Gun Digest

27th Anniversary

1973 Deluxe Edition

EDITED BY JOHN T. AMBER

DIGEST BOOKS, INC. NORTHFIELD, ILL.

We think our four-color covers for the 27th edition of Gun Digest are doubly interesting and attractive. To begin, we present the newest Sturm, Ruger firearm—the Speed Six revolver—for the first time anywhere. Next, we're delighted to show the great artistry of Jim Triggs again, and his masterful handling of the Speed Six in both normal view and in cutaway fashion—and he didn't have a cutaway to work from!

The Speed Six, designed for double-action use basically, has a three-inch barrel and a new, rounded grip frame.

Our colorful back cover carries other Sturm, Ruger arms as well—the new black powder Old Army, a 44-caliber caplock sixshooter, plus the Ruger No. 3 Carbine, the latest variant in the Single Shot rifle line. The small bronze buffalo skull by Ernest Berke, raven atop, is in Mr. Ruger's collection.

GUN DIGEST STAFF

EDITOR

John T. Amber

ASSOCIATE EDITORS

Harold A. Murtz
Joseph J. Schroeder, Jr.

ASSISTANT EDITOR

Lilo Anderson

TECHNICAL EDITORS

Bob Hagel
W. Labisky
John Lachuk
Maj. Geo. C. Nonte, Jr.
Larry Sterett
A. M. Wynne, Jr.

EUROPEAN EDITORS

Raymond Caranta
Derek Partridge

PUBLISHER

Sheldon L. Factor

MEMBER OF THE
NATIONAL
SHOOTING
SPORTS
FOUNDATION
INC.

Manuscripts, contributions and inquiries, including first class return postage, should be sent to the Gun Digest Editorial Offices, 540 Frontage Rd., Northfield, Ill. 60093. All material received will receive reasonable care, but we will not be responsible for its safe return. Material accepted is subject to our requirements for editing and revisions. Author payment covers all rights and title to the accepted material, including photos, drawings and other illustrations. Payment is made at our current rates.

Printed in the U.S.A.

ISBN-0-695-80357-3

Library of Congress Catalog#44-32588

IN THE BLACK

Jack O'Connor Retires

Jack O'Connor, long-time conductor of the Arms & Ammunition department of *Outdoor Life*, retired from his chores with that publication on May 1, 1972. He began writing the department in 1941. Well, maybe "retired" isn't fully correct—Jack will, he told me, continue to write some half-dozen stories a year for the up-front section of the magazine, but he's giving up the departmental columns for good. Jim Carmichel, well known to many of you, will take over the gun column and "Getting the Range," the question and answers section.

I've known Jack for a good many years, and over that long span I've learned something about him that I'd like you to know—there's no more deeply honest, frankly spoken, let-the-chips-fall-where-they-may guy than O'Connor. Intensely curious about all things, highly knowledgeable in a dozen different areas outside his special field, and blessed with a prodigeous memory, Jack O'Connor has offered to his world more solid, factual, basic information, more insight and sensitive discernment, than any other writer in his field. I could easily—and quite honestly—make that "any other three writers," but I don't want to spoil him.

Jack, take care.   J.T.A.

Farewell Party

After the NRA meeting in Portland, Oregon, last April, Jack O'-Connor was the guest of honor at a dinner given by Speer, Inc. in Lewiston, Idaho. Your editor (right) introduced Jack, and his successor at *Outdoor Life*, Jim Carmichel (left), gave the final speech.

Hundreds of O'Connor's friends and admirers at the big event gave him a standing ovation at the close of his interesting and humorous talk. *Hal Swiggett photo.*

Jack O'Connor, writer, world hunter and leading arms authority, receives congratulations from Bill Rae (left) editor of *Outdoor Life* on being given Winchester-Western's Outdoorsman of the Year Award. In addition to the award scroll, Jack holds the custom grade Model 21 Winchester double 20 gauge presented to him by Jim Rikhoff (right) director of public relations for the W-W group.

Townsend Whelen Award

Mr. M. L. Brown is this year's winner of our annual award for the best contribution to the firearms literature published in these pages. His excellent article, "Muskets, Powder and Patriots," deserves wide reading.

This $500 award, honoring the late Townsend Whelen—whose whole life was devoted to the rifle and marksmanship—is the 7th annual presentation. Mr. Brown's article, in the judges' opinions, best met our criteria—originality, clarity, readability and lasting value. Our warmest congratulations to the author.

Rifles for Russians

Winchester executives Charles J. Sobolewski and old friend Bill Talley (left), hold Super Grade Model 70 Winchesters presented to Soviet officials A. M. Kosygin and N. V. Podgorny by President Nixon during his Moscow visit last May. I'm delighted to print this information and show the photograph, and I'm rather pleased, too. There's a moral here someplace.

Pete Kuhlhoff
(1904-1972)

Pete Kuhlhoff, an old and very dear friend, died of a heart attack on February 9th, 1972. He was gun editor of *Argosy* magazine for 30 years. A thousand friends will miss and mourn Pete—he was one of the great, good guys.

Gun Digest IBS Trophy

The International Benchrest Shooters (IBS) Varmint and Sporter rifle championships were run at Wapwallopen, PA, August 10-13, 1971. Marlin Basset won the GUN DIGEST trophy with a 222-caliber Remington 40X rifle, his MOA for the Heavy Varmint rifle class Grand Aggregate .3774. Our warmest congratulations to Mr. Bassett.

Gun Digest NBRSA Trophy

Don Nolder, Conneaut Lake, PA., won the Heavy Varmint rifle championship and our annual award on NBRSA president George Kelbly's new range near Marshalville, Ohio. The NBRSA National Varmint and Sporter rifle championship matches were held there on August 31-Sept. 3, 1971.

Mr. Nolder had a Grand Aggregate of .3194 MOA for the 100- and 200-yd. stages in spite of rough wind conditions. He shot a 222 Hart-barreled 700 Remington. Mr. Nolder also took the 3-Gun G.A. with a .4109 MOA. Our best congratulations to him.

Dr. A. H. (Doc) Garcelon, president of the IBS, awards Marlin Bassett (right) the GUN DIGEST trophy on his winning the Heavy Varmint rifle championship.

Questions and Answers

Demands on the editors are such that not all letters can be answered, though we try. A stamped, address-to-oneself, envelope must be included. However, before writing to us for the location of suppliers, please see our Directory of the Arms pages—you'll probably save a stamp.

CONTENTS

DEPARTMENTS

Muskets, Powder

*The firearms used in the Revolution were of many types
and of highly mixed ancestry, yet they served the
patriots adequately, if not well, in their struggle to victory.*

& Patriots by M. L. Brown

GRIM-VISAGED Massachusetts Militia from Acton, Carlisle, Chelmsford, Concord and Lincoln nervously fingered loaded muskets on the muster field beyond Concord town. A dark column of smoke suddenly smudged the clear morning sky above the tiny Middlesex village and, as if on signal, determined patriots marched in double file toward the ominous beacon. Leading the van was taciturn Acton gunsmith Capt. Isaac Davis, and when his small band of citizen-soldiers approached " ... the rude bridge that arched the flood ..." they were met by a thunderous volley of musketry from three compa-

◀ The fabled "long rifle" was a novelty in the eastern colonies. In July, 1775, amazed patriots at Cambridge, Mass., watched in awe as one company of frontier riflemen placed all its shots in a 7-inch target at 250 yards—or so the story goes! Credit: Department of the Army.

Gen. George Washington faced many difficulties throughout the Revolution, among them critical shortages of artillery, small arms and gunpowder. He triumped, accepting Lord Cornwallis' surrender at Yorktown, 19 October 1781. Credit: Library of Congress.

nies of British light infantry. Davis was killed instantly, the first patriot officer to fall in battle. It was April 19, 1775, and an infant nation saw birth in the bloody throes of revolution.

Craftsmen, farmers, frontiersmen; mariners, merchants, statesmen and scholars rallied to that clarion call of freedom and they would desperately need vast quantities of arms and munitions to meet the insatiable demands of the arduous struggle ahead. As early as 1750 Parliament attempted to curtail colonial iron production and discouraged other American enterprise, yet despite severe restrictions iron production flourished clandestinely. An adequate supply of iron was available throughout the war, although the vagaries of combat often made procurement difficult while inflation escalated prices.

In 1774, as relations between stern Mother England and her recalcitrant child rapidly deteriorated, Parliament placed an embargo on all firearms exported to the colonies and, on 1 September, Gen.

Thomas Gage, Royal Governor of Massachusetts, confiscated the gunpowder stored in the public magazine at Charlestown and brought from Cambridge two fieldpieces to strengthen defenses at Boston. Aggrieved patriots retaliated when on 13 December they seized British gunpowder at Fort William and Mary.

Two months before Longfellow's immortal farmers " ... fired the shot heard round the world ...," Massachusetts organized Committees of Safety, which were soon emulated elsewhere. The committees were empowered to mobilize the militia, confiscate military stores, encourage the expansion of domestic arms-making and procure arms and munitions from domestic and foreign sources either by contract or purchase from available supplies.

It has been estimated that at the outset of the Revolution only a third of the firearms in the colonies were of domestic origin while lead, essential for casting projectiles, was

almost exclusively imported, as were prime gunflints; each was discovered to be in short supply after hostilities commenced. The shortage of gunpowder was even more acute, and a usually optimistic George Washington was forced to admit that "Our situation in the article of powder is much more alarming than I had the most distinct idea of."

Under British rule militia service was compulsory for all able males between 16 and 65. Although most colonists were prosperous enough to own firearms, and were required by Crown regulations to possess a musket and accouterments suitable for military use, they were poorly trained and equipped in comparison to British regulars. Familiarity with firearms doubtlessly sustained patriot efforts early in the conflict and, when integrated with the iron discipline hammered out by Baron von Steuben at Valley Forge in the harsh winter of 1777-78, welded the battered rebels into a more formidable foe.

Variety of Arms

Throughout the war Pvt. Yankee Doodle, of necessity, embraced virtually anything that would shoot. This was early indicated by a Pennsylvania Council of Safety report that in several units up to seven types of ammunition was required for the variety of arms in use, while at Valley Forge a perturbed Von Steuben complained that "muskets, carbines, fowling pieces, and rifles were found in the same company." American, British, Dutch, French, Hessian, Prussian and Scottish arms all found their way into patriot hands by various means, quantity generally prevailing over quality, though early in the Revolution British arms predominated; many of these were seized by patriot forces at the outset. To these were added a number of French arms, captured relics of the French and Indian War (1754-63).

The large caliber, single-shot, muzzle-loading, smoothbore flintlock musket was the mainstay of the 18th century weapons system, and in the colonies it was often used for hunting as well as military service. Its combat effectiveness was enhanced by the bayonet, and it was frequently loaded with ball or shot or a combination thereof.

The average musket had an effective range of 80 to 90 yards and, in the hands of seasoned

troops using paper cartridges containing both powder and ball, could be loaded, primed and fired four to five times a minute, while the heavy lead ball inflicted a devastating wound. Excavations of various Revolutionary War encampments and battlegrounds have uncovered musket balls of both British and patriot origin bearing obvious mutilations—some with nails driven through them—doubtlessly calculated to inflict more horrible wounds.

Lack of ranging power and low accuracy had little bearing on the effectiveness of the musket, for military tactics of that era were based on a massed volume of fire delivered at close quarters. Troops were trained to point rather than aim, firing in unison on command, and speed in loading was the essential factor. Theoretically 500 men could in 20 to 25 seconds, deliver 1,000 rounds into enemy ranks at less than 100 yards and, on the heels of the final volley, came the spirited dash with the bayonet executing even more carnage. That mortal men faced such murderous fire and the cold steel that followed is difficult to comprehend in this Nuclear Age; that they did it so regularly is astonishing.

The gradually emerging American rifle performed a minor role in the Revolution despite popular concepts to the contrary. Until the conflict began the rifle was virtually unknown to colonists in the coastal settlements and few American victories can be exclusively attributed to patriot riflemen. The rifle was primarily the weapon of the sniper, forager, picket and skirmisher, having little success except on the frontier. There it was used advantageously in the sanguinary Indian-fighting campaigns by skilled woodsmen accustomed to that deceitful type of warfare.

Highly accurate up to 200 yards, as many British officers and artillerymen belatedly discovered, the American rifle nevertheless had two distinct disadvantages when used as orthodox tactics demanded. The tight-fitting, patched ball, requisite for range and accuracy, made it more difficult and slower to load than the musket—riflemen delivering about three shots a minute—and the absence of a bayonet dictated by its less rugged design and construction often proved disastrous. That was the case at Princeton, 3 January 1777, when Hugh Mercer's Virginia riflemen were shredded by the 17th Leicesters and 55th Borderers.

Pistols were used extensively in the Revolution. Basically cavalry and naval weapons, these single-shot, muzzle-loading arms were used at short range. Generally carried by officers, they were issued to enlisted men in some units of the British Army. Many were fitted with left-side hook, attached to the sideplate, to prevent slipping when thrust into the sash or belt. Horsemen generally carried a pair of pistols in specially designed cloth or leather holsters with a brass muzzle cap. The holsters were joined by a wide leather band and slung across the saddle pommel. Some were ornately decorated.

Martial pistols were rather cumbrous, having massive butts serving as bludgeons after the initial shot. John Paul Jones, spirited captain of the *Bonhomme Richard*, used his pistols in a somewhat unorthodox fashion during the epic struggle with the *Serapis* on 23 September 1779. Angered by a gunner's cowardice, Jones threw both of his pistols at him, one of them fracturing his skull!

In addition to the various types of muskets, rifles and pistols in patriot ranks there were carbines, commonly called musketoons, wall guns and special-purpose weapons such as signal pistols and grenade-launching muskets. Carbines served both cavalry and artillery, those of the former having a sidebar and ring for attachment to a shoulder belt. Most were 10 to 12 inches shorter than the average musket, many of them made by shortening damaged musket barrels. Contemporary authors often used the word

"musketoon" as a synonym for carbine or to denote a martial blunderbuss. The latter was widely used on both land and at sea to repel boarders and to defend narrow passages such as bridges, fords, doorways, barricades and staircases. The *amusette*, known variously as the wall or swivel gun, also saw sea and land service. Considerably larger than the common musket, weighing up to 50 pounds and firing up to a 2-inch ball or shot, the amusette incorporated a swivel attached to the forestock which was mounted on the walls of forts and other embrasures. Despite its weight it was a portable weapon and often substituted for light artillery, especially on the frontier where rough terrain often made it difficult to transport heavy ordnance. Some specimens were rifled.

Until the beginning of the War of Independence Massachusetts was the hub of colonial arms-making, producing more firearms than the remaining colonies combined. Riflemaking, however, centered in southeastern Pennsylvania and, because of the variety of arms made by Pennsylvania riflesmiths during the conflict, the Lancaster area became famous as the "Arsenal of America." When war began armsmaking facilities were expanded and new installations built in most of the colonies; however, the southern colonies made fewer firearms due to shortages of skilled labor and the minimal development of natural resources, yet this was offset by the vast quantities of arms and munitions entering southern ports from abroad.

Unfortunately there is no complete record of the hundreds of gunsmiths actively engaged in fabricating arms for the various Committees of Safety, the Continental

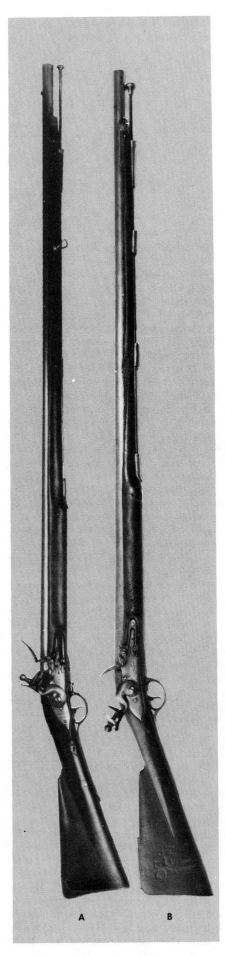

(A) John Churchill, Duke of Marlborough, introduced the 1st pattern "Brown Bess" infantry musket ca. 1714. This specimen, made by Jordan of London in 1747, probably served in the French and Indian War. "US" mark is visible on the lockplate. Credit: West Point Museum.

(B) Committee of Safety musket made by Henry Watkeys, New Windsor, Ulster Co., N.Y. (fl. 1770-80). Watkeys and Robert Boyd contracted for 1,000 muskets at £ 3-15s each for the N.Y. Colony on 13 June 1775. Stock is branded "N-Y REG." Credit: Smithsonian Institution.

◄Washington's Chief of Artillery, Maj. Gen. Henry Knox (1750-1806), reached patriots surrounding Boston in January, 1776, with a vital cargo of heavy ordnance, gunflints and lead from Fort Ticonderoga, subsequently forcing the British to evacuate the port. Credit: Library of Congress.

Congress or the infant states, and space limitations preclude listing all known makers in the text. The gunsmiths were an integral part of the socio-economic life of the colonies; most were respected community members and many were sedulous civic and military leaders. Whatever his ability and experience, the gunsmith was a skilled craftsman, either learning the trade through an exacting apprenticeship—often a maximum of seven years' duration—or under the tutelage of his father or a relative, for gunsmithing was not only a trade, but an art passed on from one generation to the next.

Gunsmiths of the Revolution

Many 18th century American gunsmiths could trace their ancestry to English arms-makers of the early colonial era. Such was Gen. Seth Pomeroy, gunsmith and French and Indian War veteran, who fought as a private at Bunker (Breed's) Hill. Pomeroy died, age 71, at Peekskill, N.Y., 19 February 1777, on his way to join Washington in New Jersey. He was the grandson of gunsmith Eltweed Pomeroy who in 1630 came to the Bay Colony from Devonshire, England, siring a family of arms-makers active until 1849.

It was a patriot gunsmith who first learned of British intentions to march on Lexington and Concord to confiscate public arms and munitions stored there. Known simply as "Jasper," his shop located in Hatter's Square, Boston, he warned the Committee of Safety which promptly sent post riders William Dawes and Paul Revere to arouse the militia on the eve of that fateful day in American history.

Innumerable gunsmiths served as armorers in the militia and Continental Army; so many in fact that Congress requested they be exempt from military service because their technical skills were vital to the war effort. Richard Falley of Westfield was the first official armorer for the Massachusetts Bay Colony and John Fitch, who in 1769 established a gunsmithery on King Street in Trenton, New Jersey Colony, served as an armorer and lieutenant in the Continental Army. Fitch made muskets for the N.J. Militia until burned out by the Redcoats in 1776. One of history's tragic figures, he is now best remembered for his pioneering efforts in the application of steam power to sailing vessels.

One of the most prominent Massachusetts gunsmiths active during the Revolution was Hugh Orr. Born in Scotland, 2 January 1715, Orr immigrated in 1737, settling at Easton, Pa. He moved, a year later, to Bridgwater, Mass. An experienced gun-and-locksmith, he established a scythe and axe works featuring the first trip-hammer forge in New England. In 1748 he made 500 muskets for the Massachusetts Militia, most of these taken from Castle William by the British when on 17 March 1776 they evacuated Boston. Shortly after the war began Orr erected a foundry, casting both brass and iron cannon while also making large quantities of ammunition. He died at Bridgewater, 6 Dec. 1798.

Another active and eminent maker of firearms for the patriot cause was William Henry. Born in West Caln Township, Pennsylvania Colony, 19 May 1729, Henry was apprenticed to Lancaster rifle-maker Mathew Roeser and from 1755 to 1760 was chief armorer to the Pennsylvania forces in the French and Indian War. During the war he was a member of Congress and the Pennsylvania Council of Safety, and served as assistant commissary general for the Lancaster district. There he supervised the manufacture of clothing and ordnance for the Continental Army. His reputation as a quality riflesmith was well known, and shortly after the war began he expanded his Lancaster rifle works to include repair work and musket and bayonet manufacture. After his death on 15 December 1786 his two sons continued in the trade, and the last family member active in gunsmithing, Granville Henry, died in 1912.

As gunmaking was primarily an individual household enterprise during this era, most shops were rather small; some no more than an addition to the man's home. There were a few larger shops and these were, from a contemporary description, "expected to contain 3 or 4 barrel forges, a grinding mill for grinding and polishing barrels, a lock shop with 7 forges, and benches for 40 filers, 10 benches for gunstock makers, a brass foundry for mountings with several finishing benches, a couple of forges for bayonets and ramrods, together with a mill for grinding and polishing them, another forge for fittings, and an assembly shop."

Committee of Safety Arms

In the tense months immediately preceding the conflict few colonies acted to secure adequate supplies of arms and munitions or to ensure future procurement; however, a few musket contracts were awarded by various colonies to independent makers. As far as it can be determined, the numerous Committees of Safety (COS) did not authorize any contracts prior to the events at Lexington and Concord, while by the end of 1778 the functions of the committees had been absorbed by other agencies within the newly formed state governments.

Such arms as were produced under COS direction can be presumed to have been made between late April, 1775, and the latter part of 1778. Firearms made prior to or after those rather ambiguous and arbitrary dates are not considered authentic COS specimens by discerning arms students and collectors. Although most COS arms were muskets it is possible that pistols were also contracted, but, no concrete data have been found to substantiate this, nor have any handguns appeared which can be definitely identified as a COS product.

Muskets produced for the various COS generally followed the pattern of the then standard British infantry musket, that is, the 2nd model "Brown Bess" although extant evidence indicates that distinctly different patterns may have been used by a few colonies. John Churchill, Duke of Marlborough, is thought to have introduced the original "Brown Bess" design between 1710-20, and it saw several minor modifications. Most COS muskets produced in early 1775 closely followed the specifications outlined by the Continental Congress in November of that year:

"Resolved That it be recommended to the several Assemblies or conventions of the colonies respectively, to set and keep their gunsmiths at work, to manufacture good fire locks, with bayonets; each firelock to be made with a good bridle lock, ¾ of an inch bore, and of good substance at the breech, the barrel to be 3 feet 8 inches in length, the bayonet to be 18 inches in the blade, with a steel ramrod, the upper loop thereof to be trumpet mouthed: that the price to be given be fixed by the Assembly or convention, or committee of safety of each colony ...."

As all firearms during this period were hand-forged and subject to the idiosyncracies of the gunsmith, and because the 'smith frequently had difficulty obtaining adequate

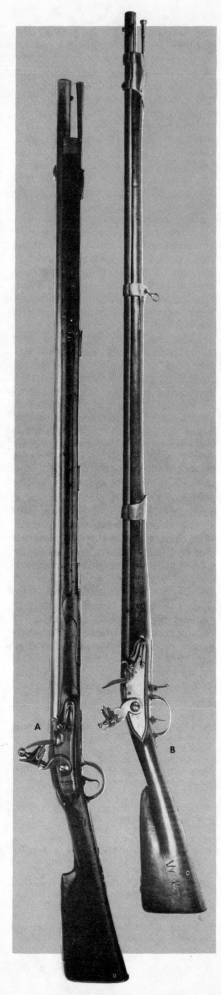

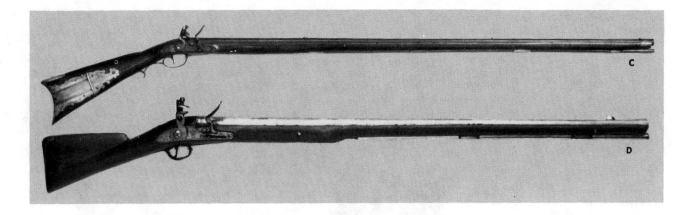

(A) Many foreign arms served patriot forces. This Prussian musket is one of two specimens believed to have been captured at Bennington, Vt., from the Brunswick Grenadiers. Credit: West Point Museum.

(B) One of the most popular imported arms serving Continental forces was the M1768 French infantry musket. This specimen, made at Charleville, has a "US" property stamp on the lock. The initials "WK" may have been those of its user. Credit: West Point Museum.

(C) A prime example of the American riflesmith's craft is this "Kentucky" rifle made by Henry Albright of Lancaster, Pa., ca. 1770. Contrary to popular concepts, rifles performed a minor role in the Revolution. Credit: The Metropolitan Museum of Art. Gift of Winfrid Wood, 1956.

(D) This full-stocked British Tower-marked wall gun with belled muzzle weighed nearly 25 lbs., with an over-all length of 72¾". Bore was nearly an inch in diameter. Credit: Smithsonian Institute.

materials, innumerable variations can be detected in the character of domestic arms produced throughout the conflict. Muskets made for the Massachusetts COS generally conformed to Congressional standards although barrels were an inch longer. Connecticut musket barrels were two inches longer and the bayonet blade was shortened to 14 inches. Barrels of Maryland COS muskets were two inches shorter, while the bayonet had a 17-inch blade.

Of whatever origin, COS muskets generally had 42-to 46-inch barrels of 75 caliber pin-fastened to walnut and, occasionally, maple stocks. Furniture was usually iron, but brass was also used. Locks were predominantly pre-war English or of European make although some were of domestic origin. Double-bridle types were ordinarily specified, but, single-bridle types were substituted when necessity dictated. Sling swivels were common on army muskets although conspicuously absent on naval models which were usually kept in racks

aboard ship, and the barrels of navy models were up to 10 inches shorter; this made it easier for marines and sailors to load when in the rigging or atop masts. The musket in the famed Minuteman statue at Lexington, Mass., is a typical navy specimen.

Massachusetts COS arms-makers were paid £ 3 each for muskets complete with iron ramrod and bayonet, that is, a stand, shortly after the war began. During this early period the average cost of a stand was $12.50, although inflation escalated prices as the war continued. A letter from a group of Lancaster riflesmiths to the Pennsylvania COS on 16 March 1776 commented that "... We are apprehensive of meeting with many obstacles in making ... a new contract. Our workmen universally complain that the sums already fixed are inadequate to their Labours; that the Sacrifice they made in *quitting their rifle business** is greater than they can well bear without some equivalent.... they cannot in Justice to their families, provide the muskets and bayonets at a less sum than £ 4 10s or £ 4 15s. We are very sensible that their observations ... are not without foundation ...." Fiscal as well as labor and material procurement problems would plague patriot gunsmiths throughout the war.

Marks and Stamps

The often repeated assertion that patriot gunsmiths refused to mark their products, fearing British reprisals, is not substantiated by fact. Most COS muskets were signed by the maker and displayed in various forms the mark of the colony as well. Connecticut required that muskets be "... marked with the name or initial letters of the maker's name." The letters "CR" and

the Rhode Island coat of arms appears on all arms purchased by that colony, while Massachusetts ordered that its muskets be stamped with the letters "MB" (Massachusetts Bay). Other markings are also found on arms used or produced by the various colonies, including captured and imported specimens.

In Pennsylvania alone COS contracts accounted for 4,500 muskets, most of these produced by gunsmiths in 11 countries between October, 1775, and April, 1776. While COS arms were generally contracted from independent gunsmiths, many colonies established and operated their own arms-making facilities. Peter DeHaven supervised musket production at the State Gun Factory in Philadelphia and, to prevent capture the works was moved to French Creek near Valley Forge in December, 1776; thence for the same reason to Hummels Town in September, 1777. The factory was dismantled and sold in 1778. The Pennsylvania State Gun Repair Shop was founded at Allentown on 26 September 1777 with James Walsh as superintendent. On 11 May 1778 Walsh reported that 800 complete muskets were available and 150 more were in the assembly stage.

In neighboring Maryland the State Gun Lock Factory was established at Frederick in 1777 with Charles Beatty, James Johnson and John Hanson named commissioners. Samuel Boone, nephew or brother to the famed Daniel, managed the works and on 17 June was directed to deliver 110 gunlocks to musket-maker Nicholas White. This installation was sold in November, 1778.

The Hunter Iron Works, operated by James Hunter on the Rappahannock near Falmouth, Va., was purchased by the colony in June, 1775. Known thereafter as

*Italics supplied. MLB.

Rappahannock Forge, the works produced muskets, pistols and wall guns for the Virginia Militia and may have made pistols for sale elsewhere as indicated by one specimen marked "CP" (Commonwealth of Pennsylvania) on the lockplate. Operations ceased in 1781. Located at nearby Fredericksburg was the Virginia State Gun Factory established by an act of the assembly on 4 July 1775 and supervised by Col. Fielding Lewis and Maj. Charles Dick. Producing muskets and bayonets, the works closed late in 1783.

Ordnance facilities were also established by the North Carolina Colony early in the war. The Charlottesville Rifle Works produced rifles, muskets and pistols for the militia in 1775-76, while at Halifax the North Carolina Gun Works, founded in 1776, made muskets under the supervision of James Ransom who served as Master Armorer there until 1778.

The Continental Congress also evinced interest in arms manufacture, and on 23 February 1776 appointed a committee to "contract for the making of muskets and bayonets for the use of the United Colonies ...." On 8 March a $10,-000 appropriation was authorized, while on 23 May the committee directed the manager of the "continental factory of firearms at Lancaster, and the manager of the gunlock factory at Trenton to deliver ... all muskets and gunlocks ... for the more expeditious arming of the continental battalion ...."

Muskets and rifles and perhaps pistols were contracted under Congressional auspices, but because of a large inventory of serviceable weapons few Continental arms contracts were made after 1778. Also noteworthy is that many state installations halted production in that year. However, thousands of arms were refurbished at the Congressional arms repair shop at Carlisle, Pa., and at Springfield, Mass.; the latter facility was established at Gen. Washington's behest in 1777 as an arsenal and powder magazine, but was subsequently expanded to include repair work and the manufacture of cartridges and gun carriages.

Musket Patterns

Continental muskets were apparently not patterned after the 2nd model "Brown Bess," for Congress furnished contractors with pattern pieces, which would otherwise have been unnecessary since most gun-

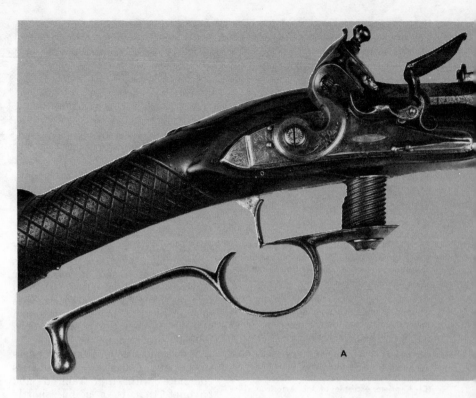

A

miths were familiar with the British musket. What patterns were used is not indicated by any extant documentation. The arms produced for the Continental Army were stamped with the maker's name or initials only, but, it was determined that a more distinctive mark of public ownership was necessary because such arms were frequently stolen and later sold. After repeated and generally unsuccessful attempts to halt this nefarious trade Congress, adopting the recommendation of the Commissary General of Military Stores, declared on 24 February 1777 that:

"... the several States ... take the most effectual steps for collecting from the inhabitants, not in actual service, all Continental arms, and give notice of the number ... to General Washington.

"That all arms or accoutrements, belonging to the United States shall be stamped or marked with the words 'UNITED STATES:' all arms already made to be stamped upon such parts as will receive the impression, and those hereafter to be manufactured, to be stamped with the said words on every part comprising the stand; and all arms and accoutrements so stamped or marked shall be taken wherever found for the use of the States, excepting they shall be in the hands of those actually in Continental service.

"That it be recommended to the

legislatures of the several States to enact proper laws for the punishment of those who shall unlawfully take, secrete, refuse or neglect to deliver, any Continental arms or accoutrements which they may have in their possession."

To this was added a suggestion by Brig. Gen. Alexander McDougall, writing to Gen. Washington on 12 April 1777, that all barrels and locks be stamped and all stocks branded with the words "UNITED STATES." That this was found acceptable can be seen on many Revolutionary War arms with "U. STATES" burned into the stock. Noteworthy is that such markings were also abbreviated to "US," while state and COS arms were also branded on the stock with appropriate letters.

As most COS muskets were made early in the war, few survived the vicissitudes of battle, while time and cannibalization contributed to the scarcity of the remainder. Continental and import-

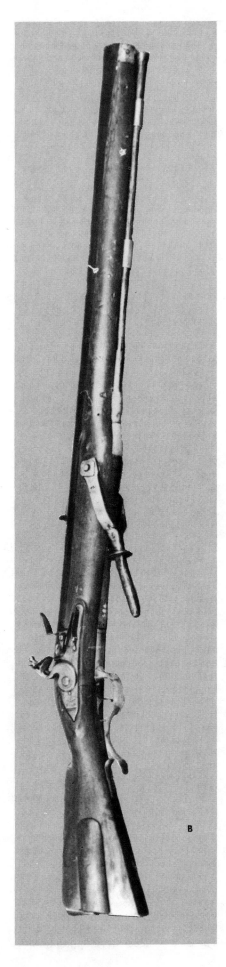

B

ed arms fared little better. When hostilities terminated, Congress, in a rare spate of gratitude, voted the patriots their arms as a farewell gift. While some were doubtlessly kept by those weary, intrepid veterans, many were sold to defray travel expenses home, for the magnanimous Congress that presented them their weapons had frequently neglected to feed, clothe, shelter and pay them during the war.

Colonial Rifles

The American rifle, termed variously the "Kentucky" or "Pennsylvania-Kentucky" rifle, slowly evolved from the shorter, more massive Jager rifle brought to the colonies around 1710 by German and Swiss immigrants setting in the Lancaster region of southeastern Pennsylvania. Just prior to the Revolution the American rifle entered its second phase of development and at this point had nearly attained the pinnacle of perfection.

Congress, by the Act of June 14, 1775, authorized 10 companies of riflemen, two each from Maryland and Virginia and 6 from Pennsylvania, and while the war stimulated the demand for rifles and production increased it was often at the expense of quality. Although many riflesmiths were engaged in producing muskets, others continued to make rifles either on a contract or individual basis. There were about three to five hundred riflesmiths in the colonies when hostilities commenced, the majority in Pennsylvania; others were located in Maryland, Virginia and the Carolinas. A few of the most prominent artisans were Henry Albright, Peter Angstadt, John Beck and Peter Humberger, Sr., all from Lancaster, Pa.; William Graeff of Reading, Pa., and Abraham Morrow of Philadelphia, who had a U.S. contract for flintlock rifles.

While there is no such things as a typical American rifle, for no two were made exactly alike, the rifles of this period illustrated similar characteristics, and were atypical of those produced after the war. The average specimen displayed a generally unmarked, hand-forged lock somewhat inferior to English or French flintlock mechanisms, and a rather straight, heavy stock with a slight drop. A patchbox was located on the right side of the stock, usually fitted with a hinged brass cover and sideplates although sliding wood covers are noted. Barrels were fully octagonal, about 42

to 48 inches long and of 45 to 50 caliber. The barrel was held to the stock by round pins and a screw passing through the barrel tang. Both front and rear sights were laterally adjustable, and an iron ramrod was provided; most furniture was brass. Innumerable variations in design and ornamentation are the rule.

Despite continuous but at times sporadic domestic production, the bulk of the shoulder and hand arms in patriot ranks during the latter part of the war were of European origin. Of these the regulation French infantry musket was commonly encountered, and it has been estimated that at least 102,-000 French long arms were imported between 1776 and 1781. These ranged in character from the obsolete M1718 to the M1768, although the M1763 infantry musket predominated.

The Blockade Guns

Benjamin Franklin, serving as one of the American commissioners to France, reported in April, 1777, that "... We have purchased 80,-000 fusils, a number of pistols, etc., of which the enclosed is on account, for 220,000 livres. They were King's arms and second-hand, but so many ... are unused and exceptionally good that we esteem it a great bargain if only half of them should arrive."

Franklin's enthusiasm was matched by his proverbial thrift, for the purchase of French muskets at an average of $5.00 each was a boon when compared to domestic prices. In June, 1777, Continental forces received an unexpected gift of 250 M1763 muskets from the Marquis de Lafayette who joined the patriot cause.

Numerous modifications marked the evolution of the French infantry musket. The popular M1768 later served as the pattern for the first (M1795) U.S. martial musket.* It was considered superior to the "Brown Bess" due to its slender profile, excellent balance, reinforced cock, banded barrel and greater range. Over-all length was 59⅝ inches with a round, 69 caliber barrel of 44¾ inches. The walnut stock was fixed to the barrel by three spring-held iron bands; the upper band fitted with a brass blade front sight and the center band with a sling swivel. Excepting the sight, all metal parts were

*Many arms historians have confused the M1768 with the M1763; the latter was equipped with a long ramrod spring between the two upper bands, a larger lock and different bands. See *The American Rifleman*, Vol. 115, No. 7., p. 19.

iron, finished bright. The flashpan was detachable from the lockplate and the lower sling swivel was attached to the trigger guard.

Like other French arms the M1768 carried such armory markings as *CHARLEVILLE* in script, surmounted by a *D* topped with a star; *MANUF ROYAL de ST. ETIENNE* with a crowned *HB;* and *MAUBEUGE* with a crowned *H* above, all appearing on the lock. Variations of the *US* stamp is often seen on the lock, barrel tang or barrel, while stocks were frequently branded *U. STATES.* In many instances these *US* markings were crudely executed, indicating that the responsible facilities had not received official dies.

Available records show that French arms shipments began in early February, 1776, when Connecticut received 3,000 assorted muskets, and continued until August, 1781, when the *Resolute* delivered 16,800 long arms to Boston. Through the efforts of Silas Deane, another American agent in France, and the support of Pierre Garon de Beaumarchais, a dummy corporation known as Roderique Hortalez et Cie was organized in May, 1776, to channel arms, munitions and other war materials to the beleaguered patriots. Hortalez was active until late 1778 when France, declaring war on England, obviated the necessity for subterfuge.

Ten ships were dispatched by Hortalez either directly to the colonies or the French West Indies ports, where vital cargoes were transferred to American vessels, mainly privateers. Only one of the 10 ships was intercepted by the British. First to arrive was the brig *Mercury* out of Nantes. In April, 1777, she made Portsmouth, N.H., unloading 364 cases of arms (11,987 muskets), 1,000 barrels of gunpowder, 11,000 gunflints, large supplies of shoes and clothing, and reported that no less than 34 other ships were clearing French ports for the colonies. Another vessel, the *Flamand,* docked at Portsmouth on 1 December with 3,000 muskets and 1,100 carbines.

Pliarne, Penet et Cie, also a French subsidized firm, sent arms and munitions to the colonies in concert with a subsidiary, James Gruel & Co. Muskets purchased from these firms were of poor quality, made at Liege. The industrious Dutch were also active in the brisk, profitable arms trade, shipping large numbers of quality muskets either directly to Massachusetts or via St. Eustatius in the Dutch West Indies. These arms are believed to have been contracted from reliable makers by Franklin, representing Massachusetts, and extant examples are marked *THONE, AMSTERDAM* on the lockplate and bear Amsterdam proof marks on the barrels of 65 caliber secured by three brass bands; the upper band distinguished by its 8-inch length.

Captured Hessian muskets were also employed by patriot forces, their characteristics varying considerably because of the different types supplied to the Hessian auxiliaries supporting the British Army. Extant specimens have brass furniture whether barrels are banded or pin-fastened, and all have elliptical brass front sights either attached to the barrel or upper band. The round barrel is 41 to 44 inches long and of 75 to 80 caliber. Lockplates are blunt at the rear and the frizzen is identified by its square top. Stocks are heavy with a massive butt and high comb. Raised carvings around the mountings are characteristic. Most were inferior to the English, Dutch, French and American muskets.

Hessian rifles also appeared in the colonies. Limited in number, they were short, heavy arms with octagonal barrels of 28 to 30 inches. Caliber ranged from 60 to 70. The stock was rather cumbrous with a massive butt incorporating a patch box with sliding wood cover and the forearm extended to the muzzle. Furniture was usually brass. Hessian rifles compared favorably to American in range and accuracy.

English rifles also served in the Revolution. These unique arms, invented by Maj. Patrick Ferguson, were the first flintlock breechloaders adopted for military use by any nation. In all probability less than 300 saw service, mostly by Loyalist riflemen recruited by the inventor. Aware of prior developments in breechloading systems, Ferguson produced a more practical version scaled to the dimensions of the standard Brown Bess. Both officer's and enlisted men's models were made. The rifle weighed 7.5 pounds and the enlisted model was of 58 caliber. Barrels ranged from 34 to 36 inches long, rifled with 8 grooves. It could be loaded and fired five to six times a minute and was accurate up to 300 yards. Traditional military resistance to new concepts dimmed Ferguson's hopes for the future of his invention, and his death at King's Mountain sealed the fate of his rifle. If the British had adopted the accurate, fast-firing rifle on a large scale the American colonies might never have won their independence. (See the GUN DIGEST, 1959, *p.* 53.)

The Patriots' Pistols

As a rule American martial pistols followed the British pattern. Those produced at Rappahannock

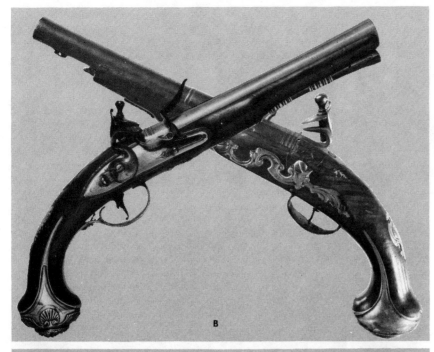

B

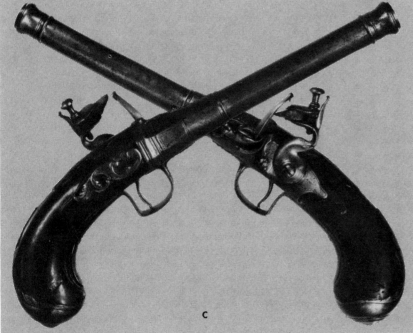

C

only the maker's name and date on the lockplate.

The new model British martial pistol was somewhat shorter and stronger, having a 9-inch round barrel of 69 caliber. Some of the brass furniture was eliminated or redesigned. The sideplate and lockplate were flat with stamped rather than engraved markings. Navy models incorporated a belt hook and retained the longer barrel of the old model. Both types were profusely copied by patriot gunsmiths.

The various Highland regiments serving the British in America were the only units in which all enlisted men were issued pistols. These unusual arms were of all-metal construction. Officer's models were primarily holster pistols, made exclusively of iron and highly ornamented, often heavily chiseled and inlayed with precious metals, while enlisted men's models were of iron with a brass stock. Ramrods of both were iron, and the soldier's type was equipped with a belt hook. Those made before 1758 were marked *HR* (Highland Regiment), those thereafter *RHR* (Royal Highland Regiment). Most were made in Scotland prior to 1762 when Birmingham and London emerged as production centers.

Highland pistols had no trigger guards or sights and all displayed button-type triggers. The lock internally resembled the so-called English dog lock, popular a century earlier, as there was no half-cock position and the sear acted laterally, protruding through the lockplate. Barrels were round of between seven and eight inches while caliber fluctuated from 55 to 57. Both types illustrated kidney-shaped, heart-shaped or fish-tailed butts, with officer's models often terminating in a ramshorn design. A removable knob, located in the center of the butt, served as a combination oiler/vent pick.

John Waters of London and Birmingham produced many plain Highland pistols, some with London proofmarks on the barrel. Another maker, Isaac Bissel of Birmingham, made officer's models characterized by a ramshorn butt with an oval petal grip design and channeled cock pin, oiler/vent pick and button trigger. Highland pistols display a wide range of ornamentation, and variations in design are common.

France, largest European supplier of muskets to patriot forces, also provided a large number of

Forge bore an exact resemblance to the new model British martial pistols appearing in 1760. They were marked *RAPa FORGE* on the lockplate and had heavier brass furniture than most domestically made pistols. Both old and new model British martial pistols served in patriot ranks, many of them captured at the outset of hostilities.

Adopted about 1714, old model British martial pistols were relics of King George's War (1744-48) and the French and Indian conflict. They had round, 12-inch barrels of about 60 caliber, pin-fastened to the walnut stock, with additional support provided by the breech-plug tang screw. The convex iron sideplate, lockplate and brass furniture resembled that of the 1st model Brown Bess musket. The bulbous butt was capped with brass as was the wooden ramrod. Most were engraved with the letters *GR* (George Rex), in script, surmounted by a crown in the center of the lockplate, while behind the cock the word *TOWER* appeared in a vertical arc. The broad arrow ordnance stamp, denoting Crown ownership, also appeared on the lock, while barrels displayed either London or Birmingham proofmarks. Some specimens have pistols. However, no accurate or complete record exists which can verify the precise number or type. Most were martial specimens. Both army and navy patterns of 1763 were popular, featuring round, 9-inch barrels of 67 caliber, held in a walnut stock by a tang screw and long, double band at the muzzle held by a retaining spring. The lock resembled that of the M1763 infantry musket with a reinforced cock and iron pan. The furniture of the army model was iron and that of the navy model brass. Each had a button-head iron ramrod, and most were produced at St. Etienne.

In 1776 France adopted a new pattern martial pistol which differed radically from the M1763. The M1776 first appeared in 1777 in both army and navy models. Each was of 69 caliber with a 7.5-inch barrel, tapering toward the muzzle. Navy models were provided with a belt hook. Frames were brass and the brass pan was integral. The cock, frizzen and ramrod were iron. There was no forestock or sights. The butt curved sharply, supported by an iron backstrap and terminated with a brass cap. Arsenal marks appeared in an arc under the cock and the stock was stamped with an inspector's mark and date. The M1777 French martial pistol served as a pattern for the first U.S. martial pistol (M1799).

The few German pistols used in the Revolution varied considerably in character and were generally inferior to other imported and domestic pistols. They commonly had brass furniture and pin-fastened, round iron barrels of 75 caliber. On some models the iron ramrod was attached to the barrel by a swivel. These pistols, normally fitted with a brass front sight, had a reinforced, convex cock and were bought by American agents in the various German states and Holland.

An undetermined number of Prussian pistols, mostly old and unserviceable, found their way into patriot hands. Many were bought by representatives of the Virginia Colony. Barrels were round, 11¾ inches long and pin-fastened to the stock. All had brass front sights, and some displayed a rudimentary rear sight consisting of a shallow notch filed into the breech plug tang. Furniture was of brass, and the stock was characterized by a heavy buttcap and fore-end cap. The lock and sideplate were flat, and there was no ramrod. Proofmarks were found on the trig-

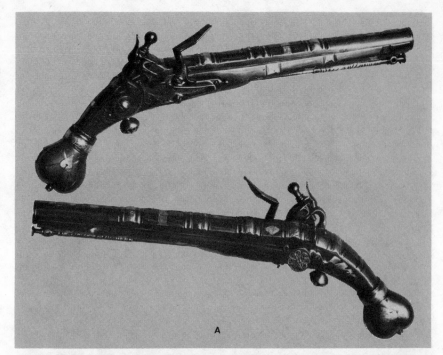

A

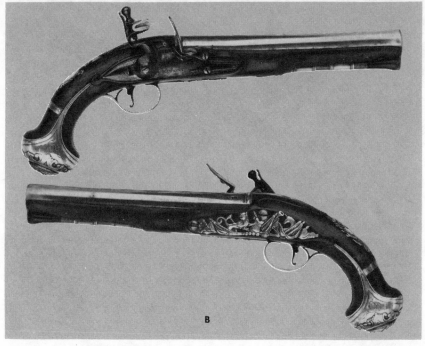

B

ger guard and barrel while the royal cipher appeared on the buttcap. Some are marked *POTZDAMMAGAZIN* (Potsdam Arsenal) on the lockplate.

Of better quality than German or Prussian pistols were those provided by the Dutch. Most are stamped *THONE, AMSTERDAM* in two lines on the lockplate. Both army and navy models were bought, the latter displaying a belt hook. Each had a 10-inch, round, pin-fastened barrel of about 69 caliber, iron ramrod, brass blade front sight and notch-type rear sight. The cock was convex and the pan brass. There was no sideplate. The stock had a bulbous butt minus a cap, while the fore-end was capped with brass.

In addition to the various types of martial pistols used in the Revolution there were numerous non-martial types of domestic and foreign origin. Most were of British make, and highly popular was the Queen Anne screw-barrel or so-called "turn-off" pistol. Early models (*c.* 1740) had the cock situated on the right side of the gun, but after about 1760 the cock was centrally hung. Over-all length was about 11.5 inches, and the round, cannon-shaped barrel was of about 60 caliber. Load-

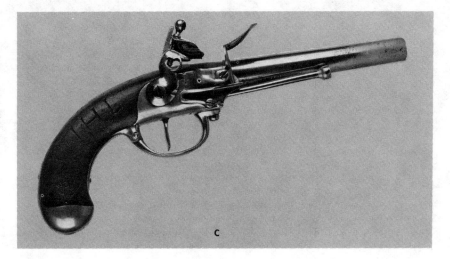

(A) All-metal pistols such as this ornate pair were carried by officers of the Scots Highland regiments. Knob in center of heart-shaped butt is attached to combination vent pick/oiler. Credit: The Metropolitan Museum of Art. Gift of Mrs. Elizabeth Cameron Blanchard, in memory of her husband, J. Osgood Blanchard, 1916.

(B) George Washington's silver-mounted, brass-barreled pistols were made by Hawkins of London (fl. 1750-75). Over-all length 13½", 8" barrels of 66 caliber. Washington is said to have owned at least 50 firearms. Credit: West Point Museum.

(C) French Cavalry M1777 pistol differed radically from most handguns of the Revolutionary War era. The 7.5" round barrel was cased in a brass housing supporting the lock and iron ramrod. The pistol served as a pattern for the first U.S. martial pistol, the North & Cheney of 1799. Credit: West Point Museum

ing was accomplished by unscrewing the barrel, pouring the powder into the chamber, placing the ball atop the charge and replacing the barrel. Those made for cavalry use often had a short chain attached to the barrel and breech to prevent loss when loading. Range and accuracy were superior to the average pistol as there was virtually no gas leakage around the ball, and in rifled specimens accuracy was extremely good. Many of these and other personal pistols were exquisitely ornamented.

Colonial riflesmiths produced pistols similar in character to the Queen Anne type while retaining features common to the American rifle. These so-called "Kentucky" pistols, made prior to and during the Revolution, differed in many respects from later specimens. The earliest known type dates from about 1740. Most reflected the Queen Anne barrel style although all were loaded at the muzzle and the majority were smoothbores. Caliber varied from 36 to 50, and barrel length ranged between 7.5 and 9.5 inches. Both brass and iron pin-fastened barrels are encountered, while brass and coin silver were generally used for furniture and ornamentation. Stocks normally extended the full length of the barrel although some were half-stocked and most had birdshead grips. Figured maple was favored for stocking, but cherry and walnut were also used, while ramrods were often made of hickory tipped with brass or silver. Specimens are found with and without sights; the sights patterned after the rifle type. Imported locks were generally used, and markings varied considerably; some specimens have different names or initials on the lock and barrel, for even during this early period specialization in

arms-making was apparent. The craftsmanship displayed on these often elegant pistols was decidedly superior to that found on most domestic specimens of the period.

The Gunpowder Shortage

With the commencement of hostilities gunpowder was everywhere lacking. Restrictions by Parliament, difficulty in procuring the ingredients in sufficient quantity, and the superiority of English gunpowder all contributed to the decline of domestic powder making. While charcoal was abundant, sulfur was exclusively imported and saltpeter production disturbingly irregular. The powder seized at Fort William and Mary in 1774 had served the patriots at Bunker Hill, but one reason for the American withdrawal was a dire powder shortage.

In July, 1775, patriot forces ringed Boston, outnumbering the Redcoats two to one, yet Washington had neither enough artillery nor powder to oust the British. Young Henry Knox, affable and brilliant Boston bookseller who became Washington's chief of artillery, proposed a wild scheme whereby captured ordnance at Fort Ticonderoga could be transported to Dorchester Heights above Boston. Despite protests Knox left in November and found at the fort 78 serviceable pieces of ordnance and 30,000 gunflints in addition to 2,300 pounds of lead. By boat, sledge, wagon, determination and pure guts he shepherded the vital cargo across frozen rivers, snow-capped mountains and frigid wilderness in the dead of winter to Boston, 300 miles distant. Arriving with 55 assorted cannon, mortars and howitzers in January, 1776, he was delighted to discover that the capture of the British supply ship *Nancy*

had provided the powder for his guns.

Shortly after the war began most of the colonies took steps to rectify the powder shortage, and mills sprang up on various locations. Oswell Eve ran a powder mill at Frankford, Pa., and it was probably there that Paul Revere studied the manufacture of powder, erecting a mill near Boston after the war. Two other mills were situated near Eve's works and another was located in Dauphin County.

Numerous complaints concerning the quality of Eve's gunpowder reached Congress and, on 7 June 1776, a committee was appointed to investigate. On 28 August the committee suggested that inspectors be assigned to the various mills with orders to mark every acceptable keg of powder with the letters *USA*. This was the first use of the marking subsequently applied to all U.S. arms and other ordnance material.

In 1780 a powder mill was constructed near Washington's winter headquarters at Morristown, N.J., concealed in the deep woods. Saltpeter for this facility was provided by the local populace, probably from natural deposits although possibly from artificial niter beds produced by soaking the earth with human urine rich in nitrate.

The estimable victory of patriot riflemen at King's Mountain on 7 October 1780 was substantially assisted by 500 pounds of gunpowder donated to the cause by Mary Patton who, in the absence of her husband serving in the army, operated a powder mill in Tennessee. It was an expensive gift, for at that time powder was selling for a dollar per pound.

The scarcity of gunpowder on the frontier was even more crucial, for

Patriot victory at Trenton, 26 December 1776, succeeded in reviving American morale and prompted French, Spanish and Dutch assistance in procuring additional troops and arms. Credit: Department of the Army.

it was there that a thin, buckskin-clad line valiantly withstood the savagery of Indian attacks promoted by the British, who supplied their numerous Indian allies with arms and munitions throughout the war. A frontier settlement obliged to defend itself expended more powder in an hour than would have been used in a year of hunting. Despite the powder shortage the generally outnumbered frontiersmen miraculously prevented British-led Indian marauders from penetrating the populous coastal settlements and harassing Washington's weary Continentals.

Patriot frontiersmen went to great lengths and took considerable risks in procuring adequate supplies of gunpowder. In 1775 George Rogers Clark persuaded Virginia authorities to part with 500 pounds of powder for the defense of Kentucky. Second Lieutenant William Linn and 15 volunteers left Fort Pitt in July, 1776, for New Orleans, where the officially neutral Spanish covertly sold powder to American agents. Linn procured 98 barrels—nearly five tons—and began the hazardous 2,000-mile return trip, eluding both British and Indians to arrive at Wheeling on 2 May 1777, just in time to meet the summer threat of Indian attacks. His party had been gone 11 months. Clark also took advantage of Spanish co-operation, and gunpowder from New Orleans bolstered his chance for victory when, in the summer of 1778, he invaded Illinois, capturing Kaskaskia and Vincennes.

Although domestic powder-making increased as the war progressed, American powder was never made in sufficient quantity to supply patriot forces, nor was it comparable to English, French or Spanish powder in quality. Due

primarily to the advancements in chemistry achieved by Antoine Laurent Lavoisier (1743-94), French gunpowder was superior to any produced in the world at the time of the Revolution, and it has been estimated that French gunpowder fulfilled 80 percent of patriot requirements. Much of it reached the colonies through the efforts of Hortalez et Cie.

The road from Lexington to Yorktown was a long and bloody road. The American War of Independence was· won not only by the inordinate courage displayed on the grim field of combat, but by the simple determination and singular purpose of a united people working toward a common goal. The contribution to victory generated by the many who left bloody footprints in the snow and survived by gnawing the bark from frozen trees was no more vital than what was given by the many who toiled long hours in the blazing heat of the barrel forge or sat hunched over a filer's bench. ●

Bibliography

Primary Sources

Carey, A. Merwyn. *American Firearms Makers.* New York: Thomas Y. Crowell, 1953.

Chapel, Charles Edward. *Guns of the Old West.* New York: Coward-McCann, Inc., 1961.

Gardner, Robert. *Small Arms Makers.* New York: Bonanza Books, 1962.

Gluckman, Arcadi. *United States Martial Pistols and Revolvers.* Harrisburg, Pa.: The Stackpole Co., 1956.

——————. *United States Muskets, Rifles and Carbines.* Buffalo, N.Y.: Otto Ulbrich Co., Inc., 1948.

Kauffman, Henry J. *Early American Gunsmiths.* New York: Bramhall House, 1952.

——————. *The Pennsylvania-Kentucky Rifle.* Harrisburg, Pa.: The Stackpole Co., 1960.

Peterson, Harold L. *Arms and Armor in Colonial America.* New York: Bramhall House, 1956.

Russell, Carl P. *Guns on the Early Frontiers.* New York: Bonanza Books, 1957.

Secondary Sources

Lancaster, Bruce and Plumb, J. H. *The American Heritage Book of the Revolution.* New York: The American Heritage Publishing Co., 1958.

Martin, Joseph Plumb (Scheer, George F., ed.). *Private Yankee Doodle.* New York: Little, Brown & Co., 1962.

Miller, John C. *The First Frontier: Life in Colonial America.* New York: Dell Publ. Co., Inc., 1966.

Perry, Clay. "Big Guns for Washington," *The American Heritage Reader.* New York: Dell Publ. Co., Inc., 1956.

Peterson, Harold L., ed. *Encyclopedia of Firearms.* New York: E. P. Dutton & Co., 1964.

Scheer, George F. and Rankin, Hugh. *Rebels and Redcoats.* New York: World Publ. Co., 1957.

Van Every, Dale. *A Company of Heroes.* New York: Wm. Morrow & Co., 1962.

Woodward, Wm. *The Way Our People Lived.* New York: Liveright Publ. Corp., 1944.

Periodicals

The American Rifleman, The National Rifle Assn., of America, Washington, D.C.

Gun Digest, Digest Books, Inc., Northfield, Ill.

Guns & Ammo, Petersen Publ. Co., Los Angeles, Cal.

THE TRAPSHOOTER–
and how he stands

by DEREK PARTRIDGE

Some champion claybirders bust 'em well in spite of their bad form and worse gun mounting. Our European smoothbore editor shows the way to better shooting via the fundamentals of good stance and style.

Fig. 1—Mattarelli shoots with forward lean, lifts his right foot.

As IN OTHER aspects of life there are many shooters, including some top-flight competitors, who shoot well *in spite of* having basically bad stances and gun mounting techniques, rather than *because of* good ones. As the success of each shot is largely determined by these two factors—before you even call for the target—they are of vital importance. Under "normal" conditions such faults can be got away with, but in bad weather, bad visibility, or when heavy competitive pressure is on, these faults can begin to tell—with disastrous results. If, however, you have a firm base in these fundamentals, such additional strains will have far less adverse effect.

Most new shooters develop their stances and mounting forms in two ways: untrained observation and through a muddle of hopelessly conflicting advice. They watch the local hotshot and assume (understandably) that because he hits more targets than anyone else, he must be doing something right! Then they try to emulate his "style." Thereafter they ask for—and are offered—endless advice by shooting ground friends. Most of it is well-intentioned, of course, but it's completely personalized, and the shooter giving the instructions

is usually without any basic knowledge of or mastery of the fundamentals. Such a "coach" has stumbled onto his own way of hitting more than he misses, so he wants to impose his style (even supposing he's capable of correctly assessing and describing what he does!) on the unfortunate and gullible novice. Many shooters have little or no idea of what they really do. It can be amusing, listening to them telling how they shoot, when a glance at them on the line shows that they do something quite different!

Some shooters have been forced by physical infirmities to adopt stances and techniques that vary considerably from any sort of norm. If they reach the top they are slavishly followed by countless fans and would-be champions—men who have never investigated what lies behind the master's idiosyncrasies. A classic case is that of Ennio Mattarelli, Olympic International Trap Gold Medalist and twice World Champion. Mattarelli has a very pronounced forward lean, which causes him to raise his back foot; he also has a somewhat unusual grip with his right hand. When he was a young man, starting to shoot, he weighed very little and he suffered from recoil—to counteract this he leaned far forward into the gun. His unusual

grip was caused by a broken wrist. Both abnormalties persist in his style to this day, because that's how he learned to shoot and it was successful *for him.* However, vast numbers of shooters in Italy, and a good few elsewhere, conscientiously ape his unorthodox style, fondly believing that it will make them champions, too. They have no idea of the handicaps they face in their paths to hoped-for glory.

Fundamentals of Form

The shooters' stances we'll examine in this article are, all of them, styles used by famous European International Trap contestants. However, what they do must be relevant to American trapshooting, as they have to cope with targets going twice as far, twice as fast, through double the lateral angulation and with height variations as well. Before looking at these shooters and their methods, let's try to establish some fundamentals on which to base an assessment of their styles. I've observed their shooting form closely for years, attempting to discover and analyse the reasons for the various idiosyncrasies shown. Then I tried to distill the essential factors and blend them with my own practice of being as natural and comfortable as possible on the shooting line.

Fig. 2—Rossini's position is about normal except for raised heel.

Our bodies are built in a certain way: the nearer we stick to the way nature intended us to be and the less we distort our bodies—in any sport—the more successful we are likely to be. One should only depart from a simple, natural stance if physical peculiarities or discomfort necessitate it.

Foot position Some shooters stand full square to the trap, which favors swinging to left-hand targets; others stand at right angles to it, favoring right-hand targets. Each drastically restricts the ability to swing to the opposite-side target. At any stand, you know the maximum angles through which your target can be thrown—or you should. If you place your feet, which position your body, to the center of these two extreme angles, then the body can swing equally to either side, instead of favoring one and hindering the other. An easy way to find this position is to hold the gun loosely between your hands, your arms hanging down by your sides. As you gradually move your feet right or left, the

Fig. 3—Carrega (above), notable for his simple, natural style.

Fig. 4—Braithwaite (center) stands a bit crouched, otherwise a good stance.

Fig. 5—Senicev (below) holds head well forward, gun quite low.

muzzle of the gun will move too. When the muzzle is pointing at the mid-point between the two extreme angles, your feet (and body) are properly aligned. This will bring the feet to an angle of about 45 degrees to the target exit point from each stand.

I have never found a valid reason to space the feet any wider or closer than one would as he stood naturally, talking to a friend. But some shooters virtually do the splits, as if digging in to take the recoil of a cannon; others place their feet closely together, wobble in the slightest breeze and sway back under recoil. Some shooters raise the back foot—we're not storks, designed to roost on one leg! We're better balanced with both feet on the ground, so you might as well leave them the way nature intended them.

Knees An astonishingly large number of American shooters go into an exaggerated double knees bend at the moment of firing. I believe this comes from hunting styles, but that still doesn't provide me the slightest clue as

to its purpose—what on earth does it achieve? Other shooters emulate the Prussian aristocracy and march to the firing line, click their heels and remain stiff and unbending, with their knees tightly locked. Not surprisingly, this makes it hard for them to swing onto angling targets. Just break the lock on the front knee, so it—and therefore the body—can have fluidity of movement to swing sideways. Some people, then, suggest placing the body weight forward, onto the front leg. I find this can cause slight imbalance, and I prefer to gently incline my body forward, from both ankles, but retaining my weight squarely distributed on both feet. I feel this gives more stability in movement to targets.

Arms and hands Some shooters place their left hand back by the trigger guard, which gives wonderful fluidity of movement, but a minimum of control over the pointing of the gun. Others (the stiff Prussian *junkers* again) fully extend the left arm, straining to reach beyond the gun's forearm, which gives fantastic pointing control, but makes it almost impossible to get the barrels moving at all! In conjunction with this, some wave the left elbow about their heads, while others snuggle it down into their bodies. It depends to some extent whether you favor the theory of left arm pointing or not. While the left arm can do the pointing, it can also act as a brake. I'm inclined to let the whole body do the pointing. The left arm/hand position is best determined by holding the gun between your hands, the right hand in position on the grip and trigger. Assuming you have a properly balanced gun, move the left hand up and down the forearm until the gun has no tendency to tip forward or back, but so that its weight feels squarely between the hands. Then shoulder it and let the left arm drop into a position that feels comfortable and natural, not too high, not too hunched in. Cradle the forearm firmly in your palm, with the fingers wrapped round it, possibly with the index finger more or less pointing the way down the barrels.

Right arms also find themselves contorted through a wide arc of angles from above the head to down by the side. The position of this arm affects the positon of the hand and therefore the important grip and placement of the trigger finger (this is also affected by the thickness and slope of the pistol grip). The trigger should be pulled from its lowest point, otherwise it becomes progressively harder to pull as the finger slides upwards—

Fig. 6—Bascagni leans forward, elbows down, left hand back.

and if the right arm is too high up in the air, it is difficult to pull the trigger from the bottom. Together, the arms should look, from the front, roughly like a slightly off-center inverted V.

Shoulder, neck and head The position of the right arm is governed largely by the position of the right shoulder, and this is where slight body "distortion" can be legitimate, especially if you have a long neck. If you mount the gun with your right shoulder in its natural, down position, you may find that the stock is some distance from your face, and you have to bend your head and neck down to it. *This is a no-no!* The stock must always be brought up to the cheek, so, by raising the right shoulder, as you lift the gun, you'll find the stock then comes into your face. At the same time as you raise the shoulder, also raise the right elbow. This opens up a hollow pocket for the gun butt to fit firmly into—if you leave the elbow down, a hard bunch of muscles will defy entry to the butt. Once the butt is in position, allow the right elbow to drop into whatever positon and level is comfortable and natural to it. The butt should be placed as far in from the shoulder as possible and comfortable, so as to bring the rib under the eye. If you mount the gun way out on your shoulder, your head is going to have to lean over to the stock, to get the eye behind the rib.

If you mount the gun so high that half the butt is visible from behind your shoulder, your neck will probably be strained backwards. If you mount it so low that it is

almost sliding out from under your armpit, your neck, head and eyes will be strained downwards—naturally, at the first movement to the target, they will attempt to return to their normal positions, result: missed target. All strain is bad, because the affected body part will always try to revert to its natural state. A good norm is to have the top of the butt *roughly* level with the top of the shoulder.

Some heads are hunched so far back on the stock that you wonder why they bothered to have a Monte Carlo comb; others are strained so far forward that you wonder why they don't get bloody noses! Neck length, face length and the height of the shoulders, all affect the distance from shoulder to eye. The short-necked shooter is

Fig. 7—Leibinger's head and cheek are above comb, right arm high.

the luckiest, as the gun will come naturally into place against his face and under his eye; it's us ostrich-necks that have problems. Holding the head a bit forward, rather than back, is favored. This position gives a better view down the rib and a better muzzle-to-target relationship. Obviously stock length is of prime importance here and a rough guide is: don't shoot a stock any longer than you have to—all that does is bring your head back along the comb, taking the gun balance out of your hands and into the muzzle.

Cheek pressure to the comb can be vertically from the fleshy front of the cheek, under the eye; from the back, nearer the top of the jaw bone; or laterally against the side and bottom of the jaw bone. The most likely to cause head-lifting is

the first, as the fleshy portion gives no stability from gun movement or recoil (when a second shot is required). The third is probably the best—it should eliminate head-lifting as there's no vertical pressure and, provided you don't have too much (or too little) lateral pressure, you should eliminate the problem of the head coming away from the stock on right-angling birds.

The above factors also affect eye alignment. The eyes should be able to view along the rib at as near their natural viewing level as possible. Again, the short-necked fellow wins out. For the long-neck, who has to lower his head some, avoid the first of the cheek-pressure possibilities like the plague, for it also causes the eyes to cant down. They must then peer up through the eyelashes and obviously try to return to normal viewing level when the target appears and the gun starts to move. Result: another lifted head and another untouched target. Don't forget to ascertain, preferably through an oculist or optician, which is your master eye. If you have frequent or even occasional equal-strength vision, don't hesitate to close one eye. My scores improved a lot after I did, for I found that occasionally my left eye was as strong as the right and took over the guidance system.

Body movement Some shooters advocate moving from the hips, others move only their arms. I believe the body should be considered as a tank, with its usual turret-mounted gun: our "tank" is our feet, and our turret-gun is the rest of the body from

Fig. 8—Renard stands with feet very close together, left hand far back.

Fig. 9—Alonso uses fully extended left hand, good style otherwise.

the ankles up. I move my whole body laterally to a target, along with a slight forward movement—bodyflow—out in the direction of the target I'm pursuing. When you swing laterally to a wide-angled target, don't lean over from the waist, but pivot on an even keel.

Gun mounting Some shooters mount their guns with the muzzle pointing to the heavens as if beseeching a blessing on their coming effort; others start so low that you wonder if they're invoking other than divine assistance! While mounting the gun level with the shoulder and eyes is a good norm, it's worth considering mounting the gun angled *slightly* upward. This insures that the gun is brought to the head, not vice versa; then, once head and gun are locked together in the correct position, the whole body inclines forward and slightly downward to the target exit.

Gun fit and clothing Both are obviously vital to the successful employment of any of the above-suggested fundamental techniques of stance and style. We're not going into either here, but just remember: alter the gun to the man—just as you would with clothes—and not the man to the gun.

Stances and Form

Now let's take a look at some of Europe's top International shooters, all of whom are members of their nations' International Trap Teams. The pictures were taken at the 1970 European Championships in Bucharest, Romania. I used a telephoto lens, so as not to disturb the competitors—hence the imperfect quality of the pictures.

1. Mattarelli, Italy: Olympic Gold 1964, twice World Champion, European Champion. Note his forward lean and lifted back foot—for reasons explained earlier. The gun

Fig. 10—Avrile—bent far forward, she holds gun almost centrally.

seems mounted slightly low in his shoulder. The unusual left-hand grip and special forearm are the result of an accident in which he lost part of his left hand. Shoots a Perazzi.

2. Rossini, Italy: Olympic Gold 1956, Silver '60 and tied for Silver '64. Very normal, natural stance, and only surprise being the lifted back foot. He comes from a family of shooters which has long shot for Italy, so he was trained in stance and style from an early age. Shoots a Beretta.

3. Carrega, France: Twice World Champion, 1970/71, European Champion. He gets my prize for best style, notable for its simplicity and naturalness. He just stands quite normally and puts the gun to his shoulder, no nonsense. Head is erect, so his eyes view on a level plane; the gun is mounted well up in the shoulder, right arm height is not exaggerated, left arm extended, but not too much; body erect, but fractionally inclined forward; feet spaced apart normally and angled about 45 degrees to the target exit. It's hard to tell from the picture if his front knee is bent. Shoots a Browning.

4. Braithwaite, Great Britain: Olympic Gold 1968. Head is well forward, and correctly angled to the line of sight. With both knees slightly bent, he appears a little crouched, otherwise this is good style. Shoots a Browning.

5. Senicev, Russia: Olympic Silver 1964, tied for same 1968. Style seems similar to Braithwaite's, but his head and neck are even more forward, and his gun is mounted strangely low. This appears to be the result of Russian schooling, as other Soviet shooters also favor the same style. Both Braithwaite and Senicev consider nearness of the eye to the rib an important factor, and this style is also common among American military International Trap shooters. Shoots a Merkel.

6. Basagni, Italy: European Champion 1971. With his head forward and seemingly down, the right arm close in to his body and the left arm well back, he seems slightly hunched. However, he is a very fast and a consistently good performer. Shoots a Beretta.

7. Leibinger, Germany: One of the handful of shooters who have broken 200 straight at International Trap. Textbook style, but with the right arm level with shoulder. Not only is he the one International Trap shooter I know who holds

a high gun muzzle, as do American trapshooters (other Internationals generally hold the gun below the ground level exit point), but his head has hardly any contact with the stock. His nose and mouth (arm covers mouth in this picture) are always clearly visible above comb. I think some of his style comes from the German expert, Walter Gehmann. Shoots a Browning.

8. Renard, Belgium: World Champion 1967. Jovial, roly-poly Renard holds his left hand so far back that I find it hard to understand how he supports and moves the gun—he must have to shove around much gun weight out front. Also, his feet are very close together. Shoots a Browning.

9. Alonso, Spain: Here we see the absolute opposite to Renard's short left arm, with Alonso's left arm extended as far as possible!

10. Bina Avrile, Italy: Ladies World Champion 1969. Another fan of the far extended left arm. Other unusual features of her stance are very high right arm, hunched over body, almost central positioning of stock (to avoid hurting her breast), and an almost square-to-front body, with straight legs. She originally took up clay shooting as therapy to recover from an illness which left her long bed-ridden. Like Mattarelli, who won his second World title when she won her first, she shoots a Perazzi.

11, 12 & 13: Author Derek Partridge, who is a member of Great Britain's International Trap Team, demonstrates his own style. He hopes it illustrates points brought out in text and is as simple and natural as his long-necked physique allows! See opening page. ●

Pressures and the Revolver

The author's invention of a system for taking gas pressures in a revolver—which had never been feasible before—revealed truly new data on gas losses, pressures and loading techniques. An outstanding development, probably the most important one of our time.

by WM. M. CALDWELL

As A MEMBER OF the ballistic team of Speer, Incorporated, the Lewiston, Idaho, bullet-making firm, it is my pleasure to work with guns and ammunition daily. In July of 1970 the Number 8 manual was at last a reality. During the development of the much-increased revolver data section for this manual, I often wondered just how much energy was lost through the gap between barrel and cylinder. No other firearm, of course, develops pressures in the same way a revolver does. Complicated though their innards may be, the utter simplicity and reliability of their function has led most of us to forgive them for their velocity losses.

About this time Speer was all geared up to start loading 38 Special and 357 Magnum ammunition. Since daily testing of this ammunition was to be part of my job, I was more than ever concerned about the effects of the revolver gap. The ammunition market is very competitive these days, and the average buyer is quite knowledgeable about the products offered him. Efforts to soup up the old 38 Special were being shot down by split forcing cones and velocities that had a way of getting lost when fired in a revolver. With these problems in mind, new testing tools were ordered.

The new lab equipment arrived, the oscilloscope very impressive with its little TV screen looking like a piece of green graph paper. The pressure barrels were tapped for a peanut-size gadget called a quartz crystal transducer. (See fig. 2.) It looked like a spark plug from my little boy's toy car. Out of place though it seemed, the development of this transducer was to lead up to the most significant advance in revolver ammunition since the days of Sam Colt. Transducers use a quartz crystal which emits an electrical pulse when pressure is applied to it. These crystals are very carefully cut so that the electrical pulse is of a known value. This pulse, or electron, is carried by way of a coaxial cable to a charge amplifier which changes the electrons to volts. The volts are then viewed on the oscilloscope screen in the form of a pressure curve.

Crusher or Transducer

The use of lead and copper crushers has long been the standard for pressure taking in the ammunition industry. There is much discussion going on these days over which is best—the crusher or transducer—and only a saint could have the patience to keep from swearing when trying to correlate between the two.

As an example, let's assume that a given lot of 38 Special ammunition is giving crusher pressures of 16,000 psi. This same ammunition would then give about 20,000 psi in the pressure revolver. I have come to expect a difference of from 15 to 20 percent between the crusher system and the transducer-equipped revolver.

While it may be possible to install a crusher system on a revolver, it would be clumsy and slow at best. I doubt if the short time duration of revolver pressures would allow much change in the crusher cylinder. An added benefit of using the transducer for taking pressures and displaying the pressure curve on the oscilloscope screen is that time may also be taken. So far, time is the only key I've found for correlating between the two methods.

After several months of pawing through pages of pressure data taken in solid (no gap) barrels by both methods, I wanted to know, more than ever, what really happened in a revolver. About this time, remembering just how small a transducer was, I began dreaming of ways to install one on a revolver. I talked to boss Ray Speer, who felt that since no one had tried taking pressure in a revolver before, we might well have another Speer "first."

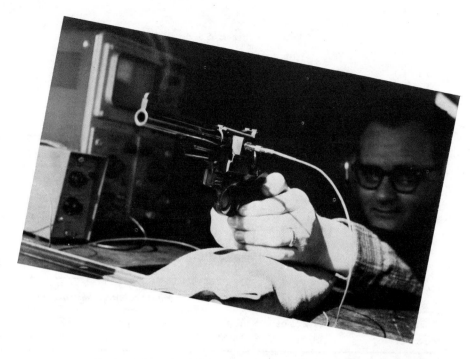

Photos by Elmer Imthern

Fig. 1—Author using 357 Magnum pressure revolver. Pressures are carried by the coaxial cable from the revolver to the charge amplifier and oscilloscope in background.

The machine shop crew was supplied with a Smith & Wesson Model 27 chambered for the 357 Magnum. Like our solid test barrel it too had a barrel length of 6 inches. Within a week the original 6-shot cylinder was replaced by a single-shot cylinder which used the original yoke to swing out for normal loading and unloading. (See figs. 3 and 4.) On its left side it was tapped for the transducer. Finally, after all the years the revolver had been in use, it was at last given its own pressure system. The replacement cylinder came from the heat treatment with a soft blue finish. When the small stainless steel transducer was installed in its side it sat there shining like the eyes of a new bride. With the impatience of a groom I headed for the laboratory to try the new test gun.

High psi, Low fps

I'll never forget how disappointed I was when I tried my new invention and found that pressures were higher. Here I was, trying to find what the psi loss was for a long list of powders, and not getting the expected loss. I thought of placing a second transducer on the other side of the gap in search of a way to measure the pressure "loss" in revolvers. Because of the gap, revolvers had always lost velocity. So why not pressure? For a long time we had known about base upset or the slugging-up of bullets in revolvers, as

some refer to it. Sure, we knew that, but who could have guessed that this unavoidable aspect could cause higher pressures. Throat diameters in revolvers will often vary as much as .002″ between the 6 holes of a single cylinder. In a 357 Magnum these 6 exit holes could be from .358″ to .360″. In any firearm the *base* of the projectile always starts to move *first*. In the revolver, with its oversize throats, the moving base upsets even *more*. Next, another feature common only to the revolver is a funnel-shaped forcing cone leading into the barrel proper—again, a place for the bullet base to upset further. The best way to realize all this is to remove the barrel from a revolver and fire a cartridge from the cylinder only. Upon recovery note that the base of the bullet, not the point, is very much upset or expanded.

At the moment of peak pressure, we now learned, there is no gap! The much enlarged bullet has it filled. It takes an average of an extra 3,000 to 4,000 psi to swage the bullet back down to groove size. As soon as the bullet clears the gap, the powder gases then escape very rapidly, thus we get a lower velocity from our revolvers. The pressure lasts only half as long in revolvers as in solid barrels of the same length with most powders. (See Table 1.)

Variables are the things that cause people in this business many sleepless nights. The gap in revolvers will vary from .006″ to .015″. Even in quality revolvers I've seen

some which would measure .006″ on one side and .013″ on the other. Barrel groove diameter for the 38 Special and 357 Magnum comes in "standard" sizes from .355″ to .358″. The groove diameter of the two solid test barrels used in this report is .3567″. The groove diameters of the revolver barrels used in this same report are .357″ for the 38 Special and .3572″ for the 357 Magnum.

By realizing that these variables do exist, it is possible to use some of them to our advantage to reduce pressures. The three most important dimensions of revolver bullets which we may vary are weight, length and, most important, diameter. We have always reduced our powder charges as the bullet weight was increased, so nothing new here.

Bullet Diameters

Bullet diameter, however, is the most important dimension related to pressure in revolvers. A change in diameter makes things happen fast. A charge of 2.9 grains of Bullseye with the popular 148-gr. hollow-base wadcutter of .358″ diameter in the 38 Special gives a pressure of 9,000 psi in the solid test barrel. The same load in the new pressure revolver gives 13,000 psi. Again using 2.9 grains of Bullseye and the 148-gr. wadcutter of .3565″ diameter, the pressure is the same in both guns but the velocity is less than the velocity of the .358″ diameter bullet. (See effect of

Table 1 — Pressure Time

Revolver vs. Solid Barrel
(both barrels 6″)

Load #1

357 Magnum, Speer 158-gr. JSP Bulletin, 15.0 gr. 2400

| | Peak | Pressures at | | |
		100 Microseconds	200 Microseconds	300 Microseconds
Solid Barrel	31,412 psi	23,020 psi	14,914 psi	9,682 psi
Revolver	33,558	22,338	9,996	5,100

Load #2

357 Magnum, Speer 158-gr. JSP Bullet, 9.0 gr. Unique

| | Peak | Pressures at | | |
		100 Microseconds	200 Microseconds	300 Microseconds
Solid Barrel	31,221 psi	17,685 psi	9,979 psi	5,829 psi
Revolver	33,201	14,943	5,967	2,907

These two popular 357 Magnum loads were used to illustrate pressure vs. time in both revolvers and solid barrels. Note that while in both loads the pressure was highest in the revolver at the peak, at 300 microseconds the pressure is only about half as much in the revolver. This then explains the velocity loss in revolvers.

Fig. 2—A "solid" pressure barrel herewith transducer fitted.

diameter with jacketed bullets in Tables 2 and 3.) The 357 Magnum, operating at higher pressures, is just as quick to detect a diameter difference in the tougher jacketed bullets as is the 38 Special with its slowest load and lead bullets. (See fig. 5.)

Bullet length becomes a factor as the weight and diameter are increased. If the seating depth is deep then more time is required for the longer bullet to cross the gap, allowing more time for base upset.

Modern lightweight bullets take advantage of all these variables to gain velocity with acceptable pressures. This again is illustrated with the 110-gr. bullets used in Table 3. The 357 Magnum is limited to one seating depth—*deep!* In the 38 Special, should one choose to use jacketed bullets cannelured (crimp grooved) for the 357 Magnum, the resulting load would not only be quite short over-all but it would result in higher pressures if the load were not reduced. However, with bullets cannelured especially for the 38 Special it is possible to reduce pressures with all bullet weights. (See fig. 6 and Tables 6 and 7.) Why? Because this bullet has only a short jump to clear the gap and doesn't have time to upset and raise pressures.

Only a few years ago the available handgun bullets were of relatively large diameter. In the 38 Special and 357 Magnum, cast bullets were .358″ to .359″ at least, and the few jacketed bullets to be had were at least .357″. The expander plug which came with a set of dies was, and unless otherwise specified still is, .3565″ to .357″. Most of these bullets were of semi-wadcutter, wadcutter, or round-nose design with crimp grooves near the point so the expanders were not only large but quite long.

Expander Diameters

Nowadays, especially, the guy who loads the 38 Special and 357 Magnum needs two or three expanders. An expander of about

Fig. 3—A Smith & Wesson K-38 with its two interchangeable cylinders, yoke and transducer.

Fig. 4—A loaded round in the pressure cylinder, ready for testing.

Table 2
Effect of Bullet Diameter on Pressure
Load #1
357 Magnum, Speer 125-gr. JSP Bullet, dia. .357", 19.5 gr. 2400

	Average Pressure
Solid barrel	36,152 psi
Revolver	39,168

Load #2
357 Magnum, Speer 125-gr. JSP Bulletin, dia. .355", 19.5 gr. 2400

	Average Pressure
Solid barrel	35,270 psi
Revolver	33,860

Note here that the .357" diameter bullet **raised** pressures in the revolver by 3,000 psi. The .355" diameter bullet in Load #2 **lowered** pressures in the revolver by 1,500 psi. The difference between the two **revolver** loads is a big 5,000 psi.

The smaller bullet has an extra .002" to upset. This gives it **time** to cross the gap with **less** distortion and pressure.

Velocity loss with the smaller diameter bullet? 50 fps.

Fig. 5 (above)—Two 38 Specials with 158-gr. SP bullets. The longer round on right will give less pressure.

.354" to .355" with a very short shank is necessary for short, lightweight bullets of the new smaller diameters or the heavier ones to be seated out with only a short portion of the bullet inside the case. (See fig. 7.) The workhorse among expanders for the 38 Special and 357 Magnum is still the one of medium shank length in a diameter of .3565". Wadcutters, especially the hollow-base types, need an expander of at least .358", with a shank about as long as the bullet to prevent a partial closure of the hollow base upon seating.

Cast bullets have been around longer than the revolver. The more knowledgeable have known for many moons that different alloys will produce bullets of different diameter and weight from the same mould. (See Table 4.) Table 5 illustrates the pressure differences for each lot of these cast bullets in both solid barrels and revolvers. The very ordinary loads of 2.7 grains of Bullseye and 5.0

Figs. 6 and 7—Expanders for light bullets (below left) on those seated out should have short shank of smaller diameter ● Both lead and jacketed bullets that require deep seating need expander of adequate length and diameter.

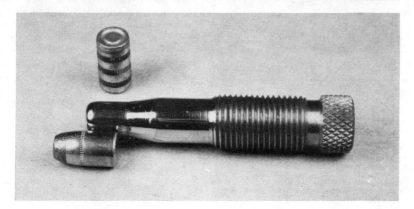

Table 3
Modern Lightweight Bullets

357 Magnum, 15.0 gr. SR-4756, Primer - CCI 500, Bullet - 110-gr. JHP, dia. .3555"

	Average Pressure
Solid barrel	38,334 psi
Revolver	33,048

By reducing bullet weight, length, and diameter it is possible to produce revolver loads which give velocity with acceptable pressures.

Table 4
Effects of Alloy with Cast Bullets

Alloy	Wgt./grs.	Dia./inch
1-200	154	.3585
1-24	154	.3585
1-16	154	.3590
1-10	149	.3595
Type metal	140	.3595

The above bullets were cast in the same mould and sized in the same sizer. The difference in weight and diameter was caused by the alloy used.

Table 5

Pressure Changes with Cast Bullets

Load #1

38 Special, 2.7 gr. Bullseye

Bullet Alloy	Average Pressure, Solid Barrel	Average Pressure, Revolver
1-200	7,064 psi	8,568 psi
1-24	7,064	10,710
1-16	7,904	10,506
1-10	8,052	12,138
Type metal	6,916	12,138

Load #2

38 Special, 5.0 gr. Unique

Bullet Alloy	Average Pressure, Solid Barrel	Average Pressure, Revolver
1-200	12,745 psi	18,258 psi
1-24	13,783	19,482
1-16	13,239	21,012
1-10	13,289	20,400
Type metal	11,609	20,400

The bullets used in the above test are the same as the ones shown in Table 4. As may be seen, alloy is important.

Table 6

Pressure Changes Related to Seating Depth with Light Bullets

Load #1

38 Special, Speer 125-gr. JSP Bullet, dia. .356". Loaded to over-all length of 1.450", 6.5 gr. Unique.

	Average Pressure
Solid barrel	18,300 psi
Revolver	19,400

Load #2

38 Special, Speer 125-gr. JSP Bullet, dia. .356". Loaded to over-all length of 1.550", 7.5 gr. Unique.

	Average Pressure
Solid barrel	17,500 psi
Revolver	16,300

Load #2 used a bullet cannelured especially for the 38 Special. This allowed a loaded length longer by .100" and one more grain of powder!
While the velocity of the two loads is the same, Load #2 gave 3,000 psi less pressure in the revolver!

Table 7

Pressure Changes Related to Seating Depth with Heavy Bullets

Load #1

38 Special, Speer 158-gr. JSP Bullet, dia. .356". Loaded to over-all length of 1.450", 5.0 gr. Unique.

	Average Pressure
Solid barrel	15,500 psi
Revolver	16,500

Load #2

38 Special, Speer 158-gr. JSP Bullet, dia. .356". Loaded to over-all length of 1.550", 6.0 gr. Unique.

	Average Pressure
Solid barrel	17,000 psi
Revolver	16,000

In this test Load #2 again used bullets cannelured especially for the 38 Special and again one more grain of powder.

While pressures were about the same in the revolver, Load #2 this time gave 50 fps more velocity.

grains of Unique were used. As may be seen from the tables, if you cast your own bullets you should try to use as near the same alloy for each lot of bullets as possible.

It has been my experience that most of the revolvers in the Speer lab gave the best accuracy with the smaller diameter bullets. It is my belief that, as the larger bullets are swaged up and down in the forcing cone, their jackets and cores are loosened and the bullet is no longer one solid unit. The smaller bullet of .355", say, crosses the gap with much less change, resulting in a more concentric projectile in flight —hence better accuracy.

Cannelure Problems

It seems there is always one fly around to fall into the soup. The fly this time is that few jacketed bullets are available cannelured especially for the 38 Special. Most sporting goods dealers' shelves are already full of items designed to catch the sportman's eye. To carry bullets for both the 38 Special and the 357 Magnum would mean twice the inventory and shelf space. It is easier to carry bullets for the 357 Magnum which may be used in the 38 Special also, even though the resulting load is not all that it could be. The low-pressure loads developed by seating the bullets out in the 38 Special should not be used with some ball powders. The slower-burning ball powders burn best at higher than 38 Special pressures with bullets seated out to maximum over-all length. When these powders do not ignite and burn properly, squib loads will often result.

It's not always that something which starts out in disappointment ends in pleasure, as happened in the case with the pressure revolver. By finding the bullet dimensions which contribute to high pressures in revolvers, and making the necessary changes, it is now possible to load revolver ammunition at lower working pressures. The fact that the same ammunition improved accuracy and did not give large pressure and velocity changes in different guns was indeed a nice bonus.

The revolver has been with us for a long time. I still find it hard to believe that it has kept its secrets from us until after man was on the ' moon. Yet we have our space-age technicians to thank for giving us the transducer. Revolvers usually last a long time. If through this Speer research your revolver lasts even longer, then our efforts were not in vain. ●

British Small-Bore Rifles

by DeWitt Bailey II

Part One—The 451 Muzzleloaders

The British 451 rifle, the small-bore of its day, grew out of a desire to improve the big-bore military rifle of the mid-1850s. The small-bore rifle— first as a muzzleloader and later as a breechloader—reached its developmental zenith in the 1880s, a period that also saw its decline and near-disappearance. The muzzle-loading 451s are reviewed here in a wealth of detail.

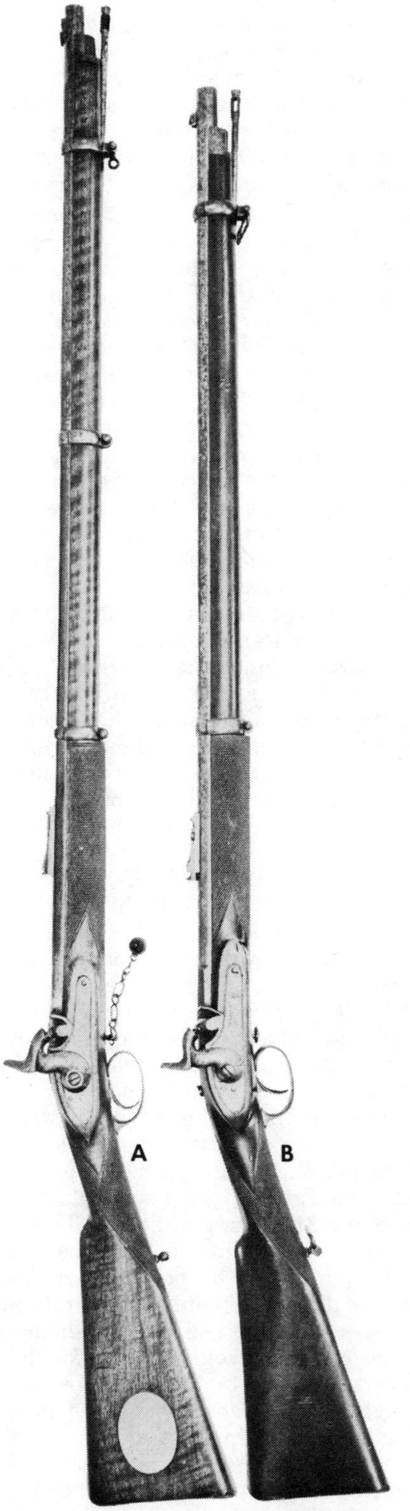

To FULLY understand the history and development of the British muzzle-loading small-bore rifle is virtually to possess a working knowledge of the British nation during the years from 1855-1870. The fabric of this historical cloth is woven of several distinctive threads, and woven into the whole is the 451 rifle. To enlarge upon but one of these threads is to miss much of the importance of the entire story and to over-emphasize to the point of inaccuracy one part of the development. A striking example of this latter tendency is the stress put upon the Whitworth rifle, at least in America, as "a Confederate sharpshooter's rifle," when, in fact, only

of London, this 33" barreled Military Rifle is one of a large number which present a problem for the student of this subject, in that the rifling system has not been positively identified. Typical of many of the cheaper forms of small-bore rifle popular in 1860-62, they were retailed by gunmakers in London and Birmingham, and often show rifling systems of obscure or original origins. That is, rifling forms not related directly to any of the patented or registered types. Although the rifling in this piece strongly resembles Henry's, there's no indication of any right to use Henry's patented system marked on the rifle. The rifle itself, because of various structural similiarities, may have been made for Wilkinson by Hollis & Sheath.

one very small part of Whitworth's muzzle-loading rifle production was ever destined for Confederate use. The actual contributions of Sir Joseph Whitworth to the development of rifled small arms have no relation whatsoever to the use of a few of his rifles by Southern marksmen during the War for Southern Independence.

The British small-bore rifle owed its existence to a request for an improvement in the large-bore military rifles made for the British government in the mid-1850s; its ultimate development was reached within a very narrow field of activity among perfectionist riflemen when the trend of the times was already moving away from the over-specialized nature of both the arm and its advocates. It ended its career in the early 1880s as an anachronism surpassed for some years by the developments in breech-loading arms and ammunition on both sides of the Atlantic. But despite these anomalies in every stage of its inception and progress the British small-bore rifle was responsible for the acceptance of major trends and tendencies in the advancement of rifled small

Fig. 1a and 1b—The most common design of small-bore rifle is the Military Rifle, which may change definition simply by the presence of a mechanically-adjustable backsight to become a Military-Target Rifle. Left (1a) *The Aston Rifle* by James Aston of Hythe, is a late example of this classification, having a 36" barrel and very refined sights although still lacking mechanical adjustment on the backsight leaf, despite its being graduated in both yards, degrees and minutes. This rifle has a plain breech, Enfield pattern lock, bronze-tipped ramrod, and a swept, separately sprung trigger. Although retailed by Aston, it was made in Birmingham by Hollis & Sheath—who made virtually all of Aston's rifles. Right (1b) Retailed by Wilkinson

arms, of both a target and military nature, from which we are still deriving the benefits today. In point of time the subject of our story occupied less than a quarter of a century, but in that space the intensive spirit of competition engendered by the initial work of Joseph Whitworth produced results far in excess of the rate of progress made over the preceding 200 years —in fact, since the invention of the rifled bore itself.

The complete story of the British small-bore rifle must be studied in terms of both the muzzle-loading and the breech-loading types. For this reason the present discussion will be divided into two parts, and each type examined in detail; for each type made positive contributions toward the ultimate design. During the muzzle-loading period— with which this article will deal— the over-all design of the rifle itself went through a bewildering number of changes, and a truly staggering variety of rifling systems was used in an attempt to equal and excel the degree of accuracy obtained by Whitworth's hexagonal bore, and to improve upon his system in terms of non-fouling, ease of loading and durability of ammunition. The efforts of designers, "military geniuses" and profit-minded gunmakers provide us with the subject of our study; fortunately for us there were a great many of these efforts which were successful enough to warrant their production on a commercial basis, thus providing the modern arms collector with a fascinating field.

The first five years of the history of the British small-bore rifle are almost entirely concerned with the birth and growth of the Whitworth rifle, and for a detailed discussion of this subject the reader is referred to the 25th edition of the GUN DIGEST, 1971.

The actual birth of the small-bore rifle was an accidental one, a by-product of the main intention of Whitworth—or at least of his original intentions. Whitworth had been asked in 1854 to design machinery for the mass-production of the "Pattern 1853 Long Enfield Rifle Musket," as the then-existing system of contracting to supply the Government with arms was not up to the exigencies of the Crimean War.

Whitworth, with little practical knowledge of the gunmaking business, set out to discover what the problems were in producing the Enfield; he found that the gunmak-ers themselves could not explain the "mysteries" of the variable performance of the Enfield arm. Whitworth then proposed that before spending much time and money in developing and building machinery to mass produce a faulty arm, steps should be taken to discover the origins of these faults and to correct them. Although given the approval of the authorities to proceed with this line of action, that sanction was obtained by a very slim margin, and Whitworth spent much of his own money as well as the government's in carrying out his experiments.

Whitworth's Experiments

The results of these showed, quite early on, that the bore of .577-inch or 24 gauge was not best-suited to the stipulated charge —2½ drams of powder and 530 grains of lead. Experimenting with bore diameter, projectile length and twist of the rifling, Whitworth found that the "ideal" figures for the above-mentioned weights were a bore of .451-inch or 52 gauge, a rifling twist of one complete turn in 20 inches, and the length of the bullet being between two-and-one-half and three bore diameters. "Length of bullet" here means the length of the actual bearing surface on the bore, not the *over-all* length of the bullet.

All this work might have been to some immediate purpose except that it took too long to accomplish and the government could not wait. They had wanted machinery to produce Enfield pattern rifles and they were not getting it. Instead their money was being spent in discovering all the faults of the Enfield rifle while the war dragged on and the supply of rifles did not significantly increase. So, early in 1856, money was allotted and machinery was purchased in America —mostly from Robbins & Lawrence of Windsor, Vermont, and the Massachusetts Arms Company of Chicopee Falls, Massachusetts, for the mass production of the Pattern 1853 Enfield. This machinery was erected at the Royal Small Arms Factory, Enfield Lock, Middlesex. By 1857 rifles were being produced at this establishment to the consternation of the London and Birmingham gun trades, but to the satisfaction of the government.

It was quite obvious, however, that Whitworth had uncovered some basic ballistic truths which could not be ignored, and in the trials of his rifles against the then current pattern service Enfield rifle the latter was left choking in the smoke of Whitworth's far superior arm. This was in 1857 and at this point a number of very pertinent problems posed themselves, problems which were never satisfactorily solved during the muzzle-loading era. Economics was the major trouble; having proceeded to set up for the manufacture of the 577 Enfield rifle, was it possible to produce the Whitworth rifle with the same machinery for approximately the same cost? Again, what with the numbers of 577 rifles already in the hands of the troops, was it feasible to re-arm them with a new caliber weapon—to spend the money to re-equip them, and the time to retrain them in the use of the new precision rifle.

While these questions were being argued in Parliament and betwen Whitworth and the Secretary of State for War and the Whitworth-Enfield Committee, both the Second China War and the Indian Mutiny broke out; by the time these had been brought under control, the financial state of the country left no doubt about the answer to at least one of the problems confronting the Whitworth rifle; it was *not* feasible to add to the cost of rifle production, nor was it thinkable to re-arm the troops unless a tremendous advantage from the military viewpoint would accrue—which could not be demonstrated as regarded line infantrymen. Whitworth had shown that his rifles could be produced with the existing machinery at Enfield for an additional 5 shillings per rifle—the current Enfield then costing £2.13.6 —about $12.84 in 1860 dollars. That 5 shillings represented a very considerable increase in cost per rifle, but this figure did not take into consideration that a better grade of iron—homogeneous iron—would be used for the barrel to withstand the far greater frictional wear caused by the long bullet and deep angular rifling of Whitworth's system. Whitworth committed what turned out to be a major blunder at this point; he offered to supply 1,000 or 1,100 of his rifles for the arming of a special regiment on an experimental basis, at a cost of 10 pounds per rifle—$48.00! This staggered the financial minds in Parliament and Mr. Sidney Herbert, Secretary of State for War, made it clear that while he would like to see the Whitworth rifle experiments carried on with a view to reducing their cost and increasing their military efficiency, there was no hope of the rifle being adopted while the price remained at anything like the present level. Whitworth hastened to explain—far too late—that his price was based upon a relatively small order of excellent quality arms made at his newly commenced works, and that the price would certainly be much reduced if a very large order were given. Too little, too late—the effect of the 10 pounds-per-rifle statement could not be ameliorated and, so far as the government were concerned, the project was shelved for the time. All of these events occurred in late 1858 and early 1859, during which period Whitworth decided to take his rifle "to the country" and enter the commercial market. This he proceeded to do about the middle of 1859. At this point our story rapidly expands and before proceeding further some definitions will be useful to the understanding of coming events.

Some Definitions

Small-bore rifle in the present context means a rifle of between .44- and .46-inch in caliber (such rifles will bear bore/gauge markings among the London or Birmingham proof marks at the breech, of between 56 and 48 gauge) with a rifling twist generally of one full turn in 20 inches; however, these may vary to as tight as one turn in 18 inches and as slow as one turn in 30 inches. This definition should also include, ideally, the stipulation that the bullet for the rifle will be at least two-and-one-half bore diameters in bearing surface length; but as this is not a factor readily discernible from the rifle itself it must be included only provisionally. Once having given a definition the exceptions must be noted; rifles of 30 caliber and approximately 40 caliber were made by several makers during the period in question (1855-1865 at the moment), notably a 30-caliber sporting rifle marketed by Whitworth on a limited production basis, and some 40-caliber offhand rifles

made by Thomas Turner, both using "small-bore" principles in the rifling. Other, "one-off" rifles of similar type may be found. It must be remembered that, although machinery was making great inroads in the production methods of this period, gunmaking was still very largely a handwork trade, and that makers would set up what their customers required—and the results can be most upsetting to the dogmatist! Most of the small-bore rifles soon to be discussed will in fact be 451 caliber or 52 guage. The smallest "standard" system was the Lancaster, with a nominal .442-inch or 56 bore, and the largest being the Metford of .458-inch or 48 bore. It should be further remarked here that although .451-inch is the nominal size for most British muzzle-loading small-bore rifles, bullets varying in diameter from .448-inch through the normal range of Lyman 457 bullets will fit many of them quite satisfactorily.

Fig. 2—Small-bore rifles by Alexander Henry, Edinburgh. These four rifles show the structural development of the small-bore rifle from its early to its final stage. From the top: (a) Military Rifle with 33″ barrel, refined Enfield back sight and wind-gauge foresight with hood. Although basically an Enfield short rifle in design, there are many minor improvements, including a patent breech with break-off, fine quality highly finished stock, bronze-tipped ramrod, detented lock and separately sprung trigger. (b) Military Rifle with 36″ twist barrel, further refined lock design, scroll trigger guard, patent breech with break-off and bronze-tipped ramrod. With the addition of a wind-gauge foresight and a mechanically-adjustable backsight, this rifle would classify as a Military-Target Rifle. It is typical of the confusion caused in classifying these rifles by the inclusion of a variety of features typical of one style but not of another, and all in one rifle. (c) Sporting-Target Rifle with 34″ full octagonal barrel, half-length pistol grip stock, and sporting pattern breech. Henry may have been the first to introduce this design to Wimbledon, which in turn led to the introduction of the full-blown Match Rifle. There is no provision for a tang sight, but the backsight (leaf missing) is of Henry's patent and is mechanically adjustable for elevation. Henry's "Patent Elevating Cheekrest" is fitted to the stock and allows the cheekpiece to be raised to suit the shooter's face by means of the screw on the bottom. (d) The Match Rifle in its most advanced state as manufactured by Henry: full-round 36″ barrel, no provision for ramrod, deeply curved pistol grip stock, and the flat plane for mounting the tang sight are all typical. The breech snails on the 1st, 2nd and 4th rifles, as well as the long stocks, are typical of Henry's production.

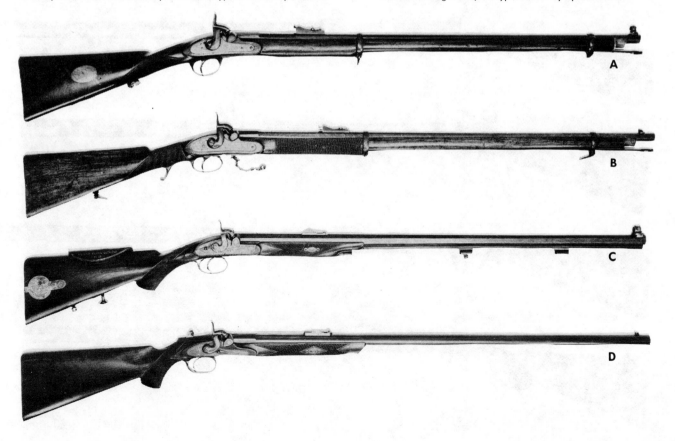

A

B

C

D

If it is not already clear from the context of the present article, the term "small-bore" is used in the original sense of the 1860s to distinguish between the "large-bore" or "government bore" of .577" or 24 gauge and this smaller size, in much the same manner as "full-bore" and "small-bore" are used today to distinguish between 30- and 22 calibers respectively.

The illustrations give an adequate conception of the various designs of small-bore rifles, but in order to prevent confusion and to allow of more precise description, here are criteria for the identification of the several distinct patterns of muzzle-loading small-bore rifles, as seen in figs. 1 and 2.

Small-bore Military Rifles. Full-stocked with band-fastened barrel and steel ramrod (sometimes with bronze tip); sights consisting of blade or hooded bead foresight (occasionally adjustable for windage) and a back sight of a refined Enfield pattern with stepped side flanges, a leaf and notched slide, which is operated by the fingers without any mechanical devices, and not windage adjustable.

Small-bore Military-Target Rifles. Full-stocked with band-fastened barrel and steel ramrod as above. Sights consisting of hooded bead or aperture windgauge foresight, backsight of either refined Enfield pattern or one of the several patented finely-calibrated sights such as Kerr's, Newton's, Whitworth's rack-and-pinion, or Blanch's. Sometimes there is provision for a tang sight and, much more rarely, for a heel sight.

Sporting-Target Rifles. Half-stocked, generally with full pistol grip; full octagonal barrel with top rib and wooden ramrod beneath. Sights consisting of hooded bead or open blade foresight, both types generally windage adjustable, and a backsight of one of the several patented patterns with mechanical elevation adjustment and fine calibrations. Tang sights are occasionally fitted. Many of these rifles do not conform to the 10-lb. maximum weight limitation imposed by most rifle associations of the time. Although obviously derived from the contemporary sporting rifle, the object in using this pattern was to concentrate the maximum amount of weight in the barrel in contrast to the military patterns which dispersed much of the weight in furniture, steel ramrods and full length stocks. External evidence indicates that these rifles were primarily intended for target shooting, but by a simple substitu-

Fig. 3. The development of the small-bore military rifle into the Military-Target rifle. From the top (a) Military rifle by Thomas Turner, the plainest of the plain; save for its more finely graduated backsight this rifle would pass for a 577 Enfield with a 36" barrel. (b) Rifle by Parker, Field & Sons, London, very highly finished and fully engraved. The 33" twist barrel has an unidentified pattern of rifling, patent breech with break-off, and a full-length flat along the barrel top. The foresight (missing) was of windage-adjustable blade pattern with provision for a sight-shade to be slid into grooves in the barrel. This is a presentation rifle of the highest quality throughout, within its general classification. The barrel is keyed through the fore-end in addition to the usual bands; also note the form of the bronze-tipped rod. (c) The London Armoury Company's small-bore "Kerr rifle," introduced in mid-1861. Every part of this rifle is interchangeable with the issue 577 Enfield Rifle Musket as made either at Enfield or by the L.A.C. (the only two establishments making completely interchangeable Enfield rifles). There are no improvements in the construction of this rifle over the standard Enfield except for the detented tumbler, the sights and the use of Kerr's ramrod (fig. 7). Bottom (d)—the Military-Target Rifle in a very advanced form, made by John Walker, Balgonie, Fifeshire. While retaining the full-length stock, steel ramrod and barrel bands of the Military Rifle, this piece contains more than the usual number of refinements which combine to form the Military Target Rifle. The breech and lock are of more sporting than military style, as is the trigger guard assembly and general style of butt, with its pistol group and capbox. The 34" barrel has a full-length flat; the foresight is a modern replacement of the windgauge hooded original; the backsight is of Henry's pattern, and there are mounts for both tang (here removed) and heel sights, all being original to this piece. Military-Target Rifles showing this high degree of refinement are most unusual.

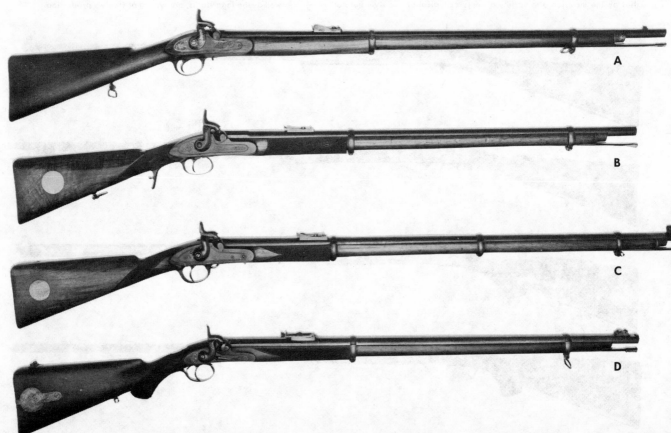

tion of more elementary forms of sights the rifle could be used for sporting purposes. They were not, however, designed for high velocity loads and were ballistically unsuited to the then-prevailing ideas on sporting rifle loads.

Small-bore Match Rifles. Half-stocked, generally with full pistol grip, and no provision for a ramrod. Full-round 36-inch barrels are normal. Sights include a hooded aperture windgauge foresight and a Vernier aperture tang sight; later rifles were occasionally fitted with a heel-position base as well. Some rifles will also have a rear barrel sight, but this is not a requisite for the pattern. For N.R.A. competitions the maximum permissible weight was 10 lbs.

The above are *structural* definitions of the basic patterns of smallbore rifles, but there are many features which may be taken as characteristics of the several types, and which in many instances will be found on more than one type, hence their exclusion from the above fundamental descriptions. These various characteristics occur in something of a chronological sequence and they'll therefore be described in "date order," However, this must not be construed as anything like definitive, for gunmakers would supply whatever the customer required regardless of the current fashion which did, of course, largely dictate the individual construction of a particular rifle.

Variant Types

The early history of the smallbore rifle was entirely of a military nature. The Whitworth experiments which gave existence to the entire system were conducted with a purely military objective in view, and the result is that the smallbore military rifle dominated the scene for about the first two years of the commercial existence of this class of rifle, that is, 1859-1861. Therefore, most rifles of this pattern will have 33-inch barrels, in common with current patterns of the service Short Rifle; and while the stocks of many are checkered with large coarse diamonds, some are plain and conform very closely to the Enfield service pattern rifle, (figs. 1 and 2). Barrel bands, ramrods, trigger guards and buttplate, and often the locks, are of typical Pattern 1853 Enfield design. They are, however, in most cases more highly finished and often bear some elementary scroll or floral engraving.

Some rifles, which generally date from 1861 or even later, will have

36-inch barrels, as this length was found to give better ballistic performance; in fact, had not the 39-inch barrel length been considered necessary for the Rifle Musket to serve adequately as a pike to dismount cavalrymen, the length of the barrel for the service rifle would have been reduced to 36 inches, as this was shown to be the ideal length for the 530-gr. bullet and 2½ drams of powder used with the slow rifling twist.

There are many refinements in construction found on these rifles—patent breeches, usually of the break-off or hook-breech type; locks with detented tumblers and lightweight, elaborately designed hammers; separately sprung triggers, locks held with but one side screw, and furniture similar to that used on contemporary sporting rifles, far more decorative than military mounts. Scroll or semi-scroll trigger guards were popular, these giving a firmer grip than the straight stock without the additional expenses of a pistol grip stock.

Some ramrods, while retaining the pattern of the service rod, have the head made of bronze to reduce the possibilities of damage or wear to the rifling during loading and cleaning, and there are a number of variant designs which also occur in bronze.

Some barrels are octagonal for a few inches at the breech before merging into a tapered round form for the remaining length, which gave a better grip when removing the breech plug, besides adding strength at the point of greatest strain. Most military rifle barrels, however, closely follow the external contours of the service rifle.

The Military-Target Rifle

The characteristics of the Military-Target Rifle are the result of experience and a refinement in fashion, carried out within the military format. Throughout the early history of the small-bore rifle the suitability of the system for military purposes was kept uppermost in the minds of all those concerned, and when a division in this attitude did occur the history of the small-bore rifle becomes a duality, one branch of which grows into an over-specialized mechanical dream world (roughly equivalent to small-bore bench rest shooting today), and the other continues actively into the field of the military breech-loader.

The refinements in sights referred to as part of the basic

definition of this class came about from obvious necessity coupled with an absence of clear-cut regulations concerning this feature—an omission which was remedied in 1864 by the adoption of several classifications of rifles and sighting equipment by the National Rifle Association.

The barrels of this pattern are mostly of the 36-inch length, and often have some refinements in design over the plain military pattern, including octagonal breeches or full length nocksforms, sporting-pattern patent breeches, or simply three flats at the breech (see fig. 3d). Because of the 10-lb. weight limitation imposed by the N.R.A. they tend to be somewhat thinner than the barrels of the shorter military rifles. (This relative thinness of barrel was undoubtedly one of the reasons for the development of the match rifle; with these the weight could be concentrated in the barrel to reduce the effects of recoil and vibration, both of which were considerable with heavy charges and must have been a disadvantage tending to nullify the advantage of the longer sight radius.)

The military-target rifle appeared late in 1860, and grew in popularity through 1861 and 1862. The refinements in construction referred to in describing the small-bore military rifle apply to this pattern as well, but in a large proportion. There are also a number of further advancements to be noted as well. Fashion may have dictated the trend and certainly it increased the elegance of the over-all effect, but the use of lighter-weight military locks and sporting-rifle or shotgun locks and furniture contributed practically to the increased efficiency of the rifle, once again by allowing more weight to be put into the barrel. This combination of military and sporting features was a relatively late improvement and must have added to the cost of the rifle as well, so that examples of this type are not as common as are the plainer varieties.

Rifles of this pattern are often fitted with the "Improved" or Baddeley-patent barrel bands, designed to avoid catching in the soldier's clothing. It was originally intended that they should be used on cavalry carbines only but were subsequently approved for all service arms in June, 1861. Their appearance on a civilian rifle, either of Volunteer caliber or small-bore, if original, will date such a firearm as of post-mid 1861 manufacture. However, they are not commonly found on such rifles save for the late type just described, and they were not universally adopted for all service rifles, but only those produced at Enfield and by the London Armoury Company. The military-target rifle represents the ultimate development of target shooting shoulder arms within a military frame of reference. Every attempt at refinement in both sights and mechanical improvement will be found on these rifles, including full pistol grip stocks, heel and tang sights, finely finished locks, and the full array of best quality sights, those which subsequently appeared on match rifles. On this latter point it should be noted that many military-target rifles, as well as the military rifle class, will have been "modernized" during their working life with more elaborate sights than those with which they were originally equipped at the time of sale, and it is often difficult to determine whether this modernization took place during the 1860s or the 1960s!

Sporting-Target Rifles

Chronologically speaking we come next to the Sporting-Target Rifle category, among which there is a complete absence of military features in favor of those of the sporting arms of the day. Obviously this form of rifle existed before the appearance of the small-bore rifle, but this particular combination of sporting rifle construction with target sights does not seem to have been adapted to the small-bore system at least until 1860 or early 1861. It is believed that Alexander Henry, the eminent gunmaker of Edinburgh, may have been responsible for introducing the pattern to the small-bore rifle system. Certain it is that both Henry and Thomas Turner of Birmingham, both prolific makers of small-bore rifles, made this pattern the standard of their production, although they did make rifles in all of the other categories as well.

As there were no regulations in force governing the particulars of non-military rifle matches before 1864 affecting stock and barrel patterns, this type was one obvious answer to the problem of concentrating the weight of the weapon in the barrel. Although the barrels were usually about 33 inches long, sometimes 36, the half-length stock and lighter lock and furniture, and the wooden rather than steel ram-

rod, allowed the weight of the barrel and rib to be much heavier. Standard characteristics of the type include a patent break-off breech; sporting pattern lock with detented tumbler and single side screw; horn stock tip; sporting pattern trigger guard and buttplate with scroll, floral or game scenes engraved thereon (and often a circular cap-box in the butt as well); separately sprung trigger (sometimes cross-hatched); checkered pistol grip and fore-end, the wood of very fine quality walnut with excellent grain and color contrast, and very highly finished throughout.

There is a curious dearth of rifles of this pattern by other makers than Henry and Turner. Odd examples are known by various makers (fig. 4) but nothing indicating any sort of preference for this design, the advantages of which over the military types are so manifest. The incentives for retaining a military design must have been very strong indeed to limit the popularity of this far more practical form for a target rifle, and this military predeliction becomes even more evident when the match rifle was introduced.

The Match Rifle

The final stage in the development of the British small-bore rifle during the muzzle-loading period is represented by the Match Rifle, which appears to have been first introduced by the Whitworth firm during 1862, and to have made its first official appearance during the Wimbledon Meeting of that year. For some reason its impact was not felt during most of 1862, but by the end of the year, and certainly by the time of the 1863 Meeting, it had swept all before it.

Until this time Whitworth had been receiving considerable competition from Henry as to which of them made the most accurate rifle, neither having established a very large lead over the other at the various rifle meetings since the introduction of the Henry rifle at the close of 1860. From this time onwards, however, until the growth in popularity of the Rigby and Gibbs-Metford rifles, the Whitworth Match Rifle with hexagonal projectiles was the most popular rifle throughout the country.

The match rifle was a precision instrument designed specifically for maximum accuracy at extreme ranges, that is, a 800, 900 and 1,000 yards and even beyond. Matches at 1,200 and 1,400 yards

were held at a number of provincial meetings although they did not figure in the Wimbledon program during the muzzle-loading period. With the development and success of the match rifle came the split in thinking regarding the practical value of pure accuracy in a rifle as opposed to accuracy plus military functionality. Even though finished to the highest degree in every particular of its design and construction the match rifle was aptly described by a contemporary marksman (who owned several and had his own private 1,000-yard range) as a "useless toy." In terms of military usefulness this cannot be denied. Delicate throughout in its design, except for the mass of its full-round 36-inch barrel, the match rifle was the perfect ballistic instrument of its time, with emphasis on the word "instrument" in all its implications of correct and careful handling by a highly skilled marksman. On the one hand it was obvious that no other arm intended for target shooting could compete with this type, while on the other it was equally as clear that such a rifle was totally unsuited for military use, and that adoption of any salient features of the match rifle into a military weapon was not practical.

As a result of the controversy which raged through 1863, a Conference of the leading riflemen of England was convened in London in January, 1864. Several decisive steps were there taken to clarify the conditions under which target shooting and military small arms advancement were to be carried on henceforth. The results, so far as the rifles were concerned, were really three-fold: the Enfield service rifle and its derivative patterns were set apart in a category of their own; the small-bore rifle was defined and separated into three classes according to sighting equipment and weight; under this last category, breech-and muzzle-loading arms came under the definitions, thus opening the way for the acceptance and development of the military breech-loader.

Match Rifle Features

Of the several characteristics of the match rifle the most noticeable is the very plain finish of the majority: the dark straight-grained wood used in the stocks, the black horn or hard-rubber stock tips, pistol grip caps and sometimes buttplates as well; the almost complete absence of engraving beyond outlin-

ing borders of lockplates, hammers and mounts, and the un-ornamental contours of the components of the entire rifle: they are constructed entirely as a functional instrument of the highest quality and finish without any of the usual fripperies and ornamentation normally associated with Victorian sporting firearms, elegant though this may often be. These rifles were furnished as complete cased outfits, hence the absence of a ramrod as an integral part of the rifle itself. The sights, of delicate construction and precision design, were intended to be removed after use and kept in a separate case with all the various elements for their most effective use under varying conditions, hence the absence of many of these sights from the rifles today. The barrels are held to the stocks with one or two keys, and the patent break-off breech is standard, as in most cases the rifles were taken into two pieces to be cased or stored. The locks are of the best obtainable quality, many of them by Joseph Brazier of Wolverhampton, the leading lockmaker of the time; they have detented tumblers, finely adjusted crisp let-offs, and sliding safety bolts which lock the hammers at half-cock (figs. 2 and 5).

Relatively few gunmakers attempted to compete with the Whitworth Match Rifle. At any rate, by the time of the development of the match rifle as *the* target arm, many gunmakers had realized that as a commercial proposition there was far more future in breech-loading shotguns and sporting rifles. There was, therefore, comparatively little interest in the increasingly anachronistic world of muzzle-loading target shooting. What interest there was, however, within this small sphere, was intense, and the specialists spared no effort to out-do each other. We are

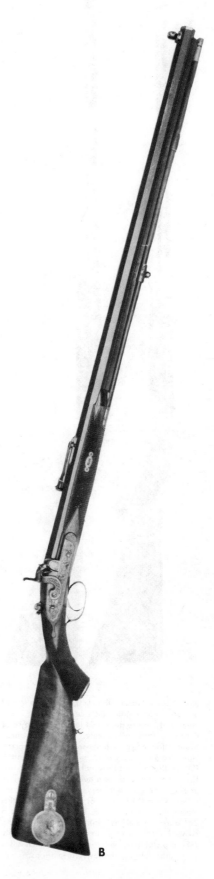

Fig. 4. Sporting-Target Rifles. Left (a) *The Blanch Rifle*, by W. H. Blanch of Liverpool, combines a Kerr barrel made by the London Armoury Company with Blanch's Patent Sights (Fig. 8) and local setting-up of the components by Blanch or in Birmingham. The 36″ military-weight barrel is unusual for this pattern of rifle; note also the use of Kerr's ramrod. Right (b) An Alex. Henry rifle that has a full set of sights (as used on many of this pattern), including a hooded wind-gauge foresight, mechanically-elevated finely-graduated backsight, and provision for an aperture tang sight. The presence of the capbox serves to remind one of the dual possibilities of this pattern, even though ballistically they were not as "hot" as contemporary sporting rifles, which used somewhat lighter bullets and larger powder charges. The shorter barrel (32″) of this example is typical of the type.

A

B

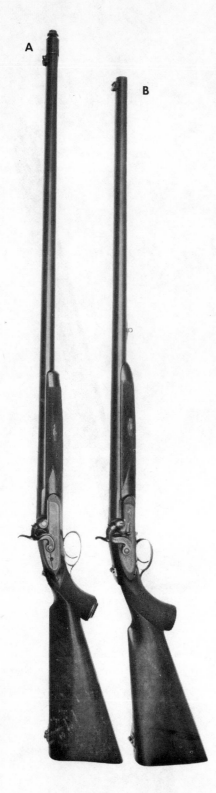

A

B

Fig. 5. Later Match rifles. Left (a) Rigby's Model of 1867, a late Match Rifle complete with false-muzzle, a feature generally found on Rigby and Gibbs-Metford rifles only. Notice the three breech flats on the otherwise round 36″ barrel, which came to be called, in America, "Rigby" flats, although certainly not introduced by this firm. The mounting for a heel sight is also quite unusual for any but very late English Match Rifles. Right (b) Ingram of Glasgow made this Match Rifle, dated 1876, unusual in having a 34″ barrel and a heel sight mounting. The sling swivel on the barrel is not original. Note deeply curved pistol grips, whereas earlier Match Rifles had longer, shallower grip forms.

therefore presented with match rifles by Whitworth, Rigby, Alexander Henry, Gibbs-Metford, Ingram of Glasgow, McCririck of Ayr, and a very small number by Turner, as well as individual examples by various other makers.

With the match rifle we come to the close of the design development of the British small-bore rifle during the muzzle-loading period. The patterns described here were to survive in varying degrees throughout the breech-loading period; in order to better understand later developments it is essential to ground one's knowledge in this earlier period, for it is upon these basic designs that the later advancements and variations were founded. General design of both rifles and sights (figs. 8 and 9), and rifling systems, were fairly well worked out during the muzzle-loading period so that there is but slight and only individual variation in these particulars encountered in the breech-loading small-bore rifles. The emphasis in these latter rifles was upon the best form of self-contained ammunition and rifling, and the most durable and functional breech system for military use.

Rifling Systems, 1854-1867

Rather than attempt to discuss briefly all of the numerous rifling systems designed between the patenting of Whitworth's polygonal bore in 1854 and the introduction of John Rigby's "imitation" of Metford's rifling in his Model of 1867—an undertaking which, in the space limitations of this article could only result in confusion and inadequate understanding—we'll confine our discussion to the seven most popular systems introduced and marketed, more or less successfully, during the muzzle-loading period of the British small-bore rifle. These are, in the order of their appearance: Whitworth (patented 1854, commercially introduced 1859); Turner, 1860; Alexander Henry, 1860; Ingram, 1860; Kerr, 1861; Metford, 1865; and Rigby, 1866-7.

Regardless of what claims may have been put forth at the time, or for that matter since, Joseph Whitworth must be awarded the palm for having brought to light and made commercially successful the basic principles of modern rifling, that is, the fundamental relationships between the size of the bore, twist-rate spiral of rifling and length of projectile. None of the systems introduced subsequently varied in any significant detail

from the principles established by Whitworth's experiments: that, in order to stabilize sufficiently for accurate flight a bullet of given weight, the bore size must be accomodated to the length of the projectile so that a rapid twist of rifling can be employed to keep the elongated bullet stable in its flight. Having been given fixed weights of 530 grains for the bullet and 2½ drams for the powder, Whitworth determined that a bore size of .451-inch would give a bullet of sufficient length, one which could be stabilized by a rifling twist of one turn in 20 inches. He had found that the government bullet was too short for the size of its bore and the rifling twist too slow for stability; by reducing the bore and increasing the twist he gave to the given weight of bullet the necessary stability. All subsequent systems—again keeping the military utility of the ultimate result always in mind—were unable to deviate far from these basics without losing the essential stability and resultant accuracy. With the exception of Metford's segmental rifling (and Rigby's, which was direct copy of Metford's in its final form) all of the rifling systems in use during the muzzle-loading period are variations upon the basic Whitworth theme, each with its own peculiarity of form and/or ammunition to justify the superior claims made for it. Of those systems which we are about to examine it may be of interest to note that the Whitworth, Henry and Ingram were offered primarily in an expensive price range, Gibbs-Metford and Rigby may be considered as of intermediate cost, while Turner and Kerr would have been in the "economy class" as far as the average range of their respective productions is concerned.

Whitworth Rifling

So much is known of Whitworth's rifling and his basic principles that only the briefest description of it will be given here. There are six angles which form the bore in the shape of a perfect hexagon, with the corner or extreme angles of each side slightly rounded off to reduce friction. The twist of the rifling is uniform at a turn in 20 inches. "Whitworth's Fluid Compressed Steel" did not come into use until after the Whitworth firm had ceased to produce muzzle-loading rifles, but Whitworth barrels during the period under discussion were in fact made of a superior and more costly metal known as "homogeneous iron." Though only obtainable from a few foundries in

England, it was more widely known and used in Germany at this time. There do not appear to have been any variations in the characteristics of Whitworth's rifling over the range of his production, nor any changes which may be considered as improvements, with a single exception: the small number of 568-caliber military rifles made late in 1863 for trials have a twist of 1 in 25 rather than the normal 1 in 20. With the exception of these and the small number of 30-caliber sporting rifles marketed by Whitworth, the entire production of his rifles was in 451 caliber.

Tom Turner's Rifles

One of the most popular small-bore rifles throughout the muzzle-loading period was that introduced by Thomas Turner of 8 Fisher Street, Birmingham, in the spring of 1860; its popularity stemmed not only from the non-fouling and accurate shooting of the rifling, but from its relatively low price. Turner's rifles always performed extremely well up to 800 yards, and could be counted upon as prize winners in the hands of capable shots at that range; beyond that they did not often get into the "magic circle" with Whitworth and Henry. Turner claimed for his rifling that it never fouled to the point of deteriorating accuracy. He advertised that 3,500 rounds had been fired through one of his barrels without cleaning or loss of accuracy. In general the claim seems to have been well-founded as there were many "unsolicited testimonials" to this effect in contemporary reports of matches throughout England. Turner's rifling was a 5-groove type with the grooves quite deep and angular at the breech; the depth and angularity gradually decreased towards the muzzle until at the muzzle it presents the appearance of 5 shallow grooves of nearly equal width with the lands, of normal form. This system is, in fact, a combination of the progressive rifling principle used in both the Enfield and Springfield rifle musket, which accomplished the self-sweeping of the bore, with the Whitworth bore size and twist. Turner's rifles were described as being of .452″ groove diameter, using a 530-gr. soft lead bullet of .441″ (plus paper patching) and from 70 to 85 grains of powder. These two charges were the standard for almost all types of small-bore rifles, regardless of the rifling system used. As previously remarked the majority of Turner's rifles were of the sporting-target pattern, closely followed by the military rifle. He produced only a very small number of match rifles. In general the quality of Turner's work would not have passed for "Best," but rather for fine Second Quality work; this is reflected in his prices, for a typical military rifle was priced between £6 and £8, while his sporting-target rifles were from £15 to £25—a top price then of about $72.

Ingram of Glasgow

Charles Ingram of Glasgow was early on the scene and late to leave it, but for all this little is as yet

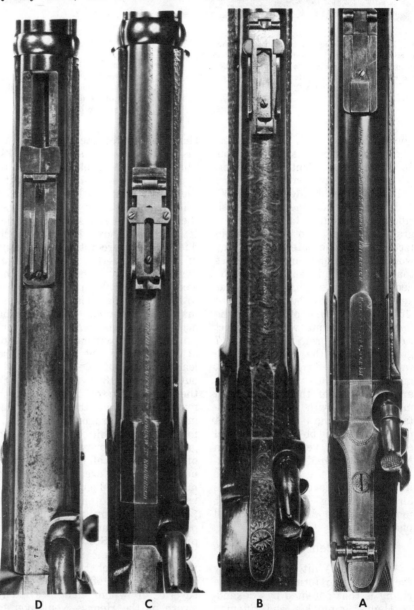

Fig. 6. Breeches and backsights on Alex Henry rifles from right (a) Plain Military Rifle breech with ordinary plug and tang, Enfield nocksform and double-shield or "Hollis breech" with flash guard both ahead and behind nipple seat. Proofmarks are on left side of barrel. The backsight leaf has been tipped forward to show dual graduations on underside of leaf, degrees on left, yards on right side. (b) Military Rifle of relatively plain finish but having a patent breech with break-off. The very plain backsight closely resembles the Pattern 53 Enfield but is smaller throughout and has smooth flanges and a slide which can be tightened in place on the leaf by the two screws shown, when the correct elevation has been determined and the slide moved up with the fingers. (c) A more elaborate interpretation of the same basic design, with engraving on the standing breech and patent breech, and a fine twist barrel. The backsight is even plainer than the one above, having a standard Enfield pattern slide; it is mounted farther away from the breech, which many riflemen thought a great improvement. (d) Match Rifle breech, the decoration restrained and of the best quality. The three separate flats on the full-round barrel (often called "Rigby" flats in America) are typical of most match rifles; they were designed to give a firm grip when removing the patent breech. An elongated tang containing the tang-sight base was one of the best means of mounting this sight, but many rifles have the mount separately let into the wood just to the rear of a normal-length tang.

Fig. 7a—Kerr's foresight is a simple barrel-shaped hood covering a thin blade, the slide being held in position by a tension screw on the forward edge of the bed. Note the Kerr pattern ramrod, also standard on the L.A.C. Kerr rifle.

Fig. 7b—Kerr's backsight, as used on the London Armoury Company's small-bore "Kerr rifle," the rifling of which was registered May 10th, 1861. Kerr's sights represent the simplest advance from the standard pattern of military sights in use on the Pattern 53 Enfield and its derivative arms. In fact the backsight is exactly the same shape and size, differing only in having dual fine graduations on both side of the leaf, and a platinum center-line on the slide and V-block. The bed has smooth rather than stepped elevators or flanges, but is of standard dimensions.

known of him and his activities. There are indications that he was an original and talented gunmaker. His rifle was present at the first N.R.A. Wimbledon Meeting in 1860, and a small coterie of Scottish riflemen continued to use the Ingram rifle well into the 1870s—in fact, during the later 1860s they won a greater percentage of prizes than they had earlier in the decade. Ingram's rifling system was again of .451" size, but a very tight .451", with a twist of 1 in 20; the form of the rifling was of distinct ratchet-wheel form, there being 7 grooves with the edges of the ratchet "tooth" forming the almost non-existent lands. Ingram's rifles are primarily of the military and match styles, with far fewer military-target and sporting-target rifles known. Fig.5b shows a typical example of a very late Ingram Match Rifle, dated 1876, which exhibits most of the salient features in the final development of this form, including the heel sight mount and the deeply curved full pistol grip.

Alex Henry Rifling

Aside from Whitworth, certainly the best-known form of small-bore rifling is that patented by Alexander Henry, gunmaker and rifleman of Edinburgh, in November, 1860. The Henry system was basically a septagon; the twist has been found to vary between rifles of from 1 in 20 inches to 1 in 30, most of them being 1 in 22 inches. In the angle of each of the seven corners of the bore is a raised V-shaped ridge, thus presenting fourteen bearing surfaces for gripping the bullet. It was this great expanse of bearing surface achieved without the very acute corner depth of Whitworth's system to which

Henry attributed the superiority of his system over his chief rival's. The Henry rifle rapidly climbed to a position of virtual equality with the Whitworth; by the time of the Wimbledon Meeting of 1861 it was the talk of the rifle-shooting world. It may well have been as much due to the more intelligent design of Henry's rifle—the sporting-target version which concentrated the weight of the rifle in the barrel—as to his rifling that this rapid success may be attributed. Whatever the actual cause the two systems continued on a virtual equality of achievement in the hands of the leading shots of the day throughout 1861 and 1862. However, with the appearance of the Whitworth match rifle and the commercial marketing of hexagonal bullets during 1862, the Whitworth rifle again gained a superiority in the minds of the riflemen of the time which no other system except the Metford managed to challenge. The Henry rifle continued to enjoy widespread popularity among riflemen in all parts of the country, especially at provincial and Scottish rifle meetings, but its name recedes notably in the Wimbledon Prize Lists from 1863, and most of the "top ten"—several of whom had previously sworn by the Henry—went over to the new Whitworth until the achievements of the Metford system attracted their attention during the 1866 season. Despite this latter comment, however, it is quite safe to say that the majority of riflemen who had any claims to superior abilities at the more extreme ranges continued to use Whitworth rifles and to a slightly smaller extent Henry rifles for the remainder of the decade. One of Henry's final contributions in the field of the muzzle-loading small-

bore rifle was the production of a patented "two-position" stocked rifle in 1878, a specialty device which allowed the same rifle to be fired with equal comfort and facility either in the normal facing-forward prone position or one of the several variations of the back-position, sometimes known in America as the "Creedmoor" or "Texas" position. Henry's contributions during the breech-loading era of the small-bore rifle were, as will be shown in Part II of this article, extensive and of paramount importance. Henry's rifles, whether breech-loading or muzzle-loading, exhibit the highest quality of workmanship and finish throughout and justify in every respect the very considerable cost of the finished product. The majority of Henry's muzzle-loading small-bore rifle production was divided between the sporting-target pattern and the match rifle, with military and military-target rifles occupying a smaller percentage of the total than is the case with either Whitworth or Turner. Fig.2 illustrates typical examples of Henry's work, while fig.6 shows several of Henry's sights. Contemporary writers often attributed a good portion of the success of the Henry rifle to the precision design of the sights and the care with which each rifle was sighted-in prior to being sold. One comparative disadvantage noted by several riflemen of the time was the proportionately heavier bullet weight and powder charge with which the majority of Henry's rifles seemed to function best—a 540-gr. bullet and from 90 to 105 grains of powder—which, in terms of the Curtis & Harvey No. 6 powder of the 1860s was a very powerful charge indeed, especially when used in a rifle the weight of

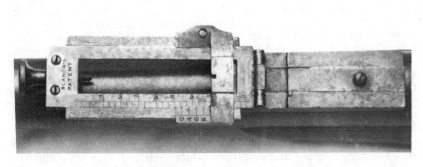

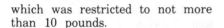

Fig. 8a. W. H. Blanch's sights, introduced at the Wimbledon Meeting of 1862. Blanch was the first to use a Vernier-scale slide coupled with degrees and minutes of elevation, a system subsequently adopted by most other makers. This method brought organizations out of confusion in recording sight readings, making the interchange of information between long-range shooters much easier. Fitted to a normal pattern of sight-bed with center tension spring, the leaf and its screw-adjusted Vernier slide were removed when not in use, as was the normal practice.

Fig. 8b. The foresight used a larger bed than normal, hence could be fitted with a very wide slide allowing for extreme windage adjustments; it was also sturdier in construction than many other contemporary foresights of the type. Note the bronze-tipped ramrod.

which was restricted to not more than 10 pounds.

James Kerr's Rifling

Next to appear on the market was the small-bore rifle of the London Armoury Company Limited, its rifling system a ratchet pattern registered by the company superintendent, James Kerr, in May, 1861. The rifle did not reach the production stage in time for the Wimbledon Meeting of that year, but appearing shortly thereafter it found immediate favor with the moderately-circumstanced riflemen. Kerr's rifling is a 6-groove ratchet with the top of each tooth cut off to form a flat land. The part of the system which Kerr registered was not the form of the rifling itself, but that a section of it for several inches at the breech was to be perfectly straight. This was in order to allow the bullet to upset completely into the grooving before beginning to rotate up the barrel, thereby assuring non-stripping and uniform upsetting. Kerr's was a somewhat undersize 451, nominally, but as with so many others it accepts .457″ bullets quite readily in most cases. The twist of the rifling is gaining for a short space ahead of the straight portion, but by the middle of the barrel it stabilizes at 1 in 20. The depth of the rifling is progressive, becoming shallower towards the muzzle, which greatly contributed to its non-fouling tendencies. The chief selling point of Kerr's rifle was not any alleged superiority in its rifling, but the twin excellences of its low price—starting at £5.16.0—and its complete interchangeability with the London Armoury Company's or the Enfield factory's Pattern 1853 Long Enfield Rifle Musket. This meant that a Volunteer wishing to

shoot in both Volunteer events (where only bona fide 577 Enfield rifles were allowed) and in Any Rifle competitions (where the only restrictions were the 10-lb. weight limitation and no set trigger), could do so with but one rifle at a very low cost. The basic L.A.C. Long Enfield sold for £3.8.0 (5 shillings more for a selected stock), and a Kerr 451 barrel complete with sights and correct ramrod could be had for £4 (fig.7). This meant that for a total expenditure of from $35.60 to $36.85 (U.S. dollar equivalent of the time) a Volunteer of modest means could equip himself with a rifle and two barrels equal to all occasions. There is ample evidence to indicate that this is just what many of them did, and the Kerr rifle long remained a favorite of those who did not indulge in the niceties of 1,000 yard competitions but were content with the wide range of events fired at ranges from 200 through 600 yards. Kerr's barrels were offered to the trade in general and are sometimes found in rifles by other makers, but the great majority are found in rifles of the London Armoury Company's fabrication. Although by 1867 Kerr rifles were offered in the full match rifle design, very few of these have been noted, no doubt because at the price at which they were offered—from £20 to £30— prospective buyers preferred the more renowned products of Whitworth, Henry, Gibbs-Metford, or Rigby. One of the most attractive features of the Kerr military rifle, aside from the excellent finish of both wood and metal parts, is the fine quality of the wood used on many of them; these show quite as much grain and color contrast as does the walnut used on the far more costly sporting arms of the

period. The earliest Kerr rifles were simply brass-mounted L.A.C. Enfields with a small-bore barrel and ramrod substituted, but by the close of 1862 more elaborate forms —including iron furniture and engraved locks with detented tumblers—were offered, and those dated 1863 form the normal production pattern (fig.3c).

Any really adequate consideration of the careers of John Rigby and William E. Metford would require far more space than is available here. The life of either could easily fill a book, even if it were largely devoted to their contributions in the quite limited field of the small-bore rifle. Therefore we can only touch in the briefest fashion upon the most important points in the careers of these men in the present context. Although their backgrounds and contributions are widely divergent, a fact of their clashing over small-bore rifles and their pursuit of the facts on the firing line lend some similarity to the discussion.

John Rigby's Rifles

The Rigby rifle made a sudden appearance on the small-bore scene during the National Rifle Association's annual gunmaker's competitions for the rifles to be used in the following season's Queen's Prize match. In February, 1862, Rigby's rifle came second to Whitworth's in this trial, out-performing Henry's, Turner's and Ingram's rifles at 500 and 1,000 yards. From this time, until he blatantly copied Metford's rifling system and bullet design, Rigby's rifling went through a series of changes. Because there is little documentary description of these, and because the Rigby firm entered upon an extensive rebarrelling program in 1866 and 1867, most of these early patterns have disappeared. One of the earliest descriptions we have of a Rigby bore is that contained in Captain Heaton's *Notes on Rifle-Shooting*. In this volume Rigby described his rifling as being octagon in form, making 1 turn in 18 inches. The grooves form arcs of circles. It is possible that this form of rifling was in use during 1863, for in July of that year Rigby introduced a mechanically fitting bullet of a hardened composition, the hollow base filled with plaster of Paris. This rifle and bullet were quite successful in matches (chiefly in Rigby's own capable hands), so we can say that the Rigby match rifle dates from 1863 or early 1864. Next to appear was a rifling system which Rigby described as "raised spiral ridges on the interior surface of the barrel, to make corresponding indentations or grooves in the bullet," and later called simply his "5-ridged rifle." It was this latter pattern of rifle which was used in the walkover of 1864 when, the other competitors having withdrawn or been disqualified (Henry's rifles were not allowed as being 1/2000th of an inch undersize), Rigby "won" the N.R.A.'s trial for the Queen's Prize rifles of 1865. He was not satisfied with this unspectacular victory, however, and in May, 1865, 15 of his match rifles submitted were given another trial. The condition of their acceptance, imposed by Rigby, was that if they did not give results equal to Whitworth's rifles in the previous three years, the N.R.A. would not have to accept them. The results made the Rigby, in the public's eye; the "figure of merit" was 1.57 feet as against Whitworth's 1.98. During 1865 the use of the Rigby rifle at matches throughout England greatly increased, and the firm opened a London branch to cater to the new interest.

Metford and Gibbs

During 1865 the Gibbs-Metford small-bore rifle made its spectacular appearance in the hands of one of the nation's most capable riflemen, Sir Henry St. John Halford. As Metford's patent was quite vague in the description of his rifling, and did not mention his new cylindrical bullet at all,* Rigby was quick off the mark to adopt the unpatented or unpatentable features of the Metford system. A

---

*Metford had, in 1864, introduced a new bullet form. This smooth-sided cylindrical bullet was rather deeply hollow-pointed, its accuracy much improved thereby. It was not until the early 1900s that this valuable aid to precision shooting was rediscovered by the builder of Ross rifles, Sir Charles Ross. Ed.

press controversy of "open letters" between the two men followed, and it must be allowed that Rigby—by Metford's own admission—had told Metford what he intended to do. There was apparently nothing that Metford could or would do, and "Rigby's new bullet" appeared in mid-1866. The status of the "5-ridged rifles" during this period is not now known, but it seems probable that they continued in use with the new bullet until Rigby introduced his "Model of 1867," the rifle with which we're most familiar. This rifle was advertised as having accuracy equal to that of the 5-ridged rifle, with a lower trajectory. It featured very shallow grooves, like Metford's rifling, but used a uniform twist of 1 in 20 rather than the gain-twist of the Metford. The new system had 8 grooves, but the grooves are nearly flat, having very slightly rounded bottom edges, and of nearly the same width as the flat lands.

From this time on the Rigby rifle was the serious competitor of the Whitworth rifle, winning almost as many prizes in the last half of the decade as the Whitworth had during the first half. There was little to choose between the results obtained with the Whitworth, Gibbs-Metford and Rigby rifles, but the Rigby seems to have been marginally more used than Metford's type; the Whitworth gradually faded from the scene until, in the early 1870s, they are rarely noted. Rigby rifles were used during the Great International Matches of the mid-1870s largely because John Rigby was one of the organizers of the Irish Teams, not because of any particular superiority over the other two, or even Whitworth's. One of the tantalizing "ifs" of history is what the results of these matches might have been had the Gibbs-Metford rifle, in the hands of some of England's crack-shots, been used.

Wm. E. Metford, C.E.

Wm. E. Metford, a civil engineer, had been a serious student of rifles and their projectiles from the late 1840s. From then until 1865 he had made numerous important discoveries in this field, many of which subsequently came into use on both muzzle-loading and breech-loading rifles. Metford's connection with George Gibbs, gunmaker of 29, Corn Ctreet, Bristol, dates officially from 1866, but the two appear to have worked together for at least three years previously. Gibbs' rifles using Metford's rifling (both muz-

zle-loading and breech-loading) should properly be called Gibbs-Metford rifles. Metford was not a rifle- or barrelmaker. Gibbs (who was Armourer to the 1st Bristol Rifles) and Metford were enthusiastic and highly skilled riflemen. They first came to public notice in 1865 as the result of a 2,000-yard match sponsored by the N.R.A. for telescope-sighted rifles. Metford had Gibbs make a 500-caliber rifle which Metford and his companion in experimentation, Sir Henry St. John Halford, used in this competition. Previous to this time Metford's work had been mostly with large bore rifles, but during 1865 a small-bore version was made by Gibbs to Metford's design and in the hands of Sir Henry scored some impressive victories over the other leading shots using Whitworth match rifles. Very few Gibbs-Metford rifles were used during 1865; not until March, 1866, did Gibbs advertise the production of the new rifle and its hardened cylindrical projectiles. The press controversy with Rigby referred to earlier may have justified Metford to some of the people who read his letters, but unfortunately his tone was rather one of "sour grapes." Although there is no question of Rigby's theft of Metford's rifling principles, Metford did little beyond engage in a fruitless public correspondence to vindicate his claims.

Metford's rifling and bullets were carefully shepherded by Gibbs, and if contemporary comment may be relied upon every barrel made by Gibbs was personally examined and tried by Metford before it went from the Bristol shop of Gibbs. Much was made of the necessity for using Metford's bullets with the rifles. All in all the impression was created of its being a superfine specialists' instrument, and perhaps for this reason it never achieved the popular usage of Rigby's rifle, and at the same time its shooting could not be said to have greatly overshadowed that of the Rigby. The workmanship is in most instances superior to that of the average Rigby, and in contrast to the majority of the contemporary Match rifles, the Gibbs-Metford is usually very finely and copiously scroll engraved. A medium and a cheap-grade rifle was offered, but apparently found little favor compared to the £31.10.0 "best" rifle. One major disadvantage of the Metford system, which combined very shallow grooves with a gain twist, was that no internal altera-

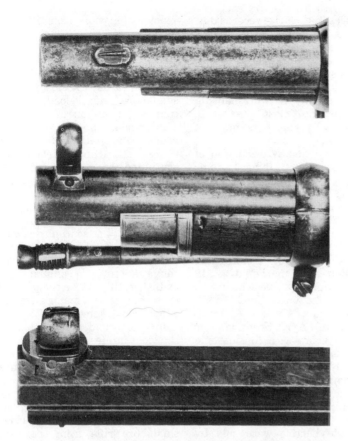

Fig. 9. Foresights. Top. Aside from the standard military blade mounted on a block (the block acting as a bayonet stud), this is the simplest form of small-bore sight; it is usually found on Military Rifles and on some Military-Target Rifles. The blade is dovetailed to allow adjustment by means of a drift and a small mallet. Middle: Hooded wind-gauge, the adjustment being made with a watch-key or similar device engaging a squared shaft, typical of many small-bore rifles. Bottom: Hooded wind-gauge with windage calibrations on the forward edge of the bed, and provision for interchangeable inserts in the top of the hood. The English rarely used the long hood so popular on American target rifles, nor was the spirit level at all widely used by English makers, nor adopted by British riflemen during the muzzle-loading period.

tions could be made on the bore, and extreme care was necessary to prevent any damage of even the slightest extent, which would spoil the accuracy of the shooting. The twist used was not constant but gradually increasing as it progressed up the length of the barrel, so it could not be successfully re-cut or "freshed-out" as could many other rifles. In addition, the rifles may have been highly sensitive to peculiarities in loading, hence the emphasis placed upon the use of Metford's specially prepared bullets, which contained a certain proportion of hardening additives. One other aspect which must have detracted from its more general popularity was that it would not use—even in a pinch—the commercially available paper-patched bullets sold by Eley Brothers and other ammunition firms; the bore of the Gibbs-Metford is .458" to .461" in diameter, and commercial bullets were of .442" diameter

patched up to .451", while Metford's projectiles began as .452" and were patched up to .460". This made ammunition problems chronic unless one dealt directly with Gibbs.

By the time the Rigby and Metford systems were in vogue and Whitworth's very deep rifling and a mechanically-fitting projectile were declining in favor, the entire emphasis in British rifle shooting had very largely shifted to breech-loading military rifles. The adoption of the Snider action, first as a conversion of muzzle-loading Enfields and then in its own right was—at about this time, 1868—viewed only as a stop-gap measure to keep pace with European developments. The basic questions of a good breech-loading action and the best rifling system and ammunition to go with it increasingly occupied the military authorities and the larger rifle meetings around the country, including Wimbledon. The

small-bore muzzle-loading rifle, although it continued in use until after 1880 was, by the latter part of the 1860s, already receding into the background even as it was reaching the zenith of its perfection and achievement. The actual scores posted during the latter '60s were far better than those of the first half of the decade; knowledge of the equipment and of the elements was superior to what had gone before. But all of these gains were misapplied by the people who had accomplished them to a highly circumscribed, extremely over-specialized field: hitting the target at 1,000 yards under the most favorable and constant technical conditions. The data gained in judging the effects of wind, temperature and humidity were of immense military value, and were used by the authorities, but rather in the sense that modern bench-rest shooting has developed, the ultimate aims were clearly separated from the main stream of practical ballistic development. It became an end in itself, not a means to an end as it had been until about 1865.

Other Rifling Systems

Several other rifling systems have not been previously mentioned because they enjoyed far less popularity or success on the ranges, but for the sake of completeness they should be at least briefly described. It must also be understood that although the majority of rifling systems were used by the patentees themselves—most of them gunmakers—there are a number of instances where the several rifling systems were used by various makers other than the patentee, usually under a licensing arrangement. This latter practice presents one of the most difficult areas of study in the field of the British small-bore rifle, but it is a highly specialized problem only to be touched upon in a general article of the present nature.

Of these several less-popular rifling systems, prominent are those of Edge of Manchester, Lancaster's oval bore, Jacob's deep 4-groove, and Aston's pentagonal. The design patented by John W. Edge in 1860 involves the combination of a flat-bottom groove with the land a curved or radiussed surface between the edges of each groove. The grooves are one-fourth the width of the curved surface of the lands. Edge patented two forms of his rifling but the one described is the type most frequently noted. The twist is one in 25, and the number of grooves has been noted as both 7 and 9. Edge's muzzle-loading rifles were made until about 1865, primarily in the military and sporting-target patterns.

Lancaster's Oval Bore

Lancaster's oval bore was the smallest of the nominal 451s, having a nominal .442″ or 56 bore. It was designed along the same lines as the far more successful 577 version, with a major and minor axis forming an elliptical bore with a gain twist increasing from 1 in 20 to 1 in 18 at the muzzle; the breech was "freed" a bit. Lancaster's small-bore rifles, although performing very creditably in the government trials of 1862, never achieved the commercial success of the government bore rifles. In the small-bore version they are almost always of the military rifle pattern, very plainly finished, and with 36-inch barrels.

Jacobs-Daw Rifling

Jacob's famous 4-groove rifling was used by George H. Daw for his 451 military rifles. This also was a scaled-down version of the larger and more popular government bore rifles and even larger sporting rifles. The twist of the small-bore Jacob is 1 in 24, and the usual barrel length is 33 inches on the plainer pattern of Enfield origin. If contemporary accounts are to be believed, most of the Daw-Jacob small-bore rifles were sent to India where they were extremely popular; certain it is that they never attained any degree of popularity in England.

Aston's Pentagonal Rifling

James Aston was the first Armourer to the School of Musketry at Hythe, and from this position he was able to absorb the ideas of many of the intelligent Volunteer and Regular officers who passed through the School's training course over the entire period we're considering. Although he does not appear in the patent records his pentagonal rifling system as used in military, military-target and match rifles is almost always described upon the top of the barrel as *The Aston Rifle.* It is a direct copy of the Whitworth rifling but has only 5 angles rather than 6. The first recorded instance of its use noted by the writer occurs in 1861. Aston rifles were quite popular as prize rifles for Volunteer units and made occasional

appearances in the prize records during the first half of the 1860s. Aston's rifles were made almost entirely by Hollis & Sheath and their successor, Isaac Hollis & Son, of Birmingham, and they do not normally exhibit a very high quality of workmanship when compared to most other small-bore rifles. A typical example is shown in fig.1a.

At the moment any discussion of the use of various rifling systems by makers other than the patentees would involve a great deal of conjecture, and be beyond the scope of this article. It is sufficient to say here that Whitworth's rifling was used under license by the Beasley Brothers of Birmingham and London, who marketed a £10 Whitworth military rifle which won a prize as early as 1862; Whitworth's rifling was also used by J. McCririck of Ayr, Scotland, for quite some years with considerable success, primarily in match rifles, and also by the Birmingham Small Arms Company who bought some Whitworth barrels in 1864 and 1865, making them up into military rifles and a few match rifles.

Kerr rifle barrels were sold by the London Armoury Company, as previously noted, and were conspicuously used by W. H. Blanch of Liverpool to make up *The Blanch Rifle* in conjunction with his own patented sights. Henry's rifling has been identified in rifles by a miscellany of makers, typical of which is the Wilkinson of London rifle shown in fig.1b. In this instance, as in most others, no credit is given to Henry for the use of his rifling. This appears to have been a typical practice save when specified in a direct licensing arrangement.

There are many rifles, chiefly of the military and military-target patterns, whose makers and rifling systems remain unidentified at this time; further study is necessary before various systems known to have been offered for sale can be positively attributed to existing examples. Many rifling systems so closely resemble one another on cursory examination that unless the examiner is thoroughly acquainted with the minute variations in appearance of each type, mistakes are often made and compounded by incorrect identification, thus greatly increasing the task of the student in this field.

We have now traced the two major contributions made to the development of the British small-bore rifle during the muzzle-loading period—basic rifle design and rifling systems

—down the years from 1855 to the middle 1860s, when technical achievement reached the point where a major division of interest and emphasis was made. From this time onwards the history of the small-bore muzzle-loading rifle is confined to the narrow circle of specialist sharpshooters at extreme ranges who, with their Whitworth, Gibbs-Metford and Rigby match rifles continued to achieve near-perfect scores up to 1,000 yards and even beyond. The study of the effect of the elements upon projectile flight and construction developed into a fine art, a study that has continued in varying forms down to this day, for England has never lost interest in extreme range shooting. The annual meetings at Bisley still feature competitions at these ranges as a major attraction to superior marksmen.

In the second part of this article the continuing development of the British small-bore rifle will be discussed in the areas of the breech-loading match rifle and its ammunition, and the divergent progress of the military breechloader, which evolved as a separate class of small-bore rifle from the time of the London Rifle Conference of 1864. The death-knell of the muzzle-loading small-bore rifle was dealt during the Great International Matches of 1874, 1875, 1876 and 1877, between the Irish riflemen and American teams armed with Sharps and Remington breech-loading match rifles. Although the victories of the breechloader were never overwhelming, considering the variety of circumstances involved in long range shooting, they were sufficiently constant to cause a growing tendency towards the use of breech-loading match rifles in England. These and other ballistic and historical developments will be dealt with in Part II of British Small-Bore Rifles. ●

The writer would like to express his sincerest gratitude to Messrs. J. B. Bell, I. McW. Davidson and M. O. A. Stanton for the loan of rifles from their collections, and to E. Holmes, Esq., for his excellent photography of those rifles.

Brief Bibliography

Heaton, Captain Henry—*Notes on Rifle Shooting.* London, 1864-1865.

National Rifle Association—"Proceedings and Annual Report of." London, 1860-1897.

The Times, London, 1860-1880.

The Volunteer Service Gazette, London, 1859-1880.

SPORTING ARMS

of
The World

The past year has seen no lessening of interest in sporting arms and hunting, even in the face of the mindless criticisms of the shooting sports that beset us daily. More hunting licenses were sold in 1971 than in any previous year—a new record for the 9th time in a row! We review here virtually all that's new in arms, ammunition and accessories, foreign and domestic, in full detail or briefly.

by LARRY STERETT, WALTER RICKELL and the editors.

IN SPITE OF repeated attempts by some so called do-gooders, and misinformed anti-hunting groups, the past year has been a good one for industry and the gun fan alike. It is hard to say there's a definite trend, but there seems to be an increasing interest in black powder arms, as forecast in our 26th edition, again in spite of legislation against black powder in some areas. There is also a renewed interest in some of the older cartridges—the 45-70 in particular—and a trend of sorts toward the use of more stainless steel in the production of sporting arms.

At least four U.S. firms have introduced new American-made black powder arms—Harrington & Richardson have two rifles in 45 and 58 caliber, plus a 12-gauge shotgun; Mowrey Gun Works has three new rifles in 45, 50 and 54 caliber, plus a 12-gauge shotgun; Esopus Gun Works has two new rifles in 45 caliber; and Thompson/Center has a new single shot pistol in 45 caliber and a double barrel 12-gauge shotgun. Navy Arms still has 4 single shot replica rolling block rifles available in 45-70 cali-

ber, but there are now at least 6 other new rifles being chambered for this oldtimer. H&R has two new carbines based on the Springfield '73 action, plus another model using their Topper shotgun action. Marlin has a new repeating lever action rifle in 45-70 caliber—the only such magazine rifle available handling that load. Ruger has a new single shot carbine-type rifle called the No. 3, available only in 45-70 caliber so far, plus the No. 1 rifle, which can be had so chambered. Clerke Recreation Products is producing a modern near-copy of the old Winchester Hi-Wall, chambered for this veteran 45 cartridge, and Artistic Arms is manufacturing a modern M1878 Sharps-Borchardt action that can be chambered for the 45-70. Apparently shooters have discovered that this century-old cartridge isn't a bad one after all.

Stainless steel has been used for rifle barrels in some calibers for many years, but Smith & Wesson started the ball rolling on its use for complete arms with their Model 60 revolver, and about 5 years ago

I field-tested a pump action stainless steel shotgun made in Sweden. Then Auto Mag started advertising their big autoloading pistol in stainless steel at about the same time the American Firearms Mfg. Co. came out with their 25 ACP autoloading pistol in stainless. At least two other firms have toyed with the production of stainless steel handguns, apparently without marked success. In early 1972 American Firearms announced three new stainless steel arms—38 Special double derringer, a 380 ACP hammerless autoloader, and a bolt action rifle. The rifle has a conventional stock with rollover Monte Carlo cheekpiece. The price varies from $400 to $895, depending on the extras.

Comments on the above and other specific sporting arms will be found elsewhere in this report, in connection with the individual firm. Over-all it looks like a good year ahead, with new products being introduced by the older firms, and a number of new firms entering the sporting arms field.

Europe 1971

My report this time on the European scene is going to be mercifully brief—there are so many good things going into this 27th edition that spare space is short indeed, so much so that some of what I put down here may be axed.

First, the good news! For some reason I'd never spent any time in Scandinavia before, but I spent a truly memorable 8 days in Sweden during late August—and I dearly wish now that I'd gone there in earlier years. It's a beautiful country, in my opinion, and certainly offering in abundance the things I've long liked—the vast pine forests stretch everywhere, even close to the big cities. In 20 minutes or so, in any direction from Stockholm, for example, there loom the great forests.

The Swedish highways, large and small, are clean and uncluttered—the never-ending billboards that disfigure our own (and some European) roadways are non-existent or nearly so. Nor does one find the long parade of shops and food purveyors lining the highways, not even as the bigger cities and towns are approached—pizza parlors and hot dog-hamburger joints, chicken-in-a-basket huts and their like, won't be found.

I saw a lot of Swedish countryside in those 8 days there, for my old friend and host, Captain Eric Claesson, drove me about in a miles-consuming, tight schedule that took us over much of southern-central Sweden.

The chief reason for my visit to Sweden was the change made in the Husqvarna Company's management and operations. A couple of years ago now, FFV (Forenade Favrik Verken), a very large quasi-governmental conglomerate, had absorbed the Husqvarna operation. The old plant at Huskvarna had ceased fabrication, with a new factory and new tools going into production at Eskilstuna, a centuries-old site of Swedish military ordnance manufacturing. I wanted to see the new Eskilstuna shops and, while I was in Sweden, several other FFV-operated concerns making products with an interest for shooters and hunters.

I spent several days in London before reaching Stockholm, a town I always enjoy visiting, but I found little of interest to report—unhappily, attrition continues its toll of the old line gunmakers—though some new gunshops have sprung up—

and the supply of arms for collectors is drying up indeed. This applies to modern, semi-modern and antique arms, and the decreased flow is reflected in the impossibily high prices. Why I wrote "impossibly" I don't know, for in spite of prices that run into thousands of dollars, often enough, the guns sell.

Anyway, London was blue-sky pleasant and I enjoyed visiting the gunshops—not that I bought anything!

Capt. Claesson, promotional manager for Husqvarna and now

Top—interior of the FFV arms factory—spacious, well-illuminated and functional. Above—FFV rifles—sporting and military—about ready for packing and shipment.

in a similar job for FFV-Sport Arms (the new company title), met me at Stockholm airport and we were soon speeding toward Eskilstuna in Eric's Volvo station wagon.

New Arms Plant

I must say I was surprised by the new FFV plant—but not unpleased. I'd thought that their new shop would, no doubt, show such modern technology as investment castings, automated machinery for making various rifle components, tape-fed milling machines and the

like. Not at all—while the new rooms were clean and spacious, brilliantly illuminated and well organized, the rifles are still being made the old fashioned way. Major components, at least, are steel forgings, carefully machined, ground and polished, with many file wielders in view! Traditionalist that I am, I was glad to see these old-school facilities and the obvious hand-made quality aspects seen in the rifles coming off the line.

I had concrete evidence of the performance built into these FFV rifles while I was at Eskilstuna. I was invited to select a rifle at random from a bank of some 38-40 sporters, all in 30-06 caliber. I did that, then waited as a 4x scope was mounted. Out at the 100 meter range I sat down at a bench, though not one like I'm used to. Most Swedish shooting is from the prone position. Wrapping myself in the sling I put 10 rounds of Norma 180-gr. soft points into less than 2 inches—1.87". In the circumstances I hold that speaks for itself—if I can shoot a rifle from rest that well it must have a helluva potential!

At Eskilstuna I also went into the military compound, where I saw a most interesting target training operation. Imagine a broad screen, some 12 by 15 feet, mounted in a slightly darkened room. Firing is done at this screen with the 6.5x55 military rifle, the ammunition an all-plastic (except for the primer) cartridge. The plastic bullet is propelled at about 1250 foot seconds, roughly half-normal velocity. When the rifleman is ready, a moving picture is projected onto the screen—I saw various game animals, these appearing to move

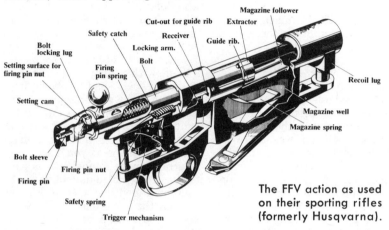

The FFV action as used on their sporting rifles (formerly Husqvarna).

rapidly or not—and in different image sizes—at the will of the projectionist. At the shot a brilliant white hole appears where the bullet struck, and a moment later the hole has vanished.

I shot some 40-50 cartridges at the moving targets, finding it a lot of fun from the offhand position—the only one tried. Range was some 10 yards or so, I believe, but the animal size can be varied greatly to simulate longer-range shooting. I haven't any cost factors on this setup, but if it weren't prohibitive, this could be a great shooting gallery sport.

Other plants visited were those of SAAB, Gyttorp and Norma, plus some 300 meter shooting which I'd rather forget about. I'd wondered why SAAB was on the schedule, having associated them with cars only, in my ignorance. I could hardly have been more mistaken. The SAAB plant Eric and I went through is a vast, multi-storied building devoted, essentially, to research and development of a wide range of precision products—gyros, navigation instruments (for SAAB-made military aircraft) scientific tools, etc.

SAAB Target Recorder

But what brought us there was

a recently-developed—and continuously being upgraded—electronic target scoring-recording device, called the BT-28, which I thought was fascinating. The recording instrument itself is positioned by the shooter, and it's adjustable in height for prone, kneeling or standing. Of moderate size (about 10"x12"x20" wide) and weight, the pedestal-mounted machine is readily portable—it can be set up at any firing position as long as there's a plug-in socket there. The face of the unit carries two concentric circles, the center one displaying a number (1 to 10) to indicate the value of the shot fired. The outer circle shows a shadowy band indicating the clock position of the shot—3 o'clock, 6, 8 or whatever. Both readouts occur virtually instantly, as the shot is made and, at the same time, the number, value and position of each shot is recorded on a moving roll of paper tape. The tape unit, quickly removable from the device, can be positioned in a master unit (which would be set up in the club house or statistical room usually), with its output, and that of any other recorders in the bank, fed to a small computer.

That describes the operation as I saw it—and used it—at 100 and 300 meters, if a trifle over-simplified, but the immense value of this equipment can be easily grasped. No target crew whatsoever is needed at the butts—a tremendous saving of man-power, time and (often) money. No target changing is required, either, for the special target used is good for an

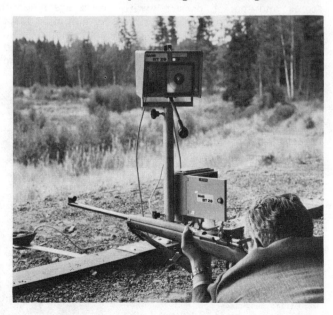

Saab BT-28 target recording unit. The shot is a 9 at 7 o'clock.

The Gyttorp Trap-O-Matic, made in Sweden by Nitro Nobel, may be chosen as the official machine for the new "Automatic Trap" competitions proposed at the 19th Olympic Games in Mexico. The provisional range layout resembles U.S. or "Down the Line," but claybirds will take off at new and unpredictable angles. The Gyttorp auto trap, always in motion, weaves up and down, back and forth, firing its target wherever it happens to be pointing when the bird is called for.

average of 20,000 rounds. That's no misprint—20,000 shots can be made through it, and the targets can then be rejuvenated to last several more thousand rounds. Even full replacement cost is relatively low, under $50. With the recorders housed in the master bank, as in a registered match or in military rifle-training sessions, there's a further great time saving. Moments after the firing of the last shot in the match, the special computer "announces" the standing of all contestants, prints their respective scores and—no, it doesn't award the prizes—the match is over, right now!

How does this machine work? Aside from the electronic circuitry inside the black box, about which I know nothing, the essentials are simple. The target is, in effect, the sending unit—made of two plastic or rubber (?) sheets separated by a dielectric (insulating) panel, one sheet transmits its signal, via a cable, to the BT-28 readout box, indicating the ring value—you shoot a 9, it reads a 9. By the way, it's carefully and precisely calibrated—a nipper -9 scores as a 9 and so on. The other half of the paired

This is the simulated—and fairly realistic—game forest at the World Exhibition of Hunting, held at Budapest (Hungary) in the fall of 1971.

screens indicates the clock position of the shot. No resetting of the unit is required—each successive shot wipes out the previous one, automatically, and records the next one.

All of this exotic machinery doesn't come cheap, of course—about $2600, I understand, buys one basic unit, not including cost or installation of the master bank-computer pieces. Obviously setting up 25 or 50 of these instruments runs into folding money, but I believe that they'd pay for themselves over the long haul. I'm going to predict that the next several years will see these SAAB BT-28 machines in general use by military forces and at ISU—Olympic ranges.

Gyttorp and Norma

Gyttorp is a fully modern shotshell plant—spotless, bright and airy—but a bit surprisingly they do not make plastic case shotshells, or they weren't when I was there in late 1971. Hold those comments, though, for Gyttorp's paper case cartridges (in 16 gauge) took top honors among 30-some other brands, in an evaluation workout conducted by the prestigious German "Schiesstechnisches Institut."

The Norma ammo plant goes back many years, but the cartridges and bullets produced are excellent in every way, as many of us here can attest. Sweden has a high number of military-rifle target shooters per capita, so to keep ammo costs down, Norma processes thousands of returned empty cases every month to supply reloaded— or manufactured—ammo. Returned cases are given the full treatment —washing, inspection, polishing and standard factory-quality powder charging and bullet seating.

Back to Stockholm, then, through

those great forests and the attractive countryside. After some 36 hours there, taking in the King Gustav Adolphus Museum (hundreds of fine arms and armor pieces, but *badly* lit) and an excellent restaurant looking down on the city—it was a Saturday and a smorgasbord luncheon was offered, the best of such I've seen or tasted! Hundreds of selections, really, and someone told me that well over a hundred varieties of herring were served in Sweden. I think I sampled about 20!

Before departing Scandinavia let me mention my *non*-hunting activities. Before leaving New York I'd talked about the chance for a moose hunt in Sweden, and Capt. Claesson did all he could to set one up. However, when I left here the seasons—two of them, with a fairly long closed season in between—had not been fixed. You must know what happened—my 8 days in Sweden came during the no-hunting period. I wasn't quite as disappointed as I might have been for I had other plans as you'll see.

Perhaps more annoying was passing up a special 3-day hunt that'd been arranged for me in Finland through the generous efforts of the Sako people—this one, though, on a tentative basis, provided I'd find the time. The plan in Finland was to spend the first day on a train, going north to some point at or above the Arctic Circle, then hunt for moose the next day. Return was on the 3rd day. I'd been told that this 3-day affair was virtually fool-proof—the moose would be there!

Unfortunately—doubly so, as events developed—I couldn't spare the 3 days. August was running out and, as I particularly wanted to spend some time at the World Hunting Exhibition in Budapest, I had to forego the Finnish hunt.

World Hunting Exhibition

I met Raymond Caranta, our Continental Editor, in Zurich, the weather bright and balmy. We set out for Hungary via Salzburg and Vienna, reaching Budapest two days later. We put in a couple of full days at the big exhibition, but because of the tremendous attendance, we'd have needed another several days to have taken everything in. Fair officials told us that over 1.70 million visitors had, by the time we arrived, gone through the gates, and that total attendance would reach 2 million. This vast display of trophies, covering scores of acres, ran for 5 weeks! Many of the national exhibits were beautifully presented, notably those by the Iron Curtain countries. The Soviet Union had assembled a simulated game forest in an indoor setting, with a dozen or so animals, fully mounted on all fours, lurking in the "woods." The East German display, while not so exotic, was a very handsome one. England had an exhibit—its first such at these quadrennial meetings, with a splendid display of roe deer trophies.

As some of our readers will know, I attended my first World Hunting Exhibition in 1967, that one held at Novi Sad in Yugoslavia, which I wrote about in our 1968 GUN DIGEST. There, as at Budapest last year, I found a large number of educational and conservational displays, but with relatively few gunmakers showing at Novi Sad. That wasn't the case at Budapest. Just about every Continental manufacturer had a display, some of them magnificently put on, so Raymond and I found much to see and many to talk to—as I've said, I wish we could have had more time. We enjoyed the nights in Budapest, too—excellent food, gypsy music in all the restaurants. Still, I don't think I'd call Budapest a "smaller Paris," as some have, but it is an attractive city, and I imagine it was a more beautiful place in pre-war days. Almost everyone we met was warm and cordial; Hungarian hospitality and friendliness are no mere myths, we learned.

The Bad News

Now I must backtrack a little. Before leaving Chicago I'd been in touch again with Omnipol and the BRNO people in Czechoslovakia, discussing plans for a renewal of my aborted visit there in 1968. I reported on that disaster in our 1970 issue as well; my day of arrival in Prague coincided with the invasion of Czechoslovakia by the Russians, so that was that. Early in 1971 Jan Bocek, head of public relations for Omnipol (Czech export-import organization), had renewed the earlier invitation to meet him in Prague, visit the BRNO works in that city and, later, get in a few days of hunting. We'd even settled on the species—I'd be allowed to take a really good

fallow deer and a mouflon, a species of mountain sheep prized as a trophy in Europe. The exact date was also set—I would reach Prague on September 1.

I made a careful selection of hunting clothes, with emphasis on lightness and the possibility of chilly temperatures in the Czech mountains. Still, the extra bag I'd use for this hunting gear weighed a full 26 pounds loaded, and it was, of course another bag to lug around—in this instance, all over Europe, in that the Czech hunt was the last affair on my program! However, now I was all set, and I was anxious and impatient to get to Prague—I kept thinking about it during my earlier travels, of course.

Caranta and I drove back to the West by way of Milan, then up through the French Alps to his home town of Aix-en-Provence, not far from Marseilles. He and I spent part of a day at the Darne plant in St. Etienne (I'll report on the unusual Darne shotgun elsewhere in this section), and I had to leave for Prague. I couldn't fly there directly, so I went to Frankfurt and checked into a hotel. I still needed a visa, which chore took me about 6 hours—lengthy forms had to be made out in quadruplicate, but no carbon paper was permitted! I wonder what my great-great grandmother's given name was?

That tedious chore over, I went back to my hotel and placed a phone call for Mr. Bocek. Are you ahead of me? Of course you are—for some mysterious reason(s), known only to some faceless bureaucrat(s), my trip to Bohemia was—once more—cancelled! Mr. Bocek was apologetic but, in the circumstances, understandably firm —I could not visit his homeland—*they* had decreed otherwise. I've yet to learn the real reason, if valid reason there was, for their refusal, but you can well believe that for a minute there I was pretty cross. I can curse fluently only in English, but I essayed a few other languages that afternoon. And when I'd think about having toted that *!!&? heavy, extra bag through a dozen cities, and about spending $6 and 6 hours getting a visa, well... Then, when I remembered the Finland hunt I'd passed up because of this Czech trip and its inexplicable ending, I got really hot. A compensation of sorts turned up later on, though, which I'll tell you about in these pages—see "Czech Bolt Actions."   J. T. A.

Main entrance to the World Exhibition of Hunting—Budapest, 1971.

Czech Rifles
M465 and Fox

Following the Czech debacle (see "Europe 1971" in this section) Mr. Jan Bocek of Omnipol and I resumed correspondence, still on a cordial basis, of course. The abrupt cancellation of my visit—which had been extended by *them*—is the sort of thing one can expect under committee-rule systems, I suppose, so I held no grudge—not after the first several months, anyway.

I'd learned at Budapest, when visiting the Czech exhibit, that the little Brno 22 Hornet rifle had been revived, if that's the word. Anyway, they were on display at the exhibit, along with the same actions, slightly modified, used to make a light rifle in 222. An olden day Hornet shooter, I wanted one of these Model 465 Czech rifles for that low-intensity 22 centerfire. I wouldn't turn the 222 version down, either, which Brno calls the Fox rifle.

I told Mr. Bocek about these desires and, after some inevitable red tape, the two rifles were delivered to me on an IRS import license. I'd been told, too, that a sample of their quite new Super Model over-under shotgun would also reach me—it did, and it was soon on its way to Wallace Labisky, our smoothbore editor *cum laude.* You'll find his searching essay on this Czech sidelock somewhere in this same edition. I'd looked the Super over briefly at Budapest, and I felt W. L. would want to see it.

Busy as we've been with the 6th ed. HANDLOADER'S DIGEST, I haven't had time to test either the Hornet or the 222 rifles at length, but I've shot them enough, I believe, to make a fair appraisal. We'll get to that in a moment.

First, let me describe the actions. The bolts are, in all important aspects, true 1898 Mausers—double locking lugs, long hook-type extractors and a readily detachable bolt sleeve. The bolt sleeve itself does differ from 98 design, but it's a sturdy small machining that functions well. Removing it lets the bolt handle fall away, too—it's not an integral part of the bolt body. Its upper section or root is split, the two flatted halves riding over another flatted section on the firing pin. Except for bolt-face treatment, the Fox and Hornet rifles have the same bolt, same design and dimensions.

Bolt release on the Hornet rifle (Model ZKW-465) is a Mannlicher style, being pushed inward to operate. The Fox 222 rifle (Model ZKB-680) has a bolt release of Mauser type. The safeties on both rifles—located at the right side of the action, just aft of the bolt handle root—locks both trigger system and the bolt. Unlike standard practice on U.S.-made arms, however, pushing the safety lever *forward* locks things up—it must be moved back to let the rifle be fired. No big thing, of course, and its reverse operation is

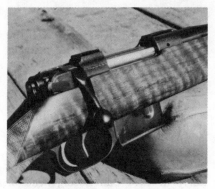

easily gotten used to. More importantly, the safety operation on both of my sample rifles is completely silent. A bright red dimple is seen when the safety is off.

The ejector—an arm of the bolt release—rides through the slotted left lug, and kicks empties out forcefully. There was no failure to eject in my shooting of some 250 cartridges, and extraction was faultless, too.

There are two round gas-escape ports in the bolt body, these venting into the left-hand raceway when the bolt is locked.

The root of the bolt handle drops, on closing it, into a recess in the side of the receiver, with a few thousandths-inch clearance. Thus the bolt root acts as a third safety.

The top of the receiver ring and the bridge carry integral dovetail scope mount bases. These are about ⅝-inch wide, and parellel-sided—not tapered as on the Sako-action. A well-made, one-piece top mount, furnished by ZB, fits these bases perfectly, but it was not usable with any of my scopes. I tried—the rings are solid, open only a small amount at the top for final tightening. Even an old straight-tube scope would have needed the adjustment turret taken off to let it be mounted.

Double-set triggers are standard on both the ZKW465 and the Fox rifles, adjustable via the usual small (and readily accessible) screw for weight of pull. These worked very well—I got both rifles down to 8-10 ounces or less, and at such light letoffs they were jar-proof, too. I couldn't get them to go off accidentally. The unset pull is a double stage type of around 8-10 pounds, but crisp when it does break.

The round barrel has about 1½-inches ahead of the receiver ring in cylindrical section, the rest a straight taper to the .575-inch diameter muzzle—which is nicely crowned. As one of my photographs shows, the Hornet barrel has a short-ramp band front sight, the Fox one with a longer ramp, but no band. Hoods are fitted to both front sights. The Hornet has an open rear sight system, the unit dovetailed in a barrel boss (a la old M70 Winchesters). A fixed leaf is used at 100 meters, the folding leaves marked for 150 and 200 meters.

The all-steel detachable magazines are well-designed and of heavy stock indeed—side walls, follower and floorplate are .020-inch stuff, very rigid and not apt to be damaged or distorted when dropped. Of single-column type, they hold 5 cartridges, one caliber on the other—they are not, of course, interchangeable.

The rear sight on the Fox 222 rifle differs. It is a folding single leaf, but may be adjusted for elevation. Lateral adjustment on either rifles is of knock-over type.

The Hornet stock, of genuine walnut, is in simple, classic design—no Monte Carlo, no cheekpiece, normal form of pistol grip, and sans white spacers. The fore-end tip shows a slight schnabel.

No so the Fox rifle—it has all

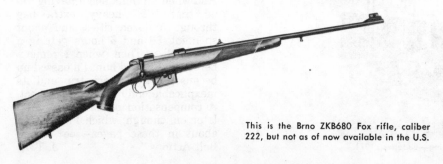

This is the Brno ZKB680 Fox rifle, caliber 222, but not as of now available in the U.S.

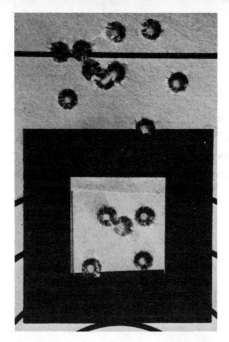

Target made with the 6-lb. Brno 222 rifle, factory ammo. Ten at top to 1.5", 5 below (pasted over square for a tighter picture) measure .78" on centers.

of the things just mentioned, though the Monte Carlo and cheekpiece are done with restraint. Both rifles are checkered at grip and fore-end, though the diamonds are typically flattened in the European manner.

Both rifles have ⅞-inch plain sling swivels fitted for and aft, and each has a hard, black plastic buttplate, shallowly dished or curved.

These Brno rifles are man-size, even though each weighs only 6 lbs., give or take a few ounces, unloaded and without scopes. The finish of all metal components is excellent, and so is the basic machining—everything shows crisp, clean workmanship. Corners, edges, flutings are properly done—sharp where called for, smoothly radiussed elsewhere.

The bolts on both rifles work smoothly, though there is a touch of light drag in the Hornet bolt if it's operated slowly—I think the side of the long extractor bears a bit inside the bridge. I can see a small burnished spot, so that'll be easy to fix.

Shooting the BRNO Rifles

As I've noted, the scope mount sent to me couldn't be used, and it took me some time to locate one that would work. I finally learned that Weaver had a tip-off type that would fit the Brno bases—a style they sell in Europe—but usable with ⅞-inch tubes only. I got two of these mounts, plus a Weaver V22 scope in 3-6x and another of theirs in 4x.

I shot the 222 Fox rifle first,

having put the V22 scope on it. Conditions were ideal at my 100-yard range—high, light overcast, no wind. I had an old lot of Remington 50-gr. HP loads nearby, these received in 1965. I put two rounds through the barrel for foulers, then moved over to another target and put the next 8 shots for record into .73", with 6 of these in .61". Another 5 gave me .78", and the last 10 at that session went 1.15". I call that pretty nice shooting for a 6-lb. rifle, a relatively low-powered scope—and me doing the shooting! As of now, a few weeks later, some 80 more factory rounds have gone through the Fox barrel, and the aggregate average makes just over an inch. Admittedly, I waited for good days, and I was also shooting the Brno Hornet during the same period.

I wish I could say that the Hornet did as well as the Fox rifle, but it didn't. Two minor faults came to light during the shooting, though I doubt they affected the

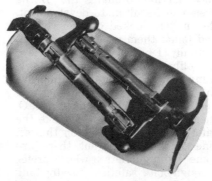

Except for face treatment, bolts for the Brno Hornet and Fox rifles are nearly identical.

accuracy—there's about .0025" excess headspace in the Hornet, and fired cases show an expansion above the rim of about .002" on the diameter. I soon learned that the bore had to be cleaned rather frequently, and I suspect there's a trace of bore roughness just ahead of the throat. The first 5 from a just-cleaned barrel go into, on average, about 1"-1.25", but groups then get progressively bigger if cleaning isn't done. Another cleaning and the first 5 do as before.

This Hornet shooting was with the 4x Weaver at first, then with the 3-6x, and with various factory 45-gr. soft point loads. The ammo brand seemed to make quite a difference—some very old Western Super-X stuff did well, while some fairly recent lots of W-W and R-P rounds didn't. My best targets, such as they were, were had using some CIL (Canadian) and Norma cartridges, which will do about

.075"-.085" steadily if the bore is kept cleaned.

Halfway through the Hornet program I gave the bore a J. B. Compound treatment, and it helped —the slight bore roughness mentioned has all but gone, and I can defer cleaning until 15-25 rounds have been shot before scattering starts. I wish I could fit an 8x or higher powered scope, for I'm sure that'd cut groups down, and I also feel that after another 100 cartridges or so have sped from the muzzle that I'll see further improvement.

Where can you buy one of these Brno rifles in the U.S.? Or any of their extensive line of rifles and handguns? As of now you cannot. I was told by the IRS, when they granted me an import license, that our readers must be told that rifled arms from Iron Curtain countries (Yugoslavia excepted, in certain circumstances) are not freely importable. Shotguns, on the other hand, may be brought in from the same sources. Continental Arms of New York City imports some of the Brno shotguns, at least, as Wallace Labisky notes in his article on the Brno Super 12/12 over-under in a story we'll do next year.

Canadian shooters have no such problem. McQueen Sales Co., Ltd. (1260 W. 3rd Ave., Vancouver 9, B.C.) offers the full Brno line, I believe, or certainly a fair representation. They sell the ZKW465 22 Hornet rifle at $149.50 and the ZKB680 Fox 222 for $179.50.

Perhaps, now that President Nixon has reached a detente, of sorts, with the Russians, we may see a rearrangement of import regulations as they affect countries behind the Iron Curtain.   J. T. A.

The Brno Fox 222 rifle in foreground, the other the 465 22 Hornet. Note differences in rear sights, bolt releases and length of receiver openings. Not seen—the right-side magazine release in the Fox and the in-guard release of the Hornet.

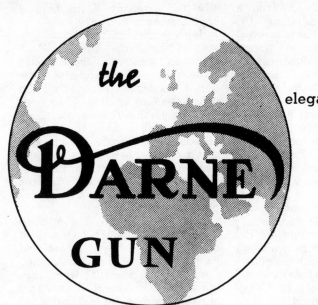

the DARNE GUN

Despite little advertising and less fanfare, the makers of this unique, handsome and elegant double gun have sold nearly a half-million of them throughout the world. They must be doing something right!

by JOHN T. AMBER

Do you know the Darne side-by-side double gun? This decidedly unusual shotgun, truly unique in its action design, has had small sale and distribution in the United States despite its several virtues and, in view of its quality construction—even in the lowest-cost grades—its moderate selling price. In point of fact, there is, as far as I can determine, no difference in quality of workmanship—metal-to-metal fit, jointing of wood and metal, polishing and finish of all components—between the lowest-priced Darnes and the highest. There is, though, good value in the extra-cost versions—stocks of better-quality, fancier-figure walnut, a greater expanse of finer-line checkering, plus various degrees and extents of engraving. There is a basic design difference, too, but a relatively unimportant one—removal of the barrels is made a little easier on the higher grades, but that's a matter, mostly, of convenience.

It's the action of the Darne that sets it apart from all other shotguns. An action that, at the same time, makes it one of the trimmest and streamlined of shotguns, yet the basic design of the action was evolved some 80 years ago—Darne guns of that age look, in their essential form and style, identical with their latest productions. One could, I suppose, look on this adherence to long-established form and design elements in two ways—one, that the makers of the Darne have resisted change and modernization, remaining locked into the original concept through inertia or

worse. Or it might be said that, once having brought the Darne design to its ultimate development, the makers looked on their efforts and found them good, even perfect, virtually. I hold to the second view, for offhand I can't think of anything that could materially improve the current Darne design—not and keep the Darne design intact. O, there are those who would like the safety repositioned—it's on the left side of the action—but there are some shotgunners who prefer through-bolt safeties to top-tang types. There is another Darne aspect, a style point, that isn't completely to my liking, and that's a stock form Darne furnishes—and one that is, I'll admit, quite popular in Europe.

This particular Darne stock has a semi-pistol grip—a long, sweeping form, with rounded end, that looks much like the type found on vintage Browning autoloaders. I'd bought my first Darne some 25 years ago, at which time this stock style was common and popular on a number of shotguns. I didn't know much then, either, though of course I thought I did.

I've used that Darne a good bit over the years, but in this job there's almost always a new shotgun to try out, sometimes several a year or season—and in recent years more than ever. For that reason I've used the Darne less and less, but that's also true of some three or four other smooth-bores I own—the shorter seasons in recent times account for some of

that, too.

During all that long usage I've never had a moment's trouble with the Darne—nothing ever broke, nothing malfunctioned.

Visit to St. Etienne

I'd always wanted to visit the Darne plant in southern France (I can't think of any arms factory I wouldn't like to see), but I'd never done more than pass through that area on previous visits. Last year, however, knowing that I'd be returning to that section of France from Budapest, to spend a few days with Raymond Caranta (our Continental editor), I planned a call on Darne. Caranta lives at Aie-en-Provence, only a short drive from St. Etienne, site of the Darne factory.

The general manager for Darne, Jean Bruyere, made Raymond and me welcome and escorted us on a tour of the buildings and shops. I don't know what, exactly, I expected to find, but I've got to say that both of us were hardly prepared for what we saw! Imagine a one-story, long and narrow shop—perhaps 50 feet wide and maybe 400 feet or more deep. The ceilings, about 20 feet above us, were dark with the soot and grime of years. Down either side of the long room, high above the workers, ran shafting and pulleys—lots of pulleys. Leather belts, small and large, fell to the machines, driving them. Here was a shop where Samuel Colt, Philo Remington or Oliver Winchester would have felt at

The elegant Darne V22, light, graceful, superbly balanced.

home. The slap and clatter of the belts and pulleys would have been familiar music. The lighting was dim, the corners dark—one had a sense of what the oil-lamped factories of a century earlier might have been like.

There *was* a touch of progress, if that's the right word. Standing in one area were two ultra-modern machines—high speed, tape fed automated milling machines. An incongruous sight, to be sure, but both were in operation. These new tools, with others perhaps to follow, may—one day—see the Darne factory a fully up-to-date plant, but for now the Darne shotgun is still fabricated, fitted and finished by hand. Men wielding files—and women, too—are there in force, particularly at a long row of benches in the final fitting and assembly stages.

Make no mistake, I've not described the Darne plant to criticize or deplore—far from it. An old pappy myself, and one who has always delighted in the genuine excellence that trained and dedicated hands can produce, I was gratified—if surprised—to view the Darne approach to gunmaking. Quality of materials and workmanship, close attention to the perfect assembly of even minor components—these are the norms at Darne.

As I've said, Darne guns are not highly expensive, even in the embellished grades. Some $500-$750 will buy their top model, I believe; compare that with certain English and Italian shotguns! No, what

puzzles me—now that I know how they're made—is how they can be sold at such attractive prices.

The Darne is a solid-frame double gun, there's no dropping down of the barrels, released to open by means of a top-snap lever. For this reason the stock can be—and is—a one-piece affair. If the inletting at and around the receiver is examined it'll be obvious that here is a hell of an inletting job. I don't think there are a dozen stockmakers here who'd want to replace a busted Darne stock—not without an aggravation bonus!

The Darne breechblock is a sliding one; the side-projecting "ears" are grasped between the thumb and first fingers, drawing it back, and the operating lever—swinging vertically in a central channel in the block—is pulled smartly upward and backward. That movement pulls fired cases fully out of the chambers; unfired cartridges are extracted only for a short distance. A roll of the gun to either side, after fired-case extractions, lets the empties fall to the ground or, if you're a reloader, into your hand. Darne calls this "automatic ejection," but cases are not kicked clear and away, as we know happens with the usual ejectors. Semantics, maybe, nevertheless their system works.

All double-gun barrels converge from breech to muzzle. In all other doubles but Darnes, as far as I know, the loaded shotshell lies in a slightly cocked position because the standing breech is not at 90°

to the long axis of the barrels. In the Darne this has been fixed—each half of the standing breech carries an obturating disk, these angled a small amount, just enough to bring them into exact square with each converging barrel. Not very important? These flanged disks, completely encircling the shell rim, are an aid to gas containment if a rim lets go. In addition, and because Darne guns are carefully gauged to have minimum chambers and headspace, Darne claims reduced recoil, increased gas thrust on the shot charge for more velocity, and better patterns. In fact, Darne fully guarantees that their barrels, in whatever gauges and lengths, will pattern 72% to 82%. That "warrenteed" performance,

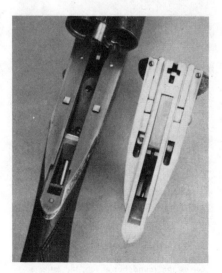

The bright "squares on the receiver are, in effect, the sears of the Darne action. At right is the actual receiver turned upside down.

note, was made before the advent of plastic shotshells and their enhanced patterning qualities.

All Darne guns, by the way, are fully guaranteed against defects in materials and workmanship for 5 years! They're also approved by "Quality France" (an honor not lightly obtained), an organization which makes sure that French products live up to their manufacturer's claims—sort of an industrial ombudsman.

The single trigger is not highly regarded in Europe, so Darne guns, like the others, have two triggers, but with the front one hinged. Trigger pulls are, in my experience, crisp and of moderate weight. I snapped some 7 or 8 guns during the factory visit, none of which showed any drag or excess heaviness. My sample Darne (which I'll describe later) has triggers that weigh, consistently, about 4-5 lbs. rear and front—and they're snappy.

Darne barrels are sleeved, that is, mounted into the breech sections via the "monobloc" system, a long-tested technique that offers various advantages—greater strength because the breech sleeve can be heat treated to better properties than conventional systems, and for less heat in assembly than is the case with brazed lumps.

Two styles of top ribs are furnished—a normal raised rib (not ventilated) and their "Plume" rib, the type sometimes called "swamped" also. This one drops away from its level position at the breech to lie between the barrels all the way to the muzzle—in effect, there is no top rib. The

The Darne V22, action partly opened, sliding safety lies above guard.

Below—The 28 gauge Darne has a "silvered" action, the stronger 10 gauge (rear) has a black receiver. One is the best-handling quail or grouse gun imaginable; the big bore is also light and lively enough for carrying many a mile without tiring the shooter.

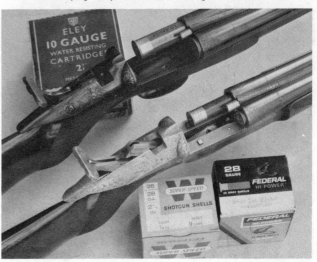

The Darne breech face, showing the obturator disks, the extractor hooks (at 6 o'clock) and the ejector pins. The large hole receives the round barrel lug, the latter secured by a vertical bolt. However, the main bolting is done by the toggle arm actuated by the operating lever, seen raised here.

Plume rib is the type to specify if you want the Darne gun to be ultra light. As you'll see, you can get them that way from Darne—no problem.

Darnes are made in all gauges extant—10, 12, 12/3", 16, 20 and 28, plus one you won't want—24! I don't think the 24s are very popular in France, either. Barrel lengths—standard is 27.6" (70cm), but lengths in 25.6" (65cm), 26.8" (68cm), 28.4" (72cm), 30" (75cm) and 32" (80cm) can be had. All Darne barrels, price range regardless, are given the heaviest French proving—the Triple Proof Test—equal to 8¼ tons psi, and the fully finished guns are again proved at chamber pressure ranging from 5.4 tons to 7.7, the exact psi depending on chamber length.

All of the specs cited apply to standard Darne guns—those that can be bought over the counter from any of Darne's world network of agents. However, Darne has long been geared to a custom gun setup —they'll make one up with virtually anything the customer wants—stock woods, engraving, barrel lengths and chokes, whatever. All you have to do is name it—and, of course, pay for it!

As I've said, Darne guns are elegant and graceful, light and excellently balanced—yet they're tough, too, and made to take it. The V22 grade gun loaned to me (while my special order Darne is being made) weighs just 6 lbs., and that's a standard weight for them. Heavier ones can be had, of course, and lighter ones as well in the smaller gauges. The Model V22 has Darne's standard stock dimensions —1½" at the comb nose, 2¼" at heel, and a pull of 14¼"-15¼" to the rear and forward triggers. I need a pull of 14¾", and I like a comb cut to 1⅜" or a hair less, hence my special order—it hasn't arrived yet, unfortunately, so there won't be any pictures of it here.

The V22 has 27.6" barrels, and for that reason it hasn't been as handy as I'd have liked in the woodcock thickets I got into last fall. The one on order will have their 25.6" tubes, which I think will help in like conditions. On the other hand, managing to get in a few days of pheasant hunting last year, I found the Darne a delight to carry and to shoot. I'd worked up some 2¾ dram loads, using an

ounce of 6s, and when I was on 'em they fell. That light load produced no bothersome recoil, either, but I had slipped on a Pachmayr rubber pad to lengthen the pull. That doubtless helped. Recoil, it seemed to me, felt about like a 3¼-1¼ load would in a gun of 7-7½ pounds.

Stoeger marketed the Darne until recently—and they may still have some on hand—but now there's a new importer—Firearms Center, Inc., 113 Spokane, Victoria, TX 77901. They'll have basic models in stock, they say, but any of the many grades may be ordered. FCI hasn't established firm prices, so far, but they are selling the Darnes on the company's standard 5-year warranty. How can you go wrong?

Elegant is the word for this delightful Darne birdgun, a 6-lb. 12 bore.

Sturm, Ruger

The black powder caplock revolver covered in our 26th edition is now available as the "Old Army." Priced at $115 in 44 caliber with 7½ inch barrel, this has to be the best thing to appear on the charcoal burners market for handgunners since the percussion cap. (A deluxe version with solid brass Dragoon style grip frame and wide trigger is available at $130.) The new carbine, also covered in the 26th edition, is called the No. 3 Carbine, made in 45-70 caliber only at $165, though other calibers are rumored. Weighing 6 pounds, with 22-

inch barrel, the No. 3 is a handy 32½ inches over-all, with sliding tang safety, folding leaf rear sight, and a straight grip, solid walnut stock and fore-end.

Another Ruger arm that is now in good production is the big Black Hawk in 45 Colt caliber—the rimmed Colt 45, that is, not the 45 ACP, of course.

That Ruger will be marketing an over-under shotgun—entirely made in Ruger Plants—is no longer a big secret. When you'll see it, though, is something else, but there is, we hear, a good chance that it will appear late in 1972. Models of the action have been seen, and this new shotgun will, I know, prove most interesting.

Right and left view of a Ruger No. 1 Single Shot rifle engraved by Albin Obiltschnig for Hal Hartley, custom stockmaker of Lenoir, N.C.

Nelson Farquharson 416 A.C.

The single shot rifle shown nearby is another one Clayton Nelson recently completed for me. The action is a true Farquharson in type, being one of several that Tom Shelhamer imported when he was with the Niedner Rifle Corp. Rumor has it that these were made in Belgium, but it was in the white when I got it, many years ago, and engraved as you see it. I'd told Clayton about it, especially its large dimensions, and because he wanted a change of pace from the unending stream of bolt actions, he said he'd like to put a stock on it and complete it.

Because it is a big action I decided to put a barrel on it with

I think Nelson did a superb job on this single shot—and if it reaches me here in time I'll made some photographs of details that don't show now. For example, there's a cartridge trap inletted ahead of the toe and a buttplate with engraved heel and toeplates of steel as well. The steel grip cap is engraved. These items were chiseled by Lynton McKenzie of New Orleans to match the original engraving—only Lynton's work is better—and he engraved other areas also.

I'd asked Clayton to carve out a fore-end looking rather like the style that was fairly standard on English-Scottish single shots, and I

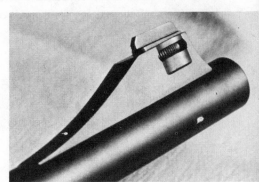

Engraved action was imported by the late Tom Shelhamer. Bullets are Colorado Custom 350- and 400-gr., the rimmed case shown the basic 45 necked down to 416. Nelson made the butt caps, Lynton McKenzie did the engraving.

a big hole, but as a rimless or belted case was hardly indicated in light of the twin extractors, I spent all of 10 minutes doping out a new wildcat. Not all that original, really, for all I did was to make use of the so-called "basic 45 case," a rimmed-head type having 45-70 head dimensions, and running 2.75″ long. These would be necked down to handle .416″ bullets, a cylindrical section running back from the mouth for about ½-inch—there's no bottleneck, just a taper that straightens out.

There are no results to report, either, for the only time I saw the rifle was at the Portland NRA meeting in May, where Nelson had lugged it to help decorate the Oakley & Merkley booth—a Mecca, a lodestone and a shrine for every rifle fan at that meeting, and of which more later.

think he did an excellent job. The pistol grip curve is shallower, too, again in line with earlier single shot rifle practices. More practical, too, for recoil won't bang the second finger as much as a tightly-curled one would.

The fancy hunk of wood Nelson transformed was got from Oakley & Merkley, and Clayton cut borderless 20-line checkering—a good choice for gripping and holding onto in a big-bore rifle—except for a long-diamond panel on the bottom of the fore-end that goes 30 lines per inch. A horn panel is set into the bottom of the fore-end at its juncture with the receiver.

Nelson handmade the heel and toe caps in the butt, and the cartridge trap set into the toe line is one made by Norm Shiffman of Salt Lake City. Nelson also made the folding-leaves rear sight and

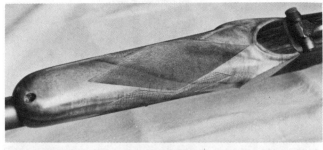

the ramp front, which offers easy switching of sight blades. The one installed now is a white "Sour-dough" style, these slanted about 45° to catch the light better.

What does 416 A.C. stand for? The 416 Amber Creedmoor, that's what. With a 400-gr. bullet game load, I believe I can easily get 2200 foot seconds at the muzzle, perhaps 2400 or so, and that's why the rifle weights about 10¼ lbs. The medium weight round barrel is 26" long, carrying open sights that Nelson made by hand.   J. T. A.

Center panel is checkered 30 lines per inch, the rest at 20. Note inset horn panel. Folding leaves are set for 50, 100 and 200 yards.

Clayton Nelson & Son

Clayton Nelson is one of our top custom gunsmiths, equally adept at wood and metal work. Readers of this department may recall that a 338 Magnum I used in Zambia a while back was made by Nelson while he was with Champlin Firearms Company. Made on a Champlin action, and stocked in the classic fashion, that rifle performed beautifully on a variety of African game—notably Cape buffalo, though a big assist must go to Nosler's and Hornady's bullets.

Clayton recently left Champlin to resume custom gun work and—it even came as a surprise to him—he's already got 18-20 months work ahead of him (as has Len Brownell, of whom I'll write about later on).

For some time Clayton had felt the need for first class, quality rifle accessories, items he'd not hesitate to fit to a fine rifle—trigger guards, floorplates, safeties, band type ramp front sights, etcetera. Most of these things weren't available or were in short supply, some were custom made and priced accordingly.

Nelson didn't have time to make these items himself, so he talked his oldest son, Bill, into the job. Nelson reasoned that with his tutelage, and using carefully-made tooling, his boy, aged 15, could make the quality parts needed.

Their first joint product was a replacement trigger guard for the Model 70 Winchester, with a floorplate release inside the front of the loop. This has sold very well and their customer list reads like a

Who's Who of custom gunmakers. (As pictured here, these sell for $15 (7 for $100) in the semi-finished stage, or at $30 contoured and finished.

Nelson has helped his son expand the line to the following items; a deep-bellied Mauser magazine, various specialized trigger guards, a Model 70 style safety for

Above—the semi-finished all-steel guards for Model 70 Winchester made by young Bill Nelson.

Clayton Nelson and his boy Bill, 15, look over some of the custom rifle fittings—guards, band-type ramp front sights, floorplates and Model 70 safeties for Mausers—that father designs and Bill makes. Excellent work, too, not to be faulted.

the Mauser action ($20), and a band-type ramp front sight. Prices on any of these—and other metal products—will be quoted, and prototype work of all kinds can be handled. That's probably the reason Clayton said, "At the moment I guess you could say our motto is 'We specialize in not specializing.' "

Asked if Bill had already decided on a career in the firearms field, Nelson commented, "At present the money earned is going into his education fund, but if Bill should decide on a firearms career I certainly wouldn't dissuade him."

Clayton N. Nelson has just issued a new price list. Send a stamped, self-addressed envelope to him at 1725 W. Thompson, Enid, OK. 73701.

Artistic Arms

In 1968 a new Sharps Arms Company was formed in Utah to manufacture a modernized version of the 1878 Sharps-Borchardt rifle. A complete line of ammunition, including some new calibers, was planned. Two years later, with only prototype rifles existing, Colt bought the Art Swanson firm. Colt planned to produce de luxe and standard Sharps rifles, but problems arose, and the situation is unresolved at this time.

Now Artistic Arms (no connection with the other two), is making 1878 Sharps-Borchardt actions that are virtually an exact copy of the original. Modern heat treated 4140 alloy steel is used in the new action, but no design changes have been made. The original Sharps-Borchardt was made for rimmed cartridges up to 45 caliber—some 40 different rimmed calibers are available here today—and so is the new replica; the use of rimless or belted cartridges is not recommended, and no guarantee is made that the Sharps extractors will work properly if such cartridges are used. Only the action—priced under $200—is offered now (to dealers), complete and ready for fitting of a suitable barrel, stock and fore-end. It is warranted free of defects in material or workmanship for one year, except for the firing pin. Barreled actions, complete rifles, kits, set triggers, and spare parts are not available yet, though a few rifles have been made, and the company will be glad to give further information if you'll enclose a stamped, self-addressed envelope.

The 1878 Sharps-Borchardt is a striker-fired, true falling block action, and can serve as the basis for a fine custom built single shot rifle.

As noted above, this company intends to make Sharps-Borchardt replica actions only, not complete rifles, at least at the start. However, for shooting trials, they sent me a complete rifle in 225 Winchester caliber, the stock a pistol grip type and the fore-end of varmint rifle style and form.

The 26-inch medium-heavy barrel came in tapped for target scope blocks and, happily, I had a pair on hand. I attached a 20x Lyman Super Target Spot and sat down to shoot at the 100-yard targets. The day was good—almost no wind and quite bright. Without scope, the 225 weighs 10¼ lbs. plus.

I'd had to work up handloads, not finding any factory stuff on the shelves. I tried 4895, using 30.1 grains at first with Remington 52-gr. hollow points, match grade of an old lot. I started low, not knowing how tight the bore and groove dimensions might be. Pressure signs well nil, though, the primers remaining rounded at the edges, and extraction easy. I put a couple through the barrel for foulers, and the next 8 went into .725-inch, with 7 into just over a half-inch (.536″), which I think is pretty good for the first effort in a new rifle—and the more so in view of a really heavy trigger pull, like over 10 lbs! Clean enough, but awful to work with.

I spoke to Mr. Metheny, head of A.A., about the trigger, and he was fully aware of the problem. Because of the unusual linkage of the trigger-sear arrangement in the S-B rifle, a good pull is hard to get.

Metheny told me he'd have, before long, a set trigger for the action.

We're running late so there wasn't time for extended tests, I'm sorry to say, but the next load, up one grain to 31.1 of 4895 and the same Remington 52-gr. HPs, did almost as well—two 5-shot strings went .683″-.702″, but I'm very sure that a light pull, say 2-3 lbs., would have meant groups on the half-inch order. A well-done action, and attractively priced at $- —. *Final report.* Larry Sterret also received an Artistic Arms S-B rifle complete, his in the rimless 243, but too late here to get in his full report. He had no target scope blocks, so he mounted a 3x-9x Bushnell, fired factory Browning and Speer/DWM 80- and 85-gr. loads for an average of 1.5 inches. He had no time to make up handloads. *J.T.A.*

New Sharps-Borchardt replica action, here made up in a heavy-barrel varminter by Artistic Arms of Hoagland, IN 46745. The 225 Winchester/Douglas barrel gave excellent accuracy.

Lan-Dav Products

C.S. Lanham and Fred Davis, Jr., operators of this gunsmith-shooter service, make a range of good products—barrel and action vises, ramp sight clamps, bolt-bending blocks, and so on. Shown here is their version of an old favorite, a double-lever scope mount, the type

that attaches to the receiver via a side plate. Four 6x48 screws are used in each ring, not two, for added grasping power. The model pictured, looking much like the old *G&H* style, is also offered in a streamlined version—sans all those sharp corners—at extra cost over the $75 this one sells for. Write for their brochure, no cost. *J.T.A.*

Remington Arms Company

New rifles and shotguns—the 541S rimfire sporter, the All-American and the 870 Light 20.

The motto of Remington for 1972 just had to be "The Year of the Shotgunner," judging by one new 12-gauge target load with a new size shot, 4 new (modified) shotguns, and special extra long 34-inch barrels for the popular Models 1100 and 870 shotguns.

Heading the list is the Model 870 All American Trap Gun—a shotgun with custom features, but available without the usual long special order wait. The stock and fore-end of the All American are of extra select American Walnut with custom cut checkering, plus a gold plate for personalized initialing inlaid in the pistol grip cap. The top and sides of the receiver, as well as the trigger guard and breech end of the barrel, are fully engraved in a scroll pattern. The left side of the receiver has a gold-plated shield embossed with a three-dimensional figure of an American eagle, and inscribed "Model 870 All American Trap Gun" in gold lettering against a background of red, white and blue. The full choke barrel is 30 inches long, and stock dimensions will be Remington's standard for trap or Monte Carlo guns. The new All American, price $550, includes a hard, luggage type, foam-lined carrying case with snap closures and a lock—a fitting (pardon the pun) tribute to a fine shotgun.

In 1970 Remington introduced a lightweight 20 gauge version of the Model 1100 autoloading shotgun. Now there is a lightweight version of the Model 870 pump action shotgun, using reduced receiver dimensions and a mahogany stock in place of walnut. All features of the regular 870 are retained, including the solid steel receiver, but the new model tips the scales at 5¾ pounds with a 26-inch plain barrel. For shooters wanting maximum range from a 20 gauge, the new lightweight is also made in a 3-inch magnum version with full choke plain barrel, cost $159.95.

Joining the Remington complement of left-hand sporting arms are new Model 1100 autoloading shotguns in 4 grades—Field, Magnum, Skeet and Trap—in 12 and 20 gauges. Except for having a left-hand bolt, barrel extension and ejection port, and left-hand safety, the new L-H 1100s are indentical to their right-hand counterparts, with similar barrel lengths and chokes.

Apparently trapshooters have been requesting longer barrels, for Remington now has 34-inch full choke, ventilated rib barrels with regular trap beads available for 1100 and 870 shotguns. The barrels, made in 12 gauge only, are $89.95 and $79.95 respectively, and only as an extra barrel; they are not furnished as part of a complete gun.

For riflemen there's a new Model 541-S Custom Rim Fire Sporter that is quite handsome. There's a selected American walnut stock with Monte Carlo comb and custom-cut checkering, a rosewood-colored fore-end tip of unusual cut and form, pistol grip cap and butt-plate with white line spacers, plus scroll engraving on the receiver and trigger guard. The 541-S uses the same action as the Model 540-X match rifle (which has accuracy of a high order), complete with adjustable trigger. The 24-inch barrel is tapped for open sights, but none are installed; the receiver is also tapped for standard scope mounts, plus being grooved for the tip-off

or slip-on type scope mount. A 5-round box magazine is standard, but 10-round magazines are available.

It's too bad that Remington had to use a magazine that hangs below the stock line, to say nothing of the stamped guard. Both detract from what is otherwise a fine looking light rifle, a rifle that is, nearly, a copy of the Remington BDL model.

The new 12 gauge target load—the RXP—the first of its kind by Remington, has "Uni-Body" construction; the shell body and base wad are one integral plastic unit. The No. 97 (star) primer has been retained, along with the "Power Piston" wad, but the new RXP primer pocket was designed to provide superior gas sealing around the primer, reducing possible leakage or primer setback. Also offered with the RXP is a new size shot— 8½. This size puts an average of 80 or so more pellets into the pattern than 8s, and about 140 more per load than 7½s, making the RXP Target Load deadly for trap shooting from the 16-yard mark. The RXP loads will also be sold with Nos. 7½, 8, and 9 shot for shooters wanting these traditional sizes. The No. 8½ shot will also be furnished as a component for reloaders.

For bench rest shooters there is a new bullet in .224-inch diameter. The jackets and bullet cores are assembled in the same manner as those constructed by hand to produce a 52-gr. hollow point bullet that has averaged as low as .16-inch extreme spread at 100 yards for a 15-shot group! A new 25-06

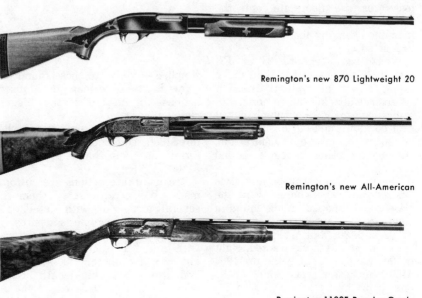

Remington's new 870 Lightweight 20

Remington's new All-American

Remington 1100F Premier Grade

load is now listed that provides flatter trajectory, via greater velocity, for use on such hard-to-reach trophies as pronghorn antelope and mountain goats. Loaded with a 100-gr. pointed soft point "Core-Lokt" bullet, leaving the muzzle of a 26-inch barrel at 3300 fps, this new round fills the gap between the previously available 87-gr. and 120-gr. loads. Another 6mm Remington load supplants the old 90-gr. 244 Remington load-same as the 6mm Remington except for the headstamp—with an increase of 120 fps muzzle velocity. Usable in rifles chambered for the 244 or 6mm Remington, the new round has a 90-gr. pointed softpoint bullet that moves out at 3320 fps from a 26-inch barrel; most rifles in this caliber have barrel lengths of 22 inches, so the useful muzzle velocity will be less, of course.

Remington 541-S rimfire sporter

Remington 40-XB rimfire sporter

Wells Sport Store

Fred Wells is another fine craftsman I met at the Portland NRA meeting—and another who helped make the Oakley & Merkley booth a top attraction at that event.

Fred had with him several examples of the rifle actions he's building from scratch. These were of 1898 Mauser design, and just about 99% perfect replicas of the 98 in all respects. The workmanship is of the finest, as good as I've seen. Wells makes the *entire* action, not just the receiver, except for the bolt sleeve. Even the bolt sleeve is Wells-made for the left-hand actions.

Wells' highest type, as it were, and certainly the most in demand, is his magnum length action, made with square, flat-tops on receiver ring and bridge. Included, of course, is the magazine well, floorplate, trigger guard with bolt-release for the floorplate, and the complete bolt. The bolt face is machined for any feasible cartridge requested.

Wells uses standard 98 or FN style bolt sleeves rather than make them, either an option. The left receiver walls are made solid, but Wells can make the thumb cut if desired, and he'll also supply his action with only one square top, shaping the other in regular round fashion.

The bolt handle can be any style desired—many customers want the classic, pear-shaped handle found in commercial Mauser sporters of the 1920s and '30s, but Wells can fabricate almost any style wanted, right or left hand, including the pre-1964 M70 Winchester type—which is the one I prefer.

Slanted magazines can also be

Remington didn't introduce any handguns for 1972, but three new handgun loads are offered—a 38 Special round designed for revolvers with 2"-2½" barrels, a dual-purpose 38 Special with 158-gr. semi-wadcutter bullet, and a 357 Magnum round with 125-gr. semi-jacketed hollow point bullet. The first short-barrel 38 Special load carries a new 95-gr. semi-jacketed HP bullet having a muzzle velocity of 985 fps from a 2-inch barrel. It should prove a highly effective law enforcement cartridge.

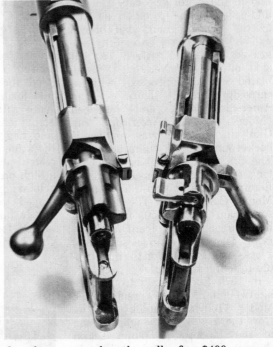

Two Mauser 98-type actions handmade by Fred Wells. At left, the magnum length with double square top to receiver ring and bridge, a left-hand version with a Model 70 bolt handle configuration. The other is of regular length, has square bridge only, standard Mauser bolt form.

supplied—similar to those found on a few Rigby-made magnum Mauser actions—for use with the bigger rimmed cases.

This double flat top action sells for $1000, complete, in right hand form; the left hand version is $1500.

Because these actions are custom made, Wells can supply them in several forms, or with details altered to the customer's desires. I saw a double square bridge type with round bottom receiver—similar to a Remington 700—at $750, and also a Magnum length action without flat-tops, this one $500. A single shot target action, made in any length, sells for $400.

Wells also will make custom scope rings for the square bridge actions, these streamlined to mate with the radiussed bridge and ring walls. The result looks like an integral part of the receiver. A fore-and-aft female dovetail, stopped at the forward end, is milled into each flat top. The rings, in two halves, carry a mating male dovetail at the bottom. This slides into the bridge-ring dovetails, then the scope is tightened by the three 8x40 screws at the top of each ring, which automatically snug the bottom dovetails to a tight fit in the female dovetails. *J.T.A.*

deHaas-Miller
Single Shot Action-Rifle

Readers of Frank deHaas' book, *Single Shot Rifles and Actions* will recall the author's intention to design and produce a single shot system. The new action is now ready, and complete rifles using it are soon to be offered.

Dean Miller (of St. Onge, SD 57729), a gunsmith-gunmaker joined deHaas in the development of the new action, and the final design shown here is the result of several prototypes constructed over the past many months.

The new action is quite compact, its short, tangless design permitting comb noses and pistol grips to be positioned much closer to the receiver than traditionally designed SS rifles would permit. The action is also very strong and rugged, safe with the highest-intensity commercial cartridges. The breechblock, a vertically-sliding type, has no plugs, bushings or welded-up holes. All action parts are contained inside the receiver and breechblock. A sturdy through-bolt attaches the buttstock to the receiver.

The trigger is fully adjustable for pre-release take-up (or creep), for weight of letoff and over-travel.

The action sidewalls are over .200″ thick, the weight of the action about 2¼ lbs. Barrels will be half-octagon. The breechblock and lever can be quickly removed by pushing out the finger lever pin, and as easily re-installed. I haven't seen the deHaas-Miller action or complete rifle, I'm sorry to say, but it looks and reads very good indeed. My only criticism concerns the finger lever—the spur seems a little spindly, the more so in contrast with the rather thick width of the forward part of the lever.

Complete rifles, Frank deHaas told me, will be built to order as far as barrel length and caliber are concerned, with only high quality walnut used. Barrels will be half-octagon, and scope mount bases/rings will be furnished. Such a rifle will cost about $660. "Nothing has been spared," Frank said, "to make this the best single shot rifle ever made." *J.T.A.*

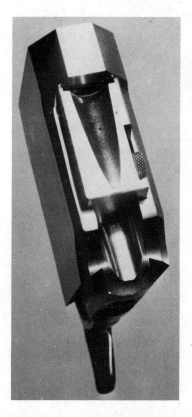

Above—the deHaas-Miller single shot custom rifle. With 26″ half-octagon medium weight sporter barrel, this fancy-walnut stocked 22-250 rifle weighs 9 lbs.

Right—top view of the deHaas-Miller compact, self-contained action. Note loading channel in top of breechblock, knurled-top safety lever at right side of block, and angled mortising of receiver rear to prevent joining edges of buttstock from spreading and splitting.

Below—the deHaas-Miller SS rifle in de luxe grade, the engraving by Neil Hartliep of Fairmont, Minn. Removal of the lever pin drops the breechblock-lever assembly intact.

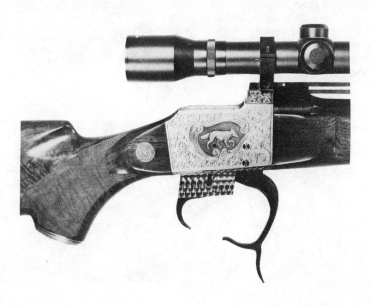

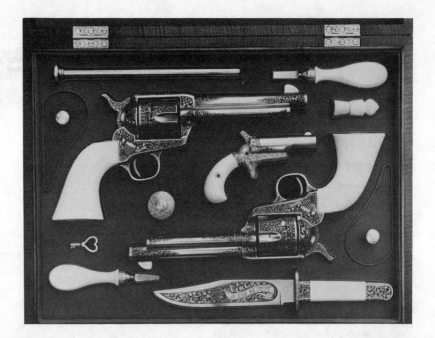

Lynton McKenzie, a young man who is already a great engraver. The cased set of Colt Single Actions shown here was done by McKenzie, including the ivory handled knife and accessories.

Albin Obiltschnig

At right—two other examples of Albin Obiltschnig's superb engraving and relief carving in metal. These guns were engraved by the great Austrian for Mr. Sol Levine of Columbus, Nebraska.

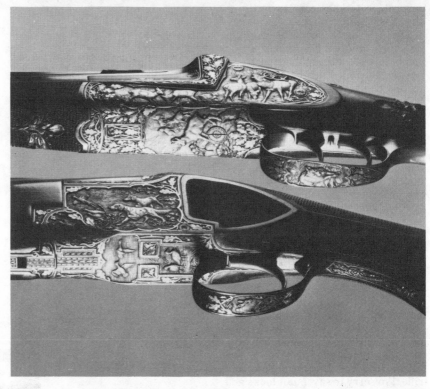

Hal Hartley

Below—Hal Hartley (Lenoir, No. Carolina) stocked this Sako-actioned 22-250 in fancy American crotch walnut, The half-octagon barrel is from Flaig's. The fine-line checkering is combined with oak-leaf carving. An excellent example of classic stock styling.

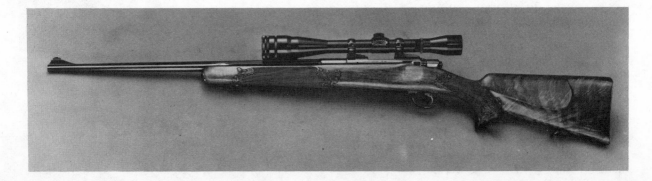

Fajen Try Gun

The average shotgun buyer uses his new smoothbore just as it came out of the box. He may have a recoil pad installed if his Model 1300 doesn't have one, but aside from that he rarely has anything done to the buttstock. In a great many cases, most of them likely, he gets a pretty good fit. Unless he's a midget or a Wilt Chamberlain the regular factory, off-the-shelf stock is a fair fit or he adapts himself—or vice versa—to the gun.

This is not to say, however, that his gun is a perfect—or even a near-perfect—fit. That's doubly true, naturally, of the real shorties and the tall guys. You can see this demonstrated whenever a girl is handed a gun and told to throw it up—you've seen that awkward, leaning-back stance, the girl's cheek about 3-4 inches from the buttplate.

What do most shotgunners do about stocks that don't suit them, about combs too high or too low, stocks overly long or short? Nothing usually. Inertia alone prevents lots of gunners from having the needed changes made—it's too much trouble, and the time isn't right. Like the guy with the leaky roof—he couldn't fix the damn thing when it was raining, and when it wasn't raining the job could wait.

More importantly, who would measure him? There weren't a dozen shops in the whole U.S. with a try gun—none were made here, and the foreign ones were very costly, when available. A few shops had skilled stockers who could tell a customer's requirements, but it was almost a black art, another of the "mysteries" of gunmaking.

It used to be different in Europe, particularly in Great Britain. Shotgunning was a sport of the well-heeled, and their guns were made to their order—and to their measurements. As an aid in giving the customer the proper gun fit the try gun appeared. With it, in the confines of his shop, the gunmaker could quickly determine—subject to a field shooting trial—the customer's dimensions required for a particular type of shooting, whether driven birds, walking up or whatever.

The try gun, of course, has an adjustable stock—length of pull, height of comb and heel, etc. A man accustomed to using one can, with a high degree of accuracy, learn in minutes the stock dimen-

Reinhart Fajen's new $18.95 cartridge trap is not hard to install, holds 3 rounds of standard ammo.

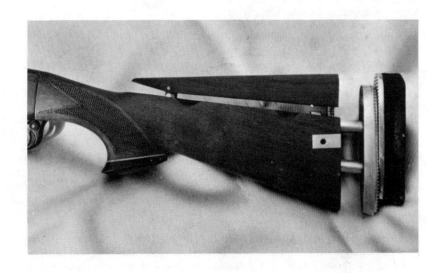

sions needed by this man or that. As I've said, the type of shooting must be considered—I've been measured at Holland's shooting school for driven-bird shooting, in which game the gun can be firmly mounted before the birds are in range, and where the shots are generally high ones, often directly overhead. That test, in warm weather clothes, indicated I'd need a stock nearly 15 inches long. That length would be quite a bit too long, I knew, for the kind of field shooting we do here, especially in the colder weather that often prevails in our bird seasons.

Now Reinhart Fajen has worked out a try gun for use in U.S. gunshops. With it—after relatively little experience—the gunsmith or the shop manager can quickly determine what stock changes or alterations the gun owner needs, if

any. Even knowing that the standard stock (roughly 1½"x2½"x14¼" at comb nose, heel and pull length) will adequately serve his build and configuration can be a form of satisfaction to the customer—or to some customers!

The Fajen try gun is fully adjustable for comb and heel dimensions, independently, and for pull length. It isn't quite as sophisticated as are the English try guns, for it does not have adjustments for castoff or pitch, but castoff is a refinement that can be foregone with no harm, except in the rare case. Pitch is important, but its correctness or not is something readily seen by the man giving the test, and allowed for in the alteration of the stock.

Fajen's try gun can be rented for varying lengths of time—write for further information.   *J.T.A.*

Browning Arms

Another caliber, the 284 Winchester, has been added to the Browning Lever Action (BLR) chamberings, bringing the total to three, and no doubt this cartridge will be added to the Browning ammunition line. Browning had some trouble filling ammo orders in 1971, but it should catch up during 1972.

New sights and a redesigned hammer were added to the 9mm Hi-Power pistol for 1972, but the big news is the 12 gauge side-by-side shotgun. Manufactured in Japan to Browning specifications the new shotgun is appropriately named the B-S/S, indicating its

New Browning B-S/S, their new moderately-priced 12 bore double gun.

type. Only the Grade 1 is available with a choice of 26 or 28-inch barrels and single non-selective mechanical trigger. Our 28″ sample weighs 7½ lbs. An automatic safety and selective ejectors are standard, as is the hand checkering on the walnut pistol grip stock and beavertail fore-end. The action is a typical boxlock with double locking underlugs. A

good looking gun, I feel, with a fore-end that reminds me of the Winchester 21s in Skeet grade. An attractive price, too, the times being what they are, and I'm quite sure the new Browning B-S/S double will find excellent acceptance. The price of $234.50 includes light hand engraving on the receiver, trigger guard, and top lever.

Garcia

Distributors of the Sako, Beretta, F.N., Rossi, Star, and the Astra line of sporting arms, Garcia has several new items available. Sako is commemorating their 50th Anniversary with a limited production of 1000 Golden Jubilee rifles chambered for the 7mm Remington Magnum cartridge. These rifles have custom inlays on the receiver bridge and ring, the trigger guard and magazine floorplate. The stocks are specially selected well-figured walnut, with handcrafted checking and carving on the pistol grip and fore-end, set off with a contrasting wood tip and pistol grip cap. Another new Sako rifle—the Model 72—has some features not common to the Standard and Deluxe Sako rifles, such as an open rear sight mounted on the barrel, quick detachable sling swivel studs, and skip-line checkering. Calibers

Garcia's new SO-6 double gun carries dummy sideplates.

range from 22-250 to 375 H & H Magnum, including the 25-06, and all the classic features of the regular Sako rifles are present.

The all-metal Bronco rifle and shotgun has a new take-down system, permitting the barrel assembly to be slipped off the breech. Ready for stowage, the Bronco rifle measures less than 20 inches overall, with the 410 Bronco going 21¾ inches—ideal for lashing to a packframe.

The BL-5 O-U shotgun is now the BL-6, upgraded by adding a pair of hand-engraved false sideplates. It still retains the excellent features of the BL series, and the

additional engraving will appeal to some. There are a few minor changes in the handgun line, with some models discontinued. The Mustketeer rifles appear to have been dropped, along with the Rossi single barrel shotgun, but there is one very welcome newcomer—the Rossi Saddle Ring Carbine. Chambered for the 357 Magnum or 44 Magnum cartridge, the new 20-inch barreled carbine is a Brazilian-manufactured replica of the popular MI892 Winchester, complete with traditional sling ring. Its weight is about 5¾ pounds, the magazine capacity 10 rounds in either caliber.

Mossberg

The bolt action 810 rifle is now available with a 24-inch barrel chambered for the 7mm Remington Magnum cartridge, this the Model 810B at $154.95. The 810A and 810B are listed without open sights, but with Mossberg 4X scopes mounted and targeted, at $146.40 and $173.40 respectively. There have been slight price changes among the centerfire rifles, but the super grade 800 D has been reduced nearly $20. Two of the 410 bolt action shotguns—with plain barrel and detachable choke tubes—have been discontinued in favor of the C-Lect-Choke Model. The slide action Model 500 line has remained the same with only minor changes in prices.

Mossberg M810, now in 7mm Rem. Mag.

The rimfire rifle line has been pared from 16 models in 1971 to 7 in 1972. Among those axed were the western style Auto, the Jack Rabbit Special, and the two "Automatic" sporter models. Remaining autoloaders include the Model 333 with the "automatic bolt-open stop," replacing the Model 430, and the Model 353 with checkered grip

and fore-end panels, replacing the Model 352K. The lever action Palamino is gone, as are the single shot bolt action 320B, the 342K with fore-end extension, the 346K with 25-round tubular magazine and the 340M Mannlicher. With the exception of the 333, all Mossberg rimfire rifles are now repeaters with detachable box magazines.

Winchester Repeating Arms Company

The Model 12 returns, there's a new line
of Model 70s, and a new 22 rimfire, the Model 9422.

The big red W firm rested on its laurels for several years and then, over several seasons, some rather liberal modifications to time-tested designs were tried. More recently the trend has been toward meeting shooters' preferences, and 1972 has to rank as one of the biggest steps in the right direction. The reintroduction of two all-time favorites— the Model 12 pump action shotgun and the Model 64 lever action rifle—will assure that.

The Model 64 was first reintroduced in 1971 as an NRA Commemorative with black chrome metal finish and an inset NRA medallion. The 1972 M64 is almost identical, but without the NRA medallion, and with a blued metal finish, is $124.95 in 30-30 caliber only. After 15 years absence the Model 64 should find many new friends among deer hunters.

The Model 12 was discontinued nearly a decade ago, except for the Super Pigeon Grade. The price of used M12s has jumped upward, if you could locate one the owner would sell. The reintroduced Model 12, made only as a 12 gauge, at least so far, comes in three basic versions—Field, Trap and Skeet— with a chrome-moly steel receiver, ventilated rib barrels 26 to 30 inches long, and buttstock and beavertail fore-end of semi-fancy American walnut. All aspects of the old M12 are retained, including hand checkering fore and aft. Old or new, the latest M12 shotguns are identical, and all parts are interchangeable! The Field gun is $350, the Skeet and Trap guns $375 or $385, either with Monte Carlo stocks. Recoil pads are standard on the Skeet and Trap guns.

The Model 70 rifles again have a new stock, the fifth or sixth in as many years. The pistol grip shows a rounder, shorter contour and, on the basic Standard and Super Grade 70s a pistol-grip cap and a slanted fore-end tip, both with black and white spacers, are used. Detachable sling swivels—for the first time—and a knurled bolt handle knob are standard on these two grades. The Super Grade (quite like the Standard, except for selected wood) is made in four calibers— 243, 270, 30-06 and 300 Winchester Magnum, at $349.95. A new model, the 70A, replaces the old 770, but it has the new 70 stock design. Prices, $149.95, $164.95 for magnums. The 670 has the M70 stock style, complete with a cheekpiece— the first for the 670. The sliding safety has been replaced with the standard three-position safety on the bolt sleeve. Calibers are the same as before—243 and 30-06—but the price is different, $133.95.

Winchester calls the stocks on the 1972 Model 70 rifles "new," and I suppose that's justified if the white line spacers now found on the standard and Super Grade 70s —along with an angled fore-end tip—constitute newness. Yet the M70 DeLuxe rifle of 1970-71 had the same white spacers at butt, grip cap and fore-end, plus the standard fore-end decoration.

True enough, the 1972 M70s have a refined grip and fore-end section, and the checkering is labeled "cut," if not actually hand cut. In any case, it is better looking checkering.

For those who don't want the California-styled 70s, there's still a choice—the African, for 458 fans, offers styling and treatment something like the Super Grades of

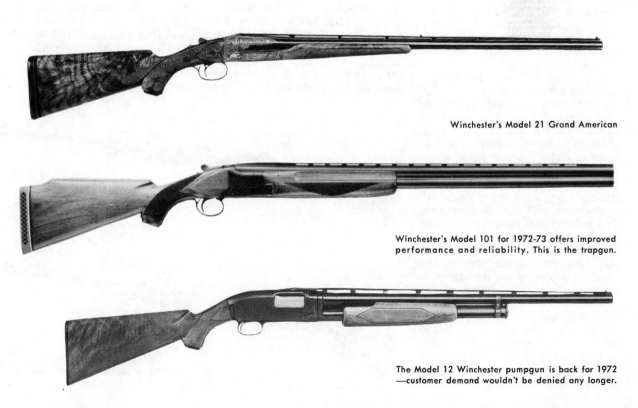

Winchester's Model 21 Grand American

Winchester's Model 101 for 1972-73 offers improved performance and reliability. This is the trapgun.

The Model 12 Winchester pumpgun is back for 1972 —customer demand wouldn't be denied any longer.

yore, including hand checkering. There's also the 70A, minus the ubiquitous white spacers and angled fore-end tip or grip cap, but it's not to be had in 338 or 375 H&H, nor 458, of course. Last, there is the plain Jane 670 rifle, not unlike last year's M770, apart from the newer stock configuration and checkering.

A few days after putting down the foregoing, a Model 70A Winchester was received here—and I'm even more of a mind that the "A" version is the better looking of the 1972 Model 70s. It is in all respects a simple, unadorned working rifle, with metal and wood finishes relatively subdued, glareless.

The new checkering is a big improvement over earlier efforts—the diamonds are sharply pointed, their crisp feel affording a good hand-stopping grasp. They're cut 16 to the inch, close as I can tell, which is a good choice if checkering is to be really functional. The wood is genuine walnut, too.

I like the new reduced-circumference pistol grip. It fits my average-sized hand better, its slimmer feel seeming to give more control, more aliveness, if that's the right word, than the older—and clubbier—handle. The fore-end is still squarish in section, the bottom quite flat, but it feels good in the hand. The well-rounded corners help, I think.

The comb-nose fluting is, generally, well done, if perhaps a little broadly. The radius ought to be rather less than it is. This fluting leaves the extreme front of the comb fairly narrow, and in the heavier calibers the guy who "crawls" forward may find the nose a bit sharp.

The bulky Williams rear sight is still used, which I don't like. Not that there's anything wrong with it as such—its half-circle opening in the shallow V is OK, and the white triangle set in underneath the notch can be helpful. But if you ever expect to use this sight, and to have to adjust it, maybe, way out there in the bush, you'd better have a damn small screwdriver with you. No other way! The well-cut radiussed ramp (for the front sight) is about 3⅝-inches long, and comes with a slide-on hood or sight protector. This ramp tapers nicely in its section, too, from its jointing with the barrel to its top, an improvement over former flat-sided and shorter ramps.

The new 70A here is a 22-250 (another small bow to old friend Jerry Gebby), the fairly stiff barrel (for the caliber) 22 inches long. My caliper says it's exactly .625" around the muz-

zle. *The trigger pull is quite crisp and clear, no trace of creep, but the letoff pull weight is a full 6¼ pounds! That'll have to be fixed, especially on a rifle in this caliber, a varminter. Weight of this rifle, with open sights, is 7½ pounds, and that's probably an ounce or so under the standard Model 70 of 1972. Why? The 70A has a blind magazine, as they're called for some odd reason. That is, there is no floorplate, hinged or not, so unshot cartridges will have to be jacked out of the magazine topside. That's no problem with the M70 action, however—just put the safety lever amidship and run the bolt handle back and forth in perfect safety. Sling swivels are plain type. The grip cap and buttplate are black plastic, the latter with moulded checkering and a WRA medallion. The trigger guard is light alloy. The bolt handle knob has no recess or hole in it, and there's a cross-bolt through the stock, ahead of the guard bow.*

*I'll have something to add about the 70A's shooting if time allows.*JTA

The really big news in Winchester rifles is a rimfire—the Model 9422. Looking almost exactly like the best-selling centerfire Model 94, the new 9422 has the shape, heft, and balance of its big brother, due to its forged-steel receiver and lever, steel barrel and internal action parts, and solid walnut stock and fore-end. It is not an exact dupli-

The new Model 9422 Winchester lever action rifle, made in 22 L.R. or 22 WMR, has already become a big seller.

cate, since loading is done in the manner common to rimfire repeaters with tubular magazines, and ejection is via a port on the right side of the receiver instead of out the top; this solid top receiver permits low mounting of a scope, the 9422 being grooved for tip-off mounts. Barrel length is 20½ inches, weight about 6¼ pounds. Two versions—standard 22 rimfire and 22 WRM—are available. Magazine capacity is 21 Short, 17 Long or 15 Long Rifle cartridges in the 9422, or eleven 22 WRM cartridges in the 9422M magnum.

In mid-1971 Winchester formed a new firm—TRAILBLAZER by Winchester—to market camping equipment and hunting clothes manufactured by two other companies in the Olin Winchester group. The new line includes a complete series of propane-powered lamps, heaters and stoves, plus tents ranging in size from cabin models sleeping 8 to lightweight backpacker types, along with sleeping bags and other related accessories. There is also a line of American Field hunting clothes, including game coats, pants, vests, game bags, and caps, camouflage suits, and a reversible hunting coat that is camouflaged on one side and blaze orange on the other. Judging by the items examined, the quality is in keeping with Winchester tradition.

Winchester's M70A for 1972 shows restraint and simplicity in stock treatment.

Winchester 670 for 1972 has cheekpiece, the 3-position safety of the Model 70s, and quickly-removable sights for scope mounting.

Creative Carvings

For the gun owner wanting to decorate his rifle with a likeness of his big game trophy or trophies, "The Alaskan Silversmith" Sid Bell has what's needed—lug heads. These hand-carved units come in sterling silver at $10, or in 14K gold for $20, and they're easily attached to stocks or floorplates. Tie tacks, clips, cuff links, pins, and bolo ties—sterling silver or 14K gold—featuring game birds, heads, and related wildlife are available at slightly higher prices—and all are hand-carved by Sid Bell.

Some of Sid Bell's inimitable creations, here in sterling silver. These 5 figures are only a few among his scores of designs, all created and hand-finished by Bell. Most of his designs are available in solid gold as well, and may be had as bolo tie ornaments, tie tacks or clips, etc. His full-color brochure tells the whole story—ask for a copy.

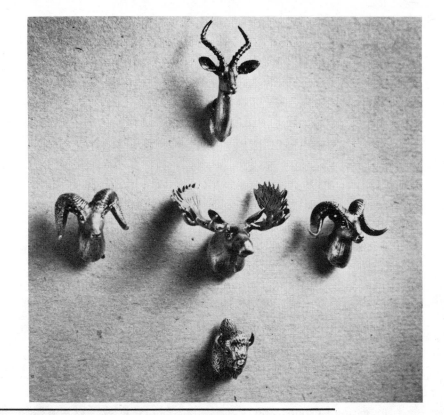

Ferguson Custom Rifle Rest

This new device was designed for benchrest shooters who compete in the "unlimited" class, which is to say those who use the heavier, return-to-battery style rifles. Ferguson will make his new rest to work with most any buttstock form or dimensions. If the stock has a rod or a track underneath, he'll make a V-block to fit the rod or furnish his rest with a ball (see illus.) for the track. The Ferguson rest is *precision made* in all respects, and it will, he says, "return to zero shot after shot." All pins are carefully ground and their mating holes honed—there is *no* slop or shake. Including a dial indicator, the cost is $76; without the DI, $65.

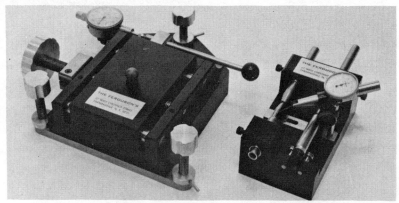

Ferguson's new rifle rest (left) and his Combo-Chek tool.

As a further custom service for benchresters, Ferguson will install a ball on a track on the customer's rifle for $10. All he needs is the buttstock, not the entire rifle. Write to The Fergusons, 27 W. Chestnut St., Farmingdale, NY 11735.

Hubert J. Hecht, who learned his gunsmithing in Europe, now has a shop at 55 Rose Mead Circle, Sacramento, CA 95831. He made the attractive and well-designed stock pictured here, the gun a rare 4-barrel by Burgmuller of Germany. The borings are: 16/16/8x57R and 22 Hornet.

Harrington & Richardson

Prices remain the same as last year on all sporting arms and handguns. The 404 and 404C double barrel shotguns have been discontinued, as has the 17/223 chambering in the 317 rifle. The limited-issue Officer's Model Springfield Rifle is no longer available (all were sold), but the new arms are enough to warm the cockles of an old timer's heart—and maybe many new timers, too! Included are a Lee Commemorative Carbine in 45-70 caliber for $200, complete with a copy of *In the Valley of the Little Big Horn*, and a shooting Cavalry Model Carbine in 45-70 at $150, or a deluxe version at $200. All three models have 22-inch barrels, and all are made on the 1873 Springfield action. There is also a black powder Springfield Stalker in 45 or 58 caliber for $150. This looks like the Cavalry Carbine, but has a solid brass ramrod beneath the 28-inch barrel. For the

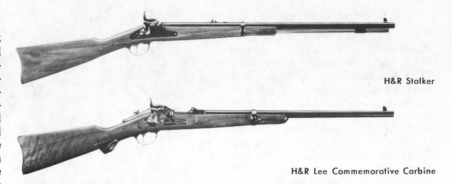

H&R Stalker

H&R Lee Commemorative Carbine

economy-minded black powder shooter there is the Huntsman in 12 gauge, 45 or 58 caliber. It breaks like the H & R Topper single shot shotgun, but in the center of the barrel breech there's a percussion cap nipple; complete with a solid brass ramrod/cleaning rod, the price is a low $59.95. A special version, called the Shikari, is chambered for the 45-70 cartridge, and the price is the same. Black powder shooters and 45-70 lovers should

have a field day.

Other H & R items include new Webley & Scott shotguns, in side-by-side and over-under models, plus air pistols and rifles, and various accessories. Prices had not been confirmed on the W & S over-under or on all the side-by-sides, but the Model 720 and 728 side-by-sides in 20 and 28 gauge, furnished in a felt-lined leather bound case, with accessories sell for $1325.

Economy Chronograph

Chronograph Specialists (Box 5005, Santa Ana, Ca. 92704) are bucking the rising current of ever-increasing prices, and that's no small achievement today. Nor are they merely holding a previous price; they're less expensive!

The 200-6P is of the binary type, which in this instance means rotating a switch lever through 3 segments to obtain a reading following a recorded shot.

The price of their CS200, which offers crystal-controlled, transistorized circuitry, is now $42.25. That price includes screen holders, cables, 20 screens, a velocity chart and instructions. Four D-cell batteries are required, but not included.

CS has three other time recorders for 1972. The CS100—hardly larger than a pack of cigarettes—is fully solid-state, and uses the BCD (Binary Coded Decimal) circuitry and readout. Just turn the switch, after the shot, to the three positions and check the result for muzzle velocity against the tables furnished. A 6V battery supplies power. With screen cables, screen holders, 10 screens, velocity chart and setup instructions, cost is $27.50—and you can't go much lower than that for a piezo-crystal chronograph!

The CS400 at $84.50 offers direct time readout—no putting down numbers and adding them up—and an automatic screen check, other-

New CS chronographs. Model 100 sits atop Model 600 DV, Model 400 at right.

wise it has the same features as the CS100, but 100 screens are furnished.

The CS600 is the top of the line, its chief feature a direct velocity readout—no turning switches, no addition of numbers—just shoot and read velocity. It is compatible with any break-type screen, and operation is by a 12V battery or 110 VAC (optional). Four large number tubes are readable even in bright sunlight. At $185 (including everything listed for the CS400 except velocity tables) the CS600 isn't exactly cheap, but even so it's the lowest priced chronograph offered today with instant velocity readout.

Screen spacing for all four CS units is 2 feet (the CS600 has a 10-foot switch, too), which makes for a compact and simpler setup.

All have 500,000 cycle crystal-controlled oscillators for 0.01% accuracy, plus or minus one (1) count.

We received samples of these new CS100, 400 and 600 instruments too late for a full Testfire Report, but we did give the CS400 a brief workout. CS screens and another brand were shot through—some 60 of them—and only one dead screen appeared in the CS batch, which is a low average. Velocities checked out very closely with results previously had with two other chronographs—using match grade 22 Long Rifles, as a standard test, plus 30-06 National Match loads with a known velocity. We rate the CS400 a good buy. Screens are $5 per 100.

Prices given are FOB factory. Send for the CS catalog—it has all the dope.

New Weatherby Shotguns

One each of Roy Weatherby's brand new shotguns were delivered to me in May of this year (1972)—the Centurion gas-operated autoloader, and a Patrician pump gun, both in 12 gauge and both with 28-inch modified barrels. Both are also handsome guns, particularly the Centurion with its full fancy-grain American walnut stock. I'm not certain if this extra quality wood is going to be standard on regular production Centurions, but if it is there's a bonus. The Centurion lists at $239.50—a highly attractive price for what the new Weatherby autoloader offers (which I'll get to shortly)—which price usually brings pretty plain-Jane wood.

The Centurion exhibits several worthwhile design aspects, notably the "Floating Piston" that operates the action. Rather than being a hang-on, as it were, to the magazine tube, as in other gas-regulated autos—the gas piston is fully independent of any other part of the actions. It can't get out of alignment, nor can it create any conditions that could result in binding or friction.

Other features of the Centurion are a patented trigger system that promises a high reliability factor; special gas ports that permit light or heavy loads to be used without adjustment; a quite different fore-end treatment which conceals the magazine cap for a more graceful, finished appearance. The fore-ends are steel-reinforced, by the way, which should obviate their cracking certainly—which some autoloading fore-ends have suffered from in the past.

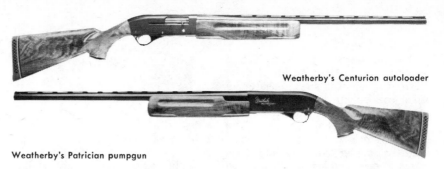

Weatherby's Centurion autoloader

Weatherby's Patrician pumpgun

The Centurion handled well for me. Its balance is excellent, the 28-inch barrel feeling neither too light nor too heavy when swung. The finger-grooved, hand filling fore-end offers very good control, as does the somewhat sharply radiussed pistol grip—I wasn't sure I was going to like the grip, judging from the photos I'd seen, but it feels good. Roy exercised some restraint in designing the curve and the slight flare it shows!

If I'm not as enthusiastic about the Weatherby Patrician pump gun, *mea culpa!* I've never been much of a slide action fan, probably because I'm too awkward or uncoordinated to handle one effectively.

Certainly the Patrician is virtually identical in form, construction quality and general appearance to the Centurion. At its price, $169.50, one can hardly except the wood to be as fancy figured as it is on the autoloader, but it does have good figure. The balance of this new pump is, in my hands, a bit different from the Centurion's—the muzzle seems to swing a little faster, which might well make this Patrician a better brush gun, the more so if it had 26-inch barrels.

There are twin action bars, not just one, which is a plus factor on a slide action shotgun—smoother, more reliable functioning will result, and in my too-brief trial of the Patrician the fore-end slid back and forth rapidly and easily. There was no slightest tendency to stick. A small, gold-plated lever, pivoting above the trigger, unlocks the fore-end to let live shells be removed, and the same hidden magazine cap is used on the Patrician.

Ventilated-rib barrels and recoil pads are standard on both of the new Weatherby shotguns. The fine-line checkering is well done and hand cut, too, and there's a generous amount of it. The wood carries a high-luster finish, which Roy says is as durable as they can devise.

The receivers in both guns are made from a hard-anodized aluminum alloy, virtually scratch proof. The breech bolts in both guns are of steel, so that lock-up with the chrome moly steel barrels is a steel-to-steel system. Both bolts are fluted, making for assured operation even if dirt and debris enter the action—to a degree, at least. Wood-to-metal fitting is excellent—no unsightly gaps or cracks on the two guns here, and Roy tells me they're all to be made that way.

Both guns are offered with 26- and 30-inch barrels, all with 2¾-inch chambers and in the usual chokes. No 3-inch chambered guns are made. Extra barrels—for both—are about $80.　　　　*J.T.A.*

John Bivins

As readers of these pages know, I'm an admirer of Bivins' truly superb skills in building flintlock rifles of the 1760-1810 periods. His mastery of the differences and subtle nuances that distinguish an early rifle from a later one is unsurpassed—his rifles look right, and they are. In addition, Bivins' rifles are *not* mere decorators—they're sturdily constructed for long shooting use, guaranteed for the life of the owner if Bivins is allowed to make the repairs. Bob Paris barrels and Siler locks are used exclusively by Bivins. He considers them the best quality obtainable.

Bivins has a new and fully infor-

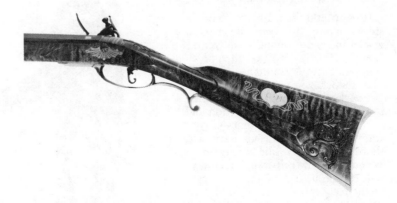

mative brochure ready, one which shows representative illustrations of the various styles of rifles he makes. His prices start at about

$650. His brochure shows an elaborate Federal period rifle, well over 100 pieces of silver worked into it, that sells at $1300.　　　*J.T.A.*

Marlin

The big news is the introduction of the lever action Marlin 1895 in 45-70 caliber—the first repeater in this caliber to be introduced in nearly 40 years. It should be most welcome to big bore shooters. The walnut stock has a straight grip, and the sporter length 4-round half-magazine is coupled with a 22-inch round barrel. Over-all length is 40½ inches, the weight with open sights about 7 pounds. The looks and feel of the rifle examined were excellent, and the price of $185 is a relative bargain, considering that some of the single shot rifles in this caliber cost almost that much. Marlin's solid-top, side-ejection design allows low scope mounting, of course.

The price line was held on the centerfire rifle and shotguns, with only a very minor increase on the rimfire line. The 22 rimfire Model 39D has been replaced by two

Marlin's Model 120 Magnum 12

rifles—the Golden 39A with pistol grip stock and 24-inch round barrel, and the Golden 39M with straight grip stock and 20-inch round barrel.

Made in limited numbers in 1970 and 1971, the Marlin 39 Century Ltd. and their 39A Article II 22 rimfire rifles—both with such special features as brass furniture, octagon barrels and inset medallions—are still available.

A new Glenfield 70, an autoloader in 22 rimfire with 18-inch barrel and 7-round box magazine, is $46.95.

Another Marlin commemorative has appeared—the Zane Grey Century model in 30-30 caliber at $150.

A dolled-up 336 lever action with brass buttplate, and receiver-inset portrait medallion of Zane Grey, the octagon-barreled rifle comes with a certificate entitling the owner to buy the entire Zane Grey Library at half price.

The long-awaited 120 Magnum slide action shotgun finally got into production. This take-down all-steel gun weighs almost 8 pounds with 30-inch ventilated-rib barrel. The walnut pistol grip stock and fore-end are checkered. 26-inch and 28-inch barrels are also offered. For the shotgunner wanting a solid wood and steel shotgun, the 120 may well be the answer. Price, with magazine filler plug, is $150.

George Hoenig made the stocks for these rifles on his Precision Pantograph, both for Tom Siatos of *Gunsa Ammo*—see text for details. He also did all metal work—quarter rib, scope mounts, special sights, etc. Top rifle is Brevex Magnum in 460 G&A caliber; lower rifle is rare double flat-topped Mauser 98 in 7x57mm. G&A photo.

Hoenig-Rodman

How would you like to have a stock made to *your* desires in weeks instead of months—or years? George Hoenig and his ultra-precision pantograph can do it—just send him a stock you want copied. You'll get back a stock with *finished* inletting, all ready to drop the action and barrel into. Not only that—if you want the stock built up here and there—cheekpiece added, say, or a Wundhammer grip-swell included, H-R can do it. In fact, the tolerances of their equipment are so small that "a wood-to-metal fit as precise as that of glass bedding" is the standard they work to, inside and out! Write to 853 S. Curtis Rd., Boise, Idaho 83705 for complete information.　　J.T.A.

Albright Buttplate

Albright Products Co. (Box 695, Bishop, CA 93514) call their new—and excellently done—trapped steel buttplate the "Easy Fit," and that's true enough. A rear flange or rim, surrounding the trap opening, is on the same plane as the buttplate's edges, so putting the plate on the buttstock is simplified. I'm more impressed, though, by the fine quality of the plate—the checkering is sharp and clean, the diamonds of long aspect, at a guess at least 3 to 1. The trap door opening, a bit over 2½" by ¾", is ample for routing out a big cavity in the wood. The Albright buttplate is 5⅛" long by 1¾" wide, and it may be had blued or in the white at $18.95.　　J.T.A.

Savage Arms

No radically new Savages in 1972, but a flock of modifications. In the 110 bolt action rifle line the 22-250 chambering has been discontinued, and the 110-D now has a hinged floorplate instead of the solid version. The 110-E has a blind magazine (no floorplate), but the solid floorplate is still standard on 110 actions and barreled actions. All 110 models now have a Satin-slide bolt, reducing bolt bind to a minimum via the use of a rail on the inside of the receiver.

The 440-BT Trap Gun is gone, a new 333-T (on the 330 action) replacing it. The 12 bore 333-T, priced at $284.95, has a 30-inch barrel with wide ventilated rib, and Monte Carlo stock with rubber recoil pad, plus the regular 330 features. A separate 20 gauge barrel to fit the 33-T, or any 330 shotgun, can be had for $110 extra, including the fitting charge. A 330 Set—any 12 gauge in this model, with an extra set of 20 gauge barrels in 28- or 26-inch lengths, complete with a black, soft case with pocket for the extra barrel—is listed at $287.95; not bad for "two" excellent shotguns. (With a "Four-Tenner" you could have three gauges on one action.) The side-by-side Savage-Fox B in 12 gauge is now chambered for 3-inch magnum shells.

The 1971-made Favorite—in the special collector's edition—is no more, but a lower-cost version is now available in two grades—the 72 Crackshot with octagonal barrel at $57.50, and the 74 Little Favorite, with round barrel, at $42.50. The Crackshot has a case-hardened receiver finish, the Little Favorite a satin black finish; otherwise the two single shots are the same—both reminiscent of a by-gone era.

Most of the Savage/Anschutz rimfire rifles cost more this year. Changes—the Mark 10-D replaces the Mark 10; the major modifications are in the stock shape and the micrometer rear sight. At $84.95 it's still a lot of value. The 22 WRM has been added to the excellent 54 Sporter rifle, and a new 22 Long Rifle sporter—the 184 at $77.95—is made for those wanting a cheaper form of the 164 Sporter.

The biggest changes are in the Model 24 Rifle/Shotgun line. The 24-S, a side-lever opener, has been replaced by a Field Grade; the top lever is now used on all M24

Above, top—Savage/Anschutz M54, now made in 22 WMR. Below it, Savage M24 Field Grade, now with top opener. Below—Savage 330 barrel set, with carrying case. See our catalog pages for pictures of the new 24-C or Campers Companion, etc.

grades, as is the separated barrel design with integral band front sight. Priced at $66.95, the 24 Field Grade has a case-hardened receiver and a walnut-finished hardwood stock and fore-end of a more pleasing shape (to this writer) that's similar to some of the older Model 24s. Another new one is the 24-V, the rifle barrel in 30-30 caliber. The 24-V receiver is satin black, its barrel tapped for scope mounts. Coupled with a 3-inch 20 gauge shotgun barrel, the 24-V makes a good choice where deer and upland game can be hunted at the same time. The 24-V is still $99.95.

Biggest news in the M24 line-up is the 24-C Campers Companion. At 5¾ pounds and 35 inches over-all, the 24-C is compact. Barrels are 20 inches —the upper one takes 22 LR, L or S cartridges, the under barrel 20-gauge 2¾-inch shells. The receiver has a non-glare, satin black finish, and the straight-grip stock has a pull of 12½ inches. A trap door in the buttplate

holds two shotgun shells and ten 22 rimfire cartridges—life insurance in an emergency. The take-down 24-C packs into a special soft case only 5 inches wide and 22 inches long; the case has loop carrying handles, plus 4 leather thongs for tying onto a pack or saddle. At $74.95, the 24-C should be standard survival equipment for pilots flying over unpopulated areas. It's also a handy item for campers hitting the open trails.

Also new are the Springfield 944 and 944-Y, side lever single barrel shotguns with straight grip stock, and the Springfield 174 pump action 30-30 rifle—a plain version of the Savage 170, which now has a running deer scene on the receiver sides. The scope line has been reduced to one 4x centerfire model and two rimfire types.

With 93 basic models in the Savage line, 4 of which have sold over a million each, the Westfield firm must be making what shooters want.

Thompson/Center

A flintlock version of the excellent T/C Hawken rifle is now available, in 45 and 50 calibers, along with two new muzzle-loading arms —a single shot duelling-type pistol with target sights and double set triggers, and a double barrel shotgun. The shotgun will be in 12 gauge, but its price and specific features still have to be determined. The prototype I examined looked good, and the production model should be equal in quality to the good Hawken rifle. The pistol is called the Patriot. It comes in 45 caliber only—at least for now— measures 16 inches over-all with a 9¼-inch barrel. It's priced at $112 alone, or at $132.50 with a special accessory pack containing all the implements necessary for shooting.

There is also a new and improved grip—very well done—for the Contender pistol. Standard on all current production models, this grip—designed by Steve Herrett— is offered at $9.40 for use on older models.

Thompson/Center Knives

T/C offers a good variety of hunting knives now—all handmade —from a classic Bowie type at

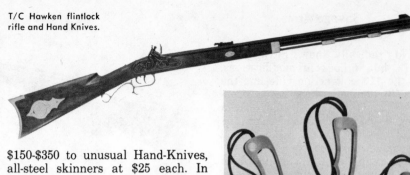

T/C Hawken flintlock rifle and Hand Knives.

$150-$350 to unusual Hand-Knives, all-steel skinners at $25 each. In between are two conventional-shaped knives, the Rifleman's Knife ($95) and the Companion at $70.

A 3-blade pocket knife, also fully handmade, is Ken's Pal, offered in 3¼″ or 4¼″ over-all length when folded. With rosewood handles, phenolic impregnated, these are $25.

All are furnished with top quality leather sheaths and sharpening stones. All are unconditionally guaranteed if used with reasonable care, and they're all engraved with the craftsman's name, date or initials.

Three blade styles are available on the Hand-Knives—a "leading" point and a "trailing" point on the two with 1½″ by 2½″ blades, the Boat & Field No.851 having a longer

and narrower (1″x3¾″) blade for use on smaller game, fish and birds.

There's been no chance to try any of these in the field, but I mean to have one of the Hand-Knives this fall—I like the skeletonized style for its lighter weight, the leather thong to prevent loss, and the fact that these could be sterilized in boiling water if necessary.   *J.T.A.*

Ithacagun

In early 1972 another Model 51 autoloader was added—the magnum. Made in plain and ventilated rib grades, chambered for 3-inch shells, the latest gas-operated 51 lists at $229.95, including a recoil pad ($25 less for the plain barrel). The Model 200E side-by-side and the 600 and 700 over/under models are now offered with silver-colored frames and black-chromed barrels, at an increase in price. Three new Perazzi models are available—the Light Game Model at $795, the MX-8 Combination Trap at $1795, with an extra inter-changeable single barrel to replace the regular over-under version, and the new Mirage Model for international events, which has tapered rib, special chokes and a schnabel fore-end, all for $1295. The Ithaca LSA-65 rifle is available in 25-06 caliber, as we noted in our 26th edition.

The Tikka Turkey Gun—the 12 gauge/222 Remington combination gun that has been handled by at least two other firms in the past— is now available from Ithaca with some decided improvements, including a solid rib atop the 24½-inch barrel, and an extra wide hammer spur. The price is $229.95, only some

Above—Ithaca Turkey Gun.

Below—Ithaca Mirage, made by Perazzi, a new version of his famed action.

$5 more than the less attractive version sold for 5 years ago. The Ithaca recoil-operated (Browning system) autoloading 300 and 900 shotguns are still available, but they have been joined by the XL series of gas-operated autoloaders. The new shotguns have aluminum alloy receivers, Roto-Forged barrels, and a self-compensating gas-system that handles mixed loads without adjustment. The XL300 receiver is black anodized, with etched scrollwork to enhance it, while

the XL900 has a silver-colored game scene on the receiver. Prices of the ventilated-rib models are $184.95 and $194.95 respectively in choice of 12 or 20 gauge, with 26, 28 or 30-inch barrels, and the XL900 is for sale in trap, Skeet or Slug Gun grades. There is also a new Model 150 side-by-side shotgun in 12 to 20 gauge. This one sells for $239.95, and it's essentially the Model 100 with a beavertail fore-end and an extensively etched scrollwork frame.

Hyper-Single Precision Rifles

As I've noted elsewhere in these pages, new-design single shot rifles are making their bow with fair frequency these days, and here is one that I've seen and closely examined. The workmanship is excellent, and the design is Sam Lair's, not a small re-working of an older type. True, it is basically a falling block, underlever actuated, but the internal elements—trigger-sear, hammer-striker, hangered twin mainsprings—are Lair's own.

Our pictures show a prototype as far as design details are concerned, but any changes will be small—the fitting for the stock-attaching through-bolt will be altered for better stock fitting, a reduction in action depth, at the front, is planned, etc.

This Lair action is rugged and strong, yet it's not overly heavy. It is made of modern steels, properly heat treated, and it has only about half the parts of comparable actions!

The breechblock operates via rollers (there is *no* lever-block linkage) and the striker rotates on needle bearings, powered by dual coil springs. Lair's trigger is adjustable for take-up, weight of pull and backlash. The lever locks in the closed position, and the safety is a top-tang type. The fore-end hanger permits barrels to be fully free-floated.

Mr. Lair sent me a sample action, and I must admit I was

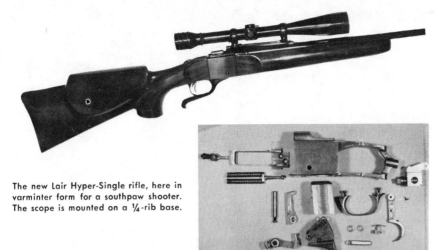

The new Lair Hyper-Single rifle, here in varminter form for a southpaw shooter. The scope is mounted on a ¼-rib base.

Hyper-Single rifle action taken down.

surprised and pleased at the quality of construction. Fit and finish of the parts couldn't be faulted, and the trigger pull was crisp and clean, letoff about 3 pounds. Lever throw to open is quite short, at a guess about 30 degrees, and the lever lockup is positive.

Ordering a Hyper-Single complete rifle will be a custom proposition. Stocking will be in AA-grade wood, to the customer's desires and dimensions. Barrels can be of any reasonable weight and length, and the barrelmaker can be selected—Hart, Shilen, anybody! The completed rifle is 100% guaranteed—material and workmanship—for the life of the original owner. Hardly more than that can be expected.

Cost of the standard rifle, chambered for any rimmed case, is $575. In light of its fully custom-made aspects, that isn't excessive—not on today's market. Chambering for a rimless or belted case is $35 extra, and for the same added cost set triggers or a stainless steel barrel are fitted. A fluted barrel adds $60.

Barreled actions only (any barrel available) are $300, the action alone $215. For $100 Mr. Lair will supply his "Smarty Kit," all action parts roughed out only.

I've always been a sucker for good single actions, I suppose—anyway, I sent Mr. Lair a deposit on a Hyper-Single rifle. I couldn't resist that handsome and handsomely-executed action.   *J.T.A.*

Ted Blackburn

The all-steel trigger guard and hinged floorplate assembly (pictured nearby) is very well done. I saw samples of these at the Portland NRA meeting, and the workmanship is most excellent. Apart from that, however, the assembly has several good features.

The magazine box fits snugly into the Blackburn floorplate frame, as well as the action, making for a stronger assembly. The side rails cover the magazine box, giving a neater look when the floorplate is opened. The bottom line of the stock is one long straight plane when the Blackburn unit is installed. The rear of the guard lies closer to the trigger, letting the second finger have more room, an asset with rifles of heavy recoil or for the gloved hand.

Though intended for the gunsmith or custom riflemaker, the serious amateur can fit this unit easily

Ted Blackburn's new guard-floorplate assembly for Model 70 Winchester rifles shows excellent craftsmanship.

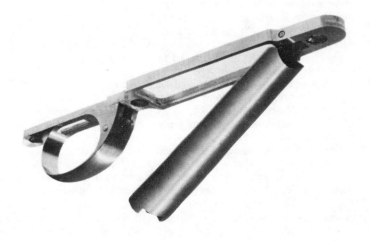

—its dimensions, 0.010″ greater than factory specs, allow for good fit into an existing stock.

Ted Blackburn (1880A Embar-cadero Rd., Palo Alto, CA 94303) gets $65 for this new guard-floor-plate-frame, and that's a moderate price for such quality.   *J.T.A.*

Chevrolet Carryall

I had an enjoyable session last fall with the rugged and efficient Chevy Suburban 4-wheel unit or Carryall (it seems to trade under both names) and my experiences with it would have been more varied and productive if it had been delivered on time!

I wasn't able to get in a lengthy hunt out West in 1971, but Jack Atcheson—who operates a world-wide hunting organization in Butte, Montana—had arranged for a scant week's trip to a friend's place in Montana for deer and antelope, and maybe—if we were lucky—an elk.

The hunt, by the way, was a mixed success—my partner and I got antelope all right, but in the section of the elk mountain I got into I saw nary an elk. Gerry, on the other hand, downed a fat spike bull and, a day later, shot not one, but two deer! Eating bucks, true, but his antelope went over 15 inches.

Because we wanted to tote the meat back home, I'd arranged with Chevrolet to loan me a vehicle for the trip, and those plans were made far enough in advance that there shouldn't have been any hangup. There was, though, for the Carryall didn't arrive at the local dealer's place until two days after we'd had to leave—big game outfitters don't wait!

Still, the Chevy machine gave me reliable service during several weeks of cold and snow. It plowed through deep drifts on my long driveway that I couldn't have managed without that 4-wheel drive system. It busted through the snow so well, in fact, that I didn't have to get my bladed tractor out—left it in the barn!

The half-ton Carryall delivered to me was a deluxe job—gold and white paint, custom interior, dual air conditioner units (one in the ceiling, forward of the lift gate) and heavy-duty 6-ply tires—or 6-ply rating, I should say.

The spec list shown here tells how the Carryall was set up otherwise. This outfit had a delivery price, before state taxes, of $6408.65. That included the 7% federal excise tax then in force, otherwise the total would have been about $5980.

What was covered by the $186.45 for "custom deluxe equipment" I never discovered, but I suppose it applied to interior trim; the "body side molding" and the "white/ochre/

Chevy's 4-wheel drive Suburban Carryall—a tough, rugged vehicle, roomy and comfortable.

Model: Suburban Carryall	$4384.00
Destination Charge	61.00
Rear Seat	124.30
Body Side Molding	42.15
Air Cond.—Overhead	658.25
Front/Rear Shock Absorbers	15.80
Front Wheel Lock Hubs	76.90
Positraction Axle	65.30
350 Cid V-8 Engine	44.25
Turbo Hydra-Matic	242.25
Comfortilt Steering Wheel	57.95
Power Steering	147.45
7.00-15.0-6 PR Tires	154.00
Heavy-Duty Battery	16.90
AM Push Button Radio	68.50
Custom Deluxe Equipment	186.45
White/Ochre/White	63.20
Parchment Trim	00
	1963.65
	$6408.65

white" paint were separate extras (at some $105), so the cost couldn't have been for those. In any case, I don't consider it a particularly deluxe interior—the Carryall is essentially a truck, and it has the looks of one inside and out, with relatively little in appointments or amenities to relieve that aspect of it. That it is a truck is all to the good from a practical use standpoint—I like that, but almost $6000 is a lot of dough for the result.

The rear seat ordered (only the front bench is standard) is bolted

in and may be removed the same way. But it's no 10-minute job. No provision is made for a folding rear seat, a la station wagons.

The Carryall was turned over to me with a few minor faults—some paint scratches near the roof, a step-strip missing from a door sill, and paint sprayed on top of a hunk of plastic still atached to an arm rest.

My big shock, though, was gas mileage! I got 7.5-8 mpg under average around-town driving, with a maximum of 9.5-10 on the toll-ways at around 65 mph. I thought that might improve after break-in, but it didn't—I got just about the same figures with 3,000-odd miles on the odometer. All of this driving was in 2-wheel range, of course, and with the Warn hubs locked out.

The Carryall has only 3 doors, not counting the rear lift- and tail-gates—two on the right side, one for the driver. I found this mildly annoying—anything needing to be put in the back—or removed—meant a trip around the front or rear of the car, unless it was something that could be thrown or tossed in. I understand that 1973 Carryalls will have 4 doors, plus other refinements. *J.T.A.*

SQUARE SHOT &

LITTLE FLYING SAUCERS

by Roger Barlow

Here are two highly unusual—not to say unique—forms of shot that few American gunners have ever heard of. Highly effective at the shorter upland ranges, too, they're not all that hard to make at home—at least until some alert outfit starts importing the FN Dispersante cubes.

Extreme close-up look at the roughly shaped cube shot loaded by FN in their superb *Dispersante* shells. (Round shot is #8)

CONTRARY TO WHAT that heading strongly suggests, Barlow, has not, repeat *not*, been hitting the bottle to excess nor has he taken up the smoking of illegal forms of flora. He has, in all truth, only been shooting test patterns and killing quail, grouse, rabbits and pheasants using shot that is even more square than Lawrence Welk—and with other shot looking very much as though it hailed from another world than ours.

These unusual, even unbelievable, shot pellets were merely some of the oddities encountered in a thorough investigation of what exists in the field of "spreader," "scatter" or "brush" loads.

As a good example of the Perverseness of Things in General, consider that no sooner did birdshooters obtain those long sought-after dense patterns (through the invention of choke boring) than some of them decided they needed, on occasion, some

way of opening up those tight patterns! So someone coined the phrase about ". . . eating your cake and having it too."

Or was it, "Wanting your choke and cylinder patterns, too?" This apparent contradiction has actually been achieved—in several different ways. Even before choke boring arrived, shooters knew they could control the pattern density of their muzzleloaders to some extent by varying the powder charge. With a normal shot charge and a light powder load they got more dense, even patterns. With a lighter shot load and a heavy charge of powder the pattern would be more open. Loading thinner than normal wadding over the powder and a thicker than normal wad over the shot was also said to produce a thinner and broader pattern. (And an undesirably irregular one, I suspect.)

I can't tell you who actually came up with the first genuine "spreader" shotshell

but W.W. Greener in *The Gun*[*], published in the 1880s, shows one which produced an open pattern from the placement of two thin over-shot wads within the shot charge. This 90-odd year old scatter load is almost identical to the modern Remington-Peters type except that the Greener load used a very thick final O-S wad. Winchester-Western "brush" loads spread their #8 shot in a thin, broad pattern by means of a cardboard X-shaped divider in the shot charge, and they close the case with a folded crimp.

Both of these U.S.-made spreader shells give something approaching improved cylinder patterns from most modified and even full choke barrels, with the distribution of shot being surprisingly even—considering all that cardboard mixed up in the shot charge; yet on occasion there are patterns with sizeable gaps.

The FN *Dispersante* shotshells, from Belgium, achieve their dispersion effect through purely aerodynamic means—with square or cube shot of about #7 size which have a very erratic flight pattern. These shells provide a somewhat more rapid opening up of the pattern at close range, as well as a more consistently even distribution of the shot, than can be managed with round shot plus those in-the-charge wads.

The Italian scatter loads carry little *disco volante* or flying saucer type pellets, securing a rapid and extensive opening of the pattern through the erratic paths traveled by these unusually shaped pellets. Although I didn't have the opportunity of shooting patterns with factory loads of this type, my own handloads made up with #8 and #6 shot—which I flattened myself in my basement flying saucer factory—performed reasonably well, although not as consistently as did the FN cube shot.

I'm amazed that Winchester-Western and Remington-Peters stick to the card-in-the-shot system, as it must be rather complicated to load these shells; with the cube or disc shot, loading would be a straightforward machine process, easy *and* economical.

---

[*]London, 1881.

Left to right—FN *Dispersante* shotshell with cube shot. Next, W-W's brush load with X-shaped cardboard divider in the shot charge. Then the R-P scatter load with two O-S type wads in the shot charge. On the far right are Italian style disc shot made by the author. These proved to be excellent pellets for homemade spreader loads.

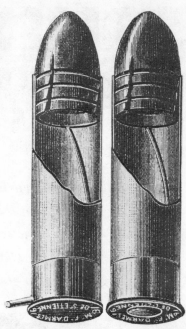

A French sporting goods catalog of 1902 listed these pinfire and centerfire rifled cartridges for use in modern smoothbores. Although the case is shown loaded with a bullet it is like those loaded with shot. To receive any spin the bullet must have been seated much deeper.

Comparison of pellets used in various scatter loads. At left are 3 of the FN cube shot (same weight as a #7 round shot)—note the bit of "tail" left on one from its fabrication; this must help it steer a suitable erratic course! The 2 round shot are #8s from a Winchester brush load. On the right are some disc shot by the author made by flattening #8 shot to varying degrees.

I'm also surprised that someone here in the U.S. hasn't either imported or manufactured cube or disc shot. Surely it would be a very simple mechanical operation to take square lead wire of the correct dimension and just chop off "pellets" at a great rate, or to flatten commercial round shot by passing them between rollers.

Considering the vast number of over-choked guns used for rabbit and upland bird hunting, there *should* be a substantial market for such products. I did say, "should be," for I suspect there really isn't a great demand for spreader loads, largely because so few people know about them or fully understand their usefulness.

Even an improved cylinder barrel throws a somewhat overly dense pattern for many shots at quail and woodcock and could definitely benefit from the use of brush loads in such situations. Certainly modified and full choke barrels are far too

destructive of game when used at 20-30 yards, but would kill without mutilating one's birds if turned into improved cylinder barrels through the use of spreader loads.

Although our U.S.-made scatter loads are offered only with #8 shot, which is perfect for quail and woodcock, they are still surprisingly effective on rabbit and grouse. The same loads are a bit light for pheasants, even at close quarters. The one size of cube shot loaded in the FN *Dispersante* shells is about the weight of our #7 shot, hence is a somewhat better all-purpose size in my estimation. Except that for quail we might better have a shot size similar to #8! But there is absolutely no reason why we could not have cube or disc shot in any size we want or need, though heavier the #7 might be slower to spread.

While spreader loads (of any type) can provide a heavily-choked gun with a good

20-30 yard "quail pattern," unfortunately they cannot endow an overlong, heavy and slow handling "duck" gun with the lively feel a genuine upland game gun should have. Of course there are a great many guns in use for rabbit, quail, grouse, woodcock and pheasants which do have fair "upland" handling characteristics, though they may be a bit too tightly choked for much of this sort of shooting. A spreader load in the first barrel will do much to make these guns more efficient for this work.

In fact, with a double, choked IC and modified (or full), one might well use a spreader load in the more *heavily* choked barrel—and fire this one *first;* the IC pattern would usually be just right (with regular shot loads) for the second shot, or for the second bird, under upland conditions. This would be one of the few times a selective single trigger would serve some genuinely useful purpose.

What about the man with a modified or full choke pump or autoloader? How is he to take advantage of a spreader load for that first shot at close-in, heavy-cover birds? Well, it's not all that complicated or difficult to stuff a scatter load in the chamber and normal loads in the magazine, is it, then reload the same way after a shot or shots have been fired.

This situation does indeed illustrate the shortcomings of the repeating scattergun, which serves well enough, when all the shooting is at targets roughly the same distance away; but it is seen to be vastly inferior to the double, which provides the shooter with an instant choice of pattern (through choke and/or load) to effectively meet widely varying field requirements. The first shot may have to be made at 20 yards, the next one might have to be taken

Even a 1-oz. load of #6s in an IC barrel is going to put too many shot into a pheasant at close range. Waiting until that bird reached the nearby trees would have more than likely meant losing him. The answer—as with much upland game hunting—a cylinder bore or a spreader load!

Here's where a quail hunter needs a scatter load, even if he is using an IC barrel! When those birds blast out of this hedgerow they'll be out of sight before they've been airborne 25 yards—so they'll have to be dropped at not much beyond 15-18 yards. This can be done with a light, fast handling gun, but the broadest possible pattern is needed as below.

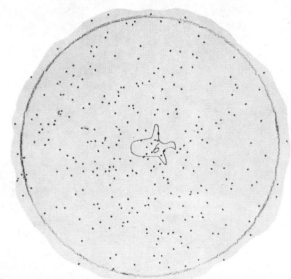

at nearer 35 or 40 yards. *One* choke and one *pattern* in a multi-shot scattergun is just about as satisfactory an approach to the practical needs of the upland game hunter as would be just *one* gear in an automobile. It is mighty rare, indeed, when I want 2 or 3 quick consecutive cylinder patterns or the same number of consecutive half- or full-choke ones!

This is one of the main reasons so many upland game shooters much prefer doubles. Sure, they're more expensive, but they're the only really satisfactory way for us to be certain of having the most suitable pattern for whatever circumstances must be dealt with when our game flushes.

I guess it would be a fair assumption to claim that pumps and autoloaders can benefit even more from using scatter loads than will doubles.

Just as we are far too much in the habit of buying our shotguns too tightly choked for the use to which we put most of them, so do we tend to value most of those shells which, we are told, will deliver "better" patterns. Better for what? Better at what range? For smashing clay targets? For duck and geese at 50 yards or more? Or for quail, rabbits and woodcock at 18-25 yards?

Our modern shells, with more effective wads and plastic shot protector cups, do deliver patterns having a more uniform distribution of the shot charge and in which slow moving, badly deformed pellets are virtually eliminated. Yet the value of these "advantages" of our latest shotshells (those slightly tighter and more dense patterns) are vastly over emphasized as far as rabbit and upland game hunters are concerned. Most upland game is killed at well under 30 yards, if not under 25, where pattern regularity is far less a matter for concern than it is out beyond 35 yards.

Slower moving, deformed pellets may arrive at the 40 yard target (clay or feathered) too late, too far off course and with far too little remaining energy to be of any use; but at 20-30 yards these deformed pellets are very little behind the main body of the shot charge, are not too far off course to be of use and they still have sufficient striking energy for effective penetration. It is entirely possible that our modern shot protector shells, which deliver those usefully more dense patterns for Skeet, trap and waterfowl shooters, may very well be unnecessarily "good" for the needs of the upland game shoter who takes his game at relatively close range and wants enough of it left for eating purposes. This would be even more true for the man using a gun made a few years ago, one choked in relation to the shotshells of that period. (Today some chokes are bored with a couple of points less constriction to compensate for the new type of shells.)

As far as the matter of the deformed shot being able to effectively penetrate a game bird is concerned, consider those spreader loads of cube or disc shot which are made up of nothing but "deformed" shot of the most distorted shapes imaginable—yet in many situations are fully as effective as any load of perfect, undeformed round shot. Certainly the penetration of the "imperfect" square or disc shot is more than adequate at the 18-30

Quailburgers on the wing! That's sure to be the result of that shot if one of those birds is well centered—regardless of how that gun is choked (unless it's completely UNchoked) and perfectly illustrates the situation which calls for the first shot to be some sort of a spreader load.

yard range at which most upland game is killed.

In France many rabbit and bird hunters find a very broad pattern (wider even than true cylinder) so useful that often they have one barrel of a double gun bored cylinder and then, to further spread the shot charge, *rifle* it with broad, slow-twist, shallow grooves! Such a barrel, shooting any ordinary shotshell, produces a wide and non-mutilating pattern useful for taking game as close-in as 12 yards and effective out to around 25 yards. With the second barrel choked IC or modified, such a gun has an effective operating range of from about 12 to 45 yards—what more could any upland game hunter want?

As I have one of these rifled or *canon raye* barrels on a light and fast handling Bretton O-U, I can vouch for this range of performance. The accompanying patterns were shot with this gun.

The French shooter has long shown an interest in wide patterns. In 1898 M. Galand, a Parisian gunmaker, patented and began manufacturing a *rifled* shotshell.

His paper case apparently had a metal liner with prominent rifling of fairly rapid twist (1 in 12) which is said to have resulted in a spread of no less than 50 inches at a little over 20 yards. Another version of the Galand shell had rifling with a twist of about 1 in 25, which reduced the spread of the shot charge to around 35 inches at 22 yards—the degree of gun choke apparently not having much effect, one way or the other.

(A similar cartridge was the somewhat earlier Courtier, also deeply rifled internally but intended for use with a special ball or slug having deep grooves to match the rifling to insure that it would not "strip" but would get a useful amount of spin in that short distance of contact.)

Ingenious as were those Galand rifled shotshells, they eventually fell into disuse for various reasons; one was difficult extraction. They could not have been inexpensive to manufacture and were undoubtedly more costly than some other solutions to the problem of getting broad patterns from a choked barrel.

Left—Using David Baker's cutting device, first, strips are cut from a 2-inch wide roll of soft lead. A ledge behind the cutting blade acts as a stop, thereby measuring equal width strips which are then fed through the machine lengthwise (right), to produce 13 cube shot at each stroke.

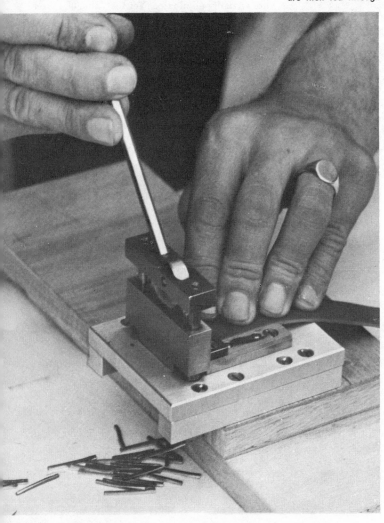

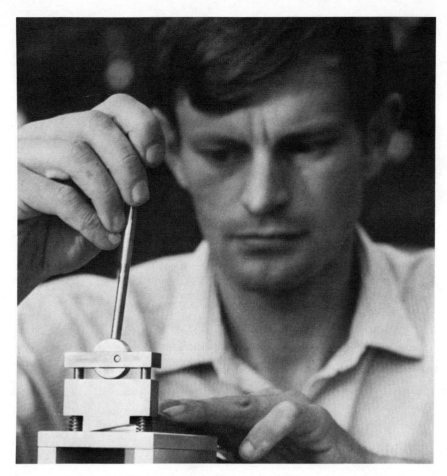

Under no circumstances can the scattergun be considered a long range arm and we should stop trying to pretend that it is. It is precisely its "scatter" that makes it so effective at short range. We should accept this fact for the virtue that it is and take full advantage of it.

Give thought, then, to buying or making a box or two of "scatter loads" for your next upland game hunt, unless you're already shooting with a true cylinder barrel —that's what is needed at close range; and it doesn't matter whether you come by it by the way your barrel is bored or the way your shells are loaded!

The modern American one-gun shooter who needs, or thinks he needs, a heavily choked gun for some of his hunting, should certainly get better acquainted with some of today's short range scatter loads. It's like having a spare cylinder or improved cylinder barrel in your pocket—and for free!

As for handloading these specialized shotshells, it requires no more skill or knowledge than does the making of the normal types.

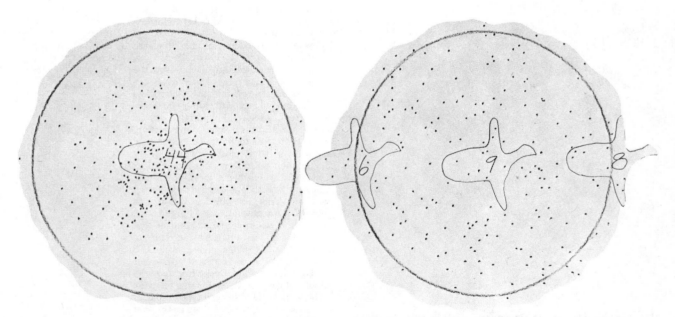

Left—One of the most noted shooting authorities once wrote that the most useful, all-round choke is the modified or half-choke, and that in his experience a modified 12 bore with 1¼ ozs. of #6 shot will grass a pheasant to about 45 yards, *yet will not shoot him to pieces at 20-25 yards.* The above pattern, made with a modified barrel using 1¼ ozs. of #6 shot, pretty clearly shows that a bird centered by this charge at 25 (not even 20) yards isn't going to be worth bringing home! Reducing that shot charge to 1⅛ ozs. of #6 shot will reduce the number of pellets in a pheasant at 25 yards to somewhere between 20 and 30, which is still too many. Even a light 1-oz. load is going to put more than 3 times the necessary number of shot into a 25 yard pheasant,

while still handicapping the shooter with a narrow spread of pattern a modified barrel gives. In a modified or full choke barrel at under 30 yards a spreader load of some type is certainly called for—unless you're such a great shot that you can count on hitting those birds with just the thin edge of those tight patterns! Right—Same modified choke barrel but this time shooting FN *Dispersante* cube shot. A pheasant size target will receive sufficient pellets for a kill out to 30 yards; and even at 20 yards will not be excessively damaged. Equally important is the fact that there is a *wide* and even distribution of pellets over a greater area, making a kill more likely even though one's hold is not perfect. This pattern would also be very effective for grouse or rabbit.

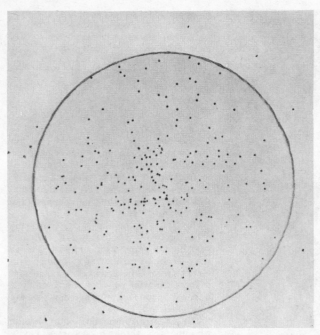

Even a true cylinder barrel delivers a high concentration of shot in the center of a small pattern area at close range. Yet there are occasions when rabbits and even pheasants must be taken at 12-20 yards.

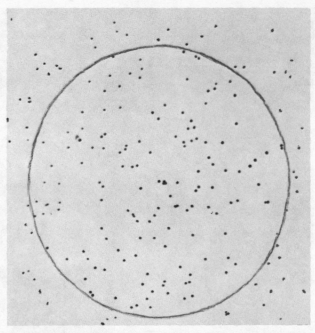

The same shot load fired in the lightly rifled spreader barrel of a Bretton O-U shows remarkably even dispersion of the pellets over a usefully wide area, makes a superb pattern for any necessary close shooting.

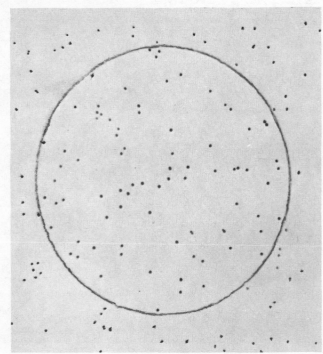

Use of a shot cup type of shell made very little difference to the pattern thrown by the French rifled barrel. But this pattern shows that this rapid means of obtaining wide shot dispersion is still effective with #6 shot for large birds and rabbits out to beyond 20 yards.

Let us start with the simplest of all spreader loads—the Remington-Peters type. No special equipment or components are required—unless the over-shot card wads are now considered to be something out of the ordinary.

Powder and wads suitable for the desired shot charge (1 - 1⅛ oz. 12 ga., 1 oz. 16 ga., ⅞ - 1 oz. 20 ga.) are inserted into the primed case and seated with the appropriate pressure. However, as the shot charge must be divided into three fairly equal portions it requires special handling. I use the charge bar and drop tube of my favorite Honey Bair press to first put each metered charge into (what else?) a whisky "shot cup." I then pour from this into a clear plastic vial which has a mark on its side indicating exactly one-third of the selected shot load. This first third of the shot is poured into a case already charged with powder and wadding and a thin over-shot card seated on top of it; the second third of the shot load is added plus another O-S card. Finally, the case is closed with either a roll or folded crimp—depending upon the amount of case available for this purpose.

The Winchester-Western type of scatter load is faster and easier to load as the shot charge can be dropped directly into the case once the X divider has been inserted. Cutting these cardboard X dividers is a job best delegated to a youngster eager to be helpful. I close these shells with a normal folded crimp, same as the factory W-W loads.

Disc shot tends to jam in the charge bars of all the loading presses I've tried and, as true-weight charges won't be thrown anyway, I weigh each charge after scooping the *plomb disco* out of a bowl with an old fashioned shot measure. So far I've made all my disc shot by simply flattening round shot with a hammer blow. To somewhat accelerate this rather slow process I ground a slight depression in my anvil where at least half a dozen pellets can be placed without rolling away before being flattened.

The degree of flattening will, of course, vary somewhat no matter how carefully one gauges the hammer blows; but for all practical purposes this doesn't really matter, especially if maximum dispersion is desired.

clothes wringer) would not be easy to build in a home workshop.

Another way of making *plomb disco* (perhaps the easiest of all) is to take lead wire of a suitable diameter and simply cut off discs with a paper cutter! A number of lengths of wire can be laid side by side so as to produce a dozen pellets at each stroke of the cutting blade.

Although square or cube shot isn't capable of quite as rapid dispersion or of such wide patterns as disc shot, nevertheless it gives adequately rapid spread of the shot charge along with the most uniform and dependable patterns of all spreader loads;

ber of these strips under the cutting blade again and off come your very own square shot! Just *how* square they are depends entirely upon how carefully you work but slightly rectangular and irregular shot will spread, penetrate and kill birds and rabbits just as well as will perfect examples.

This sort of soft lead cube shot will also jam in most charge bars so I generally drop the thrown charges onto a scale and adjust accordingly. Although FN closes their cube-shot cases with a frangible cork O-S wad and a roll crimp I prefer to use the more conveniently made folded crimp, for

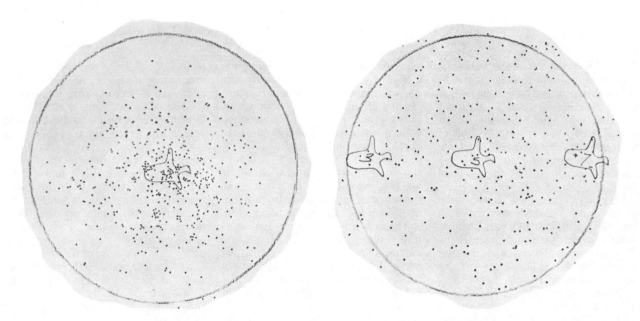

Left—The popular modified choke with the equally popular load of 1⅛-oz. of #8 shot is often used on small upland game—with the above results at average range on a quail size target. Right—What is wanted is something like the pattern shot by a 100-year-old cylinder bore Purdey.

However, if greater uniformity of flattening is wanted, just drill small holes for the appropriate size shot in a thin sheet of hard steel having a thickness equal to what you want the flattened shot to measure. A slight chamfering of the hole edges would facilitate their filling by merely spilling and rolling the shot across the plate. Once the holes are filled the shot can be quickly and uniformly flattened by striking with a large diameter hammer. Round shot could also be quickly turned into disc shot by passing it between a pair of adjustable steel rollers but such a device (somewhat on the lines of an old fashioned

it should be considered by any handloader planning to brew some shotshells of this type.

Here the only problem is obtaining the shot itself, but until some enterprising organization imports it from FN, or makes it here, we'll have to make our own. Again, because lack of uniformity in size, shape or symmetry is more of an advantage than otherwise, some fairly crude procedures are entirely permissible.

First, get some soft sheet lead, about .085" - .090" thick, from a local plumber and then simply cut narrow strips from this with a paper cutter. Next, pass a num-

the pattern spread is not noticeably affected either way.

Making your own scatter loads, especially when you use home-made disc or cube shot, adds spice and novelty to this activity, as well as providing some highly useful shells not usually obtainable at your local gunshop. Such shells will not only put more game in your bag in many situations but will also confound your less enterprising shooting companions. They'll never believe you're killing birds with square shot or little flying saucers—until after they have paid off an ill-considered bet you've cleverly suckered them into.　●

The KNIFE REVISITED

The making of handmade knives—and the collecting of them—continues to grow at an amazing rate. Shown here are the efforts of some knifemakers not covered in the 25th edition story.

by A. G. RUSSELL

INTEREST in handmade knives is growing at an unprecedented rate. In the past year, there have been no less than 10 knife articles in national shooting and sports periodicals. In the past two years my collection of knifemakers (not knives!) has increased from about 15 to over 100—most of them doing surprisingly good work.

This brief piece will cover some of the better makers not listed in the 1971 GUN DIGEST's very comprehensive article by Ken Warner. Some of these men have been making knives for several years, some for only a few months.

One of the few things all of these workers have in common is a desire to make a better knife than can be bought across the counter. Since it takes a certain amount of

business to keep even a part-time maker working, and to justify the cost of his equipment and materials, it's obvious that there must be a fast-growing body of sportsmen willing to spend goodly sums to obtain that better knife.

An important turning point in the budding knifemaker's career is when he crosses the line that separates homemade knives from handmade knives. He quits using files, sawblades, and any scrap tool steel that comes to hand. He starts looking for a superior steel. He finds, if he's good, that he cannot make knives fast enough for the people who are willing to pay for them.

Some men, of course, have never made a "homemade" knife. There's master knifemaker R. W. Loveless,

whose first knife gained him an order from Abercrombie & Fitch, and such newer makers as George Herron, Corbet Sigman and Frank Centofante, whose earliest work was quite professional. When you see a maker's work improve markedly from month to month you know he's looking more critically at his own work, and the work of others. The others, unfortunately, can seldom see the flaws in their own work, and they're often convinced that no other maker's work can approach their own.

No matter how wild a buyer's taste in knife design might be, there is undoubtedly a maker who can satisfy it. The man wanting a handmade knife can send for the catalogs of known makers, he can read such articles as this one or

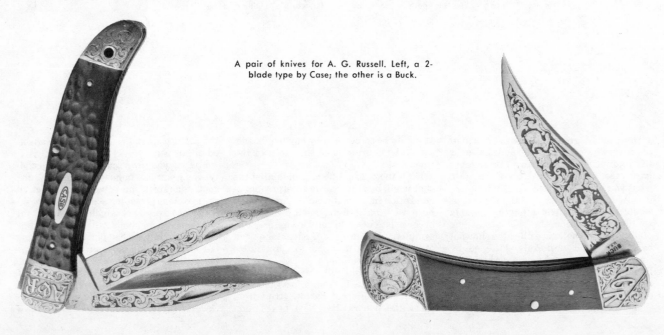

A pair of knives for A. G. Russell. Left, a 2-blade type by Case; the other is a Buck.

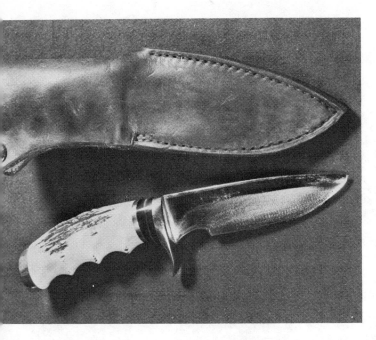

Left—This 10-oz. Fischer Custom Knife has stag-horn handles, the brass guard running over the top of the 4⅜″ blade. The biggish handle feels good, and the sheath is a sturdy piece of heavy leather.

Below—W. F. Moran, Jr. Here are three knives well worth viewing. From left—two folding pocket knives, mounted in German silver and ivory and entirely hand carved. Locking or spring, $275 each. Price of the matching hunting knife and sheath is not known, but probably $300-$350. Moran has a 4-year backlog of orders—he warned!

those in other periodicals, or he can order a knife from a maker whose pictured work suits his taste and ideas. Collectors, of course, will want them all. The collecting of contemporary hand-made knives is kept interesting by the entry of new makers, like those whose work is pictured here.

Collectors and knifemakers will be interested in the Knifemakers Guild, an organization founded in June of 1970, to promote and encourage interest in handmade knives, and to display their work once a year. Associate membership is open to anyone interested in handmade knives. Information is available from the secretary, R. W. Loveless, Box 837, Lawndale, CA 90260.

Two well done new knives by J. Nelson Cooper (Cooper Knives). The small game knife above has 4″ blade. Cooper's knives are guaranteed for life.
W. L. Rickell photo.

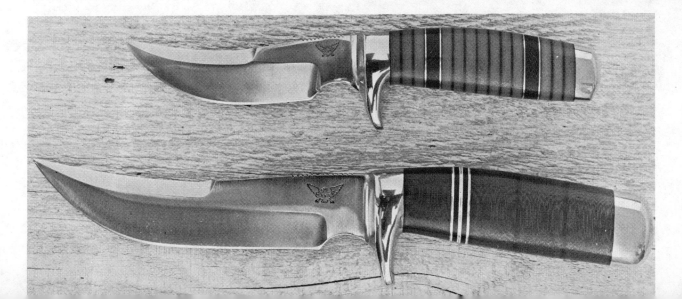

Four knives by Chubby Hueske—who guarantees them for life. His "Diamond C" steel is finished to 58 Rockwell C—or less if desired.

These larger knives were made by, from left—
(top row) Don (Zack) Zaccagaino, E. Lenaze,
Lloyd Hale, Ray Busch, Ralph Faulconer, Walt
Kneubuhler, Bob Dozier, Collins Bros., J. Nelson
Cooper, (bottom left) Geo. Herron and (bottom
right) J. Lile.

John J. Schwarz made this Bowie. He offers a
variety of blades, among them small capers
and skinners.

Medium length knives, made by the following craftsmen, from left—Davis Custom Knives, Norman Q. Dew, Ralph Bone, L. E. Brown, Dan Dennehy, Bill Sonneville, Frank Centofante, Jim Mustin and Bob Gess.

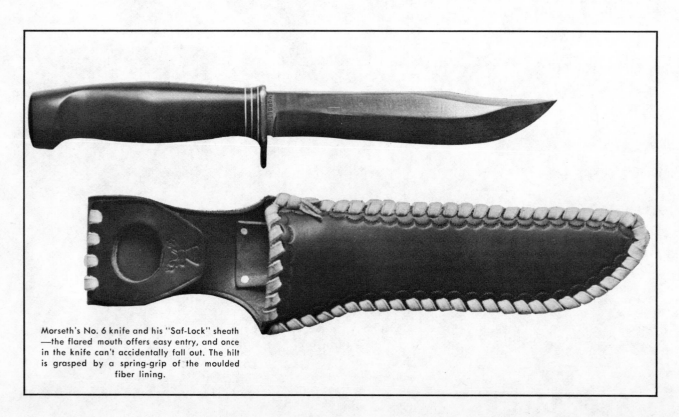

Morseth's No. 6 knife and his "Saf-Lock" sheath —the flared mouth offers easy entry, and once in the knife can't accidentally fall out. The hilt is grasped by a spring-grip of the moulded fiber lining.

The Knifemakers Guild History and Policy

The Knifemakers Guild was founded in Tulsa, Okla. June, 1970. Its membership includes most of the reputable, best-known men now working in this field. It was founded to enhance the art and craft of knifemaking; to encourage an ethical and professional relationship between customer and knifemaker; to assist the knifemaker technically, and to sponsor an annual Knifemakers Show.

Two classes of membership were decided on at the formation meeting; Voting Membership is reserved for professional knifemakers who publish a catalog and offer their work to the public. Associate Membership is open to those who work at the hobbyist level, and to all others interested in handmade knives as an ancient art and modern craft.

The Guild publishes a membership list, describing each knifemaker and his area of special interest. It also contains a full Statement of Policy, and the Guild Warranty of Delivery, for the protection of its members' customers.

To implement its Warranty of Delivery the Guild has established a special Trust Account, from which a refund is made in any proven case of non-performance by a Guild member. The Guild fully intends to honor its obligation to those who order knives from its

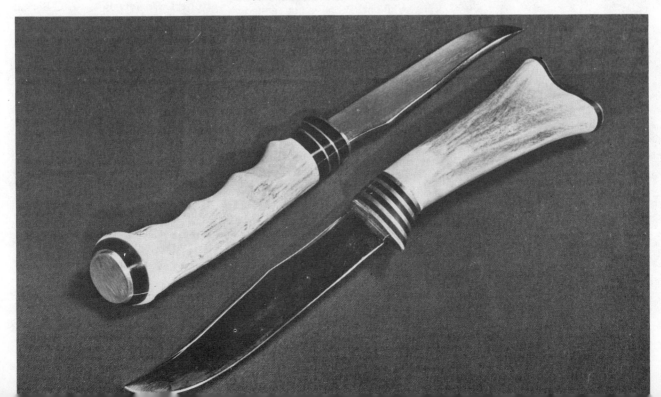

One of Western Cutlery's Westmark series, No. 703, has a 4½" blade. The heavy leather scabbard is included in the $29.95 price. Westmark knives are unconditionally guaranteed. Excellent value.

members. It welcomes legitimate complaints, and will take remedial action against any knifemaker who knowingly abuses the trust his customers have when they order a knife from him. Membership of the Knifemakers Guild have pledged themselves to a high standard of ethical performance as businessmen and craftsmen, to make deliveries as promised, and to maintain a rigorous standard of craftsmanship.

Interested readers may write to the address below for a copy of the current Membership List and the complete Warranty of Delivery. There is no charge.

The Knifemakers Guild, R. W. Loveless, Sec'y, P.O. Box 837, Lawndale, CA. 90260.

A pair of knives by the Lane Brothers, useful blades in their price range.

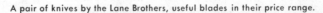

New treatment of old blade styles by Ralph Bone—skinner and caper in a solid sheath. Coco-bolo handles without butt cap for lightness. $65, the set.

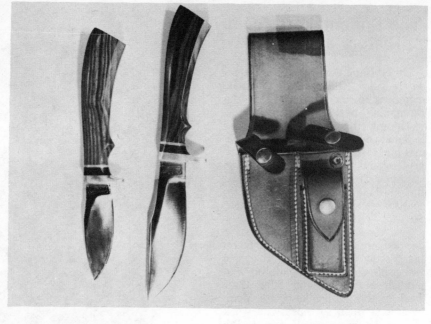

A prime example of Shaw-Leibowitz etching is seen on this Randall knife. Both blade sides are covered, as well as the guard and the pommel. The oval ivory inlay shows an elk in relief.

The Dowell integral-hilt knife—hilt, blade and tang are all one piece of A-2 steel.

A. G. Russell's List of Knifemakers

The men listed below are makers of handmade knives. The full-time makers are shown in bold face type. The majority of those listed are doing excellent work; a few are doing great work, while some others are just starting out. Usually their work shows this. Some makers charge for their catalogs; where it is $1 or more this has been noted. Some makers, so far behind that they've stopped making catalogs, are also indicated. I have many more names, but some have asked not to be included in this list, while others have not replied to my inquiries.

John Applebaugh, Box 68, Blackwell, OK 74631

Bill Bagwell, Vivian, La. 71082

Ralph Bone, 806 Ave. J, Lubbock, TX 79401 (4-color catalog, 50¢)

H. Gardner Bourne, 1252 Hope Ave., Columbus, OH 43212

L. E. Brown, 301 E. Neece St., Long Beach, CA 90805

Ray Busch, 940 Orion, Mandeville, LA 70005

Frank Centofante, Box 17587, Tampa, FL 33612

Collins Bros., 1307 Spring St., N.W., Atlanta, GA 30309

J. Nelson Cooper, Box 1423, Burbank, CA 91505

Harold Corby, Crown Gun Shop, Rt. 3, Johnson City, TN 37601

Don Couchman, Star Route, La Mesa, NM 88044

Steve Davenport, 301 Meyer, Alvin, TX 77511

Davis Knives, Box 148, Airway Heights, WN 99001

Dan Dennehy, Box 4479, Yuma, AZ 85364

Norman Q. Dew, 339 Magnolia, Channel View, TX 77530

Chas. E. Dickey, 803 N.E. A St., Bentonville, AR 72712

T. M. Dowell, 139 St. Helens Pl., Bend, OR 97701; ctlg. $1.

Robert Dozier, Box 1079, Springdale, AR 72764.

Gene Dumatrait, Rt. 1, Box 42, Orange, TX 77630

Ralph Faulconer, Rt. 3, Frederick, OK 73542

Clyde Fischer, Rt. 1, Box 170-M, Victoria, TX 77901

C. S. Fitch, 1755 Laurel St., Baton Rouge, LA 70802

H. H. Frank, c/o RWL, 1112 River St., Elko, NV 89801; engraved pocket knives.

James Furlow, 4838 Santa Fe Trail S.W., Atlanta, GA 30331

Bucker Gascon, Rte. 2, Box 332-J, Port Allen, LA 70767

Robert W. Gess, Wolfe Point, Mont. 59201

Wayne Goddard, 473 Durham Ave., Eugene, OR 97402

Lloyd Hale, Washington, AR 71862

Three knives by Jon Kirk, a few of the many styles he makes. These cost $46 to $49.

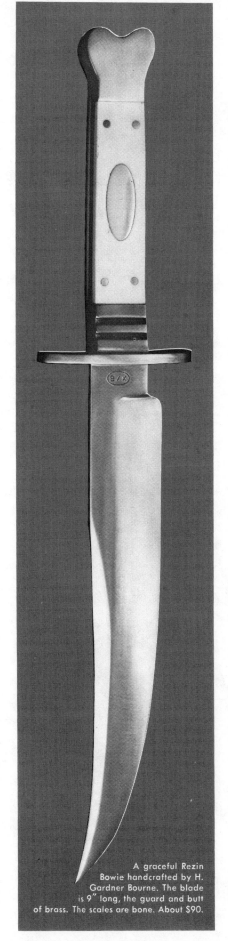

A graceful Rezin Bowie handcrafted by H. Gardner Bourne. The blade is 9" long, the guard and butt of brass. The scales are bone. About $90.

Don Hastings, Detroit, TX 75436

Pete Heath, 119 Grant St., Winneconne, WI 54986

D. E. Henry, Star Route, Mountain Ranch, CA 95246; set of photos $3. 12-month delivery or longer. Prices $200 up.

George Herron, 920 Murrah, Aiken, SC 29801

Hibben Knives, Box 773, Springdale, AR 72764

Jess Horn, Box 655, Project City, CA 96079

Chubby Hueske, 4808 Tamarisk Dr., Bellaire, TX 77401

LaDow Johnston, 563 Spitzer Blve., Toledo, OH 43604

J. Fred Jones, 858 E. I St., Ontario, CA 91762

Jon Kirk, 800 N. Olive St., Fayetteville, AR 72701

Walter Kneubuhler, Box 327, Pioneer, OH 43554; ctlg. $1.

Lane Brothers, Rt. 5, Carbondale, IL 62901

Ron Lake, 904 W. England, Taylorville, IL 62568

Emmett Lenaze, c/o A&H, 4449 Metairie Ave., Metairie, LA 70001

L. B. Lienenmann, 625 Grand Ave., Billings, MT 59102

R. W. Loveless, Box 837, Lawndale, CA 90260; ctlg. $1.

Bob Ludwig, 1028 Pecos Ave., Pt. Authur, TX 77640

Joe S. Martin, Box 6552, Lubbock, TX 79413

Max Mayers, 418 Jolee, Richardson, TX 75080

Harry McEvoy, 2110 Tremont Blvd., Grand Rapids, MI 49504; throwing knives.

John Mims, Apt. 327, 620 S. 28th Ave., Hattiesburg, MS 39401

W. F. Moran, Rt. 5, Frederick, MD 21701

Morseth Knives, 1705 Hiway 71 N., Springdale, AR 72764

Jim Mustin, Box 73644, Baton Rouge, LA 70807

Robert G. Ogg, Rt. 1, Box 230, Paris, AR 72855; folding knives.

Ed Pou, 322 Cleveland St., New Albany, MS 38652

Ralph Prouty, 5240 S.W. 49th Dr., Portland, OR 97221

Jim Pugh, 917 Carpenter St., Azle, TX 76020

Randall Knives, Box 1988, Orlando, FL 32802

Joe Rodriguez, 5241 Josephine St., Lynwood, CA 90262

R. H. Ruana, Box 574, Bonner, MT 59823

N. H. Schiffman, Box 7373, Murray, VT 84107

Jack Schmier, 16787 Mulberry Circle, Fountain Valley, CA 92708

John J. Schwarz, 41—15th St., Wellsburg, WV 26070

Merle Seguine, Box 989, Juneau, AK, 99801; over 1 yr. behind on ctlgs., further on knives.

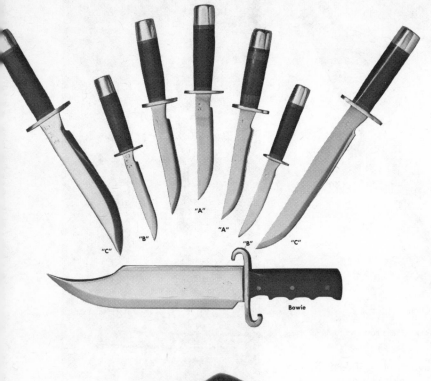

Diamond B Knives, made by L. E. Brown. All are custom made, each handfitted to its scabbard. "B" styles are $28.50, the rest up to $95 for the Bowie shown.

"C" "B" "A" "A" "B" "C"

Bowie

Bob Ogg's new folding blade locks in the open position, has lanyard hole, is highly functional yet compact.

Four skinner-capers by, from top—Jim Smith, Bucker Gascon, Weatherford Bros. and Jon Kirk.

Blackie Sewell (now Collins Bros.), 1307 Spring St. N.W., Atlanta, GA 30309

Corbet Sigman, Star Rte. 1, Box 3, Red House, WV 25168

Jim Smith, c/o J. McAlpin, 8924 Rollen, Wichita, KS 67212

Jos. T. Smith, 6048 Cedar Crest Dr., So. Haven, MS 38671

Wm. J. Sonneville, 1050 W. Chalet Dr., Mobile, AL 36608

Bernard Sparks, Dingle, ID 83233

G. W. Stone, 703 Floyd Rd., Richardson, TX 75080

D. L. Towell, Rt. 1, Midvale, ID 83645

Eddie W. Vaughn, 1905 Virginia Dr., Grand Prarie, TX 75050

James Walker, 6909 Randolph Macon Dr., Alexandria, VA 22301

Weatherford Bros., 4775 Memphis Dr., Dallas, TX 75207

D. E. Weiler, Box 1576, Yuma, AZ 85364

Gerald Willey, Rt. 1, Greenwood, DE 19950

R. W. Wilson, 145 Leech St., Weirton, WV 26062

Bob Wrench, Rt 5, Box 768, Eugene, OR 97402

Don Zaccagaino (Zack), Box ZACK, Pahokee, FL 33476

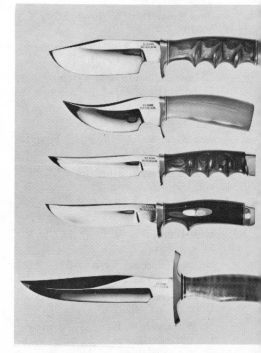

Corbet R. Sigman made this lot of attractive knives. His prices run from $50 to $100, not necessarily applicable to those pictured. Many other styles are made. Ask for his interesting booklet, "Handmade Knives."

Low Cost English Blades for Building Your Own Knives

Indian Ridge Traders, Box X-50, Ferndale, MI 48220

Bob Schrimsher, Custom Knifemaker's Supply, Box 11448, Dallas, TX 75223

Handle Makers

John Applebaugh, Box 68, Blackwell, OK 74631

LaDow Johnston, 563 Spitzer Blvd., Toledo, OH 43604

Marshall Knives, Box 96, Halabar, FL 32950

R. W. Wilson, 145 Leech St., Weirton, WV 26062

(These men will fit handles to your blade.)

Knifemaker's Equipment

Brownell's, Inc., Montezuma, IA; ctlg. $1.

Russell's, 1705 Hiway 71 N. Springdale, AR 72764

Bob Schrimsher, Custom Knifemaker's Supply, Box 11448, Dallas, TX 75223

R. W. Wilson, 145 Leech St., Weirton, WV 26062

Knife Etching

Shaw-Leibowitz, Box 421, New Cumberland, WV 26047

Commercial Knifemakers

Browning, Route 1, Morgan, UT 84050

Buck Knives, Inc., P.O. Box 1267, El Cajon, CA 92022

W. R. Case Knives, 20 Russell Blvd., Bradford, PA 16701

Colt's, 150 Huyshope Ave., Hartford, CT 06102

Garcia Sptg. Arms Corp., 329 Alfred Ave., Teaneck, NJ 07666

Gerber Knives, 14200 S.W. 72nd St., Portland, OR 99223

Gutman Cutlery Co., Inc. 3956 Broadway, New York, NY 10032

Ka-Bar Cutlery, Inc., 5777 Grant Ave., Cleveland, OH 44105

LocKnife, Inc., 11717 E. 23rd St., Independence, MO 64050

Marble Arms Corp., 1120 Superior, Gladstone, MI 49837

Normark Corp., 1710 E. 78th St., Minneapolis, MN 55423

Olsen Knife Co., Inc., 7 Joy St., Howard City, MI 49329

Precise Imp. Corp. (PIC), 3 Chestnut, Suffern, NY 10901

Schrade-Walden, 1775 Broadway, New York, NY 10019

Tru-Balance Knife Co., 2110 Tremont Blvd., Grand Rapids, MI 49504

True-Temper, 1623 Euclid, Cleveland, OH 44100

Western Cutlery Co., 5311 Western Ave., Boulder, CO 80302

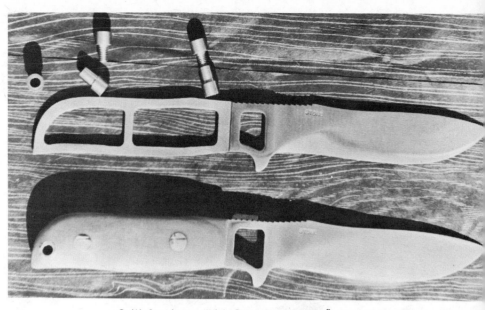

G. W. Stone's new "High Country" knife has 4″ stainless steel blade, uses SS bolts and lanyard hole bushing. Handle is black or natural phenolic. With handmade leather sheath, $100.

Bernard Sparks made these 5 knives, ranging from full-tang, high hollow ground to narrow styles—something for all tastes.

Four small knives, handsomely decorated. From left—a Collins Bros. made to A. G. Russell's design; second, a small skinner by Robt. W. Loveless; next, a gut-hook skinner by Merle Seguine and, last, a walrus-ivory handled skinner by Lloyd Hale. The Loveless knife was hand engraved by Lynton McKenzie of New Orleans. The others were etched by Shaw-Leibowitz.

One of Western Cutlery's Westmark series, No. 703, has a 4½″ blade. The heavy leather scabbard is included in the $29.95 price. Westmark knives are unconditionally guaranteed. Excellent value.

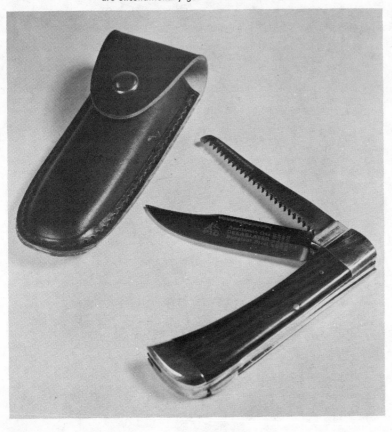

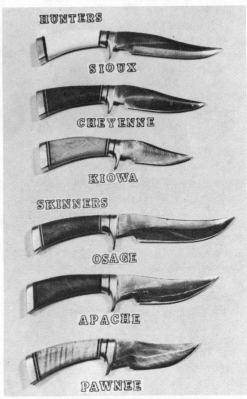

HUNTERS
SIOUX
CHEYENNE
KIOWA
SKINNERS
OSAGE
APACHE
PAWNEE

John Applebaugh—3 hunting types, 3 skinners. All are made from ¼″ stock, drawn to 58 Rockwell C for toughness. Applebaugh makes toothpicks and Bowies also.

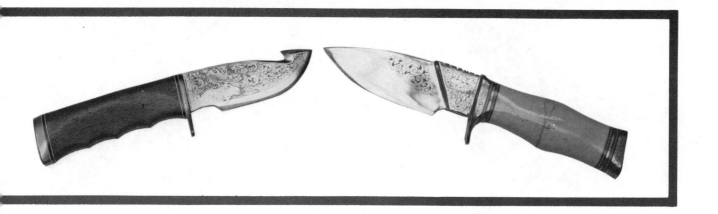

Walt Kneubuhler's rough and ready Nessmuk knife, copied from one owned by Jack McPhee for over 60 years. The sheath is in authentic style as well.

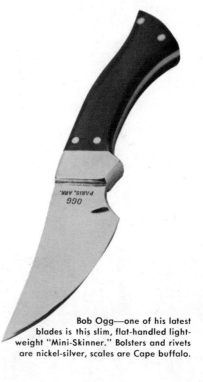

Bob Ogg—one of his latest blades is this slim, flat-handled lightweight "Mini-Skinner." Bolsters and rivets are nickel-silver, scales are Cape buffalo.

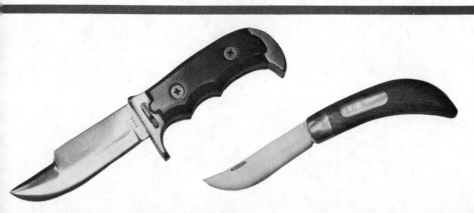

Five unusual knives. From left—a big folding knife by Ralph Bone; next, Jim Pugh shows a bronze ram's head and guard on this knife; third, a very deep, heavy blade by Wayne Goddard; next, Joe Rodriguez offers this interchangeable-blade knife, among others; last, one from the folding knife specialist, Bob Ogg, made for A. G. Russell.

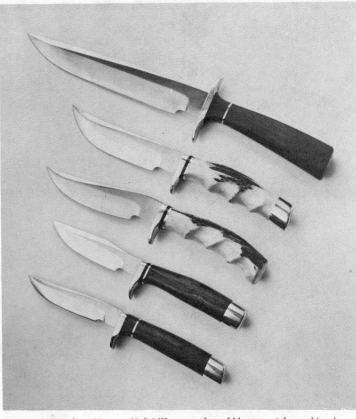

Five fine blades from Norman H. Schiffman—a few of his many styles and treatments.

Four of Dan Dennehy's "Dan-D Custom Knives." All show excellent workmanship, good design.

Highly decorated cutlery, all engraving and inlaying done by the maker, R. W. Wilson. The toothpick and tomahawk are $150 each, the Bowie costs $225.

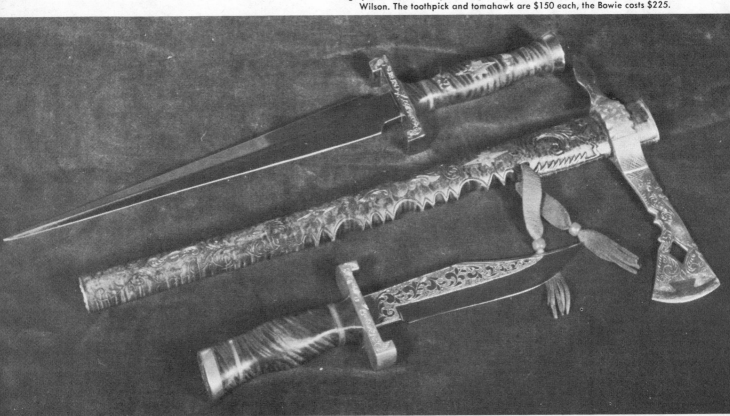

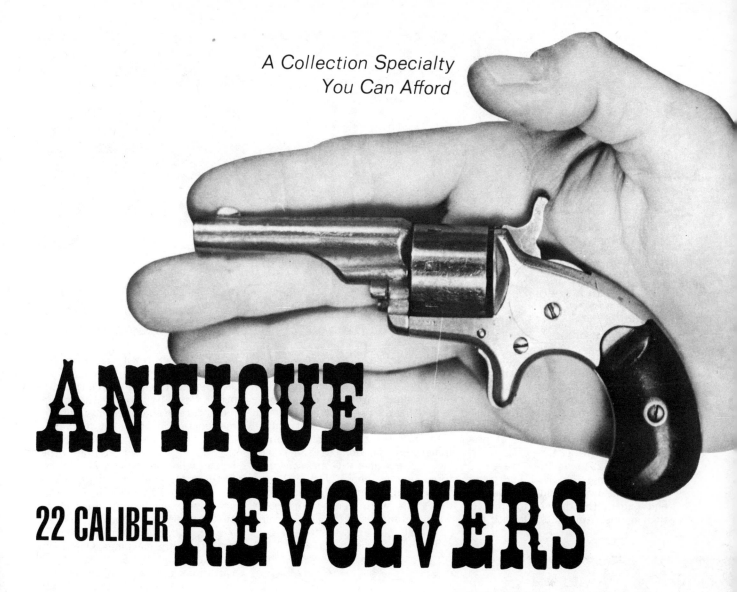

ANTIQUE

22 CALIBER REVOLVERS

by WILLIAM B. FORS

A COLT 1861 Navy revolver at a $700 asking price is a fine gun, and a worthwhile addition to any collection. But what about the gun enthusiast who doesn't have that kind of money to spend on one gun?

The percussion purist may laugh, but consider the antique 22 cartridge revolver. In that field $700 will buy 20 or more guns, these covering the period from the first American cartridge revolver, made in 1857, through the 1890 models that have most of today's modern revolver features.

The typical 22 antique cartridge revolver is a compact 7-shot arm with a two- or three-inch barrel and hardwood, birdshead grips. They'll weigh about 10 ounces, their length a little over 6 inches. Most were made to fire a 22-caliber Short, but not the 22 Short we

know now. The smokeless powder of today is too powerful for your antique 22, so don't ever try it.

22 Rimfire History

The story of the small revolvers began in 1854 with the patent of a metallic cartridge by Horace Smith and Daniel B. Wesson. To enable them to manufacture a revolver for this cartridge they had to acquire the patent of Rollin White, a former Colt employee, who held a patent issued April 3, 1855, for a bored-through cylinder to accommodate the breech-loading of cartridges. Rollin White had tried unsuccessfully to sell these rights to the Colt company. These patents, and subsequent improvement patents, gave Smith and Wes-

son the sole right to the breech-loading cartridge revolver market for 12 years, until the expiration of those rights in 1869. During this period, S&W produced some 126,-000 22-caliber revolvers in three variations of their model No. 1—plus 32-caliber types as well. Other makers were not unwilling to try to circumvent these patent rights. Rollin White, as part of his contract with S&W, defended the patent vigorously through many court cases. Many well known names were ordered to cease manufacture, among them Allen & Wheelock, Moore Patent Firearms Company, L. W. Pond Co., and E. A. Prescott. A few companies became licensees and their revolvers were thereafter marked, "Made for Smith & Wesson." These infringing guns, which usually show a marked resem-

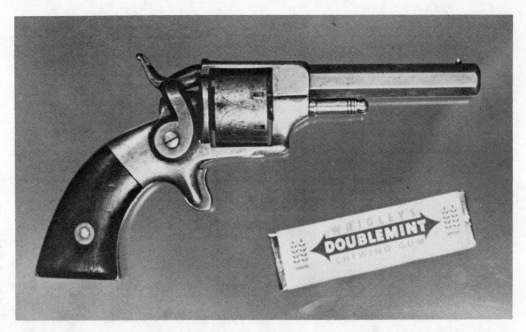

Right and far right—Allen and Wheelock in 1860 also infringed Smith and Wesson patents with a unique side hammer 22 caliber revolver. Cylinder pin removes by depressing spring under frame.

blance to the S&W original, provide an interesting comparison.

Early S&W 22 revolvers were carried by Civil War soldiers as personal pocket weapons. Their use or effectiveness was minimal but they provided some feeling of protection. Following the Civil War, the little 22 was the traveler's companion by stagecoach and train. The home-owner and shopkeeper had one in the drawer for protection against itinerants. Despite the publicity given to the two-shot derringer, ladies of the evening and gamblers often preferred the compact 7-shot revolver. Young boys found them a must for July Fourth celebrations, with blanks of course.

In 1870, the S&W patent expired. Renewal was denied, some say, because President Grant was still irked about poor Northern ordnance supply during the Civil War; the gates were opened and some 50 manufacturers began turning out 22 caliber revolvers of varying quality. Some were priced as low as 60¢, and the quality reflected this price. Possibly because the maker didn't care to share responsibility for malfunction or accident, numerous guns carried only a pet name for identity. These were sold by mail order houses who contracted with a manufacturer for their production. Most often, the mail order firm name did not appear on the gun. Such names on the barrel as *Protector*, *Tramps Terror*, *Little Giant*, ad infinitum, were the only markings. One manufacturer might produce 25 to 50 variations of the same model with only a name change and a slightly different grip or finish. Many of these "name-only" revolvers can be traced to a maker, but the process is often difficult. In the more specific area of known manufacturer's models, the author has compiled a table of some 50 makers, including brief specifications of their early 22 models and the range of their current values to collectors.

Prices and Value

This brings us to the discussion of gun values. Prices shown in the table or in any volume purporting to establish price ranges are only a guide post. It is worthwhile to remember Oscar Wilde's definition of a cynic, quoted also by C. E. Chapel in his handbook, as one who "knows the price of everything and the value of nothing." A revolver in very good condition that fills a void in your collection may be valued by you beyond any book value. Finding such a piece is an exciting discovery and a thrill

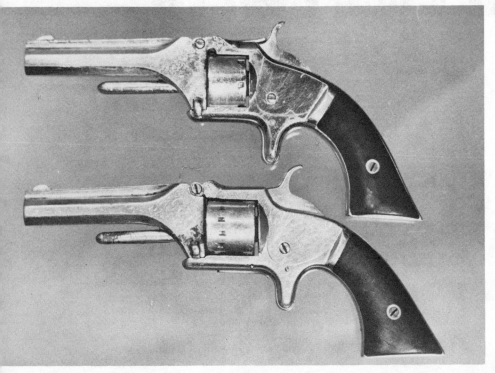

Smith and Wesson had exclusive cartridge revolver patent rights from 1857 to 1869, but infringing copies were frequent. Upper model is S&W Model 1, 2nd issue; lower gun is Manhattan Firearms Company copy.

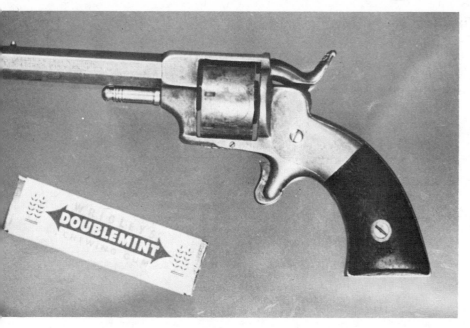

that cannot be calculated in dollars.

To pursue this area of collecting as your specialty, there are two volumes that belong in your firearm library. They are *The Gun Collector's Handbook of Values* by the late Charles Edward Chapel, and *The Collectors Guide to American Cartridge Handguns* by Dewitt E. Sell. Using the price guides and descriptive data in these two volumes will help you identify and appraise the asking price of most 22 caliber models. Interest in the small 22 caliber revolver field is increasing, but fortunately prices have not gone upward as rapidly as have many other makes and types.

If you select this area as your speciality, you will find prices range from $20 to $50 for most makes, with such better known and higher-quality names as Colt, Remington and S&W bringing $75 dollars or more. First models, obviously, are worth more, but few values have gone over $200, at least not so far!

Condition and Cleaning

Be discriminating about the condition of any antique revolver you contemplate buying. There are several "musts"—all parts should be intact and the gun in good working order. While some nicks and age marks are to be expected, 80% or more of original finish, with the markings sharp, is required to qualify as excellent. In some cases a patina or thin coating of age over the finish is found. Do not attempt to remove this for you would destroy the character of antiquity. A sanded or buffed gun, one newly-plated or brilliantly brightened, will have lost value, often drastically. Leave 'em alone!

Your first inclination on acquiring a revolver of 1880 may be to disassemble it. In a word—*don't*. The integral parts have operated for almost a century without your probing screwdriver and only harm can result from your efforts. Oil lightly if you wish, but leave the piece intact. If

operation problems occur, try to find an "exploded" or isometric drawing of the model. Then, and only then, should disassembly be attempted— and make sure your screwdrivers really fit. The general rule in the care and repair of antique models is—"the less done, the better."

Before buying that first antique 22, you should know and comply with the gun laws of your particular city and state. In many cases, antique guns (those manufactured prior to 1898) are exempt from regulations applied to modern guns. It is best, however, to have whatever "registration" is required before doing any buying. For example, Illinois requires a Firearm Owners Identification Card. Available upon application with a $5 fee, this card, encased in plastic and showing your photo, registers *you*, not your individual gun or guns.

It requires renewal in 5 years. While this card is not strictly required for buying "antique" guns, it is well to have it as a means of identification in making purchases. Your collection might include a gun made in 1899 or later, or you might be called on to prove date of manufacture of a borderline piece.

With a knowledge of values, or at least prices, you are ready to begin your search. Your local gun store may deal primarily in new or current model handguns with a stray antique offered only occasionally. Where then can you look?

Where to Look

The antique store or dealer as a source has become a "once-in-a-while" thing. Unless the dealer specializes in antique guns, prospects are poor. Since antique guns may be shipped by mail (excluding, of course, ammo or powder), the mail-order dealers found in the gun monthlies and gun newspapers are

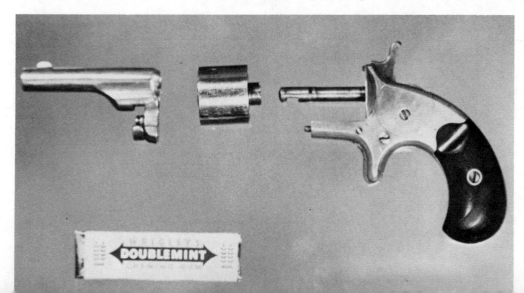

Colt open-top 22 revolver quickly disassembles into three sections by loosening screw at lower front of barrel section and turning pivot pin. Cylinder pin is fixed in frame.

22 Caliber Rimfire Revolver Manufacturers—1857 to 1900

All models are solid frame, 7-shot, single actions in 22 rimfire unless otherwise shown by footnotes below.

Company	Production Years	Specs.	Year of First Model	Markings	Book Values*	Notes
Aetna Arms New York, NY.	1880-90		1881	Aetna	$ 25-40	Possibly mfgd. by H&R.
Ethan Allen Co. Worcester, MA.	1865-71	Side hammer.	1866	Ethan Allen & Co.	35-50	New name of A&W Co.
Allen & Wheelock Worcester, MA.	1856-65	Oct. bbl.	1858	Various	40-50	1st safety notch and unique side hammer.
American Standard Tool Newark, NJ. (a)	1868-73	Oct. bbl., nickeled.	1869	American Standard Tool Co., Newark, N.J.	35-50	Fine quality—from tools of Manhattan model.
Bacon Arms Co. Norwich, CT.	1864-88	6-shot, oct. bbl., nickeled.	Unkn.	Bacon Arms Co., Norwich, Conn.	40-55	Patent date—12/10/78
Bliss & Goodyear New Haven, CT.	1860-87	Unique rd. sideplate.	Unkn.	Various brand names	20-up	Patent date—4/23/78
Colt P.F.A. Mfg. Co. Hartford, CT. (b)	1848 to date	Old line.	1871 1872	Various Various	225 80-120 50-90 250	Side rod ejector. No ejector. Detach. 2.5" bbl., no ejector. w/ejector.
Colt P.F.A. Mfg. Co. Hartford, CT. (b)	1848 to date	New line.	1873	Various	50-90	Round side plate.
D. D. Cone Co. Washington, D.C.	1860-67	6-shot, spur trig.	Unkn.	D. D. Cone— Wash., D.C.	45-65	Also marked W. L. Grant or J. P. Lower.
Continental Arms Norwich, CT.	1866-70		Unkn.	Continental No. 1	40-60	Spur trigger.
T. Copeland Wocester, MA.	1868-74		Unkn.	Unmarked	25-45	10-shot type may exist.
Daly Arms New York, NY.	?	6-shot, ring trigger.	Unkn.	Unkn.	—	Probably dist., not mfg.
Deringer Rifle & Pistol Works Philadelphia, PA.	1870-?	Bottom break.	1872	Deringer, Philadelphia	90-125	
E. L. Dickinson Springfield, MA.	1863-87	Brass frame, ribbed bbl.	Unkn.	E. L. & J. Dickinson Sprfld., Mass.	40-60	
Forehand & Wadsworth Worcester, MA.	1871-80	Ctr. hammer.	1871	Various brand names and/or comp. name	20-30	Continuation of Ethan Allen Co.
Great Western Gun Works Pittsburgh, PA.	1866-95		Unkn.	Unkn.	N/A	Dist., not mfg.
Gross Arms Tiffin, OH.	1841-86		Unkn.	Gross Arms Co. Tiffin, Ohio	N/A	Patent date—5/25/55.
Harrington & Richardson Worcester, MA.	1874 to date	W. ejector.	1871	Unkn.	20-40	
Hartford Arms Hartford, CT.	1878-?	Unkn.	1878	Various	N/A	Low quality & price.
F. A. Hood Co. Norwich, CT.	1874-87	Oct. bbl.	1874	Various	20-35	Patent dates: 2/23/75, 4/6/75, 3/14/76.
Hopkins & Allen Norwich, CT.	1867-1915	Side cyl. release.	1871	Early models marked w/brand or distrib. name & patent dates	20-up	Patent dates: 3/28/71, 4/27/75, 6/29/75, 5/27/79.
Iver Johnson (+ Bye) Worcester, MA.	1871 to date		1873	Tycoon or Favorite 1st models	20-up	
Wm. Irving New York, NY.	1861-70	Oct. bbl.	1863	Unkn.	50	(See Jas. Reid).
Lee Arms Bridgeport, CT.	1879-?		Unkn.	Red Jacket No. 1	20-up	

Lowell Arms Lowell, MA.	1866-67			Made for Smith & Wesson	25-40	(See Rollin White).
Maltby, Henley & Co. New York, NY.	1878-90	Oct. bbl.	1884	Maltby Henley & Co. plus patent dates	30-65	Earliest patent date—3/11/84.
Manhattan Firearms Mfg. Co. NYC after 1864. (a)	1855-73	Oct. bbl., bottom break.	1860	Manhattan Firearms Mfg. Co., N.Y.	40-60	Copy of S&W.
Marlin Firearms Co. New Haven, CT.	1870 to date		1872	J. M. Marlin New Haven, Ct.	40-60	**Little Joker** model probably 1st made.
Meriden Firearms Co. Meriden, CT.	1863-90	Various.	Unkn.	(See comments)		Made for these companies: Eastern, Empire State, Federal, Fyrberg, Howard Arms.
Norwich Pistol Co. Norwich, CT.	1875-87				N/A	Subsid. of Hood F. A. Co.
Osgood Gun Works Norwich, CT. (c)	1880-83	8-shot, 1-shot.	1880	Duplex and Osgood Gun Works Norwich, Conn.	100-150	Patent date—12/7/80.
Plant Mfg. Co. New Haven, CT.	1860-66	Oct. bbl.	?	Eagle Arms Co. N.Y. + patent dates	40	
L. W. Pond Co. Worcester, MA.	1859-70		1863	—	80-105	Has cartridge sleeve.
E. A. Prescott Co. Worcester, MA.	1860-63		1860	E. A. Prescott Worcester, Mass.	35-50	Looks like S&W Model 1—No. 1
Procter Arms Co. Philadelphia, PA.	1870s	Front ldg.	Unkn.	Protector Arms Co., Phila., Pa.	25-50	Trade name for Rupertus Pat. Pistol Mfg. Co.
James Reid Co. New York, NY.	1862-84	Oct. bbl.		J. Reid, New York	65-95	Patent date—4/28/1863.
E. Remington & Sons Ilion, NY.	1856 to date	Circ. sideplate.	1878	**Iroquois**	75-85	Fine quality
Rollin White Arms Co. Lowell, MA. (a)	1858-66		Unkn.	Made for Smith & Wesson	60-75	S&W pat. infringement name change, 1866, to Lowell Arms Co.
Rupertus Patent Pistol Co. Philadelphia, PA.	1858-88		Unkn.	**Empire**	35	Patent date—11/21/1871.
Thos. E. Ryan Pistol Mfg. Co. Norwich, CT.	1876-91	Oct. bbl.	Unkn.	**Napoleon**	25-35	Name change to E. Ryan, (1877-1888).
Otis A. Smith Rockfall, CT.	1873-90		Unkn.	**Smith's Patent Apr. 15, 1873 No. 22**	30-50	
Smith & Wesson Springfield, MA. (a)	1856 to date	Hinged-top, tip-up.	1857	Smith & Wesson Springfield, Mass.	175-425	1st U.S. cartridge revolver, pat. date—April 3, 1855.
C. E. Sneider Baltimore, MD. (d)	1860-87	14-shot, 2 cyl.	Unkn.	Unkn.	300-395	Patent dates—3/18/62, 2/18/65.
Standard Revolver Co. (a)	1870s	Oct. bbl.	Unkn.	Unkn.	35-45	Dupe. of S&W Model 1-2nd issue.
W. L. Uhlinger Co. Philadelphia, PA.	1880s		Unkn.		20-up	
United States Arms Co. Brooklyn, NY.	1870-78		Unkn.	U.S. Arms Co., N.Y.	20-30	Mfg. by Iver-Johnson.
Wesson & Harrington Worcester, MA.	1871-74	Oct. bbl., int. ejec. rod.	1871	**Shell Ejector.**	45	Name changed to H&R in 1874.
Whitney Arms Co. (Whitneyville Armory) Whitneyville, CT.	1841-88	Oct. bbl.		Whitneyville Armory Co. Pat. May 23, 1871.	35-50	Irreg. side-plate.
Wright Arms Co. Lawrence, MA. (e)	1870s	5-shot, folding trig.	1876	**Little All Right.**	75-125	Patent date—1/18/1876.

*Price range of book values reflects Jan. 1972 prices.

(a)—Barrel tips upward on hinge for cylinder removal.

(b)—Barrel rotates sideways for cylinder removal on Old Line and Open Top models.

(c)—8-shot 22-cal. plus 1-shot 32-cal. with 2 barrels.

(d)—14-shot via two cylinders.

(e)—5-shot 22-cal. double action.

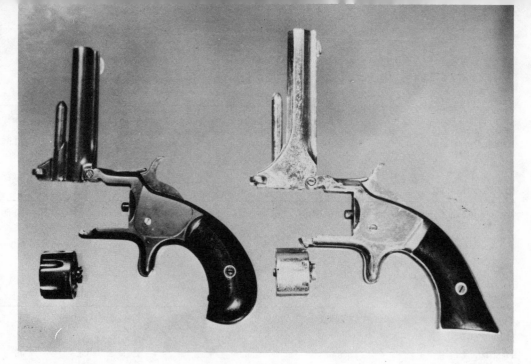

Early Smith and Wesson 22 cartridge revolvers were bottom-break for loading and spent case removal. Both Model 1, 2nd issue (right) and 3rd issue (left) were opened by latch lever on lower portion of barrel assembly.

your best bet. Most dealers offer periodical lists for a dollar or two per year. Get on several mailing lists.

If you travel for business or pleasure, make a point of checking the telephone book yellow pages as you stop in various villages or towns. A listing under "Guns" or "Antiques" may produce a store only a few blocks out of your way. The rare find is always waiting in an unlikely spot for the enthusiastic guy who is always searching. Identify yourself as a collector, your gun card comes in handy here, and ask the store owner to show you any guns he might not have on display because of unfavorable national publicity on gun control.

Secondary possibilities are garage and rummage sales, estate sales, the markets and auctions. All are usually announced in the classified section of your daily newspaper.

It is well to preserve all lists received as well as back issues of gun magazines and newspapers. These provide an additional price reference as various guns come on the market. Better still, start your own small looseleaf notebook, listing makers alphabetically with prices shown by model. Your knowledge and bargaining ability will increase. When you have acquired several specimens, you will begin to appreciate the reasons that led you to select the antique 22 revolver as your specialty. Although somewhat similar in overall appearance, you will discover interesting variations in cylinder construction, barrels and cylinder pins, grips and side plate versus solid frame construction. Like people, each make has its own characteristics.

Storage of these small, compact

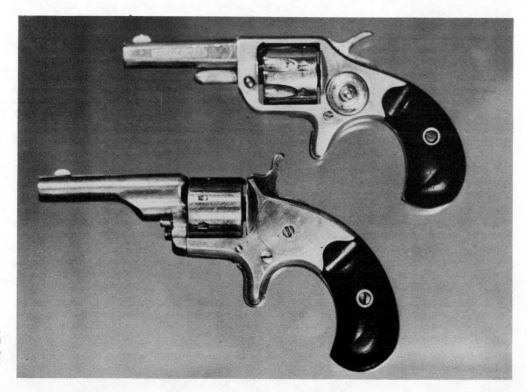

Colt open-top 22 (below) was interim model of 1872 to fill demand until Colt's New Line 22 revolver (above) was introduced in 1873.

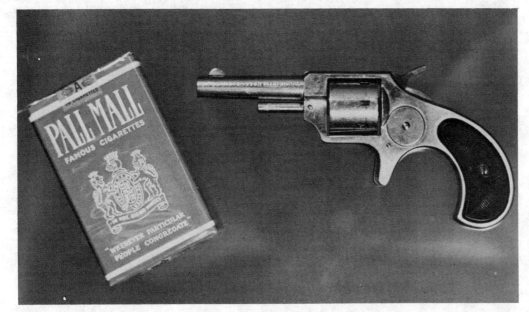

Left and below—Remington Arms made only one model cartridge revolver of 22 caliber, the Iroquois model of 1878. Author's specimen, shown here has distinction of no serial numbers and, according to Remington research director, was evidently "stolen before it was produced."

guns is relatively easy. A tool chest with two shallow drawers is perfect. Line the drawers with a soft-finished, yet firm cloth, and you'll have storage for a dozen or so guns. The top area is ideal for tools and parts.

As each succeeding gun is located and added to your collection, your knowledge and mechanical abilities will increase. The pride felt in learning these things is hard to explain, but you'll find that, a new facet has been added to your life activities. In time to come, you may even set down to write pieces like this!

Beyond the true joy of watching your collection and knowledge grow is the health-giving therapy of being totally immersed in your hobby, which often shuts out those everyday problems and worries.

As every collector knows, the peak thrill is the excitement of a rare find, at the right price, that fills a void in your collection. I defy you to match the chill that overcomes you as you spot that rare gun.

You may find it hard to convince your wife that these $30 expenditures at various times are worthwhile. If you do, point out to her

that antique guns are always a diminishing quantity through destruction by intention or accident. Demand, however, is always increasing as new collectors join the gun field. More demand, less supply means rising prices in years to come.

A representative collection of these small guns provides an historical picture of the 19th century developments leading to our modern-day cartridge handgun. The world of the antique 22 caliber revolver is a great area for a collection specialty ... come, join me!

Bibliography

American Firearms Makers, A. M. Carey, New York, 1953

Collectors Guide to American Cartridge Handguns, D. E. Sell, Harrisburg, Pa., 1963

Gun Collector's Handbook Values, C. E. Chapel, New York, 1970

Marvyn Scudder Manual of Extinct or Obsolete Companies, New York, 1928

Ten Old Gun Catalogs, L. D. Satterlee, Chicago, 1962

The Beautiful Blazers - all but forgotten!

*Only five are covered here — though there are others. These are the 22 Swift,
the 250 Savage, the 257 Roberts, the 7x57 and the 300 H&H Magnum.
They're generally regarded as obsolete now, but even a cursory examination shows
this quintet to be suitable for everything — prairie dogs to
crows to chucks to deer, antelope, sheep and elk, even the big brown bears.*

by BOB BELL

WORLD WAR II was a lot of things to a lot of people and organizations. Among other things, it was the dividing line between the reactionary and radical approaches to shooting on the part of American gun companies. In the '20s and '30s the introduction of a new rifle, shotgun or cartridge was an event to be pondered for years, both before and after the fact. Gestation periods approached those of the dinosaurs, and the subsequent offspring were coddled and brought to maturity as if they were long-awaited heirs of wealthy Republican dynasties. WW II changed all that. The fuddyduddies became swingers, so much so that that slightly *outre* group called "wildcatters" suddenly found itself without a niche in the shooting world, simply because the Remingchester twins had burped and brought forth a beautiful bunch of bangers that pretty much covered the whole shooting spectrum. Consider Remington's 222, 22-250, 244, 25-06 and 280, their 6.5mm, 7mm and 350 Magnums, as well as Winchester's 243, 284, 308, and their 264, 300, 338 and 458 Magnums. There were many others, of course—the average has been close to one new cartridge per year since H. L. Truman went for broke at Hiroshima—and, truthfully, most have been damn good. The only thing is, so far as practical field results go, not one of 'em was truly necessary.

Years before Pearl Harbor—many years in some cases—we already had cartridges to handle the gamut of North American game. Not only handle it, but do it as well as anything offered since. We could make a case for more, but to keep this within space limitations we'll consider only 5 cartridges, a group we call "the beautiful—but forgotten—blazers." These are the 220 Swift, 250-3000 Savage, 257 Roberts, 7x57 Mauser and 300 H&H Magnum. All are now generally considered obsolete, but a cursory examination suggests that this quintet covers everything from prairie dogs, crows and chucks through deer, antelope, sheep and elk on up to Alaskan brownies. Decades of use by thousands of hunters verify that suggestion.

The 220 Swift

The 220 Swift was the first good varmint cartridge I ever used. My early experience with it came in the '40s. A dedicated varmint shooter before that time, I've extensively used dozens of fine rifles chambered for many cartridges but, the simple truth is, when everything is said and done, there's still nothing better than the Swift.

A bit of background on this blazer seems fitting.

There is some disagreement on the date of the Swift's introduction. W.H.B. Smith gives 1936, while Frank C. Barnes and Phil Sharpe list 1935, Sharpe specifically stating that the rifles were released in August of that year after being put into production on April 23.* There is no disagreement on the model— it was the famous M54 Winchester, the first true commercial bolt action high powered rifle made in the U.S. The first M54 Swifts had a rifling twist of 1/16, but this was changed to 1/14 in 1936, shortly before this model was replaced by the great M70, and this twist has been standard for the Winchester Swift since that time. It reportedly gives better accuracy than the slower rate. Groove diameters were .224", barrels had 6 grooves with a width of .074". A 26-inch barrel was standard for the 220 from the first, perhaps to squeeze the last foot second of velocity out of this case, perhaps to slightly reduce its sharp report. It came in standard and target weights.

Shooters' gossip has always claimed that the early development work on the Swift was done by Captain Grove Wotkyns, who also figured prominently in the development of the 22 Hornet, and that his version was based on a necked-down 250-3000 Savage case (a design which ultimately became the Varminter or 22-250). However, when announced by Winchester the Swift was seen to be an altered 6mm Lee Navy case. Whereas the 6mm Lee's case length was 2.35 inches with diameter at shoulder of .402", base .445" and rim .448",

those measurements on the Swift were 2.20", .402", .443" and .472", the rim increase bringing it up to standard bolt face size and in effect making a semi-rimmed case out of what had been the rimless Lee Navy. The case thickness, particularly in the head area, was beefed up to handle the Swift's then comparatively high working pressures, reportedly 53,000-55,000 psi.

The first commercial loads offered for the Swift used 46-gr. hollow point and 48-gr. semi-spitzer bullets, each loaded to an advertised velocity of 4140 fps. These were followed a short time later by a 56-gr. HP bullet at 3760 fps. The 48-gr. load always seemed the preferred one, the poorly shaped 46-gr. bullet losing velocity much faster and the 56-gr. apparently being offered for those who wanted to use the Swift on deer and antelope.

There has always been controversy over the use of high velocity centerfire 22s on big game, much of it generated by the Swift. Before its appearance, few hunters thought of such an extreme approach, but apparently something about that ultra high velocity and its explosive effect on varmints got them thinking. As early as the fall of 1936, Fred Ness, then majordomo of the *American Rifleman's* Dope Bag, printed a questionnaire asking for reports from hunters who had used the Swift on big game. The results appeared in the March, 1937 issue and covered 26 kills—17 whitetailed deer, 6 blacktails and 3 mule deer—made at ranges of from 20 yards to over a quarter-mile.

As described there, the Swift seemed an incredibly good deer cartridge, with one-shot kills being the rule, no matter where hit or what the range. But after a few more seasons passed, and reports from perhaps less skilled hunters began to pile up, it became obvious that the Swift was a good deer killer when everything jelled properly, and a poor one when the bullet was improperly placed or whatever ... as is true of so many cartridges.

I have a friend whose job sometimes involves game control shooting. He has killed some 100 deer with his old scoped M70 Swift, usually with a single shot, at all normal ranges. However, he rarely shoots at a moving or excited animal, he's not excited himself, and he usually shoots from a rest and puts that tiny slug tight behind the shoulder muscle for a lung or heart shot. Almost anything is a good

*Fred Ness, in the *American Rifleman* for May, 1935, mentioned ". . . a new bolt action magazine rifle in the soon-to-be-announced .220 Swift caliber . . ." would give 4000 fps at the muzzle. Ness went on to describe the performance of the 220 Swift (in experimental or prototype form at that date) in detail, reporting on a mass of data furnished him by Capt. G. L. Wotkyns, the father of the 220 Swift in the form described by Ness, to say the least.

Then, in the September, 1935, issue of the *Rifleman*, the Winchester Model 54 rifle was formally announced as ready for delivery in 220 Swift caliber, the cartridge we know today. Ed.

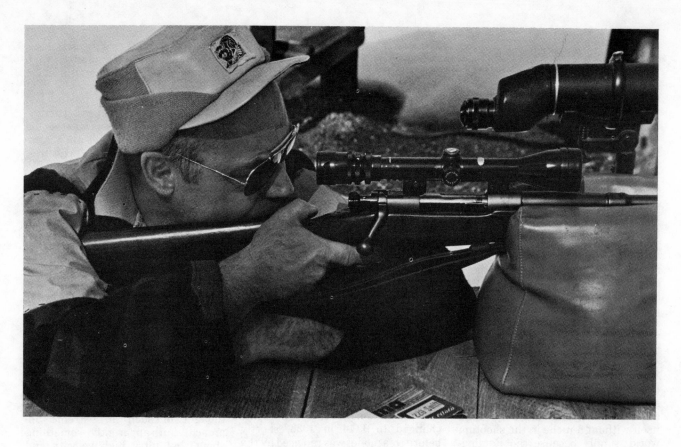

The author about to touch one off. The rifle seen is a Model 70 Super Grade 220 Swift of pre-WW II vintage. The scope is a 3x-9x Bushnell.

deer cartridge under these conditions. Personally, I've never had a desire to use the Swift or anything similar on deer. There are too many better big game cartridges available. However, if there is a truly valid reason for not using a more suitable load—a medical condition that prohibits noticeable recoil, for instance—the Swift will do the job if the bullet is exactly placed.

I got my early experience with the Swift almost by accident.

In the mid '40s the world had not yet settled down after its biggest scheutzenfest and a fella who needed a good varmint rifle, as I did, was just SOL, as we used to say. A new Model 70? Hah! There were no new guns. An *American Rifleman* ad listing a used M30 Remington 257 was answered, by phone, the first day. Gone. Still, the idea of the 257 cartridge had scads of appeal, and another ad indicated P. O. Ackley was building them on M98 Mauser actions, so the metal parts were ordered from him and a walnut blank from Bishop. A 6x Zeiss Zielsechs—the only worthwhile thing I'd liberated in Germany—already had been

sent to Schmidt & Davis in Los Angeles to have a set of rings made to fit its 26mm tube and a Redfield Jr. base, and then down to Tackhole Lee for one of his center dots. The scope was back, but the gun wasn't yet ready, and one day I was sitting in Olen Eves' Danville, Pa., barbershop bemoaning my fate, when he casually said, "Why don't you use my Swift till your 257's ready?"

It was as unexpected as stumbling into a frozen foxhole at night. "I couldn't do that," I said automatically, but already emblazoned on my mind were those fantastic, quoted-everywhere ballistics: *48-gr. bullet, 4140 fps...48-gr. bullet, 4140 fps...* Lordy me, the Devil sure do know how to tempt a guy! Particularly a would-be varmint buster.

"Sure you can," he said, and, despite my further polite protestations, I did. Fact is, during subsequent months I probably shot that particular Swift a lot more than anyone ever did before or after in a similar length of time. It was a beautiful outfit. A Super Grade 70 built in the late '30s, it had a nice piece of walnut in the stock, was beautifully inletted, checkered and finished, and had a Redfield Jr. base to accept the 6x Zeiss scope. I'd told Lee to put in a dot of the proper size for average chuck and crow shooting, and he made it

1¾ MOA. Never have I wanted it changed, though that Zeiss has since been on many rifles. It's always visible and by the time it gets too big you usually have to hold over anyhow. I got a few boxes of factory loads, zeroed in—5-shot groups went 1½ inches to 1¾ inches at 100, and man, that sharp-pitched *crack* was impressive! —and went looking for something to turn it loose on. Just above town, in one of the paper birches lining the Susquehanna's banks, I spotted a crow. It wasn't far, scarcely 50 yards, but the day was foggy and he was careless and I never gave him the chance to correct his error.

I don't know how many crows and chucks I took with that Swift, but the number was considerable. Most of them fell in the 150- to 300-yard range. Never again did I luck onto a crow stupid enough to let me get within half a football field (maybe the Red Gods set up that first one, just to get me properly hooked). It's hard to get closer to a crow than 150, even harder to hit them beyond 300. A 6x scope isn't ideal for such attempts either, and an outfit giving 1½ MOA groups can't be expected to kill more than half of its crows at the longer distance even when everything else is perfect—as it rarely is in the field.

I figured handloading was the answer to that, so I got a set of dies to fit the Pacific tool and had at it. First results were not overly impressive, though I could shade the factory stuff. It seemed to be a matter of bullets—they weren't as good then as now, at least not those that were readily available. I began to think about the hand-made ones starting to gain mention in the *Rifleman,* and then I spotted an ad by Waldemar Doering of Oklahoma. He was selling various weights of .224″ spitzers of 7-caliber ogive made in RCBS dies. I ordered a thousand in 55-gr. weight.

Surplus 4895 powder was then available from Bruce Hodgdon and I bought a 150-lb. keg of it. Cut-and-try loading led me to 36 grs. with the #12 Peters primer—and groups that now often shaded the minute of angle. One March day everything was perking right and I got 5 into a half-inch, center-to-center. It was my first "ragged-hole" group. The first two cut, the second two almost cut each other, leaving a shred of white between, and the fifth took that out. I still have that target.

Interestingly the above load, arrived at in the old-fashioned way of starting fairly low and working up while watching for the traditional (but now ridiculed) pressure signs, falls just under the maximum listed in *Hodgdon's No. 21 Loading Manual.* I went as high as his max, 37 grs., but extraction tightened up a bit, so I dropped back. Since he lists 3698 fs and 52,000 psi, I probably was getting 3625 or so. Other loading sources now list heavier loads of commercial 4895, but I'd approach them cautiously. Pressures vary in different rifles, even with theoretically identical loads.

Handloading, oddly enough seems to have been one of the two basic reasons for the Swift's death. All serious varmint shooters are handloaders, and the Swift early gained a reputation for being difficult to reload. Most of this was probably due to a widely-circulated statement attributed to J. Bushnell Smith, the best known custom reloader of the late '30s and early '40s: "The chap who 'knows all the answers' in reloading any other cartridge is just like a baby learning to walk when he tackles the 220 Swift... The Swift is the most finicky cartridge to reload in the world... The smallest irregularity ... may jump pressures 5,000 to 15,000 pounds, and without a bit of warning."

Mebbe so, but I'm dubious. I didn't figure I was an expert at the practice, but I never had the slightest trouble with handloads. Maybe it was because I didn't believe I had to constantly work with 55,000 psi. Any cartridge lengthens brass, etc., at those pressures.

The other thing that hurt the Swift was the report that barrels didn't last long. That tremendous velocity was supposed to wash them out in 700 rounds or so.* Again, I'm dubious. It might have happened to an occasional early barrel, particularly if a lot of bench shooting was done without giving the tube a chance to cool. But on varmints? Hardly. As evidence, I recently asked Olen Eves about his Swift, the one I'd borrowed back in the late '40s. He still has it, he told me, though in 1967 he had Winchester install a new barrel. The original one wasn't grouping badly, but not as well as it had earlier. So in normal hunting use, by several friends as well as Olen himself, practically all with the ultra-fast 48 gr. factory load, that original barrel lasted *almost 30 years!* I wish I never had a problem more serious than barrel life in the Swift.

Others have criticized the Swift for mediocre accuracy and for the fact that it cannot be "loaded

---

*The 20-odd years following the introduction of the 220 Swift was a period in which rifle barrel cleaning was neglected by many shooters. The advent of Kleanbore priming, prior to 1935, may have been responsible, at least in good part, for this failure to scrub the barrel thoroughly and frequently. Kleanbore priming, non-corrosive and non-mercuric, had indeed made it unnecessary to clean the bores as far as rusting and corrosion were concerned, and it is only in recent years that the harmful effect on accuracy of non-cleaning has become recognized.

Informed shooters, today know that powder residue can be "ironed" into the bore, that metallic fouling can build up, and that such conditions, if left alone for a hundred shots or more (the total depending on caliber, load intensity, rapidity of fire, etc.), can permanently—and harmfully—affect performance. As the phrase of that old day had it, the "gilt edge" was gone. Ed.

---

down." Both statements are hard to understand. Given a good barrel and good bullets, any cartridge can be made to shoot well, including the Swift.

As for loading down to 22 Long Rifle or Hornet velocities, that seems a dubious goal to strive for. However, since the claim often has been made that the Swift couldn't be handled this way while the 22-250 could, the implication being that this somehow made the 22-250 superior, I decided to have a go at it. I'd never had any interest in this back when I was using the Swift regularly, and never met anyone who did, but maybe it's something that appeals to certain shooters.

When I got to thinking about it, I concluded that the Swift is such a fast load that only one reduced load would not do. I mean, if you drop from 4000 fs down to Long Rifle speed, there's an awful gap. It seemed more logical to try for something in the Hornet class too; thus, if successful, I could decapitate squirrels at 50 yards, dispatch chucks at 125, and use normal heavy loads for the out-yonder stuff, assuming proper zeroing between shooting chores, of course.

As it turned out, the whole thing was easy—so easy I wonder if any of those writers of the late '30s ever actually tried reduced loading or merely parroted what someone else claimed. I'd been using 5/ Unique with the 45-gr. Sierra round-nose Hornet bullet in my 222 Sako. This clocks 1735 fs on an Avtron K233 chronograph and is deadly on squirrels. I figured the same load in the bigger Swift case would give lower pressure and less

An early ½-inch group—made in 1947 with the 220 Swift—and the author's first tight one! The load—36 grains of No. 4895, the 55-gr. Doering 7S bullets made in RCBS dies.

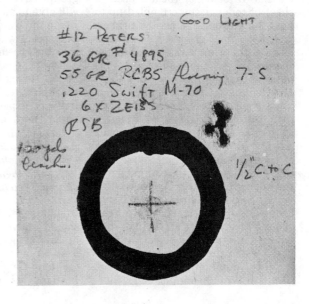

Seven 3-shot groups, fired by Bell at 100 yards with his M70 220 Swift, ran just over an inch on average. Nothing spectacular, but good enough for 'chucks.

velocity, thus would certainly qualify as a "loaded down" load. So, using the Remington 9½ M primer, I tried it in a M70 wearing a Bushnell 3-9x scope. It chronographed 1495 fs instrumental (at 15 feet), which is scarcely more than a 22 rimfire.

At 50 yards, my first group measured exactly one-half inch, with 4 in 5/16". Other groups about duplicated this. In some of them I used ⅛ sheet of toilet tissue crumpled up to hold the powder against the primer, and for some groups the Federal large pistol primer was used, but neither of these changes affected groups noticeably. I found a few old 45-gr. HP Remington Hornet bullets on a dusty shelf and tried these, with identical results. So I figured I had a squirrel load in the Swift. Such loads have wind problems similar to those of the 22 Long Rifle, of course, but that's what you get for making a pipsqueak out of a blazer. As a last effort with these loads, I fired several 5-shot groups in my basement, where I can shoot 50 feet. They ran about ⅛-inch on centers—good enough to shoot possibles on the gallery target.

For the medium velocity load, I began with 14/4198 and the 45-gr. Sierra Hornet bullet, as someone had recommended this in a letter in *American Rifleman*. Doubtless it worked in his outfit, but not in mine, which only proves again that rifles are individuals. At 100 yards, my groups went about 3 inches. Velocity was 1782 fs.

I switched to 15/4227 and the CCI primer, which gave 2187 fs on the Avtron, somewhat under the original Hornet loading but suitable for short range chucks. Two consecutive 5-shot groups each measured 1", then one went 2", followed by a 4-shotter of 7/16". A number of subsequent groups averaged about 1", which will give head shots on chucks at any range for which this load is suitable. The tissue was used for some shooting, but results weren't noticeably better than without it. I feel funny about using such stuff—I look through the bore after each shot, halfway expecting to find shreds of paper there, but I never have.

Incidentally, all of these light and medium loads should be used only in cases previously fired with heavy loads and then neck sized. Their pressures are too low to always form a gas seal with new brass.

Thus the fact that the Swift should have become obsolete is literally incredible. It was—and is—a great varmint load, the greatest long-range 22 ever marketed. Perhaps its biggest problem was that it came too soon, before the shooting populace was really ready for it. Now that we've become more sophisticated, it should be brought back. Rumors say it will be. I hope so.

The 250-3000 Savage

There was a time when the 250-3000 Savage was highly recommended as a varmint/deer/antelope load. It deserved its fine reputation. It had adequate power for such game at usual ranges, excellent accuracy and light recoil. The latter characteristic was perhaps the main reason that many gunwriters recommended it as a youth's or woman's cartridge, but doubtless most 250-3000s were bought and used by men. The world moves on, though, and shooters' eyes turned to newer blazers—particularly the 243—and in 1963 the 250-3000 was discontinued. It had had a good long life—just about a half-century, depending on whose introduction date you prefer: Sharpe gives 1913 one place, 1914 another, while Barnes lists 1915. No great matter. The important thing is that it was introduced.

The 250-3000 is credited to Charles Newton, the Roy Weatherby of pre-WW I days. It apparently was intended to be an improvement on his earlier 22 Savage Hi-Power—the "Imp"—and it met this goal. Gun lore has it that Newton designed the 250 around the 100-gr. bullet at 2800 fs, but when Savage took it over they wanted velocity beyond that of the Imp, which used a 70-gr. bullet at about 2800 fs, so they reduced the projectile weight to 87 grains, allowing them to up velocity to 3000 fs. No other commercial cartridge was reaching that velocity at that time, so the advertising possibilities are obvious. The velocity was even incorporated into the cartridge's name, and it became the 250-3000 Savage, a monicker it still wears.

Newton continued to insist that the 100-gr. bullet was the ideal weight in this case, and about 1933 Peters Cartridge Co. introduced it commercially. Powder improvements occurring in the intervening years permitted a velocity of some 2850 fs, to slightly exceed Newton's goal. He, unfortunately, died several months before the new load appeared.

The 250-3000 case can be thought of as an '06 shortened enough to work through the M99 Savage lever action rifle, and necked down to 25 caliber. Most M99 variations have been chambered for it, as well as Savage's M1920, 40 and 41, Winchester's M54 and M70, and others, including various European makes. The bolt actions permitted handloading at pressures to 50,000 psi or so, whereas most shooters prefer to stay around 40,000 in the lever guns. Nevertheless, I'm sure that the vast majority of hunters prefer this cartridge in the lever action. They go together like ham and eggs, the lightweight, fast-working M99 perfectly complementing the light, speedy load.

Factory loadings for the 250-3000 standardized at about 3000 fs for the 87-gr. slug, 2800 fs for the 100-grainer. Each of these gives about 1000 fp of energy at 200 yards, the amount many hunters feel is required for clean kills on deer-size game. However, the lighter construction of the 87-gr. bullet makes it a less desirable choice for game of this weight and, since the difference in their trajectories is small over a couple hundred yards, the heavier projectile is advisable for deer, antelope and suchlike. Theoretically, the light bullet, if planted in the lung area, will give quick kills, but this doesn't always pan out. I saw a friend shoot a whitetail buck in this manner at well under 100 yards, but it escaped. We found it the next day, soured, a half mile or so from

where it was shot. He switched to 100-gr. loads and by coincidence had a similar chance soon afterwards and made an instant kill. Two shots aren't over-powering proof, of course, but it makes sense to use a deer bullet on deer and a varmint bullet on varmints.

In the strong bolt actions, the 250-3000 can be noticeably souped up by handloading. With the 87-gr. bullet, 3200 fs can be reached, while the 100-gr. slug touches the magic 3000 fs mark with max loads of several of the slower-burning powders, a fact that should please the shade of old Charlie Newton as he gazes down from that big shootin' range in the sky. Nothing like combining both the bullet weight he wanted and the velocity that tempted the Savage people better than a half-century ago.

The same powder advances have made it possible to handload the heavier 117- and 120-gr. bullets in this fairly small case and still come up with better than 2800 fs. Highly impressive ballistics, and if the bullet is tough enough—the Nosler, say—this load could well handle elk if a chest shot is presented. I'm not saying anyone should make a practice of using this little cartridge on these critters—I like big loads for big game—but under ideal conditions it has done the job.

There could be a problem with these heavy bullets in some 250-3000s. Many rifles in this caliber had 1/14 twist, and this sometimes does not stabilize the 117-gr. or 120-gr. bullets, particularly in lever guns which must have cartridges loaded to an over-all length short enough to work through the action. Powder capacity is reduced when the bullet is seated deeply, and this lowers velocity, which in turn cuts down on the rotational velocity which stabilizes the bullet. The handloader should consider all aspects of the situation and make the best compromiser possible.

Handloaders also can go the other way, down to light bullets for varmints, if that appeals. Speer makes a 60-gr. pencil-pointed bullet that can be pushed at upwards of 3700 fs in a bolt gun, and the 75-gr. Sierra HP will reach 3400. These explode chucks and crows on contact, at least over the first few hundred yards. It's sometimes more difficult to get top accuracy out of ultralight bullets than with heavier ones, though, and my own preference for varmints in this caliber leans toward the 75- or 87-grainers.

Any way you cut it, this cartridge is a highly desirable one, and a short time ago the people up at Savage Arms decided it shouldn't be allowed to fade into oblivion. So another variant of their favorite lever gun, this one called the M99A, was chambered for the 250-3000. It's a slick rifle, with a 22-inch barrel, straight grip, schnabel-tip fore-end and tang safety. That should be enough to give this blazer a new lease on life— maybe enough to get it through the next half-century, once today's youngsters learn what a fine outfit this is.

The 257 Roberts

The late Col. Townsend Whelen called the 257 Roberts one of the most useful cartridges ever made. As usual, the colonel was right. But not even such praise by the most respected gunwriter we've ever had, as well as accolades by many other topflight authorities, most notably Jack O'Connor, was enough to save this blazer when the highly ballyhooed 243 appeared.

The basic trouble was, of course, that with factory loads and in factory length actions, the 257 just never approached its potential as a true blazer.

Major Ned Roberts, of Berlin, N.H., was one of our highly respected shooter-experimenters during the early part of this century. A dedicated woodchuck hunter, his investigations led him to believe that a 25-cal. bullet fitted to a case having about the capacity of the 7x57mm Mauser would be ideal for this use. Interestingly, this view also was held by Dr. Franklin Mann, author of the classic *The Bullet's Flight*. At any rate, Major Roberts experimented for years with this combination and eventually settled on a design having a long sloping shoulder—a style which at that time was believed to give lower pressures than the sharp-shouldered variety. His cartridge was called the 25 Roberts, and hundreds of custom rifles were built for it, primarily by Griffin & Howe and A. O. Niedner. Maximum loads reportedly gave an 87-gr. bullet 3300 fs, a 100-grainer 3000 fs, and a 117-gr. almost 2900 fs.

In the early '30s, Remington became interested in the cartridge and it was put into commercial production in 1934. However, reportedly because of manufacturing problems, the shoulder angle was changed from 15 to 20 degrees. To avoid confusion with the earlier version, the name was changed to

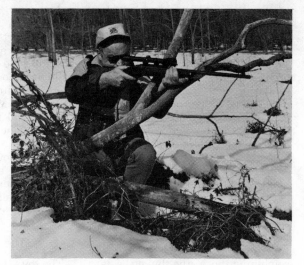

The author finds his Ruger No. 1 single shot rifle, made in 7x57mm caliber, a light and compact arm for Pennsylvania timber hunting. The scope, a Weaver K6, has been temporarily mounted for an ammo test.

257 Remington-Roberts. It was originally chambered in the M30 Remington, with Winchester adapting their M54 to it the following year and the M70 later. Remington made it in their M720, M722 and M760 pump, also. Factory ammo used an 87-gr. bullet at 3200 fs, a 100-gr. at 2900, and a 117-gr. at 2650. Good, but not spectacularly better than the smaller and much older 250-3000 Savage. Furthermore, since round-nose bullets had an accuracy edge over available 25-cal. spitzers then, Remington went with these ballistically inefficient projectiles and loaded them to an over-all length of 2.75 inches. At a much later date, this permitted chambering the short M722 for the 257 load, but the logic of it in a M30, M54 or M70 escapes me.

By the time I got my 257, techniques for making spitzer bullets must have improved radically, for I had no trouble crowding an inch at 100 yards with heavy loads and 87-gr. or 100-gr. bullets. As O'Connor's articles had convinced me the 257 was the cartridge I wanted for my varmint and deer shooting, I had the one mentioned earlier in this article built. Bump Lynn inletted the stock perfectly, which doubtless influenced its grouping ability. It shot well from the word go. Not quite as well as the Swift had with the Doering-made RCBS bullets, but close to it. In any noticeable wind, the 257 seemed superior, and of course its heavier bullets made it completely suitable for deer as well as varmints.

There had been no improvement in the 257's factory ballistics by the late '40s, despite powder improvements. Having standardized in the mid-'30s on velocities that the best

powder then (probably 3031) would give, the ammo companies apparently just used the superior propellants which came later to maintain those velocities while lowering pressures.

Handloaders of course don't think that way. Whatever gives them the most zip is what they're gonna dump in the case. More than dump—compress, squeeze, stomp—when they're using slow-burning numbers. To make even more room, they altered factory actions or used M98 Mausers to get a magazine that would accept at least a 3-inch over-all cartridge length, and seated those long spitzer bullets out where they belonged. So assembled and loaded the 257 would give the 87-gr. spitzer almost 3400 fs with 44/4895, a 100-gr. 3150 with 51/4831, and a 117-gr. 2900 fs with 44/4350, or close to 3000 fs with 49/4831. This last load gives a muzzle energy of some 2300 fp and, using the beautifully shaped Sierra spitzer boat-tail, a remaining velocity of almost 2200 fs at 400 yards, with energy there of 1200 fp—more than the factory-loaded 250-3000 has at half that distance! It equals the best handload that can be put into the ultra-modern 243—a 100-gr. spitzer bullet at 3140 fs which delivers about 100 fs higher velocity at 400 yards but no more energy. Too, the 257 has the advantage of obtaining more of its energy from bullet weight than from velocity as the 243 does. Yet the 243 was doubtless the primary cause of the 257's disappearance. Makes me wonder about all the so-called progress of the last several decades.

For Pennsylvania deer shooting—whitetails which rarely go over 150 lbs. live weight—I've had excellent results with 100-gr. spitzers of vari-

ous makes loaded to 2900 fs or so, a velocity that's easily obtained with many powders. I've never shot anything larger with a 257, but have loaded ammo for friends who used this cartridge in Canada on moose, caribou and black bear with excellent results. For such shooting, the old 125-gr. Barnes semi-spitzer bullet of pure copper-tubing jacket material, ahead of 44/4350, did the trick. Some current loading manuals don't go this high with 4350, but I fired many rounds of it with no trouble whatsoever. With all handloads, though, it makes good sense to start a reasonable amount under listed maximums and ease your way up.

If I were going to hunt antelope with a 257, I think I'd go with a good 100-gr. spitzer and a max load of 4831, but if mule deer also were on the agenda I'd prefer the 117-gr. Sierra spitzer boat-tail. Some of these critters get awfully big, compared to an antelope or the average whitetail, and if an angling shot has to be taken the heavier slug has an edge. To get top results from this slow powder, though, a barrel length of 24 inches or so is necessary. If you've cut yours to 20 inches, say, for handiness in the woods or to save weight, as I did for my wife's customized M722 257, a faster burning powder should be selected. A deer load that's worked well in this short outfit is the Hornady 100-gr. spire point and 41/ReloadeR 21, which averages 2815 fs on the Avtron K233.

Despite a hunter's desire for an all-round rifle such as the 257, most of anyone's shooting with such a rifle is on varmints. That definitely was the case with me. Taking shots. as they came, at ranges up to a quarter-mile or so on chucks, crows, Western magpies, prairie dogs, Columbian ground squirrels, etc., I can't honestly say that I've ever done much better with anything than that old, long-gone 257 Mauser. I don't mean to say I killed such smaller varmints as crows at better than 400 yards, but we did kill chucks at such ranges a reasonable percentage of the time. A crow with the feathers off is seen to have only about a base-ball-size vital area, and that's tough to hit with anything four football fields away. But I did watch my father kill one crow at 369 long downhill steps with my 257—whereupon he built one for himself.

We used mostly 87-gr. and 100-gr. bullets for varmints, but the most interesting shot I ever fired with this caliber occurred when I was using a 60-gr. bullet (a Speer, I believe, but it's so long ago I'm not positive) and a max load of 4895. We got about 3800 fs out of this combination, and some weird things happened occasionally—such as the bullet sometimes disappearing in a blue puff out there 75 yards or so. When you did hit a crow or chuck, though, results were spectacular. The shot I want to describe came at a chuck maybe 175 yards away. It was feeding and I held for the head. At the crack of the gun, the critter went up in the air, came down on its back, and lay there motionless. An ordinary shot, I thought. I walked over to get it, but just as I reached down, the chuck flipped over, gave me a startled look—I don't know what kind I gave him!—and dove into its hole. Investigation revealed that my 60-gr. slug had hit in the sod directly under the chuck's head and the concussion had knocked him out. What was left of the inside-out jacket and some core fragments were found. I dunno what would have happened had I arrived a few seconds sooner. I never had a live chuck by the tail. On another near miss with this load, the bullet smashed a piece of red shale and a fragment of stone killed the chuck, but I always felt the concussion shot was crazier.

The 257 now is dead, insofar as commercial interest goes. Handicapped from the start, the 243, 244 and various other 6mms finished it. If brought out in a full-length action and loaded to at least 3 inches over-all with spitzer slugs and a heavy load of slow-burning powder, it would do anything the average hunter could ask. For years I thought Remington would get around to this, but the introduction of the 25-06 by this company makes that unlikely and I doubt that any competitor will make a big thing of a cartridge which many semi-oldtimers still think of as the 257 Remington-Roberts.

The 7x57mm Mauser

The 7x57mm, oldest cartridge in the group we're discussing, was introduced in the 1892 Spanish Mauser, a revised version of the Belgian Mauser Model 88-89; the last had been the first service Mauser rifle issued with a box type magazine. The 7x57mm cartridge specifications at that time were: over-all length 3.08 inches, weight 377.4 grs; round nosed bullet hav-

Above—Two 5-shot groups from the No. 1 Single Shot Ruger in 7x57mm, range 100 yards. Left—139-gr. Hornady bullet over 45/4895, 1⅜". Right—160-gr. Speer and 50/4831, also 1⅜". Both high shots were first out of cold barrel. Scope was Weaver K-6.

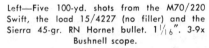

Left—Five 100-yd. shots from the M70/220 Swift, the load 15/4227 (no filler) and the Sierra 45-gr. RN Hornet bullet. 1¹⁄₁₆". 3-9x Bushnell scope.

Left and below—three 5-shot groups at 100 yards made with the M70 300 H&H Magnum, scope a 4x Weaver. Left—74/4831/165-gr. Hornady, ⅞". Below left—70/4831/180-gr. Hornady, 1⅝". Below right—72/4831/180-gr. Sierra FB, 1¼". Federal 215 primers in all loads. Scope, a Weaver 4x.

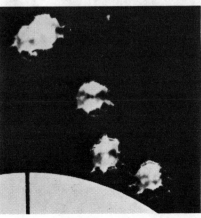

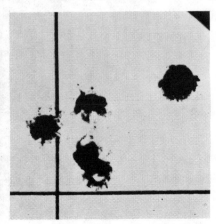

7x57 BALLISTICS

Bullet, grs.	Velocity, yds. Muzzle	Velocity, yds. 300	Energy, yds. Muzzle	Energy, yds. 300	MRT Over 300 yds.
103	3330	2060	2550	977	5.2
110	3068	2277	2300	1267	5.0
139	2710	1960	2280	1190	7.8
139	2800	1990	2420	1220	NA
150	2756	2133	2530	1516	6.2
160	2650	1780	2500	1130	NA
162	2785	2060	2780	1520	6.7
175	2490	1680	2410	1100	9.5

ing a lead core and steel jacket; bullet diameter .284-inch, length 1.21 inches, weight 172.8 grs.; powder charge 38.3 grs. of nitro-cellulose; muzzle velocity 2290 fs, pressure 45,000 psi.

Despite the fact that it has been around for 8 decades, the 7x57mm still has a wide following and factory-loaded ammunition is readily available here from Winchester-Western, Remington-Peters, Federal, Speer-DWM, CIL and Norma. Current ballistics extracted from their tables are printed nearby.

Comparing 7x57mm ballistics with some of today's popular calibers shows that the octogenarian 7x57mm, with either the 103-gr. or 110-gr., shoots as flat over 300 yards as the 243 Winchester or 6mm Remington with 100-gr. bul-

lets and delivers almost identical energy with the 110-gr., thus will make an excellent varmint cartridge given a good quality barrel. The 139-gr. loads fall into the same energy class, but are superior on deer and similar game. The 150-gr. and 162-gr. loads almost equal 300-yd. results with the great 270/130-gr. combination, exceed those of the round-nose 150-gr. 270, and come very close to 150-gr. spitzer bullet results from the larger 270 case. The 175-gr. load is essentially a short-range cruncher which, pointed with reasonable care, will take elk and moose. For that matter, the legendary elephant hunter W.D.M (Karamojo) Bell used 175-gr. solids in this cartridge for the vast majority of his 1000-plus elephants, though admittedly it was

his pinpoint shooting which made the load effective. The 175-gr. 7mm bullet is a long one, not easily deflected from its course; its moderate velocity does not explode soft points, so penetration even on rather large game is excellent.

Following the 7x57mm's introduction in the M92 Mauser, Spain used it in the well-known M93. A few years later Remington chambered their Rolling Block and Lee rifles for it and, considerably later, the M30. Winchester offered the M54 and M70 in this caliber—both now desired by many collectors as well as hunters—and recently the Ruger Number One single shot rifle has been made in this chambering, as has Ruger's M77 long action! Another single shot, the new Colt-Sharps M78, was to have been made in 7x57mm, but that rifle is moribund or worse. Many European armsmakers continue to build rifles of this caliber.

The 7x57mm is easy to handload for. Using a Ruger No. 1 Single Shot with Weaver K6 scope, new Norma brass and Remington 9½M primers, I got the following 5-shot groups at 100 yards the first time I ever loaded for the rifle. See my results nearby.

This is fine hunting accuracy from a lightweight outfit, yet doubtless can be improved with

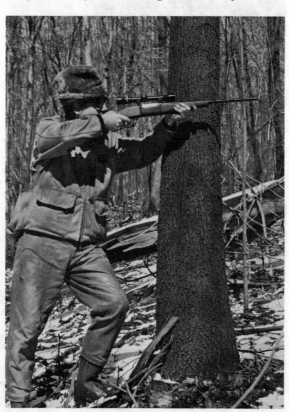

Don Lewis, gun columnist for the *Pennsylvania Game News*, readies his Savage M99 lever action rifle, caliber 250-3000, in whitetail deer country. The scope is a Weaver V7.

7x57 Accuracy

Bullet/grs.	Load	MV	Group/ins.
120 Horn.	45/4895	3000	1⅛
145 Speer	52/4831	2775	1½
154 Horn.	50/4350	2800	1
175 Speer	50/4831	2450	2

routine load development. Nevertheless, we have here, in one ordinary box of handloads, cartridges suitable for anything from 10-lb. chucks to 850-lb. elk. It's hard to ask for anything more, especially when combined with that handsome Ruger rifle.

300 H & H Magnum

The 300 H&H is unknown to many of today's Magnum Mob, or looked on as a relic from the Pleistocene by those who do recall its name. But that's just more proof of Americans' lack of respect for outstanding accomplishments of the past. For the 300 H&H was an outstanding cartridge, make no mistake about that. I say "was" because I don't think any American company is currently chambering rifles for this cartridge, but ballistically this big belted 300 is still quite a load.

It's an English development, a product of the famous Holland & Holland firm, though with typical British reserve they tended to refer to it as the Super 30. It was in America that it became famous as the 300 H&H. Basically a necked down 375 H&H, it appeared in 1920, eight years after the bigger bore. For ease in loading the European spaghetti-like Cordite powder, it was given a long, gentle (8 degree, 30 minute) shoulder. It's often been claimed that this shape is not ideal with American powders, as it supposedly funnels the granules down the bore as they are burned, increasing throat erosion. This may be true, but then again it may not. I've never done enough shooting with a 300 H&H to find out, but a longtime friend, gunsmith Al Wardrop, who has built many of the top guns competing in the current 1000-yard matches near Williamsport, Pa., for years shot a 300 H&H on targets far and near. It had a heavy Buhmiller barrel fitted to a Winchester M54 action, and when he sold it he'd put better than 3500 rounds through it. I asked about its accuracy at that point, and he said it wasn't much different than at 1000 rounds—at which time 8-inch groups at 600 yards, using 180-gr. spitzer bullets of several makes and 4831 powder, were not unusual.

I also asked Al about case life, since various reports suggest it's nothing great with this old H&H. He said 8 to 10 reloadings were common—about what he gets from several 300 Winchester Magnums he's now shooting. It has been said that the steep body taper of the 300 H&H results in case separation just forward of the belt after a few shots, but Wardrop had no trouble with this either.

Because belted cases headspace on the belt, not on the shoulder, resizing dies should be adjusted to leave the belt-shoulder dimension as long as possible. This will prevent case stretching with each shot, which happens when belted cases are routinely "full length" resized. With full loads, a few such routine resizings can cause head separations. Tailor your brass to *your* chamber and the problem won't arise.

Perhaps Al's good results are due in part to his use of slightly less than max loads. In testing a num-

ber of 300 H&H rifles at the bench, he usually got best accuracy from loads several grains under maximum. He mentioned one he built which regularly gave 2-inch groups at 300 yards, so-loaded. The customer, ignoring his recommendations, immediately went to the top manual listings, with mediocre results. After weeks of fiddling, he finally dropped down a bit and groups promptly tightened. On the other hand, it is true that some rifle-cartridge combos perform best with max-usable loads.

The 300 H&H gained sudden fame in America as a target load when Ben Comfort won the prestigious 1000-yard Wimbledon Cup Match with it in 1935. The rifle, a Griffin & Howe custom job on a M1917 action, reportedly was built in this caliber at the suggestion of Elmer Keith, the planning being done while he and Comfort were snowed in on a sheep hunt above the Salmon River. Something pleasantly satisfying about the story, huh?

At any rate, the 300 H&H dominated the Wimbledon for many years. The ammo, incidentally, was 180-gr. full jacketed boat-tails loaded by Western Cartridge Co. They'd offered the 300 H&H since 1925, though no production rifles were available until 1937, when Winchester chambered the M70 for it.

My cousin, Dave Bell, got a M70 300 H&H shortly after Winchester announced it, added a 2¼x Zeiss Zielklein in Redfield Jr. mounts, and found it more than adequate for whitetails at any range. I shot that rifle often before going into the Army in 1943, and after my discharge I used it for numerous woodchucks—an early example of overkill!

Perhaps that early usage prejudiced me, but I've always had a soft spot for the 300 H&H. I didn't do a lot of group shooting in those days, but when sighting in the 180-gr. Western open point load I

usually stayed under 1½ inches. I've recently been shooting another M70—a K4-mounted pre-WWII model—and 100-yard results (below) have been similar.

All loads used 4831 powder and Remington 9½ primers.

Bullet/grs.		Load	MV	Group ins.
150	Hornady	75	3325	2
165	Hornady	72	3100	2¼
165	Hornady	74	3200	⅞
180	Hornady	70	2900	1⅝
180	Sierra FB	70	2900	*2⅛
180	Sierra FB	72	2950	†1¼
180	Sierra FB	73	3000	**2⅝

All loads used 4831 powder and Remington 9½ primers. *4 in ⅛. †4 in ⅝". **4 in 1½".

Some gunwriters never seem to shoot a group larger than one MOA, but I don't belong to that select club. With a load as powerful as the 300 H&H, a rifle of standard weight and a 4x scope—in other words, a practical hunting rig—I don't think these are bad.

The 300 H&H gained a reasonable following in Pennsylvania, where its power obviously was unnecessary for most hunting, perhaps because its long range accuracy and punch made it ideal for ridge-to-ridge whitetail shooting in both the northern mountains and in the farm-country fields. It proved an even better choice in the Rockies and the West, as it handled antelope, deer and sheep at long range, and had plenty of energy for elk, doing all of this with a reasonable amount of recoil in a sporting-weight rifle. To top it all, it showed itself more than adequate for even the big bears of Alaska. It's hard to ask for more from a big game rifle than the 300 Holland & Holland can supply. That's why it makes up the fifth and last of our beautiful—but forgotten—blazers. ●

References

Ackley, Parker O., *Handbook for Shooters and Reloaders*, Salt Lake City, Utah, 1962.

American Rifleman, October, 1971, "Dope Bag" letter from James Hanson.

Barnes, Frank C., *Cartridges of the World*, Chicago, Ill., 1965.

Keith, Elmer, *Keith's Rifles for Large Game*, Huntington, W.Va., 1946.

Landis, Charles S., *Twenty-Two Caliber Varmint Rifles*, Plantersville, S.C., 1947.

Sharpe, Philip B., *Complete Guide to Handloading*, 2d. ed., New York, N.Y., 1941.

————————, *The Rifle in America*, 2d. ed., New York, N.Y., 1947.

Smith, W.H.B. and J. E. Smith, *The Book of Rifles*, 3d. ed., Harrisburg, Pa., 1963.

"J.M. SHOOTS TWICE"

by LUCIAN CARY

Over the long years J. M. Pyne had taken
22 deer with a single shot rifle—one shot for each of them.
His last stalk was doubly successful.

J. M. PYNE saw little flurries of snow outside the shop windows. The leaves were gone, except for those that still clung tightly to the oak trees. The meadow out toward the target butt was brown. It was hunting weather. But he couldn't go deer hunting again. He wasn't up to it. He would have to tell young Ballentyne so. He would have to tell him that J. M. Pyne was seventy-five.

He took a rifle barrel out of the boiling solution in the bluing tank. He held it by a wooden plug in each end of the bore. He had a circular wire brush mounted in the lathe. He pressed the barrel gently against the revolving brush, rolling it and drawing it back and forth to reach every part of the surface. The dull black turned brighter under the brush. It approached the dark-blue color that riflemen admire.

He heard a knock at the door and called out. Young Tim Ballentyne came in with a rifle in a leather case hanging from his shoulder. He waited until J. M. Pyne had finished brushing the

barrel and put it back in the tank for another coat of the solution.

"I should have answered your letter," J. M. Pyne said. Young Ballentyne knew that he almost never answered letters.

"But you're going with me."

J. M. Pyne shook his head. He always shook his head nowadays.

"We won't be gone long. I've just five days away from school."

"I've sold my hunting gun," J. M. Pyne said.

"The one with the twenty-two punch marks for twenty-two deer with twenty-two shots?"

J. M. Pyne nodded. The fellow had said that he wanted to give it to a museum.

"But you've got something in the shop you can shoot," young Ballentyne said.

J. M. Pyne straightened his shoulders painfully. It was only mid-afternoon, but his shoulders ached.

"Let's see your rifle," he said.

Young Ballentyne took the rifle out of the case and handed it over with pride. It was a bolt-action

repeating rifle with a stock of fine curly walnut, new and spotless.

J. M. Pyne thought it was clubby. It lacked the grace of the long-barreled, single-shot rifles that he loved. Too much of the weight was in the thick action and too little in the slender muzzle. But he knew it was strong and simple and sound. You could take the action apart without tools.

"You don't really like it," young Ballentyne said.

"It's a fine rifle," J. M. Pyne said. "I don't know of anything better than a bolt-action rifle for the .30-06 cartridge."

"But you like single-shot rifles better."

"Well," J. M. Pyne said. "I like them better for my own use."

He went to the cupboard in the corner and got out the old long-range .30 caliber rifle he had built for himself thirty years ago on a Sharps-Borchardt action. The Sharps Company had gone when the buffalo went. But their actions were well made. The rifle had a long vernier rear sight on the heel of the stock. It was designed for the old way of shooting at a thousand yards, when you lay on your back and put your left arm behind your head to grasp the butt and rested the barrel on your crossed legs.

"It's awfully long," young Ballentyne said.

"Thirty-four-inch barrel," J. M. Pyne said. "A barrel had to be long for shooting on your back, or else you were likely to shoot yourself in the leg."

He put the rifle in the vise and ran a swab of absorbent cotton through it to take out the oil and the dust. He held the muzzle up to the light and looked through the bore. It had been shot a good deal with heavy charges and jacketed bullets. But the curving knife edges of the narrow lands were only slightly rounded. The rifle would still shoot.

"You could take off that wind gauge in front and put on something else and move the rear sight up on the tang," young Ballentyne said.

J. M. Pyne shook his head. "I don't believe I've got any cartridge cases left. I chambered the rifle for an odd case I swaged down from the old .38-72. You can't buy cartridges for it."

He handed the rifle to young Ballentyne and hunted through piles of cigar boxes. He found the right box and laid it on the bench. There were fifteen or twenty of the old cartridge cases, dark with corrosion and cracked at the neck, and a few of the bullets, with a narrow swaged band at the base.

Young Ballentyne could not restrain his curiosity. He hunted through the box.

"Here!" he said. "Here are two brand-new ones, never fired."

J. M. Pyne took them. They hadn't been fired. He picked up a bullet and showed young Ballentyne that it was a push fit.

"I reamed the inside of every case neck in the lathe," he said. "The outside fits the chamber and the inside fits the bullet."

Young Ballentyne hunted eagerly through the box for more cartridge cases. There weren't any more good ones.

"If you could find just a few more," young Ballentyne said, "you could use the gun. You won't need more than ten cartridges on a deer hunt."

"You're allowed one buck," J. M. Pyne said.

"Exactly," young Ballentyne said.

J. M. Pyne straightened up. "I never in my life took more than two shots to kill a deer. Mostly I took one shot."

Young Ballentyne smiled. "You could go with two cartridges—you really could."

J. M. Pyne got out the little miner's assay scale and a can of smokeless powder thirty years old, and some primers. He primed one of the good cases and weighed out a charge of powder.

"Put up a target," he said.

He shifted the long vernier sight from the heel to the tang while young Ballentyne was putting up a target at the hundred-yard mark. He hunted for the old sight readings. He set the sight for a hundred yards. He opened the narrow window over the machine rest that he used for testing rifles, when young Ballentyne came back, and loaded the rifle. He took a couple of deep breaths and put the gun up. It wasn't so bad as he had been afraid it would be. When you have shot rifles for sixty years, you don't forget. The front sight didn't hang on the black as once it had. But when the gun spoke and the butt set back hard against his shoulder, he knew the bullet was in the black even before he heard young Ballentyne's exclamation as he peered through the spotting scope at the target.

J. M. Pyne shut the window and walked slowly back to the bench with the rifle at heel. He had forgotten something. He had forgotten how good it was to get a shot off clean. He had given up shooting, because he couldn't hold a rifle for ten shots—to say nothing of fifty or a hundred. But he could still hold a rifle for one or two shots.

He put the gun in the vise and unscrewed the wind gauge, and picked up a small brass unit and a hammer and began gently to tap the sight base out of the dovetail slot.

"You're going," young Ballentyne said.

J. M. Pyne did not answer. He got the sight base out and looked in a drawer for the large ivory bead he had always liked for hunting. He would have to do some close measuring and some more shooting to make sure he was sighted in.

"You could weigh out some powder charges and put them in glass vials, and take along primers and bullets and the re and decapper," young Ballentyne said.

"No," J. M. Pyne said. "What I can't do in two shots, I won't do at all."

II

They started north the next morning in young Ballentyne's car. It was a gray, wintry day. They came, late in the afternoon, to a bleak little town with a high stone wall on one side of the street and little shops on the other. The street was full of policemen and guards with revolvers and sawed-off shotguns. Young Ballentyne stopped the car. A policeman ordered him to keep going.

"That must be Waubun Prison," J. M. Pyne said. "I haven't been through here in twenty years, but I remember it."

It was only as they were leaving the town that young Ballentyne could stop for gas and ask the man at the pump what had happened.

"Riot in the prison this morning," the man said. "They killed three guards, and some of them got away. I hear they've stopped it now. But some of them got away."

Young Ballentyne looked so eager and excited that J. M. Pyne could guess what was on his mind.

"It isn't our business," J. M. Pyne said.

"No," young Ballentyne admitted, and drove on.

It was dark when they came to the place where they were to meet a man named Higgins with a team and a wagon. Young Ballentyne put the car in a garage.

They found Higgins in the general store. He said it would be cold. He was wearing a black-and-red Mackinaw himself, and a cap with ear flaps, and heavy gray woolen socks that came above his leather-topped rubbers and over his breeches.

J. M. Pyne was tired. The tote road was so bad the horses had to walk most of the way. J. M. Pyne wrapped himself in his long overcoat and turned up the collar and sank his chin. It took almost four hours to make the twelve miles. J. M. Pyne was so stiff he had to get young Ballentyne to help him down out of the wagon. He was glad to see the open fire inside the log camp and the hot food that Mrs. Higgins brought.

There were three other hunters there—men from New York who had got in that morning. They sat round the fire and talked hunting. J. M. Pyne saw, when Higgins introduced him, that his name meant no more to them than it had to Higgins. They were hunters, and not riflemen. They didn't know what a Pyne barrel was.

J. M. Pyne sat close to the fire when he had eaten, and warmed his shins and smoked a cigarette and listened. One of the men from New York was, he said, an experienced hunter who had killed many deer. His name was Esterbrook. The other two were novices. Esterbrook instructed them.

"The first thing you've got to learn if you want to get a deer," Esterbrook said, "is to empty your rifle. You know what I mean?"

He took his own rifle from the rack against the wall and made sure it was empty, and put it to his shoulder and aimed it at an imaginary deer and pulled the trigger and slammed the bolt hard, and pulled the trigger again and again.

"That's what I mean," he said. "You've got to keep shooting if you expect to get a deer. You've got to learn to fire every shot in the magazine before he gets out of sight." He turned to Higgins. "Isn't that right?" he demanded.

Higgins nodded. "That's why I like a lever-action rifle," he said. "You can pump lead with it faster than you can with that bolt action of yours."

He picked his own rifle, of a pattern that Americans through fifty years have made famous the world around, and showed them how fast he could manipulate it.

"You can shoot a bolt action just as fast," Esterbrook said, "if you know how."

Higgins would not admit that. They argued endlessly, as hunters will. J. M. Pyne got up and studied a local map tacked to the wall. Esterbrook interrupted his study. Esterbrook demanded to know what kind of rifle he was using.

J. M. Pyne got his rifle out of its case and handed it to Esterbrook.

"A single shot," Esterbrook said.

"A Sharps, model of 1878," J. M. Pyne said.

He did not say that he had made the barrel himself. If Esterbrook knew anything about rifles, he would note the name "J. M. Pyne" in small Roman capital letters on the barrel.

"How do you expect to get a deer with that?" Esterbrook demanded. "By the time you've reloaded, the deer will be in the next county."

"I don't like to shoot unless I see the sight on a vital spot."

"What special spot on a deer do you usually aim for?" Esterbrook asked.

"The neck," J. M. Pyne said. "About four inches below the hair. A bullet there doesn't spoil much meat." He took a bunch of keys out of his pocket. He held the keys poised. "When you hit a deer in the neck," he said, "he drops like that." J. M. Pyne dropped the bunch of keys on the floor.

Esterbrook raised his eyebrows and smiled, as younger men do smile at an old man's fancy.

"You can put a bullet through the neck of a deer that's jumping down timber as fast as he can go?"

"I didn't say that," J. M. Pyne said mildly.

"What do you do when a deer jumps and goes bouncing off through the brush so fast that all

you see is a glimpse of a white flag?"

"I like to go slow and make as little noise as possible, so as not to scare game."

"You've never seen a buck jump and go on jumping, sideways and in and out, so fast you can't get a bead on him?"

"Yes," J. M. Pyne said. "I've seen that."

"And what do you do then?" Esterbrook demanded.

"I don't shoot," J. M. Pyne said. "I stand still and figure on coming up with him later."

"Didn't you ever take a snap shot?"

"Yes," J. M. Pyne said. "But I don't shoot unless I see what I want to hit over the front sight."

"You're like Daniel Boone," Esterbrook said.

"I imagine Daniel Boone hunted more or less that way," J. M. Pyne said. "He must have. He couldn't afford to waste ammunition—not when he had to carry several months' supply of powder and lead."

"It may have been all right for him," Esterbrook said. "Game was plentiful and not easily frightened. And he was a good shot."

"I have been a good shot ever since I was a young man," J. M. Pyne said.

Esterbrook turned and smiled at the company. He made it clear that he was too kind to say what he might say.

J. M. Pyne took his rifle up to his room with him. It was an old habit with him to keep his rifle close beside him. In the old days, when he had traveled to Milwaukee and St. Louis and San Francisco to shoot in rifle matches, he had carried the gun himself. No Pullman porter and no bellboy had ever had a chance to drop the gun and knock the front sight askew.

Young Ballentyne stopped at the door. He stepped inside.

"I would have liked to tell that guy who you are, Mr. Pyne," he said.

J. M. Pyne stood his rifle carefully in a corner, making sure it would not slip, and sat down on the edge of his bed.

"He has his way of doing things," he said, " and I have mine."

III

Higgins got them all out at daylight. Higgins made a great racket with a brass bell. J. M. Pyne hated to get up. It was a laborious process to get up nowadays. He was always stiff and sore. But he made it. He dressed and got downstairs only a few minutes behind the others, and ate bacon and eggs and flapjacks with maple sirup and coffee. He was having a second cup of coffee when the thing happened.

A big man in gray dungarees stood in the doorway with a hatchet in his hand. His head was close-cropped. J. M. Pyne turned toward the other door. Another smaller man in the same kind of gray dungarees had posted himself there. He had a short length of iron bar as a weapon.

"Sit tight," the big man with the hatchet said. "Sit tight and do what you're told, and you won't get hurt."

They all sat motionless, staring at the men in gray dungarees, except Mrs. Higgins. She stood with a pan of flapjacks in one hand and a jug of maple sirup in the other, and very slowly her hands relaxed and the pan went clattering on the floor and the sirup jug landed with a solid thump. She sank into a chair.

"You watch 'em, Joe," the big man said, "while I look over the guns."

The big man turned to the living room. J. M. Pyne could see him as he picked a rifle out of the rack. They were all bolt-action rifles except Higgins' gun. The fellow laid Higgins' gun on the table, and young Ballentyne's new rifle. One by one, he picked up the three other rifles and slipped the bolts out. He did it as if he knew about bolt-action rifles, with no fumbling. He found cartridges all laid out on the table. He loaded Higgins' rifle and gave it to his partner with the piece of iron. Then he loaded young Ballentyne's rifle and stood in the doorway. He looked at Esterbrook.

"You're nearer my size," he said to Esterbrook. "Take off your clothes."

"What?" Esterbrook asked. He was wearing a gray flannel shirt and heavy woolen trousers and leather-topped rubbers. He had hung his plaid Mackinaw on the back of his chair.

Esterbrook stood up and took off his flannel shirt. The fellow made him take off his boots and his trousers and his woolen socks. He got out of his dungarees and into Esterbrook's clothes. They were a tight fit for him. He couldn't button the shirt collar, but he got into them.

"Now," he said, "I'll hold a gun on them while you get some clothes, Joe."

Joe chose to exchange clothes with one of the other men from New York.

They got a pack sack out of the shed beyond the kitchen and filled it with bread and bacon and salt and sugar.

"Now, Joe," the big man said, "you hold a gun on them while I take a look around."

J. M. Pyne heard the fellow go upstairs. When he came down he had blankets on one arm and he was dragging J. M. Pyne's rifle. He rolled the blankets up and tied them with a piece of clothesline, so he could sling them over his shoulder. Then he picked up the rifle. He studied it. J. M. Pyne knew,

from the way he looked at it, that he was not familiar with it. But he saw he couldn't slip the bolt out the way he had slipped the bolts out of the other actions. He threw the lever down. But he didn't see any easy way of putting the gun out of commission.

"Whose gun is this?" he asked.

"It's mine," J. M. Pyne said.

"How do you take it apart?"

"You have to have a vise and tools," J. M. Pyne said.

The big man looked at the rifle. He looked around the room. He saw something on the windowsill. He picked it up and tried it in the muzzle of the rifle. J. M. Pyne saw that it was a lag screw with a great rough thread, and half rose from his chair.

"Sit still, grandpa," the big man said.

He put the small end of the lag screw in the muzzle of the rifle as far as it would go and picked up the hatchet. He smiled at J. M. Pyne and brought the hammer side of the hatchet down on the end of the lag screw, driving it deep into the muzzle. He dropped the rifle on the floor and picked up the blanket roll.

"Let's go," he said to his partner.

Joe went out of the door. The big man turned as he followed. "You stay where you are," he said. "The man who sticks his head out of this door will get a bullet through it."

J. M. Pyne got up and went to the window. They were going north, toward the river. He picked up his rifle. The lag screw was jammed so tightly in the muzzle that he could not move it. The muzzle of his rifle was ruined.

J. M. Pyne turned to Higgins. "Have you got a vise?" he asked. "Have you got a hacksaw?"

Higgins jerked his thumb at the shed beyond the kitchen. J. M. Pyne walked into the shed. There was a light vise and a few tools. He laid the rifle on the bench and went upstairs and got his bag. He had a little kit of tools in a tin cigarette box of the size that holds a hundred cigarettes. He had carried that kit with him wherever he went for thirty years. It had a magazine screw driver with four blades of different sizes, and two or three files, and a small pair of pliers. He carried the kit down to the bench.

There wasn't anything to do but cut the barrel off. He put the barrel in the vise. If he cut the barrel off he would lose his front-

sight setting. He would have to file a new sight slot first. The barrel had so little taper that moving the front sight back an inch or two would make only a minute difference. He couldn't start the lag screw with the pliers. He found a monkey wrench and managed to turn it out. It hadn't gone in more than an inch. It had jammed up the muzzle and ruined the lands. But only for an inch.

J. M. Pyne marked out the sight slot and began to file. He was in a hurry. He hadn't time to do a nice job. The only thing to do was to file the dovetail slot oversize and key it into place. He could file a wire nail into a lozenge cross section and key the sight in an oversize slot.

J. M. Pyne was aware, as he filed at the barrel, that young Ballentyne stood beside him.

"They're going out for help," young Ballentyne said.

"It'll take them three or four hours to get out to a telephone." J. M. Pyne said. "And three or four hours more for a posse to get in."

"They can't go far with that load of camp stuff they took," young Ballentyne said.

J. M. Pyne filed steadily. He got the slot deep enough. He had a three-inch rule in his pocket. He laid it on the barrel and with his pocketknife scribed as well as he could the center of the front sight across the slot. Then, with a flattened nail for a drift, he drove the front sight out of its old slot and drove it into the new slot. It couldn't, he decided, be more than a couple of hundredths of an inch out either way.

He found a hacksaw. Half the teeth were gone. But it would still cut. He sawed the barrel off just

LUCIAN CARY
1886 - 1971
Lucian Cary, after a long illness, died on September 7, 1971, aged 85. A prolific writer, his last article appeared in the November 1970, issue of *TRUE Magazine.*

ahead of the new front sight. He put the rifle vertically in the vise and squared the cut with a file. He had to square it by eye. But his eye was trained by many years of work.

When he thought he had the barrel square he opened his pocketknife. He took a small blade and scraped away the burs left by the hacksaw and the file. He countersank the muzzle slightly, but enough.

He studied the muzzle with his magnifying glass. It wasn't a shop job. The muzzle couldn't be perfectly square. But it was so nearly so that it couldn't make much difference at ordinary ranges. The rifle had shot in three-quarters of an inch at a hundred yards. It must be good for an inch and a half as it stood. It was good enough for a hunting rifle.

J. M. Pyne figured that in putting the front sight back from the muzzle he might have raised it two-hundredths of an inch. He studied the vernier scale of the rear sight. It couldn't be two-hundredths. It couldn't be one-hundredth. The vernier split a sixteenth of an inch into eighths, and an eighth of a sixteenth was a one hundred and twenty-eighth part of an inch. He couldn't have raised the front sight more than that. He now raised the rear peep cup one one hundred and twenty-eighth of an inch. He couldn't be much out. He took one of his two cartridges out of his coat pocket and loaded the rifle.

"What are you going to do?" young Ballentyne asked.

"I'm going hunting," J. M. Pyne said.

"You might run into those two."

"I might," J. M. Pyne said, "if I've guessed right."

"What do you mean?" young Ballentyne asked.

"I've been thinking what I would do in their place," J. M. Pyne said.

"Yes," young Ballentyne said.

"I wouldn't drive a lag screw into the muzzle of a Pyne barrel," J. M. Pyne said. "No matter what I was up against, I wouldn't do that."

"No," young Ballentyne said, "you wouldn't do that."

"The fellow knew something about guns. I watched him. He knew that one of those rifles used the sear for a bolt stop, so he held the trigger back to get the bolt out. He knew that Esterbrook's rifle was a Springfield, with the bolt stop on the side. A fellow like that might have brains. You can see he had brains by what he did to my rifle."

Young Ballentyne nodded.

"If I were in his place I'd know my only chance was to make for the river. There's always a boat to be had along a river. You can travel farther and faster in a boat when you have a lot of duffel to carry. And a boat leaves no trace."

"There are two of them," young Ballentyne said. "They've got repeating rifles. You've got a single shot with just two cartridges."

"I'm as good as ever I was for two shots," J. M. Pyne said. "Do you think any convict out of Waubun can shoot with me? If he could, we'd know who he was. He'd have a reputation as a rifle shot."

"But," young Ballentyne said, "you forget—"

"I'll be careful," J. M. Pyne said. "I haven't hunted deer for nothing. I shan't be taken by surprise."

"I'd like to go with you," young Ballentyne said.

"Two men make too much noise in the woods," J. M. Pyne said. "And you haven't anything to shoot."

J. M. Pyne cradled his rifle in his arms.

"I'll be back before dark," he said.

IV

J. M. Pyne walked westward into the woods. He paused to listen and to watch his back trail, and turned again toward the river. They had an hour's start and they were young. They would travel as fast with their packs as he could travel with nothing to carry but his rifle. He remembered the map. The falls, with half a mile of rapids, were below him. If they got into a boat above the rapids they would have to portage.

He walked on. The rifle was heavier than ever a rifle had seemed before. He stumbled often, but he kept on. The sky was cloudy. He could see where the sun was behind the clouds. He guessed it was noon when he reached the river bank below the falls. He sat down on a fallen log with his rifle across his knees to rest. He had made about five miles.

If they were in a boat below the falls, he was too late. He could never catch them. If they were still above him, he had only to wait. He had a quiet confidence that they were upstream. He sat so quietly that a squirrel came within two yards of him and sat up, his head cocked warily on one side to study him. He gradually became accustomed to all the little sounds of the forest, so he heard only the unusual noises.

He saw an eight-point buck come down to the opposite shore of the river, a hundred yards away, and drink. He did not raise his rifle. He let the buck drink his fill and turn and go back up the trail out of sight.

J. M. Pyne waited more than an hour before something made him sit up sharply. He heard something. He did not know what. He waited, his head cocked like that of a wild animal as he listened. He heard a stick crack. Then he saw them. They were carrying a canoe bottom up. Each of them had a rifle in his right hand while he steadied the canoe over his head with his left hand.

J. M. Pyne stood up. He stood beside a tall hemlock tree. He said, "Hi!" The two men dropped the canoe. They dropped it so hard it bounced. They weren't seventy-five yards away.

"Hands up!" J. M. Pyne said sharply.

They didn't put their hands up. The big fellow half raised his rifle and stared into the woods toward the sound he had heard. J. M. Pyne raised his rifle. The fellow was asking for it.

The ivory bead of the front sight settled on the man's shoulder, swung away, swung back. As it swung back, J. M. Pyne pressed the trigger almost without volition. He heard the rifle crack. He felt the butt set back hard against his shoulder. He saw the man drop his rifle and clasp his hand to his shoulder. J. M. Pyne stepped behind the hemlock tree and peered out, exposing one eye, from the other side.

The other fellow had dropped flat on his stomach behind a log. He had that much sense. But he hadn't the sense not to shoot when he couldn't see anything definite to shoot at. He fired three shots wildly at the shadows around the hemlock tree.

J. M. Pyne opened his rifle and took out the fired case and put his other cartridge in the breech. The fellow was lying so low behind his log that J. M. Pyne could see nothing but the top of his head. He didn't want to blow the top of the man's head off. He didn't want to kill the fellow. It didn't seem necessary. So he waited.

He thought he knew, as he waited, what it was like to fight Indians. It took nerve to wait. You wanted to have it over with. And the longer you waited the more intense was your desire to have it over with.

J. M. Pyne waited. J. M. Pyne remembered to take slightly deeper breaths than usual. He wanted plenty of wind when he had to shoot. He wanted wind enough so he could wait for the sights to swing on exactly right.

J. M. Pyne remembered the oldest trick of them all. He knelt down and got a piece of a broken branch, six or eight inches long. He hung his hat on the broken branch and held it out on the left side of the tree. The fellow shot. He didn't hit the hat, but he shot. J. M. Pyne poked the hat out again and peered around the other side of the tree. The fellow was raising himself up on his elbows to shoot. He was aiming intently at that hat. J. M. Pyne waited. He remembered to take deeper breaths while he waited for the shot.

When the rifle cracked he dropped the twig and stepped out enough to see, and shot the fellow neatly through the shoulder.

It was a long way back. There were moments when J. M. Pyne paused and asked himself if he could make it as he drove those two men in front of him. They didn't know he had no more cartridges. They were completely his prisoners. But they walked too fast.

He ran them into a squad of state police and sat down beside the trail to rest. One of the troopers took his rifle for him. Another cut a stick for him. He trudged on, slower and slower, leaning on the stick. He hadn't walked so far in years. He really wasn't up to hunting any more. He was seventy-five.

Twenty Pounds of Iron

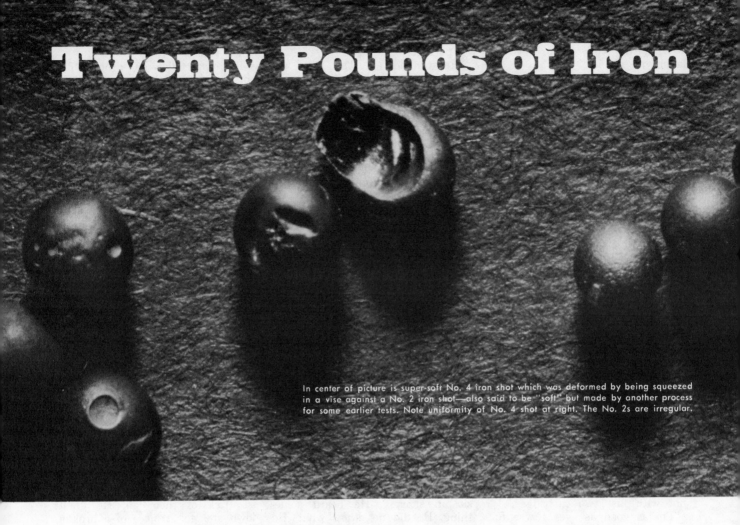

In center of picture is super-soft No. 4 iron shot which was deformed by being squeezed in a vise against a No. 2 iron shot—also said to be "soft" but made by another process for some earlier tests. Note uniformity of No. 4 shot at right. The No. 2s are irregular.

**Writer Donel Johnson shot the works
to find some answers to the weighty problems
of poisoned waterfowl—and he concludes we're close
to the day we'll be using non-toxic (iron) shot in our guns.**

by DONEL JOHNSON

A RUFFED GROUSE rocketed from the green undergrowth of the Chippewa River bottomlands in west central Wisconsin. The shot caught it, only a wingbeat away from safety, behind a big swamp oak. Nettles stung my hands as I picked up the bird and examined it. Its crop was filled with grapes and the bright red berries of Jack-in-the-pulpit. It was the first of the season.

It then struck me that it might well be another first, too. Maybe that grouse was the first ever to be felled by iron shot.

My shells were loaded with iron because I was in quest of ducks—and the opening of the 1971 season began the final phase of weeks of searching for answers in what had become a clouded and controversial issue.

In recent years it's been increasingly evident that we must find a suitable substitute for lead shot for waterfowling. The problem is lead poisoning. Great numbers of ducks and geese (official guesses run into millions) die along our flyways annually after picking up toxic lead pellets while feeding in shallow waters.

Efforts to end this deadly fallout from hunters' guns have led researchers down many dead end trails. They've tried new alloys, biochemical additives, platings, coatings . . .

Again and again they've come back to iron as the most promising substitute.

But, there've been problems.

It's not my purpose here to review all that. I have a file grown fat with research reports in this field during the past two decades. What is important is that by 1971 there appeared to have been a breakthrough—or a breakdown—in the progress the ammunition industry had been making.

Early Reports Misleading

What happened was that some very optimistic findings had been made public. Iron shot had been used in a federal study and reported not only as effective as lead in killing ducks at ordinary ranges, but harmless to shotguns!

Too, there were claims from the metals industry that iron shot meeting all specifications of the ammo makers could be produced in required quantities on short notice —and that its use would raise the cost of a box of shotgun shells only about 5 per cent.

Increasingly under the gun to find a solution, the ammunition industry now found itself under fire from all sides. When no production plans were heard, several conservation organizations, including the National Wildlife Federation, accused the industry of foot-dragging.

The International Association of Game, Fish, and Conservation Commissioners—a prestigious group indeed—adopted a resolution calling for non-toxic shotshells by the 1973 season. Questions received by the U.S. Bureau of Sport Fisheries and Wildlife from capitol hill told of a growing interest in Congress for setting a cutoff date on the use of lead shot for waterfowl shooting.

Some states indicated they might not wait for federal controls. Florida's legislature was considering a special tax (8¢ per shell!) on shotshells containing lead sold in the state. Wisconsin's conservation congress asked the legislature to take similar action, and urged the federal lawmakers to make non-toxic shot mandatory for waterfowl hunting within two years.

Nagging at both the hunter and the ammo maker were warnings from federal wildlife officials, dating back to 1966, that waterfowl seasons might have to be further cut, and bag limits reduced, unless lead poisoning losses could be cut.

To all of this the Sporting Arms and Ammunition Manufacturer's Institute (SAAMI) responded with wounded words. They were all trying, they said, and hadn't SAAMI members in the U.S. and Canada put up $100,000 to seek a solution back there in '66?

Yes, they had, and the job was turned over to the respected Illinois Institute of Technology's research institute (IITRI) which released its findings in 1969. All avenues of exploration had led back to iron, SAAMI was told, and a soft iron wire with promising qualities had already been developed elsewhere.

Using this wire, one ammunition company produced a quantity of shot using the "heading" process. A header makes little spheres from wire, and Daisy-Heddon has a battery of them banging out 54 million BBs a day, so the process is well developed. The shot was annealed to reduce "work hardening" caused by the machining. Then it was loaded into shotshells.

At its Patuxent Wildlife Research Center in Maryland, the Bureau of Sport Fisheries and Wildlife tested the "mortality efficiency" of No. 4 iron shot, and reported it to be effective indeed out to 50 yards.

Anybody who's done much shooting at ducks at known ranges (one trick is to mark distances from the blind with certain decoys in your spread) knows that 50 yards is stretching things a bit for the average gunner.

But we already knew iron shot would down ducks pretty well. What was really significant was that there'd been no discernible damage to the bores of the two test shotguns, which had fired a total of about 1,000 rounds in the tests.

Spokesmen for SAAMI said, however, that the news wasn't all that good. Some makes and models of shotguns still showed bore damage when used with the soft iron shot, it was reported. Even more vexing, it was found that, after 18 months, the shot had "age hardened" 25 per cent. That was enough, it was said, to virtually assure bore damage to any gun.

Those claims were disputed. At least two steel companies had indicated they knew how to make super soft iron to fill the bill, and Thomas M. Barret, vice president of Superior Steel Ball, New Britain, Conn., told Ducks Unlimited that it is possible to "essentially elimi-

Don Johnson examines a pair of mallards felled by iron shot.

Twenty Pounds of Iron

nate" the age hardening problem.

I'm the outdoor writer for the Milwaukee (Wis.) *Sentinel*, and it was frustrating to try to separate the fur from the feathers as such conflicting reports crossed my desk. For two years I'd tried to get enough iron shot to see for myself what was what.

Iron Shot Supplied

In the summer of 1971, through the efforts of a member of the waterfowl committee of our state conservation congress, Bill Peterburs, Jr., I did obtain about 20 pounds of the Superior Steel Ball product.

Because I was limited by resources, time, and the amount of shot I had, I had to be somewhat arbitrary about how it was used. First, it was decided to fire it all in one gun, so its effects could most fully be measured. Second, I elected to take the fastest and most direct route to developing a suitable load, and then quit fooling around at the bench and do a maximum amount of field testing instead. From clay birds I'd turn to crows, then wind things up with the waterfowl season.

Although tempted to select a gun with a chromed bore, I was more curious to learn what happened to unplated steel. The gun finally decided upon was a 12 gauge Winchester 1200 pump gun with the interchangeable Winchoke tubes. It proved a good choice.

For openers, I asked Tom Nelson, gunsmith at Badger Shooters Supply in Owen, Wis., to mike the bore for me. He took readings at two inch intervals, and found the bore to be a very smooth and uniform .732" from forcing cone to choke. The modified tube had .013" choke, the full tube .034" constriction, he found.

Then I started assembling loads on my Versa-Mec—10 rounds each of a score of combinations, using components on hand. I reasoned that, since the same volume of iron shot would be much lighter than lead, I'd run into no pressure problems with the same measures of powder and shot I usually use. More likely, the problem would be to find a powder which would burn efficiently while pushing the lighter load. And, so it was.

I'll mention only loads which proved reasonably practical, and note that autoloaders—particularly those with long recoil actions—will probably not function with any of them, with the possible exception of one that became my pet load.

Since I still had a lot of Federal paper hulls around, they were used to assemble most of the loads. Low brass plastic shells sold as field loads by Remington have the same volume and could be used instead.

Iron Shot Loads

With the paper cases, MEC's No. 12, No. 2, and 0 bars all produced loads which broke clay targets and killed crows satisfactorily. Of these, the 12 bar was best. It's supposed to drop 1⅜ oz. of lead shot—but the bigger voids around the larger shot sizes cut that down some. The equivalent volume of iron shot weighed ⅞-oz., with 160 pellets in the average load.

The 12 bar is supposed to drop 30 grains of Alcan No. 7 powder, but mine drops an average of 32.5 grains according to my Ohaus 505 scale. Behind a dose of No. 5 lead shot this has proven stout medicine for tough birds, like wild flushing pheasants and high flying ducks. With all other components the same, but substituting iron shot, I found I still had a load which would stone the crows at treetop level in the tall pines. The bore was left a bit sooty though, indicating I wasn't getting all out of the powder.

The same bar drops 19.5 grains of Green Dot, which left the bore a bit dirtier, but still pushed the iron pellets at velocities lethal to

crows called within 35 yards. In the cover I was shooting from, no longer shots were offered. Both Herter's and Winchester-Western No. 209 primers were used. The plastic wad and shot cup combo used was Alcan's No. 1 Flite-Max, factory modified and lubricated.

The No. 2 bar is supposed to drop 1⅛ oz. of lead shot. It dumps ¾-oz. of No. 4 iron, which, boosted by 23 grains of Green Dot, also proved effective on crows, although again unburned powder was left in the bore.

The 0 bar, also designed for 1⅛ oz. loads, was tried with AL 7 (30 grains) and Green Dot (19 grains). As with the No. 2 bar, the No. 4 Flite-Max combo was used. The Green Dot load was very dirty and the AL 7 load seemed even more so—and quite a few crows had to be chased after being hit.

I figured I'd found what I was looking for when I slid a 20 gauge No. 6 bar into the tool and loaded into a 12 gauge Winchester AA plastic case 26.5 grains of SR 7625 behind about ⅞-oz. of the iron shot, which was contained in a red AA wad and shot cup. Although appreciably quicker than AL 7 on the scale of burning rates for gun powders, 7625 burns more progressively than Green Dot. The combination gave a snappy, clean-burning load which produced excellent patterns and gave no indications whatever of undue pressure.

Speaking of patterns, my gunsmith friend and I remarked on the quality of patterns when we were trying a variety of loads in Badger Shooters' tunnel range, early in the tests. We didn't take time to count holes or compute percentages, but patterns at 40 yards looked uniformly good—and we've looked at quite a few of them.

All of these loads had light recoil and were pleasant to shoot at clay targets, so a lot of them were used by a young friend of the family I was introducing to scattergunning, while I swung the hand trap and waited for the hunting season.

I also asked Ed Scherer of Waukesha, Wis., a crow and grouse shooting buddy and a dozen times member of *Sports Afield's* All-American Skeet team, to try a practice round of Skeet with the test gun.

Although handicapped by an unfamiliar gun—a field gun with 28-inch modified barrel—and using No. 4 shot, Ed managed to bust 19 x 25. The load was that assembled with the No. 2 bar; 23 grains of Green Dot.

Ed's impression reinforced mine —that no allowance had to be made for differences in flight time between lead and iron shot at ordinary shotgun ranges. It's true that, with its lower sectional density, a pellet of iron will start out faster (given the proper propellant) and shed velocity faster than a lead pellet of like size. However, at ordinary gunning ranges—50 yards and under—the differences don't appear to be of an order discernible by the gunner. Weight-wise, there's about the same difference between No. 4 and No. 5 lead shot as there is between No. 4 lead and iron shot—and who thinks to lead a duck more or less when he changes from one shot size to another?

It's not that simple, of course. Density must be considered. Yet, much of the ballistic disadvantage of iron is overcome simply by using shot one size larger than we usually use. Thinner patterns then? Not necessarily. Remember that iron is lighter. A much longer shot column could be safely handled if we had the components which provided more room for shot in the standard shotshell case.

Winchester-Western Tests

Of interest here are data on some tests made by Winchester-Western, the report released late in 1965. A maximum 12 gauge load, 1½ oz. of No. 4 lead shot, was compared with another containing an ounce of No. 4 iron pellets. No information was given on powder or other components.

There were 214 pellets in the lead load; 220 in the ounce of iron. Muzzle velocities were 1350 and 1450 feet per second (fps) respectively—but at 40 yards the lead shot was traveling 795 fps while the iron had slowed to 695 fps.

Energy per pellet was computed as 4.34 foot-pounds for the lead and 2.15 for the iron at 40 yards. On this basis, W-W rated the iron shot effective at a maximum of 40 yards, compared to 50 yards for the lead.

The report did note that No. 3 iron shot would more nearly simulate the No. 4 lead, and would be more effective. However, it was said that a marked increase in choke deformation was seen when the larger shot size was used. Bore damage from annealed No. 4 iron shot was described as "minor" at that time.

Magnet holds a load of No. 4 iron shot —and demonstrates easy way shot can be handled or picked up when spilled.

Back about the same time— December of 1964 and January, 1965—some field tests were also being conducted by and for members of the planning committee of the Mississippi Flyway Council—a group which represents state conservation agencies and helps establish migratory bird hunting regulations.

I can't begin to recount the contributions the flyway council and many of its individual members have made in the search for non-

toxic shot, but let's look at what they learned while shooting mallards at Nilo Farms, the shooting preserve operated by Olin Industries near Alton, Ill.:

Four Winchester 1200s were used —two firing iron shot and two shooting lead. Shells used were 12 gauge containing 1¼ oz. of No. 2 iron or No. 4 lead shot and 3¾ drams equivalent of powder.

Careful records were kept by observing biologists. Each kill was tagged and later thoroughly examined. Of 225 mallards killed during the test, 93 were felled by lead shot and 132 by iron. Also, 53 ducks were crippled—38 by lead shot and 15 by iron. Average range of kills with lead shot was 30.8 yards; with iron shot, 31.9 yards. Iron shot kills were observed up to 55 yards. Ducks hit with the iron shot were observed to have more external damage—broken wings and legs—and more hemorrhaging as the result of shot passing through the birds.

But then came the bad part: Barrel scoring and wear were soon evident in the forcing cone and choke of guns firing the iron shot. After 300 shots a full choke gun was opened to improved cylinder.

Blamed were tiny inclusions of abrasive slag, common in most kinds of iron. It caused the shot to wear through the plastic sleeve which enveloped the shot column, the report said. It was further noted that this problem might be remedied by use of a different annealing process, already known, or by using a tougher plastic sleeve, a lubricant, or a plastic coating on the shot itself.

Alas, it hasn't been that easy.

New Wads Wanted

Back to my own findings, now: First, I learned that iron shot confronts the handloader with no particular problems, and even offers an advantage or two. Needed, as noted earlier, are combination wads and shot cups designed to provide maximum shot space consistent with good gas-sealing characteristics. Shot and powder bars could then be bored to drop an ounce or more of iron shot, and suitable charges of the most efficient powders. While only scratching the surface, my tests showed this shouldn't be difficult.

Shot cups should be thick and tough enough to keep iron pellets from contacting the bore during

Twenty Pounds of Iron

their torrid race to the muzzle. Lubrication of the plastic cup or sleeve may help. Such improvements may not entirely eliminate the effects of iron shot on bore dimensions, though I believe they'll help.

Red AA wads I recovered after firing showed many pinholes where pellets had poked through to rub against the bore. Most of this penetration apparently occurred in the choke. Much less was seen when I made some tests with the choke tube removed. This problem was not noted with the Alcan shot cups. Maybe they're made of tougher stuff, or maybe the lubrication helped. But remember, they were also used with lighter loads. There were no significant differences in performance of other components and equipment normally used.

The most vexing thing at the loader was an occasional binding of the bar. That is not uncommon when loading large shot, but the harder iron pellets did seem to need more persuasion when they jammed the bar.

A small brass hammer is kept handy on the bench. Usually a sharp rap on one end of the bar with that will do the trick. It was also observed that these hangups were less frequent—in fact, rare—if the shot container is no more than half-full. With less weight bearing down on them, the pellets resting in the way of the bar apparently

can be more easily jostled out of the way.

Another thing that seemed to make things a bit easier after a while is that the sharp edge at the top of the shot hole in the bar was gradually rounded slightly by shoving that iron shot around. Grinding a slight bevel there might help.

Big shot also hangs up in the drop tube sometimes. If it isn't noticed, the shot in the tube is sure to wait until the shell is removed from the station. It will then cascade all over the bench and floor. Right?

Ah, there's where iron shot shines. At my bench, in a cylindrical holder the size of a pencil, is a magnet. It's sold as a "stud finder" for builders, who use it to locate where nails lie behind plastered walls. A wave of this magic wand and you've collected your spilled shot!

Trials on Wildfowl

All of the shot had been loaded—and most of it used—by late summer. Forty-four of those AA reloads remained when duck season opened. There was nothing spectacular about the start of that season. I do a lot of my early season hunting while poking around in the bottomlands, sometimes jumpshooting and sometimes setting up at a pothole or beaver pond with a few inflatable decoys. In three days I fired 39 shots.

I bagged 8 ducks, plus that grouse. Nothing very spectacular about that either, but, truth to tell, that might be close to my average had records been kept over the years.

I certainly didn't get the impression that I was handicapped in any way—despite the temptation to blame iron shot for missing a few easy ones. I took the shots I usually do—no skybusting, though I reached a bit for a couple of 'em. One drake wood duck exploded from a meandering slough and was hit just as he rounded a bend. He splashed into a beaver pond beyond my view. When I got there he was floating with feet resting on upturned belly, as dead a duck as you ever saw. I called that one a 50-yard shot. Every bit of it.

Most of the others were hit just as hard. One was given a second shot because it was diving down with neck outstretched, wings still grabbing for air. I lost three. One was a wood duck on opening day. His head popped up as soon as he

hit the water, but before I could fire the finisher he dived, and was seen no more. Two days later another one hit the water hard and seemed to just keep going down. I never saw that one again either. It was baffling, because I couldn't recall ever having lost wood ducks that way before.

The other one not recovered was a mallard, hit while it was flying pretty high and fast on the morning flight. It splashed down near my hunting partner, perhaps 50 yards away, and when I heard his Chesapeake busting through the cattails I assumed the duck was being retrieved, so I turned my attention back to the sky. Not until later did I learn that my shot had not been witnessed, and the dog had been chasing another cripple. The mallard could not then be found.

If I hit any other ducks, I was not aware of it. The percentage of unrecovered ducks was unusual for me and my kind of hunting, I believe, but the sample was so small—and the circumstances somewhat unusual—that I'll draw no conclusions from that.

The ducks I got were four woodies three mallards, and a widgeon. They'd been hit from 3 to 7 times. In almost every instance the shot had bored right through. I recovered only 3 pellets, and they were not deformed. As near as I could determine, they were all that had remained in the birds. (I gave 5 of the ducks away, but got no complaints of broken bridgework.)

The Gun Rechecked

By now my curiosity had been satisfied about several things, and there had been no real surprises, that is, not until I took the gun back to Tom. I was astounded when he told me that the modified tube (which I'd used almost exclusively) had enlarged .009″ at the rear—about 1¾″ back from the muzzle. At the muzzle the tube showed .002″ less choke. To my eye, the tube had shown no indication of such changes. It did not appear to be scored or abraded in any way. In fact, looking closely, one could still see faint, concentric tool marks inside the tube. Surely they would have been erased by that much erosive wear.

And this was really significant: No change could be discerned by eye or micrometer in the bore itself. Not a scratch, after 379 rounds!

Surely more tests were called for, but winter was nearly over before

I obtained more iron shot, from a small supply the Wisconsin Department of Natural Resources had received for study. Meanwhile, I'd come into possession of some of the shells assembled for one of the earlier tests made by the ammo makers. Their red plastic cases, carrying the printed markings "Western 1320-1," held about an ounce of very irregular shot, roughly No. 2 in size. From their shapes (some almost tear drops) it seemed obvious the pellets were formed by a drop process—and my files contain, in fact, a copy of a 1951 patent to Olin Industries depicting such a process for making iron shot.

Red Winchester-Western AA wad shows severe wear after carrying charge of iron shot through bore. Pellets perforated plastic in numerous places.

The shot was surrounded by a plain plastic wrapper. Propellant was 29 grains of a dense ball powder, topped with a thin inverted cup wad and a 5/16 in. wad—both of waxed cardboard.

I couldn't wait to get to a laboratory to determine how "soft" that shot was, so I simply placed one of the No. 4s I'd been using against one of the No. 2s and forced them together in a vise. The No. 4 yielded like putty, while the No. 2 was hardly marred, even by the jaws of the vise. So much then, for the softness of some of the shot used in tests we've been told about.

But the lab would—and did—tell more.

Next stop was the Waukesha, Wis., Gun Club to enlist the aid of Vic Reinders, one of the great trap shots of all time. (Look at the record book.) I'd loaded 100 more of those AA shells, and Vic was better than a chronograph for telling me about flight time of that iron shot at the longer yardages. I asked him to shoot a round, using his usual leads, that gusty March morning. Except for a couple lofted high by the wind, Vic reduced those clay birds to puffs of smoke.

"I lost 'em due to this low comb. 'Had to cover 'em up," he explained of these misses. "There's certainly nothing wrong with the way this shot works," he added with a grin. Then he stepped back to the 23 yard line and proceeded to powder some more targets.

This time I had the full choke tube in the gun. It had been used only to fire 10 light test loads early in my experimenting. Now I had miked the tube OUTSIDE as well as inside—and I took measurements again after 25 and 75 shots had been fired. A winterlong suspicion was confirmed. The dimensional change we'd seen in the modified tube was caused by expansion, not wear. The shot was peening or stretching the relatively thin steel tube until tolerances between the

tube and the barrel were taken up. The difference was most marked at the thin skirt of the tube behind the thread—just as in the modified tube. There I measured .0045 expansion—half of what it was on the other tube. Maybe the full choke tube was a tighter fit.

At points just ahead of the threads, and just behind the knurling at the muzzle, I found the same .002-inch change we'd seen in the other tube. Further, virtually all of this change had occurred while firing the first 25 rounds of those snappy loads. Would lead shot do the same thing? Maybe. But maybe it would take longer. I really don't care that much. Not only are those choke tubes still serviceable, the patterns still look good on paper (helped by the fact there's no deformed shot, I'll bet). The last duck I shot came down as hard as the first—and the last clay bird Vic blasted at long yardage disappeared as impressively as the first as well.

If necessary, though, the tubes could doubtless be made of more unyielding alloys.

Now, examining the interior of the full choke tube with a strong light and glass, I could see a few minute longitudinal scratches. However, they appear to be simply scratches through the blueing. No such marks are visible in the modified tube, but the blueing is gone there.

But we'd gone far enough with eyeball tests, so I assembled my samples and drove to the University of Wisconsin in Madison, where Gerald Duchon, of the engineering school faculty, had already run a series of hardness tests on iron shot for the Department of Natural Resources and the state crime laboratory 6 months earlier.

I'll sum up what we learned in 5 straight hours of testing on the most sophisticated and sensitive instruments available for determining hardness of metals.

Imbedded in a plastic disc were samples of the new and old types of iron shot, a section of a barrel from an inexpensive pumpgun, and a small piece of mild carbon steel (hot rolled M1020). Comparisons were made on an optical micro hardness tester. The results given here are extrapolated from the Knoop scale to Rockwell readings, with which more gun nuts are familiar. Except as noted, these are B scale values. The higher the number, the harder the material:

Twenty Pounds of Iron

The surface of that sample of M1020 steel ranged between 46 and 53 on the scale—about the same as the softest iron shot. So, those who call the stuff "steel" shot aren't wrong. Yet, note that it is substantially softer than even the cheap shotgun barrel.

Oh yes, the Winchoke tube. We didn't want to cut it up, so just took exterior readings. They took us far off the B scale, to a Rockwell "C" of 36. (To give you an idea, a 100 at the top of the B scale is equal to 20 on the C scale.)

One more thing: We again tested the sample the professor had examined 6 months earlier. It was from the same shipment of shot which I'd received and field tested. These most exact tests showed no "age hardening" in half a year. How old the shot really was, we didn't know.

What I do know is that 479 rounds of this new ferrous shot has had no adverse effects on appearance or performance on the gun I've been using. For the average duck hunter that might mean three to five seasons of use. For a wing-shot of some experience, maybe that's 75 to 150 ducks bagged.

Remember, it's only for waterfowl hunting that mandatory use of iron shot is contemplated.

The Situation Now

So, where do we go from here? We're told that federal anti-trust laws restrict the free interchange of ideas and developments among members of the ammunition industry. Beyond that, there are rumors,

Right—After firing, steel Winchoke showed minor expansion, mainly near narrow, relatively thin area behind threads. For dimensional changes found see text.

Tom Nelson, Owen, Wis., gunsmith, measures interior of the removable Winchoke tube at start of the iron shot tests—using inside micrometer to take dimensions.

The No. 4 shot I'd been testing ranged from a reading of 40 near the surface to 72 near the center, indicating an annealing process was used after the shot was formed. Many pellets had a brassy appearance, but the hue had no bearing on the hardness.

The No. 2 shot removed from those experimental Western shells were almost uniformly hard—93 in the middle and 90 at the surface.

The cheap shotgun barrel had a Rockwell B of 93 just under the surface of the bore—very little harder than those No. 2 pellets. The outer surface was 87, and a reading of 84.5 was obtained in between. (The harder exterior and interior readings are probably entirely due to work-hardening during machining of the barrel and bore.)

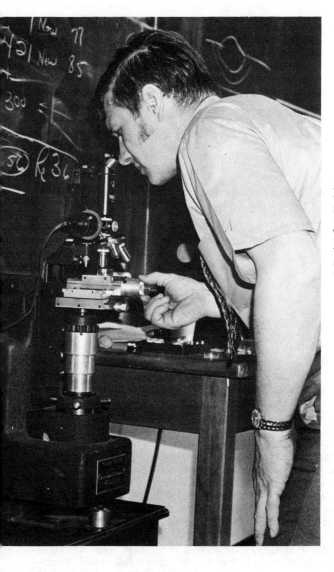

Asst. Prof. Gerald Duchon, with the sample disc under powerful microscope, studies effect of 500 kilogram load on one of the pellets. Instrument is a Wilson Tukon Tester in mechanical engineering laboratory of University of Wisconsin at Madison, Wis.

Sometimes it seemed my little experiment was raising more questions than it answered, but I did come to some conclusions:

Foremost, I'm convinced that the time is imminent when iron shot will be (1) available in commercial loadings, and (2) required for use by waterfowlers.

Second, I foresee no particular problems for handloaders. The ease with which I was able to assemble workable loads with components and tools at hand is evidence of that. Better shells will be easy to assemble when we have components and loader bars designed especially for iron shot.

Finally, I see no real handicap to hunters, although some may be hesitant (and I won't blame them) to use a fine old Parker or a Browning Superposed in the duck blind until we know more about the new ammunition.

Some have expressed fears that iron shot will be a worse crippler than lead at the longer ranges. I doubt it, and no evidence on tests conducted so far indicates it. Might it not rather be that, because it sheds energy so much faster beyond 40 yards, the iron pellet will lose ability to penetrate at those ranges where patterns get too patchy for sure kills anyway? That would be a big plus.

You know what I think? It won't be long until you too will be shooting iron in your shootin' irons. •

and rumors of rumors, which indicate a race to be in progress to see who reaches the market first with suitable iron shot loads.

Not all of those interested are established manufacturers of shotshells. Of the 70 to 100 million pounds of lead spewed from shotguns in the U.S. and Canada each year, about 12 million pounds is estimated to be fired at waterfowl. That is a big enough piece of the market to interest metals fabricators outside the ammunition industry. In 1971 at least two steel companies claimed capability of supplying the soft iron wire needed. Samples of super-soft shot were said to be in the hands of most or all potential manufacturers of shotshells, and several companies were said to be conducting their own tests. At least one, I've learned, had set 1972 as a target date for marketing shells loaded with iron shot.

For optical hardness test, two types of iron shot were moulded in clear plastic, along with a section of shotgun barrel and a piece of mild steel. To obtain interior readings, surfaces were carefully ground down; polished.

An 1897 Model Bergmann, caliber 7.8mm (7.63mm), serial No. 522, along with an original box of cartridges, loose rounds, and an instruction manual-evaluation of the pistol published by the *Revue de l'Armee Belge*.

Bergmann System

A deeply researched, thoroughly documented and detailed history of Theodore Bergmann's great contribution to the development of autoloading and automatic firearms.

ALTHOUGH RELATIVELY unknown in this country one of the most important names in the early development of the semi-automatic pistol was that of Theodore Bergmann. He was both inventor and industrialist and his factory complex in Gaggenau, Baden, in southwestern Germany and associated arms factory in Suhl, Thuringia, were the birthplace of many interesting firearms designs. Bergmann became interested in firearms in the 1880s and, through the company Eisenwerke Bergmann, held patents during that period for improved shotshell reloading equip-

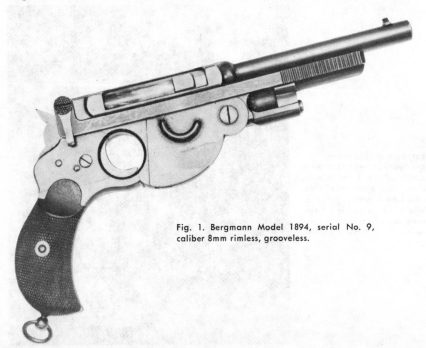

Fig. 1. Bergmann Model 1894, serial No. 9, caliber 8mm rimless, grooveless.

ment, rifle magazines and safeties, and others. It is doubtful if many of these were production items, as the company was rather fully occupied making railroad switching and signalling equipment, household hardware, stoves, wrought iron fences, and other general hardware items.

The first complete Bergmann design for a pistol, and a similar shotgun, was patented in association with Otto Brauswetter, a watchmaker of Szegedin, Hungary, in June, 1892, a full year prior to Hugo Borchardt's now famous auto pistol patent. The pistol, a long-

recoil, locked-breech design, contains the revolver-like lockwork and the unusual pivoted-side-plate, packet-loading magazine design typical of Bergmann pocket pistols. The drawings of the M1892 are quite complete and the design is basically sound. The arm was not produced in quantity but at least one example was made circa 1892-93. Records indicate the Swiss made a comparative test about that time between their revolver and the Bergmann auto, both chambered for the 7.5mm Model 1882 Swiss revolver cartridge.

Apparently Bergmann did not collaborate further with Brauswetter, and subsequent Bergmann pistol development awaited the arrival of Louis Schmeisser, gunsmith and firearms inventor who joined the renamed Bergmann's Industriewerke firm about 1893. Schmeisser was given the task of simplifying and improving the design of the M1892 with an eye to further military testing and production. This he did, and patents assigned to Bergmann in June and December of 1893 disclose the design which has become known as the Bergmann Model 1894 or the Bergmann-Schmeisser (fig. 1).

First Blowback

While the improved design retained the general configuration, lockwork and magazine of the 1892, the long-recoil locking system was abandoned and the M1894 represents the first blowback (or

Military Pistols

by JAMES B. STEWART

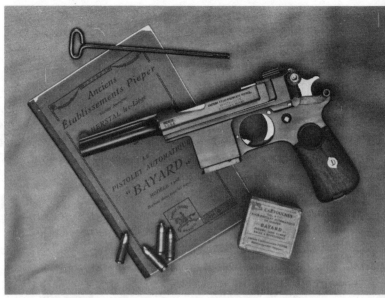

The very rare commercial version of the Anciens Etablissement Pieper Model 1908 Bergmann-Bayard. Serial No. 1954, caliber 9mm B-B, the pistol is shown with an original factory manual and cleaning rod, a box of A.E.P.-made cartridges and a few loose rounds.

unlocked breech) automatic pistol successfully built. Few of these have survived. Since the known serial numbers are uniformly low, it is questionable whether this pistol was made in any quantity. All known examples are chambered for a tapered rimless, grooveless 8mm cartridge subsequently designated by Bergmann as the No. 1 cartridge. Covered in the same gun patents is a smaller version with a folding trigger. At least one of these was made for a 5mm rimless, grooveless cartridge, called the No. 2. This was the first "pocketable." automatic pistol. The one known example is unmarked except for proof, and it is doubtful whether more than this single prototype was made.

Bergmann was still not satisfied, and modification of the M1894 led to the Model 1896 (fig. 2). These are covered by patents submitted in late 1895. When the decision was made to put the M1896 into production, conditions dictated their manufacture outside the Gaggenau facility, already overcrowded and just beginning to experiment with building automobiles. The firm of V. Charles Schilling of Suhl, already known for the manufacture of high-quality military arms, was selected and Schilling's plant was henceforth referred to by Bergmann as his "Waffenfabrik Suhl." Bergmann pistols made by Schilling are identifiable by the addition of the letters "V.C.S." and the word "Suhl" to the Bergmann "fabrik-

mark" of the miner-in-the-oval. The factory adopted a new system of pistol nomenclature at the start of production of the M1896; it began referring to the pistols not by model year but by the cartridge for which it was chambered. Thus, the 5mm pistol became the No.2, the 6.5mm, the No.3, etc.

The No.2 and No.3 pistols were essentially pocket arms and do not merit further consideration here. A modification of the No.3, however, does. This is the No.4 pistol, evidently made in small quantities about 1897, but in stock at least

until 1899. Essentially a No.3 chambered for a powerful, straight-sided 8mm cartridge, the No. 4s were made in only limited quantity and numbered in the same series with the No. 3s. All known examples fall in the serial range from 2300 to 3000.

The 1896 series pistols introduced a Bergmann feature which was to be standard on his military arms: a shoulder-stock holster that allowed the pistol to be used as a carbine. The 1896 pistols had a modified sideplate with a loop on it. A special leather holster with a

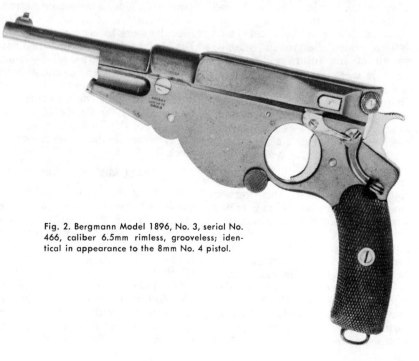

Fig. 2. Bergmann Model 1896, No. 3, serial No. 466, caliber 6.5mm rimless, grooveless; identical in appearance to the 8mm No. 4 pistol.

steel frame and a bottom projection which locked into the sideplate loop allowed it to be used as a stock.

Model 1897 Locked Breech

Up to this point Bergmann's attempts to produce a true military automatic had been rather half-hearted. In 1897 Schilling made for Bergmann, based on his patents of March and July of that year, a prototype locked-breech pistol designed to fire a powerful bottlenecked cartridge similar to the 7.63 Mauser and definitely intended for military use (figs. 3 and 4). The cartridge was designated the No.5 and, to avoid confusion with the Mauser cartridge, was referred to as the 7.8mm. This locked-breech design is unusual in that the bolt unlocks from the barrel, after about 7 millimeters of recoil travel, by a cam surface in the frame forcing the bolt head *sideways*, as in the M1892, rather than vertically, as in almost all other locking systems. The prototype had the usual lockwork, a separate spring to return the barrel to the battery position, and an interrupter to prevent the hammer from falling until the breech was relocked. The latter two features were dropped in production, a full-extension sleeve was added to protect the recoiling barrel, and the frame and trigger guard were elongated. Thus modified, the pistol was born as the No. 5 or M1897 Military.

The design did away with the typical integral packet-loading Bergmann magazine and substituted a 10-shot detachable-box magazine, which could also be loaded while in the gun from a stripper clip. This was a very advanced system which Bergmann retained on all of his future military designs. It was not, for some reason, copied by other manufacturers. There were three variations of the production pistol. The first, of which very few were made, has checked wood grips and, like the prototype, omits the typical Bergmann chamber sight-hole, but does provide cartridge sight-holes in the magazine and well. This version has a horizontal locking-spring screw. The second type, which does not bear "V.C.S." or the miner-in-the-oval trademark, has the chamber sight-hole and monogram "B" hard-rubber grips similar to those of the late model 3s (fig. 5). This second version, by far the most common, has a vertical locking-spring screw. The third type, of which apparently very few were

Fig. 3. Prototype M1897 Military, serial No. 1, caliber 7.8 (7.63mm); right side showing special sideplate for attaching holster-stock and Bergmann/Schilling trademark. Note interrupter let into side of frame.

made, has a hooked end on the locking spring, a shortened magazine well, and a horizontal screw through the ejector in addition to the vertical locking-spring screw (fig. 6).

All No.5s have a vertically adjustable rear sight graduated to 1000 meters, a sliding breech cover marked *Pistolet Bergmann*, and a tunnel at the bottom of the grip for attachment of the steel-frame leather holster-stock available for them (fig. 6). Apparently experimentation with the prototype had indicated that the loop on the sideplate was not a strong enough method of attachment of the shoulder stock to so powerful an arm. The No.5 could also be obtained with a 12-inch barrel and barrel sleeve and a full size wooden shoulder stock which converted it to a creditable carbine. This carbine could be bought in England in 1900 for £6/15. At the same time, the No.5 pistol sold for £4/17/6 or complete with holster-stock for £5/2/6.

First Military Trials

Including the carbine, which was numbered in the same serial sequence, fewer than 1000 of these interesting military arms were produced. Bergmann demonstrated a No.5 to the British Chief Inspector of Small Arms (CISA) in July, 1900, without any positive results. The Swiss also tested the No.5 in competition with several other arms between November 24 to December 8, 1899, and May 1 to

3, 1900, but chose the Luger as their official arm instead. One was even tested by the U.S. Army Ordnance Department in October, 1901, but no military contracts were forthcoming and the No.5 was dropped from production.

As an aside, it should be noted that at least one of the No.5 pistols was made to fire full automatic only, but the structure of the pistol was not up to this severe battering and no further work was done along these lines. As far as is known this was the first attempt to produce a machine-pistol or submachine gun.

Since the Model 1897 did not catch on as Bergmann had hoped, Bergmann's Industriewerke went through a period of experimentation and testing over the next few years. The records are somewhat confused, but apparently no actual production, other than of the No.5, was undertaken. The records indicate that the first request for a test was made to the Chief of Ordnance, U.S. Army, in October and November of 1899. Bergmann requested permission to submit for testing a No.4 pistol, M1896, caliber 8mm, a No. 5 M1897, caliber 7.63mm and a No.6 M1899, caliber 8mm. Apparently, no test of these arms was held at that time.

Casimir Weber, noted Swiss firearms expert, did, however, test in Switzerland two of the "Model 1899" or original No. 6 pistols in March of 1900. They were tested

Fig. 4. M1897 prototype, serial No. 1, left side. Note absence of chamber and cartridge sight holes in magazine and well.

at the military arsenal in Berne. The original No.6 used an 8mm cartridge (known first as the No.4S and later as the No.7), and was an attempt to combine the earlier packet-magazine loading system and grip frame from the M4 with the side-unlocking breech system of the No.5. These design features were covered in an English patent issued in October, 1899. At least one of these pistols, serial number 2, is still in existence.

The Swiss found this construction unsatisfactory and Bergmann redesigned it along lines considerably closer to the M1897, but using a new method of securing the recoil spring and a new type of magazine catch. Several prototype versions were constructed for a succession of experimental Bergmann cartridges known as the 7.5mm No.7A, the 7.5mm No.8, and the 8mm No.7. All were unsuccessful and the weapon was again redesigned, reduced in size, simplified, and a new cartridge designated the 8mm No.6M/06 was designed for it. This cartridge is known today as the 8mm Bergmann Simplex after the name of the production version of this pistol (fig. 7). The Simplex pistol is a simplified, mass-production, unlocked-breech pistol not up to Bergmann standards, and it suffered from constructional weaknesses. Over 4000 Simplex pocket pistols were made before production ceased about 1903. Its importance lies in the fact that the

recoil-spring retaining system and magazine catch were used in all subsequent Bergmann designs.

Bergmann-Mars

Upon returning from the unsuccessful U.S. Army trials of 1899, Earnest Zappert, Bergmann's London-based foreign representative, reported that the small caliber and complicated locking mechanism of the No.5 had weighed heavily against it during the trials and recommended that it be completely redesigned. Consequently Bergmann abandoned the sideward-moving unlocking mechanism and began work, in late 1901, on an entirely new version of the previously abandoned No.6 pistol. The new locking mechanism was based on his 1901 patents for what was to become the Bergmann machinegun of World War I fame. This excellent system had a lock using a block through which the bolt could recoil only after the block had been cammed down into the frame by the rearward movement of the barrel and barrel extension. Work proceeded rapidly, and before long Bergmann had made prototype pistols chambering the revised No.6 (that is, the 9mm No.6) cartridge, the No.5 cartridge, and two new cartridges, a 10mm and an 11.35mm. The 9mm and 7.63mm were made experimentally with 6-, 8-, and 10-shot magazines. To identify it, the exposed top of the locking block was marked

Bergmann Mars Pat. Brev. S.G.D.G. and, like all then-made German-manufactured pistols, carried the double-crown-U mark of the Oberndorf proof house (fig. 8).

By early June, 1902, work had progressed far enough that Bergmann's British agent, Wilkinson Sword Company, was able to submit to the CISA samples of the 10-shot 9mm and 10-shot 10mm pistols. The CISA indicated that the 9mm caliber was too small to satisfy their requirements and suggested that some alternate be submitted. As a result, on June 23, 1902, the CISA tested two different versions of the 10mm pistol. One, the Mars type, was referred to as the 10mm high velocity. The second, a hastily-converted example of one of the ill-fated early No.6 designs rebarreled to 10mm, used a cartridge with less powder and with the bullet seated more deeply. It was referred to as the 10mm low velocity. The CISA was still not satisfied and requested further submissions. On January 30, 1903, a Mars pistol was submitted in 11.35mm and tested, but was not reported upon favorably because of functioning problems.

In June of 1903 Bergmann's new American agent, P. J. Streit of St. Paul, Minnesota, wrote to the Army Chief of Ordnance requesting permission to submit the M1903 pistol in 11.35mm for testing. Apparently no such submission or test took place.

So far Bergmann's numerous submissions and tests had led only to frustration but, early in 1905, success finally came his way. As a result of extensive testing by Spain the 9mm version of the M1903 Mars was adopted on September 5, 1905, for issue to all officers in the active army, gendarmes, carabinerie, and police. This made Spain the third country, after Belgium and Switzerland, to officially adopt an automatic pistol as her military issue sidearm. Bergmann's troubles were not over, however. Late in 1904, the firm of V. C. Schilling had been bought out by the Heinrich Krieghoff Waffenfabrik and, with the completion of then-outstanding contracts, ended manufacture of handguns for Bergmann early in 1905. When the Spanish contract came through Bergmann found himself without adequate facilities to manufacture the pistols. He managed to get a delay of delivery from the Spanish government in order to set up a factory at Gaggenau, but apparently very few, if any, Gaggenau-made Mars pistols were delivered to Spain.

Spanish Contract

As the Spanish order was for only a few thousand pistols, Bergmann felt it necessary to obtain other contracts in order to justify installation of expanded firearms manufacturing facilities at Gaggenau. As part of this program he submitted the 11.35mm or 44 caliber Mars to be tested by the U.S. Ordnance Dept. in October, 1906. Unfortunately, because of postal regulations, the German-made ammunition was not allowed to be imported, and the 45-caliber American ammunition would not function, of course. In January, 1907, a Mars chambered for the 45 ACP was sent for testing. It was again accompanied by special cartridges, but these were loaded to a greater pressure than those specified by the U.S. Board of Ordnance. Again, unfortunately, the cartridges were not allowed into the country, so in the famous U.S. Ordnance tests of January 15, 1907, an attempt to fire 20 American-made rounds through the Mars was a failure, the pressure developed by the cartridges not being sufficient to properly operate the mechanism. Understandably the Board recommended against adoption. Bergmann's representative, A. E. Piorkowski, wrote in April, and again in May, in an attempt to get the arm retested, but with no apparent results. Because of this final failure, and with fewer than 1000 Mars pistols actually completed, Bergmann decided it was no longer economically sound to pursue the military handgun field. He began searching for someone to take over the remainder of the Spanish contract so that he might abandon this field of manufacture.

The Societe Anonyme Anciens Etablissments Pieper of Herstal, near Liege, Belgium, had a long and enviable reputation in military arms manufacture, having supplied revolvers and rifles to the Belgian and other armies. At this time, however, they were looking for new markets, having lost their Belgian army contracts to the Fabrique Nationale d'Armes de Guerre. They readily agreed to make the Bergmann-Mars design under license, and to the taking over of the Spanish contract. Before production began, several modifications suggested by the Spanish government in the interim were undertaken. These included: an interrupter, lacking on Bergmann pistols since the days of the No.5 prototype; shortening the safety lever throw; introduction of a larger magazine catch and the addition of a hammer-stop pin to prevent the hammer from battering the rear of the barrel extension. Pieper also revised the frame and barrel extension contours, and replaced the checked wood grips with patterned hard rubber grips. Even though the Spanish contract did not call for a holster-stock, the fixed lanyard loop on the butt of the grip frame which had also served as the holster-stock attachment point on the Mars (fig. 9) was retained by Pieper in their production.

Bergmann-Bayard

With these modifications the pistol known as the 1908 Bergmann-Bayard was born. Pieper also slightly modified the No.6 cartridge, reintroducing it as the 9mm Bergmann-Bayard. Serial numbering apparently started at 1000, the point at which the Mars numbering terminated. Commercial production was undertaken simultaneously to

satisfying the Spanish contract. Pistols for the contract were taken at random from the normal production run. Before the end of 1909, Pieper had completed delivery to Spain of about 3000 pistols, with serial numbers ranging to well over 5000. The Spanish contract arms are easily recognized since they bear the Spanish acceptance mark, a circle radially partitioned into thirds, on the left side of the frame bridge and on top of the breech. The pistols also carry the 4-digit Spanish issue number engraved on the left side of the frame bridge (fig. 10). These pistols were in use by the Spanish army until their replacement in 1916 by the Campo-Giro. They were in police use until after the 1936 Civil War.

Pieper, hoping to expand production, submitted to the British CISA examples of their pistols in July, 1910. These, however, were not reported upon favorably by the board. They had much better luck with the pistols submitted to Denmark in the same year, and Danish army orders *Kundgorelse fer Haeren* Nos. A 59/1911 and B 18/1911 of September 22, 1911, call for issue of a modified Bergmann-Bayard M1908 to all officers and some NCOs. This pistol was designated by Denmark as the M1910. The modifications requested were a simplification of the design of the interrupter, replacement of the fragile hard-rubber grips with wood, the addition of a key to the locking block to prevent its improper insertion when the arm was assembled, larger finger clearances for use of the stripper clip and cutouts on the side of the magazine well and corresponding grip surfaces on the magazine to allow grasping a stubborn magazine to remove it. They also recommended that the flat mainspring be replaced by one of s-shape.

Pieper made the required revisions and, in 1911, began to deliver on the contract. As with the Spanish contract, pistols were taken from normal commercial production in no particular order. A total of 4840 pistols were delivered between late 1911 and August, 1914. Original Danish contract pistols can be recognized by the acceptance stamp, a small crown surmounting a capital "D," or on replacement issue guns, a small crown surmounting the last two digits of the year of issue on the left of the frame bridge, and by an engraved army serial number ranging from 1 to 4840 on the right side of the bridge. All pistols carry full Belgian

Fig. 5. M1897, No. 5 pistol, serial No. 522 (2nd type), caliber 7.8 (7.63mm), showing adjustable rear sight and monogrammed hard rubber grips. Note barrel sleeve catch and sight holes in chamber, magazine and magazine well.

commercial proofs. Serial numbers for the Danish contract range from the low 6000s to about 11,000. Commercial pistols in the same serial number range exhibit the same constructional features (fig. 11).

Some of the commercial arms will be found with a small slot about 0.5" by 0.1" cut through the rear grip strap about two inches below the top of the grips. These pistols were modified for the holster stocks available from Pieper, the latter of wood and leather or all wood like the Mauser military holster. The Pieper system of attaching the holster both to the lanyard loop and the grip frame was much more secure than that provided originally for the Mars.

In 1912 Pieper produced a small quantity of Bayard pistols in the 12,000 and 13,000 serial number range which reverted to the M1908 style of magazine and well, these having the Bayard horse-and-rider trademark stamped on the left side of the well (fig. 12). These were intended for commercial sales only and were designated by the factory as "Modele 1912." Sometime during 1912 or 1913 a very small quantity of the M1910 type were delivered to Greece for testing. The Greeks did not adopt this arm and the fate of the test pieces is unknown. Several examples in the proper serial number range have been found with the inscription "L. Sk. 16." followed by another two-digit number stamped on the front grip strap. These may have been Greek test pieces or the marking may indicate some police usage. Several countries bought small quantities of the Bergmann-Bayard for issue to their police forces and, as a matter of fact, Denmark bought several of the arms outside the normal contract quantity and had them fitted with fancy grips and specially marked for the royal household guards.

Nazi Takeover

In August of 1914 the Germans invaded Belgium and overran Herstal. After a brief period of turmoil the Germans required Pieper to continue assembling the Bayard pistols. At first, since the proof house was no longer functioning, these occupation pistols carried no proof marking of any kind but were otherwise indistinguishable from pre-war production. Later, however, as it was considered desirable to indicate that some sort of inspection had taken place, a small mark in the form of a diamond with an apple in it (not unlike the *poincon* of the armsmaker August Gasser of Vienna) was stamped where Belgian proofing was normally placed. These occupation pistols will be found in the 15,000 and 16,000 serial number range.

At the conclusion of the war Pieper did not resume production of the M1910/12, but did assemble from spare parts several hundred pistols in the 17,000 serial number range. Rather than continue with the old design, they decided to substantially modify it to eliminate the shortcomings discovered over the service life of the original. At least one such prototype was made, mostly from old M1910/12 parts. This experimental pistol has a longer barrel, an adjustable rear sight, and a 15-shot magazine along with a great many detail modifications (fig. 13). It is proofed but not serial numbered. At this point, Pieper too, elected to retire from the field of military automatic pistol manufacture.

By 1921 Denmark found herself in the position of badly needing repair and replacement of its existing arms. With the loss of Pieper as a source of supply, on February 11, 1922, it was decreed that the Danish Royal Arsenal would produce its own version of the M1910 with several modifications that had suggested themselves. The revised design was designated "Model 1910/21." The alterations were: replacement of the original sideplate catch with a spanner screw; further enlargement of the magazine catch and replacement of the smallish wooden grips with oversized, checked grips of "Trolit," a Bakelite-like composition. It was also decided that existing Belgian-manufactured pistols returned to the Arsenal for repair would be modified in accordance with these new standards in addition to having the "S" mainsprings provided where necessary. The modified pistols are easily recognized by "M. 1910/21" stamped on the left side of the barrel extension (figs. 14 and 15).* By mid-1922 production in Danish facilities was underway. The first 900 pistols, manufactured between 1922 and 1924, were marked *Haerens Tojhus* (Royal Arsenal Factory) (fig. 16). The succeeding 1904 pistols manufactured in 1924-25 were marked *Haerens Rustkammer* (Royal Armory) the new name given to the arsenal in late 1924 (fig. 17). In all, 2204 were manufactured and serial numbered beginning with number 1. The army numbers follow those of the Belgian purchase, beginning with 4841 and terminating with 7045, and are in the same location. These pistols bear Danish acceptance marks in the form of a large crown and the last two digits of the date of manufacture on the right side. Some further service difficulties were experienced with extractors breaking and Trolit grips cracking. Therefore all pistols that were returned for repair between 1935 to 1940 had the hard rubber Trolit grips replaced by lightly embossed wood grips of the same size (fig. 16). Many of these also had the bolt replaced with a special bolt and extractor assembly, the extractor having an enlarged T-section near the claw to help prevent breakage.

Although in 1940 the Danes tested the FN Browning M1935 Hi-Power and recommended that it replace the Bayard. WWII prevented FN from delivering, and the Bayard remained the official Danish sidearm until 1946. So, more

*Fig. 15 is not pictured for reasons of space.

Fig. 6. No. 5 pistol, serial No. 737 (3rd type) showing hooked end on locking spring and shortened magazine well. Note attachment method of steel-framed leather holster-stock.

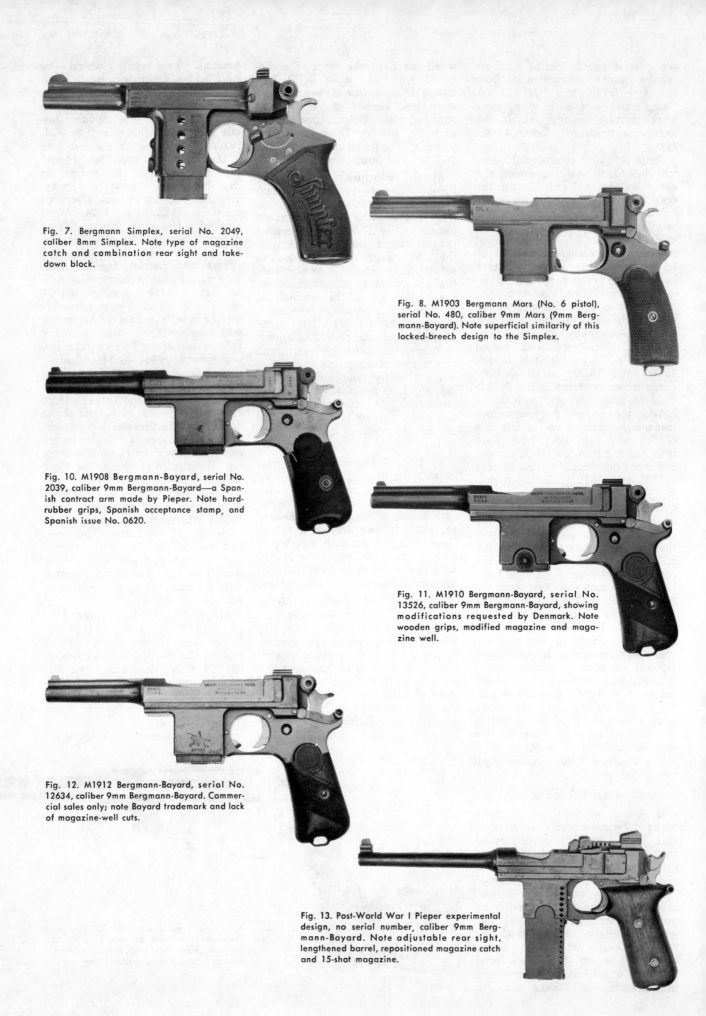

Fig. 7. Bergmann Simplex, serial No. 2049, caliber 8mm Simplex. Note type of magazine catch and combination rear sight and takedown block.

Fig. 8. M1903 Bergmann Mars (No. 6 pistol), serial No. 480, caliber 9mm Mars (9mm Bergmann-Bayard). Note superficial similarity of this locked-breech design to the Simplex.

Fig. 10. M1908 Bergmann-Bayard, serial No. 2039, caliber 9mm Bergmann-Bayard—a Spanish contract arm made by Pieper. Note hardrubber grips, Spanish acceptance stamp, and Spanish issue No. 0620.

Fig. 11. M1910 Bergmann-Bayard, serial No. 13526, caliber 9mm Bergmann-Bayard, showing modifications requested by Denmark. Note wooden grips, modified magazine and magazine well.

Fig. 12. M1912 Bergmann-Bayard, serial No. 12634, caliber 9mm Bergmann-Bayard. Commercial sales only; note Bayard trademark and lack of magazine-well cuts.

Fig. 13. Post-World War I Pieper experimental design, no serial number, caliber 9mm Bergmann-Bayard. Note adjustable rear sight, lengthened barrel, repositioned magazine catch and 15-shot magazine.

Fig. 14. M1910/21 Danish rework of Belgian contract pistol, serial No. 8758, caliber 9mm Bergmann-Bayard. Note Trolit grips, original acceptance stamp and "M.1910/21" rework marking.

Fig. 16. M1910/21 Danish *Haerens Tojhus*, serial No. 319, caliber 9mm Bergmann-Bayard, Army No. 5161. Note revised machining of barrel and post-1935 wood grips.

Fig. 17. M1910/21 Danish *Haerens Rustkammer*, serial No. 2129, caliber 9mm Bergmann-Bayard. Army No. 6971.

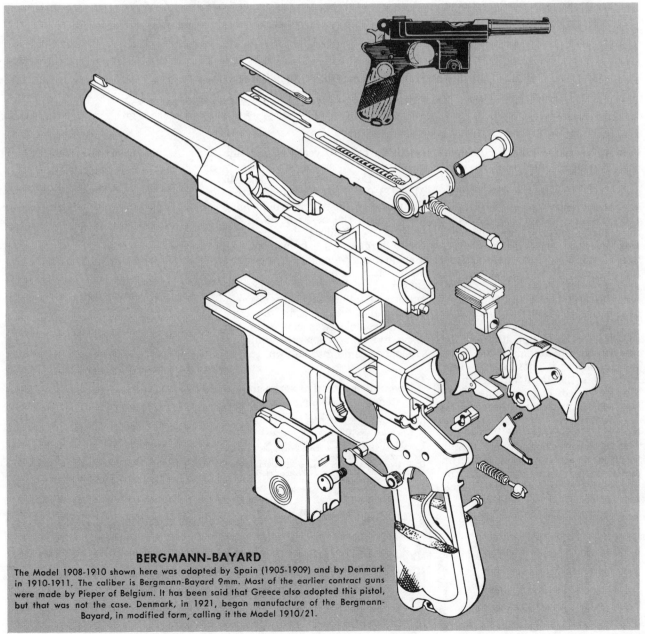

BERGMANN-BAYARD

The Model 1908-1910 shown here was adopted by Spain (1905-1909) and by Denmark in 1910-1911. The caliber is Bergmann-Bayard 9mm. Most of the earlier contract guns were made by Pieper of Belgium. It has been said that Greece also adopted this pistol, but that was not the case. Denmark, in 1921, began manufacture of the Bergmann-Bayard, in modified form, calling it the Model 1910/21.

Bergmann System Military Pistol Magazines

Fig. 18. From upper left to lower right—M1897 prototype, 7.8mm 10-shot; M1897 7.8mm 10-shot; M1903 Mars, 9mm 6-shot; M1903 Mars, 9mm 10-shot; M1908 Bergmann-Bayard, 9mm 6-shot; M1912 Bergmann-Bayard, 9mm 6-shot; M1910 Bergmann-Bayard, 9mm 6-shot (identical to M1910/21).

than 40 years after Bergmann himself produced his last military handgun, the saga of the Bergmann system military pistols came to an end.

Bergmann, one of the giants in the early history of automatic weapons development, should rightfully stand with Schwarzlose, Mauser, and Browning; his was the first practical auto pistol design; his, the first successful application of the simple blowback principle to a reliable self-loading pistol; his, the first pocket automatic; his, the first known full-automatic handarm. Bergmann's final design, the 1903 Mars, was the third military automatic adopted, and used one of the simplest and strongest breech-locking systems ever devised. The 9mm cartridge developed for it was the first to see military use and is still, to this day, the most powerful available for automatic pistols. The arm and cartridge well-proved their

worth by over 40 years of first line military use, a record equalled only by the Luger and the Colt 45 Model 1911. It is conceivable that the name of Bergmann would have been one of the best known in the field of self-loading firearms had the Bergmann's Industriewerke management seen fit to exploit the early start and notable progress they had made in the developmental era of self-loading weapons. Unfortunately, the decision to retire from the field was made at the very moment when the military self-loader came into its own. ●

I would like to thank the following people who made important contributions to this article:

D. Bady, Holliswood, New York
J. Schroeder, Jr., Glenview, Ill.
R. Alexander Montgomery, Villanova, Pa.
A. Torriani, Eidg. Waffenfabrik (Fabrique Federale d'Armes), Berne, Switzerland
D. Techy, Musee d'Armes, Leige, Belgium (retired)
J. Leconte, Musee Royale de l'Armee et d'Histoire Militaire, Brussels, Belgium
J. Paulsen, Tojhusmuseet, Copenhagen, Denmark

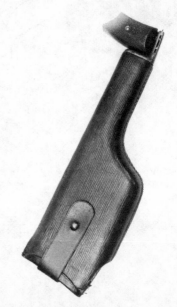

Fig. 9. "Boiled Leather" holster-stock showing attachment to M1903 Mars. An alternate steel-framed soft leather version was also available.

Bergmann System Military Pistol Cartridges

Fig. 19. From left to right—7.8 (7.63mm); No. 5; 8mm No. 4; 8mm Simplex (forerunner of 7.65 Browning); 9mm Bergmann-Bayard (virtually identical to 9mm No. 6); 10mm "Low Velocity;" 10mm "High Velocity;" 11.35 mm 45 ACP (virtually identical to 11.65mm).

The Rifles of
James
Paris
Lee

PART TWO

Born in Scotland in 1831, Lee was brought to Canada in 1836, moving eventually to Stevens Point, Wisconsin, sometime before 1860. His first military contract, made in 1864, was hardly successful. A rare dropping block design based on Lee's 1866 patent is pictured and described, as are Lee's M1875 rifle, the various trials of his rifle designs, and his 1879 system—the first one of his great magazine design, and the rifle which would prove to be the forerunner of the British S.M.L.E.

Part One of this detailed and thorough account of James Paris Lee and his gun designs appeared in our 26th edition.

by LARRY S. STERETT

REALIZING THE NEED and, possibly sensing the handwriting on the wall, the Ordnance Department convened the Board of 1882 to pick a suitable magazine rifle. By late September 1882 the Board had tested and examined a total of 53 rifles submitted by 20 inventors, including the M1879 and M1882 versions of the Lee rifle in 45-70 Gov't. caliber. Rifle No. 10 was a M1879 entry of the Lee Arms Co., and No. 36 was a Remington-Lee M1882 with an improved bolt. Rifles No. 24, 31, and 35, were Spencer-Lee rifles entered by J. W. Frazier of New York City.[9] The early

trials narrowed the field to three basic designs—the M1882 Lee, the Hotchkiss, the Chaffee-Reece—and additional testing was recommended.

> *Ordnance Office,*
> *War Department*
> *Washington, October 9, 1882*
> *Respectfully returned to the Secretary of War:*
> *A careful examination of the report ... convinces me that ... while the Lee gun is entitled to the first place, the comparative merits of the three guns put them nearly on a par in point of excellence.*
> *... I respectfully recommend that the $50,000 available ... be expended in providing the Lee, the Chaffee-Reece, and the Hotchkiss magazine guns for trial in the hands of troops.*
> *S. V. Benet,*
> *Brigadier-General,*
> *Chief of Ordnance.*

The recommendation was approved by Robert T. Lincoln, Secretary of War and Benet was asked to learn the prices of each type of gun.

Fig. 14—This is the famous U.S. Navy Rifle, M1895, or the Lee-Navy, caliber 6mm, with the rear sight leaf erect. This was the first official clip-loading rifle ever used by a branch of the U.S. military services, and was also the smallest caliber in military use up to that time—and for several decades to come. Note that the front band has both a swivel and a bayonet lug. This is also the only Lee design used by the U.S. military which had a swivel on the lower band. Another first for this rifle was the quick-detachable rear swivel which could be moved to the front of the magazine housing; the sling used a hook-arrangement which could snap into the fixed front swivel. One of the M1895 rifles was exhibited at the New York Militia Trials of 1896, as was an entry of the Lee Arms Co., Hartford. (This could have been a M1885 Remington-Lee, the 1888 Lee design, or one of the 1896 Parkhurst designs assigned to Lee), and later a Winchester-made M1895 Lee in 30-40 Krag caliber.

Fig. 15   **Fig. 16**

Fig. 15—Right side of the Lee M1895 action. What appears to be a small number 7, near the rear of the breech opening, is supposed to be the number 1. Fig. 16—Left side view of the Lee M1895 action, showing the bolt stop, bolt release and firing-pin lock. The inscription on the receiver reads, in two lines: MANUFAC-TURED BY THE WINCHESTER REPEATING ARMS CO. / NEW HAVEN, CONN. U. S. A. PAT OCT 10, 93, JAN 30, 94, OCT 5, 95.

Ordnance Office,
War Department
Washington, January 10, 1883.
Respectfully returned to the Secretary of War . . .

The Remingtons make the Lee gun, and will supply them at $16.66 each in about three months.

The prices given for the Lee and Hotch-kiss are fair. I respectfully recommend that 750 guns each of Lee and Hotchkiss may be procured by contract . . .

In this connection I have to state that as the Lee and Hotchkiss are patented arti-cles and can only be procured from parties owning the patents, the question arises whether or not contracts can be made with them without previous advertisement. If not contrary to law I respectfully recom-mended it.

S. V. Benet,
Brigadier-General,
Chief of Ordnance.

Respectfully returned to the Chief of Ordnance.

. . . the making of a contract with the proprietors of the Lee and Hotchkiss guns without advertisement is authorized for the reason that such advertisement would be a useless expense, as . . . definite articles are wanted, for which there can be no com-petition.

John Tweedale
Chief Clerk
War Department, January 10, 1883.

Ordnance Office,
War Department
Washington, D.C.,
December 15, 1885.
The Secretary of War.

Sir: I have the honor to transmit here-with a tabular statement of the results

reached in the trial of a number of each of the magazine rifles issued to the troops. (Author's note: 713 rifles each of the Lee, Hotchkiss, and Chaffee-Reece [designs] were issued to the troops, and Springfield Armory had produced 3,937 spare maga-zines for the Lee.) These guns were recom-mended for trial, in the order named, by a board of officers convened in 1881, under authority of law . . .

The reports from 149 companies have been received . . . as follows:

Comparing the three magazine guns with each other the reports are:

For the Lee, 55; Chaffee-Reece, 14; Hotchkiss, 26.

As magazine guns, therefore, the reports are largely in favor of the Lee.

Comparing the magazine guns with each other and with the Springfield serv-ice rifle as single loaders, the preference is for the Springfield, as follows: For the Lee, 5; Chaffee-Reece, 0; Hotchkiss, 1; Spring-field, 21.

Comparing the magazine guns and the Springfield for all uses, the preference is for the Lee, 10; Chaffee-Reece, 3; Hotch-kiss, 4; and the Springfield, 46; being largely in favor of the Springfield.

. . . I am satisfied that neither of these magazine guns should be adopted and

substituted for the Springfield rifle as the arm for the Service.

. . . The Springfield rifle gives such gen-eral satisfaction to the Army that we can safely wait a reasonable time for further developments of magazine systems.

Very respectfully,
your obedient servant,
S. V. Benet,
Brigadier-General,
Chief of Ordnance.

Thus, the Springfield single shot rifle was to remain the mainstay of the U. S. Army for another 7 years.

The original arrangement between Lee and Remington called for Remington to manufacture the rifles for the Lee Arms Co. This arrangement did not work out and, in 1884, Lee had entered into an agreement with Remington to manufac-ture and sell the rifle on a royalty basis. As a result, rifles manufactured after this time were marked:

**E. REMINGTON & SONS, ILION, N.Y. U.S.A.
SOLE MANUFACTURERS AND AGENTS**

On March 25, 1884, "James P. Lee and Louis P. Diss, of Ilion, New York Assig-nors to E. Remington & Sons, of Same Place" were issued U. S. Patent No. 295,-563 for a "Magazine for Fire-Arms." The basic design was for an improvement of

Fig. 17—Essential parts of the Lee M1895. Parts common to all small arms are omitted in this Figure and in Fig. 20. The parts in both Figures are numbered the same, so that they may be compared. No. 1, receiver; 2, bolt; 3, firing pin; 4, mainspring; 5, firing-pin collar; 6, cam lever; 7, trigger guard and magazine; 8, cartridge elevator; 9A, bolt-stop thumb-piece; 9B, bolt-stop; 10, extractor; 11, extractor spring; 12, sear; 13, sear fly; 14, trigger; 15A, trigger spring; 15B, fly spring; 16, elevator spring; 17, elevator-spring shaft; 18, lock pin; 19, firing-pin lock; 20, bolt release; 21, trigger-spring stop-pin; 22, trigger-spring screw.

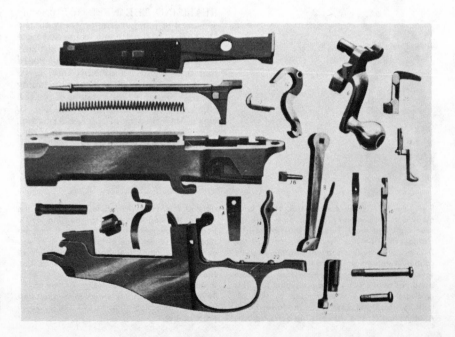

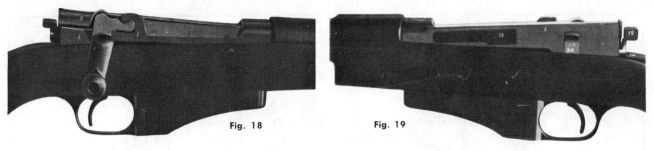

Fig. 18—Right side view of the Lee M1899. The knurled piece at the rear of the receiver is the safety. Forward of the trigger guard is the magazine cut-off, which the M1895 did not have. Fig. 19—Left side view of the Lee M1899, showing the bolt-stop and safety lock.

the 1879 model and consisted of a very light sheet-iron magazine with "... spring or detent which holds the cartridges in the box when not attached to the arm, and in corrugating the body of the box (magazine) ..." This same Diss was issued 8 other firearms patents between 1884 and 1888, with most assigned to E. Remington & Sons.

Sales to the Navy

The 1884 Annual Report of the Secretary of the Navy stated that 700 Lee magazine guns had been purchased on advantageous terms for armament on new cruisers. The model is unknown to the author: that "advantageous" might refer to a closing out of the 1879 model, but this is only an opinion.

In 1885 an improved Lee rifle appeared. This is sometimes called the 1884/85 Lee, but it is usually listed as the Model 1885 Remington-Lee. The rear locking system, with cocking on closing, was retained, but a separate bolt head was used. The extractor was attached to the bolt head, and both were held in place by a hooked piece that fitted into the guide rib and slid rearward to lock. The cocking piece was changed slightly, the flange almost doubled in size.

The barrel was 32½ inches long, and rifled the same as the 1882 model. Over-all

length of the 1885 model was 52 inches, and the weight was about 8½ pounds.

There was no upper handguard, but the two bands, the nose cap, the two sling swivels and their location, the sights, and the 5-round magazine with two vertical grooves were the same as on the Model 1882.

The Model 1885 was Remington marked, per the 1884 agreement, except that after 1888 E. Remington & Sons became the Remington Arms Company. These markings were on the upper left side of the receiver, and the serial number usually followed the second line of the marking. Rifles bought by the U. S. Navy were marked on top of the receiver ring with **U.S.N.** over an anchor: these markings sometimes had two lines below them consisting of an identification number and an inspector's initials, making a total of 4 lines on the receiver ring.

E. Remington & Sons went into receivership in 1886. (Lee recovered the rights to his designs in accordance with his contract with Remington, and apparently left for England to try to interest the British Government in his magazine rifle.) Of the Remington brothers, Sam was the businessman, so when he died in 1882 the firm started to slip slowly toward bankruptcy. Philo and Eliphalet III tried to keep the

huge Armory in operation, and if a sizeable foreign or U. S. contract for the Lee rifle had been obtained they might have been able to do so. Turning out a quality product for which the demand is limited is expensive. For two years the receivers finished the work in process and took what small orders were obtained. Then in March, 1888, Marcellus Hartley, founder of the Union Metallic Cartridge Company, and Thomas G. Bennett, son-in-law of Governor Oliver Winchester (Remington's main competitor), bought E. Remington & Sons, with all of its physical properties and its reputation, for two million dollars. The name was changed to the Remington Arms Company, but the quality products for which the firm was known remained the same.

On May 22, 1888, U. S. Patent 383,363 for a "Magazine Fire-Arm" was issued to "James P. Lee, of New York, N. Y." In the patent introduction Lee lists himself as an engineer and a resident of New York (City), although he is not so-listed in any of the other patents with which the author is familiar.

The patent relates to the 1879 patent and was "... chiefly designed to improve the construction and increase the efficiency of such fire-arms." The arm had been previously patented in England on August 18, 1887, and examination of the drawings indicates that this is the basic design for the famous Lee-Enfield rifle used throughout the British Empire for over 60 years.

The wide cup extending below the receiver breech for the attachment of the separate buttstock, so familiar a sight on later Lee-Enfield rifles, is illustrated for the first time. The removable bolt head, which could also be used as a tool for unscrewing the firing pin from the cocking piece, is covered in this 1888 patent, as is the entire striker assembly so much a part of the Lee-Enfield rifles.

Two magazine modifications, which

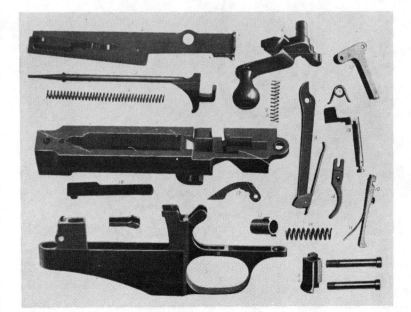

Fig. 20—Essential parts of the Lee M1899. No. 1, receiver; 2, bolt; 3, firing pin; 4, mainspring; 5, firing-pin collar; 6, cam lever; 7, trigger guard and magazine; 8, cartridge elevator; 9A, bolt-stop; 9B, bolt-stop spring; 10, extractor; 11, extractor spring; 12, sear; 13, bolt retainer (new); 14, trigger; 15, trigger spring; 16, elevator spring; 17, elevator-spring sleeve; 18, extractor-spring stop (new); 19, safety lock (new).

J. P. LEE.
MAGAZINE BOLT GUN.

No. 547,583.   Patented Oct. 8, 1895.

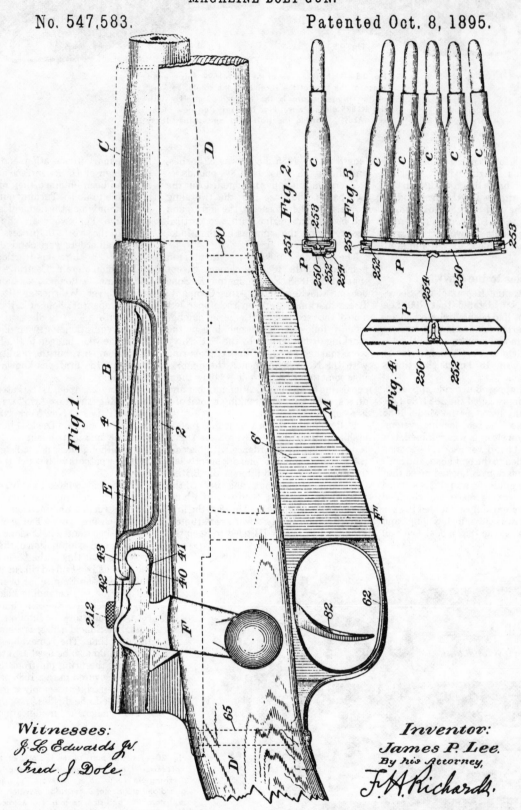

Witnesses:
J. L. Edwards Jr.
Fred. J. Dole.

Inventor:
James P. Lee.
By his Attorney,
F. H. Richards.

Lee's 1895 U.S. Patent, No. 547,583, covered his design for a
straight pull bolt action rifle. This became the Lee Navy 6mm.

make use of U-shaped follower springs instead of the common zig-zag type, are covered by the patent. Surprisingly, the cartridges illustrated in the magazine are rimless instead of the rimmed or flanged type then in use. The magazine catch is a transverse type, such as became popular later on autoloading pistols, instead of the previous lever type in the upper part of the trigger guard directly ahead of the trigger.

The Annual Report of the Secretary of the Navy for 1888 mentioned that 1500 Lee rifles ". . . of the latest construction . . ." had been bought from the Lee Arms Co. for immediate use on ships nearing completion. These would have been the M1885 design, and were no doubt manufactured by the newly formed Remington Arms Company, probably under license from Lee. So far as the author can learn the Lee Arms Company did not have manufacturing facilities, although it apparently continued to exist as a sales agency. Mention was further made by the Secretary that arms being purchased were ". . . as few as we can pending caliber reductions . . .," and that Lee had been selected as the builder of reduced-caliber Navy weapon(s), and a contract signed. Apparently the Navy, regardless of what the Army was doing, was planning to reduce the caliber from .45-inch to something much smaller, in keeping with the trend in Europe and England at this time.

In the 1889 Report the Secretary of the Navy mentioned that the 1500 stand of Lee magazine rifles mentioned in the previous report had been completed by the Lee Arms Co. and the work on them very favorably spoken of by the inspector.

Trials of 1891

The U. S. Army was still without a magazine rifle. On November 24, 1890, the Adjutant General's office issued a general order for a board of officers to select a magazine gun to replace the single-shot Springfield. The Board convened at New York on December 16, 1890, and remained in session until July 1, 1892. A total of 53 guns were examined and tests were made at Governors Island, New York, during July, 1891. Four of the rifles entered in these trials were connected directly or indirectly with James Paris Lee, as follows:

is identical to the Lee-Metford and resembles the drawing in Lee's 1888 patent closely. Speed was the name of an employee at the Royal Small Arms Factory at Enfield Lock, possibly that of the Superintendent.

Rifle No. 39, entered by the Lee Arms Co., South Windham, Conn. was probably the M1885. This address in Connecticut is not that of the 1879 firm, but the author has no other information relating to it. By whom rifles No. 25 and 26 were entered is not known to the author, but perhaps these were Remington Arms Company entries.

Again the Lee lost out, this time to the Krag-Jorgensen (No. 5) entered by a Capt. Ole Krag from Norway. The U. S. Army never adopted a Lee design as an official arm, but the U. S. Navy used Lee rifles for nearly 20 years.

Lee had apparently been busy on the new rifle the Navy had requested, for the Secretary of the Navy reported in 1892 that specifications had been given to Lee for a 236 caliber arm. In 1893 it was further reported that while the Army Krag and several European designs had been examined and compared, work was continuing with Lee on the 236.

The year 1893 was a big one for Lee. Beginning on August 19, 1892, Lee had filed patent applications for a series of ". . . new and useful Improvements in Magazine-Guns . . .," and on October 10, 1893, the U. S. Patent Office granted patents to "James P. Lee, of Ilion, New York" in profusion. Patent Nos. 506,319; 506,320; 506,321; 506,322 and 506,323 were issued for a "Straight-Pull Bolt-Gun" (first three patents), a "Magazine-Gun" and a "Fire-Arm Magazine Case" respectively. On the same date U. S. Patent No. 506,339 was issued to "Francis H. Richards, of Hartford, Conn., Assignor to James Paris Lee, of same place." Richards' patent was for a "Straight-Pull Bolt-Gun" and the application had been filed on September 26, 1892, the same date on which Lee had filed the application that became Patent No. 506,321. (Note that patents issued the same day list Lee as at Ilion, N. Y. and Hartford, Conn.) Francis H. Richards is listed in the patent drawings as being Lee's attorney, but on the specifications as a witness; the second witness on the draw-

		Magazine Capacity	Weight	Caliber
No. 1	Lee-Speed, England	8 rds.	9⅜ lbs.	303
No. 25	Lee No. 1, American	10 rds.	8¼ lbs.	303
No. 26	Lee No. 2, American	5 rds.	8¼ lbs.	300
No. 39	Lee No. 3, American	10 rds.	8¼ lbs.	300

Rifle No. 1, entered by the U. S. Army Chief of Ordnance, Washington, D. C., was apparently the Lee-Metford or Magazine Rifle Mark I, adopted by England on December 22, 1888. The first models were sometimes referred to as the Lee-Speed. This was not the official name, but Greener and several other authors of this period did not always differentiate between the Lee-Speed, Lee-Metford and Lee-Enfield. The Lee-Speed rifle shown in *The Gun* . . .*

Fig. 21—The M1882 Remington-Lee rifle as used by the U.S. Navy. Note the position and type of bolt handle; the head of the cocking piece, and the two vertical grooves in the magazine. The upper band still has two swivels. This model is often mistakenly called the M1879; it definitely is not, but it's a much better design than the original. This particular rifle is marked as indicated in the text, and the left side of the receiver has PATENTED NOV. 4th, 1879. One M1882 rifle is the Royal Military College Museum of Canada is marked on the receiver: E. REMINGTON & SONS, ILION, N. Y., U. S. A./SOLE MANUFACTURER AND AGENTS/PATENTED NOV. 4th, 1879. The rifle is chambered for the 45-70 Gov't. cartridge, and has

the 5-round magazine with two vertical grooves. The bolt handle, cocking piece, and guide rib are polished bright and the rear sight lies immediately in front of the receiver ring; the rear sight is of the type shown in Fig. 12 (See Part One of this article, pp. 48-60, 26th ed. GUN DIGEST.) except it is reversed and in the correct position. Another M1882 rifle in the same collection is completely nickel-plated, except for the highly polished blued magazine, which is without grooves. The stock on this particular rifle is checkered on the fore-end and grip, and the rifle is unmarked. This rifle was in the collection of Porfirio Diaz, once President of Mexico.

---

*W. W. Greener, London, var. eds., 1881-1910.

Fig. 22—The M1885 Remington-Lee, caliber 45-70 Gov't. The only noticeable differences from the M1882 are the size of the cocking-piece head, the method of fitting the extractor to the bolt, and the smaller cut-out of the receiver ring on the right side. Markings on this rifle are as indicated in the text. Note there are still two swivels on the upper band. Barrel length of this rifle is 32¼ inches, giving an over-all length of 52 inches. Serial number is 53142.

ings does not appear on the specifications of the first three patents. On the patent for the "Magazine-Gun" a W. G. Richards is listed on both the drawings and the specifications, and again on the specifications for the Richards patent as a witness; Francis H. Richards is listed as the inventor on this last patent (No. 506,339.) The witness whose name appears on the drawings of all the patents listed above appears to be H. Mallner.

Lee Straight Pull Rifles

The patents all relate to the straight-pull rifle that the U. S. Navy would later adopt as the M1895. The arms are designed for use with detachable 10-round magazines (staggered column) with their release in the trigger guard. The cartridges shown are rimmed, and about 30 caliber—very similar to the 30-40 Krag. Provision was made for loading the magazine with 15-round clips while the magazine was still attached to the rifle. The receiver walls are solid on this design and the ejection is upward, instead of to the right. Other than the firing-pin spring and magazine spring the only spring in this particular design was a U-shaped type that served as sear and trigger spring. There was no safety. The Lee Patent No. 506,321 and the Richards patent are for a model not quite the same as on the other

patents, and many of these particular two patent drawings appear to be the same. Basic operation of the rifles covered in the 1893 patents is much the same, as will be covered later in connection with the M1895 Lee-Navy rifle.

The 1894 annual Navy report mentioned that the Navy had designed the barrel, stock, and cartridge, and tested all. Apparently the reference is to the 236-caliber Lee rifle and cartridge, on which work had been underway to some degree for nearly 6 years.

On October 2, 1894, at the United States Torpedo Station, Newport, Rhode Island, the Navy tested 12 rifles, including the Lee straight-pull model. Two of the rifles tested were straight-pull designs, including the Lee, one was a slide-action, and the rest were turnbolt designs, 5 of these last entered by Remington. On November 19, 1894, another trial was held with three additional rifles, including a Luger 6mm rimless caliber design. One of the tests involved penetration (pine?) as related to caliber; the 236 Navy penetrated 23 inches as opposed to 10 inches for the 45-70 Gov't. cartridge, and 18 inches for the 8mm Austrian Mannlicher cartridge.

In May, 1895, a Navy Board, convened at Newport, officially adopted the Lee Straight-Pull, with the shape of the stock, fittings, sling strap, and bayonet deter-

mined by the Board. The 1895 report of the Secretary of the Navy mentioned that the 1894 Board had adopted the Lee Straight-Pull, although it may have been unofficial at that time. Bids for 10,000 rifles of the Lee design were requested, and Winchester got the contract. (Lee had sold the rights to manufacture the rifle to the Winchester firm.) However, Williamson in *Winchester* . . . says that the contract was for 15,000 of these Lee patent rifles, while factory records indicate 20,000 were made, of which 1,700 were sporting models. The factory records show that all of them were manufactured in the three years of 1896-1898, as follows:

Serial Numbers	Year
1-1917	1896
1,918-10,512	1897
10,513-20,000	1898

There were no receivers numbered from 11,719 to 12,002, 13,701 to 13,733 or 14,980 to 15,000, which cuts the 20,000 total by nearly 400 rifles.

First Official Clip Loader

The 1897 Navy Report mentions that 10,000 Lee (236 caliber) rifles had been delivered and issued to vessels in commission. Thus the Lee-Navy design became the first clip-loading rifle ever officially used by armed forces of the United States, and the smallest official caliber—disregarding the 22 rimfire—until the introduction of the 5.56mm (223) over 60 years later.

The straight-pull design was not new by any means. Austria had used at least 7 different models of straight-pull rifles by the time the U. S. Navy adopted the Lee. Switzerland had also been using a straight-pull rifle. Most of these designs had used a system of revolving or rotating locking lugs. Lee's design, patented in 1893, used a wedge-type locking lug integral with the bottom of the bolt. Although corrected in later models, once the bolt was locked down in the M1895 it could not be unlocked without pulling the trigger or pushing down on the "dead-lock actuator" on the left side of the receiver.

On October 8, 1895, U. S. Patent No. 547,583 was granted to "James P. Lee, of Hartford, Conn.," for a "Magazine Bolt-Gun." The 16 pages of drawings show clearly that this is the rifle manufactured for the U. S. Navy, even to the extent of illustrating the 6mm rimless cartridge in the 5-round clip.

The M1895 Lee-Navy uses a wedge-type locking lug integral with the bottom of the bolt. By slamming the bolt handle forward the wedge is cammed down into contact with a recoil shoulder in the receiver. Since the wedge is below the line of recoil, discharge tends to lock the breech mechanism securely. After firing a straight-back pull on the bolt handle cams the wedge up out of its recess; a continuation of the movement draws the bolt to the rear until it is stopped by the bolt-stop, which also controls the ejection.

The extractor on the 1895 design is a peculiar floating type—entirely different from that employed in the turnbolt system

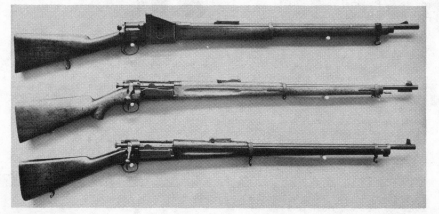

Fig. 23—Top: This is one of the improved Lee rifles with Bethel Burton magazine, of the type entered in the British trials of 1882-87. Note that barrel, fore-end, and bands are identical to those on the older Martini-Henry rifles, indicating that this may be one of the first of the Lee-Burton models. The later Lee-Burton types, which were tested extensively, had a very slim fore-end and only one band, not two ● Middle: A Norwegian 6.5x55 Krag-Jorgensen, which served as the basis for our own M1892 Krag rifle ● Bottom: M1896 U.S. Krag, caliber 30-40.

—on the left side of the bolt. It has three functions—extraction, ejection, and as a stop for retaining the cartridges in the magazine. The extractor remains stationary until the bolt has moved rearward about 1¾ inches. A lug on the bolt then strikes a lug on the extractor, imparting a violent jerk to the cartridge, pulling it from the chamber and literally throwing it out to the right. An unusual method to say the least.

The 1895 design had no safety, as such, but it did have a "firing-pin locker." This device located on the left side of the receiver wall at the breech, moved in a vertical plane only: when pushed upward it retracted and locked the firing-pin out of engagement with the sear arm. When the rifle was to be fired the "locker" could easily be pushed down out of engagement, allowing the firing pin to re-engage the sear. Two other devices appeared that were not often seen on other designs; The movable bolt stop and the "dead-lock actuator" for the sliding bolt. Located on the left side of the receiver, they locked the bolt closed, but permitted it to be unlocked to remove the chambered cartridge, and the bolt to be removed from the rifle entirely when necessary. Pressing the lock actuator downward would unlock the bolt, causing the rear portion to spring upward, after which it could be drawn back to extract the cartridge.

The 1895 design was essentially a repeating rifle. When a clip of 5 cartridges, with a confining hook at each end of the clip, was inserted into the magazine, either end up, a fixed cam released all the cartridges for feeding. There was no magazine cut-off on this model.

Williamson says that in November, 1897, after the Navy contract had been completed, Winchester introduced a sporting version of the M1895 Lee-Navy to list at $32. It was described thus:

"This gun is known as the Lee Straight-Pull Rifle, and has been adopted as the small arm for use in the United States Navy. The caliber of the gun is .236 in. (6mm) and it shoots a smokeless powder cartridge with a hardened lead bullet, having a copper jacket plated with tin, and giving an initial velocity of 2,550 feet (777.24 meters) per second. The magazine holds 5 cartridges, which may be inserted separately or at one time, in which latter case they are placed in the magazine in a pack, held together by a steel clip. The superiority of this rifle over all other types of bolt guns lies in the fact that the operation of opening and closing is by a 'straight pull' instead of the customary 'up turn' and 'pull back.'"

The sporter, sometimes known as the Winchester-Lee model, was available in 6mm caliber only, with a 24-inch nickel-steel barrel. It weighed 7.5 pounds with the sporting halfstock. The quality was good, but the price was high, and sportsmen were just not ready for a bolt action arm that cost more than the popular lever action so The Lee Straight-Pull sporter hardly got off the ground, although it was listed in Winchester catalogs until 1902.

REMINGTON-LEE MAGAZINE MILITARY RIFLE

WITH DETACHABLE MAGAZINE.—SERVICE ARM OF THE U. S. NAVY AND GREAT BRITAIN

43 SPANISH

No. 56. Military Rifles, 43 Cal., South American Model, Angular Bayonet, length 52 inches, weight, 9¼ lbs..................$18 00

EACH ARM IS PROVIDED WITH FOUR MAGAZINES.

Fig. 24—This particular rifle—listed as the South American Model and available only in 43 Spanish caliber—apparently falls somewhere between the M1882 and M1885. The front band has only one swivel; the receiver ring resembles that of the M1885; the head of the cocking piece is too large for the M1882 and too small for the M1885. The rear sight is immediately in front of the receiver ring, and is identical to the sights on the two M1882 rifles in the Royal Military College Museum (Canada). Barrel length, over-all length and weight are about the same as for the M1885. The reproduction is from the 1903-04 *Price List of Military Arms, Equipments and Ordnance Stores,* published by M. Hartley Co., of New York, listed as "Agents: Remington Arms Co." This is the same Hartley who bought E. Remington & Sons in 1888, and formed the Remington Arms Company. Hartley also owned at least three other firms, including the Union Metallic Cartridge Company, and operated all of them separately. Note that this South American Model, with 4 magazines and a bayonet, sold for only $18.

NEW REMINGTON-LEE MAGAZINE MILITARY RIFLE

MODEL 1899.

29-inch special steel barrel. Five shots. Total length, 49½ inches. Weight, 8½ lbs.

This arm is of the well-known bolt type, adopted by military organizations throughout the world on account of its simplicity, durability and ease of manipulation. The celebrated Lee rifle, formerly in use by the Navy Department, has been altered and adapted to the modern smokeless, high power ammunition, giving great penetration, velocity and flat trajectory with extreme accuracy.

In addition to the bolt locking mechanism on the large calibre Lee, this arm has double-locking shoulders on the bolt head, and is arranged to load with a filler or clip, whereby five cartridges can be placed in the magazine in the same space of time as is ordinarily consumed by the insertion of one cartridge in magazine arms of other types.

List price...$35 00
Knife bayonet and scabbard...............................   4 00

SECTIONAL VIEW, MAGAZINE CHARGED AND IN POSITION.

Made for the following cartridges: 30 Calibre Gov't. 6 M/M. U. S. Navy. 7 M/M. Spanish Mauser.

Fig. 25—An advertisement for the Model 1899 Remington-Lee rifle from the 1903-04 Hartley Price List. Note that only 3 calibers are listed as being available—two rimless and one rimmed. Bolt construction, locking lug recesses, and sear details are plainly visible in the cutaway view.

The 1895 patent mentions a previous patent—No. 513,647, issued January 30, 1894, to James Lee for a "Bolt-Gun." While this patent incorporates some of the features later used in the M1895 rifle it is mainly for a straight-pull design with a 10-round cartridge packet with an outside-mounted cartridge lifter. (Patent No. 547,-582 was for a 5-round "cartridge packet" as used in the 1895 rifle, and was issued to Lee on the same day as the rifle patent.) The right hand side of the action, as illustrated in this patent, is numbered so that the lifter arm indicates the number of cartridges in the magazine. The basic idea was good, and 16 pages of drawings are devoted mainly to the packet and the cartridge lifter, but apparently it did not reach commercial production.

Last Lee Patent

The 1895 patent was apparently the last one issued to James Paris Lee, although several later ones were assigned to the Lee Arms Company. In 1896, because of his own poor health, Lee had sent one of his two sons—George—to England with the M1895 Straight-Pull Rifle to effect its sale to the British. After examining the rifle the Commander-in-Chief, the Duke of Cambridge, is reported to have asked young Lee: "Why did you not show us this rifle before?"

Fig. 26—M1885 Remington-Lee rifle with the bolt in retracted position. Markings are as on the previous M1885, except top of the receiver ring is marked, in 4 lines: U.S.N./ /N° . . . . . . /A.C.D. (There is no number above the dots.) Serial number is 53222, and the barrel length, other details, etc., are the same as on the previous M1885. The upper band on this rifle does not have swivels or provisions for them; it may be a misplaced lower band. From the Remington Arms Company collection.

Fig. 27—The M1899 Remington-Lee rifle, caliber 30-40 Krag. The rifle is cocked, as indicated by the position of the cocking-piece. Note that this model has a handguard, while the M1879, M1882, M1885 and the South American Model do not. Note also that swivels are on the upper band and at the forward trigger guard screw. From the Remington Arms Company collection.

On March 16, 1897, U. S. Patent No. 579,096, was issued to "William P. Laraway, of Hartford, Conn. Assignor to the Lee Arms Company, of Connecticut." The application had been filed on April 20, 1896, and the patent was for a "Combined Bolt-Stop and Cartridge-Ejector for Bolt-Guns" to be embodied on a gun similar to that shown on an application of the same date made by one Edward G. Parkhurst. However, the Parkhurst patent was not issued until almost a year later. The Laraway patent, and the later Parkhurst patents, had previously been patented in England, France, Belgium, Italy, and Austria.

The Laraway invention was a very simple leaf arrangement which slid into a groove on the left side of the receiver to act as a bolt stop and to eject the extracted case out the right side of the receiver. Provision was made for the bolt stop to be depressed to allow removal of the breech-bolt.

The M1895 Straight-Pull Rifle had proved to be easily operated, quick to load and accurate, but a few years of usage revealed some weaknesses not so apparent on adoption. The extractor (not attached to the bolt) had a rather brief life; the bolt-stop was not self-closing; the sear-fly was slightly dangerous and the loading clips were of uneven tension.

To eliminate these weaknesses some new parts were added and a few were done away with completely, the result being a net reduction of 10 parts. This new rifle, the M1899 Straight-Pull, retained the best features of the M1895 and was, according to all reports, safe, sure, and reliable. However, U. S. Navy records show that the only Lee Straight-Pull rifle tested by them ended with the adoption of the M1895 design. No trials were ever held for any later models.

The 1899 Straight Pull

The M1899 Straight-Pull Rifle is covered in U. S. Patent No. 599,287, issued on February 15, 1898, to "Edward G. Parkhurst, of Hartford, Connecticut, Assignor to the Lee Arms Company, of Connecti-

cut." The patent was for a "Magazine Bolt-Gun," but it is basically for improvements on certain features of Lee's patent No. 547,583. Details in the patent follow the M1899 rifle closely, and it is worth noting that the cartridges shown in the Parkhurst patent appear to be of about 7mm caliber, rimless and bottlenecked. It had apparently been Lee's intention to make the caliber of his rifles 7mm, since this caliber had been adopted and found effective by several foreign powers. Just how effective was proved to us a few years later in Cuba, when we ran into the 7mm Spanish Mausers. However, this was the era of high-velocity and small calibers—the Army even experimented with a new rimmed 22 caliber centerfire cartridge—and the Navy apparently decided a 6mm cartridge would not only provide a flatter trajectory and deeper penetration but lighter ammunition.

The M1899 had a magazine cut-off, allowing its use as a single-shot with 5 cartridges in reserve. A bolt retainer (13)—see Straight-Pull Fig. 20—performed the same job as the sear fly (13) in the M1895 and did away with this delicate part and its spring. The bolt release or dead-lock actuator (20) of the M1895 was done away with, allowing the bolt to be unlocked by simply pulling rearward on the bolt handle. The safety lock (19) did away with the firing-pin locker (19) and performed the functions of locking down the bolt to the receiver and camming back the firing-pin, positively securing both. It performed the same function as the safeties of the Krag, Mauser, and later Springfield.

The extractor spring stop (18) of the M1899 provided a stop for the extractor and its spring during the forward movement of the bolt. This lengthened the life of the spring, since it was no longer forced out of a niche (twice as deep as it was thick) when under its greatest tension.

To remove the bolt from the M1895 the bolt stop was pressed down, where it remained after the bolt was replaced, unless it was pushed back up. If the shooter forgot to push the bolt back into place, the

next rearward movement of the bolt would remove it completely from the receiver, along with the extractor and its spring: the latter two items usually fell to the ground. The M1899 Straight-Pull design had a spiral spring which automatically forced the bolt stop back into position after it was depressed.

In the M1899 design the extractor and spring were held together with a rivet, the flanged head of which slid into a cut in the bolt. This eliminated the annoyance created by these parts in the M1895, where they could easily become lost when the bolt was removed from the receiver.

The clip for the M1899 was redesigned to facilitate loading, provide uniform tension, and retain the cartridges in place when the magazine cut-off was in use. In both the M1895 and M1899 Straight-Pull rifles the clip remained in the magazine, even though the cartridges had been released, falling out the bottom of the magazine after the first or second shot.

The M1895 had a 28-inch barrel, was 47 inches over-all and weighed 8.5 pounds with sling and bayonet. The barrel length of the M1899 was also 28 inches, with an over-all length of 47.6 inches. Other data on this model is indefinite, and just how many of the M1899 rifles were made is not known. Since the Navy was apparently not interested, perhaps only one or two experimental specimens were produced. The rear sight on both models was graduated to 2000 yards in 100-yard increments from 800 yards on the leaf. The battle sight was set for 300 yards and could be moved to 600 yards before raising the leaf. These settings were for the regular service ammunition having a velocity at 60 feet of 2460 fps. No adjustment for windage was provided, as the drift at battle settings was considered negligible.

Before leaving the M1895 Straight-Pull series one note of historical interest should be mentioned. When the U.S.S. *Maine* was sunk in the harbor at Havana, Cuba, during the Spanish-American troubles, the rifles aboard were M1895 Lee-Navies. These rifles were later recovered

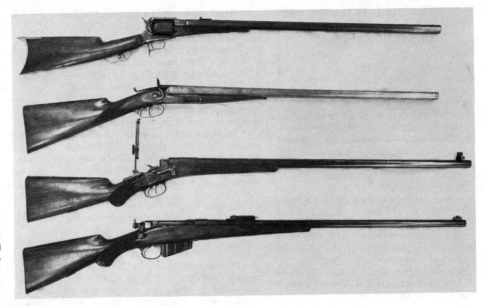

Fig. 28—Top to bottom: The Remington-Beals revolving rifle, M1858; double-barrel Remington-Whittmore shotgun; Remington No. 3 Improved Creedmoor Hepburn Rifle; and the M1899 Remington-Lee Sporting Rifle —a design which is still modern nearly 75 years later.

by divers and sold at Government auction to Francis Bannerman Sons of New York City. A list of their serial numbers appeared in the Bannerman catalog, which could identify rifles recovered from the *Maine.*

On May 31, 1898, U. S. Patent 604,904, was issued, as before, to "Edward G. Parkhurst . . . for a "Magazine Bolt-Gun." But this time the patent was not for a straight-pull design. Instead this patent covered a "turn-bolt" gun, and " . . . its general object being to provide certain improvements whereby these weapons may be rendered more durable and efficient in service and whereby their constructive features are simplified and improved, reducing the cost of manufacture . . . " One unusual feature of this design for a Lee firearm was the Mauser-type extractor, which extended two-thirds the length of the bolt. The bolt head was removable and instead of rear locking lugs there were now two front locking lugs on the bolt head. The bolt rotated 90° to unlock, and cocking was still on closing.

The firing pin was inserted into the hollow bolt body from the front, as in the previous models, and a large flange was provided to prevent the gas from a pierced primer escaping rearward. The rear of the firing pin had interrupted threads so the cocking piece could be slipped on longitudinally and locked in place with a one-eighth turn. The cocking piece now had a knurled section for easier manual cocking.

New Turn-Bolt Rifle

A main feature of this design was a clip for loading the non-detachable magazine. The magazine, an integral part of the trigger guard, assembly, projected slightly below the stock line. It held 5 rounds in a single column, and the cartridges illustrated in the patent drawings were rimmed, of about 6mm caliber. Located on the left side of the magazine was a vertically-sliding cut-off, which allowed the rifle to be used as a single shot while keeping a full magazine in reserve. The magazine lips could be contracted or expanded slightly

by means of a cam operated by a vertical-sliding mechanism on the right side of the magazine. With the lips apart the magazine could be loaded by stripping the cartridges down out of the clip. Releasing the lips prevented the cartridges from moving upward, except when being chambered in the normal manner.

The trigger and sear of this design were almost identical to the corresponding parts of the previous Lee turnbolt rifles. However, a coil sear spring was used in place of the U-shaped leaf spring of the Lee designs. Whether any rifles based on this design were actually produced is not known to the author.

The last Lee turnbolt design was the Model 1899, for smokeless cartridges. The bolt head had dual-opposed locking lugs, in addition to the rear locking lug and guide rib, and was exceptionally strong. Offered in both sporting and military versions, the receiver was marked on the upper left side:

Remington Arms Co. Ilion, N.Y.

and on the left side:

Patented Aug. 26th 1884. March 17th 1885. Jan. 18th 1887.

In the military version the caliber was stamped on top of the barrel, ahead of the middle band. Several calibers were available, including the 236 Lee, 6mm Navy, 7mm Mauser, 30-40 Krag (30 U.S. Gov't.) and 303 British. The Michigan State Militia adopted and bought 2000 of this model, chambered for the 30-40 Krag cartridge, in 1900. Cuba is reported to have bought 30,000 of them chambered for the 7mm Mauser cartridge.

The military Model 1899 weighed about 8⅜ pounds, the barrel was 29 inches long and over-all length was 49½ inches. Unlike previous models the M1899 had an upper handguard extending to the middle band. A short, straight, tangent rear sight, located about three inches behind the middle band, was graduated to 700 yards: the leaf was graduated to 1900 yards, but there was no provision for windage adjustment. The front sight was a detachable

blade, its rear face angled some 45 degrees.

The stock of the military Model 1899 was much the same as that on previous models, except for the nose cap, which was designed to support the handle of a knife bayonet. As previously, the sling swivels were on the upper band and the front of the trigger guard, and a cleaning rod was held in the fore-end beneath the barrel.

One distinguishing aspect of the Model 1899 was the extremely large knurled head on the cocking piece. This, coupled with the upper handguard and a 5-round magazine with three grooves instead of two, makes the M1899 easy to identify.

The 1899 extractor, a small leaf with a hook on the end slides into a recess on the side of the detachable bolt head; it resembles some of the latest modern designs. With the extractor in place the bolt head, which has a hole bored vertically crosswise near the rear end, is inserted into the bolt body until it lines up with a matching hole in the guide rib of the body. A locking bar, with pin to fit these two holes, is then positioned at approximately 90° to the bolt body, and rotated to line up with the guide rib, of which it will become a part; just before line-up occurs the rear end is lifted slightly to provide clearance for a positioning lug and then let down to engage a matching slot in the guide rib.

The Model 1899 cocked on closing the bolt, as did the previous models. When locked the front lugs were in a vertical plane, and the rear lug and guide rib in a horizontal plane; the left lug was slotted for-and-aft for an ejector in the left receiver wall.

The military M1899 rifle reportedly sold for $30 in 1905, with 4 extra magazines; the knife bayonet, with scabbard, was available for $5 more.

Phil Sharpe mentions that a carbine model with 20-inch barrel, weight some 7 pounds, was available in the same calibers as the rifle. It was not equipped for a bayonet, as the fore-end ended about three inches in front of the middle band. Over-all length was 39½ inches. The author has never seen one of these carbines, which reportedly listed for $28 in 1905.

Model 1899 Sporters

The sporting [10] version of the M1899 was offered in the same calibers as the military model, and a number of other available calibers have been reported by various sources. These last included the 30-30 Winchester, 32 Winchester Special, 32 Remington (rimless), 32-40 Winchester, 35 Winchester, 35 Remington (rimless), 38-55 Winchester, 38-72 Winchester, 405 Winchester, 43 Mauser, 44-77 Sharps, 45-70 Gov't. and 45-90 Winchester.

The walnut stock had a shotgun-type butt with a hard-rubber plate and a pistol grip, with cap. The grip area and the slim fore-end were well checkered, the latter with a small black hard-rubber cap. Sling swivels were not standard, but could be had on special order.

Barrels were round, lengths of 24- or 26 inches were standard. A heavier 28-inch barrel could be had on special order, as could Lyman sights and stock variations. Standard sights consisted of a rear sight adjustable for windage and elevation, and a front bead mounted on a heavier base dovetailed into the barrel.

These sporters varied from 8½ to 9 pounds, and were priced at $25 in 1905. Discontinued in 1906, they no doubt remained in stock for several years.

A limited number of "special" deluxe sporting rifles were also available. These had select English walnut stocks with full pistol grips and fancy grip caps. The butt was finished English-style with separate heel and toe plates. Checkering on the grip and fore-end was of the finest, and special attention was given to the finish on all metal parts.

Barrel length of the "Special" was 26 inches—half-octagon and half-round. Sling swivels were standard, the front unit attached to the underside of the barrel midway between the muzzle and the fore-end tip, the rear swivel attached to the underside of the buttstock.

The sights comprised a Lyman bead front, and a Lyman folding leaf rear on the barrel. In addition, there was a Lyman "wind-gauge" cocking-piece sight designed especially for the M1899 action.

The low-volume "special" sporter sold for $60 in 1905.

Although James Paris Lee's old heel wound began to trouble him shortly after the U. S. Navy had adopted the Lee Straight-Pull rifle, it was not until 1897-98 that his general health forced his confinement to bed for many months at his home in Hartford. The extent of his illness can be glimpsed from the remarks Lee made in a letter to his friend, James Young, dated July 1, 1898.

> "... I am simply a wreck in human form. This disease is surely gaining on whatever intellect I possessed. Little as it was, it is less today. I sit for hours without uttering a word, and I cannot even walk, as my old shot heel bothers me. I had to give up all business two years ago ... I live entirely in the past ... In the mornings (lie abed till noon) I think of Galt ... and would like to end my days there ..."

In April, 1899, on the advice of a Vermont doctor—a brother-in-law of his son George—Lee traveled to the Post Graduate Hospital in New York City. His troubled heel was cut open and a small portion of the bone removed. In it were found 5 lead pellets embedded there for nearly 52 years. The operation was a success. Lee's health began to improve at once and, although slightly lame, he was able to visit Galt in August of that year. He also was apparently able to return to business, at least to some extent, as indicated by the Improved Lee Model 1901 (straight-pull). However, it is also possible that his two sons were actively engaged in the business at this time.

Described as being above average height, strongly built, with dark hair and dark gray eyes, Lee's warm-hearted, easy-going manner gained him many friends. His inventions reportedly brought him several fortunes, and if he had been as successful in managing his patents and finances as he was in inventing, he might have been a millionaire. However, the expenses of his kind of an inventor were necessarily large, and the last few years were not highly productive; the 1899 models were probably the last ones to reach the manufacturing stage. Even so, Lee continued to work on his designs until his death on February 24, 1904, at South Beach, Conn.

No account of the Lee firearms would be complete without including the British portion of the Lee history. For it was in England that the Lee designs became famous, so much so that the name Lee became almost a household word.

English Beginnings

In England a Small Arms Committee was formed in 1879 to deal with several small arms problems, including the Martini-Henry rifle and the "... the desirability or otherwise of introducing a magazine rifle for naval or military use, or both." Over the next few years a number of American and European designs were examined and tested. The trials were carried out at the Proof Butts at Woolwich Arsenal by a sergeant and three picked marksmen of the Royal Welch Fusiliers. The tests performed included:

(1) Rapidity of fire without aiming.

(2) Rapidity of fire with aiming, at both stationary and moving targets.

(3) Exposure to the weather for three days without cleaning after firing; exposure to a sand blast and firing without cleaning; rough usage; safety tests.

Following the tests all weapons were forwarded to the Royal Small Arms Factory for examination.

Included in the trials held during May and June of 1880, were the arms of Hotchkiss, Kropatschek, Lee (rifle and carbine), Winchester M1876, Gardner, Green, and Vetterli rifles. The Lee arms were based on his patent of November 4, 1879, in which the mainspring was compressed as the bolt was closed. This was considered a disadvantage, as it prevented the feel of the cartridge being chambered. It was thus thought possible that a cartridge could stick or jam, yet be driven on into the chamber, causing a premature explo-

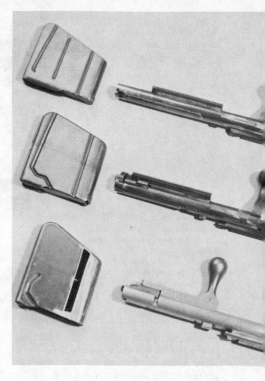

Fig. 29—Row 1: Breech-bolt of the M1889 Remington-Lee with the 3-groove magazine ● Row 2: Breech-bolt of the M1885 Remington-Lee with the 2-groove magazine ● Row 3: Breech-bolt of the M1879 Lee with the M1879 magazine. The wide slot in the magazine was apparently added later by an owner to show the number of rounds remaining in the magazine; it is not considered to be an original feature. Fig. 30—Top to bottom: Breech-bolts of the Models 1879, 1885 and 1899 Lee and Remington-Lee rifles, with the bolt heads removed to show the methods of attaching the extractors.

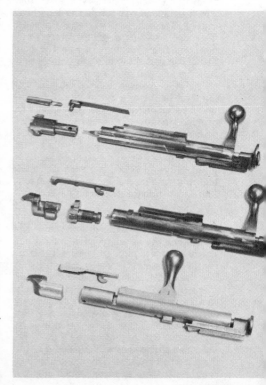

Fig. 31—The small rimfire revolver which may or may not have been a product of James Paris Lee. The octagon barrel is 2¼ inches long and the top flat is marked: RED JACKET No. 3. The 5-shot cylinder is 1³⁄₁₆ inches long and 5 chambered for the 32 rimfire cartridge. Weighing 10 ozs., over-all length is about 6 inches. It is nickel-plated and the grips are natural pearl. The revolver functions single action only, and the spur trigger has a terrible pull; the hammer does have a half-cock notch. The topstrap is marked: THE LEE ARMS CO./ WILKESBARRE, PA. in two lines, with a narrow groove passing between the two lines to serve as a sighting groove. The front sight is a narrow brass blade. Over-all construction and finish are fair, but the steel appears to be rather soft.

sion with an unlocked bolt.

The extraction was not considered satisfactory, but the chamber was partly at fault; The rifle and carbine barrels, of the 45-caliber Martini-Henry pattern, were made at the Royal Small Arms Factory, Enfield Lock; these were chambered to take solid-drawn brass-case Gatling service ammunition loaded with 85 grains of black powder behind a 480-gr. bullet. The extractor appeared to have sufficient camming action to start case withdrawal, but its form was considered poor. The guns were returned to Enfield Lock for investigation and repair.

The magazine position was well liked, since it did not alter the balance of the rifle when full or empty, and it was easily loaded. In general the Lee rifle made a good impression, and it was deemed easy to manufacture.

Specifications of the two Lee rifles tested at this time follow:

LEE RIFLE:

Caliber 45

Grooves:

Number 7
Form . . . . .Henry Rifling
Depth . . . . .0075"
Rate of twist . . . . .1 turn in 22"

Mechanism:

Closing . . . . .By bolt
Opening . . . . . .Spiral spring and firing pin

Length Over-all . . . . .53"
Weight . . . . .9 lbs. 5 ozs.
Magazine Cap. . . . . .5 rounds
Sights . . . . .To 1,400 yards

The Lee Carbine weight was 6½ lbs. and over all length was 43.5 inches. Sights on the Carbine were graduated to 800 yards.

A month after the trials were over the

Lee rifle was returned from Enfield with an improved extractor. It was then used to fire 45 rounds of the Gatling cartridges, which were easily extracted, with an average rate of fire of 20 rounds in 52 seconds. Things were looking up for the Lee design.

The Royal Navy wanted a magazine rifle, but two years later nothing had been decided. The best rifles from the previous trials were to be tested again, plus any other new designs that might be authorized; all were to be capable of firing the Gatling cartridge—the machine gun cartridge then in use.

Further English Trials

In November, 1882, the following rifles were submitted for trial: Schulhof (3), Improved Lee, Spencer-Lee, Chaffee-Reece, Gardner, and Mannlicher. On 3rd May, 1883, the Committee reported that all rifles submitted had been tried and compared to the Martini-Henry, but that all had failed on some point, and were now being altered or repaired. A new Small Arms Committee had been formed, and this time the inventors or their agents were allowed to demonstrate and fire the rifles on the range. More than half of the rifles were quickly rejected, and the inventors of several others were told that their rifles would be rejected unless they could be altered to take the Gatling cartridge. With all rifles taking the same cartridge, the trials continued until 31st October, 1883. At this time it was reported that two Lee designs—the Improved Lee modified at Enfield Lock and the Lee with the Bethel Burton magazine made at Enfield Lock—were promising, but three rifles—a new magazine rifle designed by Owen Jones, employed at Enfield Lock, the Spencer-Lee, and the Mannlicher—were still to be tested.

While waiting for the Spencer-Lee and the Mannlicher rifles to arrive, 6 additional rifles were received for testing, including a Remington-Lee model. Of the 6 new rifles submitted, only the Remington-Lee warranted much interest, but it was not chambered for the Gatling cartridge and was therefore not tested. The other 5 rifles were either too heavy, too complicated, or not chambered for the Gatling cartridge.

By August, 1885, the Small Arms Committee had examined or tried nearly 50 magazine rifles and quick-loading systems. Of these all but three had broken down during testing, or had been rejected for other reasons. The three left were the Improved Lee Magazine Rifle, the Improved Lee with Bethel Burton magazine, and the Owen Jones Magazine Rifle. All three had been improved or manufactured at the Royal Small Arms Factory at Enfield Lock, and the Lee Magazine Rifle was the only survivor of the original testing started 5 years before.

These three rifles had fore-ends of like shape, with a single barrel band a few inches behind the muzzle. A front sling swivel was attached to this band, another to the underside of the buttstock. All had a short upper handguard extending from the receiver ring to the rear sight. From this approximate location the fore-end was reduced in depth. All three rifles carried cleaning rods in a groove in the bottom of the fore-end. The Lee rifle had a one-piece stock, the others separate buttstocks. All had straight grip stocks; the two Lee models had conventional combs, while the Owen Jones was similar to the latter Enfield models without a pronounced comb.

The Lee-Burton receiver had a very long upper tang, extending almost to the comb; the rear tang of the trigger guard was as long. Both were fastened together by two bolts passing through the grip of the stock from the underside. The Burton magazine fastened to the right side of the action; in use it projected upward above the barrel about 1½ inches. When not in use it could be lowered alongside the receiver. It could be loaded with up to 5 cartridges while in the firing position, a point in its favor.

The Improved Lee trigger guard and receiver had short tangs; the guard was attached to the receiver by two bolts from below, one at the rear and one at the front, ahead of the magazine well. The magazine —a plain, ungrooved model—was readily detachable, but it could not be loaded while attached to the rifle (in this early model) and this was felt to be a disadvantage. The cocking piece differed from those on the U. S. Lee rifles.

Setback and Success

The Owen Jones rifle operated by a slide under the buttstock, and was extremely rapid but it was not as cheap to manufacture as the Lee. Still, the Committee apparently thought it superior to the two Lee models and recommended it for trial by the Army and Navy.

While the Committee had been testing magazine rifles the Enfield factory had been developing a barrel of smaller caliber for the single shot Martini-Henry rifle; they'd decided on a 402 caliber with 7-

groove Metford segmental rifling, developed over two decades before. These consisted of shallow grooves shaped to the segment of a circle. It was felt that the Owen Jones and the two Lee designs should be tested with the new 402 caliber Metford barrels before a final decision was made. Steps were taken to fit the new barrels, when suddenly the Owen Jones rifle was dropped from further tests because of manufacturing difficulties. The bottom magazine was considered to be the better position, so the Improved Lee Magazine Rifle emerged the victor.

Still smaller calibers were being developed in Europe. After some study 303 caliber barrels with Metford rifling were fitted to the Improved Lee actions and about 350 of the resulting Lee-Metford rifles were issued to the British Army for trials. The results were satisfactory and, on December 22, 1888, the Magazine Rifle, Mark I, was approved for manufacture.

British Army Orders, dated 1st December, 1889, contained the following description of the new rifle:

MAGAZINE RIFLE, MARK I

Weight	9 lb. 8 oz.
Weight of Magazine (empty)	4¾ oz.
Weight of Magazine (filled)	13 oz.
Length	49 in.

Barrel and Rifling:

Length	30.2 in.
Calibre	303 in.
Rifling	Metford segmental
Grooves	Seven
Grooves, depth	.004 in.
Lands, width	.023 in.
Spiral, left-handed	1 turn in 10 in., or 33 calibres

The rifle embodies the Lee bolt action, with rear locking. The cocking-piece is so arranged that the action can be set at half-cock, in which position the rifle can be carried in safety. Covers are fitted to the bolt and the bolt-head to protect the action in sand and mud. A safety-catch is fitted on the left side of the body, the pulling back of which, when the rifle is at full-cock, prevents any effect being caused by pressing the trigger. When springs are "eased," and the cocking-piece is in the forward position, it locks the action and prevents the bolt from becoming accidently opened.

The *magazine* consists of a sheet-steel box, inserted in the body through an opening underneath, and directly in front of the trigger guard. It is held in position by a spring in the body engaging in a notch on the magazine. It holds 8 cartridges and can be filled when in position on the rifle, or when detached . . . they are fed into the chamber by the forward movement of the bolt. A cut-off is fitted to the right side of the body which, when pressed inwards, stops the supply of cartridges from the magazine, thus enabling the weapon to be used as a single-loader. When the cut-off is pulled out, the lower edge of the face of the bolt-head, on the bolt being driven forwards, engages the top edge of the uppermost cartridge in the magazine and forces it into the chamber. The magazine can be removed from the rifle by pressing a small lever inside the trigger-guard. One magazine is attached, by means of a chain link, to each rifle: a spare magazine is also issued with each arm.

The *stock*, like that of the Martini-Henry rifle, is in two pieces, the fore-end and the butt . . .
The *butt* is secured to the body of the rifle by a stock bolt. The buttplate . . . is fitted with a trap . . . to house an oil bottle and a jag . . .
The *nose-cap* is fitted with a bar on top for the attachment of the sword bayonet, which is positioned underneath the barrel . . .
A *wooden hand-guard* is fixed over the breech end of the barrel to protect the hand when the barrel becomes hot. It is held in place by two steel springs, which clip round the barrel.

The rifle is provided with two sets of sights. The foresight and the backsight are fixed in the usual positions on the barrel.
The *foresight* is a square block, with a vertical cut through it. . . . The lowest, or "fixed" sight, is that for 300 yards . . . The highest graduation is for 1,900 yards. The rifle is also fitted with extreme range sights. The front sight, which is called the dial sight, is graduated from 1,800 yards up to 3,500 yards. It consists of a bead fixed to a revolving index hand. The index is set to the correct distance, which is marked on the edge of the dial plate, and aim is taken by aligning the bead on the object aimed at through a circular hole in the aperture sight . . . Both these sights are on the left side of the rifle . . ."

Changes, Changes

On August 8, 1891, the name was changed to the Lee-Metford Magazine Rifle, Mark I, and 5 months later on January 19, 1892, it became the Lee-Metford Magazine Rifle Mark I*, through some sight modifications.

Eleven days later, acting on recommendations to increase the magazine capacity from 8 rounds to 10, to lighten the barrel, modify the bolt head, and some dozen other minor modifications, the War Office officially approved the Lee-Metford Magazine Rifle, Mark II. The new rifle weighed 9 lbs. 4 oz., four ounces lighter than the Mark I.

Three years later a safety catch was added to replace the one which had been omitted since the Mark I*, and the rifle became the Lee-Metford Magazine Rifle, Mark II*. Other minor modifications necessary to the operation of the safety were also made at this time.

On September 29, 1895, in answer to demands from the British Cavalry, the Lee-Metford Magazine Carbine, Mark I, was approved for manufacture. Magazine capacity was 6 rounds, the barrel was 20¾ inches long, over-all length 39¹⁵/₁₆ inches, weight 7 lb. 7 oz. Other modifications to the sights, stock, hand-guard, bands, nose-cap, etc., were made at this time.

In an attempt to overcome the destructive effect of Cordite powder erosion on the shallow Metford rifling, new barrels with Enfield rifling, as developed at the Royal Small Arms Factory, were fitted.† The Lee-Metford rifles with the new barrels became the Lee-Enfield Magazine Rifle, Mark I, on November 11, 1895—the

---

†Henry Metford had, in fact, patented the so-called Enfield rifling in 1860. even prior to his segmental rifling.

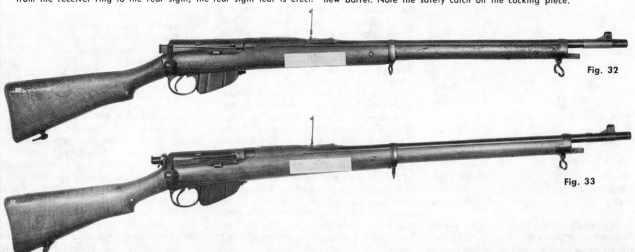

Fig. 32—The Lee-Metford Mark II. Adopted on January 30, 1892, the new rifle weighed 9 lb. 4 oz and had a magazine capacity of 10 rounds instead of the previous 8. Note the short handguard, extending only from the receiver ring to the rear sight; the rear sight leaf is erect.

Fig. 33—The Lee-Enfield Mark I*, advanced from the Mark I by omission of the clearing rod. This rifle is very similar to the previous Lee-Metford Mark II*, except for the new barrel. Note the safety catch on the cocking piece.

Fig. 32

Fig. 33

start of a long line of Lee-Enfield Rifles. On August 17, 1896, modification of the Cavalry carbine to include the new Enfield rifling was approved, with other necessary changes, and the Lee-Enfield Magazine Carbine, Mark I, came into being.

On 19th May, 1899, the clearing rod and clearing rod hole, etc., in the fore-end of the rifle and carbine were omitted, and the designation became Mark I*. The omission of the clearing rod was extended to all 303 caliber arms then in service, including the various Martini patterns.

The next L-E to be introduced was another carbine. It appeared on August 1, 1900, and was intended for the British Land Services. It had a special barrel, fore-end and handguard, weighed 7½ pounds, and was 40¼ inches long.

In January, 1900, the Small Arms Committee was completely re-organized to include representatives concerned with manufacture, inspection, requirements, and experience with service arms and ammunition. A representative of the National Rifle Association also became a member of the Committee. The Boer War was in progress and in June of 1900 the Small Arms Committee recommended that the Lee-Enfield rifle be replaced with a new one. To strengthen their position they listed 7 defects of the Lee-Enfield, and questioned whether an automatic rifle might not be desirable. They went so far as to test an Italian model.

The S.M.L.E.

In late 1900, the Superintendent of the Royal Small Arms Factory let the Small Arms Committee know that he had been able to alter the Lee-Enfield to overcome the defects they had mentioned, and could manufacture the new rifle at once at little or no increase in price. In the memorandum the Superintendent listed 12 alterations which would be made.

The altered rifle was tested at Hythe in December, 1900, and on January 12, 1901, the Secretary of State approved the manufacture of 1,000 Shortened Modified Enfield Rifles in lots of 500 each of Pattern A and B, for troop trials.

The 1000 rifles were tested by units of the Royal Navy, Royal Marines, Cavalry and Infantry, following a program of 8 parts. The rifle was well received and, on November 10, 1902, the Committee recommended it for adoption with some modifications in the sights and magazine. On December 15, 1902, the R.S.A.F. Superintendent submitted a Short Rifle with 12 minor modifications. The rifle was approved by the Committee and introduced on December 23, 1902, as the Short Magazine Lee-Enfield Rifle, Mark I, for the Infantry and Cavalry. It weighed 20 ounces less than the Enfield it replaced. The first of the S.M.L.E. rifles was a reality.

The new rifle was 41⁹⁄₁₆ inches long, its barrel 25³⁄₁₆ in. The bolt cover was omitted, the cocking-piece was shorter, the magazine was ⅛-inch deeper, and the Navy version was equipped with a cut-off. Buttstocks were issued in three lengths, a safety was located on the left side of the receiver, and changes were made in the fore-end, hand-guard, bands, nose-cap, swivels, and several other components. A few months later some additional changes were made and the rifle was re-introduced on 14th September, 1903.

On January 13, 1902, Lee-Metford Carbines fitted with Enfield barrels and extended nose-cap wings were re-named Lee-Enfield Mark I Carbines. Later, on September 6, 1902, Lee-Metford Mark II* rifles fitted with Enfield barrels became Lee-Enfield Mark I Rifles, if they had the old fore-end nose-cap; if they had the newer, more solid fore-end and nose-cap they became Lee-Enfield Mark I* Rifles.

The year 1903 was to be a busy one. The Lee-Enfield Mark I and I*, and the Lee-Metford Mark II and II* rifles were given new barrels, sights, and other minor modifications and re-introduced on January 16, 1903, as the Short Magazine Lee-Enfield (Converted) Mark II. On August

12, a new cut-off for the S.M.L.E. Mark I was approved for British Naval Service only. November 2nd, the Lee-Metford Mark I* became the Short Magazine Lee-Enfield (Converted) Mark I, a conversion which was declared "obsolete" before it was ever manufactured.

During March, April and May, 1905, as a result of a questionnaire to the British Forces in India, trials were held at Hythe between the Long and Short rifles to compare velocity, accuracy, systems of sighting and speed of loading. The trials indicated that the Long rifles were more accurate, but the Short rifles were handier and better adapted to snapshooting. A new pattern was sealed and, on 2nd July, 1906, the Short Magazine Lee-Enfield Rifle, Mark I*, was introduced. It weighed 4½ ounces more than the Mark I, and differed slightly in the magazine, buttstock and plate, swivels and screws, striker, sights, and hand-guards. On the same day a new conversion was also introduced. The Long Lee-Enfield rifles, Mark I and I*, and the Lee-Metford rifles, Mark II and II*, were converted to become the Short Magazine Lee-Enfield Rifle Converted, Mark II*, which differed from the Converted Mark II, but slightly, in the buttstock, magazine, and swivel and keeper screws. Six weeks later, on 17th August, 1906, a coin-slotted striker keeper-screw was approved for all Marks of the S.M.L.E., and on 25th October, the cut-off was returned and fitted to all S.M.L.E. rifles in the British Army—the Royal Navy already had them.

Hythe and Enfield Tests

Trials were held at Hythe and Enfield periodically in an attempt to improve the S.M.L.E. A reliable charger-loading feature was in particular demand by the troops, and several other modifications had been recommended. On 31st October, 1906, 6 rifles, which had been sent to Aldershot for testing, were reported as satisfactory. On 26th January, 1906, the

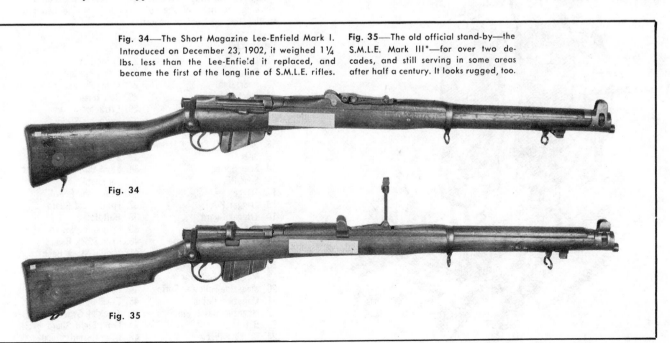

Fig. 34—The Short Magazine Lee-Enfield Mark I. Introduced on December 23, 1902, it weighed 1¼ lbs. less than the Lee-Enfield it replaced, and became the first of the long line of S.M.L.E. rifles.

Fig. 35—The old official stand-by—the S.M.L.E. Mark III*—for over two decades, and still serving in some areas after half a century. It looks rugged, too.

Fig. 34

Fig. 35

Lee-Enfield Rifle No. 4, Mark I*

Historical Notes

The No. 4, Mark 1 Lee-Enfield marks the last of an illustrious line of British Lee rifles that began in 1888 and passed through a bewildering maze of Marks and Numbers, models and revisions. After World War I, British ordnance began looking for ways to improve the old and famous Mk. III series and by 1931 developed the prototype S.M.L.E. (Short Magazine Lee-Enfield) Mk. VI. When the British revised their nomenclature system, this rifle became the Rifle No. 4, Mk I. The major improvements were an aperture rear sight, a simplified bolt-retaining system and bolt release, and a socket type spike bayonet. As is the custom in the British service, the new rifle was harshly criticized, especially the spike bayonet. (It is interesting to note that British ordnance defended the bayonet as being specifically designed to penetrate **German** overcoats). In 1939, the rifle was redesigned for mass production, but the early World War II years were fought with the Mark III*.

The No. 4, Mk. I* was the North American version. Almost one million were made at Long Branch Arsenal in Canada, and over a million by Savage Arms Corporation. The Savage made rifles are curiously stamped "U.S. Property," even though they were never intended for our use; perhaps this was prompted by political subterfuge. The major difference between the Mk. I and Mk. I* is the bolt release (see illus.).

As a military rifle, the Lee-Enfields are excellent, but they are not in the same design class as Mausers and Mannlichers. They do not lend themselves to sporterizing. British ordnance does not consider the bolts to be interchangeable. These rifles fire one type of cartridge, the 303 Enfield (British). The 303 Savage cartridge is **not** the same.

Disassembly

Raise the rear sight (3). See illustration on opposite page. **Rifle Mk. I**: depress bolt release and withdraw bolt all the way to the rear; release bolt release and raise bolt head (28) **Rifle Mk. I***: withdraw bolt until bolt head (28) aligns with cutout on guide groove, which allows the bolt head to be pushed up and out of its channel. With bolt head raised in line with the bolt rib, the entire bolt may be withdrawn. Press magazine catch (21) and remove magazine (18). Unscrew band screws (43 & 44) up over the stock. Unscrew guard screws (15 & 16) and remove trigger guard (14) with trigger (12). Work forestock (35) down and off. Buttstock (32) can be removed by unscrewing the stock bolt (33). The stock bolt is frequently packed with felt and this should be removed first. (If the buttstock is sound and tight, its removal is not recommended.) Unscrew safety screw (8) and extract safety assembly. (Reassembly can be tricky. Be sure the safety bolt and catch are in position shown in illustration before reseating). Sear (9) and magazine catch (21) can be removed by driving out their respective pins (11 & 22).

To disassemble the bolt, first unscrew the bolt head (28), then the firing pin screw (27). The firing pin (25) can be unscrewed only from the front of the bolt. This requires a special wrench. **Do not** try it with ordinary tools. The firing pin (25) and firing-pin spring (26) will come out the front of the bolt.

Unscrew extractor screw (31), insert end of screwdriver behind lip of extractor (29) and force extractor forward, then out of front of bolt head. Insert a small screwdriver between top of extractor spring (30) and upper wall of bolt head until nipple on spring clears its receptacle. From rear, push spring forward and out.

Remove magazine follower (19) by depressing the rear, allowing the front of the follower to clear the two protruding lips on front of magazine.

Parts List

1. Barrel	25. Firing Pin
2. Receiver	26. Firing-Pin Spring
3. Rear Sight	27. Firing-Pin Screw
4. Ejector Screw	28. Bolt Head
5. Safety Bolt	29. Extractor
6. Safety Catch	30. Extractor Spring
7. Safety Bolt Spring	31. Extractor Screw
8. Safety Bolt Spring Screw	32. Buttstock
9. Sear	33. Stock Bolt
10. Sear Spring	34. Stock-Bolt Lock Washer
11. Sear Pin	35. Forestock
12. Trigger	36. Rear Hand Guard
13. Trigger Pin	37. Front Hand Guard
14. Trigger Guard	38. Buttplate
15. Rear Guard Screw	39. Rear Sling Swivel
16. Front Guard Screw	40. Rear Stock Band
17. Front Gaurd Screw Bearing	41. Middle Stock Band
18. Magazine	42. Front Sling Swivel
19. Magazine Follower	43. Sling Swivel Screw
20. Magazine-Follower Spring	44. Front Stock Band
21. Magazine Catch	45. Stacking Swivel
22. Magazine-Catch Pin	46. Stacking Swivel Screw
23. Bolt	47. Front Sight Guard
24. Cocking Piece	48. Oiler (in buttstock)

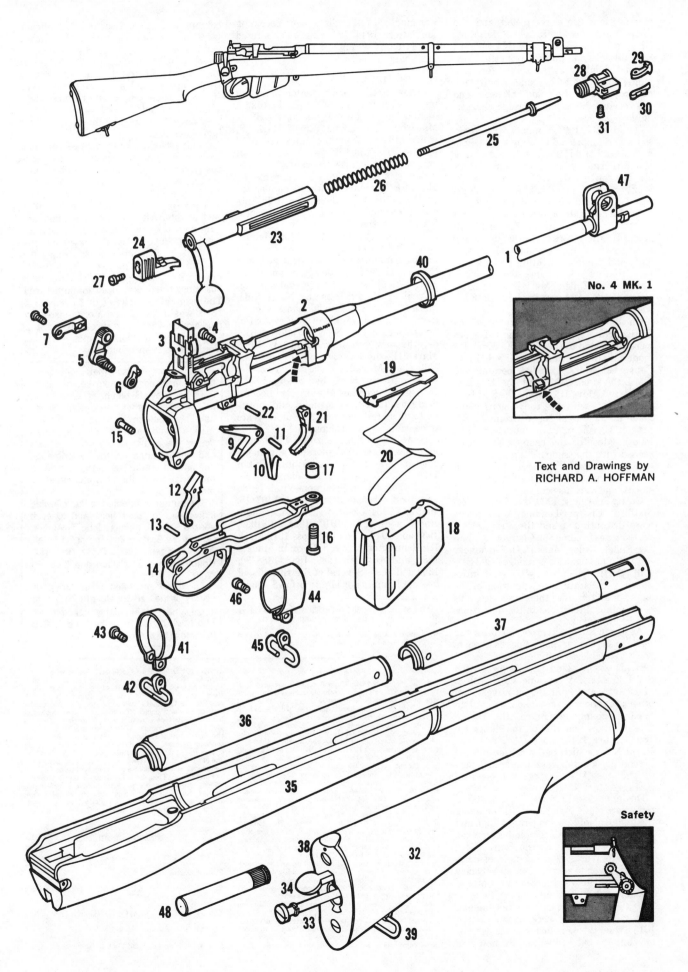

No. 4 MK. 1

Text and Drawings by
RICHARD A. HOFFMAN

Safety

modifications were completed and the Short Magazine Lee-Enfield Rifle, Mark III, was approved. The new rifle weighed 8 lb. 10½ oz., and differed from the Mark I and I* slightly in the sights, fore-end, hand-guards, cut-off, bands, buttplate, nose-cap, locking-bolt and bolt-head, and the receiver body had a bridge charger-guide.

On June 17, 1907, a number of conversions were approved to bring the Lee-Enfield Mark I and I* and Lee-Metford Mark II and II* rifles in line with the new Mark III. The converted rifles weighed 8 lb. 14-½ oz., and were listed as the Short Magazine Lee-Enfield Converted Mark IV.

On July 1, 1907, another lot of Mark I and I* Lee-Enfield, and Lee-Metford Mark II and II* rifles were converted by adding a bridge-type charger-guide, new magazine, and modified sighting system. The new conversions became the Charger-Loading Lee-Enfield, Mark I*, and Charger-Loading Lee-Metford, Mark II. Each weighed about 9 lb. 5 oz.

On January 4, 1908, a number of the British Navy's S.M.L.E., Mark I rifles were converted to the S.M.L.E., Mark I** models. Later the same year the S.M.L.E. Converted Mark II rifles became the S.M.L.E., Mark II**, and the S.M.L.E. Converted, Mark II* became the S.M.L.E., Mark II***, with the conversions being made at the Royal Naval Ordnance Depots at Chatham, Portsmouth, and Plymouth. Most of the changes were concerned with the trigger guard, magazine, and installation of a charger-guide, with minor changes in the receiver and bolt, stocks, and various screws.

On 1st February, 1909, the Mark II Lee-Metford Charger-Loading conversions were discontinued and the already converted rifles became the Charger-Loading Lee-Enfield Rifles, Mark I*. On November 3, 1910, a new service cartridge—303 S.A. Ball Cartridge Mark VII—was introduced, necessitating an alteration in the sights of all the rifles then in service, plus some minor alterations to the magazines of certain Marks.

As war in Europe approached haste was made to see that as many rifles as possible were available to handle the Mark VII cartridge. On 22nd April, 1914, the S.M.L.E. Mark I* became the S.M.L.E. Mark I***, and later the same year two other conversions were made, without an apparent change in pattern, other than a C.L. (Charger-Loading) on the sights. On 18th August, 1915, Mark I** rifles in the Royal Navy which had not been altered for charger-loading were so altered to handle the Mark VII cartridge and re-named S.M.L.E. Mark I***.

On January 2, 1916, six minor modifications were made to the Mark III, including the removal of the long range dial and aperture sight, and the rifle became the Short Magazine Lee-Enfield, Mark I*.

Prior to World War I some consideration was given to adopting an entirely new design with forward locking lugs and of smaller caliber. A Mauser-type rifle for a 276 caliber rimless cartridge was made in prototype form and became the Pattern 1913. When the war started it was decided to retain the 303 caliber and the new rifle

was modified to handle it, thus becoming the Pattern 1914. This rifle was a limited standard and was not widely used, except in sniping versions.

Advent of the Rifle No. 1

Following the war the search to find an improved bolt action went on. In 1922 a modified pattern was sealed for the Short Magazine Lee-Enfield Rifle, Mark V, which differed from the Mark III in 10 features. The Mark V was tested, but not officially adopted; it was eventually abandoned for a new design which became the Mark VI. The Mark VI was recommended on December 14, 1923, by the Rifle Subcommittee and it was to retain the best features of the Mark III. By 1924 the Mark VI was being modified for trial. By early 1926 six prototypes of the Mark VI had been manufactured for trial, and over the next 13 years the design was modified and re-modified to emerge officially on November 15, 1939, as the No. 4 Rifle, Mark I [†]. The Lee-Enfield name was no more, for in May 1926, a new system of nomenclature had been introduced. Under the new system the S.M.L.E. Rifle, Mark III—the old standby—became the Rifle No. 1, Mark III. Basic design was the same, only the name had changed. The British had used Lee-Metford and Lee-Enfield rifles for 38 years, and would continue to do so for another 38 or more years under a different designation.

Some other famous rifles which also used the Lee centrally-located box magazine include the Swiss Schmidt-Rubin 1889, 1893, 1911 and 1931; Italian Vetterli-Vitali 1887; Dutch Beaumont-Vitali 71/88 and 1888; French Berthier 1890, 07/15, 1916 and 1934; Czech ZH29; Russian Mouzin (Mosin) 1891, 1910, 1891/30, 1930, 1938 and 1944; Canadian Ross 1910 Mark III; Remington Model 8; German Mauser 1888; and Austrian 1886, 1888, 1888/90, 1890 and 1895. Several of the rifles listed use the Mannlicher clip in a fixed single-

[†]The Short Magazine Lee-Enfield, Mark II, and Mark III rifles were manufactured in Australia, and the later No. 4 Rifle, Mark I* was manufactured in Canada and the United States, but these are not considered to be a part of the Lee-Enfield history.

column magazine. Lee and Mannlicher were contemporaries and the Mannlicher version may or may not have been influenced by the Lee design. The 1895 Lee and 1898 Parkhurst designs (assigned to Lee) employ clip-loaded magazines very similar to those employed by Mannlicher. Who influenced whom? Both inventors may have developed by the same designs independently.

Today, 90-odd years after Lee's original 1879 invention, the basic Lee magazine design is used on almost all military auto-loading rifles, such as our M16, M14, and AR-18, the Soviet AK-47, the German G-3, and the British FN L1A1. Machine rifles, such as the BAR, and various submachine guns have used the design, plus most auto-loading pistols, and even a few shotguns. A number of commercial sporting rifles use the Lee-type magazine and untold numbers of rimfire rifles with detachable box magazines have been manufactured. The original Lee patent of November 4, 1879, was a dwarf in material size—two pages of drawings and three pages of text —but a giant in scope. James Paris Lee would have been proud. ●

The author realizes that many questions concerning the activities of James Paris Lee may still be unanswered. There may even be other Lee designs which have not been covered, and such information would be most welcome. In particular the author would welcome data and photographs on the experimental and limited production designs, even on the variations of the known commercial models.

The author is indebted to the following individuals for their help, and to each goes a special thanks: John T. Amber, Gordon F. Baxter, Jr., Thomas E. Hall. Daniel R. Kuehn, Judith Topaz, Herbert L. Uphoff, James S. Watson and Eldon G. Wolff.

For those interested in exploring the history of the Lee-Enfield rifle in greater detail, the author highly recommends *The Lee-Enfield Rifle,* by Major E. G. B. Reynolds (New York, 1968).

References

9. On March 6, 1883, Hugo Borchardt obtained U.S. Patent No. 273,448 for a detachable magazine for magazine guns, which he assigned to Joseph W. Frazier of New York City. (Borchardt had designed the M1878 Sharps-Borchardt rifle for the Sharps Rifle Co., to which he had assigned Patents No. 185,721 and 206,217 on December 26, 1876, and July 23, 1878, respectively. This would place him in Bridgeport at about the same time as James Lee.) Frazier had filed his patent application on January 4, 1883, and on December 18, 1883, U.S. Patent No. 290,636 for a "Magazine Fire-Arm" was granted to "Joseph W. Frazier, of New York, N.Y., Assignor, by Mesne Assignments to the Spencer Arms Company, of Same Place." This patent covered the adapting of the Lee detachable box magazine—patented by Lee on November 4, 1879—to the slide action rifle patented by Christopher M. Spencer and Sylvester H. Roper on April 4, 1882, in U.S. Patent No. 255,894. The Frazier design consisted of the Spencer-type slide action rifle, with its breechblock pivoted at the rear and free at the front to swing above and in line with the chamber of the barrel. The box magazine was attached to the breechblock and moved up and down with it in normal operation, but was still readily detachable for replacement with a loaded magazine. The chambering and ejection of the cartridges were covered by the Spencer-Roper patent. This then became the basis for the Spencer-Lee rifles entered in the U.S. and British rifle trials of the 1880s.

10. Alden Hatch relates an incident involving a Remington-Lee Sporting Rifle that shook Bridgeport almost to its very foundations. A local lad, returning home empty-handed from a deer hunt, decided to take

a short cut through a field loosely fenced with barbed wire. On the field were a number of half-sunken stone structures resembling beehives. Deciding that one of these would provide a safe backstop for some rifle practice, he fastened a piece of paper onto the wooden door of one and paced off a hundred yards. Adjusting his sights, he took careful aim with his Remington-Lee and pulled the trigger. With a blinding flash of light the sky vanished and the earth split open with a thunderous roar. Three days later, when the lad came to in a hospital, he learned his "safe" backstop had been one of the U.M.C. powder-storage magazines. Bridgeport had shivered and windows had been broken as far away as Long Island. That the lad survived was a wonder. Shortly thereafter the present Powder Park—now a part of the Remington Arms Company complex—was obtained. The new Park is tightly fenced, closely guarded, and the powder magazines are bullet-proof.

Photo Credits

Figs. 16,19,22,23,24,26. U.S. Army, Rock Island Arsenal.

Fig. 36. National Park Service.

Fig. 37. British Crown Copyright. By Permission of the Controller, HMSO.

Fig. 17. Remington Arms Co. Collection.

Fig. 21. Globe & Mail, Toronto.

Patent Drawing—E. I. Du Pont de Nemours & Co., Inc.

Experimental Lee and Lee-Type Rifles

A 30-caliber bolt action rifle having a single-line box magazine permanently fixed in front of the trigger guard appeared in Norm Flayderman's catalog No. 69, along with a pump shotgun and a pump 30-caliber rifle of similar workmanship. No information is available, other than the arms are believed to have belonged to an executive of the old Savage Arms Co., and whether these could have been Lee designs is not known. It is a fact that Arthur Savage, who later absorbed the J. Stevens firm, was perfecting his lever action rifle at Remington's Armory in 1892, and might have met with James Lee. Or Savage may have decided to experiment with the Lee magazine, which Remington was manufacturing as a part of the Remington-Lee rifles, the rifle mentioned above representing the pilot model of a design Savage intended to explore further.

In the last catalog of Martin B. Retting, issued at West Hurley, N.Y., a number of Lee rifles were listed, including several M1879 and M1895 Lee-Navy rifles, and a M1899 Improved Lee Straight Pull rifle. Two other rifles were advertised as follows:

"Original factory pilot model of British Lee-Enfield rifle; 30-inch barrel, caliber 303 British, similar to the standard S.M.L.E. with magazine cut-off and made without safety. Safety was provided for through halfcock notch on cocking piece; two-piece stock with buttstock showing the beginnings of the well-known pistol grip. Bayonet lug on side of rifle (sic). This rifle was obtained from the family of Westcott, Treasurer of the Lee Arms Co., Patentees of the Lee bolt action rifle system, and was probably made at the Remington factory. Two of these rifles were manufactured, one for the English trials at which it was accepted, with the other retained by the Treasurer, Mr. Westcott. A very interesting, historical rifle, original condition throughout."

The second factory rifle was listed by Retting as a Remington factory experimental bolt action magazine rifle with a bolt of Modified Remington-Lee design with three locking lugs in rear of bolt, forward of the bolt handle. A special magazine was designed to fit on the left side of the receiver feeding from the top downward; special hinged folding magazine guides close the magazine port when not in use. The rifle was listed as having a 32-inch barrel, chambered for the 43-77 (sic) Remington cartridge. Another rifle in this caliber was listed as having an improved type bolt head and extractor so that cartridges could be loaded into the magazine through the top of the receiver. The barrel length of this rifle was also 32 inches.

After Retting moved to California other Lee rifles were listed in later catalogs. One such listing appeared in the green catalog as follows:

"Russian Berdan Infantry Rifle, 2nd Model, 42 caliber. Armory modification changing to Lee detachable box magazine system; extension fitted to trigger guard containing magazine with quick detachable thumb release. Bottom of receiver milled out, magazine cut-off fitted on left side of stock."

Fig. 36—Right side views of two experimental Lee rifles in the Winchester collection. The upper rifle is the Johnson modification, the lower rifle is Mason's.

Fig. 37—Left side views of the two rifles shown in Fig. 36. The furniture and fixtures on these two rifles are very similar to those of the M1895. The upper model does vary slightly, having finger grooves on the fore-end not found on any of the other models, and having bands, both upper and lower, which are slightly different.

A similar rifle (possibly the same one) was listed in *World's Guns* as a "Colt-Berdan II, 42 caliber Berdan . . . with 5-shot Lee-type magazine." The same publication also lists a "Dreyse patent bolt-action repeating magazine rifle, special 9mm four-shot, 25-inch barrel. Lee-type magazine swings out to the right for loading. Weapon cocks on closing. Thumb safety. Single large cocking lug in rear. Mannlicher-type stock with cheekpiece." While Lee may have had a hand in designing such a rifle it seems doubtful since most of the Lee magazines were the detachable box type or fixed, rather than swinging.

In a white-paper 1965 Retting catalog another interesting Lee variation is listed as a "Japanese experimental Murata-Lee Carbine with a Remington-Lee type magazine." It was full stocked to the muzzle, with two bands, and had side sling swivels. A grip safety was located on the underside of the grip, behind the trigger guard. The 8mm barrel was 18 ½ inches long, and a reversible angular bayonet could be locked onto the muzzle with the blade housed in the stock fore-end. The butt had a hinged trapdoor for accessories, and both barrel and action were stamped with serial number 1.

In the author's opinion it is possible that Lee could have attempted to interest the Japanese in using his magazine design, since the Type 22 (1889) Murata carbine had a tubular magazine. The Type 22 rifle differed from the carbine in having a longer stock and barrel, with a tubular magazine holding 8 cartridges. The Type 22 rifle and carbine and the earlier Type 3 (1880) rifle were invented by Major Murata Tsuneyoshi, and were copies of the French Chassepot. They left a lot to be desired, and the Lee

magazine would have been a definite improvement.

The 1949 Bannerman catalog, and possibly previous editions, showed two Spencer-Lee rifles in pump-action form. Rifle No. 1 had a 32-inch barrel, the upper band fitted with a stud for bayonet attachment. The checkered wooden fore-end was similar in shape to that on some modern shotguns. The top of the frame was solid, the cartridges ejecting out of a breech opening on the right side of the receiver in the same manner as modern pump shotguns and rifles. The box magazine projected below the stock in front of the trigger guard a la Lee design, the release a small lever inside the trigger guard. What is apparently a lever safety appears on the right side of the receiver, below the ejection port.

Both No. 1 and 2 rifles are of so-called hammerless design, or streamlined with inside hammers, but may be cocked separately without operating the slide by the use of an opposed forward trigger; this same feature was also used on the Spencer pump action shotguns and the Ohio-manufactured Union shotguns of two decades later.

While Rifle No. 1 was apparently made up in an attempt to interest some European governments, Rifle No. 2 was tested by the U. S. Army Magazine Gun Board in 1882 and was officially known as Gun No. 35. It differed from Rifle No. 1 in several ways. The fore-end was metal and the box magazine was not in contact with the trigger guard, but was located a short distance forward. The slide mechanism is slightly different and ejection was through the top of the receiver in the same manner as on the Spencer pump action shotgun. The No. 2 rifle was cham-

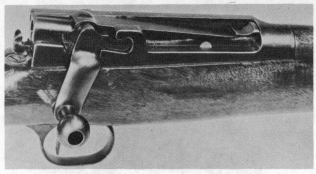

Fig. 38   Fig. 39

bered for the 45-70 cartridge and the magazine appears very similar to that used on the early Remington-Lee model Rifle. (The caliber of Rifle No. 1 is not known.)

According to the Bannerman catalog both rifles were manufactured by the Francis Bannerman firm in New York and later sold when government contracts were not obtained. The present whereabouts of these two very interesting rifles is not known to the author. It is possible that at least one of the rifles, or another model of the same basic design, is in England in some reference collection. A Spencer-Lee rifle was entered in the British small arms trials of 1882-1883, which ended with the adoption of the Improved Lee bolt action rifle in 1888.

The author has also heard of a connection between Lee and the Mosin-Nagant rifles produced under the Russian Czar. However, there is no concrete evidence of this connection at present.

Although the M1895 Straight-Pull was made by Winchester only during 1896-1898, it was almost a decade later before the last of the rifles were cleared from the Winchester warehouses. During this time some experimental modifications of the basic M1895 were made. Two such modified rifles from the Olin collection are shown in Fig. 36 and 37. The top rifle, chambered for the 30-40 Krag cartridge, has a magazine bottom loading device designed by Thos. C. Johnson, the very able designer of the famous Model 12 shotgun. This particular rifle was used in the New York State trials at

Fig. 38—Right side of the improved Lee straight pull action. The piece at the rear of the bolt is the cocking piece. The M1899-type safety lock on this particular rifle has been lost. The white semi-circular piece seen in the bolt is part of the extractor, which differs slightly from that of the M1899. The front of the bolt also butts against the receiver more solidly than either the 1895 or 1899 models. This is one of the two types mentioned in the text. **Fig. 39**—Left side of the improved Lee action. Note similarity to the M1899, although the receiver is not milled out to receive the extractor-spring stop, and the magazine is considerably different. The magazine is of the Mauser-type and is lettered on the floorplate, in two lines: EDWARDS PATENT/NO. 13124. The small lever ahead of the receiver, on the side of the fore-end, is a magazine follower depressor. The inscription on the receiver, in block or capital letters, appears to be hand cut. The inscription reads: IMPROVED LEE STRAIGHT PULL PATENT/BRITISH & FOREIGN/ LEE ARMS CO. Ltd LONDON.

Creedmoor. The second rifle, chambered for the regular 6mm (236) Lee-Navy cartridge, looks almost exactly like the M1895 from the right side. However, the left side shows part of the modification made by William Mason, a special two-inch long spring for controlling the extractor is held in a cut in the left side of the bolt. Another spring, also visible, comes in contact with the rear end of the extractor and prevents it from moving forward with the bolt. This rifle has a swinging bolt stop, which projects down by the top of the trigger guard.

Johnson and Mason were co-workers at Winchester. Johnson worked there from 1885 until his death in 1934. Mason had learned his trade at Remington's in Ilion, N.Y., then worked at Colt's for 13 years before joining Winchester in 1882. He remained there until his retirement in 1910. Both men were at Winchester during the time the M1895 Straight-Pull was being made, and no doubt worked with Lee.

Two other unusual Lee Straight-Pulls are known to the author. (See Figs. 38, 39 and 40.) Both are chambered for the 7x15mm Mauser cartridge, appear to be modifications of the M1899 Straight-Pull, and are marked on the left side of the receiver:

Improved Lee Straight Pull Pattern
British & Foreign Lee Arms Co. Ltd. London

Though both specimens have the same dimensions (31-inch barrels, 50.4 inch over-all, weight 8¾ pounds) they don't have the same type of magazine, and neither uses an inserted clip. The gun shown has a magazine-follower depressor (arrow) on the left side, pushing down which lowers the follower, allowing cartridges to be dumped into the magazine without forcing them in against the tension of the magazine spring. The other version has a Mauser-type magazine without the follower depressor.

The rifle illustrated *may* be the Lee Model 1901, that guess based on a magazine patent. The floorplate of the rifle shown is lettered EDWARDS PATENT NO.13124. This British patent for an improved, faster-loading magazine, was granted to Owen Henry Edwards, 1 Richmond Terrace, Aberdeen, Scotland, on November 23, 1901. Details of the patent drawings are carried out in the rifle shown here.

Since the buttstock on this rifle follows the shape of the "issue" British rifle it seems possible that Lee or one of his sons might have again been trying to interest the British government in another of his rifles.

A native of Scotland, Lee may have visited there on his travels, and could have met Mr. Edwards. Since the latter's patent is dated from June 27 to November 23, 1901, it seems logical to assume that the rifle was manufactured about the same time. With the exception of the magazine the Improved Lee differs little from the M1899 Straight-Pull.

Certainly other modifications of the Lee Straight-Pull may exist. The writer knows of one with a very minor difference—its bolt handle knob is solid, and apparently original, yet all other knobs examined, seen or viewed in pictures (including the Government manual), show the knob with a cavity. Possibly the very early knobs were solid, but the receiver of this particular M1895 is so badly pitted that the serial number cannot be read.

Fig. 40—Above: Right side view of the improved Lee. Note Enfield type pistol grip buttstock, made without comb and having a straight buttplate. Both the M1895 and M1899 have the regular type pistol grip stocks and curved buttplates. The upper handguard on this model does not extend beyond the rear band—this variation also appears on another modification. The upper handguard on the M1895 and M1899 extends forward beyond the rear band one by

1.5 inches. On the M1895 the stock proper extends beyond the upper band and is rounded. On both the M1899 and improved models the stock proper is flush with the front of the upper band. On the improved model the front sight is a large block, tapered to serve as the sight. The smaller block, with the pinned-in blade of the M1895 and M1899, does not appear on the improved model. Below: Left side view of the same rifle. Note the magazine follower depressor. The longer barrel of this model is very evident.

A Way of Life

by C. P. BARAGER

It takes a dedicated craftsman, perhaps, to instill his enthusiasm, the same feeling for good work, in a promising youngster. Old Bill Campbell, master gunsmith, did just that.

CANADIAN SHOOTERS often bemoan the fact that top gunsmiths are hard to come by in their own country. This reasoning is hardly true. Canada does have some good gun craftsmen, but the question arises: Why are they so little known?

The answer, maybe, is because a really good gunsmith gets more work than he can handle. Therefore, he sees little point in advertising to bring in additional business.

One of them told me that if he had more to do, he'd have to hire help, but that young men today have little interest in the gun trade. The financial returns are not high enough compared with many other easier, more lucrative occupations.

Nevertheless, this vast country—stretching between two great oceans and as far north as the Arctic circle—does have some outstanding craftsmen. Two of them may be found, any time you visit Winnipeg, at 1580 Wolseley Avenue, hard at work in a small but up-to-date gunshop.

Bill Campbell, the senior partner, has been in the business all his life. Long known as a gunsmith's gunsmith, when others find the going tough they bring their problems to Bill. Bill has the reputation of never yet having seen a gun with a missing part that he cannot make and replace. He's a genius at figuring out how a gun should tick.

Don, the younger partner and Bill's nephew, has only been at the business 10 years. At the age of 20 he began doing stock work in his spare time. Bill's work was so far behind that he persuaded Don to try his hand at stock fitting and checkering.

The lad had previously shown a natural aptitude for working with wood, so Bill started him doing stocks at home evenings after fulfilling a regular job in a creamery. A few years later, Don became a partner, specializing in stock work.

When Bill repairs a gun or builds a rifle, it has to be right; nothing less will do. As a consequence, young Don had to win his spurs before his uncle would accept him in the business.

In 1967, the Campbell shop turned

First custom-crafted Canadian Centennial rifle is presented to the writer (right) amid happy smiles. A 6mm varminter, the scope is a 15x Unertl.

out specially-made rifles to commemorate Canada's Centennial. The buttstock carried an inscribed nameplate and the owner's name on the breech in gold lettering. The writer received the first one, a 6mm with medium weight 26-inch barrel. These guns already are collectors items.

My stock was a piece of cherry wood brought from Ontario a few years earlier. The trigger mechanism is a Campbell creation, and as fine a piece of workmanship as you'll encounter on any firearm. In having a rifle custom crafted, you may choose any type of wood from the Campbell selection or send in your own.

Don puts a pronounced palm swell

on all of his stocks unless the customer says otherwise. An ardent varmint shooter himself, Don says there's nothing like the palm swell to help you get off an accurate shot. "It's the only thing that gives you the right grip for a proper trigger squeeze," he told me.

My own rifle, built for varmint shooting, weighs 12¼ lbs. with 15x Unertl scope, and it produces groups well under an inch at 100 yards. Picking off crows and gophers near the 300-yard mark is easy—on my better days!

If you're ever in Winnipeg, call at the Campbell shop. Bill and Don are never too busy to talk guns. They'll tell you it is their way of life. •

The ever-changing
Shotshell

The American shotgunner who uses factory cartridges is a lucky guy, for tough competition insures top quality and top performance. The author reviews the past decade and examines closely the current developments.

THE AMERICAN shotgunner who shoots factory ammo is without question the world's most fortunate. Keen competition among shotshell manufacturers is practically a guarantee that the fodder he feeds his pet smoothbore, whether it be loads for clay targets or for game, will be the ultimate in terms of reliability and performance.

What we have at our disposal today is a long, sky-busting shot from what we had when this writer was a fledgling shooter back in the 1930s. To such old-time shotgunning greats as Captain Bogardus and Fred Kimble, the shotshell of the 1970s, if they were here to shoot 'em, would surely seem like something out of the pages of science fiction.

Much of what has happened in the shotshell field has occurred since the close of World War II, and particularly over the past decade and a half. Significant advances in the field of plastics have played the greatest role. Plastic shells and plastic wads are as commonplace today as brass shells and felt wadding were in the late 1800s, or as paper shells were only a few years ago.

What the future holds is anybody's guess. In the meantime it might be interesting to review briefly some of the highlights of the past decade, and to take a little closer look at those developments which are fresh off the production line.

Winchester-Western

ALTHOUGH Winchester-Western (W-W) did not turn to the use of polyethylene for shotshell bodies until late in 1963, the big red "W" outfit had long recognized the value of such pattern-improving measures as a cup-type over-powder (O/P) wad, fold-crimp closure and shot-protecting sleeve.

W-W adopted the fold crimp at the close of World War II; and, if memory serves, the "umbrella-type" O/P wad pressed into service at about the same time. This "Super Seal" cup, constructed of thick, durable, gas-proof paper, is shaped to expand readily to seal off the shell's "combustion chamber." It is still very much in use today, doing yeoman duty in W-W's field, high-velocity and magnum loads.

The well-known "Mark 5" plastic shot collar came along in 1962, being offered initially in 12-ga. target loads. This protector is simply a rectangular strip of plastic surrounding the shot charge. It cannot prevent pellet deformation caused by set-back forces, but it does eliminate the abrasive-type damage that would otherwise occur through pellet contact with the bore. This innovation not only increased pattern density, but it also improved the distribution of those shot pellets comprising the main body of the pattern. As a fringe benefit, lead fouling in the bore disappeared almost completely. The

Mark 5 approach was an immediate and unqualified success, and its use was soon extended to many other loadings in the W-W line.

When the W-W compression-formed (C/F) plastic shell made the scene in 1964, it was hailed as a major breakthrough in shotshell development, which it most certainly was. The manufacturing process, a combination of injection moulding and final die-forming under tremendous pressure, made possible a design in which the basewad became an integral part. In other words, the C/F shell has no basewad *per se*, but in its place a head section of solid plastic which is a continuation of the tube walls.

The strength of this C/F shell is so great that it could have been marketed without a brass head, but W-W felt that such a move would constitute a too radical departure from the traditional. Initially, the C/F shell was used only for 12, 16 and 20-ga. high-velocity loadings in both Super-X and Super Speed brands; and, like their paper-tube predecessors, these also employed the Mark 5 collar.

Also in 1964, as a companion to the C/F shell, W-W introduced a poly-formed (P/F) plastic shell which was of built-up construction. It took its designation from the manufacturing process, a procedure which rearranged the molecular structure of the polyethylene to give the material increased strength. The P/F shell, identifiable

Story

by WALLACE LABISKY

by its corrugated (ribbed) tube surface, used the same basewad that had seen service for so many years in W-W paper-tube shells. At first the P/F shell was used only for standard field and target loads in Xpert and Ranger brands, but later various loads in Super-X and Super Speed brands were also put up in the P/F shell.

A fresh concept in buckshot loads was inaugurated by W-W in 1963 by wrapping the "blue whistlers" in a plastic sleeve and using granulated polyethylene to fill the considerable space between the layered pellets. The buffer material proved to be most effective in reducing pellet damage due to jamming during the inertia set-back and this, in turn, produced a dramatic improvement in patterns.

Tight chokes seem to give the best results with these "Super Mark 5" buckshot loads, and it is not unusual to get 90% or better patterns at 40 yards. The writer has a full-choke magnum 12 that will consistently place the entire charge of 15 pellets of 00BK in a circle no larger than 28 inches, and frequently in one as small as 23 inches. As an extra bonus, pellet energy remains high, because the undeformed pellets shed their velocity at a lesser rate than those which have become badly deformed or mis-shapen.

The Double A Loads

Few competitive trap and Skeet

shooters will forget 1965, for this was the year that W-W gave clay-birders the Double A (AA) target load (12 and 20 ga.) in the C/F shell with extra-hard shot. Introduced simultaneously was the AA plastic wad column. This marked W-W's first use of a one-piece shot-protector wad in factory ammo, though a unit-type column called the Win-Wad had been offered earlier (1963) as a handloading component.

The AA plastic shell quickly became a favorite among the hand-loading clan because of ease of "reloadability" and long life. The high-brass C/F shell, however, created some handloading head-aches due to a much heavier inside taper which severely limited wad choice. Eventually the heavy taper was eliminated and today all W-W C/F hulls are of the same inside dimensions, or very nearly so.

That same year (1965) W-W put the finishing touches on a 12-ga. tracer load, the first and only shot-shell tracer ever to be offered by a U.S. ammo company. The tracer load is useful for showing the budding trap and Skeet shooter the error of his ways, and even for helping the experienced shooter to climb out of a hard-to-shake slump.

The W-W approach was to use a spherical, aluminum capsule with a short tail for aerodynamic stabilization, and its size is such that it has the same in-flight ballistics as a pellet of No. 7½ shot. The tracer

mix is ignited by the powder gases, via an opening in the center of the wad column. In flight, the tracer "pellet" stays well inside the shot cloud, seldom straying more than 10 inches (usually less) from the pattern center at 40 yards. It is seen by the shooter as a glowing dot of yellow-white flame. Burnout time for the loads (1965 vintage) tested by the writer was approximately 65 yards.

It was in 1968 that W-W came out with a special, long-range 12-ga. load in the 2¾" C/F plastic shell. At first it was dubbed the High Density Magnum (see 25th ed. GUN DIGEST), but it is now called the Double X (XX) Magnum. Intended as a load to reduce crippling losses in waterfowl shooting, the XX Magnum carries 1½ ounces of hard chilled shot in Nos. 2 and 4 only. The load delivers exceptionally tight, dense-center patterns that usually average 85%-90% out of full-choke barrels. This high level of performance is made possible by combining the Mark 5 shot sleeve with granulated polyethylene for maximum effect in reducing pellet damage, the same approach as with W-W Super Buckshot loads.

Immediately following the introduction of the XX Magnum, many shooters expressed hope that W-W would follow with a similar loading in 12- and 20-ga. 3" magnums. Although a 12-ga. 3" XX load has been listed in past W-W catalogs, it has not yet made an appearance, and the prospects are dim, as a Winchester official has recently passed the word that the company has no immediate plans in this connection.

Another step in the total switch to plastics occurred in 1970 when W-W came out with an AA 410 Skeet load in 2½" length (C/F plastic shell) which has as its wad column a one-piece plastic design similar to the Federal 410 wad. Later that same year the use of the C/F shell was extended to include 3" 410 field loads in Super-X and Super Speed brands. The wad column in the 3-incher is a spartan affair, consisting of only the paper Super Seal O/P cup topped by a card wad and a Mark 5 collar. But despite what seems to be a lack of cushioning, the 3" C/F load prints excellent game-killing patterns.

Upland Shells

Recent word from W-W tells us that the poly-formed plastic shell is being phased out completely, a fact which serves to explain the introduction of the new Upland loads (12, 16, 20 ga.) early in 1971, these loads replacing the long-familiar

The ever-changing
Shotshell Story

Xpert and Ranger field loads. But despite the new brand name and the use of the stronger C/F plastic shell, wad columns in the Upland shells have seen no change. Still used are the paper O/P cup, fiber fillers and the Mark 5 sleeve.

As a final major move in 1971, W-W brought out the AA Handicap load for trapshooting and, as the name implies, it is intended to provide an extra edge in performance at high-yardage distances and for the second shot at doubles. It uses the same hull as the regular AA load, except that the color is black for quick, positive identification. Extra-hard shot is used, along with a freshly-designed plastic wad column. Offered in 12 ga. only, the Handicap load is available in Western and Winchester brands in shot sizes No. 7½ and 8.

The new AA Handicap wad pretty much parallels the design of the regular 12-ga. AA wad except for notable changes in the cushioning section. Three strap-like posts, each being .335" wide and .405" in length, are used to link the O/P and shot cup sections together. The posts are thinned slightly over their central portion and the inner surface of each is partially concave; the purpose of this is to insure that they will fold *outward* rather than inward as they undergo compression. As such, the center of the shot cup is more or less unsupported during the acceleration set-back and, at least theoretically, this should alleviate some pellet damage due to jamming. The end result is a more dense pattern.

After a considerable delay, the Handicap wad has finally been released as a handloading component and it can be used in any W-W compression-formed shell. The Ball powder used in the Handicap load is not available to handloaders, but W-W recommends using DuPont PB, Hercules Green Dot or Alcan AL-120 for 3-dram equivalent loadings.

According to catalog data, 10-ga. loads (both 2⅞" and 3½") were switched from paper to P/F plastic shells in 1971, as were 28-ga. field and target loads. W-W advises that starting sometime during the summer of 1972, all 28-ga. loads will be put together in the C/F plastic shell. Presumably the 10-ga. offerings will also receive the same treatment, and this goose hunter, for one, is hopeful that W-W will eventually see fit to offer the 3½" 2-oz. shell in the XX Magnum loading. Incidentally, W-W now loads only No. 2 shot in the 2-oz. 10-ga. package.

Remington Arms Company

IT WAS DURING the early 1960s that Remington Arms Company rolled back the curtain on two shotshell developments that made scattergunners everywhere sit up and take special notice. The first occurred in 1960 when the "SP" plastic-tube shell was introduced, and without a shadow of doubt this was *the* move which sparked the current revolution in shotshell design. The second major development was the birth of the famous "Power Piston" wad column, the first single-unit, all-plastic wad ever to be used in factory-loaded shotshells.

The SP shell features built-up construction with a non-integral basewad which, in shells of current manufacture, is made from an asbestos-like material that is moulded to shape under tremendous pressure. The "S" part of the designation, incidentally, refers to the brass-plated steel head, while the "P" stands for the polyethylene tube.

Scuffproof, waterproof and with slick-feeding properties, the SP shell was used at first only for 12-ga. high-velocity loads. Then, in 1962, "express" loads followed in 16- and 20 ga. By 1963, a low-brass version of the SP shell was used for Remington "Shur Shot" and Peters "Victor" field loads in 12, 16 and 20 ga. That same year, too, all 10-ga. loads were switched over to the SP shell.

The equally revolutionary Power Piston made its initial appearance in 12-ga. target loads in 1963. The excellent cushioning section, in conjunction with a shot-protecting cup, contributed to a high level of pattern efficiency. A second advantage was a noticeable reduction in apparent recoil, this stemming from the wad's light weight and the fact that less powder was required than with conventional wadding. It's small wonder that claybirders were quickly sold on the new one-piece wad. In fact, that same year, the Grand American Handicap was sacked with a perfect score of 100 straight from the 21-yard line using Power Piston loads in Peters brand. This not-so-easy feat put a cash prize of better than $9,000 in the pocket of Indiana shooter Albert G. Kees.

Prior to the entry of the Power Piston, Remington-Peters (R-P) trap and Skeet loads were assembled in a paper-tube shell having a low basewad of paper construction. But the over-powder (O/P) wad used in the old corrugated-tube load was as modern as tomorrow. This was the plastic "H" wad which was cupped on both ends so that the filler wadding could expand the upper "skirt" for a secondary gas seal.

The adoption of the Power Piston did not immediately kill off the "H" wad. It was sold as a handloading component for several years thereafter, and it was used also for "heavies" in the SP shell—until replaced, step by step, by the Power Piston in its various forms. Just as all current R-P loads are in plastic shells, so do they all employ the Power Piston, except for the buckshot loads and all 10-ga. offerings, the latter still being turned out with a card O/P wad.

First PP Loads

When the Power Piston target loads first came out, the new wad was teamed with a smooth-walled paper-tube shell having a high fiber-type basewad. This shell had an extremely short production life, being replaced in 1964 by a plastic-tube shell with a plastic-covered basewad and a rib-style 8-point fold crimp. The head was brass, rather than brass-plated steel. Handloading trap and Skeet buffs welcomed the new plastic hull, for it gave much longer reload life than its paper-tube predecessor. The new shell was designed to accept the larger 209-size battery-cup primer (#97 Star in Remington brand).

By 1965 Remington had extended the use of the Power Piston beyond 12-ga. target shell application. Included were 20-ga. target loads, 12-16-20 ga. high-velocity loads and 28-ga. loads. Then, the following year, the power piston replaced the "H" wad and felt fillers in 12-16-20-ga. low-brass field loads, as well as in the 2¾" and 3" magnum loadings in these gauges.

Remington's Post Wad came along in 1965, being used in 12-ga.

target loads. This plastic column was largely identical to the Power Piston, except for the addition of a tapered post in the center of the shot cup. This was was specifically designed to produce evenly distributed patterns from full-choke guns when shooting clays from the 16-yard line. Apparently the Post Wad loading has been permanently shelved, as it has not been listed in Remington catalogs for several years.

By 1966 Remington had traveled full circle in the changeover to plastic shells, with the introduction that year of 2½″ and 3″ 410 loads in the SP shell. These sub-smallbore hulls had a paper basewad, used a card-and-filler wad column, and were closed with a 6-point fold crimp. The battery-cup primer was the usual Remington #69, which is a #57 size. The 3″ shell had an actual length of only 2⅞″.

Prior to 1967 R-P buckshot loads were simply "straight loads" in which the layered pellets were given no protection against becoming mis-shaped during the initial accelerating thrust of the expanding powder gases. In the new "Power-Pakt" loads that appeared that year, the pellets were nested in granulated polyethylene to eliminate much of the damage that occurred during the ignition setback. In terms of pattern performance, there was no comparison—the new loads stood head and shoulders above the old loads. The wad column in the Power-Pakt buckshot loads consists of the "H" wad in conjunction with felt fillers —not the Power Piston as some gun scribes have erroneously reported.

In 1968 the R-P 12-ga. plastic target shell underwent a minor design change in that the covered basewad was replaced by one of solid plastic, and these loads were then branded "All-American." The new basewad gave increased head strength and, according to Remington, produced faster and more uniform powder ignition.

This was also the year that Remington turned to color coding for 20-ga. shells (yellow) to lessen the likelihood of the smaller shell being mistakenly loaded in a 12-ga. gun, in which case it could slip far enough forward to permit the chambering of a 12-ga. shell behind it, thereby setting the scene for a hazardous barrel burst.

Skeet shooters were pleased in 1970 when Remington made changes in the 2½″ 410 shell. The SP hull was given a solid plastic basewad and the old multi-wad column was tossed out in favor of still another Power Piston. The result, of course, was improved gas sealing along with more dense and evenly distributed patterns. The redesigned shell was also given a larger diameter primer designated as the 97-4 (209 size). This new primer is "balanced" to the light 410 powder charges and it provides a larger area for firing-pin impact than did the old 69.

A similarly redesigned 3″ 410 load followed in 1971. Again the Power Piston was called upon, this version being tailored to accommodate the heavier ¾-oz. shot charge. This shell is of full 3″ length and, like its 2½″ teammate, it has the larger diameter 97-4 primer. Both lengths carry a neat 6-point fold crimp and feature improved properties at the mouth for easier wad insertion when handloading.

The Modi-Pac

Another fairly recent Remington development, though one far removed from the usual gunning scene, is the "Modi-Pac" shell (Modified Impact Shotgun Shell). This roll-crimped load in the SP plastic shell is intended for use by law-enforcement agencies—namely, for riot control and similar confrontations.

These 12-ga. loads contain a ¼-oz. charge of .120″ diameter, plastic pellets, or about the same size as a pellet of No. 5 shot. Pellet count per load runs about 320. The charge exits the muzzle at close to 1,600 fps, but the light "shot" pellets lose velocity very rapidly. At 15 yards they are moving only about 200 fps, and maximum range is said to be on the order of only 25 yards when the gun is fired in a horizontal attitude. Pattern spread is claimed to be around 10 feet at a distance of 10 yards, presumably from a cylinder-bored riot gun, Owing to the fact that chamber pressure is low, the Modi-Pac loads will not function reliably in auto-loading guns.

Essentially, the Modi-Pac load serves as an effective deterrent, psychologically as well as physically, yet it does not create a situation that is hazardous to innocent bystanders. As an afterthought, this innovation probably would be the ideal solution to discouraging the neighbor's pooch from romping through the petunias!

This year, 1972, the big news from Remington revolves around a new 12-ga. target load called the "RXP," and it is being offered in both Remington and Peters brands in the traditional green and blue colored hulls. The RXP loads carry the hardest shot ever used in Remington's long history, in the usual 1⅛-oz. charges of Nos. 7½ and 8 in trap loads and No. 9 in Skeet loads. A new No. 8½ size pellet is also offered

Winchester-Western "Ranger" and "Xpert" field loads have been replaced by a single "Upland" brand. The new loads are put together in the one-piece compression-formed plastic shell, have a conventional wad column and the "Mark 5" plastic shot collar.

The ever-changing

Shotshell Story

in the trap loads, this being recommended for 16-yard shooting, as well as for the first shot at doubles. The 8½'s are said to increase pattern density by about 80 pellets over regular 8s, and about 140 pellets over 7½s.

The RXP shell is different from anything previously offered by Remington. It is an all-plastic shell, of course, but one which features "unitized" construction via an integral basewad. Like the Winchester Double A hull, the RXP has a solid head section that is a continuation of the tube walls. This type of construction offers several advantages over built-up shells, particularly where handloading is concerned.

Since the base section is integral with the shell tube, there is absolutely no chance that powder gas can find its way to the rear and contribute to brass failure, or to cause excessive expansion of the brass which might give rise to problems during resizing. Another bonus for the handloader is that the extra tube strength near the head practically guarantees there will be no case buckling as a result of pressure applied during finish crimping. Last, but perhaps not least, the handloader never has to worry about basewad failure, either through break-up or loosening.

The capacity of the RXP shell is substantially greater than that of the All-American, the difference amounting to nearly ¼-oz. of No. 9 shot. Because of this, Remington had to whomp up a new Power Piston (W29930), roughly ⅛" longer than the W23694 used in the All-American shell. The extra length was achieved by adding an extra tier of cross tunnels to the cushioning section.

Although the RXP tube has an inside taper, it is only over the last ⅜" forward of the solid head section that the walls begin to thicken appreciably. In order to match this inside configuration, the RXP Power Piston was given an inward taper at its O/P end—there's roughly .030" difference in the outside diameter between this

new wad and the W23694 for the All-American shell. While it will be possible to use some of the other 12-ga. Power Pistons for certain loads in the RXP case, light charges of dense propellants will definitely call for the new contour-hugging W29930 wad.

The primer is the 97 Star, and the 8-point fold crimp is of the style that is flat across the recessed portion. The shell mouth is skived (thinned) to facilitate easy recrimping. All RXP components, including the shell itself, are being released to handloaders.

The tube of the RXP shell is typically R-P in that its surface carries the familiar grooved or corrugated pattern, except for a smooth ⁷⁄₁₆" panel immediately forward of the non-cannelured brass. "RXP" appears on this panel in bold gold lettering, with the usual load markings appearing on the opposite side—also in gold. All in all, the RXP is a pretty classy looking shotshell but, more importantly, one that is engineered for top-drawer performance.

The only other change in the R-P shotshell line for 1972 will be a redesigned shell for the 28-ga. target load. The moulded compositon basewad will be replaced by one of solid plastic, similar to that used in the All-American shell. The change is scheduled to be made about mid-year.

Federal Cartridge Corporation

THIS YEAR, 1972, marks Federal Cartridge Corporation's 50th year of activity in the shotshell field, and during its half-century of operation the Minneapolis-based firm has become one of the world's major producers of ammunition. In addition to scattergun fodder, the firm also offers both rimfire and centerfire ammo.

Some of the many milestones in Federal's history include the disintegrating top wad (1946); color coding of shotshells starting with 20-ga. loads (1961); the "Champion" 12-ga. target load with the "Pellet Protector" plastic wad column in paper-tube shells (1964); and the first-of-its-kind one-piece plastic wad column in 410-bore loads (1969).

Federal began the switch to plastic-tubed shells in 1965 when 12-ga. "Hi-Power" loads were offered with a pattern-tightening shot cup and exta-hard shot, the cup being used in conjunction with their "Altite" filler wadding. The following year plastic-cased loads were offered in 12 and 20 ga., and color coding was broadened to include all gauges. At the present time Federal has only two paper-shell loads in its line; these 12 and 20-ga. target loads represent a concession to the clay-bird buff who still prefers the paper-tube shell for handloading. Both loads are also offered in plastic cases.

One of the many "firsts" for which Federal can take credit was the "short magnum" 28-ga. load with 1 oz. of shot. Later, in 1967, a ⅞-oz. field load was introduced as a replacement for both the ¾- and 1-oz.

One of the most recent additions to the W-W shotshell line is the 12-ga. "AA Handicap" trap shell. Only a 3-dram equivalent loading is available in shot sizes No. 7½ and 8. Tube color is a distinctive black for quick identification.

hunting loads. Plastic hulls are now used for all 28-ga. hunting and target loads, these with conventional "Altite" filler wadding teamed with a plastic shot cup.

By 1968 Federal had perfected the "Triple-Plus" wad column. This is a two-piece all-plastic design consisting of a gas-sealing O/P cup with an integral hollow pillar for "shock-absorber" cushioning. Federal's well-known "Long Range Shot Cup" comprises the other half of the column.

The "Triple-Plus" wad is now a standard offering in all Federal high-velocity and field loads in 12, 16 and 20 ga. However, all magnum loads in these gauges, both 2¾- and 3-inch length, are turned out with "Altite" filler wadding topped by a plastic shot cup. The reason, of course, is that the "Triple-Plus" column does not leave enough room for the heavier shot charges.

Federal's break-through with a one-piece plastic wad for the 410, in 1969, revolutionized the handloading side of this sub-smallbore round. More importantly, the 410-bore finally came into its own as a field gun, the plastic shot-cup column producing high-efficiency patterns that were only dreamed of before.

At the same time the switch was made to plastic hulls for the 410-bore loads, first in 2½-inch length and eventually in 3-inch. Although factory loads in both lengths are put together with a plastic wad column, only the 2½-inch shells with shot sizes 7½ and 9 have a fold crimp. All others are roll-crimp loads. But Bill

RXP 12-ga. Skeet and trap loads are available in both Remington and Peters brands. The loads employ extra-hard chilled shot, and a new No. 8½ shot size is being offered.

Horn, Federal's vice president in charge of marketing, says that the 410 crimp picture may see some changes in the not-too-distant future. There is the possibility that the built-up plastic shell will undergo redesign by way of a lower basewad. This will serve to increase case capacity, and fold crimping will then be possible with some of the larger shot sizes.

First Plastic Targets

Although Federal's first plastic-tubed loads appeared in 1965, it was not until 1969 that a plastic shell was adopted for target loads. This first plastic 12-ga. "Champion" shell was of built-up construction with a basewad of solid plastic rather than paper. Then in 1971 it was superseded by a redesigned version which has an integral, flexible lip around the top edge of the basewad, the purpose being to prevent powder gas from working to the rear where it might cause loosening of the basewad and/or shell-head damage. The 8-point crimp was also changed slightly from a rib-style to a flat closure similar to that found on Federal's field-type loads.

A very reliable source has informed us that Federal's research and development people are hard at work perfecting a unitized plastic shell, one like the popular AA type in which the conventional basewad is replaced by solid-head construction. As a matter of fact,

This cutaway view of Remington's RXP target shell shows the new W29930 Power Piston with its long cushioning section. Shell body is of one-piece construction with an integral head of solid plastic.

one such Federal design is currently being manufactured (under special license) by a competitive company. Our source adds that when Federal does eventually come out with a one-piece plastic shell under its own banner, it will take a backseat to no other design.

Interestingly, during 1970 Federal began a changeover to brass-plated steel shell heads, with 12-ga. "Hi-Power" loads receiving first attention. Company officials report that the switch will probably include most other gauges and loads by the end of 1972. Excluded will be the 12- and 20-ga. target loads, which will be continued with all-brass heads.

Two new offerings will expand Federal's buckshot line-up in 1972. Both are short-magnum 12-ga. loadings—a 20-pellet charge of #1 Buck, and a 34-pellet charge of #4 Buck. The latter loading will probably be welcomed by those who like to call up within shotgun range such larger varmints as fox and coyote. Goose hunters, too, may go for it in a big way, but personally I've never been able to see #4 Buck as a waterfowl loading.

All Federal buckshot loads, by the way, are roll crimped in plastic hulls, and they don't use granulated polyethylene to buffer the pellets against damage during ignition set-back.

There have been no changes in Federal's rifled-slug loads, made in all gauges except 10 and 28. Like CIL, Federal uses a plastic insert in the cavity of the Foster-type slug to prevent wad-caused distor-

The ever-changing
Shotshell
Story

tion and to further accuracy.

For the first time in Federal history, 1972 will mark the use of nickeled shot in sizes 7½, 8 and 9 in the 12-ga. International load. This 1¼-oz. loading will be put together in the new "Champion" plastic-tube target shell, using the very efficient "Pellet Protector" wad column and its air-chamber cushioning. The load will also be available with extra-hard chilled shot.

A new shot size, No. 8½, will also make its appearance in 1972 in Federal 12-ga. target loads, in both paper and plastic-tube shells. Like the chilled shot used in all Federal "Hi-Power" and target-type loadings, the 8½'s will be extra-hard, containing a higher percentage of antimony to better resist deformation. As most hep shotgunners know, any measure that serves to reduce pellet damage results in tighter patterns, better velocity retention for a shorter shot string, and more striking energy at the target.

Of special interest to competition shooters is a new 12-ga. International load to meet the requirements of the International Shooting Union. The new ISU ruling, which will go into effect in 1973, calls for a reduction in shot weight to 1⅛ ozs. and the elimination of nickeled and copper-plated shot. Federal has met these requirements well in advance with a 3¼-dram, 1⅛-oz. load in plastic-tube "Champion" shell, using extra-hard shot in sizes 7½, 8 and 9. Again, the wad column will be the "Pellet Protector." Muzzle velocity of the new load will be 1,250 fps, in contrast to the heavier 1¼-oz. loading at 1,220 fps—a little less shot, but more striking energy per pellet.

Canadian Industries Limited

SHOTGUNNERS in this country annually fire millions of rounds of Canadian ammo, principally that produced by Canadian Industries Limited (CIL). Most of the shotshells intended for the U.S. market, as well as centerfire ammo, are loaded at CIL's Plattsburg, New

York, plant, where operations were started in 1966 (CIL Ammunition, Inc.). The bulk of the target-load shotshells, and also rimfire ammo, are manufactured at CIL's Brownsburg, Quebec, plant, which has been continously in operation since 1885.

CIL 12-gauge target loads have been upgraded from time to time over the past decade. The first improvement involved the "Plus 10" concentrator, which was used in conjunction with felt wadding. Then, in 1966, CIL made the switch to a two-piece all-plastic wad column called the Ram-Wad. During 1971 the Ram-Wad loads were phased out, the replacement column being a new plastic design called the Dynawad.

Like its predecessor, the new Dynawad is also a two-piece column. The lower or over-powder (O/P) end consists of an obturating cup and a cushioning section, while the upper part is a four-segmented shot cup of 1⅛-oz. capacity. The samples we've seen weigh 37.5 grs. for the total column. The Dynawad runs a bit lighter than the Ram-Wad

it undergoes compression. The secondary gas seal is formed by the cupped base of the shot container, and here there are 12 angled ribs around the inner perimeter to facilitate even compression of the O/P section.

We've had no opportunity to try the Dynawad loads for pattern, nor on claybirds, but the wad column looks like it will really carry the mail. Dynawad target loads are assembled in the low-brass "Canuck" plastic shell, which has a ribbed surface and a paper basewad. This hull, along with all other CIL offerings, takes the 209 size battery-cup primer, and it is well liked by handloaders. Incidentally, CIL wads and other shotshell components for handloading are *not* offered on the U.S. market.

Another recent change in the CIL line is that the 12-ga. "Canuck Heavy" load was boosted from 1⅛ ozs. to 1¼ ozs. of shot, with the powder charge now being 3½ drams equivalent. The "Canuck Standard" load in 12 ga. is now a 1⅛-oz. offering at the 3¼ dram level.

Except for 410-bore and 28-ga.

Cutaway view shows Federal's "Triple-Plus" wad column in a loaded shell. Over-powder section has an integral, hollow pillar, which crushes down on firing to provide cushioning. Shown at far right is a T-P wad after firing; note how the pillar has been compressed.

and, accordingly, along with what appears to be an improved cushioning section, apparent recoil should be somewhat softer.

According to a CIL spokesman, the Dynawad provides a dual gas seal. The O/P section serves as the primary gas seal, of course, but this part is designed with a hollow, compressible center column in conjunction with a thin outer wall, both of which crush down to provide cushioning for the shot charge. Additionally, there are four reinforcing ribs on the outside of the walls, their purpose being to keep the two-part unit aligned as

loads, all CIL shotshells are now put together in plastic shells, these of the so-called "built-up" construction with paper basewads. All high-velocity and magnum loadings, including buckshot and rifled slugs, use the extra-high-brass "Imperial" tubes, while target and field loads are put up in the low-brass "Canuck" case. Crimps are the now-standard fold closure.

CIL has not gone overboard by way of plastic wad columns. Except for 12-ga. target loads, wadding consists of either a card wad or plastic O/P cup in conjunction with felt fillers. Plastic O/P cups combined with filler wadding is the story for 20- and 28-ga. target shells.

Like most U.S. companies, CIL uses the Foster-type projectile in its rifled-slug loads, these being offered in 410, 28, 20, 16 and 12 ga. However, it is only in 12 ga. that the "Poly-Kor" rifled slug is used, and it takes its name from the fact that a plastic insert is used in the slug's base cavity. This polyethylene core serves to prevent wadding from being driven into the cavity and distorting the slug. The practice is said to stabilize the slug in flight and enhance accuracy.

The most interesting aspect of CIL buckshot loads is that pellet size designations differ from what U.S. shooters are accustomed to. A trio of 2¾-inch 12 ga. loads are available. These contain 34 pellets of size AAA buckshot (#4 Buck); 12 pellets of SSG (#0 Buck), or 12 pellets of Special SSG (#00 Buck).

In 3-inch 12s, CIL's single buckshot offering is a load containing 15 pellets of Special SSG. There is likewise only a single loading offered in 16 and 20 ga.—12 pellets

From what we have been able to gather, the Alcan line of factory shotshells will be kept in production. There will also be a new line of premium-quality loads under the S&W-F label in 1972. Let's look over the Alcan loads first. These include Trapmax (12 ga. only), Skeetmax (12 and 20), Gamemax (12-16-20), Ultramax (12-16-20 high-velocity loads in a highbrass shell), and Magnamax (12-ga. 2¾" Magnum only).

Prior to 1967 all Alcan shotshells were loaded in paper-tube cases, but the conversion to plastic was started and completed that year for all gauges. Although some plastic hulls for handloading (10-ga. 3½" and 12-ga. 3") are imported from Europe (Fiocchi), all shells used for the factory loads are made in the company plant. This is also true of primers and wads.

The plastic shell used for Alcan factory fodder is of built-up construction, with a low basewad of the wound-paper type. Like most polyethylene shells, the tube surface is ribbed or corrugated. All crimps are the modern fold closure.

er in color than 700-X.

Wadding in the Alcan factory shells consists of the excellent Air-Wedge plastic over-powder (O/P) wad in conjunction with Feltan-Bluestreak (fiber) fillers. The one exception to this is the Trapmax load which, starting in mid-1971, uses the unit-type Flite-Max wad with a shot-protecting cup.

S & W-F Line

The S&W line of premium-quality loads will pretty well blanket the field in 12, 16 and 20 ga. Twelve-gauge loads are headed by a 2¾" Waterfowl Magnum shell loaded to a 4½-dram equivalent velocity with 1½ ozs. of copper-plated shot in sizes 2, 4 and 6. Also included in the line are regular short magnums in 12 and 20 ga.

Others in the new S&W line are high-velocity loads in 12-16-20; a 12-ga. heavy field load; both regular and light field loads in 12-16-20; Skeet loads in 12 and 20; and light and heavy 12-ga. trap loads.

S&W 12-ga. buckshot loads are being offered in #00, #0, #1 and #4 pellet sizes. There is also a 12-ga. Police Slug load.

Like the Alcan brand shotshells, the new S&W loads are put together in a plastic hull of built-up construction, with the basewad also being of the same type and height. The polyethylene shell has the usual ribbed surface, the color a deep blue (yellow for 20 ga.). This, along with an uncannelured nickel-plated steel head (height of 9/16+" for all loads and gauges), makes for a highly attractive looking round. Primer is the 220 Max-Fire, of course, and crimps are a 6-point fold with heat-fused center. The trap and skeet loads, however, carry an 8-point crimp and the mouths of these shells are skived for easier crimping when handloading.

A careful look at the shot charges shows that the pellets are not only brightly polished but also possess excellent roundness. S&W-F hasn't said, but it's our guess that the lead has been alloyed with a higher-than-normal percentage of antimony to make the shot extra-hard for tops in patterning.

Both the 12 and 20-ga. field loads carry a plastic shot-cup wad which is similar, but not identical, to the Alcan Flite-Max unit sold for handloading. The 12-ga. column has a shallow obturating cup at the O/P end which is of about the same depth as that found on the Remington Power Piston wad. The shot cup itself is 1³⁄₁₆" deep, and for the 1⅛-oz. loading holds two ⁵⁄₁₆" fiber

Federal's "Champion" target loads in 12-ga. have the "Pellet Protector" plastic wad, which uses trapped air for cushioning. Shown (second from right) is a wad recovered after firing, and at far right is the over-powder cup.

of SG (#1 Buck) and 20 of AAAA (#3 Buck), respectively.

Smith & Wesson-Fiocchi (Alcan)

THE ALCAN operation is so widely known among shooters that it is perhaps redundant to remark that for many years this firm has supplied shotgunners with top-quality handloading components, as well as factory-loaded shotshells. But what some of you may not know is that Alcan recently became part of a larger corporate family. Although still doing business at the same old stand in Alton, Illinois, the firm is now known as Smith & Wesson-Fiocchi, Inc. (S&W-F).

The shell heads, of brass-plated steel (⁹⁄₁₆+" height for 12-ga. field loads) are not cannelured. Head-stamps now read SWF over USA, along with the gauge size. Load data is inked onto the plastic tube in a longitudinal pattern.

As might be expected, the "ignitor" is the high-energy 220 Max-Fire primer. It was somewhat of a surprise to find that the powder used in the Gamemax loads broken down by the writer is not one of the "AL" numbers sold for handloading. Rather, it is a perforated, round-flake propellant with a granule size about like that of Hi-Skor 700-X, though a shade or two dark-

The ever-changing
Shotshell Story

fillers for cushioning and for regulating crimp space. Like most shot cups, this one is of 4-segmented design, with the slits extending back ⅜″ from the mouth.

Other details of design include 4 reinforcing ribs on the inner surface of the shot cup, these starting ⅜″ from the mouth and continuing down to the cup's floor. The ribs are integral with a network of cross-bracing in the bottom of the cup and against which the filler wadding rests.

The plastic column in the 20-ga. field load is of much the same design. The 4-segmented shot cup has a depth of 1¼″, has 3 reinforcing ribs on the inside, but has no cross-bracing on the floor. The 1-oz. loads use two ¼″ insert fillers for cushioning.

S&W-F's 12-ga. 9-pellet load of #00 buckshot offers "pattern control," meaning that granulated polyethylene is used to fill the pellet interstices. As was discussed earlier, this practice is highly beneficial to patterns and, secondly, the undeformed pellets arrive at the target with more striking energy because they retain their velocity better. So this S&W-F loading should prove to be very effective for whatever use it is put to, whether it be brush-range shots at a bounding whitetail or some form of police work.

The wadding in the buckshot load consists of an Air-Wedge O/P wad topped by a ⅜″ Feltan-Blue-streak filler. No wrapper or sleeve is used to surround the shot charge. These #00 pellets, by the way, represent the highest quality buckshot the writer has ever seen, and when you start with pellets possessing excellent sphericity, you're already one jump ahead in terms of pattern performance.

Sabot Slugs

The projectile used in the S&W-F Police Slug load is the Kelly-McAlvain 12-GA/500 sabot bullet which was conceived and developed by Ballistic Research Industries (BRI), Sebastopol, California (see *Hand-*

loader's Digest VI). The West Coast firm has now licensed S&W-F to manufacture, load and market this slug, which stands as a major breakthrough in design and performance.

To quote from the S&W-F box, "The Smith & Wesson Police Slug loads have superb rifle-like accuracy. They are for law enforcement situations where it is necessary to penetrate automobile engine blocks, bodies and heavy barricades. The extra-hard alloyed Police Slug is centered in the gun bore by a plastic sleeve (sabot), which falls away when the slug-sleeve assembly leaves the gun barrel."

As it comes from the S&W-F molds, the slug is about .035″ longer than the Police Alloy version that was marketed earlier by BRI, but this is the only difference of note. It is of .50″ diameter at the front and rear, has a wasp waist and weighs a full ounce (actually a nominal 440 grains). The various

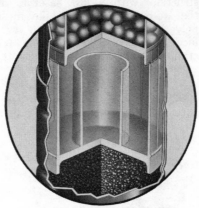

Section view of the CIL Dynawad in a loaded shell shows design details of the wad's over-powder and cushioning sections. Hollow post can be seen in center.

surface angles are designed to utilize air flow and promote stability in flight, though the plastic-filled base cavity lightens the tail end, and this probably helps to maintain a point-forward attitude.

The sabot consists of two halves made of high-density polyethylene, each with an inside contour that perfectly matches the surface configuration of the slug. Encased in this manner, not only is the slug perfectly centered in the bore at all times, it never makes bore contact, all of which makes a substantial contribution to accuracy. Using the BRI sabot bullet in handloads, for example, the writer has fired 5-shot groups at 50 yards that measured as small as 1⅜″ (center to center of widest hits). This was from bench rest using an improved cylinder barrel that was topped with a 2½x scope. So

the obvious conclusion is that the sabot bullet does have excellent accuracy potential.

But an equally important aspect of the sabot approach is that it allows the use of sub-caliber projectiles for a vastly improved ballistic coefficient. Note that the sectional density of this 50-caliber slug is 134% greater than that of a conventional rifled slug of the same weight. This means that the velocity loss will be less and the delivered energy higher. This, in turn, translates into greater effective range.

The S&W-F Police Slug is recommended for use only in cylinder or improved cylinder barrels. Tighter bores may cause the slug to snap in two at the wasp waist as it passes through the choke section.

The wad column is spartan, but adequate, consisting of an Air-Wedge plus a .135″ nitro card. This is a roll-crimp load, of course, and the plastic shell with 220 Max-Fire primer is the same as used for the field and buckshot loads described above. Like the buckshot load, packaging is in handy 5-round boxes.

It is our understanding that S&W-F has a 12-GA/500 Deer Slug load in the works, one which will be suitable for use even in full-choke barrels. It will probably be available in time for the 1972 hunting season, if not sooner.

Whitney Shotshells

THE NEWEST name in the shotshell field is Whitney Cartridge Company, Inc. (WCC), now relocated and in production in Cortez, Colorado (P. O. Box 608). This firm was spawned about two years ago in Pasadena, California, when C. David Whitney, a claybird shooter and handloader, put into practice some rather bold and futuristic ideas pertaining to shotshell design.

The Whitney concept has been described earlier in the firearms press as a revolutionary approach, and one would be hard pressed, indeed, to come up with a more fitting description than that. The WCC shell is of truly all-plastic construction, and certainly there is nothing unusual in that. But what brings out the old double-take is this rather startling fact: Not only is the shell made up of two separate parts, but these pieces (head and body) are screwed together in a nut-and-bolt fashion to form the complete unit!

While this may sound like madness, there is a method in it, not only on the handloading side, but also offering benefits to those shooters who do not handload. We'll get to this aspect shortly.

From its very inception, the WCC shell was developed essentially as a target-load proposition. A last-minute communique from WCC advises that current production is limited to 12-ga. trap and skeet loads, and that an expansion of the line to include other gauges is not foreseen for the immediate future.

The various components comprising the WCC factory load are all readily available to handloaders. The primer is the CCI-209, the propellant Hercules Green Dot. The wadding, a one-piece plastic shot-cup column made by Whitney, is also available in component form. This wad column, incidentally, is a "Remington size" in terms of volume displacement, and it appears to be identical, or very nearly so, to the "Pattern Control" wad developed by the United Cartridge Company (Casa Grande, Arizona).

The WCC 3-dram equivalent loading with 1⅛-oz. of shot is powered by 17.5 grains of Green Dot. With the CCI-209 primer, this charge gives an average muzzle velocity of 1,198 fps at a very mild average chamber pressure of 7,540 lup. Tests carried out by the H. P. White Laboratory show the ballistics of the factory-loaded offering to be highly uniform, the extreme variation in velocity for a 10-round sample being only 29 fps.

Factory loads are offered in two forms—either as a complete ready-to-shoot shell, or as a loaded but headless round. More than a few nickels can be saved by purchasing the WCC "refills." The price situation may be slightly changed by the time these comments see print, but early quotation show an 80-cent savings per 25 rounds by going the refill route.

All the shooter has to do is unscrew the shell head, or base piece, from the fired shell and re-attach it to the headless load and he is ready to bang away. The savings would be very substantial for any claybirder who burns up thousands of rounds annually—enough in many cases, for example, to cover the cost of a new shotgun.

The refill approach (and no tools are required) means that the shooter will need a few boxes of ready-to-shoot loads to start with. Or, he can buy the shell bases separately, for that matter. The bases (jet black in color) are constructed of a very tough polymer plastic, a material so durable that it will withstand anywhere from 20 to 40 firings.

The bright orange Whitney shell tube, (with its integral base-end projection which forms the primer pocket and has the male threads for mating with the head), is made of a less costly and less strong material—a linear, high-density polyethylene similar in strength to the plastic used for most other shotshell bodies. Surface of the tube is smooth. It is designed to produce optimum ballistics for one firing only, and that means it is not intended to be reloaded, though some handloaders will surely ex-

The new Dynawad used in CIL 12-ga. target loads is a two-piece design of lightweight plastic. Lower part of the wad forms the primary gas seal and has compressible walls and a hollow center column (not visible in photo), both of which cushion against the shock of firing. Angled ribs at base of shot cup insure even compression of the over-powder section.

periment along these lines. Doing so will not be hazardous, but the ballistics of such loads will be questionable.

For handloading, WCC offers a package deal. A minimum quantity of 500 shell tubes and 500 Whitney wads is priced at $16.50. The wads can also be bought separately at $5.85 per 1,000; and the shell heads are priced at $2.50 per 100. Since none of these components is subject to federal law regulating interstate shipment of ammo, they can be mail-order bought directly from WCC. Shipping charges are extra.

Handloading the WCC offering is a bit less involved than for conventional shells. Resizing and decapping are not required. The fired tube with its dead primer is simply unscrewed by hand and discarded. After attaching a new shell tube to the old head, the usual loading steps follow—priming, powder charging, wadding, shot charging and crimping.

An 8-point fold crimp is recommended. Since tube-wall thickness at the mouth is reduced about .015″ on the outer surface over a 7/16″ distance, crimp starting and finishing present no problems. With most loading tools the end result is fully equal to the factory closure in all respects.

In addition to the Green Dot load listed above, WCC suggests 16.5 grs. of Hi-Skor 700-X behind 1⅛-oz. of shot. This gives a velocity of 1,213 fps and a chamber pressure of 8.660 lup when used in conjunction with the CCI-209 primer and the Whitney wad.

The Whitney method of using a new shell tube for each reload may seem extravagant, but it is not without certain advantages. Foremost is the fact that the new tube is neither expanded in the body nor weakened in the crimp area, and this contributes greatly to a minimum variation in ballistics. In other words, it makes possible the ultimate in consistent load-to-load performance in all respects.

Partly because of the better confinement offered by a virgin shell tube and partly because of the internal configuration of the Whitney shell, target-load velocities can be reached, as we have already seen, with a rather considerable reduction in the powder charge. Too, let's not overlook the fact that less powder results in less recoil and a lower chamber pressure, all of which means, in turn, that the gun's mechanism will be subject to less strain.

Surely the Whitney operation will thrive and prosper, but it will be interesting to see which side of the market will topple the larger share of the mortgage. Will the factory-loaded headless refills do it, or will it be the handloading components? From the shooting side of the fence, both of these approaches have their merits. ●

The Little Twenty — a wildcatter's wildcat!

by G. O. ASHLEY

What will a 20-caliber rifle do that a 222 or the increasingly-popular 17 won't? Nothing, really, but you can get in on the ground floor development now—the field is wide open.

20:28A (left) beside author's 6x47, both based on 222 Remington Magnum cases.

A WIDE OPEN fresh frontier is here, for wildcatting—and mildcatting—in 20 caliber. No crowd is in on the development effort now, but such work needs to be done, and some of mine is reported on here. Your development might connect your name to posterity with such as the "Lynch Sharp-Shouldered Puma Pranger 20." But you have to start somewhere, and the 20:28A reported on here is a good place to begin.

The 20-28A is the Remington 222 Magnum brass squeezed down to accept .205″ bullets. Off the shelf, 222 empties will have a powder capacity average of 28.5 to 28.8 grains. The neckdown reduces neck diameter, while increasing shoulder slope, with a sample of cases averaging about 28.3. Dropping decimals for convenience, we begin with a good capacity in strong brass, a first point that made me begin my 20-cal. developments on this combination.

The base of the 222 Remington Magnum brass fits many actions on the market now, without any need for bolt face conversions—a second useful consideration before you make the plunge. My 20:28A was a straightforward rebarreling on a Remington 788 action originally barreled in 222. A key point is to begin your planning with a sound, comparatively new action, for the little 20 does cook up a bit of pressure at full loadings.

Half a dozen of the more foremost and custom barrelers will produce a 20 barrel for you, with a fair lead time. P. O. Ackley has made two for me in 20 caliber, one chambered for a far larger wildcat version. Ackley is equipped to cut barrel grooves at .1965″ up to .2065″, depending on how you take to details of a 20-numbering system. Based on what I've learned from correspondence with other 20 fans, however, there is a tendency for most to settle for .205″.

Other barrel makers who could furnish a 20-cal. tube are: Douglas, Hoffman Rifle Barrel Co., Walker Machine Tool Co., A&M, Harry McGowen, Clyde Hart and Ed Shilen. Wm. H. Hobaugh might, too, but don't bank on it!

Remington's prematurely-proposed rimfire 20, announced in late 1967 and early '68, called for a groove diameter, I believe, of .2045″. But it might not be prudent to hold your breath waiting for either a tube of that diameter or the rimfire case to experiment with; what finally appears may not be exactly like the original.

That's why the emphasis here is on the developmental pleasure you may get working up a 20. You have to enjoy handloading, for no corner hardware store now has 20-cal. cartridges for sale. Bullets are a problem, too, but more on these later. Your first taste of exceptional performance, though, with components handmade all the way, makes for a lasting enjoyment. I said earlier this is a fresh frontier, because we have so many good cases to tinker with now—as compared to older days. The caliber itself

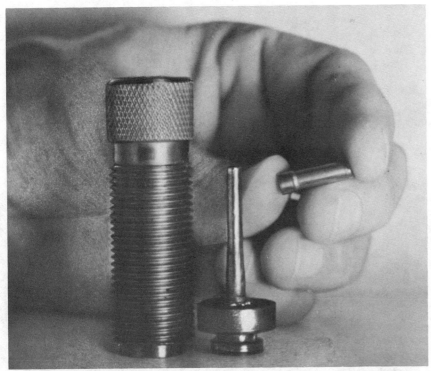

Fig. 2—Rough reshaping die author uses to resize 22-cal. Sierra .705" cups to 20-cal. pre-size dimensions, before making 53- or 56-gr. bullets. Part-sized cup is in his fingers.

is an old one, really, as we'll see.

A key question at about this point is whether the 20 will shoot effectively. Fig. 1, benchrest shot at 100 yards with a 56-gr. bullet I make, displays about all that needs to be said about the 20's potential performance, but here are loads that have shot well for me:

20 Caliber Loads

Grs./powder	Bullet/grs.	MV
22.5/4198	45.5	3587
23/4198	44	3570
22/4198	50	3326
24.5/N201	53	3737
22/4198	29	3699
23.5/3031	44.5	3492

The 26" barrel of the 20 reported on here is an asset. It will consistently group slow fire into ¾" and ⅞"; with 53- and 56-gr. bullets, it stays mostly below 1½" at 200 yards.

20-Caliber History

Evidence shows German, Swiss, and Mexican developments in 20 caliber, some ranging back into the last century. Case size experiments ran from small ones, equivalent to the 218 Bee, up to those as large in capacity as some of our modern belted magnums. Bullets, reportedly, ranged from 28 grains to about 108.

That gave me a first capacity fix on the 20:28A. Consider, I thought, how fine it would be to have a case holding a grain of powder per grain of bullet weight! So far, however, the little 28-gr. bullet has not done well in my rifle.

Historically, Mexican General Mondragon experimented with several vintage .205s, in various weights and capacities. He is said to have made up a straight-pull bolt action and an automatic rifle in this tiny size. Mondragon cases I've seen had almost no neck, with shoulders even more abruptly angled to case necks than Gibbs or ICL "improvements." The Swiss and German experiments covered far

more modest cases, with longer, more conventional necks. From the data I've seen, neither nation thought a bullet was suitable until it was as long as the burgomeister's toothpick.

Closer to home, developments over 30-plus years have been with more modest-capacity cases, with bullets more normal to American eyesight and ogive preference. Cases used so far for someone's wildcat include the 218 Bee, the 223, the 222 and 222 magnum, 22 Hornet brass necked down and "improved," a la Kilbourn, and 250 Savage brass reduced and reshaped. Your development of yet another case, then, or that of mythical Mr. "Lynch" may make the next great 20-caliber breakthrough.

Unless you can invent a remarkably different shape for the surplus 223 brass, however, don't hook your hopes too high that you'll create a new one. Bob Forker (of Hutton Rifle Ranch fame) made one of the first trips with 223 brass, and several versions—shortened, sharpened and formed otherwise—have appeared. Most of them got down to near-222 case capacity. At this juncture, so far as I know, C. H. Stocking deserves the palm for the first work on 222 brass to 20 caliber. He has now tucked away almost a score of years use of it against targets, critters up to and including coyotes, and satisfying match performance.

20-Caliber Bullets

Before the recent pinch on mail-order sales, 20-cal. bullets of high quality could be ordered from the following people, perhaps others: C. H. Stocking, Hutchinson, Minn. 55350 and Frank Hemstead, P.O. Box 281, Sunland, Calif. 91040. L. L. Franssen, LLF Die Shop, 1281 Hwy. 99 No., Eugene, Ore. 97459, Ted Smith, SAS Dies, P.O. Box 250, North Bend, Ore. 97459. Special negotiation is required to get bullets from: Fred

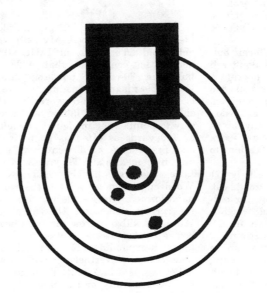

Fig. 1—Three shots from the author's 20:28 at 100 yards, bench rest, went into 9/16 inches. Load was 26 grains of 3031, average MV 3652 foot seconds.

Fig. 3—The 20 atop the author's chronograph at the Green Valley Rifle and Pistol Club, Columbia, Mo. That's an Oehler Model 10 "count'em'up" chronograph shown, Ashley's favorite.

Huntington, RCBS, P.O. Box 1919, Oroville, Cal. 95965; Fred Wood, Bahler Die Shop, P.O. Box 386, Florence, Ore. 97439; E. L. Sweet, Oregon Technical Institute, P.O. Box 2129, Klamath Falls, Ore. 97601.

Through access to an FFL licensed dealer this can still be done. Rumors that three bullet makers are going to begin stock production are cruel things to pass on, because they raise hopes which may be a long time becoming satisfied. Remington's early announcement mentioned a 38-gr. Powr-Lokt bullet (which will be an achievement when we see it) even if it is designed for rimfire velocities. All our shots, of course, needn't be loaded to the limit.

Despite that list above, 20-cal. bullets are hard to come by. I don't sell mine, since I don't want to operate a store. So be prepared, perhaps, to have the pleasure of making your own. That's a logical and sensible extension of the handloading skill many of us practice, and it develops an extra technique that adds gratification to fancy or difficult shots.

A punch die shown here (Fig. 2) has been used to neck Sierra 22-cal. .705″ cups to several lengths, for outstanding bullets in several weights. A partly-formed case, shown in my fingers with the punch, is step one of bullet preparation. That step can be by-passed if you can buy 20-cal. cups, ready made. Fred Wood plans to offer these in stout form by the time this is in print. The next component,

lead cores, may be bought, for example, from Division Lead Co. (7742 W. 61st Pl., Summit, Ill. 60502), in ⁵⁄₃₂″ rolls. They are prompt and responsive on special work.

The actual swage die shape and ogive you select is a part of the development fun. It is reasonable to predict you will get two, before you've broken one in well, just out of curiosity as to how other shapes and ogives perform. Suffice it to say there is still much room for development, pending the day the big producers offer good production bullets.

Tests

The 28-gr. bullet, 28-gr. powder idea had to be dropped. My case will only hold 26.5 grains of IMR 4198, and seating compresses that. A 28-gr. bullet in 20-cal. is no long thing. From this maximum loading, no longer recommended, there were dub results. The bullets didn't know which way to point. They made 90° keyholes at 100 yards as often as going front end first—some even went rear end first, it seemed to me. They were tough little buggers, though, made with Wood cups from a cull lot, the cores hand-formed from soldering lead of the correct dimension. One at about 130 yards killed a crow that was dead before he was aware he was hit, from *two* non-expanding holes through his midsection. Nevertheless, with that bullet it was a lucky hit. They do not print consistently or group snugly, at extreme velocities.

Perhaps twist rate had something to do with this performance. Ackley suggested 1 turn in 12″, which both of my 20-cal. barrels have. Ernest L. Gardiner, the Rockford, Ill. bullet maker (now forced out of business via the GCA of 1968) tried 8″ and 12″, then settled on a 10″ twist. Bob Forker, I've heard, prefers 12″, using 36-gr. bullets. C. H. Stocking, I believe, likes a 12″ twist. The Germans, I've heard, went as fast as 1 turn in 7½″, while Mondragon used 1 in 9″, I understand. I don't believe anyone *knows* the correct twist.

Coming back from velocity fantasyland with the little 28-gr. bullet, useful plinking performance chronographed with my Oehler count-em-up model shows 3699 fps from 22 grains of 4198. Using a die setting that leaves about ¹⁄₁₆″ hole up front, and soft lead coring, the bullet will now open up on crows, and is respectably predictable in accuracy.

As of this writing. I've made up three effective bullets that perform with high accuracy and proper expansion. One is in 40-gr., two are 53- and 56-gr., all Sierra cups. The main difference between the latter two is a tip of lead out front on the heavier one, with the lighter one a shallow hollow point. On varmints up to coyote size, both expand uniformly and well. The 40-gr. bullet has become a stock bullet for groundhog shooting and target work.

Mainstay bullet for varminting is the 53-gr. hollow point ahead of 26 grains of 3031 at an average 3562 fps a reliable load.

The 20-Caliber Rifle

Earlier I mentioned that my rifle was on a standard Remington 788 action. The barrel, just over 26", allows 90% loadings to produce full thrust behind a feasible bullet, for regular purpose shooting.

Photographs (Figs. 3 and 4) show details of the piece as a whole. I put Bushnell stud mounts and rings on it, to keep over-all weight down, and so far they've stayed put. The scope is a Valor 10x40, with crosshairs. In varmint usage so far this economical scope has proved sharp, crisp and reliable. With the little German sling in place, and loaded with three rounds, over-all weight is still under 8 lbs. From a stick rest or benchrest, then, there is enough weight to absorb almost all recoil. The long barrel diminishes almost all muzzle blast, except for the final sharp, authoritative report. No Missouri farmer on whose land I've shot has had concern about his herd being stampeded, and the invite-back rate has increased since I've allowed each of them to shoot a few in the 20. In central Missouri, at least, the 20:28A has committed fans!

With the 28-gr. case capacity, 90% loading density behind bullets of 53-56 grains has provided outstanding worn-in performance. Over 1000 rounds have been fired through my 20:28A so far, and its tuning gets better each time I use it extensively. It has been with me to Wyoming for marmots, across part of the Dakotas for prairie dogs and coyotes, and has made stew of both cottontail and jackrabbits in the six states where that type of shooting is authorized. I have not used it on deer, and don't intend to.

Fred Huntington's able craftsmen made me up a set of case-forming dies, mirror smooth and functional. I use another die, near 20, before I socket cases up fully for final reloading/sizing in the caliber dies. Brass loss just hasn't happened, so far.

Longest shot I've made so far was 311 paces across a swale into the chest of a waddling badger. The 53-gr. bullet opened well, taking out a ¾" disc of striped fur on the far side. Bullet remainder found after about 20 minutes of sifting and scratching weighed, back home, 32 grains. A drop of epoxy cement I sometimes put in the base of the hunting bullets I make held the remains of the cup and core together.

Why the 20-Caliber

What will the 20 caliber do that a high speed 17 or 224 won't do? Can-

Fig. 5—20:28 case flanks C.H. Stocking's excellent 20-cal. bullets; from left: 44, 48 and 50 gr. Next, cup in formation.

didly, nothing. Well loaded, it will press and pass some of the whiz-velocity 17s. Since I have chronographed 17s and 20s, I know about that aspect. Since I am also a committed fan of the .224s, now owning three, I am aware of their capabilities from many years of satisfying shooting.

The key point is that fully acknowledging the merits of the other calibers does not require one to *exclude* developmental attention, with enthusiasm, to the place in between for a 20:28A, or any offshoot you may develop. The usefulness is in the developmental experiences. There is no requirement to trump up some contest, which on unbalanced rules would "exclude" another caliber. But if developmental curiosity is dormant in you, and if you prefer to buy ready-made all components you use, then the 20 isn't your cup of tea. We'll stay friends, anyhow. ●

Fig. 4—Right side of the 20:28A, made on a Remington 788 action, the author sighting from a favorite stick rest.

Stocking does use a 12" twist in his 20-222 Sako-A&M L46 rifle, which he described as being "... one of the most accurate light sporters I have ever shot ... " However, Stocking intends to have A&M build another barrel, this one to have a 10" twist, which he feels may do better with 48-gr. bullets.

Here are some of Stocking's loads, those that have performed well in his 24" barreled Sako, muzzle diameter .565":

Powder/grs.	Bullet/grs.
Ball C/22	50
Ball C/22.5	50
Ball C/22.5	45
4895/23.5	45
4198/19	48
4198/20	45
Norma 200/20	48
Norma 200/20	45

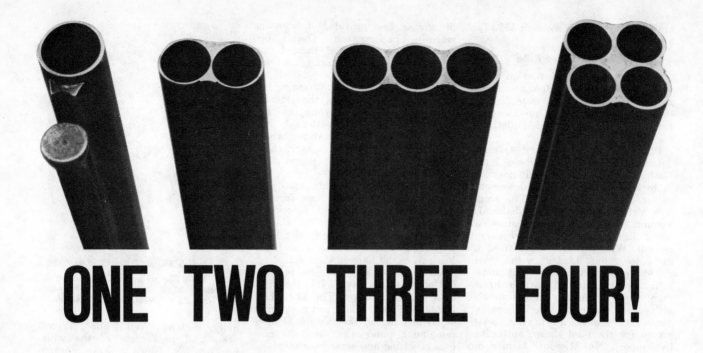

ONE TWO THREE FOUR!

Barrels, that is—an early Manton caplock single, a double by Lang, a John Dickson drilling and a Lancaster quattrocannone. All eminently usable, too, bringing down game in all seasons to Barlow and Black Dog.

A STRANGE TITLE for a shotgun article? Not at all—that's precisely the number of the barrels to be found on four of the guns I hunted with last season!

One barrel: a Joseph Manton 12 bore percussion muzzleloader.

Two barrels; a Joseph Lang 20 gauge pinfire.

Three barrels: a 16 gauge John Dickson round action.

Four barrels: a Charles Lancaster 20.

Every one of them a gun of some considerable interest; the youngest over 80 years old, the eldest 150 years or not far off it.

Because it is the most simple, the oldest and was made by the most famous of all the great shotgun makers, let's examine first the single barrelled percussion muzzleloader of Joseph Manton. This is not one of the *great* Joe Mantons, not being one of his renowned flintlock doubles or ever having been owned by Col. Hawker! Indeed, there could even be some doubt about it be-

ing a *genuine* Joe Manton gun, for it has no serial number on the barrel, breech or lock, nor are the maker's initials on the barrel or lock. Still, there are examples of authenticated Mantons which have no serial numbers, so nothing definite is to be concluded from that fact.

The high grade two-stripe Damascus barrel has every appearance of belonging to a Manton product—the octagonal breech becoming 16-sided 5 inches forward

and then, 4 inches further on, being rounded off for the rest of its 32-inch length. It appears that both Charles Lancaster and Wm. Fullerd, two of the greatest barrel-makers of the day, did make barrels of this type for Joseph Manton at this time.

The rib bears the words—*Joseph Manton Hanover Square London*—which means that it was made between 1819 and 1825, the only years this address was occupied by Manton.

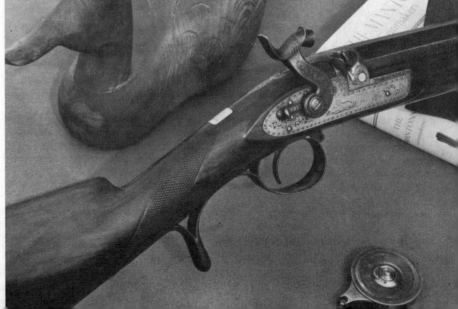

Note the unusual trigger guard of the single barrel Joseph Manton, more like that of a rifle than a shotgun.

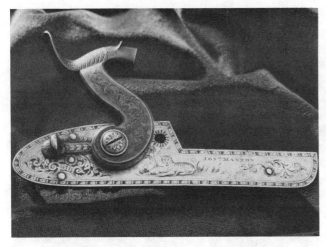

by ROGER BARLOW

Of course this gun might have been assembled from parts on hand after Manton went into bankruptcy 1826. It might also have been sent out to Manton & Co. in Calcutta, as this branch was formed just about the time financial disaster hit Joe Manton. Indeed, there is very good evidence that this gun was at least intended for someone in India or someone going there; the lock is embellished with a tiger, the trigger guard shows a charging boar, the breechplug carries a boar's head (where Manton's stamp should be found) and there's a deer on the tang of the metal buttplate. But why such decoration on a shotgun? And why the unusual un-shotgun-like trigger guard so much like that belonging on a rifle? I think this rather heavy-barreled smoothbore was intended as a dual-

purpose gun; for shot, of course, but also for use with a heavy powder charge behind a solid ball when hunting boar or deer. Indeed, at 5 to 10 paces a 12-gauge ball, carefully placed, might well stop a tiger, though an 8 or 10 would certainly be a more logical choice.

I suppose the tiger is there on the lockplate merely to say, "India," with the gun actually expected to be used on birds and 4-footed game appreciably less dangerous than tigers. The heavy barrel (and its length) certainly denotes the intention of the maker to let it be safely fired with relatively heavy charges. Most Manton singles and doubles had lighter and shorter barrels than does this gun.

The safety on the lockplate is of the type Joe Manton used on some

This detail of the Manton lock shows its unique device for blocking the half-cock catch or "bent." In a normal lock the hammer can be placed in half-cock from either full cock or the fired position. Fig. 1 (above) shows that when this Manton is at full cock the free-swinging, pivoted "blocker" arm will deflect the nose of the sear and prevent it from entering the half-cock bent. Fig. 2 (below) shows that when the hammer is brought back from the fired position this blocker swings to the rear and permits the nose of the sear to enter the half-cock bent. When the hammer is brought to full cock the blocker swings back to the position seen in Fig. 1. The writer can see only one reason for this mechanism's use; it permits a very deep and secure half-cock bent in the tumbler, the blocker being there to prevent the sear from catching it when the hammer falls from the full-cock position and the trigger is quickly released. Just the sort of complication Joe Manton loved—like his "gravitating" locks which prevented his flintlocks from firing when they were being loaded.

The boar's head is engraved in the area where Manton's stamp is usually found. The two bright bands are gold.

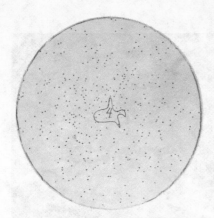

The old Manton's cylinder barrel throws a very even pattern of 8s, which is effective on quail out to 30 yards. This was shot at 20 yards using 1⅛ ounces of shot.

Upper right—The handsome 109-year-old Joseph Lang double. One of the early "modern" breechloaders using the pinfire cartridge. Lower right—The drawing shows the Lefaucheux break action design which inspired Mr. Lang to introduce the breechloading shotgun to the English market. However, he held the barrels of his gun more firmly to the action by placing the locking lug nearer the standing breech.

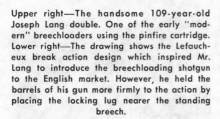

of his shotguns—it locks the internal tumbler rather than the external hammer, as was the more common practice. Details of the lock mechanism seem in the best Manton tradition of workmanship and design. The "dolphin" hammer is, with the exception of the engraving, almost identical with those on Hawker's famous "Old Joe" after Manton had converted that flintlock to percussion.

One final reason to believe this gun to be a genuine Manton is that it hardly seems logical to go to such lengths to fake a *single barreled* gun, when there'd have been so much more profit in a double! Also, if it is a fake, I think there would be a number and some initials on it simply to allay suspicion. More likely, as I said, it might have been unfinished at the time of Manton's failure in 1825-6, and completed by Joseph Lang, who acquired all of Manton's stock. Anyway it is a gun to provoke endless speculation (until someday when W. Keith Neal* can examine it).

Basically this old gun is in superb condition, having only a very few small dents in the stock plus some powder stain near the hammer and nipple. I've not had the breech plug out but as far as I can tell the bore is in quite good

---

*Co-author with D. H. L. Back of *The Mantons: Gunmakers*, New York, 1966.

condition (the barrel is perfect outside with, I am certain, the original browning). However, out of respect for its age, and my own fingers, I shoot it only with a light load—2½ drams of black powder and 1 to 1⅛ ounces of shot.

I've mainly shot doves with it for, although it weighs only 6 lbs. 13 ozs., the barrel is rather long and the gun too muzzle-heavy to handle well for me on upland birds. However, I've also shot quail with it, the cylinder patterns being ideal for such close shooting. But the stock doesn't really fit me well enough for such fast gun mounting. Nevertheless, to go afield with a gun that is the product of one of the world's great gunmakers, and built when Thomas Jefferson, Beethoven, and Napoleon Bonaparte were still alive is a mighty satisfying experience! One really feels a link with history.

Although this isn't in any way supposed to be a history of the shotgun, but merely a recounting of my own shooting experience with guns having barrels in numbers one to four, let us proceed to the gun with 2 barrels and a little

relative background information.

The Early Lang Pinfire

Now there isn't anything very startling about a shotgun with two barrels (at least not in 1972), for flintlock doubles came into use during the late 1700s. However, the one to be now considered is representative of an important milestone in the development of the shotgun. Although the first practical break-action, breechloading double barreled shotguns came into use in France about 1835 these guns made very few converts outside their native land. But by 1850 the pinfire cartridge had been greatly improved and the London gunmaker, Joseph Lang, was so impressed by the potential of the French-made examples he saw at the Crystal Palace Exhibition of 1851 that he immediately undertook the manufacture of such guns (with improvements) at the time when every gunmaker in England was making muzzleloaders only. Joseph Lang (who might have worked on that Manton of mine) is credited with having literally forced the breechloader upon both the con-

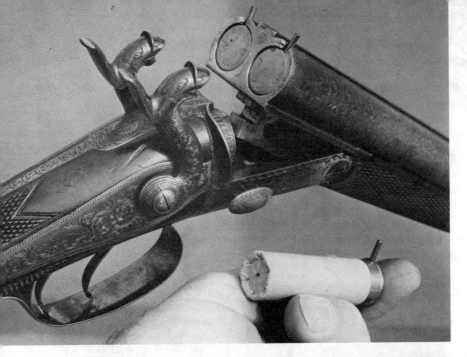

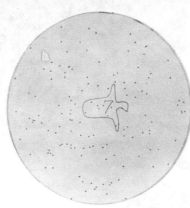

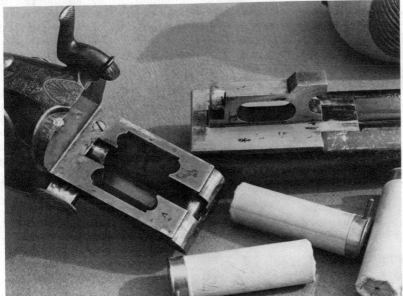

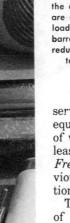

Top left—The 20 ga. Joseph Lang pinfire. The oval "button" on the side is pressed to open the action. Barlow's handloaded pinfire shells are given a modern crimp on a conventional loading press. Left—Note how the action and barrel lug of the Lang have been cut away to reduce weight. Below left—A pheasant brought to bag with the old Lang pinfire double.

servative British shooter and his equally conservative gunmakers, all of whom were reluctant, to say the least, to find anything good in a *French* invention regardless of its obvious advantages over the conventional muzzleloaders of the period.

The main weakness or drawback of the French-made break-action double was in the way the barrels were held against the action—there was usually enough "give" to permit the breech end of the barrels to lift slightly when the gun was fired, causing the muzzle to drop and the charge to fly lower than it should. This occurred because the single locking lug was too weak and too close to the hinge-pin to enjoy a very favorable leverage.

Joseph Lang built similar guns but appears to have moved the hinge-pin slightly forward and the locking lug much nearer the standing breech. This improved design was such a success that before 1860 every gunmaker in England was building his own version of Lang's gun. Most of them, though, continued to use a side-pivoting under-lever to actuate the "bolting" mechanism. This was certainly slow and awkward to operate, but it still beat stuffing powder, wadding and shot down the muzzle!

My 20-gauge Lang pinfire is also an example of the next big improvement in breechloading shot-

Above left—This portrait of the 90-year-old 3-barreled Dickson shows its sleek and graceful lines. (The lion on the cover of the old John Dickson catalog is just to remind a customer that this Scottish firm built rifles as well as shotguns.) Above right—Details of the 3-barreled Dickson, showing the twin set of double "Purdey" locking lugs.

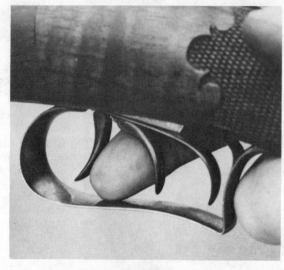

Right—Both the first and second triggers are hinged to swing forward when the shooter's finger reaches for the second or third trigger, therefore only requiring slightly more movement of the shooter's hand on the grip than when only two triggers are used.

Below—The 3-hole Dickson drops a ringneck.

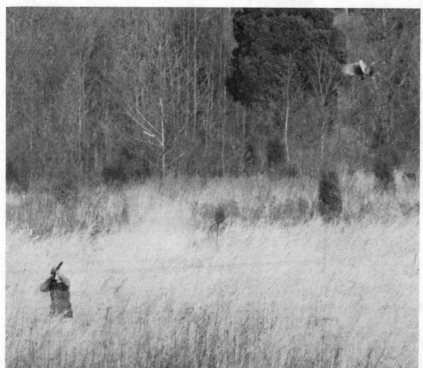

guns, for it is a "snap-action" gun. A button on the right side of the action is pressed to open the gun but the bolting mechanism "snaps" into its locking position automatically as the gun is closed, thereby greatly speeding up the reloading operation. About 1862 Westley Richards, Purdey, Greener, Lang and others all had patented their own "snap guns."

My Lang, made in 1864 to the order of a Mr. R. Guville, is listed in the company's records as one of their "best" grade models. Weighing a mere 5 lbs. 2 ozs., with 28-inch barrels, and also appropriately muzzle light, it is a delightful upland game gun. I load its pinfire shells with 2 to 2¼ drams of black powder and ⅞- or 1 ounce of shot. The barrels are, of course, true cylinder, so the patterns are ideal for quail at the normal 18-25 yard range these birds are taken and are effective on grouse and pheasant to a little beyond 30 yards.

The Civil War was raging and Abraham Lincoln was still alive when this most elegant little gun— with its fine Damascus barrels, handsomely engraved locks and action, dolphin hammers and stock of magnificent walnut—was made. It adds something special to any hunt —when one isn't actually shooting it there's such a genuine pleasure in just *looking* at it! (Something I cannot say for any modern autoloader).

The Dickson Three-Barrel

If two barrels are good *three* would be even better, would they not? John Dickson (the younger) and Arthur Graham Murray apparently thought so for, on February 23rd, 1882, they filed a patent, in Edinburgh, for just such a gun. This was based on the justly-famed hammerless Dickson "round action," and the patent specified three side-by-side barrels, or two side-by-side barrels and one centered above them, or two side-by-side barrels with one centered below. It appears doubtful that any guns having the latter two configurations were ever made by the Dicksons. Indeed, only 11 of the style I have were ever constructed. Why it was never more successful is hard to understand. It is an exceptionally graceful gun, relatively light and well balanced, and perfectly suited, certainly, to the shooting of driven game. Nor would it be at all unsuited for walking up birds.

My 3-hole Dickson was actually made for Mr. Murray, the joint patentee, in 1882. It is a 16-gauge (a 12 would not be nearly so light or graceful) weighing 6 lbs. 14 ozs. and has 28-inch barrels. These are choked, right to left, true cylinder, modified and full. I assume the barrels are made of what was then called "fluid steel," hence suitable for smokeless powder, but as it was only proofed for black powder loads I stick to those. This Dickson shows very little evidence of its 90-plus years of use, and it is a truly magnificent example of a "best" gun of the period. All it lacks are automatic ejectors which, presumably, the makers left off because of the additional weight and complication. I don't miss them. The 3 triggers are set a bit more closely together than two usually are, but as the first two are hinged there's no awkwardness about using any one of them, or one after the other.

The broad sighting plane offered by the 3 side-by-side barrels is a bit strange but not the least disturbing. One sights naturally along the top of the center barrel, which is exceptionally well outlined by the black of the sunken ribs on either side.

Opening is by means of a side lever which is so smooth, effortless and convenient that one wonders just why the top lever opening became the most popular system.

Regrettably I haven't yet shot as much with this gun as I would like, and I haven't had the chance of trying for three birds on a covey rise, either!

Lancaster's Quartet

The 4-barreled gun I have was patented by the firm of Charles Lancaster about the same time as the Dickson, but it was the invention of Mr. H. A. A. Thorn, who had taken over this firm upon the death of the son of the founder.

The 4-hole Lancaster, rather more than the Dickson drilling, is

Above—Close-up of the 3-hole Dickson showing the rich engraving and the fine fit of metal to metal.

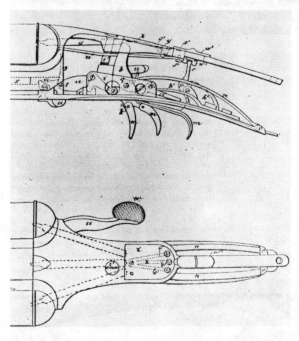

Left—Part of the patent specifications of the 3-barrel Dickson. Note the long firing pins angled sharply inward to permit this gun to still have the customary graceful and thin Dickson grip. The three locks are grouped closely together on the trigger plate; also a feature of the Dickson 2-barreled "Round Action" guns.

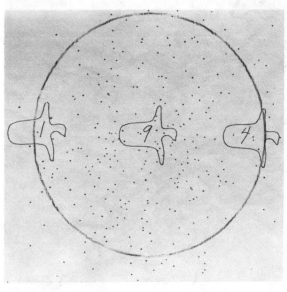

The left (full choked) barrel of the 3-hole Dickson produces a useful 40 yard grouse pattern with 1 oz. of 7½s.

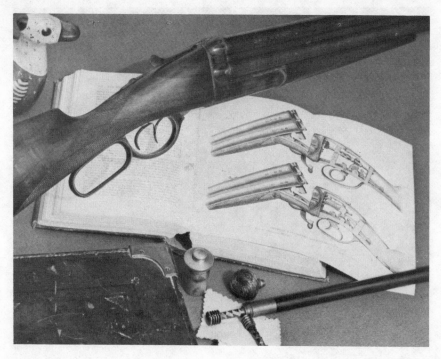

The writer's 4-barreled Lancaster, the final version of this design, was initially bolted by means of a strong but rather clumsy underlever. The first guns of this type were cocked and fired by pulling the ring trigger—which made for rapid use of all the barrels but at the expense of a too-heavy trigger pull. The second version provided for cocking by the rear trigger and firing by the forward one. The third and last version, as exemplified by Barlow's gun, is quite different in many respects—the gun is bolted with the snap action "Purdey" bolt operated by a top lever. The underlever is for cocking the two hamers, which are fired in the usual way with two triggers—then, to fire the remaining two barrels, the lever is actuated again to recock the two internal hammers and to rotate the striker assembly.

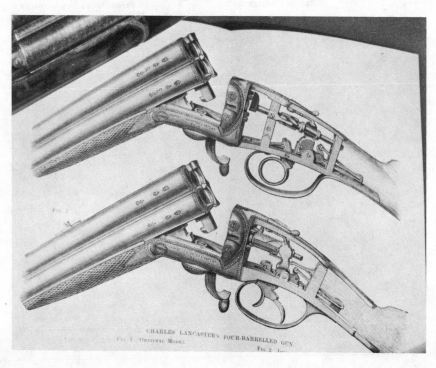

CHARLES LANCASTER'S FOUR-BARRELLED GUN
Fig. 1 Original Model

a direct outgrowth of the tremendous amount of driven game shooting which took place in Great Britain during the latter half of the 19th century. Lord Walsingham, in 1888, shot 1070 grouse in one day, using a gun loader. The skilled shooter found it possible to take two birds out of an approaching covey, switch guns with a "loader" as the birds passed overhead, and then take two more out of the same covey as they were going away! Obviously the idea behind the 4-barreled Lancaster was to do away with the need for a second gun and a servant-loader!

As the shooters of driven birds do their work from a stand or butt, little if any carrying of a gun is involved, so it was probably felt by the designer that the considerable weight of a 4-barreled gun would be no handicap. This might well be true for a dozen or so shots, but by the time a man has swung any 9-10 pound gun 20 to 50 times he is going to be getting arm weary, which may well have been the reason for the failure of this gun to catch on. Bear in mind, too, that the 12-gauge doubles popular for this sort of shooting weighed around 6½-7 lbs and were relatively muzzle light. They were much less tiring when dozens of shots might be made in only a couple of minutes.

My 80-year old 20 gauge 4-hole Lancaster weighs 9 lbs. 4 ozs. and also, as would be expected, is very muzzle heavy. Hardly an ideal gun for carrying afield after quail and grouse! Yet I find that I shoot this monstrously heavy shotgun as well, or even better, than any gun I own—at least until my arms tire. I credit this to the outstanding job of gun fitting carried out when it was stocked for me by Ian Crudgington of Bath, England, a first rate gunmaker and collector who deserves to be more widely known. Anyway, I lugged those 9¼ pounds around the Shenandoah Valley on more occasions last fall than I ever anticipated, killing quail, woodcock, grouse and pheasant with it—but never being able to make use of that 4-shot capability. It would take driven game, and a fair lot of it, to do that.

Because all 4 barrels of this Lancaster are choked modified (they haven't been opened up for I want the gun to remain original) I've used cube shot in my black powder handloads to get the more open patterns I need for much of my shooting. As this gun has

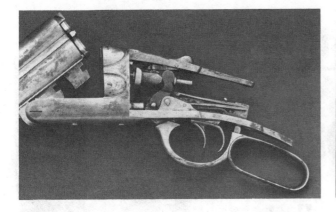

Damascus barrels, and was only proofed for black powder, I hesitate to use nitro in it.

One, two, three or four barrels—which are best? Happily I don't have to make a decision to discard all but one of this quartet. I would certainly dislike having to do that, for every one of them has so much to recommend it.

A single barrel (single shot) shotgun is, naturally, commendably light and a short barreled modern one usually has a fine, lively balance; it is a far more effective game getter than most shooters realize. Today, unfortunately, there are no top quality single barrel *field* guns being made. Trap guns, of course, are too heavy for upland bird hunting.

But basically the double-barreled gun has clearly proven its many virtues over the past 200 years, and if today it is the world's most popular type for use on what we call upland game, it has reached this position for very good reasons. The good two-tube gun is almost as light and well balanced as a single-barreled gun, but it does have that highly desirable second shot capability, that extra cartridge that lets the hunter drop a pair of birds on a covey rise instead of only one. As the opportunity of collecting *more* than two birds out of a flushed covey doesn't present itself very often, and our present-day bag limits and bird populations don't encourage such shooting, there is little if any reason to seek more than two-shot capability. It is highly doubtful if any 3- or 4-barreled guns will ever again be manufactured, which makes going afield with examples of the few existing guns of this type so rewarding. They *are* intriguing firearms, made even more interesting by the quality of their workmanship and their pedigrees.

One, Two, Three, Four—two *is* best, though I must admit I'm prejudiced and love them all! ●

Above left—It was in this state the writer acquired the 4-barreled Lancaster. It had been put into production in 1891 but after passing proof no further work was done on it. The barrels were never browned, the action never engraved and case-hardened nor was it stocked. It remained "in the white," rusted from sweaty hands, until 1971 when it was completed exactly as if the original workmen, long dead, had done the job. This final work was done by Ian Crudgington of Bath, England. Note that the underlever and the rear trigger are bent, probably through the gun having been dropped at some time.

Above—The first ruffed grouse Barlow took with the 4-hole Lancaster, using handloads of 1 ounce of 7½ shot and 2½ drams of black powder.

Detail of the barrels and action of the 4-hole Lancaster. The double barrel lugs are a bit wider than usual and a top extension is fitted to firmly bind the high standing breech to the barrels when the gun is closed.

Breech of the Lancaster 4-holer showing the "newness" of this recently completed 80-year-old gun, the richness of the color case hardening and the beautifully browned Damascus barrels.

The choked barrels of the 4-hole Lancaster can be made to print usefully wide and not over-dense patterns for quail (and grouse) at close range—this one shot at 20 yards with ⅞ oz. of cube or square shot!

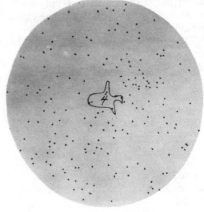

High Performance Handgun Loads—

and how to handle 'em.

by GEORGE C. NONTE, Jr.

Cannelure at left is adequate, that at right is too shallow to be of much help.

If you're going to duplicate today's light bullet, high velocity pistol and revolver cartridge, you'll have to forget some old rules. This is a new ball game!

TIME WAS WHEN the average handgunner who rolled his own ammunition was satisfied with essentially just two loads each for revolver and autoloader. Invariably, one load was the lightest, cheapest, and most accurate that could be assembled. This one was used in the largest quantity for serious paper-punching and, occasionally, plinking and other forms of powder-burning amusement. This was, for revolvers, a flat-nosed, home-cast, lead wadcutter bullet propelled with the lightest pinch of Bullseye that would produce acceptable accuracy. The same type of load was assembled for autoloaders, primarily in 45 ACP, but different in that the cast lead bullet was of semi-wadcutter form so as to feed reliably. Powder charges, of course, were a bit more hefty in order to supply sufficient recoil impulse to work the gun's action.

The second load class for revolvers was a relatively heavy Keith-style, semi-wadcutter bullet (also made at home) driven at better-than-factory velocities by hefty charges of Hercules Unique or 2400 powder. These were serious loads, intended to give deep penetration on game and enemy alike, along with as much expansion as could be coaxed out of cast bullets at the velocities that could be safely produced.

Loads for autos were somewhat similar, though round-nose bullets predominated to insure 100% reliable feeding, with powder charges and velocities not quite as impressive as those from revolvers.

Odly enough, relatively few handloaders attempted to duplicate the standard service revolver loads —simply because for target use their power and recoil were more liability than asset, and for hunting and defense they were less effective than the heavy loads. For automatics quite a few people felt the factory-load duplicate with lead bullets did well enough for defense work—and they were probably right inasmuch as the big 45 ACP was the almost universal choice of caliber.

But, came the 1950s and a few pistoleros no longer believed that it was impossible—as they had been told for decades—to produce *jacketed* handgun bullets that would expand well in animal tissue. First there was Jim Harvey, with his short-jacketed "Jugular" bullets, which expanded well but possessed a few shortcomings. Others followed in his tracks, but the inherent lead-fouling problem existing with short-jacketed bullets prevented really wide acceptance of this type, even though it gave tremendous expansion by normal standards.

A number of experimenters extended the jacket forward, over the bullet ogive, still using pure lead for the core. This development eliminated leading at the expense of expansion.

Two factors prevented most shooters from obtaining the performance level sought: adherence to traditional bullet weights in most calibers; and the use of jackets too thick and sturdy to allow proper expansion at the velocities that could be produced with those relatively heavy bullets.

First Effective HP Loads

Some people made stabs at correcting one or both of those problems, but success and market acceptance eluded them all. All, that is, except one Lee E. Jurras. Lee reduced bullet weight and bearing surfaces below previously accepted standards as much as he felt he dared, in order to obtain velocities sufficient to insure expansion with the very thin jackets he had specially made. He also carried the jacket well forward over the ogive to prevent slugging and leading, and used the softest lead available for cores.

Jurras's experiments resulted in his obtaining explosive expansion in game (and in people, too, as various law-enforcement officers put his custom-loaded ammunition to use), and velocities exceeding 1400/1600 fps in 38 Special and 357 Magnum respectively with 110-gr. bullets. As the design developed, he was also able to obtain accuracy surpassing that of many standard factory service loads.

By the early 1960s Jurras had formed the Super Vel Cartridge Corp. to produce and market ammunition loaded with the bullets and by the techniques he had

Typical factory high-performance loads for autoloaders, with and without cannelure. Uncannelured cases use case-mouth lacquer to hold bullets securely against feeding impacts.

Left case is cannelured to prevent bullet from receding; at right is plain case.

developed. Market acceptance was phenomenal, especially among law enforcement agencies, and the plant has been undergoing almost continual expansion ever since. In 1971 Super Vel produced (and sold) more high-performance handgun ammunition than all the other U.S. makers combined.

Not until 1969 did the major ammunition makers wake up to the fact that the upstart in their midst (Super Vel) had something almost every handgunner wanted. Since then, a score or more of Jurras-type loads have been offered by other makers, but to date none has achieved the wide acclaim of the original Super-Vel.

This high-performance ammunition—as we began calling it a couple of years back—can be safely duplicated by the advanced and experienced handloader. Almost from the beginning Jurras offered components and loading data for those who wanted them, which has spurred handloading interest.

In the past two or three years virtually every ammunition and bullet maker—with the single exception of Winchester-Western—has introduced a line of handgun bullets intended to compete with Super Vel. Some do so quite well, others just *look* like good expanding bullets and give indifferent performance.

New Loading Techniques Needed

But it takes more than simply an abundance of good bullets to insure handload performance that will equal that of the original article. New or different techniques must be mastered, often new tools acquired, and very careful attention must be given to the choice of propellants.

My own testing indicates that a wide variation exists in the expansion capabilities of bullets that look almost exactly alike. Too much generalization gets one into trouble, but to avoid an excess of detail, let's say that Super Vel bullets sit at the top of the list in accuracy and expansion characteristics and the ability to produce highest velocities at acceptable pressures. They are followed closely by the nearly-identical Sierra line, then Hornady and Speer, Remington and, finally, Norma. Many smaller makers also produce high-performance handgun bullets, but their numbers and limited output, the wide variation in performance, make it impractical to include them here.

Be not surprised in examining your first such bullets if they measure less in diameter than what you've come to expect for the caliber. The soft cores and thin jackets essential to good expansion allow them to upset easily enough to fill the grooves correctly and give good accuracy—yet that slight undersize condition helps hold down peak pressures and allows maximum velocities. It gives the bullet a sort of running start.

Bullets of this type are deliberately light in weight, as already mentioned. When loaded properly, probably the best balance of all factors is produced by: 110 gr. in 38 Spcl.; 125 in 357 Mag., 180 in 44 Mag.; 90 in 9mm; 105-110 in 38 ACP; 80 in 380 and 190 in 45 ACP. Choose heavier ones and you may not be able to drive them fast enough for good expansion.

Because of this low weight the traditionally-favored powders won't produce best results. As an example, Hercules 2400 has been virtually the *only* powder used in the magnums for so long that few people think anything else will work. It does have an excellent reputation with heavy bullets, but it burns far too slowly for light, high-performance bullets in any existing handgun caliber. Much faster powders generally associated with light target loads are needed. Actually, 2400 is *not* an efficient powder for heavy 44 and 45 loads with even the heaviest practical bullets!

Powders and Charges

In the 38 Spcl. and 357 Magnum, Olin 230-P, Bullseye and Unique

Undamaged bullets are standard factory loads; expanded slugs are Super Vels, fired at same time and distances, and into same material.

are highly efficient. The big 44 Magnum requires slower-burning fuel, and H-110 seems to be at the top of the heap.

In the smaller-capacity autoloader cases, about the slowest powder that can even be considered is Unique in the 45, with 230-P, Bullseye and Red Dot needed for the smaller 38, 9mm, and 380.

Factory loads (all makes) often use special powders which produce optimum burning in different barrel lengths, that is, 2", 4", 6", etc. By very careful study of propellants available and their performance in different barrel lengths, it is possible for the handloader to tailor ammunition to specific barrel lengths—that is, to develop maximum velocity safely in the shorter tubes. This in itself is too extensive a subject to go into here, but such loads are possible for the advanced handloader.

As for size of powder charges, be mighty cautious. When working at the upper limits of those pressure levels generally considered safe in handguns, a change in bullet brand or a very minor change in weight can easily push chamber pressure well over the red line. Even an invisible change in jacket thickness or core hardness will do it. This has been proven too many times in laboratory tests to be argued against simply because you've tried it and your gun didn't blow up in your face.

The CH canneluring tool.

High-Performance Handgun Load Data With Super-Vel Bullets

380 ACP (4"bbl)

Bullet	Dia.	Powder/grs.	MV	PSI
88/JHP	.3550"	B'eye/3.0	932	12,800
88/JHP	.3550"	230-P/3.0	965	13,600
80/JHP	.3550"	B'eye/3.3	1018	12,800
80/JHP	.3550"	230-P/3.5	1020	13,200

9mm Parabellum (5"bbl)

Bullet	Dia.	Powder/grs.	MV	PSI
90/JHP	.3550"	230-P/5.0	1422	30,000
90/JHP	.3550"	B'eye/5.0	1415	32,500
90/JHP	.3550"	N-1010/5.5	1409	33,500
112/JSP	.3555"	230-P/4.5	1240	28,600
112/JSP	.3555"	Herco/7.0	1324	28,100

38 Super Auto (5"bbl)

Bullet	Dia.	Powder/grs.	MV	PSI
90/JHP	.3550"	Unique/9.0	1580	30,000
90/JHP	.3550"	230-P/7.0	1452	32,500
112/JSP	.3550"	230-P/6.0	1321	30,000
112/JSP	.3550"	Unique/8.0	1431	*33,000
112/JSP	.3550"	AL-5/9.5	1390	28,100

38 Special (6"bbl)

Bullet	Dia.	Powder/grs.	MV	PSI
110/JHP	.3565"	Unique/7.5	1280	19,000
125/JHP	.3560"	Unique/7.0	1200	19,500
125/JHP	.3570"	Unique/8.0	1150	———
125/JHP	.3570"	2400/15.0	1210	———

357 Magnum (8⅜"bbl)

Bullet	Dia.	Powder/grs.	MV	PSI
110/JHP	.3560"	Unique/10.0	1780	28,500
110/JHP	.3560"	AL-8/15.5	1780	29,000
125/JHP	.3570"	Unique/9.5	1640	28,000
125/JHP	.3570"	AL-8/14.5	1660	29,000

45 ACP (5"bbl)

Bullet	Dia.	Powder/grs.	MV	PSI
190/JHP	.450"	Unique/7.5	1060	19,000
190/JHP	.450"	230-P/6.0	1000	18,500
190/JHP	.450"	Herco/8.0	1030	19,000

All above loads represent maximum working pressures and should be reduced slightly to start. Changes in bullet make should also be compensated for by a slight reduction in powder charge.
MV = Muzzle Velocity. PSI = Pounds per Square Inch.

The loading data given here are for use only with Super Vel bullets, with which they were developed under laboratory conditions. If used with other makes or weights, powder charges should be reduced 10% as a starter. Substitution of a same-weight bullet with a harder or thicker jacket, or a bit longer bearing surface, or a slightly larger diameter, can boost pressures 5,000 pounds/sq. inch (psi) or more in a flash.

Having selected powder, charge weight, and bullet, you may think the problem is whipped. Not so at all. First is the matter of getting the bullets into the case and keeping them there in their proper relationship until they're fired. Resizing dies and expander plugs that worked perfectly with lead or older jacketed bullets may leave the case mouth too large for high-performance bullets.

Case Necks and Bullets

Seat a bullet of your choice in a resized and expanded case, but do not crimp. If the bullet can be turned or pushed deeper into the case with your fingers, the problem is obvious. If it can't, try pushing the bullet *hard* against a solid surface. If the bullet can be pushed in deeper without straining your arm, a tighter case is needed.

Polishing the expander plug smaller may do the job; *so may simply omitting the expanding operation.* If both fail, obtain a smaller die, or switch to thicker-walled cases. The bullet *must be tight.* RCBS, Box 1919, Oroville, CA 95965, can furnish special tight dies and expanders.

Since some high-performance bullets have sharp-edged bases, proper chamfering and flaring of the case mouth for them is unusually important. The mouth must be opened up enough to let bullets be hand-

Smith & Wesson's Combat Magnum.

Colt's National Match.

started *straight* in the case, and to remain that way as the assembly is placed in the die. With a short bearing surface and sharp base, a tipped bullet will almost invariably be deformed in seating, often ruining the case as well.

Also, even those high-performance bullets that are jacketed fully to the nose are quite soft, relatively fragile, your old practice of using only one or two round-nose or semi-wadcutter seating punches with all bullet shapes won't work. It will deform soft bullet noses badly. This not only looks like hell, but can cause leading, and will also close up hollow points to the extent that they won't expand properly. Most tool makers can supply punches to fit any H-P bullet correctly, so obtain and use them—or else fill one you have with sealing wax or epoxy to make a perfect nose fit.

Since high-performance loads produce relatively heavy recoil, especially in the lightweight guns favored today by many, a tight crimp

is essential if bullets are to be retained in their cases during recoil. All good H-P revolver bullets have fairly deep cannelures, made so to permit a heavy roll-crimp. You'll not be able to get an adequate crimp on a smooth uncannelured bullet except by badly deforming it.

The time-honored process of seating and crimping in a single operation just doesn't work on many H-P bullets. Nor is it the best system with standard bullets, either. The die often begins to turn the case mouth in before it is over the cannelure, which results in deformation of the soft bullet and the case mouth. This may not seriously affect accuracy or expansion, but it sure as hell doesn't improve them. Seating to proper depth first, followed by crimping as a separate operation, produces better results.

With new or only once-fired cases, crimp strength is important to velocity uniformity. It needs to be uniform, but it won't be if cases vary much in length. Trim cases

Cases must be flared sufficiently—but no more—to permit bullets to be started by hand, to avoid bullet damage.

uniformly. However, as cases are fired, the mouths work-harden, and crimp strength becomes less of a consideration. Assuming a normal hardness gradient, new cases do require a strong and uniform crimp, while well-used cases do not because of the much harder mouth and consequent tighter grip it produces on the bullet. However, this is *not* a valid reason for ignoring crimp as a means of avoiding recoil-induced bullet movement in revolvers. Use a good crimp for this purpose —always.

Auto Pistol H-P Loads

Self-loading pistol ammunition of H-P type requires a bit different

Typical factory H-P revolver loads show the heavy crimp that must be applied also to handloads.

treatment. In order to feed correctly and reliably, bullets must be held very tightly in the case. Where revolvers tend to draw the case *off* the bullet during recoil, autoloaders tend to drive the bullet *deeper* into the case. The reasons are simple—in the magazine the loaded cartridge is slammed repeatedly against both front and back of the magazine by recoil—and later in being fed through the mechanism, the nose of the bullet is rammed very hard against the feed ramp, sometimes also against the chamber wall or barrel tang, as it is driven from magazine to chamber. H-P bullets are not only lighter, but have less surface engaged by the case, and are thus doubly likely to be rammed deeper into the case than conventional bullets.

A heavy roll crimp will, at least partially, overcome this problem in revolvers, but it is not practicable in autoloading cases, which headspace on their mouths as most do. Consequently, H-P bullets intended for autoloaders are not generally supplied with a crimping cannelure.

The handloader's solution is to make the resized case as tight a fit as possible on the bullet, and at the same time expand the case

Taper Crimps and Cannelures

With all this done to insure that the bullet is as tight as possible in the case, a slight *taper* crimp must be applied to remove the remains of the original mouth flare—and it will also add some support to the bullet.

In extreme instances, especially with thin-walled cases, it may be necessary to roll in cannelure into the case against which the base of the bullet may rest. This is easily done with the SAS or C-H bullet/case canneluring tools. A single canneluring operation is good for several loadings if care is taken not to iron it out when the mouth is again expanded after resizing.

Of course, the factories solve all this autoloader problem by placing a sealing compound inside the case mouth before the bullet is seated. It is applied in liquid form, then turns *almost* hard and remains in that state; when the bullet is seated everything is bound together very strongly.

If you really want to go first cabin, you might also waterproof completed H-P rounds. This is not difficult and the primer end is simplest. Merely place cartridges bullet-down in a compartmented ammunition box. then lightly spray

from having more than an infinitesimal effect on powder ignition or combustion—if any.

Care and Inspection

High performance handloads, of course, should be even more carefully inspected and tested than your regular run of home-brewed fodder. Its main purpose is to defend your tender body from the baddies, and if it doesn't work you could be in real trouble—not like with a paper target or an empty beer can. These hardly ever shoot back.

Then, too, it should go without saying that the very best cases should be used for H-P loads. Certainly no more than once- or twice-fired, and in top, thoroughly clean condition—and tumbling in ground nut hulls is the best way I know to get them clean and bright. My own H-P loads are generally loaded in new unfired cases, but that isn't always possible. Besides, it kicks the cost way up there.

Questions are often asked about "loading down" H-P ammunition for reasons of increasing accuracy, cutting recoil, reducing gun stress and wear, etc. There is just one problem—*load down and it's no longer high performance ammunition.* The bullets are the key, and they are designed to perform their best at high velocities. No high velocity, no high-performance load. It's as simple as that. Powder charge reductions, up to 10% or so, can be made without seriously affecting expansion in most calibers, but in the 380 auto, for example, the full charge is already so small that even a slight reduction in powder takes it out of the H-P class.

If you want high-performance ammunition, then load H-P ammunition. If you want a lighter load, then load it, but don't expect it to perform anywhere near the same.

In the final analysis, the only *good* practice and training for the use of high-performance ammunition is the firing of that same ammunition in the gun which you'll use if and when the balloon goes up. If you feel the need—or just the desire—for H-P loads, make up lots of them and spend most in practice. You'll need that practice because the gun will perform differently, will shoot to a different point of aim, and it will affect you differently in recoil, muzzle blast, flash, and other ways you'll notice the first time out.

The last few years have demonstrated that there is no substitute for high-performance ammunition. It's the best there is. ●

Old HP loads use heavy lead and half-jacket bullets at left, while today's generation uses light, long-jacketed bullets, as at right.

Revolver bullet at left is factory-canneluler for crimping; auto bullet at right is not.

mouth only down to 1/64-1/32" *above the point* that will be reached by the base of the bullet when it is fully seated. This usually means buying an undersize resizing die and expander plug. Even then the plug won't be quite correct for the job. Its working surface must be shortened so that when the die is adjusted to decap the case, the lower end of the plug's working surface leaves a slight shoulder just above where the bullet base will fall. Though it may seem a very shallow shoulder—and it is—it will still provide a great deal of support for the bullet when it is slammed hard against magazine wall or feed ramp. In seating, the bullet is rammed tightly against this shoulder, displacing it just enough to insure solid and lasting contact between the two.

the case heads with an aerosol can of clear lacquer. This sounds messy but isn't, and the lacquer will run in around the primer and seal the pocket quite effectively against any moisture or liquid which does *not* contain a lacquer solvent.

At the bullet end, simply pick up the cartridge and place a drop of thinned clear lacquer at the junction of case mouth and bullet by means of a small brush, wire, or toothpick. It flows freely into the entire joint, and when it hardens (a matter of minutes) the seal will be complete. If bullet/case assembly is tight, as it should be, there is no likelihood that the lacquer will penetrate to the powder charge—even if it does, the small amount used, and the fact that it hardens so quickly, will prevent it

Handgun Hunting

by BILL DAVIDSON

Arizona handgunner-guide Ollie Barney Jr. with near-record-class mountain lion he bagged with his S&W 44 Magnum revolver. Barney guided author to hefty javelina a few years ago, specializes in "pigs," lion, bear.

Today's sporting revolver shows an accuracy equal to—and often better than—what a saddle carbine gave 25 years ago. Let some legislators—and Presidential hopefuls—consider this before buying the fable that handguns are not precision, sporting instruments.

PEOPLE—the social-conscious gospelers and others—who argue that the handgun is no sporting instrument are deep amid tricky conditions. First of all, they are arguing an untruth. All this, of course, is aside from the doubtful social premise that handguns should not be kept as personal weapons for self defense.

But even more pertinent for shooters, the handgun banners are obviously ignorant of the latest results in target competition, nor are they aware of the bolder facts about modern sporting handguns.

What the match model semi-auto pistol will do is pretty widely known among handgun fans, but there is considerably less knowledge about the potential of the sporting revolver, even among gun fans who should know more.

The sporting revolver—the modern, sound, magnum-caliber revolver with adjustable sights—is capa-ble of accuracy that, a generation ago, would have soothed most hunting riflemen—accuracy at least equal to what a pre-war saddle carbine would do and, in many cases, measurably superior to this.

It is something for Senators, attorneys-general and various presidential commissions to consider before slipping hysterically off half-cock with ridiculous recommendations to ban completely all privately-held handguns.

Any time that you or I—and I am not even a low Master-class shooter and I gave up handgun competition some years ago—can fire a revolver from sitting rest, two-handed, and cluster 3-shot groups inside 3 or 3½ inches at 50 yards and inside 6 inches at 100, the conclusion must be that the handgun has reached a singular level of effectiveness. It would be intriguing to show such results to the anti-gun clique. It might even convince a few, since I cannot avoid the suspicion there are among the gun haters a few, at least, who sincerely buy the fable that handguns are not precision or sporting instruments.

Oh yes, I know—we even have in the gun-writing trade a few people who, from some stifled yen for notoriety or whatever, write big-headlined pieces alleging that handguns are not accurate nor suitable for deer-class game or even coyotes. But these people are like the Southwestern guide who "gave up" hunting to loud headlines in the anti-hunting press and then went sneaking back into the tules every chance he had.

At the end of about two years of periodic but serious testing of magnum handguns, and some others, a few friends and I compiled the following group averages. While not sensational, these are indicative of a sound accuracy potential in modern sporting handguns. The two principal shooters who obtained these groups (Prescott, Ariz. sportsman and gun dealer Don Sieh and the author), are reasonably accomplished pistol shooters. High-Class, match-experienced veteran handgunners would do much better. Some of the guns used in these tests would probably do slightly better with properly-mounted pistol scopes. We preferred not to use scopes as a matter of taste and convenience and since we would not be using scopes on any of these guns in the field.

The figures should be self-explanatory in terms of what handguns *can* do:

Caliber	50-yd. avg.	100-yd. avg.	200-yd. avg.
357 Magnum	2.495″	4.893″	8.301″
9mm Parabellum	7.18	—	—
41 Magnum	—	4.813	9.500
44 Magnum	3.47	6.100	10.38

Notes: 1. Among mixed-quality, dealer-stock used 45-cal. Model 1911 semi-auto pistols tested at about the same time, one shot into 4.14″ at 50 yards (5-shot groups; all other groups cited here were 3-shot ones).

2. Best individual groups were:

Bob Emmitt wields an earlier Ruger Super Blackhawk 44 Magnum offhand, the gun rising to 90 degrees at the shot.

Two 3-shot groups fired by Don Sieh at 100 yards with tuned Ruger 44 Magnum. Either would be coyote or deer getters.

At 200 yards: 3.63″ by a 6″ 357 Magnum Python.

At 100 yards: 1.063″ by another 6″ Python (However, similar tests with a 44-cal. black powder Remington replica cap-and-ball revolver, a Navy Arms Model 1858, produced one 100-yard group measuring 1.062″. The 44 cap and ball over-all average was 5.037″ at 100 yards).

3. In all cases reported here, the sitting, two-handed bench-rest hold was used, with only the two cupped hands resting on a cushion atop the rest; in such tests, I try to avoid allowing any portion of the handgun—frame, barrel, whatever—to touch anything, since most of my field shooting with handguns is done from either standing or sitting. It is possible that a severe variation in methods of holding would provide some difference in point of impact at 50 or 100 yards or more.

Twenty or 30 years ago, results like these would have been improbable from all but a few target-tuned, strictly match handguns. Escalating improvements in manufacturing quality (with occasional lapses), in sighting equipment, in factory-loaded ammunition and components and in reloading gear, have combined to make today's revolver precise indeed within the context of a hand-held firearm. This applies largely to the generality of well-made handguns, from the 44 and 41 through the 357, the 38 Special, some 45s and such newer ones as the 30 M1 carbine-cartridge revolver, the 22 Jet, 221 Fireball and 256. The bigger ones have almost as much punch and accuracy as many of the slab-sided old big bore carbines our fathers wielded, and the smaller magnums are ultra-destructive, high-speed items with a potency approaching the prewar 22 Hornet. Now, of course, we have Thompson-Center's Contender available even in the Hornet!

Another shooting friend, Bob Emmitt, and I had an unusual, almost unbelievable opportunity to field-test hunting handguns in Southern Arizona not long ago. Predator and rodent control personnel of the Department of the Interior had by mischance poisoned a coyote area two years out of three—instead of the usual one in three. After the second wide application of poisons, baits and traps, there were few coyotes stirring in a wide zone

Colt's New Frontier Single Action, shown in 357 Magnum version, is also made in 45 Long Colt.

between the San Pedro River and Oracle Junction, Ariz. Rabbits—the coyotes' natural prey—had exploded in population as a result. There was an astonishing glut in both cottontails and jackrabbits, with no set season and a daily or possession limit of 10 in effect on cottontails (none on jacks). For perhaps 6 months Emmitt, my nephew Andy and I were treated to rabbit shooting almost impossible to describe; it was so good, certainly, that taking rabbits only with handguns became an article of honor

with us. Even so, we usually managed to collect 10, 15 or 20 on each trip afield. We wasted only the obviously sick, keeping the cottontails for Emmitt's hasenpfeffer and the jacks—stringier, strictly survival rations—for feeding our dogs.

Withing a few months, the natural consequences of artificially-stimulated overpopulation had set in and rabbit hunting was back to near normal. But until rabbits started dying from a high incidence of disease, and until a new crowd of hungry coyotes started filtering in, the opportunity for learning about handgun load performance was unparalleled.

We used mostly 38 Special and 357 magnum revolvers on the rabbits; our 22 rimfire magnums were not especially effective for humane kills out beyond 50 and 75 yards—and we had plenty of shots beyond those ranges. The big 41 and 44 magnums were even more effective, but they were unnecessarily violent in recoil for the purpose. As the prime rabbit shooting fell off, we switched to calling coyotes and trying for deer and other bigger game with the 41 and 44 (I packed my respected 41 on an elk hunt, too, but had no shot at one with it). In addition, we gave the 45 Colt caliber—the old Peacemaker cartridge—thorough use on most kinds of handgun hunting although, unlike the big magnums, the 45 is not legal for handgun hunting in Arizona. We also used the 9mm Parabellum, the 45 ACP and the Super 38 semi-auto load to a considerable extent. The semi-auto loadings were discarded fairly soon because the empties they spew out

Sam Green, Prescott, Arizona handgun hunter, handles recoil of Ruger 44 Magnum better than many—big hands and stout arm muscles help!

Ruger's 357 Magnum Blackhawk, here with 6½" barrel, is also offered in 30 Carbine, 44 Magnum and 45—both rimmed Colt and ACP.

are tricky to locate in typical dun-colored, rocky Southwestern habitat. Nor did any of them have anything special to redeem them from this fault. The 45 Colt was excellent within its twin limitations —thin-shelled cases and less metal between cylinders than the big magnums have.

Emmitt fixed a lot of hasenpfeffer, and our dogs got fat. Almost all our rabbits were "bought" with copious amounts of pistol powder, semi-jacketed and home-cast bullets, primers and all the other necessaries. We ate a lot of flour tortillas and drank plenty of coffee and bouillon around mesquite fires, in heat and cold, wet and dry, calling up coyotes and chousing rabbits. We frequently got into such wild and feverish shooting that we'd burn up 59 or 60 rounds a day per man; on occasion, one or two shooters might wind up expending a hundred rounds apiece in a flush day. We averaged about one rabbit killed for every 4 to 5 rounds fired. Such shooting made us the component-makers' staunch friends. It was a little like the way some of the old wolfers must have done in the Depression, when they shot jacks or coyotes or whatnot to stay alive; we did it primarily for sport and to learn what handguns would and would not do on game at 50 or 100 or 150 yards.

This gave us the formulas for a lineup of handgun reloads that were effective on game of various sizes. We tried a variety of bullets, including most recently the new Winchester-Western and Remington-Peters magnum-type ones. We found that most quality bullets, including the factories', were somewhere near a certain high level of efficiency, and that home-cast bullets, while acceptable, seldom were as consistent—for obvious reasons:

For almost all bullet-casters, the quality control is not there, and the variables take over just when you need one round extra-well delivered. We ended up using cast bullets only for combat courses and other practice.

The great advantage to the new W-W and R-P 9mm, 38 Special and 357 magnum ammunition is the ready availability in a finished package if you want some rounds in a hurry. Too, and for the first time, there are 9mm, 38 Special and 357 magnum factory loadings available in a versatility equal to almost any careful reloading effort. There are 100- and 110-gr. light-weight sporting or stopping bullets; 115-gr. lightweight hollow-points; 125-gr. hollow-points, and 158- to 160-gr. jacketed HP and SP bullets that put the 38 Special and 357 in a special class for diversity. Both Winchester and Remington have zipped up the 9mm Parabellum with hunting-type loads as well. I'm hoping next to try some 380 loads in one of the new Browning pistols with longer barrel and adjustable sights, for the accuracy potential of

the 380 cartridge remains largely unplumbed.

The following are our best loads —the ones we settled on for hunting after range-testing, and which we still use in the field:

41 Magnum

Powder/grs.	Bullet/grs.	Notes
4227/20.5	210 SJ	hunting
2400/18.5	210 SJ	general
2400/19.0	210 SJ	hunting
4227/21.0	200 SJHP	hunting
4756/12.0	Any	defense, combat-course
Unique/10.0	212 lead	general, inc.

44 Magnum

2400/21.5	240 SJ	general
4227/24.0	240 SJ	general
4227/25.5	225 SJHP	hunting
2400/22.5	225 SJHP	hunting
4227/20.0	265 Jkt	big-game load

357 Magnum

2400/14.5[1]	146-160	hunting, heavy combat load
5.0 grs. Red Dot	150-160	light load
4227/12.0	200	heavy combat-course load
4227/15.0	146-160	hunting

38 Special

Unique/6.5[2]	146-160	all-around load
2400/12.0	146-160	hunting
4227/9.5	200	heavy-duty load
4756/6.0	146-160	all-round medium load
7625/4.6	146-160	DA combat-course load

9mm Parabellum

Bullseye/4.0	100-125	medium load
Unique/6.2	110-125	heavy load
7625/4.6	110-125	general

45 ACP

7625/6.5	215-230	general
Unique/7.5		heavy-duty load
Bullseye/5.0	185-215	heavy-load

S&W's Model 29 in 44 Magnum, while their Model 57, the same gun, is in 41 Magnum caliber.

45 Colt SA

Powder/grs.	Bullet/grs.	Notes
2400/18.5	250-265	hunting
FFg Black/35-38	250-265	general
Unique/10.0	250-265	hunting
Red Dot/5.5	#8 or #9 shot	survival

SJ-semi-jacketed. SJHP-semi-jacketed hollow point. Jkt-jacketed.

The 45 Colt is surprisingly versatile; it will shoot well with almost all existing powders, including marginal rifle-pistol powders like 2400. With FFg black, the 45 Colt perhaps reaches its maximum efficiency, provided you don't mind the extra cleaning work. With a prop-

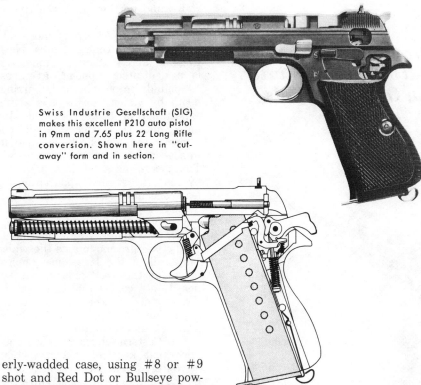

Swiss Industrie Gesellschaft (SIG) makes this excellent P210 auto pistol in 9mm and 7.65 plus 22 Long Rifle conversion. Shown here in "cutaway" form and in section.

erly-wadded case, using #8 or #9 shot and Red Dot or Bullseye powders, it will serve as a substitute "bird" gun or a snake-killing weapon without peer in the one-hand gun field. The 18.5/2400 load is the same medicine that Elmer Keith and friends used so widely in 44 Specials before the big 44 Magnum appeared. A modern 45 Colt SA will do as well with this load as a 44 Special. If a man had only one centerfire handgun, and that one would be used almost entirely outdoors—hunting, backpacking, fun shooting and so on—he'd be crazy if he didn't consider the 45 Colt.

1: Most 357 fans like 15.0 grains of 2400. I have never had great luck stuffing quite that much 2400 in my 357s. In DA combat-course work with the 357 about 14-14.5 grains of 2400 is preferable because

there is less chance of a marginally stout load binding up the cylinder in sustained firing.

2: The 6.5-gr. Unique load in a strong, tight 38 Special is the best all-purpose load I have used, except in snubnoses. Many sources will call this load too stout. It is certainly not recommended for decrepit 38s; it should be used only in top-shape 38 Special revolvers, and then only with considerable caution in approaching the load. *Care is advised from 5.5 grains of Unique and on up.*

The handcannons we tried afield and on the range were all relatively new, tight guns. In 357 Magnum we generally used two 4″ barreled Smith & Wesson Combat Magnums, a 6″ Colt Trooper and two Colt Pythons with 6½″ barrels and two Rugers, one with a 4⅝″ tube and the other a 6½-incher. In the 41 Magnum—my favorite of all the magnums—since it attains all necessary punch (for me) with a bit less turbulence than the 44, we used a Ruger Blackhawk with 6½″ barrel and a S&W "plain" Model 58 Military & Police with a 4″ barrel. In 44 Magnum, we tried two Super Blackhawks, each with standard 7½″ barrels, and one pre-Super type Blackhawk with the old 6½″ barrel (it did as well as the

latecomers, I should add). We also used an assortment of 38 Special S&W revolvers—a K38, several Combat Masterpieces and one exceedingly accurate fixed-sight M10 S&W with heavy or "Border Patrol" barrel.

The 9mm pistols tested were two Browning military models, one with ancient tangent-style sights. The 45 Colts were single-action Colt revolvers of post-war resurrection. We also shot numerous semi-auto pistols chambered for the 45 ACP round, including two match-tuned hardball guns—and the aforementioned replica 44 cap and ball of astonishing performance.

Thus we have some evidence of what the modern centerfire handgun will do. There is much other evidence obtainable from better shots, from more controlled conditions, from a much wider cross-section of loads and field exposures. People like Donald Hamilton, Frank Higginson, Ray Tourigny and other really top Masters could, if they decided to go in for handgun hunting and range-testing, make these results look fat and sloppy indeed. I hope they do. For one of our great problems, as gun owners, shooters, hunters and particularly as handgunners, is lack of a way to reach non-shooters with The Message. If the average listener to "The Advocates" debate on handgun legislation, or the average Time-Life or LA Times or Washington Post reader could learn that a 357 Magnum revolver will group three shots inside 3 inches at 50 yards or inside 6 at 100, we would be on the way to convincing him of the asininity of the handgun-ban bleating. Or if he realized that the maximum danger range of even a 44 Magnum factory round is less than a mile and a half—compared to two and a third miles for the 30-06 class of rifle cartridges—he might begin to comprehend there is indeed a strong case for sporting handgun ownership. Ownership of handguns for self-defense is or should be an inherent right and deserves treatment elsewhere—and gets it. But delivered by a reasonably skilled shot, a magnum-caliber handgun bullet is effective on game out to 200 or perhaps 250 yards under optimum conditions. It is something we should respect and broadcast as widely as possible. Brought home to the uninvolved public in the best way, it is a message carrying far more punch than the meandering unreason of those who would ban handguns to soothe their own peculiar urges.●

Target - The Woodchuck

by ELLIS CHRISTIAN LENZ

A delightful and informative essay by an oldtimer at the game—a veteran varminter, whose beat is the lush Ohio farmlands.

OUR SUBJECT, or target, is the common Eastern woodchuck. He has several names, other than those flung at him by his reluctant host, the farmer. This burrowing rodent is variously identified as 'chuck, groundhog, or whistle pig. The Cree Indians knew him as *wuchak*. The groundhog has national status as the Weather Prophet of Punxsutawney (Pa.), without whom February Second would have no special distinction. For those who take their names straight he is *Marmota monax*, a member of the numerous marmot family. On this continent the species is found in differing sizes and colorations in a range extending through our southern states and northward to the Arctic Circle.

The Eastern 'chuck is most numerous in our central states, New England and southern Canada. He is a dedicated tunneler, averages 10 pounds in weight and, barring death by violent means, has a life expectancy of 13 to 15 years. His hairy hide is worthless to all but himself, and his efforts to keep it intact border on the supernatural. The species as a whole is unloved by man, beast, and apparently, at least one bird. A totem pole in the Yukon depicts a bird reputed to have gotten its jollies by dropping rocks on hapless Arctic marmots. In the western mountains the whistling call of the large hoary marmot and the rock 'chuck can be heard at considerable distances. Their chief concern is to avoid appearing on the menus of local grizzlies and mountain lions.

The Eastern 'chuck has two enemies that keep his alarm system at concert pitch—the precision rifleman and the farm dog. While the shooter may frown upon competition from a 'chuck-hunting canine, he must respect the dog's eagerness for single combat, and possibly some fresh meat. A cornered 'chuck can be more than a match for an incautious dog. However, once the dog perfects his approach, grip, and follow-through he'll kill a score of 'chucks during a season.

Our 'chuck was originally a forest dweller to whom the clearing of land and crop cultivation brought a higher standard of living. To be near the new bounty he burrowed into fence rows, briar patches, slab piles and open fields. In short, the Indians' "little man of the forest" became a sly free-

A 'chuck sniper's firing position. This "sawbuck" posture is quickly assumed and basically stable.

loader and unwanted tenant. Live stock could break legs in his field diggings, and the blacksmith prospered making mower repairs. One description of a high 'chuck population is that of the hay wagon with always at least one wheel sagging into a 'chuck hole. Any field excavated to that extent would surely be the 'chuck hunter's view of paradise.

The farmer sees the 'chucks as he goes about his work, but he's too busy throwing dice with Mother Nature to hunt the varmints down. The 'chucks, too, seem to have acquired some degree of divination that assures them they can't be shot with the farmer's hoe, rake or axe. Crows have long distinguished between a gun and an implement and have possibly passed this arcane knowledge along to the ground forces.

Being classed as a pest, there is usually no closed season on the 'chuck—more's the pity. Many largely rural counties have an old statute that directs a bounty payment for dead 'chucks, but funds are now seldom allotted for this purpose. In 1883 a New Hampshire law placed a bounty of 10 cents on each 'chuck killed, but with this pious restriction: "Provided, that no bounty shall be paid for any woodchuck killed on Sunday." The dime was then of robust value and a 'chuck slyly slain on the Sabbath was in no condition to tattle.

Due to its period of hibernation the 'chuck is apt to be mistakenly related to the bear family. The 'chuck is a true rodent with incisors similar to those of the beaver. These teeth continue to grow as gnawing wears them away, and they are also the 'chuck's only immediate means for self-defense.

The animal's short, muscular legs and hand-like paws are efficient digging tools. Given time the 'chuck may dig as much as 40 feet of interconnecting tunnels. The ejected earth and stones mark his main entrance, which also serves as sun porch and observation post. When a rock pile or farm building covers the burrow entrance the tunneling is not so extensive, nor is there need for drop-away holes. In a well-established tunnel system in open terrain these fairly invisible holes may be 15 feet from the noticeable main entrance. The drop-aways, usually hidden by field vegetation, may actually be used as much as the more visible means of exit and entrance. These secondary holes are reminiscent of the discreet Ladies Entrance of the old-time saloon.

The Coming of Fall

After a summer of gorging on farmland bounty the 'chuck holes up in late October or November. Fallen leaves drift into the den entrances and down below one or more 'chucks are snug in grass-lined nests. The heart beat slows to 3 to 5 times in five minutes and body temperature drops to 38 degrees. When the sleep ends, somewhat before the momentous February Second, the male 'chuck begins to have a private concern that, with suitable cooperation, results in a litter of 3 to 9 juveniles.

In the early spring the adult 'chucks wander farther afield in search of food than they do later on, when crops are up nearer the den. Spring travels are also undertaken by yearlings who leave the home den bent on carving out independent careers. Location of the new burrow usually reflects the old engineering knowhow, but occasionally a less gifted digger will be flooded out by an ordinarily friendly stream.

Apparently the 'chuck has little inclination to frolic. 'Chucks may be seen chasing each other, but without evidence of doing it just for fun. On occasion one will climb a tree or be seen on the roof of an isolated shed. In doing this he can be on the lookout for enemies while sunning himself. After all, living one's whole life in an unlit subway is for the moles!

There is some question as to whether our 'chuck is completely herbivorous. He has been reported to vary his diet with an occasional insect, possibly a grasshopper that didn't hop. My own evidence in the matter is of doubtful quality. Many years ago I shot a 'chuck as he emerged from a river. I had not known a 'chuck to swim and I mentioned it to the farmer whose land adjoined the stream. He assured me that his riverside 'chucks ate mussels they dredged from the shallows. Was the farmer treating me to a bit of hayfield humor, or had his 'chucks been tutored by racoons that infested the area?

Many otherwise astute farmers do not know that their 'chucks whistle. The Eastern chuck's whistle is not loud and can be mistaken for a bird call. The note is tremulous and, starting in a high pitch, ripples to a fadeout. The 'chuck uses it when alarmed. Short bursts are the female's call to her stray-

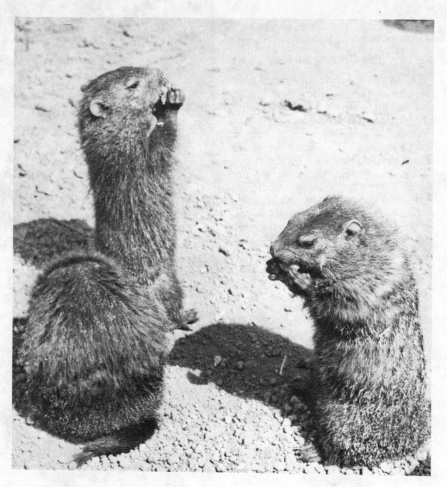

A trio of young 'chucks busily engaged in becoming larger 'chucks.

ing young. The 'chuck will also set his teeth achatter when angry. I've heard this sound interspersed with whistling coming from the depths of a den. This is when he correctly suspects that danger lurks above, but a ravening stomach is presenting practical reasons for him to surface.

The 'chuck's coat is not always of an unattractive gray color. There is an occasional albino. The Ohio albino I have pictured nosed his way into a box trap set for cottontails. Even rarer may be the coal black 'chuck. In 1932 I had one in my sights. I was satisfied to merely study it through the glass. Some older 'chucks have a brownish coat, merging into lighter color on the belly. An occasional prime 'chuck will have hair less coarse than usual; the pelt will be dense and fairly soft to the touch. I have seen an experimental vest made of 'chuck hides. It was quite attractive—to moths. They attacked it in broad daylight!

The 'chuck seems free of serious diseases. An occasional seedy looking specimen will show the pres-ence of warbles, skin swellings caused by maggots of the botfly. These also afflict horses and cattle. 'Chucks are not born tailless, but I have shot a few minus the tail. Only the 'chuck would know how he lost it. A dead secret.

The Golden Ones

In 1969 I shot two unusual 'chucks; their coats were of rich orange color. They were probably from the same litter. As they moved about in the sunlight on a distant hillside their coats glowed like burnished gold. Lacking interv-ening cover, I could not stalk with-in 250 yards. A good hit at that range would tax my holding ability and the killing power of my 222 Remington cartridge. I decided try a shot when one of the golden 'chucks was erect. I took my relia-ble sawbuck sitting position and waited, 10-power scope at the ready. A 'chuck stood up. I held the crosswires on his head, the rifle cracked and he crumpled. An in-stant kill, a chest hit. The other 'chuck streaked down the slope and disappeared into a thicket.

Two weeks later I glassed the remaining golden 'chuck. Facing my position, he was down and feeding, only looking up occasional-ly. I waited, but he would not come erect. Down, he presented a small target, and at that long range I'd have had to hold over his head to compensate for bullet drop. (I'm normally sighted in to hit an inch high at 100 yards.) I fired, but I over-corrected and the bullet passed over the 'chuck. The shot did not spook him. My second shot proved to be a head hit.

Each of these golden 'chucks pulled 12 pounds on my pocket scale. Their successful bagging was largely due to a well-targeted hand-load, no crosswind, and a good portion of sniper's luck. I try to avoid shots that tax my holding ability and cartridge performance. It's so easy to only wound a 'chuck even at moderate range. A 'chuck's survival mechanism is programmed to get him back to the den, and it functions tenaciously to the last muscular twitch. One should try to confine hits to the upper third of a 'chuck's body. Such hits are most humane and speak well for the rifleman's ability. I may seem over-ly concerned about the manner of this varmint's demise, but even a medieval headsman took pride in a smooth job!

Many 'chucks are shot at close range, 25 to 75 yards. They are shot in late June, when the first clover crop is up and before hay-ing. A female shot then is not likely to leave an unweaned litter to die in the den. This short range shooting is quite sporting because the rifleman is on a slow walk and must fire quickly from the offhand position. A 'chuck's head will ap-pear above the ground cover in any quarter and the shot must be taken before the target vanishes. Or the 'chuck may drop to all fours before a shot can be let off and scurry for a hole. Reaching it he may look about momentarily before diving in; that short interval allows a final chance to fire. A successful hit at that time, say at 50 yards, may require more skill than a hit at long range. The 'chuck trips the timer.

Safety Measures

In the field I carry a referee's whistle. Its unusual burble can arouse a 'chuck's inherent curiosi-ty. This curiosity in a young 'chuck has yet to be outbalanced by ma-ture wariness. Hearing those dulcet notes he may expose himself sufficiently to become a satisfactory target. The whistle can also serve as a discreet warning to other persons who may be in the area, such as berry pickers and, in the autumn, when squirrel hunters are afield.

Safety precautions must not be relaxed when hunting on any kind of terrain. Field workers and live stock are ever on the move. A tempting target on the skyline must be ignored. That shot is not worth the smallest risk. A careful, and interesting, stalk will sometimes put the rifleman in position for a safe shot. Hunting is the name of the game; patience and good judgment must regulate every squeeze of the trigger.

An aid to the summer's 'chucking is the Maytime exploratory trip. On that occasion the hunter examines new hunting areas and notes changes on familiar acreage. Last summer's clover field is now planted to oats, or the slab pile that harbored 'chucks has gone to fuel wintertime stoves. Many 'chucks' diggings will show signs of Spring housecleaning, or of having been vacated. New digs are noted, holes that will be concealed by summer foliage. Much of this information will later prove useful in preventing incautious approaches and loss of shots.

The 'chuck's acuity increases with hunting pressure and is a normal reaction. The 'chucks of 50 years ago would seldom scurry to the den upon sighting a shooter on their feeding ground. The 'chuck of that day might come erect and eye the intruder a bit and, if no unusual movement was made, drop down and resume feeding. The first 'chuck I saw killed was shot in the head at 10 feet with a 22 Short. The unsophisticated 'chuck may still be found in remote areas, but not on farmland convenient to a modern highway.

A very old and unusually large 'chuck is now seldom bagged. On shot-over land a 'chuck seldom survives longer than several summers. During that time he has fulfilled his family obligations, but the chance of becoming a grizzled elder is remote. Modern cartridges and optics have effectually united to reduce the 'chuck's life span. The 200-300 yard kill, once a feat, is not unusual. The 'chuck must now hope to be eyed by a mediocre rifle marksman. Many 'chucks are lucky in this respect.

The heavy 'chuck here pictured, a female, was shot in the fall of 1969. She and others inhabited a large den whose main entrance was at the base of an oak tree. In the surrounding pasture grass were several dropaway holes. I glassed this 'chuck from a nearby hill, as she and a smaller one wandered about under the tree. The range was 200 yards. She finally ceased moving and raised her head. I then managed to put a 50-gr. spire bullet into her shoulder. The impact rolled her on her back, stone dead. This 'chuck weighed 15 lbs. 7 oz., and was the largest the Amish farmer had seen. After examining her he exclaimed, with mock regret, "There went my breeding stock!"

I am occasionally asked what I *do* with the 'chuck carcasses. I try to leave them where they will be found by scavengers. Turkey buzzards, crows, foxes and dogs have a taste for the remains. In one area where I repeatedly made kills I'd find buzzards awaiting my return. Those birds have a useful function, but I consider it a dubious honor to become their banquet caterer. I've seen 5 buzzards tearing at a 'chuck within an hour after it was shot. Hardly time for the meat to ripen.

A Place to Hunt

Yet to be considered is the suitable place to hunt 'chucks. The farmer controls that place. He is traditionally more liberal in the matter of trespassers than is the owner of urban property. But the farmer's generous attitude has hardened. He has endured the actions of gun-toting persons in hunter's garb who have left behind them a trail of open gates, broken fences, shot-up buildings and theft. Much farmland is now posted. Some premises are posted against any trespassing; other postings aim to limit hunters to those who ask permission and are willing to be identified. Still another farmer may simply wish to shoot his own rabbits or pheasants.

Most 'chuck hunting is done during the summer, but that hunter is not privileged to trespass because it isn't "hunting season." But the way is opened to 'chucking territory, often on posted land, if the propective 'chucker will first visit the farmer on a friendly basis. Once the farmer feels his applicant to be a responsible person, competent to carry a gun on the premises, and knowing the purpose, he will generally welcome the 'chucker.

For the past 20 years I've shot 'chucks on excellent farms in northeastern Ohio. Much of this land is tilled by the heaviest concentration of the Amish sect in the United States. It is horse-and-buggy country, and motorists are warned: ENTERING HORSE DRAWN VEHICLE AREA. On the back roads and lanes an atmosphere of the 19th century prevails. Many of the Plain People have become my friends. As a 'chucker I'm welcomed rather than endured.

Now, some fashion hints. The 'chucker should dress quite conser-

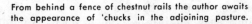
From behind a fence of chestnut rails the author awaits the appearance of 'chucks in the adjoining pasture.

A lage Ohio woodchuck, weighing 15 lbs. 7 oz. Gray hairs of muzzle and pelt attest to the animal's considerable age.

also are the handbooks which list tested loadings. One need spend little for the reloading tools. Indeed, the less expensive equipment is recommended for the occasional handloader; the outfit is slower in use than a bench press but the completed round can be of target quality.

The 'chucker's .222 rifle need not be expensive. I have targeted those of domestic and foreign make, and all provided accuracy expected of this cartridge. Naturally, the rifle of handsome lines and finish allows greater pride of ownership, but I have yet to know whether the 'chuck desires to be felled by my sturdy and inexpensive Savage or my svelte Remington. As these rifles perform equally well, the 'chuck must hope for human error to allow him another sunrise. Each rifle weighs 9 pounds, complete with 10-power scope and carrying strap.

For steady holding the rifle's scope should not exceed 10x. A variable-power scope allows use of a lower power for short-range and offhand firing. The rifle's scope can be used to study the field but it is an awkward viewing device. It is better to carry a small binocular for this purpose. However, its continued use is habit forming, for it can bring on a severe case of birdwatching. True, the wary 'chuck is given to flight, but always on the ground.

The 'chucker's score for a trip can be anything from zero to 4 or 5. The uncertainties of the hunting field—without them hunting wouldn't be a sport—account for a percentage of muffed shots. But a capable rifleman and stalker should average 7 kills in 10 shots. A quick shot will occasionally be lost because of time required to release the rifle's safety; but the safety should always be effective when the piece is otherwise ready to fire. The uncertainties of hunting cannot include careless management of the rifle.

The hunter will have an occasional scoreless day in an area known for its 'chuck population. Prime grazing time for 'chucks often coincides with the farmer's milking time, but on this day no 'chuck is visible. One can then only surmise that the 'chucks are attending underground services for one of the tribe who failed to return from lunch!

'Chuck or not, the hunter has had a fine day afield. He never loses. His coin always comes up four-leaf clovers. ●

vatively. Neither farmer nor 'chuck is favorably impressed by unusual raiment. I dress for summer comfort and low visibility. The gray matched cotton shirt and pants, these the better for a few patches, make me appear indigenous—and just short of indigent. Also, well-worn shoes, possibly burdened with some barnyard detritus, makes everyone feel more at ease! The shoes should have non-skid bottoms and 8-inch tops. That top, with bellows tongue, supports the ankle and excludes weed seeds. This smart ensemble is topped by a washable cotton cap. Unlike a hat, the cap does not snag on brush, and it may be wetted for coolness on a hot day.

Rifles and Calibers

Finally, the 'chucker's rifle. The story of my own progress in that area is long, but it all started with Stevens Favorite models firing 22 and 32 rimfire cartridges. For many years the sighting equipment consisted of metallic sights and a sharp eye, although the rifles became more sophisticated—likewise the 'chucks. Eventually I used scope-sighted and sporterized military rifles, chambering the 30-06 and 30-40 (Krag) cartridges. These were handloaded to give accuracy at about 1700 fps. The bullets were hard-cast, hollow-pointed and gaschecked. They accounted for many kills, but beyond 150 yards those bullets' high trajectory was objectionable.

Later, I had flat-shooting accuracy with 30-caliber 110-gr. express bullets fired at high velocity. The sharp report of that full load could set cowbells tinkling. I was noticeably over-gunned for 'chuck shooting. This was also the era of the wildcat cartridge—a necked-down bottle of ballistic lightning that usually bore some fanciful designation. But through all this the 'chucks remained available in the old standard model.

In the 1950s the 222 Remington cartridge was introduced as a factory-developed varmint cartridge. In appearance it is a mini 30-06 round, about two-thirds the size of the military cartridge. The similarity does not end there; the 222 performs reliably in all appropriate loadings. The 50-gr. jacketed bullet has a muzzle velocity of about 3200 fps. and assured effectiveness at 250 yards. The firing report is not disturbing. This is an excellent 'chuck cartridge.

A 222 rifle may fire factory loadings or the more economical handloads. The latter will generally give better target accuracy in a given rifle. At bench rest, 5 shots should print under a nickel at 100 yards. This degree of accuracy, combined with the bullet's low trajectory, can result in kills at the longer ranges.

Handloading

It is not difficult to handload this cartridge. Handloader's cartridge components—primer, case, powder, bullet—are readily available, as

The 45-70–A Century Later

Born 100 years ago, and still going strong, the big caliber
cartridge wins new adherents daily—as well as rifle manufacturers.
Here's history, rifle and loading information, useful
material for the 45-70 shooter-hunter.

by FRANK C. BARNES

1973 MARKS THE centennial year for the U.S. Model 1873 single shot military rifle and its 45-70 cartridge. Not only is ammunition of this caliber still loaded in sporting version, but in addition Harrington & Richardson in late 1971 offered a replica of the 1875 Officers Model 45-70 Springfield. To that H & R has just announced the addition of the 1873 carbine. Other rifle manufacturers have also added the 45-70 as an available caliber, thus we have the interesting phenomenon of an obsolete military cartridge staging a remarkable comeback in popularity. The 45-70 has survived (along with the 44-40 WCF) as one of our oldest centerfire cartridges, primarily because it fills a special niche among the available calibers as a brush or short-range "knockdown" load.

When the 45-70 was adopted it replaced the earlier 50-70 cartridge, which had originated in 1866. The reduction in caliber from 50 to 45 resulted from studies that had demonstrated greater efficiency and improved performance for the smaller caliber. Although the 45-70 cartridge was adopted in May of 1873, quantity production of the new ammunition didn't get underway until after January, 1874. The original cartridge case was the Benet type inside-primed centerfire, and it was not reloadable. These cases look like a rimfire but can be identified by the cannelure just forward of the rim. The Boxer type primer, which has its own anvil, was eventually adopted as standard, but some lots of contract ammunition made by private companies used Berdan primers and cases. In these the anvil is formed as part of the primer pocket.

The original issue 45-70 cartridge was loaded with 70 grains of musket powder and a 405-gr. bullet, being known officially as the 45-70-405 round. There was also a carbine loading with the same bullet, but there were three felt wads between powder and bullet to reduce the powder charge to 55 grs. The purpose of this lower charge was to reduce recoil of the lighter-weight cavalry carbine. Muzzle velocity of the standard loading was 1365 feet per second; that of the carbine load 1150 fps.

Early experiments had indicated that more efficient powder combustion could be had by using a heavier bullet, and the weight was eventually increased from the original 405 grains to 500. The muzzle velocity of the heavier bullet was 1315 fps, a loss of only 40 fps. However, the 500-gr. bullet developed a muzzle energy of 1875 foot pounds as against 1670 ft. lbs. for the 405-gr. projectile, a gain of 205 ft. lbs. The heavier bullet had greater energy and penetration at practically all ranges, but its higher trajectory was not favored by most

The author's son firing heavy black powder charge from rebuilt Remington rolling block rifle. Note muzzle rise from recoil. Black powder "kick" is somewhat more uncomfortable than that from smokeless loads. Standard factory 405-gr. bullet smokeless loads as well as a variety of black and smokeless handloads were checked out in the 1-14" twist barrel. Accuracy ranged from good to outstanding. Shooting proved that block powder will perform OK in quick twist rifling.

hunters. After 1881 the 45-70-500 round gradually replaced the 405-gr. version except for carbine use.

The 45-70 cartridge is of considerable interest to collectors because over the years quite a variety of case types, primers and loads were manufactured, both military and commercial.*

Early cases were made from copper, the later ones of brass. There were also copper- and tin-coated brass cases. Both folded- and solid-head cases were used; all modern 45-70 brass is of the latter type. Bullet weights varied from 140 to 240 grains for light gallery loads to over 500 grains. The military used multiple-ball loads for guard duty, and there were also shot, blanks and other special types. In addition to the extensive variety of black powder loadings there was also a good choice of smokeless loads offered after about 1900. For quite a few years both Remington and Winchester produced a high velocity smokeless loading with a 300-gr. soft point bullet at a muzzle velocity of 1885 fps. This load, intended only for smokeless powder rifles, would have wrecked many of the old black powder actions. Since people don't read labels and a number of accidents resulted therefrom, the high velocity load was discontinued about 1936.

Shortly after its introduction, a number of changes were made in the 45-70 case. The head was thickened to make it stronger, the case walls were also thickened, and the outside diameter was slightly re-

*See HANDLOADERS DIGEST, 5th edition, p. 139, "Fodder For Forty-Fives", by Charles H. Yust, Jr.

duced. As the result of these changes the capacity of the case was lessened a little and the solid head construction reduced this even further. Modern 45-70 brass won't hold the original 70-gr. black powder charge unless the bullet is seated farther out of the case than standard. This doesn't matter with many single shot rifles, but may lead to feeding difficulties with repeating rifles. There is no problem with smokeless powder loads because the full charge doesn't fill the powder space anyway. Modern cases will only hold 55 to 60 grains of FG black powder if the 405-gr. bullet is seated to its proper depth.

Early Rifles

A great variety of military and sporting rifles were at one time or another chambered for the 45-70 cartridge. The Union Metallic Cartridge Co. catalog of 1905 lists the 45-70 as: "Adapted to U. S. Springfield, Sharps and other military and sporting rifles; Winchester, Model 1886 and Hotchkiss, Model 1883, repeating rifles; also to Gatling and Maxim guns." However, that is only part of the story because Remington, Marlin and practically everyone else who made centerfire rifles turned out at least

one model in 45-70 caliber. A few of the old black powder rifle actions were quite strong, but most of them are suitable only for black powder pressures and, as a matter of safety, handloads must be kept at or below this point. Bear in mind that the design of most black powder rifles doesn't include a provision for handling escaping high pressure gas, and when the action lets go—everything goes!

For the above reason it is necessary to divide 45-70 loading data on the basis of what rifle actions the loads can safely be used in—weak or strong. The standard factory-loaded 45-70 cartridge with the 405-gr. soft point bullet produces only about 20,000 psi, and that is probably tops for most black powder cartridge rifle actions. Modern-made replicas have much better material than the originals they copy, but the matter of design strength also enters the picture. An inherently weak design will retain that property no matter what it is made of.

Of all the old 45-70 rifles the U. S. 1873 "trapdoor" Springfield has one of the weakest action designs when it comes to handling pressure above that generated by black powder. On the other hand, these rifles

Springfield is another newcomer, as is their 1873 carbine, but these must be confined to black powder pressures as with the original. All of these good rifles open up a new chapter for the 45-70 buff.

The 45-70 is an easy cartridge to handload, presenting no special problems. The big straight case allows considerable flexibility in the choice of performance and the excellent variety of cast and jacketed bullets available permits rifles of this caliber to be adapted to small game or anything else on up to the toughest big game found in North America. Lyman lists about 10 different bullet moulds specifically adapted to the 45-70, and there are three or four others that can be used for special purposes. The new Ohaus line includes 45-cal. moulds, too.

Loading Dies

Loading dies in 45-70 are offered by practically all the die and tool manufacturers, including C-H, Herter, Hollywood, Lachmiller, Lyman, Pacific, RCBS, Redding and SAECO. The 45-70 case is of the straight-walled type, and the use of 3-die sets, in which sizing, expanding and seating are separate operations, is the preferred system. Use Lyman shell holder J17 or X17, RCBS 14 or equivalent in other makes. Large rifle (.210″) primers are the correct size, although when loading black powder, large pistol primers usually work equally as well. Empty cases, offered by Remington and Winchester, can generally be found in the larger loading tool establishments or ordered by local dealers. Hornady turns out a good selection of jacketed .458″ bullets in weights of 300, 350 and 500 grains. Remington and Winchester make 405-gr. jacketed bullets.

The original military bullet was usually made from an alloy of 16 parts lead to 1 part tin and this hardness still gives very good accuracy with black powder. However, it has been my experience that when using smokeless powder an alloy of 10 parts lead to 1 part tin gives superior results. Naturally, if

are perfectly safe to fire if this fact is understood and all handloads kept within design limits. The author has owned and fired a goodly number of these old rifles with both black and smokeless powder without accident or difficulty. The formula for success is very simple —use moderate loads that duplicate black powder performance and forget about "improved" performance.

There are a few other weak action black powder rifles that should be mentioned. These are the Ballard, Burgess, Colt Lightning, Maynard and Whitney, among others. These, along with early models of the Remington rolling block, should be placed in the black-powder-only category.

Old rifles with what are generally regarded as relatively strong actions are the Farrow, Peabody, Sharps Borchardt, Winchester single shot, Peabody-Martini, late model Remington rolling blocks and the Remington-Hepburn, all single shots. Repeating rifles with strong actions are the Winchester Model 1886 lever action and Hotchkiss bolt action, original Marlin Model 95s, and the Remington-Lee bolt action. All of these rifles were, at one time or other, available in 45-70 caliber. These rifles have

stronger action designs than most black powder rifles, but the date of manufacture and the material used have a bearing on the ultimate strength. Few of these older actions are suitable for the modern high pressures developed by cartridges fired in some bolt action rifles.

Although factory 45-70 ammunition has been continuously loaded from its introduction right up to the present time, the same cannot be said of 45-70 rifles. The last rifles in this caliber were discontinued about 1930, and only recently has the caliber been re-introduced. In the interim all 45-70 rifles have been custom jobs, with suitable actions becoming an increasing problem. Currently, the Ruger No. 1 rifle and No. 3 carbine are available in 45-70. Navy Arms is importing an Italian-made replica of the Remington rolling block in that caliber. Marlin has recently announced that their new Model 95 lever action repeater (based on the original 444 action) in 45-70 caliber. All of these are strong actions, capable of standing handloads well above the black powder level, raising the performance of the old 45-70 to a formidable level. The Harrington & Richardson 'Officers Model' replica of the U. S. 1873

The author bench rest testing black powder loads in 1-14" twist barrel. Accuracy with 405-gr. bullets was equal of smokeless-load groups. 300-gr. bullets and black powder charges did not group as well.

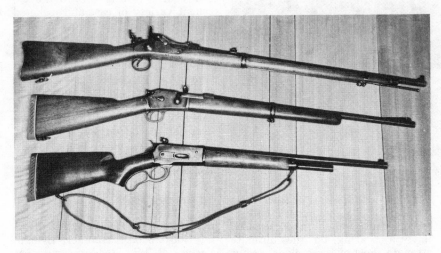

Above—A trio of 45-70 rifles. From the top—1873 Springfield single shot, Winchester Hotchkiss bolt action and Model 1886 lever action. Below—Gunsmith Franklin Frye checks out the author's caliber 45-70 Winchester Model 1883 Hotchkiss, a bolt action rifle that is fairly rare today.

attempting to achieve the maximum velocity-accuracy combination an even harder alloy may be required, something like type metal or a similar alloy. Some shooters say they get top accuracy with a very hard alloy regardless of the velocity involved.

Bullet diameter for the 45-70 is given in some manuals as .457" and in others as .458". I have sized cast bullets to both of these diameters and can't make an absolute statement on the subject one way or the other. In general, the smaller diameter appears to give best results with soft alloys and black powder whereas the larger diameter is the correct one for almost all smokeless powder loads, particularly with hard alloys. This probably varies with different rifles and rifling twists and, like bullet hardness, is something requiring a little individual experimenting. Over the years I have settled on .458" and size all my cast 45-70 bullets to that diameter.

Powder Choice

Some of the older powders that gave very good results in the 45-70 and similar black powder cartridges are no longer available. Such propellants as Hercules Sharpshooter and Lightning have been off the market for so long that the new crop of handloaders never heard of them. DuPont 4759, another good one, was discontinued only a few years ago, but dealers' stocks are now completely exhausted. Of the current crop of smokeless powders, probably DuPont 4198 and 3031, along with Norma N-200, are the most useful; they burn well with the widest variety of bullet weights and charges. However, for light loads, Hercules Unique and 2400 and DuPont 4227 are very useful. The reader is cautioned to be very careful in checking his charges when using these last three faster-burning powders because the normal charge does not bulk well in the big 45-70 case; it is possible to get a double charge into the case with possibly disastrous results. I know of several accidents caused by this, so make a double check of all charge levels before seating the bullets. For full charges with 300-gr. jacketed bullets and heavier, the slower-burning DuPont 4895 and 4320 work well. There is actually a good selection of powder to work with; it is just a matter of knowing which ones work best in this particular cartridge.

In addition to the 1873 Springfield, I've fired and experimented with quite a variety of 45-70 rifles. It has been one of my favorites since I was a boy, and I've found them an enjoyable and interesting study. I have had two Winchester 86s, an original Marlin Model 95, a Winchester Hotchkiss, several Remington rolling blocks, a Sharps Borchardt and a bevy of custom built 45-70s on various actions. My latest acquisition is a custom built job on a 7mm smokeless powder Remington rolling block action with a 22″ barrel and a 1-14″ twist. I'll have more to say on the subject further along. Fact is, the author has had ample opportunity to shoot 45-70 rifles and work up useful loading data. Two separate loading tables are presented; one covers data for the 1873 Springfield and similar weak-action rifles, including the new H&R replica, while the other applies to the Model 86 Winchester and other strong action rifles. The reader is cautioned to be certain he is using the correct data for his particular rifle.

Although normally considered a big game cartridge, the 45-70 can be adapted to any game or shooting conditions by the simple process of picking the right bullet and load for the job. In assembling the loading data for this article the author has attempted to present at least a few basic loads for every bullet type and weight available for the 45-70. The emphasis is more on good practical loads and accuracy than absolute top performance. The lighter bullets, even in weak-action rifles, could be loaded to higher velocities than those given. However, accuracy suffers and the author has therefore selected the velocity range that experience has shown to produce the most consistent results.

45-70 Bullets

The 144-gr. collar button bullet, 146-gr. round ball and 193-gr. 455 Webley revolver bullet (sized .457″), make good short range squirrel or rabbit loads with good accuracy out to 60-70 yards. At initial velocities of around 1200 to 1300 fps they will kill cleanly without mangling or ruining edible meat. These bullets, along with the 210-gr., are also excellent for plinking and short range target shooting.

The 250-gr. gas check and 255-gr. plain base 45 Colt revolver bullets make nice all-round loads for shooting anything from small game up through deer at ranges out to 100

45-70 LOAD DATA

For U.S. 1873 Springfield Rifles, H&R Officers Model,
1873 Replicas and other Low-Strength 45-70 Rifles.

Powder/grs.	MV	Notes
144-gr. bullet & 146-gr. round ball		
Unique/8	1135	
2400/15	1300	Small game and plinking loads. Accurate
4227/18	1390	to 60-70 yards.
4198/20	1350	
193-gr. 455 Webley revolver bullet		
Unique/10	1350	
2400/16	1260	
2400/18	1365	Accurate small game and plinking loads,
4227/18	1320	also good for 50-yard target work.
N-200/19	1330	
4198/21	1350	
210-gr. bullet		
Unique/10	1330	
2400/17	1310	
4227/18	1295	This heavier bullet does not perform well
N-200/20	1325	in all rifles.
4198/22	1400	
250- & 255-gr. Colt revolver bullets		
2400/26	1480	
4227/27	1440	Good short range small game through deer
N-200/28	1460	loads. Bullet 454485, 250-gr. GC appears to
4198/34	1630	give best all-round accuracy.
3031/37	1510	
300-gr. bullet (cast)		
2400/25	1370	
4227/28	1450	
N-200/30	1430	Varmint through deer loads at ranges to
4198/32	1480	125 yards. Also accurate for targets to 100
3031/37	1410	yards.
4895/40	1465	
300-gr. bullet (Hornady Short Jacket)		
4227/29	1440	Accurate varmint and deer loads at moder-
4198/34	1525	ate ranges.
3031/42	1560	
330-gr. Gould hollow point		
4227/26	1360	
N-200/28	1390	Excellent deer loads at short to moderate
4198/32	1430	ranges.
3031/38	1385	
350-gr. bullet		
N-200/26	1310	
4198/31	1370	Deer, black bear loads, possibly larger game
3031/40	1380	at short ranges.
4895/41	1360	
395-gr. GC and 405-gr. plain-base bullets		
4198/30	1320	Loads for any No. Amer. big game to 100
3031/37	1300	yards, or farther under ideal conditions.
4895/40	1265	
500-gr. GC and plain base-bullets		
4198/28	1210	Short range loads for any No. Amer. big
3031/35	1180	game.
4895/38	1160	
535-gr. Postell bullet		
3031/33	1130	About the heaviest practical 45-70 bullet.
4895/36	1140	For short range use on heavy game. Good
4320/40	1120	penetration.

WARNING: The above-listed loads should be considered as maximum for older type rifles, and it is strongly recommended that they not be exceeded. They should be used only in rifles in first class condition. If there is any doubt as to the strength of action or its condition, do not use smokeless powder. Load only black powder.

45-70 LOAD DATA

For Winchester 1886 and other Strong-Action Rifles

WARNING: The loads listed in this table must not be used in the U. S. 1873 Springfield or similar weak-action rifles. To do so is to invite instant disaster.

Powder/grs.	MV	Notes
300-gr. Hornady Short Jacket		
4198/37	1610	
4198/40	1750	
3031/45	1490	Good allround loads. For any No. Amer.
3031/50 (Max.)	1840	game, large or small, to or beyond 150
4895/46	1470	yards, depending on hunting conditions.
4895/50 (Max.)	1690	
330-gr. Gould hollow point		
4198/34	1520	
3031/45	1600	Cast of type metal. Big game.
4320/47	1565	
350-gr. jacketed		
4198/33	1420	
4198/35 (Max.)	1540	
3031/43	1400	Big game loads.
3031/52 (Max.)	1820	
4895/46	1375	
4895/50 (Max.)	1580	
395-gr. GC bullet		
4198/37	1535	
3031/44	1600	Cast of hard alloy. Big game loads.
4895/46	1580	
405-gr. jacketed bullet		
4198/32	1350	
4198/37 (Max.)	1480	
3031/40	1410	
3031/50 (Max.)	1760	Big game loads.
4895/42	1350	
4895/48 (Max.)	1710	
4320/50	1620	
500-gr. GC bullet		
4198/32	1380	
3031/40	1420	Cast of hard alloy. Big game.
4895/45	1400	
500-gr. jacketed bullet		
4198/32 (Max.)	1300	
3031/42 (Max.)	1350	Cast of hard alloy. Big game.
4895/47 (Max.)	1430	

Other 45-70 Load Sources

Ackley, Parker O., **Revised Handbook for Shooters & Reloaders.**

Herter, G. L. and J. P., **Professional Loading** ...

Hodgdon's Reloading Data Manual, Nos. 20 and 21.

Hornady Handbook of Cartridge Reloading.

Lyman Reloading Handbook. 44th Edition. (Also older editions)

National Rifle Assoc., **NRA Handloaders Guide.**

Pacific Rifle & Pistol Manual.

Ballistics of Commercial and Military 45-70 Loads

Bullet Type Weight/grs.	MV	ME	Notes
285 lead	1450	1332	45-85-285 Marlin
300 SP	1885	2070	Obsolete HV, Rem. and Win.
330 lead HP	1380	1405	Gould Express, UMC
350 lead	1325	1365	45-70-350 Marlin
405 lead	1365	1670	Military rifle
405 lead	1150	1190	Military carbine
405 SP	1320	1570	Modern sporting
500 lead	1315	1875	Military rifle

yards or so. I prefer the gas check bullet as it appears to give better accuracy at the higher velocities. These bullets have more oomph than those listed above, yet are still economical of lead and powder. Loaded to over 1600 fps produces a load comparable to the 44 Magnum in effectiveness.

Bullets weighing 300 grains or more are primarily for big game, but may also be used to extend the effective range on varmint type animals. Probably the most useful of those is the Hornady 300-gr. short-jacket bullet. Even in relatively weak-action rifles the velocity can be stepped up to around 1500 fps, which tends to lift the 45-70 a notch out of the 100-yard brush busting class. In a strong-action rifle a velocity of around 1800 fps flattens the trajectory and improves the effective range to a satisfying degree. These bullets have proven very good killers on deer within permissible velocities.

The 405-gr. bullet is considered by many experienced hunters as the best all-round big game bullet in 45-70 rifles. Unfortunately the factory 405-gr. bullet is designed to expand at the relatively low velocity of the original black powder loading. When the velocity is stepped up to over 1700 fps, these bullets have an explosive effect at short range and tend to go to pieces without penetrating deeply enough. Elmer Keith and others recommend the 500-gr. bullet for elk, moose, bear or anything larger than deer. Incidentally, Keith's favorite load for the 45-70 is a good 400-gr. bullet backed by 53 grains of 3031 for an initial velocity of 1827 fps and 3000 ft. lbs. I have used this load and it is certainly effective, but it must be fired only in suitable strong rifles.

As a matter of personal observation and experience I've found the 350-gr. Hornady to be an excellent all-round big game bullet for strong 45-70 rifles. It has a tougher jacket and does not expand as rapidly as the factory-made 405-gr. bullet, so it's a better high velocity projectile. It is at its best when used in strong action rifles where velocity can be stepped up to the maximum. There have been some complaints that this bullet failed to penetrate well on elk and heavy game, but that may be due to the particular hunting conditions involved. Other reports and my own experience to date have been favorable.

When loading cast bullets weigh-

CAST BULLETS

For 45-70 or other 45 caliber rifles

Weight/grs.	Mould*	Notes
144	457130	Collar button
146	457129	Round ball
193	456401	455 Webley revolver
210	457127	Lightweight 45-70
250	454485	45 Colt GC
255	454190	45 Colt plain base
300	457191	45-60, 45-90
330	457122	Gould hollow point
350	456192	45-75 Winchester
395	457483	45-70 GC
405	457124	Standard military
500	457125	Standard military
500	457406	458 Winchester GC
535	457132	45-70 Postell

NOTE: All bullets fired in 45-70 rifles should be sized either .457" or .458". GC = gas check.

*Lyman mould numbers

A U.S. Model 1873 "trap door" single shot and a Winchester Model 1883 Hotchkiss bolt action, the actions open. The Hotchkiss has a tubular magazine in the buttstock, its capacity 6 rounds. Made in military and sporting versions, the Hotchkiss did not achieve great popularity.

Reloading Data and Factory Ballistics

Bullet (grs.)	Powder/grs.		MV	ME	
Loads for Old Black Powder Rifles					
300	4759	26	1375	1265	Mild load
405	4198	29	1300	1520	Dup. fact. ball.
405 Lead	Fg-Blk.	70	1350	1640	30" bbl.
500 Lead	Fg-Blk.	70	1315	1560	20" bbl.
Loads for Modern Smokeless Powder Rifles Only					
300 SP	4759	30	1660	1840	Jacketed bullet in all cases
300	HV-2	53	2140	3048	
405	3031	53	1850	3080	
405	HV-2	47	1820	2978	
500	3031	50	1655	3040	
405	FL		1320	1570	200 yd. MRT = 13.0"

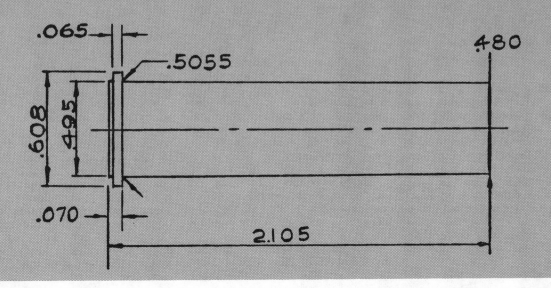

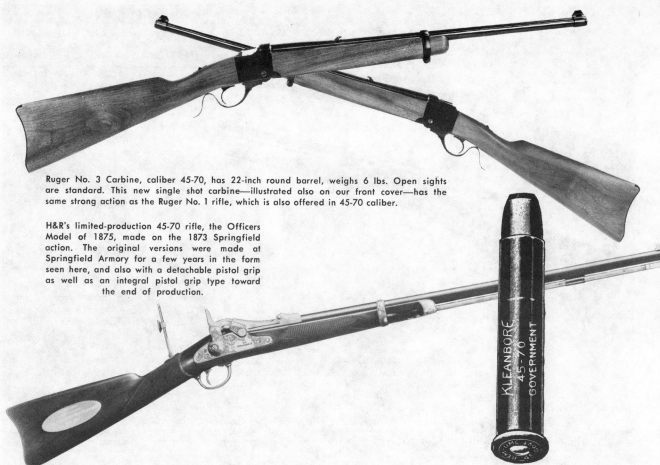

Ruger No. 3 Carbine, caliber 45-70, has 22-inch round barrel, weighs 6 lbs. Open sights are standard. This new single shot carbine—illustrated also on our front cover—has the same strong action as the Ruger No. 1 rifle, which is also offered in 45-70 caliber.

H&R's limited-production 45-70 rifle, the Officers Model of 1875, made on the 1873 Springfield action. The original versions were made at Springfield Armory for a few years in the form seen here, and also with a detachable pistol grip as well as an integral pistol grip type toward the end of production.

ing less than 300 grains the normal powder charge does not fill the case very well. I would suggest using one- or two-grain tufts of dacron or kapok as over powder charge positioners. I prefer this to the usual corn meal filler. As a word of warning, *don't* use cardboard wads seated on top of the powder with a large air space between the wad and the base of the bullet. This practice has been known to bulge or ring the barrel in the forward area of the chamber. It's OK to use wads tight against the base of the bullet, but not way down in the case.

45-70 Twist Rates

The U. S. 1873 Springfield and most other old black powder rifles have a rifling twist of 1 turn in 22 inches, which twist works all right for most shooting with black powder or at black powder velocities. Some rifle makers used a twist of 1 turn in 18 inches, and anyone who's had much experience with 45-70 rifles knows the quicker twist is much more satisfactory. In *Modern American Rifles,* first published in 1891*, the author wrote that 45-70 rifles with a rifling twist slower than 1 turn in 18 inches wouldn't shoot ac-

*Arthur C. Gould, Boston, Mass., 1891.

curately at all ranges with all of the various bullet weights available. My own experience with different twists in various 45 caliber rifles bears this out. I discovered years ago, in working up loads for the 45-70, that a twist of 1-16″ or 1-14″ would give much better general accuracy with different bullets and loadings than the slower twist. As the result, I'll go Mr. Gould one better—if there was any way to avoid it I wouldn't have a 45-70 rifle with a twist slower than 1-16″.

Anyone buying a 45-70 rifle in this day and age is going to end up handloading, because that is the only way to get the maximum flexibility and use out of the cartridge. The modern shooter is not going to do much if any black powder shooting, and he isn't going to be satisfied with factory-loaded ammunition. It's too expensive and it doesn't bring out the full potential of the rifle or cartridge. Under these circumstances a 1-16″ or 1-14″ twist will give much more satisfactory results. Unfortunately, all the new factory-made 45-70s have the old 1-22″ twist of the black powder era. In my opinion this is a mistake.

As mentioned earlier, I ordered my latest 45-70 rifle with a 1-14″ twist and, like other 45 caliber

rifles with the same twist, it shoots extremely well. I can't honestly say that it outshoots the 1-16″ twist because both seem to do accurate work with just about whatever I've fed through them. I'm well satisfied with its performance. All the wise boys, lacking experience to back up their opinion, will tell you that a 45-70 with a twist faster than 1-18″ just won't handle black powder. The bullet is supposed to "jump the rifling" or something like that. Well, this simply isn't true. I can't claim any really tight groups with black powder, but even my 1-14″ twist barrel will shoot 4-inch groups at 100 yards with this propellant, and the average 45-70 hunting rifle with the slow twist won't do any better than that.

In conclusion, then, the 45-70 has survived the hundred year mark because it is basically a good cartridge design and it fills a definite, though specialized, need in the modern cartridge lineup. It can be adapted to a much broader spectrum of use by handloading to fit specific game and hunting conditions. It is hoped that the information provided here will assist owners of 45-70 rifles in achieving the maximum potential of this fine old cartridge.

●

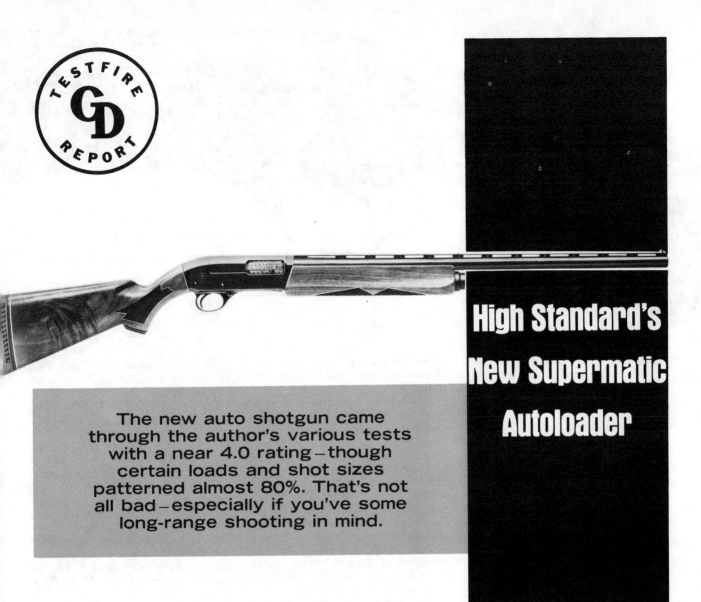

High Standard's New Supermatic Autoloader

The new auto shotgun came through the author's various tests with a near 4.0 rating—though certain loads and shot sizes patterned almost 80%. That's not all bad—especially if you've some long-range shooting in mind.

by WALLACE LABISKY

EARLY IN 1972, High Standard announced redesigned models of the Supermatic autoloading shotgun in both 12 and 20 gauge. There are two major improvements. These consist of changes in the various action parts to parallel the highly successful Model 10-B police shotgun, and a newly styled fore-end that's less bulky than on preceding models. The Supermatic guns, of course, feature a self-compensating gas system.

As in the past, the new models are non-takedown, with the barrel factory-attached to the receiver—"lock-aligned" as High Standard describes the practice. This means that the Supermatics do not offer barrel interchangeability; and also that when barrel cleaning is necessary the job must be tackled from the muzzle end.

The new Supermatic line-up in 12 ga. includes a model for every avenue of shotgunning. Hunting models are offered with plain or ventilated rib barrels, and with the usual choke options (full, modified or improved cylinder). There is also a 27″ vent-rib barrel gun decked out with an adjustable choke device. Other models include Skeet and trap guns, both with ventilated ribs; a deer gun equipped with rifle sights and a duck gun chambered for 3″ ammo, this last made in both plain and ribbed-barrel styles.

On the 20-ga. side, the Supermatic can be had with either plain or vent-rib barrels in the usual chokes, as well as with a raised rib, 27″ adjustable-choke barrel. There is also a raised-rib barrel Skeet gun in 20 bore. All 12 and 20-ga. models, except for the Skeet guns, carry a recoil pad with white-line spacer as standard equipment.

Notes on the Supermatic

The Supermatic test gun received by GUN DIGEST was a 12, its 28″ modified-choke barrel wearing a vent rib and having a standard 2¾″ chamber. The first order of business was a close look at the gas system.

Gas for operating the action is taken off through two barrel ports, these about 9¾″ ahead of the breech. The piston travels ⁹⁄₁₆″ to the rear before it clears the gas chamber, at which point total gas relief occurs. It is also at this point that the breech bolt begins to unlock The piston then carries through of its own momentum to provide the power for extracting, ejecting, and the feeding of a fresh round from the magazine.

The gas piston is linked to the bolt slide by a sturdy twin-arm action bar. The entire piston assembly, including the action spring for

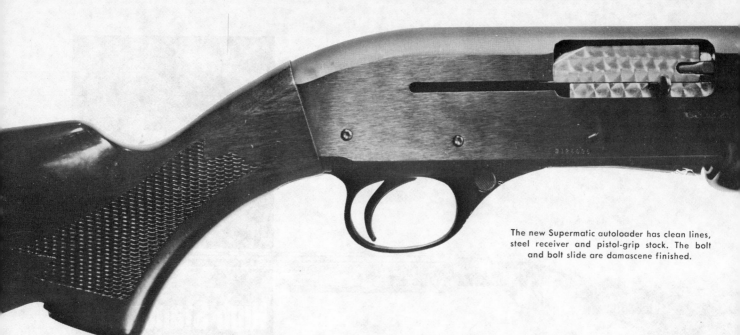

The new Supermatic autoloader has clean lines, steel receiver and pistol-grip stock. The bolt and bolt slide are damascene finished.

returning the bolt to battery, is housed outside the magazine tube. Thus magazine capacity is not affected, this being four 2¾" shells.

The gas venting-off system closely follows that used on earlier High Standard models. There are 7 small ports ringing the forward part of the gas chamber for bleeding off excess gas. This is diverted through an arrangement of washer-type wavy springs (8 in all, in a series of 4 pairs separated by washers), and the amount of tension on the

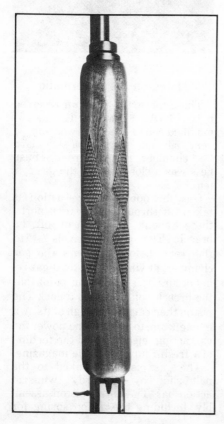

wavy springs regulates the amount of gas that can escape before the piston clears the gas chamber.

The factory adjustment of these wavy springs is such that the system automatically compensates for all 2¾" shells, ranging in "gusto" from light target fodder to full-house magnums. The Duck Gun model is factory adjusted to function properly with 2¾" and 3" magnum loads only.

In putting this gas system through the high hurdles, the writer ran 60 factory loads in different brands through the test gun. These consisted of 2¾ and 3-dram equivalent (DE) target loads, light 3DE field loads with 1 oz. of shot, high-velocity shells with 1¼ ozs., and 4DE magnums with 1½ ozs. At times the loads were randomly mixed; at other times three of a kind were loaded.

Shooting the Supermatic

It can be reported that the Supermatic took more than the lion's share of these in stride. There were two malfunctions involving a 3DE target loading. In each instance this happened on the third and final shot and the empty shell was left hanging in the ejection port. Obviously, it was a matter of the breech bolt not moving rearward with enough force to give complete ejection.

The 2¾ DE loads tried gave no trouble in this respect; however, they were of a different brand. So, on the face of things, it appears that we simply chanced across two 3DE rounds that were loaded on the light side, be-

Bottom view of the newly-styled Supermatic fore-end shows checkering pattern, which is of the die-impressed type.

cause a number of other loads from the same box of shells cycled the action perfectly.

One other spot of trouble surfaced during the above test session. This was definitely a bonafide malfunction, but not one that can be blamed on the gas system. In this instance the gun was fully loaded with 3DE target loads. As the action cycled following the first shot, the left-hand cartridge stop failed to retain the last shell in the magazine. It ended up on top of the shell lifter where it prevented the complete chambering of the preceding shell. Other than these incidents, functioning was perfect throughout the shooting, which also included a workout on claybirds as well as patterning.

Particular attention was paid to both recoil and the force with which the various loads worked the action. Target loads were very pleasant to shoot, naturally, and the ejected hulls landed only a few feet away. With 3¾ DE high-velocity cartridges there was more shooter awareness of recoil! It follows that recoil with short magnum loads was quite pronounced, though it was not actually disturbing to this shooter, and empties landed as far as 15 feet from the gun.

That the action was being subjected to plenty of vigor with the heavy loads was evident not only in the distance of ejection, but also in the condition of the fired shells. In many cases an ejector imprint was visible on the shell headface, and invariably the brass received a conspicuous dent as a result of rather violent contact with the rear of the ejection port.

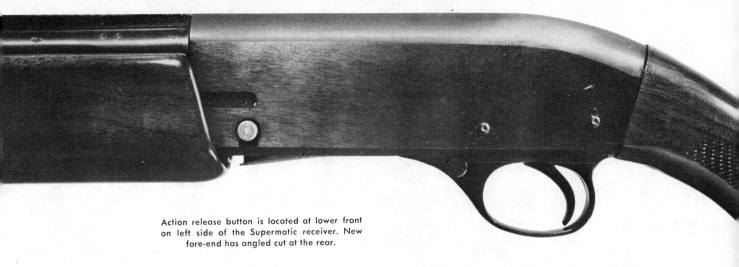

Action release button is located at lower front on left side of the Supermatic receiver. New fore-end has angled cut at the rear.

Heavy Load Adjustment

By way of personal observation, I think that if one were going to feed this Supermatic a steady diet of high-velocity and short magnum loads, as many shooters probably will, it would be a sensible move to adjust the mechanism to vent off more gas through the forward escape ports. Not only would this result in slightly less apparent recoil, it would also ease wear and tear on the various action parts. This adjustment, by the way, calls for a special spanner wrench and, unfortunately, none is furnished with the gun. However, any gunsmith should be able to take care of this matter in just a jiffy.

Breech lock-up on the Supermatic is handled by a round stud of ½" diameter, which is cammed vertically to engage a bolt cut in the ceiling of the steel receiver. Bolt alignment is taken care of by the action bars, each of which travels in its respective channel in the receiver walls. The bolt and bolt slide carry a damascened finish.

The plunger type ejector is enclosed within the bolt on the back side. When the bolt terminates its rearward travel, the ejector projects fully ¼" or more from the bolt face and, as we have already seen, exerts considerable thrust on the empty shells. The single extractor is of the conventional hook type.

The guard and housing for the trigger group—cast from a nonferrous metal—are finished to match the blued receiver. All working parts in the trigger group are of steel, of course, and the shell lifter is finished bright. Aluminum is used for the action release button. It is located well forward on the

Action-open view of the Supermatic gas system shows piston fully to the rear and action spring compressed. Wavy springs for regulating escape of excess gas can be seen forward of the gas chamber.

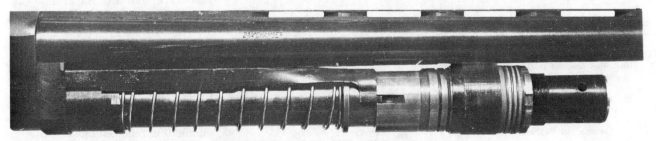

Details of High Standard's self-compensating gas system can be seen in this action-closed view. All parts are outside the magazine tube.

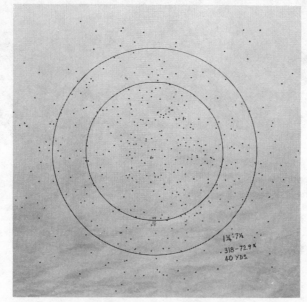

The Supermatic 28″ modified barrel averaged over 76% with the Federal International/Flyer 1¼/7½ loading, and all pattern centers showed high density. This pattern with 318 hits ran 72.9%.

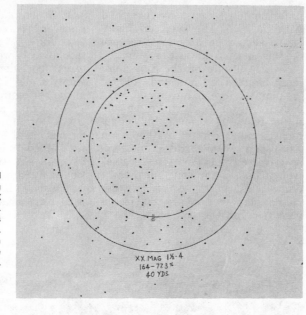

The Supermatic's modified barrel also took a strong liking to Winchester's XX Magnum load with 1½ ozs. of 4s. Average for 5 shots at 40 yards was 79.3%. With 164 hits, this pattern went 77.3%. All had dense centers.

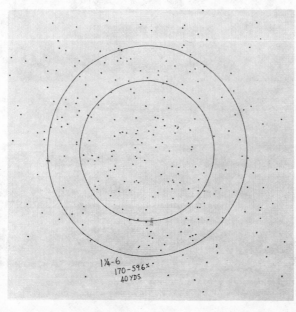

Modified-choke patterns with balanced pellets distribution were the story with Federal Hi-Power 1¼/6 loading. This pattern, with 170 pellets registering in the 30-inch circle, went 59.6%. Average was 60.1%.

left side of the receiver—a position which may at first seem a little awkward to those shooters accustomed to having the release on the starboard side.

Trigger pull on the test gun is somewhat heavy, weighing close to 6½ pounds, and the let-off is preceded by rather lengthy travel. The pull is also a bit rough, but this can be expected to smooth up somewhat with continued use.

Loading and unloading procedures for the Supermatic parallel those for most other autoloading shotguns. There is no cut-off mechanism for locking rounds in the magazine.

Installation and removal of the magazine plug calls for first removing the fore-end cap, which is retained by a coin-slotted screw, and then screwing out a slotted cap from the end of the magazine tube. Both steps take only a few moments. The fore-end cap, made of aluminum, is contoured to give a press fit over the fore-end tip, and it's finished to match the barrel bluing.

Stock and Fore-end

Although the new fore-end has been reduced in circumference, it is still of a highly functional shape. Length is 11¾″ and the rear of the wood is cut on a pleasing angle. In section, it is round over the lower half, with the upper half "scooped out" to give a comfortable purchase for the shooter's thumb and fingers. It should fit all sizes of hands very well. Interestingly, the fore-end is slotted in the barrel channel at the front end, allowing it to spread slightly as it is pushed home. This provides for a snug, rattle-free fit.

The buttstock comb is moderately full and the pistol grip comfortably shaped. The wood is straight-grained American walnut. Finish is a soft-sheen oil type. Both the grip and the fore-end carry a checkering pattern of the negative die-impressed type.

Width of the non-tapering ventilated rib on this Supermatic 12 ga. is .315″ (about ⁵⁄₁₆″) and it extends to within ¹⁄₁₆″ of the muzzle. The receiver is grooved and the rib has no ramp at the breech end, so the sighting plane is dead-level. The rib's surface is cut with longitudinal lines and additionally has a wavy pattern which, along with the matte finish on the receiver top, is very effective in eliminating reflected light.

Bore inspection is a muzzle-end-only proposition, but from what I

40-YARD PATTERN TESTS

High Standard Supermatic 12 Ga.

28″ Barrel — Modified Choke

Load	Density 20″ Circle	Density 30″ Circle	Efficiency 30″ Circle	EDV 20″ Circle	EDV 30″ Circle
Federal International Triple-Plus wad 3¼-1¼-7½ (436)	209	334	76.6%	35	31 (7.1%)
Federal Hi-Power Triple-Plus wad 3¾-1¼-6 (285)	95	171	60.1%	31	17 (6.0%)
W-W Super Speed XX Magnum 4-1½-4 (212)	103	168	79.3%	16	10 (4.7%)

Comments: Extra-full-choke performance with 7½s and 4s; modified choke performance with 6s. Pellet distribution in the 30″ circle with 7½s and 4s shows the high center density that is usually the rule with a full-choke barrel, pellet distribution with 6s was more balanced.

EDV = Extreme variation in pellet hits between the high and low patterns.

Pellet counts and percentages shown represent an average of 5 shots.

could see, the finish looks good. Bore diameter at a point 5″ behind the muzzle is .728″ and the muzzle checked out at .708″, with roundness here staying within .001″. Thus the choke constriction of .020″ is in perfect agreement with the modified-choke marking on the barrel. The choke section, of the conical-parallel type, has a total length of about 1¾″. The parallel portion at the muzzle is about ¾″ long.

Patterning The Supermatic

At the pattern board it was learned that the barrel centered its patterns on the point of hold when a small amount of rib was seen— just enough so that about half of the front bead was visible above the center "guide" bead. Pattern results with three different loads and shot sizes ranged from modified to extra full.

With the Federal Hi-Power 1¼/6 loading, the barrel printed as marked, giving a 60% average for 5 shots at 40 yards. Pellet distribution was nicely balanced. But with the Federal International Flyer 1¼/7½ loading, the barrel turned in an extra-full-choke performance of over 76%, and pellet distribution showed high center density. With the Winchester XX Magnum loading—1½ ozs. No. 4 shot—it was much the same story. Average efficiency leveled off at a fraction over 79%, again with predominantly high density in the pattern cores—all of which is fine and dandy if long-range shooting is on the

agenda. Whether or not all High Standard modified-choke barrels will print this tight a pattern, I certainly wouldn't care to hazard a guess.

Clay Bird Test

As a check on what to expect of this gun's handling and pointing, a portable clay-target trap was set up and the writer shot 25 pair of doubles. The shooting was done from a gun-down position to simulate field conditions as closely as possible.

The fact that I was able to post a score of 46x50 with a gun that was still virtually a stranger in my hands, speaks very well for the

Supermatic, I think. A companion also did some claybird busting and he shared my opinion that there certainly was no struggle in getting on the target.

From where I sit this Supermatic looks like a good buy for the money. It combines clean lines and good workmanship with a time-tested action; it handles nicely and puts the pattern right where you're looking. On the practical side, there is not much more one can ask for.

If my ship comes in between now and then, I plan to be shooting a Magnum Duck Gun model during the coming waterfowl season. It should be a winner. ●

SPECIFICATIONS
High Standard Supermatic Deluxe Shotgun

Model: C-1200, solid frame.

Action Type: Autoloading, gas operated, self-compensating.

Gauge & Chamber: 12; 2¾″.

Barrel & Choke: 28″; modified.

Safety: Cross-bolt type through front of trigger guard.

Sights: .120″ metal bead front, and .090″ center bead on ventilated rib.

Magazine Capacity: Four 2¾″ shells plus one in chamber, providing 5 shots (3-shot plug furnished).

Weight: 8½ pounds (empty) for test gun.

Over-all Length: 48″.

Buttstock & Fore-end: American walnut; fluted comb; pistol grip with plastic cap; die-impressed checkering; recoil pad.

Stock Dimensions (test gun): Length of pull 14⅛″; drop at comb 1½″; drop at heel 2⁵/₁₆″; downpitch 1″; zero cast-off.

Price: $184.95.

Mfr: High Standard Sporting Firearms, Hamden, Conn. (Leisure Group, Inc.).

Remarks: Barrels not interchangeable.

Rifles and Cartridges for

Much depends on where you hunt, more perhaps on how you shoot. Here's a rundown on all the popular choices, with good handload data for a sweetener.

by NORMAN E. NELSON, JR.

ELEMENTARY, my dear Watson." Holmes chuckled as he etched a patriotic VR with revolver shots in the apartment wall—which is one way to break a lease. "The ideal rifle for *Odocoileus hemionus*, the North American mule deer, should weigh three pounds when carried, 12 pounds when aimed, and fire a cartridge producing about 2000 foot-pounds of bullet energy at 400 yards without causing excessive meat destruction at 50 yards. The cartridges should retail at two cents a round and produce not more than 8 foot-pounds of recoil."

Although Dr. Watson was such a simple clod that he thought VR stood for Vapo-Rub, not Victoria Regina, he replied severely, "Holmes, something tells me you've been hitting the cocaine pretty hard again." That was the year's easiest diagnosis, for no one but a complete hophead would expect to find that in a rifle.

Muleys in their range from Mexico's Sierra Madre into the snows of British Columbia are hunted in heavy timber, open sage plains, semi-dense brushlands, barerocked sheep country, or even agricultural fields. Like gold, mule deer are

where you find 'em, though that can be reasonably predicted by local geography, weather and time of year.

Varied hunting conditions require a compromise rifle. By contrast, arming for the forest-loving whitetail poses no problem. To bushwhack whitetails in the beech and maple ridges of the East, the balsam and birch forests of the northern Midwest, or the thick canebrakes of the South, a hunter could make out all his life with a shotgun. A good 30-30 or 300 Savage could well be the most rifle he'd really ever need. A genuine zapper in the big magnum class may be a downright disadvantage for the 50-yard whitetail shooter in recoil, rifle weight and meat destruction.

There are two approaches to choosing a rifle for mule deer. One is to go the compromise route, picking a rifle model, caliber, and sight combination *most likely* suited to the country and the conditions prevailing where you expect to hunt. The other is to cheat (on your wife and the family bankroll) by having more than one rifle for your muley hunting.

The trouble with the single, all-purpose rifle for mule deer hunting goes right back to the wide variety of conditions under which you may wind up hunting muleys. On a single, relatively small ranch in northwest Wyoming, I've hunted and seen mule deer on cross-canyon situations where a 350-yard shot was moderately "close" and down in creek bottom cottonwoods and greasewood where a 35-yard shot would be a moderately long one. For the one situation, a genuine magnum of the 7mm Remington or bigger category in a somewhat heavy rifle is desirable. For the other, I'd prefer a lever gun or an autoloader in a power class not to exceed the 300 Savage, since I have a great fondness for eating the venison I successfully smoke with gunpowder. Shots at any deer in timber at 35 yards are likely to be going-away shots; and I doubt if even Roy Weatherby would honestly recommend the big magnums for this to venison lovers.

The problem is best approached by arbitrarily lumping mule deer rifles into three basic groups and relating these to the kind of country most likely to be hunted. They

Muleys

should also be personally correlated with how experienced a rifleman you are. If you're an urban dweller with little chance to shoot between seasons, you're automatically handicapping yourself if you choose a king-sized magnum. Mule deer are not difficult to kill, nor are they particularly big deer in most of the western ranges. Sure, some exceptional muleys are taken, but on the whole a 200-lb. live-weight buck is a big one.

Class I mule deer rifles could include all that give 1000 to 1500 foot-pounds of energy at 200 yards. I arbitrarily pick that range because it probably represents the maximum effective hitting range of many, if not most, hunters—and I'm being optimistic. A westerner with considerable guiding experience tells me flatly that 100 yards is more realistically the limit for the average hunter, and he's seen standing deer missed cleanly by some of his pilgrims at 50 yards.

Choice of Calibers

To meet our dogmatic standard of at least 1000 foot-pounds at 200 yards, we have the 250-3000 (100-gr. bullet for 1020 ft. lbs.), the

underloaded 257 Roberts (100-gr. for 1080 ft. lbs., but 1400-plus in good handloads), the Remington 6 mm and Winchester's 243 (100-gr. at 1570 and 1430 ft. lbs. respectively), the 300 Savage (1240 to 1530 ft. lbs.), the 30-40 Krag (1340 to 1660 ft. lbs.), such off-beat but good loads as the Swedish 6.5x55mm, (1400 and up) and numerous similar cartridges in this general class. Marginal by this yardstick are the 30-30, the 32 Winchester Special, and their obsolete Remington counterparts. Out of the running are the 35 Remington (don't confuse with the Bridgeport firm's 350 Magnum!), the hotter 22 varmint rounds, the 44 Magnum, the half-forgotten 25-35, and quite a few others that make respectable 100-yard deer rifles (the 22s do not).

Admittedly, in the hands of cool (or lucky) shots these will take deer at 200 yards, but we're speaking here of the "minimum desirable," not the "marginally possible."

The main virtue of these Class I cartridges is in their genial recoil and relative lack of muzzle blast. All things considered, they're easier on the shooter than bigger cartridges, often inherently more accu-

rate (such as in the 6mm family of the 250-3000), and lend themselves to genuinely light rifles which can be shot without producing a mild concussion in the shooter.

Perhaps in a more useful category are the Class II cartridges. These have more power (1500 to 2000 ft. pounds at our arbitrary 200 yards), are more reliable on that day when you have to take an end-on rump shot at the big buck topping the butte, and can double as reasonably effective elk or good-sized-bear rifles—an important consideration for many western hunters.

They would include: the 6.5mm Remington Magnum 120-gr. (1640 ft. lbs.), the 270 Winchester 130-gr. (right on the top margin at 2000 ft. lbs.), various factory loadings of the 280 Remington (1800 to 2000 ft. lbs.), the fat and formidable 284 Winchester (1800-plus ft. lbs.), the Norma (or handloaded equivalent) loads for the 7x57 with medium-weight bullets (Norma lists 1810 ft.

Mule deer hunting can be a close-range affair in some situations, but in open hill country like this in northeastern Wyoming a fairly heavy, long-range rifle shines.

lbs. for their 150-gr. load), such 30-06 loads as Federal's 150-gr. (1760 ft. lbs.), some of the better 30-40 Krag loads (1600-plus), top loads of the 303 British (180-gr. at 1750 ft. lbs.), the big game loads of the 308 Winchester (from 1500 to 1760 ft. lbs.), the little-known 358 Winchester (1610 to 1760 ft. lbs.), and a host of like-potential wildcats in various calibers.

The newly standardized 25-06, at close to 1800 ft. lbs. with the 120-gr. bullet—or suitably hand-loaded—would make Class II very nicely, of course.

For the top-drawer rifleman who knows how to shoot, who can handle recoil and muzzel blast, and

chester family (2430 to 2640 ft. lbs.), the 350 Remington (on this category's threshold with 2000 to 2180 ft. lbs., depending on bullet choice), and the King Kong entries like the 375 H&H, the 350 Norma Magnum and the bigger Weatherby rounds. The proprietary Weatherby cartridges are represented in all three classes depending upon caliber and case choice.

Bullets and Weights

Does the mule deer hunter need as much rifle power as the Class III cartridges offer? Ordinarily, no. Any cartridges in all three groups have trajectories flat enough for useful, 200-yard shooting or

heavy-jacketed moose missiles should be avoided. If in doubt, err on the lighter side, and you'll get quicker kills. A 257 with 100-gr. bullets kills muleys like dynamite; with the best of 117-gr. handloads, it's not anywhere near so impressive. Generally speaking, the 150-gr. '06 loads anchor muleys in their tracks quicker than the 180-gr. loads.

If you go up a notch in rifle power—replacing, say, a 257 with a 25-06 or a 30-06 with a 300 Weatherby—it's worthwhile shifting up to heavier bullets for better long-range ballistics and to avoid excessive bullet blow-up when a muley gets right out of the rockpile

The West means mule deer—and a variety of hunting conditions, running from short-yardage shots to those at barrel-rupturing ranges.

doesn't mind a heavier rifle (nor some dynamited venison at closer ranges), we shift into Class III mule deer rifles. These would take in the so-called magnums (not always titled as such), starting with the 264's 140-gr. (2270), any of the 7mm Remington full-power loads (2100 to 2470 ft. lbs.), the hottest 30-06 loads in factory or hand-stuffed rounds exceeding 2000 ft. lbs. at 200 yards, the 300 Winchester (from 2480 to 2790 ft. lbs.), the 300 H&H (barely edging the better '06 loads), the walloping 338 Win-

beyond, but if he can handle it, the more powerful cartridges offer more potential on longer shots. The hooker in the deal is that qualifier: "... if he can handle it." Many shooters would do nicely with a Class I rifle, passably with a Class II choice, but turn into flinching, near-spastic, ballistic cripples when using one of the more severe of the Class III rifles or even a very light, short-barreled Class II rifle.

Bullet choice is important in mule deer cartridges. The extremes of featherweight varmint slugs or

under your feet.

Basically, good bullets for mule deer call for some compromises between the ranging, wind-bucking virtues of longer, thus heavier bullets, and the quicker expansion and frequently better killing power of the somewhat lighter bullets.

Now hear this. The following handload suggestions should, as always, be approached by other loaders from below, using lighter charges and working up to these in small incremental increases. Meanwhile, watch for the usual signs of excessive pressures, such as extraction problems. I like loads somewhat on the conservative side, since they tell me it's quite a trick to learn Braille. But I have no way of knowing what "conservative" or "58 grains" means to your powder scale or rifle chamber.

30-30 Winchester Admittedly marginal with the usual 170-gr. factory loads, but don't laugh. With 150-gr. bullets and decent sights, it's not a bad mule deer rifle, within reason. Use flat nose bullets for tubular magazines. Charges of 35 to 37 grains of 4064 or 4895 give 2300 foot-seconds velocity on up to 2400-plus. One problem: some thin-walled 30-30 brass is so springy that it's hard to full-length

257 Roberts Try 48/4831 or 45/4350 behind a 100-gr. bullet, Sierra or Speer (Hornady in this weight is rather violent on the eatin' meat). Noticeably superior in performance over factory loads.

25-06 Remington Better dual purpose cartridge, for various reasons, than the 6mm family or the 270, if you want a varmint-deer rifle. My favorite muley load calls for 54 grains of 4831, 117-gr. Sierra boat-tail or flat-base. This rivals 270/130-gr. performance. Don't use 100-gr. bullets in the 25-06 for deer unless you really like your venison shoulder roasts converted to instant bouillon.

243 Win. and 6mm Rem. Lots of loading data involving chronograph

300 Magnums The only excuse for these cannons on muleys is the range potential. Therefore, it's amazing that more 300 magnum lovers haven't tumbled to the fact that a 200-gr. spitzer will outrange even 180-gr. loads, while 150s are a waste of the large magnums' potential talent. Working from various loading tables and using caution, you can get close to 3000 fps in a 300 Weatherby, while the Norma and Winchester versions aren't far behind. Naturally, this velocity with a 200-gr. bullet is going to mean lots of action on both ends of the rifle, but it should give you an honest 500-yard mule deer musket . . . if you know how to use it.

270 Winchester Its reputation was

Big muleys like rugged country—tough areas calling for a light rifle. Author's favorite is a featherweight Mauser-actioned 257.

size for use in 94 Winchesters or Marlin lever guns—the cases spring back at times. After sizing, try running unloaded cases gently but firmly into your 30-30's chamber, and discard the balky ones.

6.5x55mm Swedish Mauser Fine deer cartridge. A lot of these floated in with the tide as surplus weapons in the early '60s. Don't be misled by the moderate ballistics. Even with mild loads of 47/4831 or 38/4320, a 140-gr. bullet will rake a big deer from stern to stem, I've found. Trajectory is flat enough for 250-yard shooting.

tests show that factory ballistics for these are almost as optimistic as Egyptian air force communiques. Just use slow-burning powders like 4350 with deer-weight bullets. Probably 100-gr. bullets are best for muley hunting with a 6mm. If you stalk muleys in lodgepole forests, you might try Speer's 105-gr. round nose, a favorite of mine when hunting timber whitetails on Lakes States forests. If you insist on one, all-round 6mm bullet for varmints and deer, try Sierra's 85-gr. and just hope you don't hit a buck in the hindquarters.

made with 130-gr. bullets, but the classic 150-gr. spitzer handload with 58/4831 makes a beautiful long-range deer load. It's hot; approach it with caution. Out-performs the 130-gr. considerably.

30-06 Good, 150-gr. spitzers like my favorite, the Remington Bronze Point, are hard to beat, using 54-55 grains of 4320 or 60/4350. Velocity will be in the 2900 fps area. The 165-gr. bullet, like the Speer, is ballistically superior to the 150, dropping deer better than any 180-gr. spitzer. In a good bolt gun, start at 57/4350 and work up carefully to 58 or 59 grains ... maybe. This will give close to 2900 fps at the muzzle and will outshoot any 150-gr. load at longer ranges.

Accuracy is more important in selecting a mule deer rifle than a whitetail weapon, simply because of the likelihood of longer shots. Fortunately, almost any modern rifle with the poorest of factory ammo will turn in acceptable 3-minute accuracy for deer-sized targets about as far as the average shooter can expect to make hits in any event. The more serious mule deer hunter will likely opt for the bolt rifle's generally superior accuracy with an eye toward the time when the margin of performance is important.

And sometimes it is, too. One of my better muley bucks was a 4-pointer taken in mountain twilight at 230 paces as he grazed within one good jump of dense cottonwoods—no likelihood of second shot. Worse, his rump was facing me. To avoid a rearend shot and the likely loss of a fatally wounded deer as the light failed, I shot for the neck as he turned his head, grazing, to one side. It called for varmint rifle accuracy, and fortunately my custom 257 could provide just that. The buck never heard the shot that caught him in the spine just ahead of where the neck fairs into the shoulder bones.

On the other hand, the hunter who likes a saddle scabbard on Jeep, horse or Honda may prefer a lever gun, a trombone action like Remington's 760, or one of the autoloaders—maybe the new Browning Automatic Rifle that's fast making a name for itself with the kind of accuracy that reasonable people ordinarily would expect only from a bolt action—a *good* bolt action.

The mule deer hunter who likes to walk 'em and stalk 'em, working the edges of the canyons and brushy draws, will want to compromise. The small carbines are fine to carry but, being muzzle-light, leave something to be desired for that now-or-never off-hand shot. On the other extreme is something like my 11½-lb. 25-06, which grows a pound an hour even in the more accessible country! Years of climbing the rimrock have convinced me that a good weight range for the mule deer rifle is from 7½ to 8½ pounds. Lighter than that they're hard to shoot accurately, particularly when you're panting from the scramble up that last 200 feet of shale slope. Heavier than that means a more

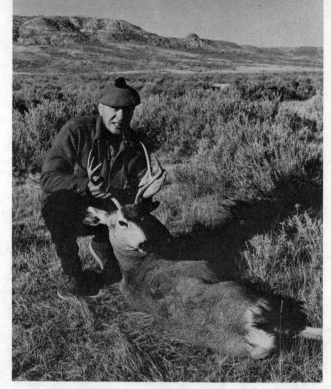

Open country in much of the West doesn't always mean long shots. This buck was shot at very close range when he sprang up from a bed in open, sagebrush country.

tired hunter looking for an excuse not to climb that last ridge where a 5-pointer could be bedded on the other side.

Two Rifles?

This brings us back to the alternative of having two specialized mule deer rifles, also known as the coward's way out or the Classic Excuse To Buy Another Gun. An example of this rationale would be to acquire a lightweight Class I rifle for tough hunts involving lots of walking and climbing or the day your horse runs away, leaving you to hoof it 7 miles back to camp. This would be backed up with a heavier model of Class II or even Class III rifle for the sit-and-watch hunt at dawn or dusk along your favorite 400-yard canyon. I went this route years ago with a featherweight 257 and the afore-mentioned heavy 25-06 and, some 40 big game animals later, never regretted the choices.

What kind of sights should the mule deer rifle wear? A good 4x scope is difficult to beat. However, the variable powers offer some advantages, particularly for glassing a distant canyon wall for a cleverly bedded buck's antlers. The 2½x class, excellent in timber, can't hack it hunting muleys in the hills. For one thing, picking out the buck from a herd of does at longer range may be impossible with a 2½x glass, as I've learned the hard way. On the other

hand, avoid using too high-powered a glass or magnification setting. It simply may not give enough field of view to properly lead a running deer. I learned that the hard way, too, using a 10x varmint scope for kicks one time. On a standing shot, it would have been fine, but on running targets, all I got were the kicks—which make very thin stew.

Summing up, there are many choices both in cartridge and rifle model when it comes to picking a good mule deer rifle. The guidelines are influenced by the kind of hunting you do, how well you handle a rifle (i.e., don't overgun yourself to the point of being a chronic flincher), and even such factors as whether you'll use the same rifle for other purposes. For example, one of the 6mm tribe would make a fine off-season coyote and prairie dog rifle. But if you want one rifle for both muleys and elk, you'd be better off with an '06, a 270, or one of the stouter magnums, if you're an experienced shooter. Meanwhile, "The most important factor is still, as always, the man behind the gun," Holmes continued, while reloading his Webley.

"Come, Holmes; you're being trite," his listener said.

"But true, Watson, true," Holmes drawled, smiling up at the mounted head of Professor Moriarty on the wall above the sideboard and gasogene. ●

The Guns of John Brown

by LOUIS W. STEINWEDEL

John Brown, the popular image. This old Currier & Ives pictures Brown as he appeared to the Northern public — the popular martyr, a near saint against a background of almost classic symbolism.

Some believed him a saint, others said he was Satan, this fierce guerrilla leader they called "Osawatomie" Brown. Whichever, he fought to abolish slavery years before the Civil War — and paid with his life. These are the weapons he used in "bleeding Kansas" and at Harpers Ferry

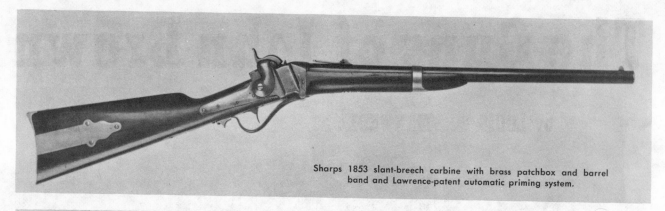

Sharps 1853 slant-breech carbine with brass patchbox and barrel band and Lawrence-patent automatic priming system.

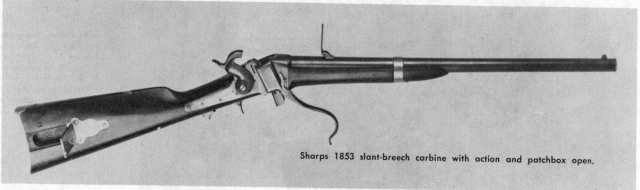

Sharps 1853 slant-breech carbine with action and patchbox open.

IRONY AND contradiction are often the warp and woof of history, but there are enough unnatural measures of the unknown in the lurid story of John Brown to spin many a tale weird enough even for modern television. Most of these are best left to the historian, psychologist or armchair thinker to ponder, but at least one of the curious circumstances of Brown's bloody career is of interest to gun collectors—how Brown came to defy Virginia, the Union and the world with 200 of the best rifles money could buy and an equal number of probably the worst revolvers.

The so-called "John Brown Sharps rifle" is fairly well known to collectors, the slant-breech model of 1853 with brass patchbox in the buttstock and brass barrel band and buttplate. The raiders' guns were not, as some people apparently still believe, the similar but more modern vertical breech model 1859 Sharps which appeared the same year as the storied seizure of the Federal armory at Harpers Ferry. Less well known to collectors are two other facets of the fanatic's armament: his long standing personal association and preference for Christian Sharps' advanced rifles and his extremely unlikely supply of sidearms.

John Brown bought his first Sharps rifle in 1848, the first year of the gun's introduction, and became—in his own way—one of the first boosters of this remarkable breechloader. For some reason known only to Brown, he wanted this personal gun unmarked,

and that was the way he got this potent, accurate arm that served him well through the years of border war in "bleeding Kansas." The Sharps was the ideal weapon for the early day guerrilla warfare that he and his free-soilers waged and perfected in Kansas. Settlers backed by fiery New England abolitionists and opposed by equally determined Southerners anxious to replant slavery to fresh Western soil bled along with Kansas through the 1850s on a miniature Civil War battleground.

Determined that the advocates of slavery in the West would do the bulk of the bleeding, Henry Ward Beecher and other less vitriolic New Englanders sent the best guns they could buy to be sure that their version of right was backed by a sufficient supply of might. Crates of sparkling blue, brass, and casehardened Sharps breechloaders sallied forth secretly from their native New England with the incongruous deception "Bibles" neatly blackened on their white pine sides. Beecher (along with his sister Harriet Beecher Stowe, authoress of *Uncle Tom's Cabin*), shouldered probably more personal liability for the Civil War than any other one man, possibly even more than Brown himself. He got a little extra claim to fame when his Sharps rifles blazed their way across the Kansas prairie nicknamed "Beecher's Bibles." It was altogether fitting.

Brown's Personal Revolver

John Brown's personal sidearm

through much of the Kansas bloodletting was the perfect complement to the advanced rifle he carried—an 1851 Colt Navy 36, recognized from the Barbary Coast to Balaclava as the best friend a man could have in his holster. Of graceful lines, beautifully balanced and comparatively light for its day, the Navy was patently impressive, either coming out of leather at full speed or simply lying at rest on the green felt of a gaming table. How Brown got his Navy Colt, the fifty-one thousand and tenth to be made, and how he parted with it is another ironic twist to the Brown legend.

William F. Arny, a canny Kansas politician and abolitionist, eyeing the bearded fanatic's devotion to the cause with appreciation, strategically chose to overlook the more disagreeable facets of Brown's quixotic personality. Arny believed that this ardent fighter in Kansas' "holy war" should be materially rewarded with a token and, fittingly, gave him a gun. Arny chose the best, the long barreled Colt Navy 36, plain finished except for the usual naval battle scene rolled onto the cylinder. Brown accepted it and conscientiously carried it in Kansas. For two years it became a witness to the most Inquisition-like page in American history.

"Osawatomie" Brown, as he liked to be called, after the best known site of the Kansas conflicts, was a psychologically fascinating man. He was burdened with precious few scruples over murder on the coldest terms when it furthered his cause, or even

John Brown's Colt Navy revolver, presented to him by abolitionist William F. Arny for his service in "bleeding Kansas." When the donor later disapproved of his savage methods, Brown returned it.

over feeding his sons to his hopeless ambitions at Harpers Ferry, yet he was meticulously honest. Eventually Brown's bloody Biblical-like vengeance mercilessly visited upon the "offenders" sickened even the devoutly abolitionist Arny. When Brown learned that he had fallen from favor in the mind of the donor of his revolver, he reasoned that the gift was conditional and that he no longer had any right to it. Accordingly, W.F. Arny promptly received from Brown one Colt's Navy 36, serial number 51010. However, the slim Colt had apparently been to Brown's liking since he soon acquired another one, with his own cash no doubt. Such a gun, or at least the remains of one, was found in the aftermath of the Harpers Ferry debacle in 1859, though not used there. Its barrel was sent to Hartford as a souvenir for Samuel Colt.

By the middle of 1856 a shaky peace had descended upon Kansas. At this time, however, a shipment of 200 more Sharps 1853 carbines was on the way from Massachusetts, creating a situation not far removed from the Russian missiles-in-Cuba crisis of about a century hence. The New England financiers of the "Kansas Crisis" began to fear that Federal military authorities in Kansas might take a dim view of the presence of this many rifles considerably superior to their own. Also, with the usual ingrained Yankee regard for hard cash, there was an investment of some $5500 to protect.

Brown Gets Rifles

So, the Sharps shipment was secretly diverted to a depot at Tabor, Iowa. The attempt at secrecy did not of course include so trusted a warrior as John Brown. That, as history shows was a mistake, because the power in-

herent in 200 superb rifles was simply too much for the Kansas guerrilla, who saw bigger things in the wind to resist. It did not take much persuasion for Brown to get possession of the guns with the stipulation that he sell them privately and distribute the proceeds as relief funds. Brown did nothing so charitable, and the Sharps carbine showed up three years later on the rented Kennedy farm a few miles from the U.S. Armory at Harpers Ferry. Osawatomie Brown was apparently willing to compromise even his lofty principles about rightful possession when the "cause" stood to profit by an abuse of the Eighth Commandment.

The fast, accurate, easy handling Sharps served Brown astonishingly well in his otherwise botched raid at Harpers Ferry, permitting seventeen men to, as Henry Ward Beecher phrased it in a sarcastic sermon, "overawe a town of two thousand brave Virginians and hold them captive until the sun had gone laughing twice around the globe."

The Sharps was a splendid weapon, but the revolvers which Brown carried East stood in stark contrast to it. These were tiny 31-caliber revolvers made by the Massachusetts Arms Co. for the firm of Wesson & Leavitt. Some 200 of these handguns, complete with such accouterments as flasks, nipple wrenches and bullet moulds, had originally been sold to Boston abolitionist George L. Stearns. Through some espionage they ended up in the hands of John Brown in Iowa in 1857, and they too made it to the Kennedy farm in Maryland two years later.

This Massachusetts Arms Co. revolver was about as far as you could get from John Brown's hefty Navy Colt, and a highly unlikely nominee for the quasi-military foray on the

banks of the Potomac. It was chosen, apparently for financial reasons; these 31-caliber jobs cost only $6.50 complete with accessories while a Navy Colt cost roughly double that—and was worth more.

The Massachusetts revolvers were unusual in concept and appearance, not unlike some of the very early attempts at revolving repeaters. With the exception of a topstrap over the cylinder which served to hold the cylinder pin and barrel to the rest of the parts, the gun appeared almost frameless, like a dueling or target pistol with a cylinder added as an after-

John Brown, the private image. This rare, unbearded view of Brown was regarded as his best picture by the family. He appears less ferocious than usual here, but the cold and expressionless eyes are the perfect symbol of his character.

thought. The revolver's only touch with the times was its Maynard automatic tape primer which was intended to eliminate the necessity of a separate percussion cap for each shot. The system had been invented in 1845 by a Washington dentist named Edward Maynard and enjoyed a measure of popularity by the 1850s, particularly when adapted to the muzzle-loading military musket.

The Maynard system was simple. When the hammer of the gun was cocked a small arm pushed up the end of a coil of waterproofed paper containing small fulminate charges, almost exactly the same as toy caps for children's cap pistols. On musket conversions the original percussion nipple was retained, so ordinary copper caps could be used in a pinch. However, the Maynard adaptation to the revolvers which Brown's men used completely did away with the usual nipples at the rear of the cylinder. Instead, the roll of caps was fed to a single nipple mounted in the frame which communicated the flash of the cap explosion through a tiny vent in the rear of each chamber in the cylinder. This was one of those ideas which look great on paper but which have a way of turning out to be unmitigated disasters.

It is understatement to say that the Maynard system was not noted for its reliability. Despite its claim to waterproof caps, a Maynard equipped gun often would not fire during damp weather. During such conditions, the militiaman could slip an old-fashioned copper cap on the nipple of his musket and be sure of a kick when he pulled the trigger, but the Maynard priming system was exclusively and forever married to the Massachusetts Arms revolver. Having the ignition system reach the powder chambers by a small vent hole was a throwback to the flintlock, and had the same problem of black powder residue fouling the vent after the first or second firing. These two factors combined made the Massachusetts Arms revolver dependable for little more than casual Sunday afternoon shooting, yet fate capriciously sent it along on one of history's boldest expeditions.

By another quirk, fate chose a U.S. colonel named Robert E. Lee to yank Brown from his makeshift fortress with the gracefully arched windows and the top-heavy looking cupola. The breaching of the armory firehouse took only three sweeps of the minute hand of Colonel Lee's big gold watch, but it quickly became popular history that is still providing fodder for movie and television screens.

The whole thing was a holiday in the picturesque Virginia hills and it did not take the revelers long to locate the bulk of Brown's private arsenal at the rented Kennedy farm a few miles away in Maryland. One of

1853 Sharps and stocked Colt Navy carried by John Brown, Jr. The Collins cavalry officer's saber was presented to Brown, Jr. by his Civil War regiment. Wooden canteen was the senior Brown's.

the regiments at the farm, the "Baltimore Greys," did not consider it unprofessional to re-appropriate some of the expensive abolitionist carbines as spoils of war.

Collector's Sharps

Fortunately for history, one of the shiny brass-bound Sharps carbines found its way into the hands of Colonel A. P. Shutt, commander of the 6th Regiment of Maryland Volunteers. In civilian life Shutt worked for the Baltimore & Ohio Railroad and was in Harpers Ferry mainly to protect company property from the gun-toting mobs that had swarmed in for the carnival and free whisky. The colonel was one of the few recipients of Brown's guns that sensed a bit of drama about it rather than a simple windfall of a good gun. He gave the unused carbine to his son and the lid of the inlaid brass patchbox was later engraved: "Captured from insurgents at Harpers Ferry, Va. October 18, 1859 by Col. A. P. Shutt and presented to his son Augustus J.C.L. Shutt." Today, the gun belongs to the Maryland Historical Society. It is the most authentic of the extremely few Brown guns and relics that survived the years after the raid. Its serial number is 15864.

Officially, 102 Sharps carbines and an equal number of Massachusetts Arms revolvers were removed from Brown's rented base of operations, so apparently the better part of a hundred of each were carried off by enterprising souvenir seekers. Some of the other remnants of Brown's shat-

tered dream of a slave rebellion included 23,000 percussion caps and 100,000 percussion pistol caps, ten kegs of powder, plus spears, pikes, and assorted martial hardware with which Brown had planned to arm the slaves which never rose to follow him. The guns were removed to the Federal arsenal, where they were appropriated once again when the town later was captured by the Confederacy and—the greatest irony of all—the guns for John Brown's "holy war" vanished into the ranks of the rebel cavalry.

The scene of the raid seemed to suffer a fate under Brown's curse which no other piece of American territory has ever had to endure. Like some little European border town, with spectacular Rhineland-like scenery to complete the comparison, Harpers Ferry was alternately shelled by armies as they advanced, pillaged of its machinery while they were there and burned as they retreated, until by the end of the war it literally ceased to exist. Years later the ghost of Osawatomie Brown seemed to still haunt the spot with a vengeance as the usually placid Potomac swallowed it.

* * *

John Brown was a saint or a satan, generally depending on which side of the Mason-Dixon line the opinion originated, but there is no argument that he was an enigma, a strange blend of idealism and savagery, something mysteriously apart from the ordinary mould of men—and that the exotic about him extended even down unto his armament. ●

Short reviews of five firearms—Savage 24C and 99A, Richland 10-gauge Model 810, the Omega III and Dumoulin rifles.

by Larry S. Sterett

Omega III Rifle

The Omega III (mentioned in our 26th edition), has now been given a limited amount of shooting, and with a variety of loads. My test rifle has a classic stock with cheekpiece, but no Monte Carlo. The 24-inch barrel is chambered for the 7mm Remington Magnum cartridge, and the complete rifle weighed 8 lbs. without sights. The action is tapped for most scope mounts, and a Redfield 4-12x variable scope in the excellent Conetrol mounts was soon fitted to it.

One of the unusual aspects of the Omega III is the 2-piece stock, designed to provide an interchangeable buttstock and/or fore-end. The rear of the fore-end fits into the front of the magazine well, and is secured by the front swivel stud. The buttstock fits into the rear of the magazine well, secured by the rear guard screw, no more—and no through bolt. One thing to be checked was whether this arrangement would cause battering of the front portion of the buttstock. After 100 rounds—500 or 1000 would have been more conclusive, but time didn't permit—no noticeable battering had occurred. This included firing loads with bullet weights ranging from 125- to 175 grains. The buttstock afterwards appeared to be the same as when first examined.

A second unusual feature of the Omega III is the rotary magazine. (Two popular sporting rifles—Savage's M99 and the Mannlicher-Schonaure—have similar magazines, but they date from the turn of the century). The last such rifle introduced was the seldom seen

semi-automatic M1941 Johnson. The Omega magazine holds 4 magnum cartridges, fed one at a time in a counterclockwise direction. The magazine may be emptied in a hurry by pressing a button located ahead of the trigger, in the top of the trigger guard. (The same button serves as a bolt release.) The cartridges come out in a hurry, and it is advisable to have a hand ready to catch them.

The unusual bolt has an octagonal body and a square head. The square head does the locking, instead of the usual locking lugs. This permits locking to occur without having to move the bolt handle as far; it works and bolt operation is definitely faster than with most bolt actions of the same caliber size. The bolt body rides on the vertices of the bolt flats and, with less metal-to-metal contact, binding is reduced to a minimum, making the Omega III a slick action to operate.

Four different ammo brands—CIL Imperial, Federal, Norma, and Remington—in three different bullet weights were shot at the bench, but time did not allow for handloads. Using sandbag butt and fore-end rests, 3-shot groups were fired at 100 yards. Repeatedly, 3 shots

would form a neat triangle measuring about 1½ inches, regardless of brand or bullet weight. The smallest group was had with 175-gr. bullets in the Norma brand—⅞-inch on centers for 3 shots; another group had two shots in less than ½-inch. The Omega III can produce minute-of-angle groups, or less, and with the right ammo, factory or handload, it will probably group consistently into less than one MOA.

The bolt head has the current style of pinned-in extractor, and plunger ejector, fired cases being thrown to the right and slightly to the rear.

Wood and metal finish and fit is near-perfect—better than on some rifles costing considerable more. Grip and fore-end are smooth, without checkering; none is intended. A contrasting fore-end tip, and a silver pistol grip cap with gold initial, are standard.

The Omega III rifle is certainly unusual, from its large push-through safety at the rear of the trigger guard to the square bolt head. Its features are not found together on any other rifle, and all do what they were designed to do. We'll be seeing and hearing more about the Omega III from Texas.
L.S.S.

Savage Model 99A •

The basic M99 rifle and the 250-3000 cartridge was a time-proven combination on whitetail deer, and on varmints, too, with the 87-gr. bullet, but in recent years the newer cartridges have been getting the limelight. Apparently someone at Savage realized the need for this pre-war combo, and its return is most welcome.

There have been some changes since the first M99 in 250-3000 appeared, and all have been toward making the rifle modern in every sense. The sliding tang safety certainly beats the old lever safety, and the magazine rotor is now aluminum; the brass version is no more. The action has been tapped for scope mounts for years, but it wasn't 'way back when.

Topped with a weaver Classic 6x scope in Savage mounts, the 99A weighed in at 7¾ lbs., putting it out of the lightweight class. The extra weight may aid accuracy, but the minor recoil of the 250-3000 cartridge doesn't require it. The straight-grip stock is fluted on both sides of the comb, a style I prefer to the pistol-grip 99, and the comb is high enough for use with a scope.

Some know-it-alls scoff at the accuracy of lever action rifles with two-piece stocks, but the 99A takes a back seat for no one. From the bench at 100 yards it performed better than some bolt action rifles I've shot, most of which have one-piece stocks. Dominion 100-gr., Gevelot 87-gr., plus Winchester Super-X 87- and 100-gr. loads were put through the 99A, the firing done with the aid of front and rear sandbag rests. Some 3-shot groups with 87-gr. bullets went just over an inch. The smallest was made with Gevelot 87-gr. SPE-RN bullets —27/32-inch! Thus, even with 87-gr. factory loads, the 99A is suitable as a varmint rifle. Switching to 100-gr. loads the group sizes doubled, going to just over two inches, and indicating the preference of this particular rifle for the lighter weight bullet. But even this performance is still very acceptable for deer hunting, and handloads may decrease spread.   *L.S.S.*

Richland 810

This big gun, the Model 810, was mentioned in our 26th edition, but a test gun didn't arrive until the end of the goose season along the Mississippi Flyway. For this reason testing was limited to patterning

Sterett shooting the 250 Savage 99A.

and use on some clay pigeons—this latter practice isn't exactly recommended for a full time diet; it could loosen your fillings.

Manufactured in Brescia, Italy, by Armitalia de Lucchini Stefano, the test gun tipped the scales at an even 11 pounds. The barrels measure a hair over 31⅝ inches, carry a wide ventilated rib, and are chambered for 3½-inch shells. Examination of the barrels—both choked full—revealed smooth bores and chambers, and long, rough forcing cones—this latter feature is thought to have an advantage over smooth cones, at least by some shotgunners.

The action is a boxlock with Kersten top locking. Extractors that raise firing and unfired shells about ⅜-inch, double triggers—the front trigger is not hinged—and a non-automatic safety are standard. Trigger pulls proved to be heavy, though on a 10-gauge gun a light pull is definitely not desirable. I'd prefer the pulls to be lightened on this gun to about 5- and 10 pounds respectively.

The stock and fore-end are of dark European walnut, plain, but satisfactory, with some fair 20 lines-to-the-inch checkering. Length of pull is 14⅝ inches, between triggers, and there's a ventilated rubber recoil pad. The beavertail fore-end provides a very comfortable grip—a decided asset when swinging on a big honker. Metal finish is a glossy black on the barrels and dull black on the receiver, with a polished blue trigger guard. Engraving is almost nil, but this 10 gauge is intended for use, not to be hung on the wall and admired.

Alcan, Remington, and Western Super-X factory loads were patterned at 40 and 50 yards with Nos. 2 and 4 shot. With the 2⅞-inch shells the plastic-cased Remington load—1⅝-oz. of 4s—produced the best 5-shot average—62.5% for the top barrel. (This cartridge uses a roll

crimp with overshot wad.) The best 5-shot average at 40 yards was made with some paper-case Super-X Magnum 3½-inch shells throwing 2 ounces of size 4 Lubaloy shot—69.9 percent. With No. 2s the average ranged between 50% and 60% at 40 yards; at 50 yards the averages dropped about 10 percent. But anytime you send 2 ounces of shot on its way, even a low percentage can put a lot of shot where it counts.

It's doubtful if any average shotgunner is going to wear out a 10-gauge shotgun, unless he uses it for trap for a couple of decades, bag limits on ducks and geese being what they are. The 810 should perform well. Surprisingly, the recoil is not as much as with some 12-gauge over/unders, partly because of the weight and partly to the stock design. At least I didn't mind shooting the 810, even during the rather long patterning sessions, when there were no moving targets to shoot at.

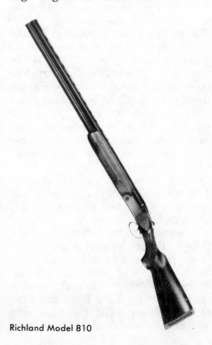

Richland Model 810

Dumoulin Carbine

The 270 test rifle we received had an FN Supreme Mauser action, but current production is on Sako actions. The carbine has a 20-inch barrel—button rifled—and a slim one-piece full length stock of select French walnut. A rollover Monte Carlo with cheekpiece, rosewood teardrop pistol grip cap, Pachmayr recoil pad, and fixed European-style swivels are standard.

Right out of the box the Dumoulin rifle tipped the scales at 7⅜ lbs., without sights. Depending on the particular scope and mount, another pound should be added, although open sights can be had at extra cost. The trigger pull was a uniform 1⅞ lbs., crisp, without any noticeable creep. It is adjustable and weight of pull can be increased if desired.

Before going to the range the new 270 was taken down to examine the inletting—and a pleasant surprise awaited. The long slim fore-end can be a source of warping, but on the Dumoulin the barrel channel and action areas were completely finished—a sign of a quality product. The inletting was well done everywhere including the trigger guard area; in fact the inletting was so close that the barreled action stayed in the inverted stock, after the guard screws were removed, until the barrel was tapped lightly with the heel of the hand. The outside is finished with a high luster material which appears to be plastic; the grain had been filled before the finishing applications, and the surfaces were very smooth. A metal plate in the stock, behind the receiver recoil lug, helps absorb the recoil and prevents possible stock splitting. One stock feature I particularly like is the slimness of the grip. I have nothing against larger grips, but a slender hand grip permits better control of the rifle.

Finish on all metal parts, with the exception of the polished and engine-turned bolt body, is a highly polished blue—no waves or ripples are noticeable anywhere.

I put a Weaver V8 scope, with a rangefinder reticle, on the Dumoulin, and went out to my bench for some shooting. Firing for accuracy was done at 100 yards, using sandbag fore-end and butt rests and, since the Mannlicher is a hunting rifle, 3-shot groups were fired, with all cartridges fed from the magazine. Test loads included the 130-gr. and 150 gr. Speer/DWM, Frontier, and Hy-Score. Accuracy was more than acceptable for a hunting rifle, the Frontier 130-gr. load producing one group measuring 1½ inches. Most of the groups ranged around two inches, with the Speer/DWM 150-gr. load making the smallest group for this bullet weight—1¾ inches, not bad for a carbine or a rifle.

No difficulty was experienced with the Mannlicher during the firing of over 100 rounds. This is a relatively small amount of shooting, but considering the quality of the Dumoulin workmanship, I don't foresee any problems. The price ($269.50) is in line with the quality, and the accuracy is better than many hunting rifles show—at least it was with the test rifle. Other models may vary slightly, but on other models examined, the workmanship was quality all the way. *L.S.S.*

Savage 24C Camper's Companion

The Savage 24 has been around for almost as long as I can remember, in one form or another, but the 1972 version has to be best. From time to time various improvements have been made—most of them good, such as replacing the selector button on the receiver (it often came loose and got lost) with a selector lever on the hammer; for 1972 it was replacing the small screw-attached front sight with a one-piece barrel band and front sight that should never get lost the way the old one often did. But this was only a start; the barrels were separated on all grades to allow air circulation—not really needed on single shots, but it permits the use of the muzzle barrel band—and several new grades were added, including what should become one of the most popular, the Camper's Companion. With 20-inch barrels—22 Long Rifle over a 20 gauge chambered for 2¾-inch shells—straight-grip walnut-stained hardwood stock with 13¾-inch pull, this is a handy little sporting arm. One thing I particularly like—and which would be a good idea on all Model 24's—is the trapdoor buttplate. This has a panel that slides out to the right from beneath the buttplate. A fingernail can catch the panel lip and move it out to expose cavities below capable of holding ten 22 LR cartridges and two 20-gauge shotshells.

The 20-inch barrel of the 24-C has no choke, or, if you prefer, it has a straight-through cylinder choke. Since it is intended as a camp gun shots are supposed to be at short range—at rabbits, etc. For this reason it was patterned at 25 yards, instead of the usual 40 yards, Federal's Monark and S&W-Fiocchi 2½ dram field loads holding 1 oz./7½s and 1 oz./6s respectively, were used. The 5-shot averages were 58.2% and 54.3% in the 30-inch circle. In addition, the Czech S&B papercase field load (2¼-⅞-7½) was patterned. This S&B load has a top wad and rolled crimp, so it was expected that the pattern average might be down slightly. It wasn't. The 5-shot average turned out to be 54.5%, right in line with the new S&W field loads, except for having ⅛-oz. less shot.

The 24-C rifle barrel was checked out at the bench with CCI Mini-Group and Mini-Mag, plus Western Super-X 22 LR cartridges. All firing was done from 25 yards, using sandbag rests and open sights. I'd intended to fit a 4x scope, but after trying to mount two Weaver scopes, a Bushnell and a Tasco without success—the barrel is grooved, but the rear sight is so high it prevents the scope tube from sitting low enough for the mount base to fit in the grooves—this idea was dropped. At 25 yards the Mini-Group loads made the smallest 5-shot groups, some just less than one inch, with the Super-X cartridges doing almost as well. Ample accuracy for small game or plinking, in view of the open sights.

Except for the scope mounting problems, the 24-C is entirely satisfactory. Light and handy, it should be welcomed by many backpackers, RV campers and hunters. *L.S.S.*

BETTER GET USED to Austin and Hodgdon imported black powder, also referred to as Curtiss and Harvey*. It is nearly the same in chemical composition as Du Pont powder, but its burning rate is slower and the granulations are not the same. These details and new ballistic data are presented here to bring muzzle-loading shooters up to date. It is the only black powder available, regrettably.

This turn of events is, at least in good part, the result of an explosion at the Moosic, Pa., black

offer a bulk type smokeless powder to replace their black powder, their Explosives Department has just informed me that there is no basis for the reports—Du Pont will not, I was told, resume the making of black powder! This makes the imported ICI powder the only propellant available for muzzleloaders, at least in the U.S.

The Austin Powder Co. of Cleveland, Ohio, through their subsidiary Red Diamond Distributing Co., the Hodgdon Powder Co. of Shaw-

Pont sizing, a grade can be selected to handle the whole range of loading needs *except for maximum power*. The former loading and ballistic data for Du Pont black powder no longer applies.

When the correct (matching) grain size of the ICI powder is used, the same charges formerly used with Du Pont powder will be suitable, but note carefully our detailed comments. The different granulations make a difference. In general the same charge of the corresponding grade of ICI powder will produce less velocity and less pressure than Du Pont black powder. Most shooters will only know that their velocity is lower because they read about it. Their guns will sound and feel much the same as ever, but they'll have to raise their sights a bit more for long range shooting.

Black Powder 1972 –

a new situation

by EDWARD M. YARD

When DuPont ceased manufacture of black powder for sporting purposes in 1971, the outlook for the future was bleak indeed. Now there's a rift in the pungent pall, as the author shows.

powder Du Pont plant in June, 1971. Damage was enough to make it uneconomical to rebuild for renewed production of black powder, and there were other needs for that plant area. In view of the sale/use of less than 200,000 pounds per year, the decision is understandable. While there have been rumors that Du Pont would

nee Mission, Kansas and CIL of Canada, are importing the ICI powder. It is available in four grain sizes and, while these do not correspond exactly to the former Du

Because this lower velocity is accompanied by lower pressures, too, loads can usually be increased, with safety, for a partial recovery of lost foot seconds (fps), but usually not fully. Some heavier charges can't be increased because the finer granulations of this powder can (and do) give high pressures.

The high pressures are not hypothetical. Several such instances were actually measured with a pressure gun during the ballistic tests that were conducted in working up the load data presented here. These results are tabulated. Since there is only a partial equivalence to former Du Pont granulations and results, a new look at how these ICI powders apply is of first importance:

ICI Black Powder Range

Austin	Hodgdon	Application
Musket & Shotgun	F	Muskets, large bore shotguns and rifles.
Rifle	FF	Rifles to 55 cal. and shotguns.
Pistol	FFF	Pistols, small bore rifles and shotguns.
Pan Powder	FFFF	Priming powder for flintlocks.

*The original Curtiss & Harvey's black powder was made in a plant near London. It is now made by the Nobel Division plant of ICI at Stevenston, Ayrshire, Scotland.

This is the pressure-recording device designed and built by Thompson/Center, makers of the interchangeable barrel T/C single shot handguns and the Hawken muzzle-loading rifles. The heavy steel box or "yoke" accepts muzzle-loading barrels in various calibers, their breech ends projecting inside the yoke, in line with the heavy-duty steel screw seen. A lead crusher cylinder, positioned between the screw and a sliding piston inserted into the breech plug, compresses on firing. The reduced-length crusher is then measured to determine the pressure of a given shot, using standardized (tarage) tables. As pictured, the crusher is in position, the nipple capped and the hammer cocked, ready to be fired by the lanyard.

Even though Hodgdon uses an F series similar to old Du Pont markings and Austin uses a descriptive designation that sounds like the applications of former Fg grades of powder, there is not an exact interchangeability. Trouble will seldom result by assuming equivalence or from using earlier published black powder load data, but three of the new granulations are finer than Du Pont FFg, FFFg and FFFFg respectively, which they seem to stand-in for. We did get high pressures with Austin Pistol and Hodgdon FFF (ICI FFF) in rifle loads that did not occur with old Du Pont FFFg. A more detailed discussion follows.

Grading The Powders

Austin Musket & Shotgun granulation or Hodgdon F may be loaded in the same charge weight where Du Pont Fg was formerly used. It is slower burning and will produce less velocity and pressure than an equal charge of Fg. Charges may usually be increased by 10 percent without exceeding former pressures. But is is well to remember that the large bore guns in which this grain size is used are often old muskets and shotguns or poorly made replicas that are not strong, so use some judgment before upping any powder charge.

Austin Rifle and Hodgdon FF (ICI F) is finer grained than the Du Pont FFg which is approximately replaces. Its composition is slower burning, but its finer grain size tends to offset this. In most applications it will give less velocity and pressure when loaded in the charges as used for FFg. But because it is nearly as fine as old FFFg we advise caution in using it for heavy loads in 8- and 10-gauge shotguns or in 58, 69 and larger muskets. For normal loads there should be no problem.

The Austin Pistol or Hodgdon FFF (ICI FFF) is finer grained than Du Pont FFFg, almost as fine as FFFFg, and while its composition is the same as its fellow ICI powders (it is slower burning than the Du Pont formulation), it produced high pressures in a number of heavy loads fired with it. Pressures of 10,000 to 20,000 lead units of pressure (LUP) were registered with it in rifles of caliber 40, 45 and 50 with loads heavier than normally used but yielding less velocity than lighter charges of old Du Pont FFFg. It will be a temptation to equal Du Pont ballistics, but don't overload this ICI powder. It is fine grained enough to jump pressures up sharply, and when this happens you will get *less*, if

not more, velocity—by the chronograph. It is for use in pistols, revolvers, new rifles of caliber 36, 40, 45 and 50 in moderate charges. The load table presented herewith shows where the pressures jumped. It has no place in muskets or large bore rifles. It really should not be used for shotguns but it would be all right in the lightest loads. Treat this FFF stuff cautiously.

The ICI priming powder, Austin Pan Powder and Hodgdon FFFF, is solely for priming flintlocks. It is almost a powder literally, being everything that will pass through a 70 mesh per inch screen. *It has no propellant applications.*

Breech-loading guns are generally stronger than muzzleloaders, and they give the shooter a warning of too high pressures through extraction difficulty and case expansion, primer flattening, extrusion and marking. The muzzleloader gives no distress signs, an accident being usually the first indication. So take careful note of the fact that we did measure high pressures during the testing of various. loads, and that a number of black powder guns have been blown up. Generally there is no known cause or explanation for these mishaps. But it is quite evident from the measurements shown here that a heavy charge of a too-fine grain black powder is certain to cause stress and strain, if not actual failure.

Judgment Needed

When used in proper grain size and in sensible loads, however, Austin and Hodgdon black powder is as safe as the gun it is used in. It is tolerant of charge variations, hence reasonable care in measuring charges is all that is necessary. Bulk measuring is sufficient, but be sure you really know what *your* bulk measure charge weighs. Check it on an accurate reloading scale. In finding a load that suits your rifle, bear in mind that a few grains up or down will have little effect on ballistics. Changes of 1 to 5 grains in a 45 caliber, when checked with a chronograph in a pressure gun barrel, would be hard to distinguish from the readings. In the correct grade, 10% heavier charges than used with Du Pont will normally cause no trouble. The cautions cited are to make sure the reader realizes that black gunpowder is capable of causing serious accidents. But it isn't fussy if you aren't foolish.

The correct load for muzzleloaders is the one that makes it shoot best—which is seldom the heaviest load it will handle. Every black powder shooter has his pet loads, often a different one for each gun he shoots. If you are experienced and have worked out your own loads for Du Pont, then try the same charge with the corresponding grade of Austin or Hodgdon, using our earlier table of applications and our powder comments as a guide. You may also try increasing the charge in one- or two-grain steps to 10% more. A novice muzzle-loading rifleman may, if he likes, try a charge equal to 60% of ball weight in bores through 55. Do not use this old rifle-load formula for Civil War type rifled muskets of caliber 54 to 58 or in 69 caliber rifles or smoothbores or in any larger bore flint or percussion guns. Some guide books give the old military loadings in the 60- to 80-gr. range, and some suggest using the Austin Pistol grain or Hodgdon FFF in these guns. Looking at our pressure test data, we recommend you do *not* take that chance, using instead the Austin Rifle or Hodgdon FF in these big bore old guns.

Blank or "salute" loads, where there is no wadding or projectile to obstruct the bore and provide resistance to the powder gas, can surprisingly produce serious pressure, even enough to damage the musket in which they are fired. Such loads should be held to the least amount of powder that makes enough noise, and not too much more than they usually take for regular ball loads. In a 50-caliber rifle barrel 100 grains of ICI FFF gave a pressure reading of 3700 LUP, and 125 grains went to 5000 LUP. Both of these values exceed what a musket was intended to handle, though not an overload for a rifle barrel that was used with the pressure gauge. There was a satisfactory noise with the 100-gr. load.

After the Du Pont accident black powder was in short supply for a while, and information about what the Austin powder was and how to use it was equally scanty. Hodgdon powder was not in full distribution here in the northeastern U.S., and his new *Black Powder Data Manual No. 1* was not then generally known. Even now it is quite possible that many black powder shooters don't know that the powder they buy is different or what the difference might be.

Sometimes an improvised container is offered, perhaps a paper bag, with no more than a handwritten mark to indicate the corresponding Du Pont grade. Just what was in the package no one really knew. Confusion reigned.

If you're offered powder in a hand marked container you should refuse it and demand factory-packaged stuff. The unidentified container is illegal. Should you, in some circumstance, have to take it that way, you may learn to recognize it by eye. If you have any of the Du Pont grades left, save a little of each in glass vials for making visual checks and proper grading. Our earlier comments about grain sizes and the tabulated comparison should be enough.

Some shooters are now claiming that this ICI powder leaves less fouling in the bore, and that they can load several times without cleaning. This would appear to be a subjective view and, in view of the almsot identical chemical composition, perhaps more a matter of loading and cleaning practice than a major difference in fouling. There are some differences, however, which will be covered.

The writer uses a tight patch, and a second ball goes down harder in any bore. More impressive is the difference in ballistic performance.

Bore Cleaning

The difference we do notice is that the fouling cleans out easily if done the right way. It is soft and moist and can easily be wiped out with wet patches. The cleaning liquid should contain water, oil and a detergent. The old-fashioned standby was hot water and soap. The best bet is to clean the bore at the range as best you can, and then finish the job at home or in camp that day. Don't wait until next morning, not on account of rusting (which may happen), but because an adherent film forms in the barrel. It seems waxy to me and is tough to remove. It is better not to let it form.

Bore condition, whatever it may be, has other effects, including an

Front view of the special Thompson/Center pressure gun, showing the dual cradle setup to position and hold the barrels (all of them used in the author's tests were also furnished by T/C) in permanent alignment with the chronograph (at right) screens. Velocity and pressure were recorded simultaneously with each shot fired.

Black Powder Rifle Ballistics

Cal.	Charge, grains	Powder Rifle or FF Vel. fps	Powder Rifle or FF Press. LUP	Powder Pistol* or FFF* Vel. fps	Powder Pistol* or FFF* Press. LUP
36	40	1455	3900	1720	6500
	50	1630	4400	1880	7000
	60	1800	5000		
	70	1880	5000		
40	50	1550	4900	1795	6500
	60	1665	5100	1870	7000
	70	1770	5500	Press. 11,000	
	80	1870	6000	Not tried	
	90	1920	6500	Not tried	
45	70	1425	4400	1640	6200
	80	1550	4700	1750	7000
	90	1665	5000	1860	7500
	100	1815	6000	Press. 14,500	
	110	1920	7000	One shot 20,000, damage to pressure gun.	
50	80	1440	4300	1560	4900
	90	1500	4600	1625	5200
	100	1560	4700	1690	6000
	110	1625	5000	1775	6800
	120	1690	6000	Press. 10,000	
	130	1750	6500	Not tried	

*See text: This ICI FFF powder designated "Pistol" by Austin and FFF by Hodgdon is not well adapted to heavy loads in rifles. It should be restricted to moderate loads when used at all.

Velocity is for a 28″ barrel. Calculations based on this data indicate velocity would rise 7½ fps per inch of longer barrel length and fall about 10 fps per inch shorter, to about 20″.

alteration in ballistic results. All shooters should be aware that gun bore condition will surely affect its shooting performance, for with lead bullets we've learned that degrees of bore cleanliness affects velocity and, consequently, accuracy.

Target shooters clean out the fouling between shots. This is usually done with a patch wetted with Hoppe's, Hodgdon or some other cleaner, followed by one or more dry patches. Some of these "dry" patches are re-used. No bore wiped with a wet patch and dried with only one dry patch is really dry, nor will a re-used dry patch and a new one do the job.

For uniform testing procedure with chronograph and pressure gun it was necessary for me to thoroughly clean and dry the test gun bore after every shot! Among some of my results I noticed a large spread in velocity, up to 250 fps, and a pressure variation as well. Suspecting that I had not dried the bore adequately after each shot, I re-tested the loads with a very well dried bore and the velocity variation shrank to as little as 2%, which is as good as metallic cartridge reloads can claim.

So, talking one of our bore-cleaning targeteers into chronographing his paper puncher, we found about the same thing, a velocity spread of 275 fps. It spoiled his day. I don't know if he has yet figured out a good bore-drying technique, but you can be sure that your bore must be *free of oil and water* if you expect uniform ballistics. This is one of the good things a chronograph can do for you.

Other hazards in this situation are misfires and hangfires. The velocity spread, of course, is indicative of fast hangfires that will ruin accuracy, and I've watched others getting misfires from carelessness in drying their cleaned barrels. The percussion cap is not a very strong igniter, and it doesn't take much moisture, oil or dirt in the flash hole, bolster tube or the chamber to obstruct the cap flash and cause a hangfire or misfire. Please note that this has nothing to do with the new powders—the old black would act the same way. These comments are just a by-product of the tests and observance of the phenomena, the tell-tale instruments at hand.

Black Powder Pressures

One of the unexpected things revealed by these tests is that black powder pressures, when loading within the proper range, tend to be very uniform. It is not unusual to get three or four identical pressure readings in five shots, the other one or two being only 100 or 200 LUP away. Black powder test shots were usually within 30 to 60 fps total deviation. Velocity spreads for shots from a truly clean dry bore are as small as those for smokeless powder, where a variation of 50 fps is normal. The ill effects of oil, bore cleaners or water in the barrel have been mentioned, but there must be other things that will vary from shot to shot, small differences that may affect the velocity and pressure of each round. So the experienced shooter's advice to do everything exactly the same for every shot has merit.

In determining proper charges for Minie balls the same amount of Austin Musket & Shotgun grade

The moment of truth. Test shot breaks chronograph screens and fingerprints its pressure on a lead crusher cylinder at the same time.

or Hodgdon F will replace Du Pont Fg—and the author feels this is the powder to use for these heavier bullets. Since high pressure occurred using both Austin Pistol and Hodgdon FFF (and some similar indications with Du Pont FFFg in heavy loads), it is possible that Austin Rifle or Hodgdon FF, being finer grained than Du Pont FFg, will get into a high pressure area with heavy bullets. The ICI F grade that is Austin Rifle and Hodgdon FF, has been used in 58-caliber rifled muskets with the Minie ball in 60-gr. charges. Probably 70 grains of this should be considered a maximum in big bores with Minie balls or slugs.

Double balls have sometimes been loaded. One published source suggested using 100 grains of Du Pont FFFg and two balls in a 45-caliber rifle. This certainly must have produced high pressure. The same charge in that caliber with *one* ball, using ICI FFF (Austin Pistol and Hodgdon FFF) produced high pressure. Such a double ball load will, I believe, wreck a lead crusher pressure gun. Never try this load with the new ICI powder, and I think it inadvisable to use FFFg as well. Until reli-

du Pont FFFg Test

Cal.	Charge, grs.	Vel. fps	Press. LUP
45	60	1720	5700
	70	1820	6700
	80	1920	8600
	85	1960	9100
50	80	1770	6700
	95	1950	8500

able data can be worked up, do any irresistible experimenting only with Musket & Shotgun or F.

Black powder is a mechanical mixture of potassium nitrate, sulfur and charcoal. It usually contains 1% of water which, with the sulfur, serves as a binder. It is not hygroscopic up to 93% relative humidity. When ignited, charcoal burns with oxygen in the potassium nitrate, giving off intense heat. When the temperature reaches about 445° C the sulfur vaporizes and carries ignition throughout the charge mass. There are many references to the effect that certain charcoals have on the burning of black powder. It is generally thought that dogwood charcoal is best for small arms powder as it is faster burning. The ICI Nobel plant making the imported powder distributed by Austin, Hodgdon and CIL, indicate they are

du Pont and ICI Powders Compared

du Pont		ICI	
G.D.*	Sieve	**G.D.***	Sieve
		T.P. Cannon	8 x 20
Fg	12 x 16		
FFg	14 x 30		
		F	18 x 24
FFFg	20 x 40		
		FFF	24 x 70
		Priming powder supplied as everything passing 70 mesh	
KNO$_3$	74.0 ± 1.5%		75.0 ± 1.5%
Charcoal	15.6 ± 1.0		15.0 ± 1.0
Sulfur	10.4 ± 1.0		10.0 ± 1.0
Moisture	0.85% Max.		1.2% Max.
Spec. Gravity	1.72 — 1.80		1.70 Min.
Burning Speed (lead fuse)	75 - 80 sec./yd.		90 - 100 sec./yd.

*G.D. - Granulation Designation.

ICI believes their two "F" grades may be substituted for Du Pont FFg and FFFg without noticeable difference.

ICI is reported to produce less fouling than Du Pont. It has a graphite surface glaze.

How this will be packaged and marked by the three known importers remains to be seen.

The importers are: Austin Powder Co., Hodgdon Powder Co., C.I.L.

Black Powder Grades

	Designations			Uses
Austin	Hodgdon	CIL		
Musket & Shotgun	Fg	Fg		Muskets, big bore shotguns and rifles.
Rifle	FFg	FFg		Rifles to 55 caliber and shotguns.
Pistol	FFFg	FFFg		Pistols, small bore rifles and shotguns.
Pan Powder	FFFFg	NA*		Priming powder for flintlocks.

*Not available.

CIL are building, they report, a warehouse in Plattsburgh, N.Y., and that by mid-January, 1972, sporting and fireworks grades of black powder will be available. They will distribute this via former DuPont dealers. It will be in 1 lb. tins bearing a C&H label with Fg, FFg and FFFg size indications as shown in the comparative table above for the current three importers.

using alder or dogwood charcoal to the extent of their availability. The other two ingredients are of controllable high quality today.

Caseless Black Powder

Service Armament Co. is planning to import black powder "caseless" charges. Prototype samples have been tested, these consisting of compressed cylinders sized to fit the 36-cal. Navy revolver chambers. The intention is to supply these packed in cartridge boxes with a suitable bullet, possibly in a glassine envelope or collodion sleeve. The exact details are still to be worked out by RWS and Val Forgett early this year.

The samples tested were of small-grain size, the individual grains clearly visible, and looking like

FFFg. The 24.7-gr. units were of correct length and 36-cal. diameter for the Navy replica. Another, which we tested in a 36-cal. pressure gun barrel, weighed 31 grains, was too long for the revolver.

Three shots with the 24.7-gr. sticks produced 620 fps with a .380" lead ball in a 36 Navy revolver. The same load gave a pressure of 3500 LUP in a 36-caliber pressure barrel. These ballistics would be fine for short-range target shooting or plinking, with very low pressure strain on the gun.

While the prototype compressed charges burn more slowly than would a like weight of loose powder, the samples were limited, and no final conclusion is possible at this time. This is a new idea, and a good one, I believe. ●

Last Minute B. P. Report

SINCE WRITING the preceding report on the new black powder situation, there has been time for more tests, particularly in such areas as the effects of different patch materials and lubrication, pressure with double-ball loads, and new observations about the imported black powder.

The supply situation is still the same. We depend on powder imported from Scotland. Samples of stick or solid charge powder, made with German black powder, were received and given limited tests, but the stuff isn't yet available. Neither is the German powder. We are trying to obtain samples of Australian black powder and the manufacturer is looking for a distributor. At this writing neither has been accomplished.

Despite earlier assurances that black powder would be in good supply after the first few months of transition from Du Pont to our new source, black powder supplies are scarce. Dealers' stocks are depleted. In most areas only one brand is usually available.

Further study of and testing the Scotch powder indicates that the *coarser two grades*, marked FG and FFG by Hodgdon and C-I-L,* and designated by Austin as Musket & Shotgun and Rifle, respectively, are so close to the same average grain size of Du Pont Fg and FFg, (although having different sieve grading specs), that they should be considered equivalent granulations. This does not alter my earlier comments about the two grades or their application. It is simply a more accurate physical comparison. In describing FFG (Rifle) we would not now use the word "finer" in comparing it to Du Pont FFg. It is about the same.

The above comments *do not* apply to FFFG (Pistol) powder, which is much finer than Du Pont FFFg. Our earlier comments about it have been re-inforced by additional test results. It must not be regarded as a replace-

*C-I-L black powder is not reaching dealers here yet.

ment of old FFFg. Heavy loads that were safe with Du Pont FFFg may be unsafe with this. It will give high pressure in all bore sizes above 35-36 caliber with patched round balls. It is unsuited for use with conical- or Minie bullets. It should be regarded in the same way smokeless pistol powders would be for centerfire rifle loads.

The round ball patch, for best ballistic results, must be tight and uniform. The tighter the patch and ball fit, the higher the velocity and pressure of the shot. Thompson/Center patching material, which runs .020″ to .022″ thick, is about as tight as you can seat manually. A look at the attached table of results with different patches and lubricants reveals the importance of this. Note the velocity increase when the T/C patch is lubricated with Crisco instead of a water-base lube, and the losses with only slightly thinner patching. These results imply that there is gas blow-by with normal patched balls.

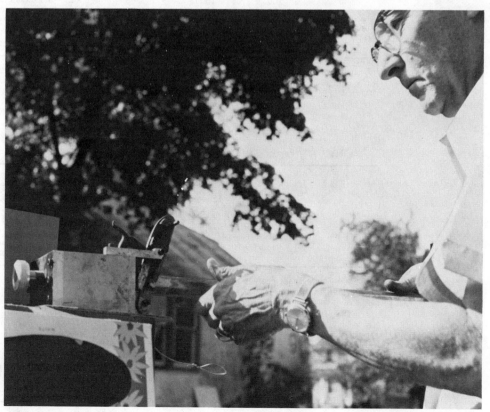

Barrels were removed from the pressure breech, thoroughly cleaned and dried after each test shot, then replaced for loading. This step is necesary for uniform ballistic results.

These observations suggested a wax impregnated patch, so some T/C material was soaked in parafin. These stuck to the barrel but slipped on the ball, letting it punch right through the patch! This area could benefit from experimentation. We also found that if there is any clear difference in the seating force from shot to shot, velocity and pressure will both be higher for the tighter load in clean barrels.

Two-Ball Loads

Double balls double pressure for the same powder charge. As we have observed with other heavy loads generating high pressure with black powder, there is considerably more variation from shot to shot. This is reason enough for me to condemn them, even if the shooter is willing to risk the pressure, but there is a more important warning against their use. The second ball may become a bore obstruction. Air trapped between the first and second ball while loading can cause a separation between them.

Under primitive conditions loading two balls may have been the best available way to obtain greater striking energy. Without technical knowledge, the risk may have seemed acceptable. Our statement that double balls double pressure is based on measuring actual breech pressures with such loads. Theory predicts the result because a double ball load has twice the sectional density, and would require twice the force to accelerate it. Measurement and theory agree.

A better solution today is to use a conical bullet of greater weight and the next larger-grained powder. This eliminates the bore obstruction risk, though one must still make sure the load chosen is within reasonable pressure limits. Heavier bullets cause higher pressures than lighter ones with the same charge weight. There is a need for more black powder load data covering this area than now exists.

Muzzleloaders have only three grades of black powder with which to do everything. There isn't the wide range of burning speeds we get with smokeless. The surest way to more muzzle-loading energy is to use a bigger bore.

More tests with salute loads, or blanks, where a black powder charge is fired in a clear bore without wad or bullet—just loose powder—indicate that pressures similar to those generated by regular ball loads result. These pressures rise with increasingly heavier blank charges. A table of our results is attached.

Black powder ballistics show a distinctly diminishing return for indefinitely increasing charge weights beyond 70% of bullet weight. As black powder combustion products are 56% solids, these must be accelerated as well as the ball. Very heavy loads, above 100% of bullet weight, start losing velocity rapidly, but pressure continues to rise.

There is still much to learn about our old gun powder. Black powder is a propellant, and it behaves like one, but it has its own low pressure personality. Using it at much over 7000 to 8000 LUP is misapplying it. ●

Patch Effect Tests

Powder Austin Rifle (ICI-F)

Caliber	Charge, grs.	MV	LUP	Patch Lube
45	100	1900	7500	T/C .021″ Crisco (saturated)
	100	1850	6000	T/C .021″ Water + soluble oil
	100	1800	4300	Ticking .018″ Water + soluble oil
	100	1740	3700	Ticking .016″ Water + soluble oil
	100	1720	3600	Ticking .011″ Water + soluble oil

All charges were weighed. All shots were fired from cleaned, dried bores. 28″ T/C Hawken barrels. Balls were .440″ in .440 bore, .450 groove barrels.
MV = Muzzle Velocity. LUP = Lead Units of Pressure.

Blank Salute Loads

Caliber	Austin Powder	Charge/grs.	LUP	Noise Effect
45	Pistol	90	3600	Reasonable for drill ground use.
		100	3800	Satisfactory, little more than 90 gr.
		125	4700	Satisfactory, little more than 100 gr.
50	Rifle	90	3400	Reasonable for drill ground use.
		100	3500	Satisfactory, little more than 90 gr.
		120	3800	Satisfactory, little more than 100 gr.
		150	4200	Satisfactory, little more than 100 gr.

All Blank Salute Loads charges were weighed and fired in 28″ T/C barrels. No wadding or restriction of any kind were used.

Double Ball Pressures

36	60 grains Austin Pistol	(ICI FFF)	— Single ball —	6300 LUP
			Double ball —	12,300 LUP
45	100 grains Austin Rifle	(ICI F)	— Single ball —	6400 LUP
			Double ball —	12,600 LUP

Locked Breech 380 Autos

By DONALD M. SIMMONS, Jr.

Photographs and drawings by the author.

Only a handful of recoil-operated 380 pistols ever attained series production—and some are rarely found today. Here they are—all eleven of them!

THERE IS ONE caliber size of automatic pistols which seems to be neither fish nor fowl. This group comprises the 380s, also known as the 9mm short, Kurz or Corto. Some 380 inventors used blowback actions, others designed a recoil-operated type. I'd like to comment in detail on the recoil-functional 380 autos, a small and unusual company. First, though, let's see how both types work.

Just about *all* self-loading pistols can be divided into two basic classes, depending on their actions. One of these classes is called the "blowback" type, the other group is "recoil" operated. The blowback action, characteristically, uses a relatively low-pressure cartridge. It is by far the most common action because of its lower cost of manufacture. The recoil action is usually found in pistols with high chamber pressure, often the military type of pistol. Like any rule there are

many exceptions to the above. These exceptions are a fascinating subject— they run the gamut from recoil-operated automatics as small as the Frommer 1901 and the Roth-Sauer to the massive blowback Kimball and Walther Model MP. The first two fire a low-power 32 automatic cartridge, the others a super powerful U.S. 30 Carbine cartridge and the 9mm Parabellum respectively. Of particular interest in this article are not the extremes but rather the type of pistol which fires the in between-powered round, the 380 ACP. Pistols that use this cartridge are not nearly as numerous as those that chamber the 380's sister cartridge, the 32 ACP. The 380 auto cartridge was a joint development of John M. Browning, for Colt, and William "UMC" Thomas of the Remington Arms Co. Outside the United States, as noted, the 380 ACP is called the 9mm Browning short,

among other names. Its first use was in the Browning-designed Colt Pocket Model M of 1903, which was first made in this caliber in September of 1908. These Colts were of 100% blowback design and, from the original Colt to date, there has been a surprisingly small number of automatic pistols designed to use the 380 ACP. This relatively small group consists of about 40 pistols and, of this number, some 25% of them were designed for recoil operation or had some nonblowback action design elements. This would seem to indicate that some designers were a little unsure whether the 380 ACP was a low-pressure or high-pressure cartridge. These recoil-operated and partial blowback pistols make an interesting collection of automatic pistols. They further exhibit some of the most unusual actions ever designed.

The 380 ACP is held in almost

From the left—the Savage Models 1917, 1915 and 1907, the latter in nickeled finish. All three are chambered for the 380 ACP pistol cartridge, all have the unusual Savage locking systems.

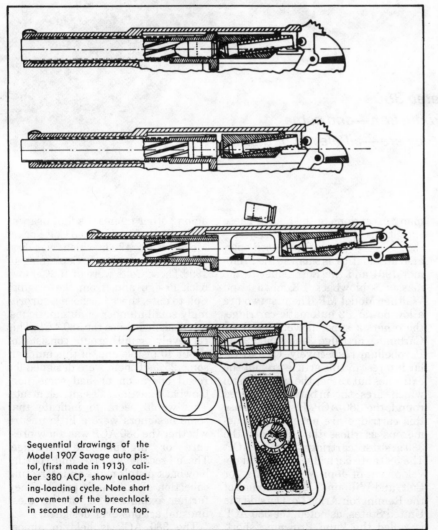

Sequential drawings of the Model 1907 Savage auto pistol, (first made in 1913) caliber 380 ACP, show unloading-loading cycle. Note short movement of the breechlock in second drawing from top.

total disdain in the U.S., but this is not at all true in Europe. There we find the police, even the military, armed with pistols using this cartridge. At least two of the automatic pistols which we'll discuss later on were the standard issue Army pistols of Czechoslovakia.

Recoil Operation *Versus* Blowback

About any pistol ammunition *could* be designed for use in a blowback action. The only reason we don't find highpower blowback 45 autos and 7.63mm (Mauser) pistols is that to safely use these hot rounds the mass of the recoiling parts would be too heavy to make a practical handgun. Blowback action relies on the weight of the recoiling parts and spring compression to keep the slide from opening dangerously far before the projectile has left the barrel. Of course when the bullet leaves the muzzle, the pressure rapidly drops to that of atmosphere. In this short period of time, between the bullet's departure and the final drop in chamber pressure, the entire automatic cycle of a blowback is completed. The slide is started to the rear by the empty shell under the force of the gas acting as a sealed piston. The pistol is then recocked, the empty shell ejected and a live round fed into the chamber. If, in the design of a blowback pistol the recoiling parts are too light, then the slide opens too soon—while the chamber pressure is too high. This premature movement could result in a dangerous ruptured shell case, since the cartridge's brass walls are not strong enough to resist the initial chamber pressure when completely unsupported. In recoil-operated pistols we have a different situation, the barrel and slide being locked together for a distance. The degree of locking is further subdivided by comparing the length of the locked distance to the length of the pistol's cartridge. When locking occurs for only a portion of the full slide travel, the system is called the short-recoil type. If, on the other hand, the locking occurs during the greater part of recoil, then it is termed a long-recoil system. I'll soon be describing in detail the more common short-recoil system, the rare long-recoil types, and those hybrid actions which don't fall into either category. Let's look now at the locked 380s in the order of their appearance.

The Savage Models 1907, 1915 and 1917

The Savage Arms Co., then of Utica, N.Y., began manufacture of their excellent line of pocket automatic pistols in April, 1908. These pistols were designed by Major Elbert H. Searles, a Philadelphian. The inventor claimed, in part, that he had designed a simplified form of locked breech, one in which it was unnecessary to have the barrel recoil. His main principle was this —when the slide/breechblock recoiled, it forced the barrel to rotate 5 degrees clockwise. Searles contended that, as the bullet was traveling down the barrel clockwise, this torque force twisted the barrel counterclockwise, and that these forces tended to balance, thus locking the barrel until the bullet left. So we have a recoil-operated pistol which, over a very short period of time, has an additional force operating which locks the barrel to the breech. I believe that Searles' principle is correct for two reasons. First, he was able to make a caliber 45 ACP pistol using his system and, second, I have tested penetration by using the Savage pistol against a regular blowback autoloader, both with the same length barrel. The Savage, in every case, had more penetration, suggesting that there was less gas escape in the Savage than in other systems! The Savage Model 1907 didn't appear in 380 ACP (called by Savage the 380 ASP, for Automatic Savage Pistol) until 1913. From that date until all Savage pistols were discontinued in 1929 (includ-

Right—Frommer Stop locked-breech auto pistol. Left—Frommer Baby, made to same design as the Stop. Both in caliber 380 ACP.

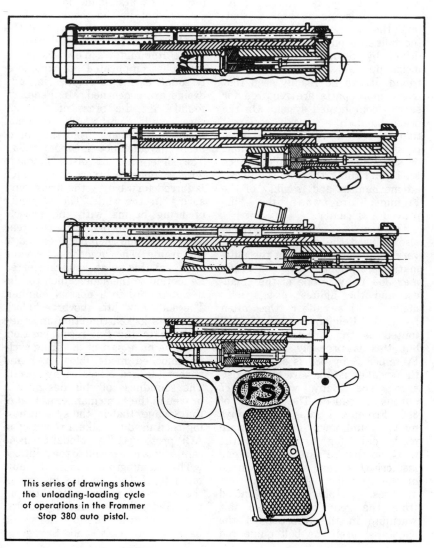

This series of drawings shows the unloading-loading cycle of operations in the Frommer Stop 380 auto pistol.

ing all three models, those of 1907, 1915 and 1917) only about 29,000 were made in 380 caliber. This makes them a relatively rare 380.

Frommer Models of 1912 Stop and Baby

The Frommer 1912 was manufactured in the Fegyvergyar Arsenal in Budapest, Hungary. It was made in two barrel and frame sizes—both in a long barrel or "Stop" Model and in a short barrel or "Baby." Before World War I, these two types of pistols were made only in 32 ACP, but almost immediately after the war the two styles were adapted to the 380 cartridge. The 32 ACP Frommer was actually used as an issued side arm in WW I by the Hungarians. The Frommer 1912, designed by Rudolph Frommer, had many of the features of his earlier pistols.

These Frommers have the long-recoil type of action. This means that the barrel and bolt are locked together during the full travel of recoil. The barrel then flies forward, driven by its own spring. As the barrel is almost back in battery, the empty shell is ejected and the bolt is then released. The bolt, driven by its own separate spring, picks up and chambers a fresh round. It can be readily seen that many more parts are required for such a complicated system. On the other hand, it is quickly apparent that in such a design there is no possibility of premature gas escape, or subsequent loss of bullet velocity. I don't think that the complicated mechanism and fragility of the Frommer are worth the "improved" efficiency.

The use of a long-recoil system also allowed the designer to use a very lightweight bolt—not the automatic's traditional slide. The Frommer 380 Baby is one of the smallest and the lightest pistols ever made in this caliber. One often hears the Belgian Bayard of 1908 touted as the smallest 380 ACP, but this is probably because the Frommer Baby 380 is so rare that the speaker is unaware of its existence. The Baby weighs 15.17 ounces unloaded. The number of 380 Frommer Stops and Babys made is unknown, but they were made only for 10 years at the most, so they're rare. There is one last criticism that should be made of the Frommer system. The bolt of these pistols is disassembled from the rear or, to give fair warning, in the direction of the shooter's face! The bolt guide rod has two small ears, and these are the only deterrents to the bolt continuing straight back, right off the frame of the pistol. The design of any pistol should be such that, no matter how many possible failures occur, the shooter is safe. While the Savage technically has its breechblock disassembled from the rear, it is unlike the Frommer in that there are large interrupted ribs which absolutely lock the breechblock.

Remington Model 51

The Remington Model 51 was designed by an American genius, John D. Pedersen. He worked months on the shape of the grip alone. He worried about getting the pistol thin and flat, about lowness in the hand, about matting the rib between the front and rear sights. Mr. Pedersen even designed an entirely original type of action, one with features of both blowback and recoil-action systems. The Remington Model 51 was first sold in 1919. Unlike many of its competitors it was first made in 380 ACP caliber, not in the more usual 32 ACP. It was not until 1921 that the 32 ACP caliber was marketed.

The Remington's blowback/recoil action is complicated but completely sound as far as engineering and design are concerned. Mr. Pedersen found that the brass of the 380 case could withstand a small amount of setback from the chamber. This distance is about .083". The slide of a 51 pistol is made with a separate breechblock, which is forced forward by the firing pin's spring in the slide. The sequence of firing begins with the breechblock being gas-blown to the rear about ³⁄₃₂" and then being locked to the frame. The breechblock, while locked at this point, has transferred its motion to the slide, which continues rearward in a normal manner. The slide now lifts the breechblock out of its locked condition and they both go to the full recoil position. Thus we have part of the firing cycle in unlocked mode (blowback) and part of it locked, albeit briefly (recoil). The soundness of this design was proven in the same manner as that of the Savage, that is, the system having been used to make a working 45 ACP prototype. The Model 51 in 45 caliber was never sold to the military.

The Remington Model 51 came too late, I feel, in the history of the American pocket automatic pistols. Had it been issued in the first decade of the century it would have given Colt and Savage a definite run for their money. As it was, only some 60,000 of the 51s were sold in 380 ACP. This is a great shame, it seems to me, for here was a pistol which could have held its head high even in such exalted company as the Walther PP and PPk, the Sauer 38 (H) and Mauser's HSc.

Czechoslovakian Models 1922 and 1924

Josep Nickl, an Austrian designer in the German Mauser Works, developed a method of making the blowback 1910 Mauser Pocket Pistol into a high powered locked-breech handgun. Nickl made this system from 1909 to 1914. The Mausers converted to 9mm Luger Parabellum by Nickl's method survive in very few numbers. Probably because of WW I nothing ever came of this recoil-operated Mauser in Germany.

In 1919 the newly-formed republic of Czechoslovakia was looking around for a handgun with which to arm its soldiers. The Czechs liked the Nickl design and decided to make the gun using the 380 ACP cartridge, then rare in Europe. The first of two different Czechoslovakian service automatic models was made in 1922, though the Models 1922 and 1924 are identical in action. I don't believe there were any of these pistols made for civilian use. All that I've ever seen have been military types, with regimental identification numbers stamped in the foregrip.

The Nickl recoil action is somewhat like the Savage, but with the Nickl there can be no question that it is a true recoil operation. The barrel is locked to the slide by two lugs, these rotating 30 degrees to unlock. The slide and barrel move almost ¼" before the slide can travel, unlocked, to the rear. This is a classic example of short recoil. Notice also that the barrel merely rotates, it does not change its axis with reference to the line of sight.

By 1927 the Czechs had made two basic changes in their service automatic. They eliminated the recoil operation elements in the design, reverting to a straight blowback system, and they reduced the caliber to 32 ACP. The first change was obviously prompted by a desire to reduce the cost of manufacture, but the second change is, to me, inexplicable. The Model 1922 was made until 1924, with only around 20,000 manufactured. The Model 1924 was made until 1937-38 and about 190,000 were issued. Both models were then made obsolete by the advent of the Model 1927, again in caliber 32 ACP. Of the recoil-operated 380 automatics, the Czech Model 1924 is the most common.

Llama IIIA

The Llama IIIA pistol, made in Spain by Gabilondo & Co. after World War II, is an almost perfect copy of our Colt Model 1911A1, caliber 45 ACP. The most obvious difference is that the Llama is only about three-quarters the Colt's size. The Llama IIIA, quite a fine pistol, was introduced into the United States by the Stoeger Arms Co. in late 1951 or early 1952. The IIIA mechanism is an exact copy of the Colt. The only difference, and a small one, is that the grip screw bushings of the Colt are not found in the Llama. This minor deletion might be thought of as an improvement by those shooters who have ever had a bushing(s) work loose in the Colt. The extractor in the Llama is of the common pinned and external type, unlike the Colt's internal self-locking one.

The recoil action of the Llama is John M. Browning's classic single link dropping barrel. At firing, the slide and barrel move to the rear, locked by matching lugs and grooves. The rear of the barrel is dropped and unlocked by the link swinging to the rear and downward. This downward dropping of the barrel breech, during unlocking, causes an angular alteration in the bore's axis. However, this downward shift comes after the bullet has left the barrel, thus there's no disadvantage as far as accuracy is concerned.

There appears to have been some 160,000 IIIAs made, but this figure includes the more popular XA, a blowback in 32 ACP.

Star S and DK (Starfire)

The Star line of automatic pistols is made by Bonifacio Echeverria of Eibar, Spain. Two models of pocket automatic pistols are made, both in 380 ACP, and both use the Browning dropping barrel system. These pistols have an external resemblance to a (small) Colt Model 1911A1, but without the latter's grip safety. Inside it is all Spanish, not Browning—the typical rigid pinned sear, side-mounted disconnector bar, and pinned trigger. The Star has an assembled recoil spring and recoil-spring guide, which are big improvements over the Colt 1911A1.

The Model 51 Remington autoloading pistol, caliber 380 ACP, is an ultra-slim, well-styled and engineered handgun. It was also made in 32 ACP caliber.

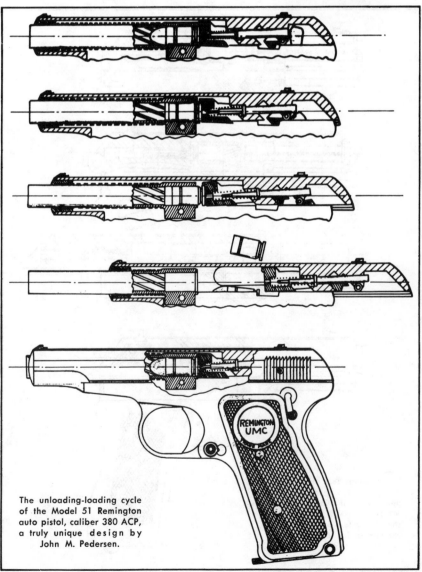

The unloading-loading cycle of the Model 51 Remington auto pistol, caliber 380 ACP, a truly unique design by John M. Pedersen.

Left—The Czechoslovakian Model 1924 auto-loading pistol, caliber 380 ACP, this specimen made in 1927. Right—the Czech Model 1922, of similar locked-breech design, this one made in 1923 and also in 380 ACP caliber.

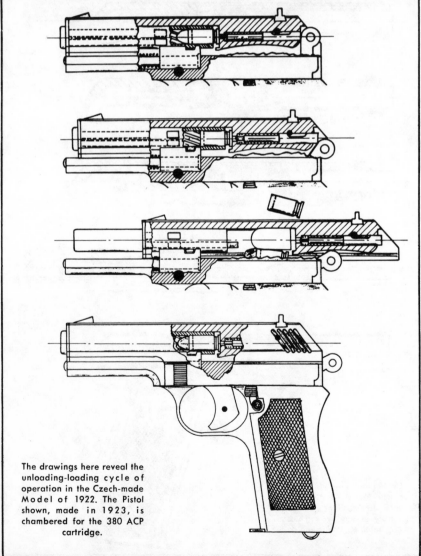

The drawings here reveal the unloading-loading cycle of operation in the Czech-made Model of 1922. The Pistol shown, made in 1923, is chambered for the 380 ACP cartridge.

The first model was the S1 later called the Super S offered here in 1952. Dimensionally it is a typical pocket automatic with a steel frame. The DK or Starfire offered here in 1960, is almost as small as the Frommer Baby. In fact, it actually weighs a little less, 14.87 ounces. The DK/Starfire has an aluminum frame, a shorter barrel, and a magazine capacity reduced to 6 rounds. The two Stars, well-finished and attractive pistols, will probably never be seen again in the U.S., for which we can thank the current federal restrictions on importing handguns that don't meet an arbitrary set of standards, so-called.

In trying to guess the number of Star Model S and DKs manufactured, we again run into the same trouble found in the Llama. The 32s and the 380s run in the same series. Serial numbers in the low 300,000 range are known while my DK is in the mid 700,000 bracket. I have seen very late DKs with serial numbers approaching the 1,000,000 mark. Since these pistols are still being made, there is little doubt that in time there will be more Star recoil-operated 380s in existence than any other like 380 ACP pistols.

Nine of these 11 pistols have external hammers; the Savage 1907 and 1917 Models have a cocking piece attached to a striker. The Remington Model 51 has a concealed hammer, while the Savage 1915 is a true hammerless pistol.

The recoil operation of these pistols varies from the just-barely-locked Savages to the ultra-locked Frommers. In these 11 pistols we find unlocking accomplished by turning barrel, dropping barrel,

Right—Spanish Llama auto has locked breech, as does quite similar Star pistol (left), also made in Spain. Both are chambered for the 380 ACP cartridge

turning breech piece and, lastly, the Remington Model 51 with its blowback/recoil system, a never-duplicated action.

These 11 automatics are the only recoil-operated 380 autos ever made in production quantities. Some of them are rather rare or scarce, while others are still being made. The Frommer Baby 380 is very rare, as is the 1915 hammerless Savage, but the Star DK/Starfire can certainly be bought today by the collector. Good hunting. ●

Acknowledgements: H. Milton Every, Charles Walker, Daniel Stern, James Carr, Dr. J. Howard Mathews, Mrs. D. M. Simmons, Jr., Paul Hendel (photographer)

Bibliography

Automatic Pistols, H. B. C. Pollard, London and New York, 1920.

Textbook of Automatic Pistols, R. K. Wilson, Plantersville, S.C., 1943.

Automatic Arms, M. M. Johnson & C. T. Haven, New York, 1941.

Pistols & Revolvers, Vol. 1, W. H. B. Smith, Washington, D.C., 1946.

Savage Automatic Pistols, James R. Carr, St. Charles, Ill., 1967.

Ten Shots Quick, Daniel K. Stern, San Jose, Calif., 1967.

Firearms Identification, Vols. I & II, J. H. Mathews, 1962.

Collectors Guide to American Cartridge Handguns, D. E. Sell, Harrisburg, Pa., 1963.

Remington Handguns, C. L. & C. R. Karr, Harrisburg, Pa., 1947.

The Mauser Self-Loading Pistol, Belford & Dunlap, Alhambra, Ca., 1969.

The Gun Digest, Stoeger Catalogs (Various years).

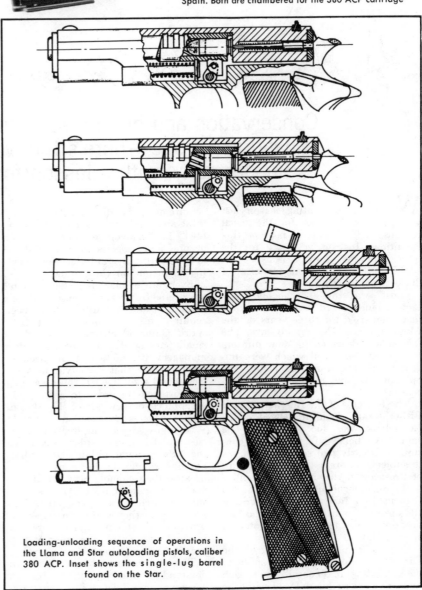

Loading-unloading sequence of operations in the Llama and Star autoloading pistols, caliber 380 ACP. Inset shows the single-lug barrel found on the Star.

A NEW LESSON FROM THE OLD WORLD

by Lt. Col. JACK RANDOLPH

Conservation and hunter education go hand in hand in Europe—here's the way it's done in Germany, with a lesson for us all.

WE LOST a hunting season last year. It was lost not for the usual reasons, lack of game or poor nesting conditions. Instead we lost it for the most ludicrous of all reasons — we couldn't distinguish one species of ducks from another!

"Lost" was the experimental September blue-winged teal season, which had been tried for three years on the Mississippi and Central Flyways. The season was designed to allow hunters to harvest those teal which were migrating in fair numbers before the opening of the general waterfowl seasons.

The Director of the Bureau of Sport Fisheries and Wildlife, Dr. John S. Gottschalk, was too kind when he said, "We believe it unwise to continue this early teal season as long as it subjects hunters to the possibility of prosecution through their inability to identify legal species." He added that in 1967 forty-seven per cent of the observed hunting parties who had an opportunity to fire upon protected species did so.

One can't help but wonder if the Director's rationale wouldn't apply to duck hunting in general? Isn't each hunter in every blind faced with the requirement to distinguish between legal and protected species of waterfowl? Is the average hunter capable of practicing species management, or is he shooting them all down and sorting them out on the ground?

Ever since biologists have found more effective ways of managing our wildlife resources hunters have been required to learn more about their sport. Game identification is only a small part of it. Some of the better management practices have been so revolutionary that conservation agencies found they needed the assistance of sportsmen in order to gain public acceptance of new ideas. The killing of doe deer is an excellent example.

In many cases conservation agencies found hunters harder to convince than the general public. Doe killing remains repugnant to many hunters because they cannot recognize it as a necessary management tool. As a result of such experiences authorities are learning that wildlife management programs must have the understanding and support of sportsmen if they are to be successful.

The obvious way to gain this understanding and support is through conservation e d u c a t i o n programs.

Through the use of magazines and special booklets published by the various agencies, by means of movies and expert speakers, the message is carried to various groups. Generally these programs are reasonably successful as far as they go. Unfortunately many, if not most, sportsmen do not belong to the clubs or groups reached by conservation education programs. Some seldom buy an outdoor magazine or bother to go out of their way to learn on their own. Consequently the success of our programs is somewhat limited.

Hunter Training Needed

Many of us maintain that there is no substitute for experience. Many years ago, when we hunted as much for food as for sport, we spent a great deal of time afield and gained a great deal of experience. The modern hunter does not have this opportunity. Because of our jobs and the relatively short hunting seasons we can seldom spend much time in the woods. For example: a New Jersey deer hunter who hunted deer in the Garden State for 25 years has only about 22 weeks of actual experience, and that only if he had hunted every day of the six-day season!

We are slowly learning that we need a more aggressive approach to hunter training and conservation education. The National Rifle Association's Hunter Safety Program is a step in the right direction.

This program, which began in 1950, has reached 39 states and 6 Canadian provinces. One additional state and one Canadian province operate similar programs, but not in cooperation with the NRA. Although most of these programs were originally introduced on a voluntary basis, most of the states in the program now require Hunter Safety Training as a mandatory prerequisite for obtaining the first hunting license.

Emphasizing hunting safety, the basic NRA course is four hours long, including the examination. Included is instruction in basic marksmanship, range procedure, hunting laws, and safe practices when hunting. In the various states the subject matter is augmented with practical hunting subjects. In Maryland, for example, the course contains 6 blocks of instruction, the two additional subjects being game identification and principles of game management, which also includes instruction in courtesy and sportsmanship.

It appears that we are slowly recognizing the value of mandatory training before we are allowed to hunt. In not too many years it is likely that the basic NRA courses will be developed into a far more comprehensive conservation education program than was originally envisioned.

We are not the only nation in the world that faces this problem. Germany recognized the need for this type of training many years ago and introduced a mandatory hunting course as early as 1934. The Japanese recognized the value of hunter education and introduced mandatory schooling in 1964.

The Japanese course is somewhat different than our NRA training and a great deal less exacting than the German system. Only consisting of 5 hours of instruction, the Japanese course spends two hours on hunting laws, two more on game identification and only one hour on safety. A unique feature of the Japanese system is that licensed hunters must take a three-hour refresher course every three years.

West Germany's Hunter Education Program is perhaps the most comprehensive one of its kind in the world. In order to appreciate how well the training is adapted to the German environment, one must understand the system it serves.

The basic difference between our philosophy and the German's is that our game is managed and held in trust for us by the state while, in West Germany, almost all game is privately owned but must be managed under laws established by the state. In Ger-

The author with a bag of Japanese ducks.

many game, besides being a source of recreation, is a saleable commodity. A great deal of emphasis is placed upon the philosophy that all land must be managed for multiple use if at all possible, to produce a combined yield of crops, forests, wildlife and recreation.

The German System

In order to appreciate the effectiveness of the German wildlife management system take a look at the amount of big and small game produced in your home state during an average hunting season; now consider that Germany's area is about 96,000 square miles or approximately the size of Oregon. Also consider that Germany's population is about 400 persons per square mile when you note that, during the 1965-66 season, slightly more than 200,000 hunters accounted for over 500,000 head of big game! This bag included more than 600,000 roe, red and fallow deer; 23,000 wild boar; 1,000 chamois; 950 mouflon; more than a million rabbits and hare; 750,000 pheasants; 200,000 Hungarian partridges; 250,000 ducks; 250,000 doves; 100,000 foxes and considerable other game.

Over 90% of the available hunting land is managed for hunting.* These lands are organized into areas called "reviers." Each state has laws governing their size, the rule being that the revier must be sufficiently large to allow effective management of the

game population. Generally a tract of 200 acres, owned by one man, is the smallest area that can be managed as a revier. Holdings of less than 200 acres must be combined to form an area of at least 375 acres, which may be cooperatively managed or leased. Usually they are leased. A small game revier is leased for 9 years while big game areas are leased for 12 years.

The lessee has considerable responsibility to both the landowner and the state. He is responsible for all crop damage by game and all damage to property by hunters. State laws prevent him from exploiting the game or trying to carry too much game on the land. Usually the lessee must hire a qualified game manager to handle his revier.

To insure proper management of big game the state requires each revier owner to prepare an annual "Abschuss Plan" and submit it to county officials for approval. This consists of a census of all big game on the revier by sex, age and quality. The plan shows which animals will be harvested and which will be carried over to the next year. The carry-over depends upon the size of the revier and the winter feeding program. The plan must be strictly followed or the revier owner will be penalized. Sometimes, particularly late in the season, it's almost funny to see a revier owner scurrying about looking for someone to help him harvest a few barren does. Germans dislike doe shooting as much as we but they must adhere to their plan. They generally attempt to keep a one-to-one ratio between bucks and does.

Much importance is attached to the quality, rather than the quantity, of the game. In German game management heredity is considered of high importance in producing good trophies. Most American biologists believe that range conditions are the most important in the production of trophies. The German practice, however, is to harvest the poorer trophy animals before the breeding season, allowing the quality game to breed. Later, those quality animals that must be harvested under the plan are taken. A good quality buck is allowed to survive as many years as possible, and is taken usually in his last prime year.

After the better trophies are taken an effort is made to find and harvest barren does or any poor quality game that may have been missed earlier. Only wild boar, which move about too much to be counted, and small game, are exempt from management under the Abschuss Plan.

Most revier owners find that their's is an expensive hobby. Some of their investment is recouped through the sale of game. Most hunting is done by invitation and there is seldom a limit on the amount of game which may be bagged. It is common for several hundred hare and a hundred pheasants to fall during a one-day drive hunt. All of the game taken, however, belongs to the revier owner. If a hunter desires to take home game he buys it at the going market price. All game not bought by the hunters is sold through the game market.

Big game hunters usually pay a fee for the trophy. Some trophies are quite expensive. The best red deer or an auerhahn (capercailzie) are expensive in any currency. The trophy fee only entitles the hunter to the head, heart and liver of the animal. If he wants the carcass he buys it at market price.

Partially because of tradition and partially because of the market value of game, great emphasis is placed on a clean, one-shot kill. Wounded game that drops on a neighbor's revier belongs to the neighbor. This is sufficient incentive for careful shooting. Strict laws concerning rifles legal for various game also contribute to clean kills.

By law rifles are grouped into three categories: those suitable for roe deer; for chamois, and those for all other big game. For hunting the little, 45-lb. roe deer a rifle must be capable of delivering 723.3 foot/pounds of energy at 100 meters (109 yards). This law eliminates such rifles as the 22 Hornet and the 30-cal. U.S. Carbine from consideration.

Rifles to be used for long shots amid the alpine peaks for 70-lb. chamois must be capable of producing 1,446 fp of energy at 100 meters. Here such old reliables as the 30-30 and the 32 Special bite the dust.

The final group, rifles for all other cloven-hoof game, including red deer, fallow deer, mouflon and boar, must have a bore diameter of at least .256" (6.5mm) and fire bullets weighing not less than 154 grains *or* deliver a velocity at 100 meters of not less than 2,788.71 fps.

Compliance with the latter law is tricky. Many calibers that are otherwise legal may not be used with lighter bullets, such as 90 to 100 grains. Like Americans, however, there are lots of hot stove discussions among Germans as to the relative merits of various loads and the wisdom of the German law. In the United States such a law would be virtually unenforceable, but it can be handled in Germany because most hunters usually pursue only a certain single species on a hunt, and they're accompanied by a guide who checks 'em out for compliance with the law!

As unwieldy as the German law is, it beats some we have in many of our states. We have three big game states that set no minimum size on rifles that may be used to take big game, 7 that allow anything larger than 22, and 8 that simply specify centerfire ammo only. It would seem wise for these states to establish tougher limits to prevent indiscriminate wounding of game. Many of our states, however, do have realistic laws in this regard.

Because the average German hunter is required to know more game management than the average U.S. hunter, and because he is usually personally involved with the entire conservation program, the law requires that he undergoes an intensive period of training before he may purchase a license. This course lasts about a full year, the student attending once or twice a week.

During this year he studies animal biology, diseases of game, hunting techniques, weapons and ballistics, safety, dressing game, handling trophies, hunting dogs, game manage-

Wagon load of 101 hare taken on a community drive hunt in Bavaria.

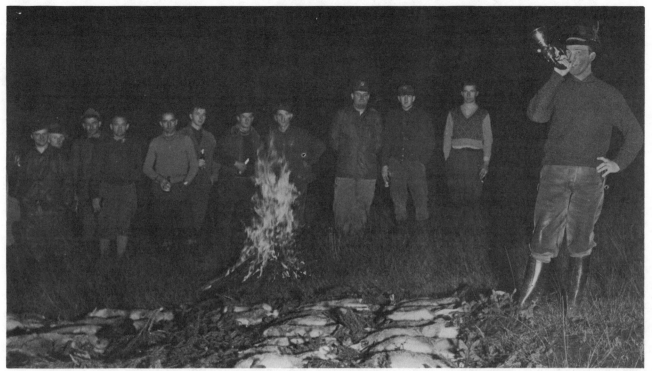

German hunter salutes game taken on a drive. A special call is played for each species.

ment, hunting laws and customs and traditions of the hunt.

Upon completion of his year's training the applicant must pass written and oral examinations. He must also qualify on the range with rifle and shotgun. The test is administered by an examination board consisting of 6 people, three of which are appointed by the county hunting authority. One must be a professional hunter, another a member of a hunting club, and the last a county official. Each of the appointed members selects another to sit on the board with him. In the hunting year ending in March, 1967, a total of 7,525 persons attended classes and took the examination, but only 5,340 passed.

After getting by his examination, the new applicant must purchase his hunting insurance. For a fee of a little more than $6.00 the hunter receives a policy covering him for $6,250 property damage and $62,250 personal damage.

With this certificate of completion of the hunting course and insurance policy in hand, the new hunter may now buy his hunting license at a cost of about $11.00. This entitles him to hunt only on his own revier, as a guest on another and, in some cases, on state lands.

Armed Forces Program

A modified training program has been established for American servicemen stationed in Germany. This is a relatively short, 20-hour course of instruction which has been developed on the assumption that most Americans have had previous hunting experience at home. The modified version

treats firearm safety, customs, laws and traditions, but dwells mainly upon familiarization with German game and hunting techniques. More than half of the course deals with teaching identification, habits and hunting methods for each game animal. It's a safe bet to state that the average American, upon completing this short course, has a greater depth of knowledge of German game than he does of his native species back home. The training not only enhances the student's enjoyment of German hunting, but it stimulates his desire to learn more about wildlife and conservation.

The German system, while apparently excellent for Germany, would not be practical in its entirety in the United States, but the concept of providing the hunter with a well-rounded conservation education within practical limits is an excellent one. There is much we can learn from the German system, but they can also learn from us.

Occasionally the German Hunter Safety record is held up as a model for comparison. Frankly, there is no basis for comparison between hunting safety in America and Germany. Unlike the United States, much of the German hunting is either controlled or, in the case of big game hunting, there are no other hunters in the area save one or two. The Germans don't "car hop" as many of us do, and most German hunters have much more actual hunting experience than their American counterparts. The German can hunt a full 12-month year, and enjoys extremely long seasons on several species. Their safety

record is good, but it could be better. During the 1966-67 season they experienced 105 accidents involving guns, 43 of which resulted in injuries.

While German hunters are extremely safety conscious, their traditional forest green hunting outfits are nice to look at, but really impractical from a safety viewpoint. Often, on a drive hunt, it is difficult to locate your fellow standers among the greens of the countryside. On bird hunts it is tricky to see your fellow hunters out of the corner of your eye. Undoubtedly if tradition were bent just a little and blaze orange caps substituted for the green, the German fall scene would become a little more colorful and their excellent safety record a little bit better.

As a result of our Hunter Safety Programs, American hunting is becoming safer. The day is not too far away when our safety programs will be expanded so that we, too, will be fielding knowledgeable hunters who know not only the laws, but the why of them as well. Perhaps some day, we'll even be able to tell one duck from another. ●

*Actually 9% of all hunting lands in Germany is state-owned. Much of the big game Armed Forces personnel are allocated is taken on state or federal lands, though such lands may be leased to private individuals. Generally Americans, by agreement, are entitled to a third of the male and a quarter of the female big game meant to be harvested. The trophy fee, entitling the hunter to the trophy and heart, liver, etc., is paid, under an agreement, by the military at no expense to the hunter, but if he desires the meat of big game or small game the hunter must buy it at the going market price.

On the same point, most commands employ a German citizen as a "Hunting & Fishing Clerk." He arranges hunts on both state and privately owned lands. The Germans have been generous hosts and a high proportion of our hunting has been as their guests.

Scopes & Mounts 1972-1973

by BOB BELL

A detailed and up-to-date review of the scopes, mounts and related products that are now being shown.

IT'S ALMOST 35 years since I got my first scope—a Weaver 29-S, which I still have, mounted on my first 22, a M72 Winchester—and sometimes, looking back that far, I feel a bit old. But there are few ways I'd rather spend my time than squinting into a good glass sight solidly latched to a top-grade hunting rifle, so I don't consider such time misspent. And who knows—maybe Allah, who allegedly does not deduct time spent fishing from a man's lifespan, will take similar pity on a feller whose right eye seems to have crosswires emblazoned on it. At any rate, here's the dope resulting from this year's efforts. . . .

Bausch & Lomb has no new scopes this year—it would be hard to find a slot they don't already cover, so this is no surprise—so we'll take a little space to comment on their Trophy mount. This aluminum alloy bridge mount came out with B&L's line of internally adjustable scopes a few years back, also called Trophy models. I've tested them on a number of rifles and have permanently installed them on a couple—my old favorite 7x61 S&H Magnum, here it carries a 2½-8x B&L, and on my wife's customized M722 Remington 257. I also often use one on my HB Sako 222. The bottom of the base on this one is machined to accept the integral male dovetails of the Sako, making for a very solid setup, as well as an attractive one. A pair of allen screws further bind the unit to the gun.

The Trophy rings also lock with allen screws, which I consider commendable; they can be turned up extremely tightly, and there's little likelihood of boogering up the hexagonal holes—something that can't be said about regular screwdriver slots. The rings, dovetailed on the bottom to fit the base, are locked

to it by transverse allen screws, which fit into recesses to prevent slippage under recoil.

The bases have extra slots, which permit fore and aft movement of the scope to help adjust for eye relief. The holes in the rings are slightly eccentric and by reversing them it is possible to get as much as 13 extra minutes of windage adjustment. This is a big help with old-style scopes that don't have constantly centered reticles, and can be useful even in the new ones, as it's always better to keep the reticle as near the optical center of the scope's lens system as possible. All in all, a sturdy and attractive mount.

Product manager Howard Palmer says that this year the Trophy mount has been made even more adaptable. The rings are now made to fit Weaver-type bases, which gives shooters a wider choice in solving their mounting questions. Surprisingly, a price reduction has been made here. Trophy rings to fit either the B&L base or Weaver type are now $9.95, down from $11.95.

Buehler, Inc., has fully engraved one-inch split rings for those shooters who want to dress up a fancy rifle with a fancy mount. Offered with deep engraving and in three heights —.075", .136" and .212"—these should harmonize well with a Sunday-go-to-meetin' rifle, while at the same time they provide the solid positioning of scopes for which Buehler mounts have long been noted. The three heights of course, permit mounting of any scope with an objective up to 2¼" in diameter. $34.50 per set.

Also new this year from Buehler are mounts for the round receiver

version of the M77 Ruger (its profile is the same as the Remington 700's); a two-piece base, Code BL-2, for Browning's BLR lever action rifle; and a two-piece base for the Mossberg M810 and M812 rifles, Code 81.

Other Buehler mounts, long made, fit most readily available rifles, of course, and over the years they have earned a reputation second to none for this Orinda, Cal., company.

Bushnell, now a division of Bausch & Lomb, Inc., has expanded its Scopechief V line from last year's single entry to three, including a pair of variables, the 1½-4x and 3-9x models. With the earlier 4x, these are unique in having the Lite-Site reticle. This was covered in last year's scope review, but for new readers we'll say that by means of a switch resembling an adjustment turret (on the adjustment housing in the 4x, on the ocular lens unit of the variables) an integral battery operated bulb projects a circular lighted dot on the intersection of the crosswires. This permits aiming under conditons of darkness when any other reticle we've used is useless. This dot, incidentally, subtends 5 MOA in the 4x, 13-5 in the small variable, and 6-2 in the big one, the larger sizes coming at the lower magnifications, of course. The conservative oldtimer who is still debating the relative merits of open sights *versus* scopes (and there still are a few such) will doubtless cringe at the very thought of this innovation, but the fact is, the Lite-Site works, and it can make the difference on a expensive hunt where your only chance might come before true dawn or in early evening darkness.

The two new variables are of conventional design otherwise, and should cover most hunting situations. The 1½-4x is listed at $84.50, the 3-9x at $98.50.

Another reticle now offered by Bushnell in the Scopechief IVs is the MX (Multi-X), which combines crosswires and 4 posts in the now familiar design available for some time from various makers. This is perhaps the best choice for all-round use, I feel, as it's conspicuous and yet makes precise aiming possible. Bushnell does not offer the Command Post (crosswires with flip-up post) with the MX.

All Bushnell scopes suitable for high-powered rifles except the Scopechief IV-DM (complete with detachable mount) have neoprene eyeguards on the ocular lenses now. These are intended to reduce the cutting effect if you are accidentally slapped in the eyebrow by a recoiling rifle scope. I can't say from personal experience how well they work as I've never had the nerve to try one out deliberately and I'm careful about eye relief before I shoot. But obviously they're far preferable to the metal scope tube.

Rimfire riflemen have two new options this year, a 4x Scope Chief ($17.95) and a 3-8x ($24.95). These are built on ⅞" aluminum alloy tubes with integral mounting rails. For heavy handgun fans, the Phantom scopes in either 1.3x or 2.5x have been beefed up to take the recoil dished out by the Magnums, so naturally they're called the "Magnum" Phantoms. Prices are four bucks over standard versions—$33.50 and $43.50.

Also new are a couple of mounts. One is an aluminum alloy, split-ring design for one-inch tubes. The socket screws that lock the rings to the Weaver-type bases make it quickly detachable, and it comes in two heights. Rings are $6.95 per set, 2-piece or one-piece bridge base $1.40. The second mount is a pivot design, similar to the above except that it can be flopped aside to use iron sights. Rings, $7.95 per set, 2-piece bases $1.60, one-piece bridge base $1.40.

Del Sports, Inc., imports the good Austrian-built Habicht (Hawk) hunting scopes in 4x and 6x. The 4x models, which have 32mm objectives, are made with steel or alloy tubes and with w. and e. adjustments or just elevation. The alloy tube models have mounting rails, while the others take 26mm rings. The 6x42 is available with steel tube only, either single or double adjustments. Prices range

The Browning Auto Rifle and four of their scopes.

Browning's two piece ring mounts and barrel mount base (left) and 1 inch split rings and scope mount base (right).

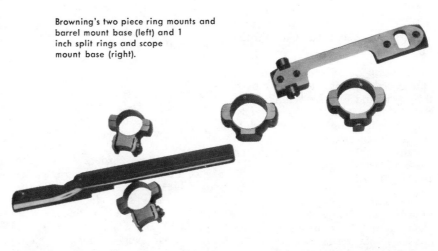

Davis Optical's target scope has precision click mounts, comes in 10, 12, 15, 20 ,25 and 30 powers.

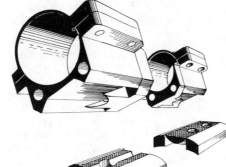

Firearms Service's Duo-Speed Mount absorbs recoil shock and permits instant demounting or remounting of the scope for iron sight use.

from $70 to $80, with an integral spirit level to eliminate canting at $5 extra. All models have rotating eyepieces for exact focusing, and there is a choice of four reticles—crosswires, crosswires with three or four posts, or three posts alone.

Of special interest to drilling (3-barrel guns) owners is the fact that Del Sports proprietor Franz Achleithner can supply and install claw mounts to attach these Habicht scopes to many of the German-made combination guns (as well as various Mausers and Mannlicher - Schoenauer rifles) from which the glass sights have disappeared. This quick-detachable design has long been popular in Europe.

Del Sports also markets a 30x75mm spotting scope at $125, including a tree screw, which eliminates the need for a tripod, at least up to timberline.

Mrs. Emma Achleithner, incidentally, is a fine gun engraver, with a European background and training.

Firearms Service, makers of the Duo-Speed mount, recently moved from Oakland to 2 Llewelling Blvd., San Lorenzo, CA. 94580, has redesigned their mount to accommodate the large objectives typical of some variables. They have also deepened the knurled top groove to simplify iron sight use.

Freeland's, Inc., has long been known for riflemen's accessories—shooting mats, benchrest stands, sun shades for target scopes, gun cases, custom fore-end stops, etc. Of particular interest are his fine spotting scope stands, available in a number of styles to satisfy the small-bore rifleman's needs. A few years back, noting the need for a model tailored to the International shooter, Al Freeland engineered and produced his International Shooting Stand. This unit has a 2-inch diameter upright shaft of anodized aluminum fitted with a head assembly that mounts a spotting scope and has a horizontal neoprene-covered bar on which the rifle can be rested between shots from the standing position. Three wide-spreading legs support the unit. Each has a short spike which can be forced into the earth outdoors, or the ends can be rotated to use suction cups on hard surfaces. In trying to locate bullet holes in the 300-meter target, the slightest movement of the spotting scope can drive you batty. This stand can go a long ways toward eliminating that problem—and the eyestrain

that accompanies it. The head can be used at any height, from standing to prone. Complete, it weighs about 16 lbs., sells for $100.

J. B. Holden Co. makes the "Ironsighter" scope mount, a slightly raised unit which permits use of the iron sights through oval openings beneath the tube. It's now made for many rifles and shotguns (steel receiver models). A friend, John Plowman, has been using one on his M721 Remington '06 with a Weaver variable scope and likes it well, expecially in the miserable weather that's typical of Pennsylvania's deer season. The Ironsighter is now made for grooved-receiver rimfire rifles also. Made for ¾", ⅞" or 1" tubes.

Hutson Corporation's 1x handgun scope and Chromatar 60 spotting scope, both notable for their small size, were announced in last year's GD. Now a slightly more powerful model—a 1.7x—scope is offered. This will doubtless be welcomed by handgunners who like to try their luck on the smaller varmints. $49.95 with mount.

Lyman Gun Sight Corp. announced the 20x LWBR (Light Weight Bench Rest) scope last year, and it has turned out to be one of the most wanted high-power models in the country. According to their manager of customer services, orders have been twice those anticipated, so supplies are a bit slow in some areas. By the time you read this, chances are this problem will have been fixed.

This LWBR weighs barely 15 oz. and is just over 17" long. A member of the All American family, it mounts solidly, normally putting all its weight on the action rather than partly on the barrel, which benchresters don't like. Its eye relief of 2½" makes it usable on rifles of the 308 class without much worry about recoil. Internal adjustments—¼- or ⅛-MOA—are available, and there's a choice of fine or extra fine crosswires, or a center dot as small as ¼-minute. Price is $109.95.

The internally adjustable 20x Lyman All-American has attracted a fine following among benchresters in the few years it has been available. It is short enough to mount on the action (at least for target work, where its overhang isn't the problem it might be on a hunting rifle), so can't affect barrel vibrations as a conventionally-mounted target scope might.

I put my sample on a 40XB-BR Remington 222 rifle and shot it quite a bit on the bench and a

little at chucks. This one has ⅛-minute clicks, the only scope I've ever used with this fine an adjustment. Quarter-minutes also are available and doubtless will handle most shooting requirements; still, it was interesting to experiment with these. They proved very accurate. In one test at 100 yards, moving 32 clicks, horizontally or vertically, should give a 4-inch adjustment. I consistently got 4¼ inches between group centers. This gives a value in this particular scope of a whisper over ⅛ MOA—like .0078 over, if my math is correct. One possible problem should be mentioned—eye relief. It's about 2 inches on this 20x Lyman and, on rifles that noticeably recoil, such as the 308 favored by many competitive shooters, this should be considered. In a solidly mounted model like this, the scope recoils right along with the rifle, rather than standing still while the rifle moves beneath them as the externally-adjusted target jobs do. If the gun is held loosely, as many benchresters advocate, the scope might bump your eyebrow or shooting glasses.

Optically, this 20x All-American is fine. I could easily spot 22-cal. holes in 200-yard targets.

Marlin Firearms Co. has dropped several scopes from its line and added one, the Marlin 425. This is a 4x with 32mm objective. It's built on a 1" tube, has ¼-minute adjustments and a new reticle called the 1-MR. This is the Marlin Tri-post arrangement combined with cross wires. List price is $29.95, but when bought in combination with various Marlin rifles and mount, special reduced prices prevail.

Mashburn Arms Co. reports it is no longer producing its scope mount or adjustable triggers. Both were fine items.

Normark Corp. offers the unusual Singlepoint Sight, which resembles a small scope (1-inch tube, 6¾" long, 7½ oz.) but does not magnify and which gets its name from the projected red dot which is its aiming point. The Singlepoint requires the shooter to keep both eyes open, for the "aiming" eye, which sees the dot, actually does not see the target. The other eye watches that—and thus the "field of view" is in a sense unlimited—the brain automatically combining the two to form a normal sight picture. With such a setup, eye relief is absolutely no problem either, and this unit can be mounted conventionally on a rifle action, ahead of a top-ejecting action, or on a handgun to be held at arm's length. It can be fitted to a shotgun also, and for such use a 42-minute dot is available. Normal size is 16 minutes, which means the Singlepoint is essentially a woods outfit on a rifle, but since it does not magnify, that is how it normally would be used anyway.

The Singlepoint is, in effect, an acrylic light-collecting system which gathers and transmits the red light rays. Rain and snow will not affect the unit so long as there is some kind of view at the ocular (rear) lens. In use, you look at the target with both eyes, bring the gun to the shoulder, which lets you see the dot with the aiming eye, put the dot on the target and squeeze. Internally adjustable for w. and e. $24.95.

PGS, Inc. (Peters Gun Shop) has for years been supplying rubber shields that slip over both ends of a scope to keep the lenses dry in bad weather. Most of these are made to fit specific models, but a newer design is more universal in that two sizes fit all scopes, including those with large objectives such as the bigger variables. These are split cylinders which are fastened on with black plastic tape instead of being a close friction fit.

These PGS scope shields do not actually cover the lenses, but rather act as tube extensions to keep rain and snow off the glass when the rifle is held more or less horizontally. Raised rings on the inner surfaces prevent droplets of water which enter from migrating to the lens; they act as tiny dikes which direct such moisture to the open slit at the bottom, where it drops free. $3.98 per pair.

Pacific Gunsight Co. also has discontinued its line of scopes.

Precise Imports Corp. offers an extensive line of scopes, straight powers and variables, for rimfires and centerfires. Latest model is a 1½-5x with 32mm objective for big game hunting. It has a field of 55 feet at bottom magnification, 20 feet at 5x. Internal adjustments are of ⅓-minute.

Realist, Inc. has dropped a couple of their Camputer Auto/Range scopes this year—the 4x and the small 1½-4½x variable—according to their latest literature. I imagine that those long-range riflemen who like this rangefinding system prefer the extra power of the 3-9x or the straight 6x, which are still offered.

Four of Redfield's variable-power scopes. From the top—6-18x, 4-12x, 1-4x and the 1¾-5x Wide Field. All are available with Accu-Range.

S&K's Insta-mount on a German M-43 rifle.

Swift Instrument's 2½-8x variable scope.

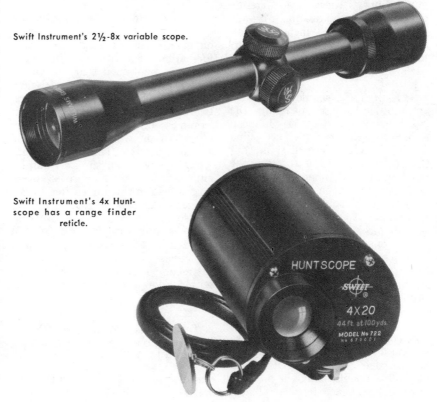

Swift Instrument's 4x Hunt-scope has a range finder reticle.

Both variables are still supplied (without the CA/R system), as are 2½, 4 and 6 power models for big game and a pair of scopes for rimfires.

Redfield Gun Sight Co., long recognized as a leader in scope and mount manufacture, and particularly well known for variables, has added another model to this group. The latest entry is a 1.75-5x, apparently intended to give big game hunters a choice between the long-popular 2-7x and the small 1-4x. This new model, built on a 1″ tube, of course, is 10-¾″ long and weighs 11½ oz. It has a slightly enlarged objective, tube diameter here being 1.24″. This gives a 4mm exit pupil at 5x, adequate in any hunting light. Field is 70 feet at bottom power, 27 at top, and eye relief is a strong 3″—enough for any high powered rifle if mounted correctly. This is a Widefield scope, featuring the larger than normal horizontal field. It has the usual glossy black Redfield finish and is available with most of their usual variety of reticles. Price is $95.95, $10 more with Accu-Range. This should be a popular item with the hunter who does most of his work in the woods but occasionally needs a bit of extra magnification for a shot across a valley or on an open hillside.

Also new from Redfield this year are See-Thru bases to accept the Frontier rings (thus permitting use of iron sights in emergencies), priced at $4.95, and Frontier shotgun mounts. These are currently made for the Remington 870 and 1100 models, the Winchester 1200 and 1400, Marlin 55, Breda autoloader, and High Standard 8216, 8117 and 8246. Price, $4.95.

S&K Mfg. Co. should soon have yet another Insta-mount ready—the latest being for the 1941 Johnson semi-auto military rifle, according to Sid Haight. No price yet, but the Insta-mount is quite often the most suitable rig made for getting a scope onto a somewhat uncommon military rifle, both from the viewpoint of quality, price, and convenience. We've had a chance to use one on an M1 Garand, and it works. We've also seen them used on other ex-military rifles, with complete satisfaction. These are milled steel units, incidentally, and they're nicely finished.

Savage Arms continues to increase its gun line, but has dropped a number of scopes. Currently, only a pair of rimfire models—a 4x and a 3-7x—and one 4x big game model are listed.

This centerfire model, of conventional design, sells for $29.95.

Selsi Co., an importer of a wide variety of optical goods, supplies several rimfire scopes and three big game models. Both the 4x and 2½-8x have 32mm objectives, while the 3-9x features a 40mm for good light transmission at the top power. Prices are $27, $44 and $49 for the centerfire models.

W. H. Siebert, who lives out in Issaquah, Wash., and spends considerable time shooting at little critters like ground squirrels, likes high power scopes but doesn't like long target models. So he converts conventional varmint models, usually the high Lyman powers in the All-American line or the Weaver Ks of 8, 10 or 12x, to considerably higher magnification ... 15x to 30x. The conversion increases scope length by less than an inch and maintains good eye relief. Prices are $25 or $30 depending on the particular scope and the magnification wanted. He can also install extra fine crosshairs or dot for $10.

Southern Precision Inst. Co. will have two new scopes in its lineup by the time this review is in print. We have no complete rundown on them, but according to Nat Halperin both will by 4x, built on 1-inch tubes, one having a 32mm objective, the other a 40mm. Both are wide angle designs, giving about 25% more field.

Tasco continues to expand its line of scopes, with now over two dozen big game models, 5 for 22s and a pair for target or bench shooting. Last year we mentioned that the Omni-View scope was in the works. It's now available in 5 models—two 4 powers, two 3-9x variables, and a 3-8x with 24mm objective. Each of the others is offered with a choice of 32mm or 40mm objective. The term "Omni-View" comes from the horizontally enlarged ocular, which gives an enlarged field in this dimension. Prices range from $49.95 to $99.95.

Also new here are a 4-12x40mm ($79.95) and straight 10x ($69.95) and 12x ($74.95) models with 40mm objectives—all with focussing adjustments for range. These large lenses give a lot of light for the power.

Tradewinds, Inc., has discontinued handling scopes and mounts, according to B. L. DeFazio.

Unertl Optical Co. introduced the BV-20 (Benchrest-Varmint 20x)

something over a year ago, and John Amber wrote it up in last year's Scope Review. This scope is unique, I believe, in that the unit which focuses for range is located just ahead of the ocular lens assembly—considerably more convenient when you're seated at a bench than the usual arrangement at the objective end. We won't go into detail here, as the BV-20 was covered fully in GD26, but we can say we've seen a number of these around and their users seemed well satisfied. Price of the Super Grade with Posa mount is $158—down a couple of bucks from last year—while the Standard Grade, which has standard target mounts and clamp ring, no recoil spring, is still $148.

The same reasoning which leads a conventional benchrester to get his target scope off the barrel is being followed by some 1000-yard riflemen. However, many of these fellows prefer lower magnifications than the guys who are trying to hit an aspirin ten times at 200 yards. They know they're not going to get eighth-minute groups—in fact, MOA groups are not everyday occurrences—so they don't need 20x-30x scopes. Oftentimes, mirage makes these big powers unusable when firing at a half-mile plus. So 10x or 12x scopes are getting considerable play, usually in the target models, of course, but of late some riflemen have gone to the so-called varmint models. One friend is trying the 10x Unertl Vulture in target mounts, which puts all the weight on the rifle action, has enough power to easily quarter the 12″ aiming bull, and has reliable external mounts. Adjustment values are greater than with normal spacing, but this is no particular problem in such shooting. I've a hunch there will be more movement in this direction soon.

Universal Firearms Corp. now has four rimfire models (a 4x and a 3-7x on ¾″ and ⅞″ tubes), 8 fixed-power scopes for high-powered rifles (all standard powers from 2½x to 10x), 4 variables of conventional power and design, and a 4x wide angle. Prices are on the low side, the most expensive one the 4x32 wide angle with Quadraplex reticle at $59.95.

E. D. Vissing's Supreme lens covers again proved their worth to me during the past hunting season. A sloppy snow combined with rain made conditons miserable all of opening day, but these covers kept my Weaver V4.5

usable. Viss says a price increase to $6.95 will be in effect shortly. They're still a good buy. I'd hate to be without 'em in the kind of country I hunt.

Weatherby, Inc., is best known for its potent high-velocity rifles, of course, but for many years a matching line of scopes—the Imperials—has been available in the common magnifications—2-¾x, 4x and 6x straight powers and 2-7x and 2-¾-10x variables. These are somewhat unusual in that both w. and e. adjustments are positioned under one cap on top of the tube, while immediately adjacent (under another weatherproof cap) is the eye-focusing dial. In operation this is somewhat more convenient than the common method of screwing the eyepiece in or out.

The adjusting setup is a bit unusual too. An outer ring controls elevation, with ¼-minute clicks, while an inner dial, movable with a coin, permits extremely small reticle movements. This is convenient when trying to bring an outfit into exact zero, for some scopes seem absolutely unwilling to settle precisely on aim, hopping back and forth across the desired point.

A second line of big game scopes is now offered by Weatherby—the Premier models. We mentioned two years ago that these were in the works; now you have a choice of a 2¾x or 4x at $59.50 and $69.50 (30 bucks less than the Imperials of those magnifications) and a 3-9x at $79.50.

These have conventional adjusting systems, that is, windage and elevation are in the usual separate turrets. Eye focussing, however, is a bit different—a knurled ring lies ahead of the eyepiece, and turning this focus ring to right or left of a zero mark focusses the scope. A lock ring then holds the adjustment.

The 3x-9x variable sample seems to be very well made, and I like the matt, non-reflecting finish. I like the neoprene eyepiece, too—having been, in my time, banged by a recoiling scope! All reticle types (5 are offered) are non-magnifying and constantly self-centered. W & E clicks are ¼-minute, easily read, and movable with the fingers. Fog proof and waterproof, of course, being gas filled, and that applies to the 3x-9x also.

The Premier 3x-9x tried out here has Weatherby's "Lumi-Plex" reticle, the type with heavier crosshairs reducing at their intersection to fine wires. In this reticle, though, in dark lighting the reticle glows or becomes illuminated. It's

Weatherby's Premier 3-9x variable power scope.

Williams' Sight-Thru mount, seen here on a Model 100 Winchester.

Williams' Dove-Tail Open Sight is easily, quickly installed without driving.

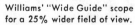

Williams' "Wide Guide" scope for a 25% wider field of view.

Vissing's Supreme lens cover.

a rather eerie but highly useful effect. No batteries are involved, and in broad daylight the reticle appears normally very dark or black.

This appears to be an excellent glass, and I'm looking forward to using it this fall. *JTA*

The Weatherby Mark XXII 4x rimfire scope, built on a ⅞" tube with integral mount for grooved receivers, is still offered. This is a high-grade glass with long eye relief (3 inches-plus), half-minute click adjustments, and enlarged ocular and objective lenses, which give unusually good relative brightness (50) for a rimfire scope, and a full 25-foot field. Price, $29.50.

W. R. Weaver Co. is resting a bit on its laurels this year, as well it might, with 5 handsome Classic models now on the list, 8 long-famous K models, 4 V (for variable) designs—all the foregoing built to take the recoil of any shoulder arm—plus three 22 scopes and the Qwik-Point aiming devices for rifles, shotguns, and—new this year—rimfire rifles.

This Qwik-Point gizmo seems to be a real sleeper, selling surprisingly well over most of the country. It mounts over the action like a scope and projects a red dot out yonder as an aiming point. Said dot can be zeroed in to coincide with the center of your shot pattern or with your rifle bullet. A hunting buddy, Wes Bower, has one on his 870 Remington 12 gauge and I've shot it at trap with good results. It's sort of weird to see that luminous dot floating ahead of the bird, but when you see it there and keep swinging, that bird busts.

I've hunted with Wes a number of times when he made some very long shots on cloverfield cottontails, and he claimed the Qwik-Site helped at such shooting. He is even more enthusiastic about it on passing geese and ducks—his favorite kind of shooting—and it does seem probable that this is where the Qwik-Site really shines. At any rate, Model R-22 is now offered for rimfires (at 6¾ inches and 7½ oz. it's slightly smaller than the other models), and it could be a whale of a lot of fun for some kinds of shooting. All models are $39.95 including mount.

We mentioned the Classic V900 last year, but hadn't had a chance to shoot it much at that writing. Since then this scope has been given a good workout on several rifles—a 222 for testing accuracy and consistency of adjustments and several high-powers to see if we

could shake anything loose. The only thing that noticeably got shook up was me—as I expected. Many years of shooting have proved to my satisfaction that Weavers are tough, and I think most hunters will agree that these Classics are handsome too.

So many reticles are available now from different scope manufacturers—some of them truly wondrous to behold—that I'd like to take a moment to mention an old but extremely practical one that Weaver has been supplying for a dog's age—the Range-finder. Almost any reticle can be used to estimate range, if its subtension in minutes of angle is known, along with the approximate size of the target. However, some designs are better at this than others, and quite often the simpler things prove more suitable than the complicated ones at this business.

The Range-finder is simply conventional crosswires with a second horizontal wire 6 MOA beneath the regular one. Elmer Keith proposed this idea many years ago and described how he had one installed in a Lyman Alaskan before WW II, if my memory is accurate. He could well have suggested the design to Weaver—or perhaps they came up with it on their own. The important thing is that it can be had and it serves very well. By comparing the known separation of the horizontal wires with an animal's size, you get a good idea of its distance. By spending a few afternoons on the range to learn your pet load's trajectory over normal hunting ranges, you can zero in to take best advantage of the two distinct aiming points this reticle supplies.

With many high velocity loads, zeroing about 3 inches above the top wire at 100 yards will mean you can use one or another aiming point, or an easily judged point between them, to 500 yards or so, and that's about as far as any of today's rifles can be expected to kill cleanly. The Range-finder is available in all Weaver big game scopes except the K1.5, K2.5 and K3, at no extra cost. I've used one in an old V7 for many years, and it works.

Williams Gun Sight Co. has got into the scope business in a big way, since it began offering the Guide-Line models in 1970. Besides that line, which includes a 4x, 1½-4½x, 2-6x and 3-9x, the Williamses—a real shooting family—now also have a

somewhat less expensive line called the Twilight scopes and a new Wide-Guide model.

The Guide-Lines start at $75 for the 4x, go to $105 for the small and intermediate variables, and $115 for the 3-9x, while the 2½x Twilight is $32.50, 4x is $36.50, 2-6x $54, and 3-9x $62 with crosswires. Five bucks extra for the T-n-T reticle (Thick 'n Thin).

All the Twilight scopes are built on inch tubes, only the 2½x having an unenlarged front end (20mm clear objective lens). This is big enough to give an 8mm exit pupil, which is larger than the human eye can fully use insofar as light transmission goes, but it does make quick aiming easy. Smallest exit pupil in these scopes is 4.2mm in the big variable at the 9x setting—still plenty for any hunting use. All have half-minute internal adjustments.

The 4x Wide-Guide is an interesting scope. It has a field which measures 35 feet horizontally, 27 feet vertically—which is becoming sort of routine since Redfield introduced the wide-angle characteristic a few years back—but this Williams glass has a traditionally round ocular lens, instead of the oval typical of various others.

The Wide-Guide is built on an inch tube, enlarged to 1.61" at the front end and 1.75" at the ocular. Just over a foot long, it weighs 14 oz., a bit more than some other 4x scopes, but that apparently is part of the price paid for the wide-angle design. Exit pupil is a big 8mm, for a relative brightness of 64, and eye relief is 3¼", which makes it usable on Magnum calibers when properly mounted—a job that various Williams mounts can handle, of course. Adjustments are internal, of half-minute value. Choice of CH, T-n-T or Guide reticle (a diamond-shaped aiming point atop a slim tapered post). Price, $75.

Zeiss is without a doubt one of the truly legendary names in the field of hunting scopes. However, at this time they are being imported only on special order. Their prices in this country—obviously high when compared to American- or Japanese-built models—will keep them out of most hunters' hands, but anyone who wants a top-grade item and is willing to spend the money can get full value from Zeiss. Three models currently listed are the Diatal DA, 4x32, in a lightweight mount with w. and e. adjustments, without mounting rail, $199; the Diatal DA 6x42, $219, and the Diavari DA, 1½-6x, $299.

GREAT GUNS!

Winchester's Model 9422s.

Speak of Winchester and the average listener thinks of lever action rifles, more particularly the Model 94 nowdays. Combine that worldwide recognition with 22 rimfire cartridges and you've got the new 9422—in both regular and magnum chambering. Handsomely styled, well made in the old fashioned way, flawlessly functioning and accurate, the new Winchesters are, indeed, great guns.

by JON R. SUNDRA

CERTAINLY NO NAME is more synonymous with lever action rifles than Winchester. Equally certain is the fact that the Model 94, now in its 78th year of production, is among the best loved rifles ever made. Team these two factors with the world's most popular cartridge, the 22 rimfire, and you should have all the requisites of a great gun.

It was precisely this kind of-reasoning, me thinks that prompted Winchester to introduce its new Models 9422 and 9422 Magnum (WMR). Previewed at the recent NSGA Show, these new lever-actions caused quite a stir—and well they should have. These new rifles are impressive by any standards—

especially when one considers that "It's a Winchester" has carried the weight it once did.

Spit and Image

As the name implies, the 9422 is patterned after the perennial 94, and a striking facsimile it is, too. Except for its slightly thinner grip, physical size, weight and silhouette of the two guns are almost identical. Tipping the scale at 6½ pounds, this 22 is a man-sized carbine in every respect.

The pleasant heft and feel of the rifle no doubt result from its "old-fashioned" construction. If my test rifle, one of standard 22 caliber, had any non-ferrous alloys or plas-

tic parts on it, I certainly couldn't find 'em. The 9422 is a genuine, all-walnut/steel rifle; a rare breed these days!

Looking at the gun's exterior, the wood-to-metal fit of buttstock and fore-end is quite good. At the fore-end, for example, instead of the usual practice of putting a U-shaped notch in the bottom of the barrel channel to accommodate the tubular magazine, a separate hole is used—even though there's less than 1/16″ between barrel and magazine tube. The fit of the buttstock to the tang is equally good; however, because the wood stands a little above the metal all the way around, there's an initial impression of ill fit.

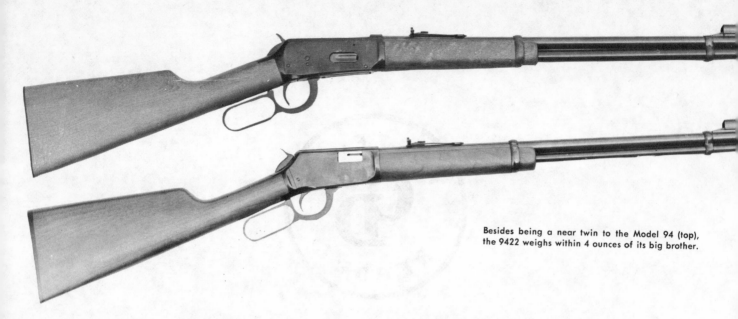

Besides being a near twin to the Model 94 (top), the 9422 weighs within 4 ounces of its big brother.

On closer inspection though, the uniformity of overlap and the glove-like fit throughout are evidence to the contrary.

Mechanism Details

Unlike its big brother, the 9422 has side rather than top ejection, and a solid-top receiver. The bolt is a two-piece affair, and lock-up is achieved by using a single lug, which engages a recessed shoulder milled into the inside top of the receiver. This ingenious old Browning design is still used in many areas; Model 12 Winchesters and Ithaca 37 scatterguns, to name a couple, though both are slide-operated rather than lever-actuated. Nevertheless, the lock-up principle is the same. As the bolt all but completes its forward travel it is cammed upward, allowing the locking lug to engage the recessed shoulder. The pivotal point for this vertical movement is provided by two lips at the front of the bolt, these resting on a sill at the front of the receiver, just beneath the barrel.

Bolt movement on the 9422 is through direct action of the lever, with no linkage or cams for mechanical advantage. Lever throw on the test carbine is 64°. The trigger engages the hammer directly, which has a half-cock or safety position.

In addition to relying on magazine tube spring pressure to feed cartridges onto the carrier, this gun also *pulls* cartridges from the magazine. When the action is fully open, the rim of the cartridge sits within a vertical raceway machined into the front of the flat bolt face. As the lever is closed, a cam-actuated finger pushes the cartridge (sliding it upward within the raceway) up to chamber level, where it is then pushed home by the closing bolt. It's not a new design by any means but it is ingenious—and positive. During the test-firing of 150 rounds the feeding, extraction and ejection were smooth and faultless.

Speaking of ejection, rather than having a slender, finger-like spring fixed inside of the receiver wall as do some designs, the 9422 uses an

Lock-up is provided by single, massive lug which fits into recess at top of receiver.

Take-down of Model 9422 requires only a few seconds. Because Barrel and receiver remain mated, scope settings are unaffected.

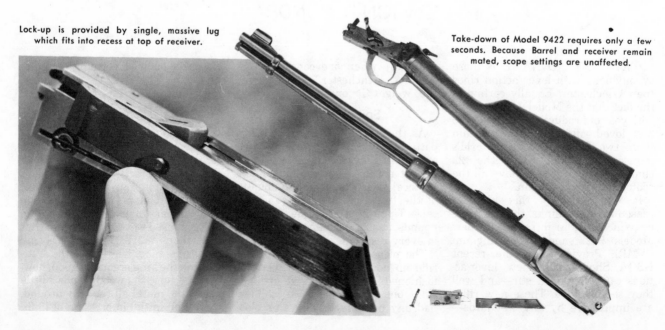

Left—9422 fore-end has that extra touch—a separate hole is made for the magazine tube instead of cutting a notch in the bottom of the barrel channel.

Above—Semi-buckhorn rear sight provided on 9422 is better than average.

Left—Wood-to-metal fit on 9422 was very good. Take-down screw (arrow) to gun's 4 main component parts takes only the twist of a coin and a few seconds.

Left—Protruding lips on bolt face provide pivot for vertical lock-up movement. Note vertical raceway for feeding cartridges up from magazine level.

ejector rod that slides within a groove on the bolt itself. It's a system which should prove to be positive as well as durable. Even a deliberately sluggish working of the lever easily tossed empties clear of the port.

Magazine capacity of the 9422 is 21 Shorts, 17 Longs or 15 Long Rifle; the 9422M holds 11 of Winchester's 22 Magnum Rimfire cartridges.

Acceptable Accuracy

Getting back to the outside of the gun, sitting atop the 20″ barrel is a hooded ramp front sight with bead and a semi-buckhorn rear. As iron sights go, they are quite good and a refreshing change from the stamped, sheet metal variety. Groups fired from bench rest at 50 yards average around 1½″. Most shooting, however, was done with the excellent little 4x Bushnell Scopechief XXII clamped onto the receiver, which is grooved for standard tip-off mounts. Using it, 5-shot groups shrank to an average 1⅛″ with Remington and CCI hollow points. Another ⅛″ was cut from that with Eley Tenex match ammo, run through for comparison. I felt no need to use shorts or longs in a hunting rifle such as this, but I'm sure they'll at least function as well as the long rifles.

Although not advertised as being take-down rifles, the 9422 and 9422M are certainly that. A coin to turn the single assembly screw and all of 30 seconds are required to dismantle the rifle into its four major components, for easy carrying or thorough cleaning. Because the barrel and receiver remain mated, scope settings are unaffected by disassembly.

All in all, these new Winchesters should capture the fancy of lever lovers everywhere. As critical as I tried to be I could find nothing to criticize! Basic design and execution of the Model 9422 are truly superb, and they're well worth the retail price of $100. All I suggest is that Winchester furnish a hammer extension, as does Marlin on its Model 39, so the hammer can be thumb-operated with a scope mounted. ●

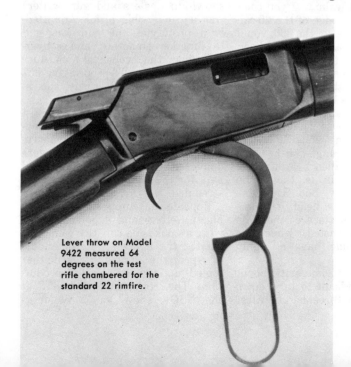

Lever throw on Model 9422 measured 64 degrees on the test rifle chambered for the standard 22 rimfire.

The turn of a coin disassembles the M9422.

HANDGUNS

U.S. & FOREIGN 1972-73

BY BOB STEINDLER
GEORGE C. NONTE
AND THE EDITORS

THE LAST several months have seen the introduction, or at least the announcement of impending introductions, of a number of "new" semiautomatic pistols. Some of these guns have actually reached the production stage, and can be found on dealers' shelves. Others have been on the drawing board or in prototype for so long that it seems doubtful that they'll ever reach production status. Usually, sixguns and semiautomatics run just about even when it comes to new ones—or should we say old ones in a new get-up?—but this year the self-loading pistols overshadow the new revolvers.

The designing of a new pistol, and then converting the drawings into a gun that actually functions, is not difficult, since most of the worthwhile pistol designs of today are merely copies of well-proved designs of yesteryear. If a designer has really been kissed by genius, you may find that older designs have been modified, actually making them better for today's production methods and shooter demands. For instance, stainless steel pistols present some peculiar manufacturing problems. Licking those is tantamount to designing a selfloading pistol from scratch as far as complexities and new gray hairs on the designer's head go.

Threatened anti-handgun legislation had not materialized as this lead was being written, but the airwaves are filled with reports about the attempted assassination of Governor George Wallace in Maryland. Even before the first medical bulletins were issued, Sen. Birch Bayh of Indiana had called for stringent handgun regulations and laws. King Richard of Daleyville on the Lake—Chicago, for those not initiated in midwestern English—went on the air with his own brand of anti-gun hogwash. Boss Daley wants the U.S. to shut down all domestic handgun makers and stop the import of all handguns. Only the cops and the military would have handguns if Daley had his way—or that's the way it's supposed to work.

Just the week before the Wallace shooting, the Illinois solons defeated a move to legislate against handgun ownership on the state level, thus dealing the powerful anti-gun clique from Chicago its second defeat in as many years. However, the Wallace shooting might well rekindle this, as well as other anti-gun legislative attempts on the state and national level.

Here then, in alphabetical order by manufacturer or importer, are the new semiautomatics.

American Firearms

The Mark X 25 ACP stainless

A Survey of Semi-Automatic Pistols

steel pistol now has a big sister, or is it brother? The Safeguard 380 is mechanically identical to the 25. A magazine safety prevents the gun from being fired when the magazine is removed and, with the safety in the "on" position, a stainless steel block interposes to prevent the firing pin from falling. The gun is permanently lubed with molybdenum disulfide, and yes, there is the now practically mandatory loaded-chamber indicator. Over-all length of the pistol is 5½", barrel length is 3½", and the gun weighs in at a hefty 21 oz. The stock panels are plain walnut. If you compare the forward edge of the 25-cal. magazine with that of the 380, you'll notice that the base plate has been changed—gone is the forward sweep that caused problems in the speedy unlimbering of the smaller pistol from pocket or holster.

As of the moment, it is uncertain if the 380 will also be offered in a blue finish. The 25 ACP is so-made, both in a high-polish finish and in what is called a Military & Police finish. This is the name given the gun by Bob Saunders, American Firearms' head. It means that the upper surface of the slide has been sandblasted, while the sides of the slide have a highly polished blue.

There has been some static about the 25 being difficult to take down unless you had three hands. After

reading a couple of these statements, I took the gun to a neighbor who doesn't know the difference between a revolver and a pistol. After telling him what I wanted, and without help from me, he stripped the gun easily and speedily, with two hands and without losing a single part.

Bob Steindler

Auto Mag Sold?

The company has been advertising the 44 Auto Mag for nearly two years. At the NSGA show in Chicago in Feburary '72, the gun shown to dealers and gun writers was a convertible pistol. Admittedly a prototype, the gun was said to function smoothly, and conversion from the proprietary 44 Auto Mag to the equally proprietary 357 Auto Mag was made easily, speedily and without tools.

Unfortunately, test guns for most writers never did make their appearance, although it has been rumored that over 100 guns were delivered to customers who had paid for their guns in full and then screamed the loudest.

Repeated attempts since then, by phone, letters and a personal visit with a spokesman of the company, elicited the following. As of middle of April, the company was neither tooled up, nor set up for production. The convertible 44-to-357 at the NSGA show was a non-func-

Prototype of American Firearms stainless steel Safeguard 380. Note lack of markings.

Auto Mag's new Hardballer is more compact and trimmer than its big brother; note arched back strap that is checkered. Barrel assembly is easily removed. The ejector, not spring-loaded as in the Model 180, is actuated by the bolt stop.

tioning prototype. The test gun that was to be furnished to Editor Amber or me, another prototype owned by a company VP, was not capable of firing the 357 Auto Mag ammo. In other words, there doesn't appear to be a gun available that can be studied, and a comparison of some of the published reports and the company's literature read suspiciously alike.

Bob Steindler

News From Auto Mag

Something new from Auto Mag may sound odd when they can't deliver the big 44, but production is moving on the latter and deliveries are being made, slow as they are. Despite these delays Harry Sanford, Auto Mag's president and designer, found time to develop new versions.

First is the Auto Mag 357 extra barrel assembly at $150. (The new 357 case is merely a necked-down 44 Auto Mag). The standard Model 180 44 Auto Mag pistol is easily converted to the new round simply by replacing the 44 barrel with the new one—all other parts stay the same, even the magazine. No final factory loadings have been set as of yet.

Second is a totally new version of the Auto Mag pistol, this one called the 45 Hardballer. This new pistol, of course, is designed to take advantage of the shock-absorbing

qualities of the Auto Mag action. The 45 Hardballer is a scaled-down version of the big gun and only two experimental models exist at this time. Production, though, is underway, supposedly.

The grip is similar to the Model 52 S&W target pistol. The prototype pictured here is made of stainless steel but production pieces will use standard steels with wood grip-panels. Recoil in the 45 HB is light, rather similar to that of the 38 Special waductter round, hence the double-stage recoil common in the 1911 with 45 ACP ammo is absent. No whipping to the side, taking you completely out of the black and making recovery difficult. The relatively gentle push barely takes you out of the black. Accuracy is comparable to or better than most accurized 45 autos, but further modifications will be required to make the pistol comply with the national match rules and regulations. One of these is sight radius, which can only be 7 inches maximum. Otherwise the 45 HP complies with the rules, and it also conforms to NRA regulations, it's said.

This 45 HB by Auto Mag should find favor with the competitive pistol crowd at the modest $225 price, compared with twice that much for some custom pieces.

Third, 44 Auto Mag commercial ammo is now ready—or so we're

told. Made by *Cartuchos Deportives de Mexico* at Morelos, the new round carries a 240-gr. bullet of Auto Mag's own design. Muzzle velocity out of the 6½" barrel is 1375 feet per second. Also planned is a 225-gr. 44 cartridge and the 357 AMP stuff later this year. The new ammo is packaged in a bright red, white and black box, with the Auto Mag logo prominent in the design. The head stamp is *AUTO MAG—CDM—.44.* Virgin brass cases are also to be offered, these with the new head stamp, but prices are not yet settled.

Another new idea from Auto Mag, among several, is their multi-barrel setup. The basic Auto Mag, 44 or 357, may be had with the standard 6½" barrel or 8½" and 12" versions in either caliber. All of these barrels, length regardless, weigh the same, for uniform weight is critical to the functioning of the Auto Mag.

To sum up, the Auto Mag is now available (?) in 44 AMP, 357 AMP and 45 ACP, plus several wildcat calibers, all of these simply necked-down variants of the basic 44 Auto Mag brass. Among those tested were the 41 AMP, 8mm AMP, 30 AMP, 25 AMP and 6mm AMP. Most of these are still in the experimental stage, but some are already being used by the serious wildcatter, for it takes only a barrel change to convert any Auto Mag model, except the 45 Hardballer, to these calibers. *W. L. Rickell*

Bauer Firearms

This appears to be the year for pocket pistols of various kinds. Bauer Firearms (a new name) engineers have been working on their 25 ACP stainless steel gun for well over a year—I saw a prototype in the spring of '71—and guns are now being shipped.

Basically a copy of the Browning blowback design as manufactured by FN in 1906, the new pistol carries the unimaginative label "Bauer 25 Automatic."

The gun is made entirely in the U.S. Parts are precision machined and then fitted carefully. Nearly everything inside the gun is made from stainless steel, and the high quality of the gun became obvious during my test firing. One of the hardest tests a semiauto can be put to is the feeding, and then the hoped for firing, of mixed lots of ammo from the magazine. Some European 25 ACP ammo, especially German and Austrian stuff, appears to be somewhat hotter. At least 5 other pocket pistols I used to compare the Bauer's functioning and accuracy jammed solidly or exhibited severe primer cratering or even primer piercing. The Bauer gun digested every last round without a complaint.

The gun has a magazine safety and another that locks the sear and prevents the slide from moving to the rear. At the rear of the frame is the loaded-chamber indicator pin which can be seen as well as felt. Empty, the gun weighs barely 10 oz. Its distinguishing feature is the rudimentary rear sight. While certainly not in the target class, the eared V-notch does help in deliberate aiming and shooting. The gun can be had with plastic stocks that resemble mother of pearl, or walnut, and you can even have the gun finished in a good deep blue. In either finish and with a pistol rug, the $69.95 you spend for that Bauer pocket pistol buys you a darned fine gun in a caliber that is once again in vogue. If the 25 ACP doesn't appeal to you, wait a few months—the 380 should be out by next spring. *Bob Steindler*

Beretta Model 20

This recently introduced Beretta auto pistol is probably the one 25 ACP auto pistol which gives the most firepower for its weight and size.

Ordinarily I'm not too enthusiastic about 25 ACP pistols, but this one offers unusual attractions for

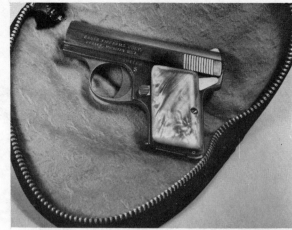

Bauer Firearms' 25 ACP stainless steel pistol, resting on the "rug" it comes with.

The Beretta Model 952 Special.

The Beretta Model 20.

Beretta Model 20
Specification

Caliber	:	25 ACP (6.35mm)
Total Length	:	4.7″ (119mm)
Height	:	3.34″ (85mm)
Thickness	:	1.06″ (27mm)
Barrel Length	:	2.36″ (60mm)
Empty Weight	:	11 oz. (310g.)
Magazine Capacity	:	8 shots
Double Action Pull	:	6.6 lbs.*
Single Action Pull	:	2 lbs.*

Tip-up barrel; Thumb safety.

*Test Specimens

its class; an extremely smooth double-action pull (6.6 lbs.) combined with a quite remarkably light single-action let-off of only 2 lbs.

The tip-up barrel and recoil spring mounting are reminiscent of the old Le Francais design.

This gun fits the hand surprisingly well, for its size; the slide and barrel have no play, and accuracy is outstanding at 25 meters.

Using the M20 slow fire at 25 meters, 4-inch groups were easily achieved, the shooting offhand; that's pretty incredible for such a tiny pistol.

The receiver is made of "Ergal"

light alloy, and the magazine capacity is 8 shots. Unfortunately, sale of this small wonder is reserved for the international market because of the GCA-68 regulation. A pity. *Raymond Caranta*

Beretta Model 952 Special

In addition to its tiny Model 20 vest-pocket auto pistol, Beretta now offers to centerfire target shooters its new 952 Special, a target version of their famous Brigadier pistol, in military service for years with the Italian, Egyptian and Israeli armies.

While the service Beretta is or-

Beretta Model 952 Special
Specification

Caliber	:	30 Luger (7.65mm Parabellum)
Total Length	:	9.8″ (248mm)
Barrel Length	:	5.9″ (150mm)
Empty Weight	:	34 oz. (960g.)
Magazine Cap.	:	8 shots
Trigger Pull	:	6.6 lbs. (on test specimen)

Steel receiver; target grip; rear sight, adj. for windage and elevation.

Hold-open device; external hammer; push-button thumb safety.

Left side of the MKE 380 lacks the panel seen on the 32 (inset). Note that *Made in Turkey* appears on test guns used by Steindler, also the name of the importer.

Browning's revised 9mm auto pistol is available with two different sight systems and a modified hammer spur. Upper pistol has fixed sights, the lower gun has fully adjustable rear sight and 1/10″ wide blade front.

dinarily chambered for the 9mm Luger (Parabellum) cartridge, the 952 Special—which is intended for paper punching—fires 30 Luger ammunition. That round shows excellent accuracy (about the same as the 38 Special), very mild recoil and great reliability. Furthermore, Fiocchi in Italy is manufacturing special low power target ammunition.

The wrap-around walnut grip has a well-located thumb rest and the rear sight is adjustable for windage and elevation.

I've found only one weakness in this Italian target pistol—that's the 6.6 lb. trigger pull, which will need some handwork to place it on a par with the best centerfire automatics. Nevertheless, the new Beretta is highly accurate, well made and pleasant to shoot.   *R. Caranta*

Browning's 9mm Autoloading Pistol Revised

Target sights and a new hammer spur—for easier cocking—were announced by Browning Arms early in January of 1972. As our picture shows, the pistol at bottom has the new fully adjustable click-type rear sight plus a new ¹⁄₁₀-inch ramp front sight, serrated to reduce light reflections, and the new hammer. The standard Browning 9mm pistol, still to be available, also carries the new rounded hammer but has the regular fixed sights, as before.

Eventually the new slides, with target front sight, will be stocked, as will the separate target rear sights. Thus an old Browning 9mm pistol could be converted. The new hammer will also be stocked.

With fixed sights, the suggested retail price is $137.50; the target-sighted model, $151.50, and both are furnished with red-lined rugs—zippered carrying cases—at no additional cost.   JTA.

Clerke Firearms

This appears to be another ill-fated venture for Bo Clerke. The California-based company has once again been sold, and plans for actual manufacture appear more uncertain than ever. Two company spokesmen refused to submit test guns—though the 22 LR and the 32 S&W revolver have been in the stores for some time—and the target automatic, slated to be chambered for 22 LR and 380, is still on the drawing board. The same

situation prevails with the single-shot rifles and shotguns displayed at the NSGA show. *Bob Steindler*

Firearms Center

This Texas-based importer handles a number of really fine European rifles, plus two semiautomatic pistols named the MKE Defender. If that MKE doesn't ring a bell, try Kirrikkale. That, of course, is the Turkish government arms plant, and the pistols are fairly exact copies of the Walther PP. In 380 chambering it's also the side-arm of the Turkish army. The 32 ACP - 7.65mm version is nothing more than a scaled-down 380.

Takedown and functioning are identical with the German original and when placed side by side it's hard to tell them apart, aside from the markings. Unlike the Walther originals, both guns studied showed some internal tool marks. In functioning and accuracy tests, however, the MKE pistols held their own, shot for shot, against other European double-action pistols I tested.

The price of $87.50 is a definite plus factor for these Turkish pistols. In firing both of them—using 200 rounds of sundry ammo in each—I must report that there was not a single failure to feed, extract or eject. This speaks well for the original design and for the shooting quality of these selfloading pistols.

Bob Steindler

Garcia

The Gun Control Act (GCA) of '68 has not only affected the importation of guns in general, it's been especially hard on semiautomatic pistols. Enforcement of the point system now gives all of them a sameness that's disconcerting and disheartening.

The Astra Constable, offered in 22 LR, 32- and 380 ACP, is a tidy double-action package. A small frame gun, the empty pistol weighs 26 oz. in any of the three calibers. The grips are plastic, with a thumb rest on the left panel. The gun has no loaded-chamber indicator pin, which I really don't miss. When I carry a gun, I know damned well whether it's loaded and, if someone points a pistol at me I'll have other things on my mind rather than looking over the guy's shoulder to see if an indicator pin sticks out.

The Astra I tested was a 380, and my only complaint—a minor one—was that the slide stop release was a bit difficult to manipulate. It requires a heavy, forceful push to move the lever downward

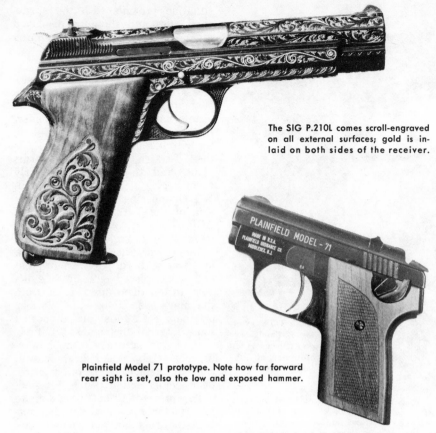

The SIG P.210L comes scroll-engraved on all external surfaces; gold is inlaid on both sides of the receiver.

Plainfield Model 71 prototype. Note how far forward rear sight is set, also the low and exposed hammer.

so the slide can go into battery. This all-steel pistol just under $90, is definitely a quality gun.

Bob Steindler

Plainfield Machine

Long and best known as makers of M1 carbines in 30 and 5.7mm calibers, plus stocks and sundry accessories for these shoulder guns, the company showed a tidy new pistol at the NSGA show. Gary Wilhelm, designer of the High Standard lineup of semiautomatic pistols, is the guiding light behind the new group of pistols that will be shortly making their appearance under the Plainfield Ordnance Co. label.

There will be at first 4 guns, all in straight blowback design. A small frame, in 22 RF and 25 ACP, will be known as the Model 71. Slightly larger frame guns will appear later, these in 32- and 380 ACP, with a military-sized 9mm Parabellum chambering due to appear in about 6 months.

Frame and slide will be of stainless steel, using carefully controlled investment castings. The guns will incorporate the Wilhelm lock piece and spring principle, and there's to be full interchangeability of all parts among the different calibers of the same model. Guns will have a wide target-type trigger, a Teflon

coated firing train for smooth functioning, and a somewhat constricted bore that increases MV and striking power. Because of the close tolerances to which parts are held, the gun will, in effect, be accurized at the factory. The smaller calibers will sell for about $70, the 32 and 380 will be $10 more. The price of the 9mm Parabellum has not yet been determined.

The prototype gun I examined was very well finished, inside and out. The checkered stocks and the weight of the gun—25 oz. empty—give this small pistol that nice balance that so many of its counterparts don't have. The prototype had an exposed and somewhat angular hammer and a rear sight that, though not adjustable, gave a good sight picture. The 25 ACP will hold 9 rounds in the magazine, the rimfire magazine 10. The first two chamberings will have a 2½" barrel, over-all length will be 4⅞", height 4" and width at grips 1".

Bob Steindler

Nonte Comments

Our samples felt boxy and bulky. Though the exposed hammer spur is partially shrouded, it isn't well-designed for pocket or other concealed carrying. The manual safety at the frame left rear offers little thumb purchase and it isn't very convenient in operation.   *G.C.N.*

New SIG Custom Grade Automatic Pistol

SIG (Switzerland) will produce a small batch of fancy automatic pistols. Called the P.210L (for "de luxe") these are scroll-engraved on all external surfaces and gold inlaid on both sides of the receiver. The wrap-around stockplates, made of selected walnut, are also scroll engraved. The slides carry the Swiss cross, in an escutcheon, in front of the rear sight. The workmanship is beautiful indeed, the gun itself a masterpiece of modern precision engineering.

SIG P.210 pistols (chambered for the 7.65mm and 9mm Luger rounds), while of the simplest design, are among the most expensive in the world since they are exceptionally well made and of the finest possible materials. Barrels for 22LR caliber are also available.

Their excellent accuracy results from a particularly efficient barrel mounting, and a very snug slide fitting, a la Luger. The lock mechanism is removable by hand, as a unit, for cleaning or for checking sear engagement.

A highly reliable pistol is the P.210 as well, for samples have withstood the firing of over 10,000 rounds of high power ammunition. One specimen, in Danish trials, is known to have fired 18,000 service rounds! Field stripping is very fast and the gun consists of only a few components. P.210 pistols are in service with the Swiss and Danish armies, with the German Border Police and with several other police departments.

Trigger pull runs 5 pounds on the standard models, and about 4 pounds on target guns, all with two-stage pull.

Specially-tuned target models are available with micrometer rear sights, adjustable trigger stops and choice of two barrel lengths.

Made to special order only, the SIG P.210L pistols will sell for about $500. Benet Arms is the importer.   *R. Caranta*

Sterling Arms

No matter how you slice it, the 25 ACP is having a hell of a revival! Recent tests at my range showed that factory loads—in various expansion media at an average range of 20 feet—raised enough hell to make me want to be some place else when those little metal-clad pills began to fly around. Perhaps a better bullet design would make the experts—who have never been shot at with anything—a little more charitable about this old cartridge.

Sterling Arms, which in the last two years has produced three 22 autoloaders and a 380, now offers the Model 300. This blowback vest pocket 25 ACP auto sells for a nickel less than $40! Total length is 4½", height is 3¾", weight is 10 oz. empty, and magazine capacity is 6 rounds. The all-steel gun is offered in matt black or a satin finish. The Cycolac grips, impact resistant and checkered, will be available in white or black. If you're familiar with the Model 9 Galesi 1952 issue, you'll recognize Sterling's Model 300.

Because of rushing deadlines, I managed to borrow a very low serial number gun, one still undergoing testing at Sterling's factory near Buffalo, N.Y. The simple groove in the slide merely guides the eye to the target—there are no sights as such—thus aiming is neither easy nor very precise. At 25 feet, the results of the first three clips of Remington ammo were downright disappointing. Shooting from a solid rest, the first 6 shots were literally all over the target, with most of the shots grouping in a 5-inch pattern somewhat high and left. During this test firing of 18 cartridges, a live round fed into the chamber while the slide completed its forward travel before the spent case was ejected. This was cleared easily by moving the slide back a fraction of an inch.

A real surprise came with tests 4, 5, and 6. Without changing my hold, the rest position or the brand of ammo, these 18 bullets printed just 2" high and directly above the point of aim. Moreover, the gun seemed to have settled down, for there were no more ejection failures. Another run of 5 clipfuls produced similar results—a shade high, with groups measuring around 3½". Considering my big hand and the smallness of the gun, plus the lack of sights, I consider this ample accuracy for the gun's intended purpose—self defense.

Bob Steindler

Unique DES - 69 Target Auto Pistol

The *Pistolet Olympique* is easily one of the most popular 22 Long Rifle autoloading target pistols produced in Europe during the last few years. The Unique DES-69, made in France by the Manufacture d'Armes des Pyrenees Orientales in Hendaye, near the Spanish border, has been specifically designed around the Interna-

The Sterling 25 has no sights—there's only a groove, but that doesn't appear to hamper performance in any way.

tional Shooting Union (ISU) rules applicable to the "Standard Pistol" event. However, it also perfectly matches the American Smallbore pistol regulations of the U.S. National Rifle Association.

A highly sophisticated target pistol of international class, it offers most advanced design characteristics combined with a very personal styling. Note the unusual mounting of the fully adjustable rear sight, and the maximum sight radius afforded. DES-69 pistols are available in the United States from Garcia. They're made with custom

Unique DES-69 Target Auto Pistol
Specification

Caliber	:	22 Long Rifle
Total Length	:	6.5" (255mm)
Height	:	3.7" (145mm)
Thickness	:	1.96" (50mm) max.
Sight Radius	:	8.6" (220mm)
Barrel Length	:	5.9" (150mm)
Empty Weight	:	36 oz. (1000g.)
Magazine Cap.	:	10 rounds
Trigger Width	:	.47" (12mm)

Micrometer rear sight, adj. for windage and elevation. by .31" (8mm) clicks at 25 metres (82 feet).

Walnut target grips with thumbrest and adj. palm shelf.

Trigger, click-adj. for weight of pull, backlash, sear engagement and sear-spring pressure.

Manual safety; slide hold-open device; dry-firing device.

left-hand grips for southpaws on request. *Raymond Caranta*

New Pocket Auto

I've been sworn to secrecy for some odd reason, but this much can be told—there's a new single action auto pistol in the works, caliber 380 ACP, and if the catalog sheet I'm looking at (complete with isometric view, all specs and parts numbers) is any real indication, the new 380 should be on the market by September, 1972, maybe earlier.

The new auto will weigh about 20 oz., be 5½" over-all and have a 3⅛" barrel. The magazine holds 6 rounds, there's a thumb safety and the sights are fixed; true, the rear sight is drift-adjustable for windage.

Made in the U.S., I believe, this latest pocket auto pistol looks quite like that old warhorse, the Colt 45 ACP, even to the arched housing (without grip safety, though), the slide stop, safety and magazine release button.

Straight blowback, locked or semi-locked, I don't know, but the barrel is positioned by a link, and the drawing shows what may be locking grooves cut into the barrel top ahead of the chamber.

This same handgun may be offered later in 22 LR as well, we hear, but prices are not known at this time. Less than $100, I'd guess, but probably not much less.

HANDGUNS

U.S. & FOREIGN 1972-73

New Handgun Roundup

INTEREST IN—and demand for—handguns has never been greater. Depending on whose report you choose to believe, it would appear that something over 2½ million new handguns were made and sold in the U.S.A. during 1971. That's a powerful lot of short-guns, anyway you view the situation. It would certainly seem to indicate that be he country boy or city slicker, the American Male is by no means ready to bow his head to the utopians and meekly give up his handguns.

In such a climate, certainly, new models are bound to proliferate. There's no shortage of those this time around but, as usual, it's sometimes hard to determine what is *really* new. Facelifting purely for the sake of change is becoming more common, as is the practice of announcing "new" items long before they actually become available at your local shop. Often what was reported as a new gun last year never got west of New Jersey, so it appears new again this year (or next) by virtue of actually becoming available.

Me, I'd rather see more technical advances in design and production methods than facelifting. Also, I'd prefer to see some genuinely new designs in the small gun field, rather than the perennial modified copies of old Browning designs circa 1910. But a fair return on the investor's money is the name of the game, and in the current seller's market, that means conservatism is the order of the day. Anything new and serviceable will sell almost as fast as it can be turned out, so there is no great incentive for a company to spend a million or three dollars to develop and tool for a truly new design. On the other hand, it would seem that right now—when massive sales pour bundles of money into corporate coffers—is the time when such development should be done. Later, if and when the market levels off, it will cost more and there'll be less money available.

Be all that as it may, there are quite a few "new" models to drool over. Let's take a look.

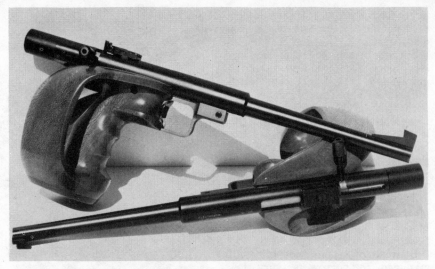

The Electroarm Free Pistol.

Colt

Colt's continues to upgrade its entire line, as begun a few years ago with the Mark III and Mark IV series. There isn't as much new this time as before, though we except some more goodies in the near future.

The Detective Special has been revamped, with the first deliveries of the new model shipped to the trade back in March.

Continuing the Python, Diamondback, and Mark III trend, the new DS barrel has an integral ejector-rod housing on its underside. By leaving only a thin section up front, room is made for the original full-length ejector-rod with its .875" stroke (which is longer than on most competitive 2" guns). On top, the barrel carries a low integral solid rib and a new Baughman-style front sight sloping up from the frame. The usual square-notch-in-frame rear sight is there, of course.

Crane, cylinder and lock work remain unchanged; the frame differs only in being matched to the new barrel profile, and made with a stub grip frame.

For the first time Colt has fitted semi-combat style stocks as standard equipment. The design is far better than earlier DS stocks, but still well short of matching Herrett's Shooting Ace grips on like styles.

The 1972 Colt Detective Special handles much better than its predecessor. It is 2 ounces heavier, with balance shifted well forward, thus aiding control and recovery in rapid DA combat shooting. Our sample guns handle very well in this respect, and give excellent accuracy. Too, at least to date, the new guns seem a bit better fitted and finished than a good many other Colts seen over the past couple of years.

Geo. Nonte.

Electroarm Free Pistol

Independent Research & Development, Inc. (Box 28188, San Antonio, TX 78228), developers of this match pistol and its electro-mechanical sear assembly, appears to be getting into production. Deliveries may begin late in 1972.

Chief feature of this truly unique 22 rimfire single shot pistol is its unvarying and ultra-short lock time—3.8 milliseconds from shot to shot within .00002 ms. Further details will be supplied by I.R.&D. *J.T.A.*

New Hammerli 150 match pistol.

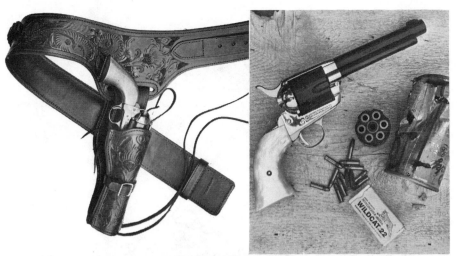

Left—The new Hawes Federal Marshall, shown here with the new Monrach Buscadero belt, sports one-piece walnut grips and case hardened colored frame. Right—Hawes' Silver City Marshall has alloy frame and cylinder, the latter is sleeved with steel chambers.

Hammerli 150 Free Pistol

Hammerli Match Pistols 106/1.02 are no more. They were phased out in December 1971, their place to be taken by the Model 150, a wholly new design. The 150 barrel, mounted low for straight-back recoil, is fully free-floated for better accuracy. The loading-cocking lever is on the left side. The oversize thumbrest grips allow for shaping to the individual hand, and the backstrap-to-trigger distance is quite short as standard, permitting comfortable operation by those with small hands.

The Martini action is retained, in hammerless form, and a new direct-action trigger is adjustable for weight of pull and location—both are said to be vibrationless and ultra fast in lock time. The rear sight is a micro-click type, low mounted.   *J.T.A.*

Two New Revolvers From Hawes Firearms

Hawes Firearms, importers of the Sauer single action revolver, has introduced two model variants in this quite complete line of cartridge and black powder revolvers. The Western Marshall, an alloy-frame 22 rimfire/magnum combina-

tion, has been dolled up with a solid brass grip frame, nickel-plated cylinder frame, blued cylinder and barrel, plus a pair of pearl grips. Called the "Silver City Marshall," it lists at $69.95 for the standard model or $79.95 with the extra magnum cylinder.

Also new is the Federal Marshall, a de luxe variation of their larger steel-frame centerfire revolver, already offered in several versions including one with adjustable sights. Several 2-cylinder combinations, such as the 45 Long Colt/45 ACP, 357 Magnum/9mm, are available at extra cost. The new model differs in having the traditional color case-hardened frame and one-piece walnut grips. The price is $99.95.

To round out their western and black powder firearms line, Hawes now has the Monarch leather goods —there are products for police and sporting use, black powder and western style holsters, belts, etc. Good quality and workmanship are evident, and the prices are modest.
Walter L. Rickell

Ruger Caplock

The one "new" Ruger item is the Old Army percussion revolver, announced last year but just now

becoming available. It's been described in detail elsewhere, but is essentially a traditional-style, 6-shot, 44 caliber percussion revolver based on the Ruger Blackhawk SA design. The front of the frame is extended to provide space for loading, a rammer has been fitted beneath the barrel, a percussion cylinder fitted, and the hammer modified to handle caps.

In extensive shooting we obtained excellent accuracy and reliability, and have but two minor complaints: rough-finished nipples made fired caps hard to remove, and slightly larger than standard 44 balls (.455″ diameter) were required.

Ruger now offers a brass grip frame with square-back trigger guard as an option on the SA Blackhawk series.

It's a great gun, the first genuinely modern caplock sixgun, and the first improvement of the breed since befo' the Wah. A welcome addition to our battery. G. C. N.

Smith & Wesson

The conservative, old-line approach is standard here. With no advance advertising or publicity— only the usual grapevine information—S&W introduced stainless steel versions of its tremendously popular Model 10 (M&P), Model 15 (Combat Masterpiece), and Model 19 (Combat Magnum) revolvers. These are called Models 64,67, and 66 respectively.

These guns are mechanically and otherwise identical with their plain-steel companions for all practical purposes. The esteem in which the basic models are held insures success of the stainless counterparts. While we've examined samples of all three "new" models, there's been no opportunity to run them through range tests. There is no reason to expect them to do less well than the Models 10, 15, and 19.

Stainless steel requires costly fabrication and finishing methods, so

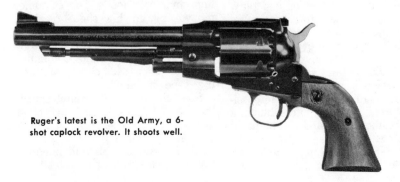

Ruger's latest is the Old Army, a 6-shot caplock revolver. It shoots well.

S&W's latest version of the Combat Magnum is this stainless steel Model 66.

the new guns run roughly 30% higher than the plain-steel models.

Magnum fanciers bemoaning slow delivery of the big-frame S&W guns will be pleased to learn that frame production has been speeded up. New facilities devoted solely to making Magnum frames are in operation, and will greatly increase output of all guns in that class.

It is also fairly common knowledge in the trade that S&W is readying a 15-shot version of the alloy-framed M-39, 9mm autoloading pistol. Actually, we had expected to see it before now, but apparently there are still a few bugs to be worked out.   G. C. N.

10-Ring Precision

I know, I didn't believe it either, but the piece pictured is a muzzle-loading handgun. Made by the firm named above (1449 Blue Crest Lane, San Antonio, TX 78216), they're described as "Match grade" quality, and each has triggers adjustable for pull weight and backlash. Made in flintlock ($175) or as a caplock at $150, both are caliber 45. The prices include bullet mould, ramrod, powder measure and loading data. This is all we have—write for more.

Dan Wesson Arms

For a time there D.W. couldn't make enough of his D.A. revolvers to fill the orders. He must have caught up, though, for now you can get his sixguns tastefully engraved, the cost about $325 over the gun's price.

This year saw a fixed-barrel Dan Wesson revolver appear, one that must be sent to a gunsmith or the factory for removal or replacement. These revolvers, called the M-14, will be made with 2½", 4" and 6" barrels, choice of 38 Special or 357 Magnum calibers.

Another new version, the M-15, with target sights, can be had in nickel finish, bright or satin blue. These two new revolvers, as well as all other Dan Wesson sixguns, will take the new grips to be described next.

Dan also has a new line of grips for his revolvers, these made in 4 styles—combat, target, Michigan and Sacramento. His standard grip form is the traditional, smaller style. These new styles are optional extras, each $9, and all are made of genuine walnut, hand finished.

No, it's not a gag! That's a real live flint pistol, with Match accuracy claimed for it.

An example of the "Grade B" engraving available on Dan Wesson Revolvers at $325 over the cost of the gun.

The latest Dan Wesson revolver, Model M-15, is a fixed-barrel version, here seen in satin blue finish.

Accessories

Bar-Sto Precision Machine

Bar-Sto stainless steel barrels and bushings for 45 Auto pistols (with 9mm and 38 Super calibers to follow) are not, please note, merely SS replacement barrels, valuable as such barrels might be from a non-rusting, long life standpoint. Bar-Sto barrel-bushing sets are different. The regular Bar-Sto SS barrels are designed to fit GI or "service pistols," a *slightly* higher lug and longer "hood" allowing a barrel lockup without appreciable vertical movement or end play, and headspace held to a minimum. This alone enhances accuracy, and Bar-Sto bore and groove dimensions are uniform—in a given barrel—to 0.0002", plus or minus. Moreover, the inside finish is excellent, so smooth that bore leading is virtually impossible. These "regular" barrel-bushing sets are about $35, and can be fitted by the customer.

All Bar-Sto bushings (collet or National Match type optionally) are of a different type of stainless steel, one highly resistant to galling. The collet type is most popular because it grips the barrel muzzle firmly, holding it tightly in position radially and full forward in the slide, thus returning the barrel to the same position after each shot. The collet bushing, in effect, "offers target accuracy with combat performance," according to Irving Stone, Jr., Bar-Sto's man-in-charge.

Bar-Sto match-target barrels, however, must be factory fitted because they are made with high lugs and long hoods. The customer must send in his slide, receiver, slide stop, link and link-pin. These barrels can be fitted to Colt Gold Cups, N.M. pistols and Commanders, the price $49, choice of bushing type included.

Six-inch or longer match grade barrels can be ordered, price to be quoted, but these take some 4 weeks for delivery.

All Bar-Sto barrels and bushings are unconditionally guaranteed, but

Bar-Sto Stainless Steel barrels and bushings, made for Colt 1911-11A1 and Commander pistols. See text for details.

New Ransom Master Series Rest for handgun testing (left), with holding unit (above right) and semi-soft insert pieces.

they're not returnable if altered in any way.

Bar-Sto also furnishes a full set of stainless steel springs for the 45-38 Auto—3 magazine springs and one each for sear, firing pin, magazine catch, slide-stop/safety-plunger, mainspring and recoil-guide; the 9 springs for $9.50 or so. Extra magazine springs, $4.

A sample regular barrel and collet bushing, plus the full spring kit, were furnished to us for trial, but there wasn't time to conduct an adequate appraisal. Included were a stainless steel link and link pin. It was no trouble to fit the barrel to an old UMC pistol—though getting the collet bushing home proved a small job—and after 60 rounds of lead bullet shooting there wasn't a trace of lead.

This old GI 45 is by no means a competition handgun, but the average of those 60 Remington wadcutters, used in the new Ransom Rest, was just over 2 inches at 25 yards—several 5-shot strings made an inch or so, and some went over 3 inches. I consider that a pretty nice improvement for relatively small cost.　　　J.T.A.

C'Arco

The long-awaited Master Series Ransom Rest has finally arrived, and a well-made device it appears to be on all counts. Handsomely finished, this latest Ransom rest for precision testing of a handgun's grouping ability—or the same quality in ammunition—is a sturdy, 7-lb. machine. While the base section is essentially the same as the earlier Ransom Rest (now discontinued), which absorbs recoil via special friction discs and a heavy spring, the Rocker Assembly is new and different. Instead of mounting

the auto pistols (which type of handgun the old rest was limited to) on an internal support, inside the magazine housing, the new rocker grasps the gun — auto or revolver — in individually-fitted mounting blocks, or "grip inserts" as C'Arco calls them. These metal paired blocks, lined with a semi-soft rubberlike material, clamp onto the grip frame of the gun; this gun-clamp assembly is then held tightly against a base unit metal wall. In this construction, the handgun may be fired from a loaded magazine or cylinder, a decided

improvement in more convenient and faster operation.

The new C'Arco Master Series rest is $112.50, including one set of grip inserts, these last now ready for the 45 Colt (or like frame 38s), the models 41 and 52 S&W autos, the military High Standard 22 auto and the S&W K-38 revolver. Other grip inserts (Browning 9mm, Luger, Ruger 22 auto, et al) are in the works. They're all priced at $12.95 a pair.

The Rocker Assembly, usable on the earlier Ransom rest, sells for $67.50, without any grip inserts.

Day 30X Conversion

Taking over where Editor Amber left off in the previous issue of GUN DIGEST, I have enjoyed using the Day Conversion. As Amber told you last year, this simple-to-install unit will change your 45 ACP to 22 LR in a big hurry.

I began with a recently-made commercial 45 auto, putting 100 rounds of various 22 LR ammo through the gun to find out if there were any glitches in the thing. There were none, I then switched the Day Conversion unit onto a well-battered, much-used GI gun, and again the Day unit gobbled up any brand of ammo without a bobble. The last step for Bob Day's creation was my match gun, which has been customized by one of our best pistolsmiths. Once more the Day unit functioned without hesitation.

I had only one small problem, this with the GI gun. The insert magazine of the Day unit should not be loaded with more than 5 rounds. Stick more ammo in the magazine, and she won't feed. On this particular gun, despite only 5 rounds in the magazine, releasing the slide in the usual manner failed to feed the cartridge every time. It then turned out that a slight tap on the base plate of the magazine was apparently needed to seat it properly so that the slide, in its forward movement, could strip a cartridge out of the Day magazine lips and into the chamber.

By that time, Dick Lee's pistol rest had arrived, so I decided to try the same 3 Colts with Lee's rest, using the Day Conversion. With the match gun and two brands of match ammo, I fired five 5-shot strings, the best group just

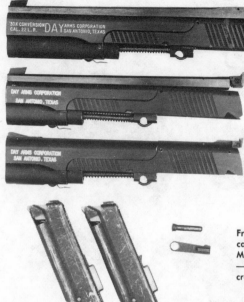

Hogue's Combat Grip.

From the top—Day Arms 30-X Conversion unit with a 6″ barrel, caliber 22 LR. Second is the 5″ version. Bottom is new El Macho variant. Also shown are two 22 cal. magazine adaptors —which slide into the 45 ACP magazine—and the slide stop/ cross pin assembly used to connect the 30-X unit to the frame.

barely 0.75″, the worst 1″. While the commercial gun groups were almost identical to Amber's, the GI gun groups were somewhat larger than Amber's semi-accurized gun gave, most measuring 1½″. All shooting was at 25 yards, with the Lee machine rest mounted on a solid bench.

I think the Day Conversion unit could be of value to the fellow who has rough going on the 45 course of fire, who wants and needs practice with his 45 but can't get to the range often enough, or who wants to use rimfire ammo for reasons of economy or whatever. One other use was brought to my attention by a shooting crony. A cop, he shoots his 45 on the regulation course set forth for his department. As he said when he saw the Day unit: "That conversion idea appeals to me since I like the feel of the 45, and I've never found a 22 plinker worth the money."

Bob Steindler

In addition to the Day 30X unit described here by Steindler, Day now offers a plinker/combat version of the 30X called the El Macho. It's essentially the same unit but lacks the heavy rib, and has an adjustable target sight mounted on the slide. Overall length is the same as the standard 1911 Colt and it sells for $89.50. The El Macho comes with a "10-Plus" magazine, which fully replaces the regular 45 or 38 magazine, rather than using the 5-shot adaptors furnished with the 30X conversion.

Day Arms also offers a complete line of 45 auto accessories, both target and combat, such as sights, ribs, accurizing and custom work. Send for their catalog.   *WLR*

Alton S. Dinan, Jr.

Dinan, one of the very few full-time pistolsmiths, does *all* the work that comes to him, no one else. He guarantees the highest degree of satisfaction.

His specialty is the rebuilding of the 45 Colt auto pistol into a match performer, but he works on other handguns as well. His services are too varied and numerous to list here, but the full accuracy job on the 45 (or 38 Super) auto is $65, and he'll convert a 38 Super to 38 Special for $75.

If you want the best there is in handgun work, write for Dinan's brochure. We recommend him highly.   *J.T.A.*

Gil Hebard Guns

Those of you interested in handgun shooting in any form—hunting, competition or plain old plinking— can and should have either or both of Gil's new handbooks. They're indispensable, believe me.

His latest catalog, *Gil Hebard Guns,* is the 21st edition, and in its 112 pages, plus colorful soft covers, you'll find virtually every handgun and related accessory known. I say "virtually" because Gil does not have 100% coverage of such products, but if he's left out anything (aside for some foreign handguns he doesn't sell) it probably isn't worth showing.

Nominally priced at $1, the new Hebard catalog contains a $2 credit certificate good on a $10 order.

The Pistol Shooter's Treasury, edited and published by Gil Hebard, is now (for 1972) in its 2nd edition, enlarged and revised. Hebard maintains—and rightly so—that this book

"could make you a great pistol shot." Will it do that? Maybe, maybe not, but that depends on you, for between its covers there's everything you need to know on how to shoot a handgun. The top experts in the field, match winning shooters all, impart the no-secret secrets—men like Blankenship, Weston, Toney, McMillan, Jim Clark and Gil Hebard himself, to name a few contributors.

There are 30 articles in the new 128-page paper-bound book ($2.95 prepaid), and I recommend it unreservedly.   *J.T.A.*

Hogue

Hogue Custom Grips (Box 1327, Cambria, CA 93428) has a new catalog ready ($1.00) that shows their complete line of custom made stocks for all handguns, these handcrafted from 3 rare woods— Brazilian rosewood, Gancalo Alves and Pau Ferro. New this year, though not pictured, are rosewood stocks for the Auto Mag pistol; about $40, checkered on both sides. Shown is their new combat grip for revolvers. These have one finger groove, an open back-strap, and the lower section of the frame peeks through the grip's front strap filler. This gives the little finger more relief and comfort. About $24, fine-line checkered both sides.   *WLR*

Hornady Pistol Loading Data

Joyce Hornady has prepared an 8½″x11″ booklet with the above title. There are 17 pages within the soft covers devoted to handgun loads or to handgun cartridge loads intended for

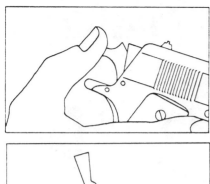

Swenson's Dual Safety.

Hammer pressure holds Pin-Pad in place—between hammer and firing pin—until hammer is cocked. Then the spring-loaded Pin-Pad self ejects.

The Matich Quick Load.

use in rifles. Included are 30 Carbine, 380 Auto, 38 ACP (standard and Super), 38 Special and 357 (handgun and rifle), 41 Magnum, 44 Special, 44 Magnum, including rifle loads, 45 ACP and Auto Rim, and 45 Long Colt.

Hornady notes, in the new booklet, that some things were learned in the process of researching the load data. He says it was startling to learn that "maximum loads fired in a revolver produced much *higher pressure* than in a rifle."

Jeffersontown Specialty

A perennial question among 45 ACP shooters is: "What's the best way to carry a 45 with a live round in the chamber?" The 45 Auto is becoming more and more popular with police departments, but most officers, naturally, are reluctant to carry the gun with the chamber empty. Having to pull the slide back and them release it to feed a round and cock the hammer in a dark and silent alley is a dead give-away, both as to your location and your intentions.

Jeffersontown Specialty has introduced a spring-loaded plastic device called the Pin-Pad. Handling the Pin-Pad is simple. Chamber a round, then lower the hammer slowly while holding the Pin-Pad in position with the curvature forward and seated down as far as possible so that the spring-activated pin is pushed all the way into the Dayglo red plastic. Now, on cocking the gun, the Pin-Pad—thanks to the spring—will eject straight up. Practice inserting the device while the gun is empty for safety's sake, unless you know how to

uncock the Colt with a live round in the chamber.

I carried a 45 with the Pin-Pad in place for some 3 months to test any possible spring fatigue. The Pin-Pad ejected as strongly after 90 days use as it did the day I first inserted the device. The Pin-Pad can be used in any pistol made to Colt or Government specs, including the 9mm Commander and the NM gun. *Bob Steindler*

Matich Loader

Made for all Colt or S&W revolvers with swing-out cylinders, this "Quick Load" device works very fast—just position the taped rounds over the cylinder, yank the tab off and your gun is loaded. Reusable, of course, and the cost is $2.98 each. A combat holder, to carry two Q.L. loaders, is $7. Box 958, So. Pasadena, CA 91030.

Mustang Firearms, Inc.

If the ordinary plastic handgun grip—shiny and slippery—puts you off, these Mustang Duro 300 handles may well appeal. Made by solid pouring of a superior polyester resin, these new grips offer a wood-grain appearance and a wood feel. For now, at least, only a finger-grooved combat style is offered ($12.95), these in ebony, rosewood or ivory color.

Mustang is well known, of course, for their extensive line of real wood grips, made in a very wide range of types and styles—too many to detail here. Mustang will send brochures on both the Duro 300s and their wood grips. Write to 13830 Highway 395, Edgemont, CA 92508.

Swenson Dual Safety

Armand Swenson (3223 154th St., Gardena, CA 90249) has finally put into production his patented ambidextrous thumb safety for the 45 Colt auto pistol. The unit lets a left-handed shooter use the thumb safety when carrying the old warhorse in the cocked-and-locked position.

The safety comes in three different models, all basically the longtang style pioneered by Swenson. The two sides are linked together by a male and female tongue arrangement. The right side of the safety is held in place by the right grip panel. The cost is $29.95, and it can be installed by the shooter; the only alteration required is some wood removal from the right grip panel. They're also available in blued steel or hard chrome finish at slightly higher cost.

Swenson's standard long thumb safety is still offered, too, for $15.95. For full information on these thumb safeties and other custom services contact Swenson's 45 Shop. *W. L. Rickell*

David R. Woodruff

Got a worn, rough, rusted or pitted auto pistol barrel? Woodruff (116 Stahl Ave., Wilmington Manor, New Castle, DE 19720) can reline it at modest cost. All calibers are available—22 to 45—and the job includes barrel removal, relining, chambering and headspace adjustment. He prefers to have receiver and barrel of Lugers, but it's not mandatory. Prices on Lugers run from $5 (4″ barrel only) to $17.50 for the 8″ artillery barrel.

A History of Proof Marks

 ## Gun Proof in Hungary

This is the 6th installment of the new and fully up-to-date series "History of Proof Marks" initiated in our 22nd edition. The author, Mr. Lee Kennett, is highly qualified to have undertaken the definitive research required, and we feel certain his comprehensive and detailed work will prove reliable, interesting and valuable.

While Mr. Kennett used the framework of the late Baron Engelhardt's "The Story of European Proof Marks" as a structural guide, he personally visited and talked with Proof House officials in many countries in his research. He will continue to do so until all nations in the survey have been covered. When that time arrives, we will publish the complete book.

With this issue we present "Proof Marks in Hungary." The completed and published book will carry a full account of the origins and historical background of proof marks.

by Lee Kennett

Proof in Hungary

HUNGARY EMERGED from World War I as a small independent state. Like most of the other successor states to the old Austro-Hungarian Empire, Hungary continued for some time to use the Imperial proof system of 1891, retaining the old marks as well (see under Austria-Hungary). In 1929 a new set of proof rules and marks were introduced; at the same time Hungary adhered to the Brussels Convention, so the new system conformed to international standards. The basic provisions were as follows:

Smoothbores underwent a provisional proof of unjoined barrels in the rough state (mark no. 1). Barrels for multi-barreled smoothbores could also be submitted to a voluntary second provisional proof after joining (no. 2). Both of these proofs were made with black powder. Shotguns took definitive black powder proof at 8800 psi (pounds per square inch) (mark no. 3), or definitive smokeless proof at 12,000 psi (mark no. 4). Rifles, revolvers and autoloading pistols were proved with loads generating pressures 30% greater than the strongest commercial cartridge load, taking mark no. 3 or no. 4, the latter if smokeless powder were used. All arms bore the number and year of proof. Shotguns bore the words NEM GOLYONAK (not for ball) if choked, barrel weight to tenths of a gram, and bore diameter to tenths of a millimeter.

The state of proof in Hungary since 1945 is unfortunately known only imperfectly. As late as 1958 Baron Engelhardt found evidence that proof was still being administered with the 1929 rules and marks, although the post-war Hungarian government declined any full participation in the Brussels Convention. Though no information has been received on this subject from the Hungarian authorities, there is evidence that proof has been altered slightly. Shotguns of Hungarian make now appearing on the Western European market still bear the mark of provisional proof (no. 1), but the old definitive proof mark is no longer stamped. In its place appear the English words SMOKELESS POWDER. Choked barrels now bear bore diameter of the choked portion, as well as the English words NO BULLET. Nominal gauge and chamber length are now placed in fraction form inside a lozenge. Number and year of proof are stamped as before. It is quite possible that some of these marks, particularly the words in English, are special marks applied only to guns destined for export to the West; however, for lack of definite information, this can only remain a conjecture.

Proof Marks on a Hungarian Shotgun

This 16-gauge gun is an interesting example of double proving. It was manufactured and proved in Hungary in 1963, then exported to France. Since Hungary is no longer a member of the Brussels Convention, her marks are not recognized in France; the gun was subject to obligatory proof in France, in this case at the Paris proofhouse. Note that bore diameters are given for the choked portions of the barrel only. Cylinder bore in this gauge being 16.8mm, the left barrel has 1mm of constriction, or full choke; the right barrel has .7mm constriction, or three-quarter choke.

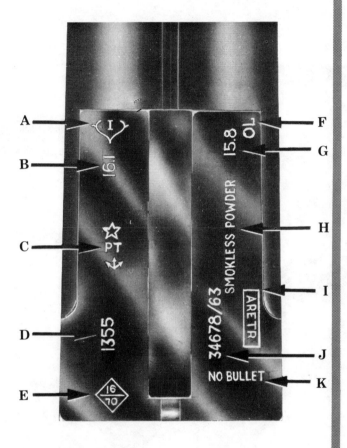

A — Provisional proof mark.

B — Bore diameter at choke.

C — Star and PT — French definitive nitro proof for a gun in completely finished state.

D — Factory number.

E — $\frac{16}{70}$ in lozenge, gauge and chamber length.

F — 70 — chamber length (French stamping).

G — Bore diameter at choke.

H — SMOKELESS POWDER — for nitro proof. (Ed. note: the Hungarians know how to spell "smokeless," it's our artist who can't spell.)

I — AR.ETR. — French stamp for a foreign gun *(arme etrangere)*.

J — 34678/63 — Serial number and year.

K — NO BULLET — designating a choked barrel.

Hungarian Proof Marks

In this table the mark numbers at left are those assigned by the author, and keyed by him to the text for reference. The 2nd column shows the true form of the proof mark and gives the period of its use. The last column tells of the marks' significance.

Rules of 1929

1	⟨I⟩	Provisional black powder proof of rough, unjoined smoothbore barrels.
2	△II	Second provisional proof of joined smoothbore barrels.
3	BP	Black powder definitive proof.
4	BP FN	Smokeless powder definitive proof.
5	NEM GOLYONAK	Means "not for ball," indicating a choked bore.
6	2064/30	Proof number and year; here, 2064th proof administered in 1930.
7	1026.8	Barrel weight in grams and tenths.
8	16.8	Bore diameter in millimeters and tenths.

Some Current Marks on Shotguns

9	SMOKELESS POWDER	Designates smokeless definitive proof.
10	NO BULLET	Indicates choked barrels.
11	◇12/70	Nominal gauge and chamber length in millimeters.

Jerry A. Fisher
French walnut, 24-line fleur-de-lis checkering, steel buttplate and grip cap, 30-06 barrel by Bliss Titus. All metal work by Tom Burgess (except damascening and bluing), including new floorplate and guard, checkered bolt knob, custom safety and scope bases. M98 Mauser action.

R.E. Anderson
338 Win. Mag. on a Weatherby Mark V left-hand action. French walnut, 28-line wrap-around checkering, Leupold 2-7x in Conetrol mounts. Screws and fittings checkered or engraved, parallel aligned. Classic style.

Richards Micro-Fit
This thumb-hole production stock lets shooter use regular hold or hole, offers good value.

Custom Guns

Russell R. Zeeryp
French walnut, multi-point checkered, stocks this Sako-actioned 270, the grip cap and fore-end tip of rosewood.

C. D. Miller
New deHaas-Miller single shot action, barreled and stocked by Miller. For full details see "Sporting Arms of the World," elsewhere in this 27th edition.

Shaw's-Finest in Guns
Feather crotch Claro walnut, carved to oak leaves and acorns, was used to stock this Sako rifle, caliber 300 Win. Mag.

Reed Gun Shop
FN action, Apex-barreled in 22-250, stocked in well-figured American walnut.

Dale Andrews
Shilen-barreled Sako action, stocked in dense native walnut, 6mm Rem. deer and varmint rifle.

Earl Milliron
Mauser 98 action, classically fashioned. Metal work—guard, floorplate release, scope bases—by Tom Burgess.

Talmage Enterprises
Stocked in birdseye maple, with rosewood trim, the 24″ Douglas Premium barrel is on a 98 Mauser action.

Robert M. Winter
Classic stocking in fancy American walnut of a Shilen-barreled Mauser, cal. 22-250. Double set triggers.

Mike Conner
Mauser '98 in 375-06, the ribbed barrel octagon-to-round. French walnut, fleur-de-lis checkering, D.S. triggers.

Clayton Nelson
This 25-06 Champlin A&M octagon barreled action is stocked in French walnut of good figure. 24-line checkering, with 32-line inset; checkered bolt knob, buttplate and grip cap; bolt and follower engine-turned. 10x Leupold scope in Buehler mounts.

Paul Jaeger
FN Mauser, stocked in the classic style in highly figured European walnut, the receiver, scope base and rings, etc., engraved and gold inlaid.

Kess Arms
Mauser 98, 30-06 Douglas barrel, striking French walnut, carved and checkered in Mannlicher style.

Abe-Van Horn
This Mauser M1898 action is barreled in 22-250 caliber, the wood Bastogne walnut of good contrast.

Edw. O. Hefti
Mauser '98 in 35 Whelen, stocked in Flaig's Circassian walnut, the extensive checkering multi-pointed.

Hal Hartley
Ruger SS in 375 Magnum, engraved by A. Obiltschnig, stocked in close-grain fiddleback maple, channel checkered.

Kay Bowles
Pre-'64 M70 stocked in California Claro walnut for Fred Huntington, Jr., caliber 257 Roberts.

J.K. Cloward
375 H&H Douglas barreled pre-1964 M70, French walnut, finely checkered, shows graceful cheekpiece.

Hollis Gun Shop
Springfield '03, with 25-06 Douglas barrel, stocked in Circassian walnut, carved-border checkering, ebony trim.

Smitty's Gun Shop
Bob Smith built this 7mm Rem. Mag. on a southpaw Savage 110, reworking action, receiver ring and bolt. The wood is fiddleback walnut.

Ahlman Custom Guns
Featherweight 308, Mannlicher style, stocked in French walnut with horn fittings.

Len Brownell

A typical Brownell job—which means unexcelled in design, execution and first class materials, as witness the highly-figured wood.

A   E

Dale Goens

Dale made this outstanding stock for John Johnson of Albuquerque NM, the action an Argentine Mauser, cal. 280. The checkering is a variant of the Jack O'Connor pattern.

B   F

Jerry A. Fisher

This G33/40 Mauser was stocked for Jerry's wife. The barrel is a Shilen, the scope an old Lyman Alaskan, the superb English walnut from Oakley & Merkley.

C   G

Keith Stegall

Crisply stocked in fancy French walnut, the checkering an interesting multi-point pattern. The late Arnold Griebel engraved the grip cap and floorplate, one of his last jobs.

D   H

Smitty's Gun Shop

Bob Smith stocked this 98 Mauser, cal. 277 Smith Magnum, with imported English walnut. Special checkering reveals owner's initials.

R. J. Maberry

A 250 Savage Douglas XX barrel on a Mauser 98 action, the scope a 6x Lyman. 22-line skip checkering.

Hubert Hecht

Well done classic stock on an M70 action, all metal and wood work by HJH, and made for Joe Oakley of Oakley & Merkley, fine stock blank purveyors.

N. H. Schiffman

Sako-actioned sporter with elegant traditional stock in fancy walnut. The scope is a Leupold.

EPROUVETTES

An Illustrated History

by LEE KENNETT

Black powder in years gone by varied greatly in quality and power. Eprouvettes—powder testers—were in general use for at least 400 years.

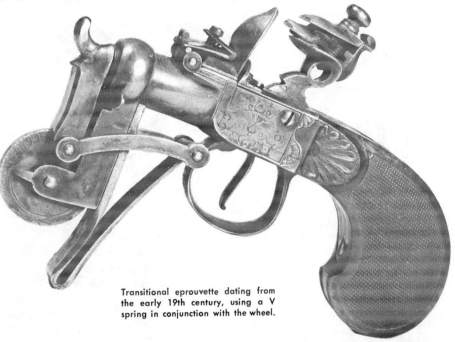

Transitional eprouvette dating from the early 19th century, using a V spring in conjunction with the wheel.

TODAY BLACK POWDER enjoys the reputation of an old but reliable propellant, simple in composition, uniformly high in quality and exceedingly regular and dependable in performance. But in preceding centuries this was not the case, for powder could vary enormously in composition and quality. Even as recently as a century ago, whenever sportsmen gathered they frequently discussed the quality and "strength" of their powders. The Englishman William Baldwin, who hunted African game with a ponderous 7-gauge gun, noted in his journal in the 1850s: "My powder this year is excellent. I only wish my nerves were as good."

If finding good powder was one problem, keeping it good was another. Even the best quality propellant could deteriorate from improper storage. This was especially true when it was kept in fortresses or aboard ships, where dampness was a constant enemy. The problem was a serious one; in the years 1790-1811 the British Navy had to return nearly 200,000 barrels of deteriorated powder for remanufacture.

For these reasons both the sportsman and the soldier needed some way of determining the quality of gunpowder, and the first simple tests appeared quite early. One of the earliest involved igniting a small charge on a piece of paper. Good powder would leave no residue. This technique, mentioned in the 16th century, was still in use in the 19th. Another test, somewhat more risky, called for igniting a pinch of powder held in the palm. Good powder would presumably be consumed before it could scorch the hand. Early artillerymen sometimes used still a third method. They poured a train of powder along the ground and judged its quality by the rapidity with which it burned and volume of smoke it produced.

Since these rule-of-thumb tests lacked precision, another solution was soon found. William Bourne, an early English authority on ordnance, wrote in the 1570s describing a "little boxe" used for the testing of powder. A small charge was placed in the box and ignited, and its explosion (burning, really) lifted the lid; the more powerful the powder, the higher it raised the lid. From the description, it is clear that Bourne was writing about a very early form of *eprouvette,* or powder tester.

Though they varied greatly in details of construction, eprouvettes all functioned on the same principle. A carefully measured charge of the powder to be tested was required to perform a mechanical task by its explosion—to lift a weight, for example, The degree to which it performed this task could be measured exactly; hence the strength of any powder could be established, comparatively, at least, by the reading it gave.

The first eprouvette in general use seems to have been the vertical ratchet type. It is also called the Furtenbach eprouvette, since it was described by Joseph Furtenbach in his *Halinitro Pyrobolia,* which appeared in 1627. This device consisted of a tiny mortar, positioned vertically, and whose muzzle was covered by a weight. Upon firing, the weight was driven upward between two upright supports; a ratchet and pawl mechanism prevented it from falling all the way down again. According to Furtenbach, a charge of good quality cannon powder would drive the weight up 4 inches, while the reading for good musket powder was 5 inches, and that of the best hunting powder 8 inches.

The Furtenbach eprouvette was superseded in popularity by the less cumbersome wheel type, also called the Saint Remy eprouvette, after a late 17th century French artillery officer. This type is most frequently seen in collections, and was in continuous use for three centuries. It generally takes the form of a pocket pistol, with the muzzle surmounted by a tight fitting lid. The lid it attached to a ratchet wheel, so that when the ignited charge repels the lid, the wheel is turned. This latter must overcome the friction of a flat spring pressing against its notched rim. The number of notches the wheel was moved indicated the strength of the powder. In a common variant the wheel was not notched, but marked off with a numerical scale.

With the beginning of the 19th century, further modifications appeared, most of them designed to correct the erratic performance of the springs.

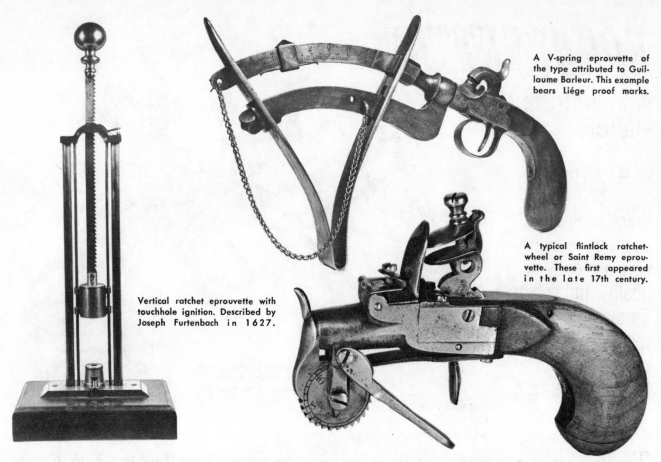

A V-spring eprouvette of the type attributed to Guillaume Barleur. This example bears Liége proof marks.

A typical flintlock ratchet-wheel or Saint Remy eprouvette. These first appeared in the late 17th century.

Vertical ratchet eprouvette with touchhole ignition. Described by Joseph Furtenbach in 1627.

One type used a V-shaped spring whose tension could be easily measured; the charge compressed the spring, the use of friction being discarded. This form of eprouvette probably originated in Liége and is sometimes attributed to the Liége gunmaker, Guillaume Berleur. In 1810 the French physicist Regnier introduced his hydrostatic eprouvette, which did away with springs altogether. This mechanism was composed of a floating cylinder; the explosion of a charge of powder on its top would drive it down into the liquid in which it floated, the depth depending upon the propulsive force of the powder. At about the same time an inventor named Hoer perfected an eprouvette

consisting of two arms, hinged together like a schoolboy's compass. One arm contained at its extremity a cavity for the powder, while the other, which fitted over the cavity, carried a weight. On explosion the weighted arm would fly away, the distance being measured on a graduated arc.

Eprouvettes were made in a bewildering number of variations; rarely are two found that are identical. A Belgian gunmaker who manufactured considerable quantities of them recalled that "each maker produced this instrument according to his own particular idea." The lack of standardization presented no problem, since testing with the eprouvette was empirical and comparative. Once the instrument

had given a reading for a powder known to be of high quality, the performance of other powders was compared with it.

A similar but much larger device was the eprouvette mortar or proof mortar used by the military for acceptance tests on gunpowder delivered to the government. The eprouvette mortar of the French Army, in use by 1686 and possibly before, was rather typical of such devices. It closely resembled an ordinary mortar, but was manufactured to rather closer tolerances. It fired a copper globe at a 45° angle; to be accepted, three ounces of the powder being tested had to propel the globe 50 *toises,* about 320 feet. It is interesting to note that

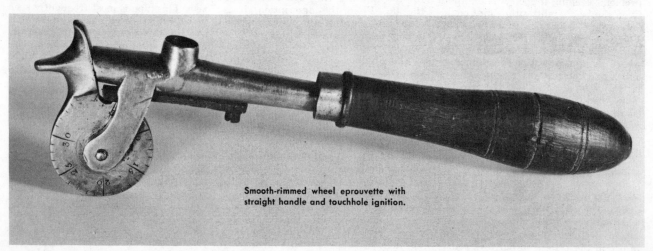

Smooth-rimmed wheel eprouvette with straight handle and touchhole ignition.

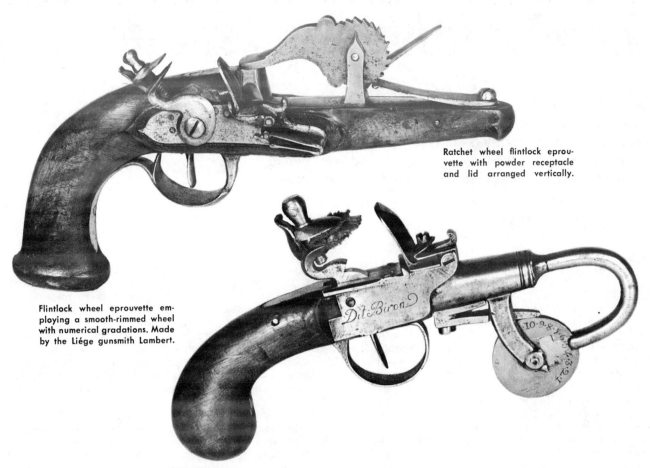

Ratchet wheel flintlock eprouvette with powder receptacle
and lid arranged vertically.

Flintlock wheel eprouvette em-
ploying a smooth-rimmed wheel
with numerical gradations. Made
by the Liége gunsmith Lambert.

while the mortar remained essentially the same for two centuries, the standards for powder rose steadily; by Napoleon's time acceptable powder had to propel the globe 100 toises and the government paid a premium for any that propelled it 120 toises. This is rather graphic evidence of the gradual improvement in the manufacture of black powder over the years. As might be expected, these mortars varied from one country to the next. The Russian model, for example, fired its ball straight up, also true of the mortar used in the Swedish service; but in this case the projectile trailed a silk tape behind it as it rose, facilitating measurement. Needless to say, manufacturers of commercial powders also tested their products with the eprouvette mortar.

The use of eprouvettes declined in the course of the 19th century, this for several reasons. Even the most sensitive eprouvette was a relatively crude mechanical device. It purported to measure a powder's "strength," ignoring the fact that this word masked a whole series of ballistic properties. Consequently, the eprouvette might give a higher reading to a weak, quick-burning powder than to a stronger, but slower-burning one. By the mid-19th century the chronograph and the crusher gauge could tell the ballistician much more than an eprouvette. Finally, higher manufacturing standards for black powder made it less necessary for the consumer to test it, while the introduction of smokeless powders made such home testing virtually impossible.

As is so often the case, the eprouvette remained in use for some time after the need for it had ended. Thus in the 1880s, despite the existence of the crusher gauge, the authorities at the Birmingham Proof House in England were still testing their proof powder with a wheel eprouvette. Even at the end of the century, at least one European sporting goods firm still offered the Hoer eprouvette to its customers. But, by and large, the eprouvette had been discarded by 1900, and was on its way to becoming the curiosity it is today. ●

Eprouvette designed by Devoitille and made by Francotte of Liége. The spring presses a "shoe" against the wheel. Ignition is by touchhole. A piston within the cylinder drives the numbered wheel.

Photographs from the Musee d'Armes, Liége, Belgium.

Handloading Centennial

Reloading metallic cartridge cases began about 100 years ago.
The practice faltered at times, over the long years,
but handloading today is enjoyed by millions.
Here's a review of the new, interesting and worthwhile
tools and equipment offered the home cartridge maker.

by JOHN T. AMBER

Ohaus Loading Equipment

The biggest news in the hand-loading world for 1972-1973 has to be Ohaus, a long-time maker of weighing scales for laboratory and industrial uses. Except for loading tools or presses—which they'll probably be offering a year or less hence—the brand-new Ohaus line includes virtually every product the average reloader needs. True, they are not showing such esoteric items as bullet spinners or case-neck cutting tools, but there is so much else that we're going to be hard pressed to find space in this department for all of them.

As many of our readers know, Ohaus has been making an excellent line of powder scales for some years. Some of these have been marketed under the Ohaus name (the Models 304 and 314, both of over 3100-gr. capacity), with others made for and sold by Lyman—the D-5 and M-5 types. (Lyman, by the way, no longer offers these Ohaus-made scales, but offers instead their D-7 model, described elsewhere in these pages.)

The Ohaus 5-0-5 Reloading Scale, the first to use magnetic damping, and probably the most popular scale available, is now improved for better visibility of calibration and easier adjustment. Instead of the former 2-poise system, there are now 3; the increments at left of the self-aligning, agate-bearings beam are calibrated in 10-gr. divisions, while the two poises at right adjust from 0.10- to 1 grain and from 1- to 10 grains. The advantage is an important one—all beam notches can be cut wider and deeper, thereby helping materially the avoidance of error via accidental— or mis-read—shifting of the poises, and the potential dangers such movement might involve. The new

Ohaus 5-0-5 is $17.50, only $1 over its older counterpart, the now-discontinued Lyman-Ohaus D-5.

Newest design among Ohaus popular-priced scales is their Model 510 with, I believe, a truly unique adjustability, at least in production scales—this is a rotating micrometer-type poise that turns in adjustment, the range running from 0.1-gr. to 10 grains. A positive locking system holds the adjustment. While the 510 scale has the standard Ohaus features—magnetic damping, hardened steel knife edges and agate bearings, 510-gr. capacity and 0.1-gr. sensitivity—it offers other worthwhile things as well. An enlarged leg has been included with the heavy die-cast base for greater stability, and the pan is held in a bracket arrangement to prevent its tipping if a bullet, for example, is placed off center in it. Ohaus calls this new scale construction the "Approach to Weight" system, the user being "alerted to beam movement before the pointer reaches the zero scale." Price, $19.50.

Top-priced Ohaus scale—aside from their Models 303 and 314—is the 1010. Identical to the 510 in all important aspects, including the new micrometer poise system, this version offers 1010-gr. capacity by

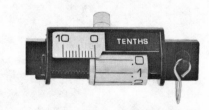

Ohaus Micro Poise on 5-10 and 10-10 scales.

means of a furnished 500-gr. auxiliary weight, and the base designed to hold the beam elements for storage or when the scale is carried. A dust proof cover is furnished at no extra cost, which is $19.50. The 1010 also has enhanced stability of both body and pan.

All of these Ohaus scales carry a table converting ounces into grains, a handy reference for the shotshell loader checking shot charges, while the 1000-plus grains capacity of the Model 1010 allows weighing of cases, some loaded rounds, and so on.

With that many powder scales Ohaus ought to have a powder measure, too—and they do. It is quite different from any other measure in design, in that the new Du-O-Measure's rotating drum carries two metering cavities, not one, and both are fully adjustable. The small cavity (clearly marked "S") has a capacity of 0.5- to 15 grains, and it's intended for handgun charges, of course. The "L" marked rifle cavity has a range of adjustments from 15- to 100 grains. Either cavity is quickly made operative by the removal and re-insertion of a single stopscrew, and both adjustment systems may be critically set and recorded by means of carefully calibrated scales engraved on the arms.

The closely-fitted drum is chrome-plated for smooth, trouble-free operation. The sharp-edged cavities should cut through the coarser powders easily, with more uniform charges resulting. A quick-dump arrangement lets powder be drained fast. While a reliable scale must be used to check charges thrown from any powder measure, especially when full or maximum-usable charges are used, Ohaus provide a handy wall chart for the rough approximation of charges, in both rifle and handgun powders, thrown by the Du-O-Measure cavities, small or large. The powder reservoir holds a pound of powder, its brown plastic, low-profile form having a spout for easier emptying. With two drop tubes and a steel mounting bracket, the new scale sells for $31.95.

I was particularly pleased that Ohaus furnishes an Instruction leaflet for the Du-O-Measure, an 8-page, fully illustrated pamphlet that thoroughly explains the operation and care of their new powder measure. A pleasant and gratifying surprise.

Ohaus has entered the cast bullet field in a big way, some 68 different moulds being now available in rifle and handgun types, not to mention 19 round ball moulds in sizes from .311″ to .662″. Most are made in 4- and 2-cavity style as well as single-cavity. Nose punches are available also, designed for use with lubricating-sizers of Lyman, Saeco or other make.

Tungsten carbide cherries are used to cut the precision cavities in the Pearlitic malleable iron blocks—which are carefully well-vented. The alignment pins are hardened, as are the sprue cutters. Sprue holes are ground to a sharp knife edge to assure flat-based bullets and effortless sprue cutting. One universal handle size fits *all* Ohaus mould blocks, the handles long enough for cool operation.

Packaging of the Ohaus mould blocks has obviously had intelligent attention—bold block lettering on a white panel carries full information on the mould within. Caliber, weight, nose and base type, code number, suggested sizing diameter, top punch style and its part number, plus whether a single- or double-cavity mould, all this data is there, besides a clear photograph of the cast bullet the mould makes.

Again, as with the Ohaus Du-O-Measure, a fully informative and illustrated booklet of 8 pages comes with each mould, its title "Guide to Better Bullet Making." Mention is made of the additional casting equipment needed—lead pot, dipper, fluxing material, and so on—the techniques of preparing and managing a bullet alloy, how to go about casting good bullets, and several examples of what not to do. An excellent idea, these comprehensive manuals—it should be emulated.

Lead bullet shooters will, I'm sure, welcome this new Ohaus line of well-built moulds. Until their advent only a few people have offered bullet moulds in recent years, and some of those not easy to obtain in a reasonable time.

I've only one minor criticism to

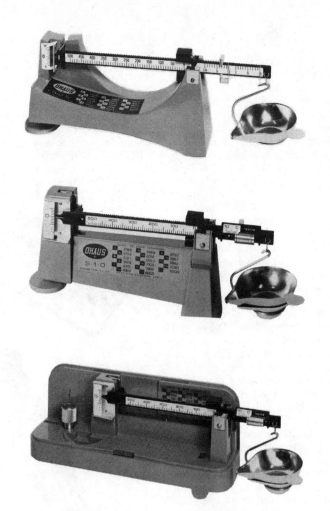

Three new Ohaus powder scales. Top—5-0-5 has 3-poise system, 5-1-0 (middle) and 10-10 have Micrometer Poise and approach-to-weight features. See text for details.

offer on the Ohaus moulds—I believe the sprue cutters should have been made a bit thicker. I've had no trouble at all with the two blocks I've used (45 ACP and 30/170 gr. GC), I freely admit, but in rough service I'm wondering if an angled belt with the mallet wouldn't bend the cutter.

Ohaus 1-cavity mould blocks are $10 for plain or gas check base types; $14 for hollow base designs (H.P. styles are not so far offered); two-cavity blocks, plain base or GC only, are $13.50. Handles only (these fit either type) are $4.95.

Ohaus also has casting accessories—a bail-handle, flat-bottom cast iron melting pot, with pouring and tilt lips, holding about 10 lbs., is $2.50. A dipper or ladle, long-handled for coolness, has an oval pouring spout exactly contoured to

match Ohaus mould sprue cutters. Its open top picks up a sizeable quantity of molten mix, too. The price is $2, which is also the price of a 4-compartment ingot mould. A sturdy hardwood mallet, expressly designed and lathe-turned to bang sprue cutters efficiently, is $2.49.

We'll now touch lightly on the rest of the Ohaus product array for handloaders. An alloy-steel based powder trickler, made for good stability, is $3.50, a crush-proof plastic powder funnel, designed to accept all metallic cases, is $1, while a flip-over loading block, made of unbreakable plastic, has 80 holes on one side, 40 on the other, cost $1.69. Though Ohaus calls this an all-caliber block, I'd consider the smallest holes much too shallow for good stability with anything but 222-based cases.

RCBS

While Fred Huntington hasn't announced any major products for 1971-72, there are several new items for the handloader of metallic ammunition—especially for the 17-caliber shooters.

Foremost among all of these is a sensitive, low-leverage priming tool that offers smooth, uniform seating of primers. With this new "Precisioneered" tool, the primer can be felt going home into the primer pocket, which means that a loosened or over-tight pocket can be readily detected. In addition, the pockets can be easily checked before seating the primer.

An auto primer feed is also supplied with the RCBS Priming Tool, but if the reloader already has RCBS Auto Primer Feed Tubes and RCBS Shell Holders, he can get the new Priming Tool for $21.95, including both large and small Primer Rod assemblies, plus the Auto Primer Arm. For $3 more he gets the Primer Feed Tubes. RCBS shell holders are still $2.40 each.

Now that Remington 17 caliber rifles and ammo are readily available, RCBS will doubtless see a splurge in sales for their 17-caliber equipment—which they've had for some little time, for Fred wasn't to be caught napping on the mighty midget!

The 17-caliber tools include a Funnel ($2.40), a Case Neck Brush (60¢), a Drop Tube ($3) for the RCBS Uniflow Powder Measure, and a Burring Tool at $3.60. RCBS has, of course, loading dies for the Remington 17, as well as die sets for many older wildcat 17s.

Other new RCBS items are: Plastic-cased lube pads, the foam pads removable for cleaning, cost $3, and plastic handles ($1) for their case neck brushes—the latter at 45¢ for all calibers but 17. These new handles also take the RCBS Primer Pocket Cleaner Blade (which handles large or small pockets) at $2.40.

RCBS again has some money saving combination offers on presses. The Jr Press, which is an

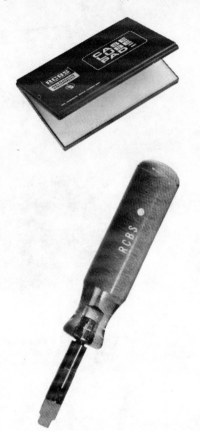

excellent choice for the beginning handloader, comes with Shell Holder, Primer Arm (for small and large primers), Primer Catcher, a set (2) of RCBS dies and a sizing lube at $43.50, a $48 value. The Rock Chucker press, a heavy-duty O-frame with the RCBS patented compound leverage system, may be ordered with the same tooling above for $64.50, a $69 value.

Both of these RCBS loading tools, even at their regular prices, offer top value, but if you may want to form cases or swage bullets, buy the Rock Chucker. That patented linkage makes the chores easy. I've used RCBS presses for many years, starting with Fred Huntington's early Model A, and if I could only have one loading tool . . .

The third "package deal" from RCBS is the Ammo-Crafter, an outfit that combines everything the loader needs in one handy container. There's a Powder Scale, Powder Measure, a Case Lube Kit (pad, handled brush, lube), Powder Funnel and Burring Tool, plus the $1 RCBS Reloading Guide, for free, and all for $49.50 versus a regular price of $53.25.

RCBS has a big 1972-73 catalog available for the asking, and the *RCBS Reloading Guide* has been revised and updated, the price still $1 postpaid.

Another RCBS publication, *Handloading Rifle and Pistol Ammunition*, a work of love by John (the Beard) Jobson of *Sports Afield*, is a 10-page booklet that shows graphically how to begin home loading. Fred will be glad to send you a copy, and it's a valuable work for the novice.

RCBS products, from left below—A2 press, Ammo-crafter Kit, JR press. Above, Lube Pad and reversible primer pocket cleaner.

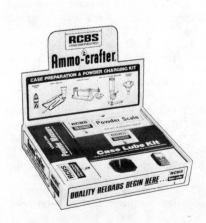

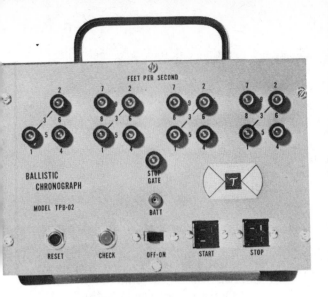

Far left—Latest Telepacific Electronic chronograph reads directly in foot seconds, has bullet-form correction for reading true MV, and uses photoeye screens for continuous shooting.

Left—Telepacific's unusual photoeye screens are battery operated, use only ambient light to trigger readings.

Telepacific Electronics Co.

Col. Burt Miller reported on Telepacific's then new Model TPB-01 chronograph in our 26th edition, a chief virtue of which was its multi-shot screens. These special screens permitted the firing through them of 10 to 20 shots before replacement was required. I ran my own tests with the type TPB-01 later, and found the instrument and the screens fully reliable and accurate.

The new system, named Model TPS-02, includes a TPB-02 chronograph and a set (2) of TS-E Electroscreens, all of which are illustrated nearby. Cost of the TPB-02 is $265, plus shipping, from 3335 Orange Ave., Anaheim, CA. 92804.

That price is well over the cost of Cooke's TPB-01 at some $135, but wait until you learn what the new outfit promises—which I consider little short of amazing at that price!

The operator of this electronic instrument will be able to fire continuously, never leaving the bench, and he'll read out *true* muzzle velocity in foot seconds. He won't have to set down time figures and—then or later—convert them to fps. Also, by turning a dial on the face panel to correct for his particular bullet's ballistic coefficient (using an Ingalls Table figure), *true muzzle velocity* is recorded. This is the first use of an MV Corrector, as Cooke calls it, thus it's a genuinely unique feature.

Fully solid-state electronic circuits are used in the TPB-02 system, plus the latest computer technology, so reliability is assured. Battery operated (two 6V dry cells) the unit is fully portable, and the setting up is compact and easily managed. Screen spacing required

is only 4 feet for MVs from 500 fps to 5,000. Shorter screen separation is feasible as well for air rifles, BB guns, et al. Battery life in operation is said to be about 30 hours of use time.

Accuracy is 1/4 of 1%, plus or minus (plus 1 fps, plus or minus) if screen spacing is held to within .050″ (1/20″) of nominal spacing. In point of fact, the inherent accuracy of readout is maintained despite minor errors in screen spacing. Reading may be slightly more or less, but *uniformity* of reading-to-reading will be held.

Operating the TPB-02 system is uncomplicated—just make sure there's an adequate bullet backstop. Distance from muzzle to first screen should be about 5 feet, the line of fire about 4 inches over the photo sensitive pair of screens. A paper target, clamped to and projecting above screen 2 serves as an aiming point—its only function.

The MV Corrector is set for the bullet loaded, the reset button is pushed (if a previous reading is still displayed on the panel) and the shot is made. The new velocity is then read from the 4 grouped lights—thousands, hundreds, tens and units, from left to right. If no light appears in any group, the reading is zero (0). If one lamp lights, the numeral shown is read; if two lamps are illuminated, the number between them is the recorded figure. Three or 4 lamps are never lit. An admirably simple system, which leads us to the photoeye screens, unique in their own right.

These screens, each measuring 3″ by 2″ by 5″ high, detect the bullet's passage over them. Only the ambient light, usually skylight, is the light source for triggering the

screen, and no adjustment, collimating device or other light source is needed.

The MV Corrector adjustment does not appear on the panel pictured, which shows an earlier instrument. The "Check" button is used to determine if all circuitry is "go." Pushing it lights all bulbs, but at half brightness, if all is well. The "Stop" window lights up after a shot if the shot has been successfully recorded, and it also serves to warn the operator that he needs to hit the "Reset" button before proceeding with another firing. If the "stop" light does not come on after a shot, you can suspect something's gone wrong—the bullet may have missed the 30-degree (approximate) cone-of-fire area, for example, which the paper aiming target should reveal.

The Cooke literature says nothing about protecting the photo-eye screen, but protected they sure as hell should be, and I leave you to guess what'll happen if you don't! I'd suggest placing each of them behind a bullet-proof steel plate or other energy-absorbing material. I use barnyard limestone, commonly available at under $1 a 50-lb. bag. A 6″-10″ depth of this stuff is ample for stopping—by disintegration—any bullet at any velocity except, perhaps, armor piercing types. I haven't tried those.

All in all, this latest TPS-02 Chronograph System sounds highly attractive, and I'm anxious to check one out. I like the easy setup, the battery capability and—most importantly—the MV Corrector, the direct foot-second readout and the surprisingly simple screens. All this for $265 is hard to believe —any other system with similar advantages is much more costly, and none has the MV Corrector.
J. T. A.

Lee Custom Eng.

Richard Lee's rapidly growing young organization has already spun off a new group, Lee Precision Mfg. Co. Between the two of them, they've produced so many interesting and useful articles for the handloader that it's hard to know where to begin—or where to stop!

The best known Lee tool—and I imagine still a best seller for them —is their Lee Loader, a simple, low-cost set of tools for the shotshell man with a bit of time on his hands. Which is simply to say that the Lee Loader (10, 12, 16, 20, 28 and 410, but be sure to indicate chamber length when ordering) lacks speed compared to some bench presses. But it gets there, and it does a good job as well; at $9.95 still, despite everything, there is no better value.

Lee, though, has improvements planned for the veteran Lee shotshell tool. The new Deluxe Lee Loader will include a full length wad starter, 6- and 8-point crimpers and a full set of measures, with all this for only $2 more—or $11.95 for the new outfit.

The same-price Lee Loader for metallic cartridges isn't all that new, either, but the old price yet holds at $9.95, and its mention here affords a good opportunity to comment on the wide range of accessories Lee has developed in the meantime for the tool—there's a Primer Pocket Cleaner (both sizes, .175″ and .210″), a pocketable one-hand priming Tool, a Base-Decapper for crimped-in primers, a Case Spinner for motorized trimming of case necks, chamfering or pocket cleaning, and more.

The latest Lee products include a Bullet Mould that shows design features found on no others—the blocks are of aluminum, which means they'll heat up faster, and lead won't stick to them, either. They're fully vented, too, and the sprue cutter holds its adjustment indefinitely. The Lee Bullet Mould is offered in a good selection of bullet types and weights, for handguns only so far—from 32s through 38/357 and 41/44s to 45 ACP and Long Colt. By the time this is in print Lee may have moulds for rifles and black powder arms— they're definitely on the way. Price? A low $8.98, handles included!

To augment the new bullet moulds, Lee has a Lubricating and Resizer Kit, at $5.98, that includes a pan for holding the lube, a lube

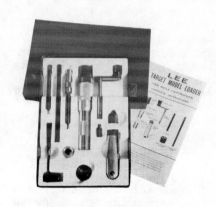

Lee Target Loader

Lee Shotshell Loader

cutting out tool, a resizer with its mating punch, and 2 oz. of grease. A 4-lb. lead pot and a lead ladle are $1.48 each.

The Lee Target Model Loader has been mentioned before, but it should be noted that this special outfit differs in important aspects from the standard Lee Loader. The big item is the combination straight-line bullet seater and inside reamer. The latter tool leaves case mouths of uniform wall thickness (to within a few ten-thousandths), which means that neck tension and bullet pull is also uniform—and there's no argument that sustained uniformity in all phases of handloading is the open secret of enhanced accuracy. The straight-line seater, of course, does just what the name implies, so there's no angled or cocked bullet entering the rifle's chamber. In addition, the Lee Target Model Loader contains other tools for precision loading—the case trimmer assures cases all of the same length (uniformity again) and of minimum length as well. An undetected over-long case in the chamber can impair accuracy and create dangerous pressures, too. Other pieces not found in the standard Lee Loader include a mouth chamfering tool (inside and out), a primer pocket cleaner and Lee's portable recapper. In short, a complete, self-contained set for producing target-class cartridges, all for $24.95.

Lee's very latest tool is a spring-loaded Automatic Primer Pocket Cleaner. A fast push on the handle drives a spiraled rod, its end squared to clean the pocket as it rotates under thrust—our picture will convey the operating principle better! It works well enough, no question of that, but I find it unnecessarily complicated, bulky and expensive. They're $1.98 each, while Lee's own, all-steel pocket cleaners are only 49¢ a copy. I prefer the latter.

Lee Handgun Rest

Lee Bullet Mould

Lee Lube Kit

Alignment Gauges

Norman E. Johnson, operator of the Plum City Ballistics Range (Rt. 1, Box 29A, Plum City, Wis. 54761) now offers a companion tool to his earlier Case Neck Gauge, which checks neck-wall thickness and sells for $30.50 postpaid, including a dial indicator, or at $19.50 without the D. I.

His latest tool is another D. I. type, this one for determining bullet runout in the loaded cartridge. With the D. I. it is $29.50, without $17.50. The same D. I. can be used with either gauge.

See Johnson's article, elsewhere in this edition, on the use of such gauges in predicting—and attaining —accurate shooting levels.

Bitterroot Bullet Co.

Production rate for Bill Steiger's excellent Bonded Core bullets has improved greatly, with all of the various calibers now available for reasonably fast shipment. However, don't be impatient if your order suffers a short delay—those potent big game bullets are not quickly made, and Steigers may be temporarily out of one caliber or another. Six calibers are available now—270 in 130 and 150; 7mm in 140, 160 and 175; 30 (.308″) in 165, 180 and 200; 338 in 200, 225 and 250; 358 in 250, 275 and 300, and 375 in 275, 300 and 325, all grain weights. Prices run from $6.00 to $9 for 20 bullets (that's right, 20, not 50), but BBC bullets are something extra special. Ask for the BBC brochure and you'll see why.

Retained weight of these two BBC 300-gr. 375 bullets is 295 and 297 grains!

Canadian Notes

Our north-of-the border readers may now turn to a new organization for their needs in reloading tools, components, and firearms generally, we've just learned. Amm-O-Mart, Ltd. (P.O. Box 66, Hawkesbury, Ontario) have taken over the mail-order business of Xelex, Ltd. A-O-M is also the exclusive distributor for Star handguns, Italian-made replica arms, and others.

XL Munitions, Ltd., at the same location as A-O-M, has bought the bullet-making equipment of the Curry Bullet Company. Curry bullets will now be made in Canada, but how soon the full line will be available is not known at this time.

Curry bullets are accurate and good; we've used them over the last several years in most of the calibers they make—from 22 through 8mm including all the popular calibers in between—and their performances were in Class A.

Carbide Neck Buttons

Pacific Tool Co. (Box 4495, Lincoln, Nebr. 68504) has begun manufacture of highly precise case neck expander units—made to fit Pacific Durachrome or RCBS dies—which now use tungsten carbide expander buttons. Made in calibers from 22 to 30, Pacific guarantees the TC element for life against dimensional wear. These TC expander balls will permit near-effortless case-neck expansion, with inside neck lubing unnecessary. Quantity loaders are sure to appreciate the new TC unit, and the price is not excessive—$5.50 for either type.

Pacific, of course, continues to offer a complete line of tools and accessories for shotshell and metallic case reloading. Their catalog is free.

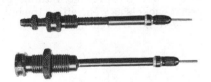

Case-Gard Ammo Boxes

There are 5 sizes/heights offered now, against 3 last year—the PS3 for 38 Special and like size cases, and the PL4, meant for 41 to 44 Magnum and 45 Auto. For rifle cartridges of small size (222 Rem. and similar) there's the RS-50; for 22-250 through 35 Rem., ask for the RM50, and for all the big stuff you'll want the RL50. $1.25 each in the handgun types, $1.95 for the others.

MTM's Adapto Powder Funnel is truly unique—it has 4 interchangeable tubes, each one providing an exact fit for its case or range of cases. This No. AF5 all-caliber funnel is $1.89, and there's another, the UFI, of conventional type, at 75c.

The new Case-Gard No. 150 Loading Tray, of sturdy plastic, has 100 holes on one side—50 each for large and small rifle cases, foreign or U.S. The other side has 50 holes for such cases as the 9mm Luger and 45 Auto. 7.62 Russ., 45-70 and 30-40 are not accommodated. The AF5 is $1.89.

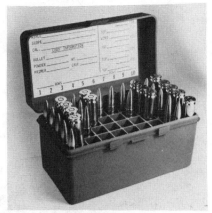

Above—Case Gard 50

C-H Tool & Die

In addition to their No. 301 Case Trimmer—a good tool at a moderate $13.50—complete with one hardened case holder—C-H has a new model this year, the No. 325C. Heavier and sturdier, the new type uses standard shell holders, not steel sleeves, to hold and position the case. The cutter head carries a tungsten carbide blade for a lifetime of use, and a cam-type locking device assures uniform trimming of every case mouth. Subsequent burring, inside and out, of the trimmed necks, is not necessary. The No. 325 Super Case Trimmer, complete with one shell holder and one pilot (your choice) is $24.95. Extra pilots are $1 each, extra shell holders are $2.50 a piece.

C-H will have two brand new items soon, perhaps as you read this. One is a sensitive, low-leverage primer seater of lever type, an eccentric-cut cam assuring, I'm told, positive seating. The price, about $22, will include auto primer feed tubes (one large, one small), but not a shell holder. Equally new— we haven't seen either of these tools—is a canneluring machine of all-steel construction, adjustable for location and depth of the grooving. Cannelures produced will, we understand, equal or better factory cannelures on jacketed handgun bullets. $14.95.

C-H has a bunch of other new and/or interesting stuff for the handloader—powder funnels and drippers, a burring tool with tungsten carbide cutting surfaces for years of service ($4.95), plus others.

Consult our Directory pages for the location of firms or individuals mentioned.

John Dewey Gun Co.

Dewey has a new version of his excellent Bullet Spinner (no longer available as such), one that measures concentricity of both bullets and cases in the one tool. Including a .0001″ dial indicator unit, $89.

JD's Cartridge & Bullet Spinner.

For those who make their own bullets, and particularly for those who do so with an RCBS A-2 or Rockchucker press, Dewey offers a Bullet Ejection Assembly that's quite different, as our picture shows. It does a first class job, of course, but unlike some other ejectors it leaves ample room for working, and it isn't hard to adjust. Pretty much custom made, the new ejector costs $30.

His benchrest quality Neck Sizing Die is the drive-in type, serving also as a primer decapper. The decap rod is included at the low price, but as these are custom made, four fired cases must be sent with the order. These cases should be of the style being shot, that is, reamed or neck-turned if that's your method. $10.00 for this NS Die, (plus $1.00 postage) or $30.00 postpaid for it and a matching Straight Line Seater. The latter is $19.00 separately, plus $1.00 shipping cost. Calibers available—17 on up.

New Half-Jacket Dies

Clymer Mfg. Co., long-time makers of quality chambering reamers, headspace gauges and other shop tools for the gunsmith, are now producing swaging dies for forming half-jacket bullets. A well-made lead-wire cutter ($14.95) is also offered, and extra bullet-nose punches to fit their new swages are $4.75 each. The bullet swaging dies, made in 30, 38, 44 and 45 calibers, sell for $18.95 each.

These new Clymer dies are truly precision made, the finish inside and out faultless, the machining first class. Heat treated and hardened to 52-55 Rockwell, the interiors are honed to 4-6 micro inches, which is mighty smooth.

Threaded ⅞-14 for use in any loading press of good power, there's a flange or rim on the base of the nose punches that lock into the press shellholder. The die is adjustable for any bullet weight, and nose punches can be had in various styles—conical, round nose, wad cutter and SWC.

I've received Clymer swage dies in two calibers—38 and 45—and I was surprised at the ease with which bullets could be made. I've used other swage dies in years past, and none that I recall of this type made bullets with so little effort. The ultra smoothness of the Clymer dies must make the differ-

ence. Bleed off of excess lead is through a hole in the end (not the side) of the Clymer nose punches, so it should be possible, I think, to use ¾-jackets as well, letting the bullet ogive be covered high enough up

or forward to eliminate leading in the bore.

However, so far I've not been able to locate any ¾-jackets, so I can't tell you just how the new Clymer dies perform with those. On the other hand, the several score ½-jacket .357″ bullets I've made are beautiful and they've shot as well or better than any others of like style I've used in the past—aside from some leading, which I'd expected. My Clymer bullets average 157 grains, after final adjustment, the lead dead soft, of course. Using 13.4 grains of Norma 1020, with CCI regular primers, I got good accuracy from a 6½″ barreled S&W Magnum for about 20 shots, from a 2-hand rest. First groups kept within a couple of inches at 25 yards. But then I began to get some leading near the muzzle and accuracy fell off.

Left—Clymer Bullet Die Set.
Below—Clymer Lead Wire Cutter.

Part 2—Components

Remington

Late in 1971 Remington introduced three more handgun cartridges, and it's confidently assumed that the components, including the new bullets—new ones—will be offered to handloaders as well.

First of these is a 95-gr. loading in 38 Special, the round and its charge designed especially for use in short-barreled (2"-2½") revolvers. The new semi-jacketed HP leaves the short barrel at 985 fps. This increased muzzle velocity gives the rapid expansion now considered desirable in police use. (However, for longer-barreled revolvers, Remington suggests the continued use of their 125- and 158-gr. HPs.)

Next is a 38 Special carrying a new 158-gr. semi-wadcutter bullet, useful as a dual-purpose cartridge —target or service.

Last on the new list is a high speed 357 Magnum loading, its 125-gr. semi-jacketed HP moving at a truly fast clip—1675 fps at the muzzle, though from an 8½" barrel, true. Even so, this should make a first class hunting load, for at a full 50 yards it's still going strong—1420 fps and 560 ft. lbs. of energy. At 100 yards, 1215 and 410, but that's a long handgun distance, despite what you may have heard.

Shooters of the Remington 17, using BDL 700 rifles, have all reported (I know of no exception to date) excellent accuracy with factory ammo and off-the-shelf rifles. Average 5-shot groups of one inch or less are common under good conditions—which means that there had better not be much wind! My own sessions with the 17 Rem. produced just about those figures at 100 yards, with Remington ammo. I haven't got room here to list the various handloads I tried, but my best results—and all at 3900 fps, give or take 50 feet— were with 18.4 of 4198 or 20.8 of ReloadeR 11. Both shot well under an inch several times, usually with Hornady's 25-gr. bullets, these from his current production.

Our own chronographing (and that of others also) failed a full 4020 fps with the factory 25-gr. loads, some 3945 being closer to a general average. However, that isn't a great difference—and handloading can close the gap easily enough—and past performance of almost all earlier 17s has been better, if

accuracy is your goal, at MV levels on the order of 3850-3950.

The Remington seminar in late 1971 revealed a bunch of interesting things to the assembled writers and editors—new firearms, of course, among them a handsome little 22 rimfire rifle, looking much like a reduced-scale version of their M700 BDL bolt rifles, and a de luxe, engraved version of the M870 pump shotgun, a truly handsome piece.

Most serious benchrest shooters make their own bullets or buy them from some custom maker. Such bullets, obviously, aren't available to the average shooter ordinarily—the custom bulletmaker has no great output, and the cost of such bullets is fairly steep. The benchrester who rolls his own has trouble enough finding time for his own needs, much less selling any. Remington proposes to change this situation, at least as far as 22 bullets are concerned.

At the seminar Remington's Mike Walker showed us a new 52-gr. HP bullet of .224" diameter, one that will be, he said, comparable in performance to the best handmade 22 bullets available. These new match bullets will be made to tolerances not heretofore obtainable with commercially made production bullets, we were told, and it begins to look as though Remington is right!

In their own tests, using benchrest rifles, the new bullets gave an over-all average of 0.24" extreme spread at 100 yards. In several Remington 40XB-BR rifles with their 20x scopes mounted, the new bullets *averaged*, note, as small as 0.16" for 15 shots, not just 5!

Among the centerfire rifle cartridges, Remington has two new offerings for 1972. One is a 100-gr. "Core-Lokt" bullet for the 25-06 cartridge, initial velocity 3300 fps, and intended for flat, long-range shooting on such game as antelope and whitetail deer.

The other new load is a 90-gr. pointed SP in the 6mm Remington case, but with 120 fps more than the older 90-gr. load for the 244 cartridge (a nice boost), which it supplants. So 244 rifle owners now have a choice of 80- or 90-gr. loads, while the 6mm rifle user can shoot these last two or a 100-gr. load as well. The 100-gr. bullet may not

Remington's new shot shell, the RSP, has one-piece plastic base wad-body construction, offers long reloading life.

stabilize in some 244 rifles, note, because of the slower twist that many of them have.

Remington has a new shotshell, the RXP for claybird busters, and even a new shot size—8½! Remington research shows, we were told, that this new size has ample velocity and energy for dusting clays, but offers 80 more pellets per load than do 8s, and 140 more than 7½s carry. However—coppering the new bet to a degree—Remington will also make the RXP shells with 7½, 8 and 9 shot, and all four sizes will be the hardest shot they've ever made.

Remington has taken special pains with the design and construction of the RXP cartridges. The plastic shell body and the base are integral, the base forged to impart dimensional stability and a lessened need for resizing. This makes the RXP a tough and highly reloadable case. Its primer pocket, also newly designed, gives a superior gas seal, reducing gas leakage or primer setback.

Remington wisely held onto the good features of their target loads —the better venko crimp, which produces a better looking re-crimp on reloading, and stays crimped; their "Power-Piston" wad and 97* primer. These RXP loads will be on the shelves early in 1972, and so will the components used in them.

Remington's Tips on Better Reloading

To aid handloaders wanting to use the new RXP target cases and related components, among others —the same as the factory employs —there's a new 12-page booklet available, the title *Remington's Tips on Better Reloading.* I think this is a first for Remington, as I can't recall any earlier such brochure issuing from Bridgeport. Loads are listed for 12, 20, 28 and 410, with such powders as 700-X, Red Dot, SR-7625, etc., and all are target-type. All wads are of Remington make, clearly indicated as to code number. Understandably, the booklet stresses "Matched Performance" through the use of Remington components, and there's no doubt at all that excellent reloads will result if the reader does just that.

See your dealer for a special plan Remington offers until June 30, 1972 on RXP-12 wads. Fill in the form he'll supply, add $1 and four (4) RXP box tops, then mail to Bridgeport. You'll soon receive 250 RXP plastic wads and a copy of the booklet just described.

Downrange Ballistics for the 25-06 Remington*
100-gr. Pointed Soft Point "Core-Lokt" Bullet

Range (yards)	Velocity (ft.-sec.)	Energy (ft.-lbs.)	Trajectory**
0	3300	2420	—
100	2960	1940	+1.5"
200	2640	1550	0
300	2350	1230	—6.6"
400	2080	960	—19.4"
500	1830	740	—40.4"

*From 26" test barrel, 1 in 10" twist.
**Iron sight height of 0.9", rifle zeroed-in at 200 yards.

Downrange Ballistics for the 6mm Remington*
90-Gr. Pointed Soft Point Bullet
(Interchangeable with 244 Remington)

Range (yards)	Velocity (ft.-sec.)	Energy (ft.-lbs.)	Trajectory**
0	3320	2200	—
100	2980	1770	+1.5"
200	2670	1420	0
300	2380	1130	—6.4"
400	2110	890	—19.0"
500	1860	690	—39.3"

*From 26" test barrel.
**Iron sight height of 0.9", rifle zeroed-in at 200 yards.

Federal Cartridge

Here's a rundown on what's new from Federal for 1972-73, now in its 50th year of production.

A transparent weatherproof plastic box contains 100 Federal Hi-Power 22 cartridges, Long Rifle or Long Rifle Hollow Point. The box, made of sturdy Cycolac for resistance to breakage, has a sliding cover that permits dispensing 5 or more cartridges at a time.

A 3¼ dram, 1⅛-oz. target load to meet the requirements of the International Shooting Union for 1973. The new rules will eliminate nickeled shot and reduce the shot load weight to 1⅛ ozs. Federal's new shell Code F125 has the famous Champion wad, and extra hard lead shot in sizes 7½, 8 and 9 in a plastic hull.

Their 12 gauge Champion target loads are now available in No. 8½ shot, a new size for 16-yard trap. Buckshot loads are now offered in 12 Gauge 2¾" Magnum #1 Buck, with 20 pellets, or with #4 Buck, 34 pellets.

They've added another rifle cartridge, the 44 Remington Magnum with 240-gr. hollow point bullet.

Hercules Powder

I imagine that most of our readers have already learned that Hercules ceased manufacture, late in 1971, of their ReloadeR line of propellant powders—Numbers 7, 11 and 21 are no more, sad to say, for they were highly useful powders. Hercules cited economic reasons for their decision, contending that the ReloadeR brand hadn't sold well enough to justify its continuance. My own feeling is that Hercules didn't give the line enough time to become popular.

For shotshell loaders Hercules has a new and interesting device, a sort of circular slide rule in effect. Rotating the inner wheel until a pointer lies within a selected brand and type of shell case reveals the charge weight of powder for a choice of pellet weights, while another segment of the wheel indicates the wad selected. Some 5 to 9 makes and types of plastic wads are shown for each shell case type.

One side of this new Handloading Data Guide is devoted to Red Dot powder, the other to Green Dot. Twelve gauge only loads are found on the Red Dot side, but 12- and 20-gauge cases and loads are covered for Green Dot. I think this Hercules tool will sell well at its $1 nominal price.

Nosler Bullets

We've heard recurrent rumors that there'd be some new Nosler bullets appearing before long, but on questioning a company man on this point, we got a firm noncommittal answer! Well, these "we can't confirm or deny" replies hardly serve to squelch any grapevine reports, so keep your eyes on the ads.

In any event, for those who've not used the famed Nosler bullets in the field, let nobody tell you that there's any other game bullet quite like the Nosler Partition type. Its performance record has been outstanding for many years, its controlled expansion and high retained-weight qualities making it a deadly projectile. Many big game hunters won't use any others, whether in North America, Africa or Asia.

Hornady-Pacific

Bulletmaker Joyce Hornady now owns Pacific Gunsight of Lincoln, Neb. Hornady noted that "Precision bullets for reloading and precision equipment to reload them with are a natural combination. It has always been our goal to provide the shooting fraternity with the very best product we are capable of producing. We intend to continue the same high quality in our reloading tools and accessories that we have maintained in Hornady bullets."

Early in 1972 Hornady announced two new rifle bullets, both intended for long range varmint shooting. Both show Hornady's secant-ogive shape and inner-grooved jackets for high ballistic performance and maximum expansion, even 'way out there. The 110-gr. 270 HP and the 120-gr. 7mm HP, loaded to 3400-3500 foot seconds respectively, retain 2136 and 2231 fps at 500 yards, good figures indeed, as are their remaining energy numbers as well—1114 and 1327 ft. lbs. at the same distance. Both bullets should perform very well on varmints and lighter game at the longer distances.

Hornady has a Data Sheet that will interest 17-cal. shooters. Good load data, using a half-dozen powders and the Hornady 25-gr. bullet, is given for muzzle velocities from 3500 to 4100 fps, and ballistic data for those same velocities to 500 yards—which might strain a 17-cal. rifle a trifle! Write for this 17-cal. table and for Hornady's Bullets for Handloading List—no charge.

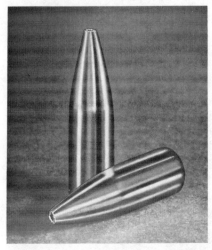

Above, Hornady 7mm 120-gr. HP and 110-gr. 270 HP.

RWS Anvil Primers

Stoeger is now the exclusive distributor in the U.S. for anvil type RWS primers—the kind that all American made cases can take, metallic or shotshell. Many RWS calibers, too, now accept anvil-type primers.

RWS primers are, of course, non-corrosive, non-mercuric and also non-erosive. They're offered in all sizes—small and large handgun, small and large rifle, plus a 209S type for shotshells with .240″ diameter pockets. They're excellent primers, as well, in uniformity of ignition and other performance aspects—we've used thousands—of—them with complete satisfaction. Prices to consumers and dealers—are very attractive.

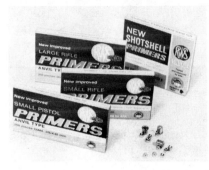

Whitney Shotshells

A new firm, Whitney Cartridge Co. (P.O. Box 608, Cortez, Colo. 81321) is marketing a novel plastic shotshell, in fully loaded form or as components. They're *all-plastic*, too, including the screw-off heads! That's the basic idea—the tubes and the plastic shot sleeves are shot once and discarded, but the base or head sections are retained—and these heads are said to offer 25-40 or more firings. The tubes are colored a brilliant orange shade for easier finding in the grass or brush.

Fully loaded Whitney cartridges (12 gauge only so far) will be about $2.75 a box of 25. Shoot these up, save the heads, and buy the Whitney loaded tubes ($1.85 for 25) or 25 tubes plus wads at less than $14 for 500 of each. Bases are about $2.50 for 100, wads only are 500 for $3.50 or so.

Whitney had a series of tests conducted by the H.P. White Labs, these for patterning essentially, though proof rounds were fired as well. Surprisingly tight patterns were made with some of the loads (up to 95% and more), and at pressures and velocities comparable with conventional loads.

Write to Whitney for further data, current prices, etc.

Speer

Most recently Speer made available a companion bullet to the 224″/70-gr., the newest one a 228″/71-gr., which users of the 22 Savage cartridge will welcome. I wonder how many there are?

Speer also has a new 8mm bullet, this one a 225-gr. SP of .323″ diameter, which should offer excellent heavy brush-timber performance in the 8mm-06 or 8mm belted magnums. Two new handgun bullets for 1972 also—a 9mm of 100 grains in HP form, and a 45 revolver bullet (.452″), their 225-gr. Magnum H.P.

The Speer .451″/200-gr. SP, for 45 ACP use, has been changed for better expansion characteristics—it will be a jacketed HP for '72.

Speer has a new .257″ bullet also, this a 100-gr. hollow point designed for varmints in rifles of the 25-06 class. The big open point means an explosive blowup on the smaller game, and accuracy is said to be superb—first trials by Speer *averaging* well under a half-inch for 5 shots at 100 yards. Sectional density is .216, ballistic coefficient .328, cost is $5.35 per hundred.

I gave the new 100-gr. HP a brief 100-yard trial in a standard barrel Remington 700 BDL, using Speer's mid-power load for 4350 of 53 grains first, with Remington's 9½ primers. Cases had been twice fired, then partially sized. Velocity average for 5 shots—at 15 feet—was 3190, with easy extraction, no signs of pressure. Going to 54 grains, all else the same, showed 3280 average, and there we stopped. Accuracy was good but not excellent—two groups with the 53/4350, 5 shots, went into .89″ and 1.05″, while the grain-higher load tightened these figures slightly—.78″ and .73″. I had the feeling that a bit more powder, say a half- to 1 grain, maybe even a little more, would have tightened things up.

Speer has several new load data sheets available for the asking—though a stamped envelope, with your name and address on it, would be helpful. One of these is on the 17-223, another on the 17 Remington (both using the 25-gr. Hornady bullet), a third covers the 44 Special and Speer's new 200-gr. jacketed HP bullet. The last data sheet is on the 44 Magnum, using the same 200-gr. JHP.

> **Consult our Directory pages for the location of firms or individuals mentioned.**

Robert W. Hart and Son

New Hart neck-turning tool works well.

Latest Hart tool for benchresters—or other high-accuracy fans—is a compact neck-turner that works very nicely. I've just turned a small lot of 22 Hornet necks! The tool does a slick job, the necks smooth and without chatter marks—a carbide cutter does the trick. As with such devices, getting the initial adjustment just right is also a trick. An adjustable step controls depth of cutting on the neck. Cost—$26.45.

For more on other Hart products —neck sizing dies, bullet seaters and such—write to the Harts at 401 Montgomery, Nescopeck, PA 18635.

The Fergusons

The Combo-Chek offers, for the first time, a tool to test bullet run-out and case concentricity in one compact unit. Including a dial indicator of .0001" type, the new instrument is $65.

Their Neck Sizing die is usable at the bench via a mallet or arbor press, and in which the used primer is ejected as the sized case is pushed out. A special virtue of the Ferguson N. S. dies is this: cases fired in one's rifle need not be sent in because Ferguson will supply "custom sized buttons" to let the customer size his case necks to one or another dimension. These special buttons ($3.50 each) are used with the Neck Sizing unit, which sells for $21. All that Ferguson needs is the outside dimension of the "new case" perhaps neck-turned for a smaller OP—thus saving the cost of another $21 die unit.

Ferguson tools are precision ground, lapped and polished, and they all carry a lifetime guarantee to the original owner, barring abuse or obvious neglect.

I thought the original small arbor press made by the Fergusons was just about the last word in such tools, and it's been so-described in these pages. Precisely made, and perfectly efficient, it was—and is—a handsome, well-finished press, ideal for such jobs as neck sizing via knock-out type dies, straight-line bullet seating, and so on.

Still, their latest arbor press, pictured here, offers even greater convenience, though it's as well put together—if not more so—than the older one. The big improvement lies in the vertical adjustability. Loosen a ball handle at the head and that unit may be quickly moved up or down on the sturdy steel column, moved to just where it's needed for short tool or long die work. The die pictured is Lee's target type, longest made that I know of, and the head can be lowered enough to let the rack/ram touch the steel platform.

An excellent bit of tooling, and I have to say, I don't know how Ed Ferguson does it at the price—about $45.

Above, right—Ferguson's latest arbor press offers quick vertical adjustability, shows top quality craftsmanship. *Don Pease photo.*

Below—New Ferguson Combo-Chek tests bullet or cartridge runout.

Reloading the 9mm Luger

Handloading the 9mm Parabellum cartridge can be easy, even with cast bullets—just trim the cases to a minimum, even length, use bullets of the correct shape and hardness, plus the right powders, and you're in business.

by BOB STEINDLER

DEVELOPED BY DWM (Deutsche Waffen-und Munitionsfabriken AG) in 1902 for Georg Luger's toggle-linkage pistol in caliber 7.65mm, the 9mm cartridge came into its own in 1904 when the truncated bullet was introduced for the German Navy pistol of the same design. The German Parabellum pistol was adopted by the Army in 1908 and the pistol, to this date, is known as the *Pistole 08*.

The German munitions makers replaced the truncated bullet for the service cartridge with the round nose bullet in 1915, but truncated loads were manufactured in Europe for pistol and submachineguns until the end of 1930.

As a military round and defense or police cartridge, the 9mm Luger has long been considered as the nearly ideal design. Its small size allows a greater magazine capacity; the recoil is minimal, therefore enabling even the rankest recruit to get on the target and stay on it, or at least darned close to it.

Logistically, the 9mm round has two other military advantages. Its very smallness, and therefore its relatively light weight, permits handling more rounds within the same space or weight limitations, and the cartridge is eminently suitable as handgun, carbine and submachinegun round.

Since the end of WWI, the 9mm Parabellum round has been adopted by numerous military services, with either new guns being designed for the cartridge or existing guns redesigned to handle the round.

Because of its popularity—in Europe the 9mm Luger is a favorite target round—a great many case and bullet designs have been offered. During WW II, the Germans used a steel core bullet as well as a sintered iron bullet. The Swiss at one time made 9mm Parabellum cases from aluminum, and Norway produced a short-range plastic cartridge during the 1950s. A number of munitions makers, here and abroad, have also developed special-purpose 9mm Luger rounds. Among them are armor piercing, signal and subsonic rounds for silenced pistols. Tracer and even teargas cartridges have been developed, although most of these have seen but limited service and distribution. These are now of primary interest to cartridge collectors—and believe me when I say that collecting the various types of 9mm Luger rounds is almost a full-time job.

It took a few years for shooters, handgun fanciers and U.S. arms makers to realize that the 9mm Luger was a well-balanced cartridge. Six years after the end of WW II Colt's introduced the Commander chambered for the 9mm, and from then on the 9mm round and the guns chambered for it have come into their own. The addition of hollow point bullets has made it a handgun hunting cartridge.

For a number of years, when military surplus ammo was plentiful, the warning about not using submachinegun ammo in handguns was repeated with regularity. The explanation was that the SMG ammo was loaded to higher pressures, was therefore hard on handguns, notably the PO8. More recently, and somewhat belatedly since SMG ammo has attained collector status, pressure tests on SMG ammo have revealed that pressures were not excessive for handguns, with the possible exception of the M1910 Glisenti Pistol, which is chambered for the 9mm Glisenti cartridge. This round is interchangeable with the 9mm Luger round, but the Italian ammo is

Above left—One of the most popular domestic 9mm guns is the double action Model 39 S&W. This gun was one of the autos used by the author to test loads, and it has seen service as hunting pistol • Above right—The French MAB autoloader is a handful of gun, has greatest capacity of any 9mm autoloading pistol—a full and hefty 15 rounds.

Below left—The World War II German service P38 pistol, in original condition, was also used as test gun for load developing • Below right—New arrival from Europe is the Spanish Star. Now modified to some extent, it's a close copy of the Colt 45 ACP.

Shotgun Powder Loads for 9mm Luger
Jacketed Bullets

Bullet/grs.	Charge/grs.	MV
90 HP Sierra	8.0/AL-7	1280
	5.8/Red Dot	1385
	8.0/Herco	1472
	5.1/700-X	1400
	5.7/AL-120	1412
	7.9/HS-6	1470
	5.8/Top Mark	1400
95	4.7/Red Dot	1175
104 AP Norma	4.9/N2020	1260
115 HP Norma	7.0/Herco	1340
	4.8/N2020	1165
	4.8/AL-120	1210
	4.7/700-X	1250
116 FMJ RN Norma	5.0/Red Dot	———
	4.4/5066	1102
124 FMJ RN Rem.	5.5/5066	———
125 SP Speer	7.5/AL-7	1140
	7.0/Herco	1260
	5.0/Red Dot	1127
	6.6/HS-6	1130
	5.0/Top Mark	1160

Pistol Powder Loads for 9mm Luger
Jacketed Bullets

Bullet/grs.	Charge/grs.	MV
90 HP Sierra	7.0/Unique	1400
	5.3/Bullseye	1425
95	6.2/Unique	1280
	5.0/Bullseye	1250
115 HP Norma	4.8/Bullseye	1160
	6.6/Unique	1300
116 FMJ RN Norma	4.4/230-P	1100
124 FMJ RN Rem.	4.3/230-P	1075
125 SP Speer	5.0/230-P	1120
	4.8/Bullseye	1170
	6.0/Unique	1140

considerably underpowered when compared with the German or Canadian 9mm Parabellum cartridges.

Berdan primed cases are not worth the trouble reloading since Boxer primed brass is plentiful. The German steel cases, marked "St" on the case head, are hard on dies and although they can be reloaded, it is best to discard them in favor of brass cases.

Ammo Specifications

SAAMI (Sporting Arms and Ammunition Manufacturers Institute) long ago settled that the maximum chamber pressure for the 9mm Parabellum round would be 33,000 psi. Similarly, the bullet diameter should not exceed .3555″, although some of the older European autos will digest bullets with a slightly larger diameter; this is usually the

case with war production guns which have slightly over-size barrels. This has been one of the most frequently encountered problems with pistol ammo, notably Luger ammo. Another trouble spot that has led a good many handloaders into giving up loading for the 9mm is the fact that feeding troubles are likely to develop.

Feeding problems are usually due to errors in bullet selection. The home-swaged or cast bullet is often too soft, thus will hang up or become deformed during the feeding cycle. Bullet design is the other trouble spot. The truncated, or truncated cone bullet seldom gives feeding trouble. The round nose bullet won't hang up unless over-all cartridge length has been exceeded. The total length of the 9mm Luger round should not be more than 1.169″, with 1.16″ being considered as most suitable for the majority of the autoloaders.

Case length is usually specified as .754″, although some guns will handle cases ranging from .740″ to .756″. Longer cases have a tendency to hang up or fail to chamber. More mention will be made about minimum case length when headspacing is discussed.

When the American shooter "discovered" the 9mm Luger, handloaders, too, became seriously interested in this cartridge. (This was the time when you could buy a reasonably clean WW II service PO8 for $50, with a virtually mint condition gun setting you back about $65.) These handloaders invariably followed some of the older and underpowered load data, and failures of these handloads were common, especially in the PO8.

Some of the softer loads sometimes recommended for autoloaders won't function the toggle-linkage of the PO8. If you find that your loads won't function your Luger, your best bet is to see if the gun will function with either factory or surplus ammo. If the gun then operates normally, the fault lies in your handloads, but if the gun still malfunctions, there is some mechanical trouble that must be located and repaired before you can enjoy your Luger.

The standard 9mm Parabellum barrels have a 6 groove, right hand 1:10 twist. However, a few off-beat barrels appear every so often, and if loads recommended here or elsewhere fail to give you reasonably good accuracy, you should check the number of lands and grooves of your barrel. I've found that

some of the lighter bullets, shot with near maximum charges, develop the tumbling habit in such off-beat barrels. Some experimenting proved that a slight reduction of the charge or a heavier bullet often miraculously "restores" the accuracy of the gun. It seems that the shorter bullets with their smaller bearing surfaces don't stabilize in these odd-ball tubes and that obturation or bullet upset is not complete. Hence the relatively poor target performances with such barrels.

In contrast to some other handgun cartridges, the 9mm Luger round headspaces on the case mouth, therefore cases should not be crimped into the bullets. This rule also holds for cast bullets. Because of the manner in which the case headspaces, a short case, that is one measuring less than .751″, should not be used, and .751″ is the length to which cases should be trimmed if that job is required.

Powder Choice

In contrast to many rifle cartridges and some handgun rounds, the 9mm Luger, the 38 special, the

Pistol Powder Loads for 9mm Luger
Cast Bullets

Bullet/grs.	Charge/grs.	MV
115 RN Ohaus #9115R	6.1/Unique	1260
123 B&M	4.8/Bullseye	1125
	6.0/Unique	1300
124 Ohaus #9124C	4.6/Bullseye	1170
	5.9/Unique	1230
125 RN Markell	5.5/Unique	1083
125 H&G #115	4.0/Bullseye	1055
125 Lyman #356402 or #358242	4.6/Bullseye	1170
	6.0/Unique	1245
	3.6/230-P	1000
158 Lyman #358311 *	3.3/Bullseye	940
	4.4/Unique	1041

*This rather heavy bullet gave satisfactory accuracy and performance in only two of the test guns. It is too heavy for my customized PO8 and none of the 158-gr. loads tried in this particular gun was found fully satisfactory.

Shotgun Powder Loads for 9mm Luger
Cast Bullets

Bullet/grs.	Charge/grs.	MV
123 B&M	5.5/5066	1100
125 Lyman #356402 or #358242	6.0/Herco	1170
	5.5/5066	1100
	6.4/HS-6	1200
	4.6/Top Mark	1100
158 Lyman #358311	4.5/Herco	1000
	4.8/HS-6	960
	3.4/Top Mark	900

357 Magnum and several other handgun cartridges can be reloaded with a wide variety of powders. Some of the shotgun powders, especially those offered by Hodgdon, are very well adapted for use in the 9mm Luger case.

The most popular powders are: Bullseye, Unique, Herco, AL-7, 230-P, and Red Dot. Of the Hodgdon powders, I found HS-6 the most suitable. Not only does HS-6 burn clean, it also gives, grain for grain, the best accuracy and the highest velocities. This powder was originally designed for shotshell loaders who stuff magnum hulls.

Hercules Green Dot burns somewhat slower than Red Dot, a powder that has long been used in handgun loads. Hodgdon's Top Mark burns just slightly faster than Red Dot, while DuPont's 700-X, also suitable for loading handgun ammo, has a burning speed that is about halfway between Red Dot and Green Dot.

Winchester's AA20S and AA12S, Hodgdon's Grey B, and Norma's 2020 shotgun powders can also be used for loading the 9mm Luger, and the data given in the special table are those published in various manuals.

All of the loads listed in this article are within the SAAMI chamber-pressure specifications for the 9mm Luger cartridge. While each of these loads has been tested in four different guns, there is always the outside chance that your gun won't digest a certain load. Therefore, these loads, like all other such published information, should be worked up to.

Cast Bullets

While cast bullets for rifles and revolvers should be made from carefully alloyed metals, or even pure lead, casting for most of the selfloading pistols requires a hard bullet metal. Linotype metal is the best of the readily available choices, and bullets should be cast as hard as possible. Cast bullet diameter should not exceed .3555″, and slightly undersized moulds should be used, thus reducing the need for too much bullet sizing. Suitable moulds are offered by Hensley and Gibbs, Lyman, Ohaus, Lee Engineering, and Belding & Mull.

If you want to shoot cast bullets, but are not inclined to mess around with casting or have only limited space for your loading hobby, excellent cast bullets can be bought

Cast bullets. Top three, from left—Markell 125-gr. RN, 125-gr. RN Golden Arrow, 125-gr. Spire Point. Bottom, from left—125-gr. Spire Point Golden Arrow. Last is 125-gr. bullet cast from Hensley & Gibbs # 115 mould. Bullets should be sized not larger than .3555″.

from many sources.* To test the performance of factory cast bullets, I tried the Markell brand. These bullets, delivered sized and lubricated, are cast to the correct hardness. This company offers four different types of 125-gr. bullets suitable for loading 9mm ammo. I

*See the HANDLOADER'S DIGEST catalog pages.

Factory jacketed bullets. From left, top—Norma 115-gr. HP; Speer 125-gr. SP. Second row—Super Vel's 108-gr. JSP and 90-gr. JHP. Bottom—Sierra 90-gr. HC and Norma 116-gr. SPRN.

especially liked the performance of the round nose and spire point bullets which, with a heavy copper coating, are tradenamed Golden Arrow. Accuracy was on a par with any of the jacketed bullets. As a current radio commercial says: "Try it, you'll like it!"

The use of cast bullets usually means that there'll be a certain amount of leading. With the hard cast 9mm bullets, there is little of that, and routine gun cleaning is all that is required. After my actual load testing was done, I had about 60 rounds of sundry Markell loads left. I cleaned one of the guns I had been using, then fired 40 rounds, using the rest of the loaded ammo for another accuracy check. Fouling was identical, or very nearly so, to the degree of fouling that occurs when the same amount of jacketed ammo is run through an auto.

The bulk of the load testing was done with CCI 500 and Remington 1½ Small Pistol primers. I also tried 20 rounds with my last lot of Federal 100 primers, and in comparison with Remington and CCI primers, there was little variation in the velocities, and accuracy didn't appear to vary beyond the normal limits.

For loading large quantities of handgun ammo, I'm partial to a turret press since it allows me to leave the dies set up, and priming on the Lyman turret press is simple and speedy. For the testing I took the time and trouble to clean the primer pockets, but for plinking ammo, I seldom bother with this step in reloading. I've found that cleaning the brass ultrasonically, by tumbling, or chemically with either Brownell's Case-Brite or Birchwood-Casey's Case Cleaner (after two firings) not only makes the brass look factory-new, but the process also removes all of the primer residue in the primer pockets of the cases.

Since the case mouth needs no crimping, the brass in this area of the case is not worked nearly as much as that in the 38 Special cartridge, for instance. Hence, case life is good and if you can recover your cases when shooting an autoloader, your shooting fun can go on for quite a spell with the same batch of cases. Cast bullets are inexpensive, primer and powder costs are small, and even if you blast away with jacketed bullets, the cost per round is still quite low—and that's what reloading is all about. ●

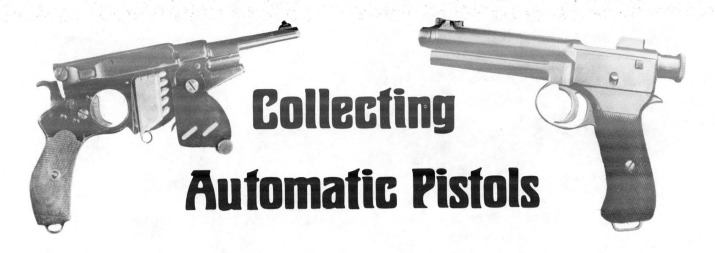

Collecting Automatic Pistols

*In spite of their greatly increased interest for collectors, over a
relatively short span of time, many auto pistols may
still be found at attractive prices. Here is how to begin collecting,
what to guard against and a check list of average prices.*

by J.B. WOOD

THERE WAS A TIME, not many years ago, when an excellent Luger pistol could be purchased for around $30, and a decent Polish Radom for less than $20. There was also a time when I knew all the other serious automatic pistol collectors in a surrounding three-state area. Both of them! Well, for good or bad, those days are gone forever.

To better understand what has happened over the past 25 years, let's look back to the "early days." Of course, self-loading pistols have been commercially produced since the last decade of the 19th century, and there were, no doubt, individual collectors who got started at about that time. However, the majority of the world military powers did not complete the change from revolvers to automatic pistols until the mid-1930s, while interest in collecting self-loaders really came to life only after WW II, a result of souvenir and surplus pistols brought in by returning troops and enterprising dealers.

As is usually the case, the publication of many articles and several books during this period spurred collector interest. One of the earliest such books, Datig's fine volume on the Luger,* resulted in much collector concentration on the Pistole Parabellum, and the price of the P-08 began to climb. Even popular fiction had a small effect:

*The Luger Pistol, 1962 Borden Pub., Alhambra, Ca.

Above left—The 6.5mm Bergmann Model 1896 commercial, with magazine gate open and a clip of 5 cartridges in place. The rounds and original clip are even more rare than the pistol. Above right—The 8mm Roth-Steyr Model 1907 has a unique firing and locking system. Semi-double action, striker-fired, with a double-lug rotating barrel locking system and a marvelously complicated takedown. These are getting harder to find. Below—Pistols for the 9mm Parabellum round are a good collecting field. Top to bottom: Browning Model 1935 commercial with stock slot and tangent sight. Walther P-38 military, made by Mauser in 1943. Radom Model 1935, early Nazi-occupation type.

Following Ian Fleming's improbable James Bond, the Walther PPK became a most desirable item, and so was any sidearm purported to have been a "favorite of the Waffen-SS."

Determining the exact time when collecting automatic pistols came into its own would be almost impossible. However, it can safely be said that more serious collections were begun during the past 20 years or so than in the previous 50. As the number of collectors has grown, the value and scarcity of certain items has increased accordingly. Monetary inflation has been a relatively small factor.

As in other areas of firearms collecting, time has produced several realms of specialization. Perhaps the first to evolve was a select group interested only in the Luger. Its graceful lines, esoteric appearance, unique mechanism, and infinite variations quickly made it a favorite. Although it was produced in great quantity, the rarity of certain types has resulted in a continuous rise in prices which has affected even the more common models. As an example of this, a 7.65mm DWM Model 1923 commercial I bought for $30 in 1950 would now easily bring around $200. In excellent condition, with all numbers matching, even an ordinary WW II military model is now valued in excess of $125. Luger values today run from an absolute

A trio of Astras. Top to bottom: Model 400 (1921), 9mm Bergmann-Bayard (Largo), the scarce Navy type. Model 600 (1943), 9mm Parabellum, commercial type without Nazi Waffen-Amt markings. Model 300 pre-WW II commercial type in 9mm Short (Kurz).

Buy now, boast later. Quite reasonable at present, these three will become scarce and expensive in years to come. Top to bottom. 8mm Nambu Type 14, 7.65mm Long French Model 1935-S and 7.65mm Dreyse Model 1907.

low of about $75 to a maximum of more than $1000. This estimate, of course, does not include the rarest of all Lugers, the original 45 ACP model, of which two only are known to exist! They're priceless.

While I don't want to sound too discouraging, it's obvious that anyone now beginning a collection of Lugers should have a comfortable supply of money. Another absolute necessity for the Luger collector is reference material. I can think of no other pistol for which accurate identification books are so important. Besides Datig's book, here are

two of the best: *Luger Variations* by Harry Jones,* and *Lugers At Random* by Charles Kenyon, Jr.†

Another popular form of specialized collecting is the single manufacturer concept. This works well only if the manufacturer chosen has produced enough of a variety to allow a collection of respectable size. For instance, trying to gather an example of each pistol bearing the Walther name would make an interesting and impressive display. At the other extreme, a good exam-

*Torrance, Ca., 1959   †Chicago, Ill.,1970

ple might be the Ortgies pistol: One each of the three calibers, 25, 32 and 380 ACP, an example of the original Ortgies-produced type (before Deutsche Werk took over), and one of the 380 types with the manual safety. A total of only 5 pieces, and the collection would be complete. Also, in this particular case, there is so little variation in mechanism and appearance that the interest aroused would be very limited.

Collecting by caliber or cartridge has become a common system. This is a good plan, as in some calibers,

"Papa" and "Baby" Czech pistols, unusual in that the firing system is double-action *only*. That is, the hammer does not remain cocked when the slide cycles, but returns to "down" position, and a full revolver-type pull on the trigger is required to fire again. Upper: 9mm Short (380 ACP) Model 1938. Lower: 6.35mm (25 ACP) Model 1945.

The new breed, currently in production. Upper: 9mm Beretta Model 951 Brigadier. Beautifully engineered, superb balance, with a modified Walther P-38 type locking system. Lower: 9mm MAB Model PA-15, having a turning barrel locking system and the largest magazine capacity currently made, 15 rounds.

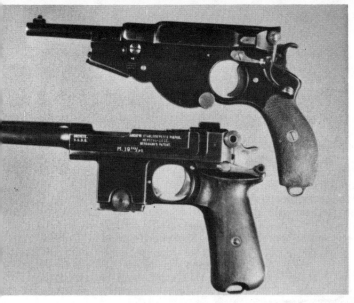

Commercial and military Bergmanns. Upper: 6.5mm commercial, Model 1896. Lower: 9mm Danish military, Model 1910/21, made for Denmark by Pieper of Belgium.

Scarce variations of otherwise common pistols. Upper: 7.65mm Czech CZ Model 1927, Pre-WW II commercial type. The common type has "Pistole Modell 27" in large letters on the left slide flat. Lower: 7.65mm Ortgies. Slide marks differ slightly from the common type; the more obvious clue is the "H.O." monogram on the grips, this one made before Hermann Ortgies leased production rights to the Deutsche Werke in Erfurt. Both of these are more difficult to find, and more valuable, than the usual types of the same pistols.

such as 25 or 32 ACP, the variations are seemingly endless. When caliber alone is the standard, 9mm is an excellent field. If a single cartridge is chosen as a guideline, however, the collection may be severely limited. The 9mm Browning Long, for instance, has had only three pistols chambered for it and produced in quantity: The Browning Model 1903, the Webley Military and Police, and the Le Francais Model 1928. An interesting, but exceedingly small, collection.

There are several other forms of specialization: One collector I know is interested only in contract pieces, those manufactured in one country for sale to another. Some collect only military sidearms, others the pistols of a specific era, such as World War II.

My own collection is an example of still another pattern: I am interested mainly in pistols having unusual firing or locking mech-

anisms. My pieces range from the ultra-rare Smith & Wesson in 32 ACP to the realtively common but mechanically intriguing 7.65mm Hungarian Frommer-Stop. I like the unusual semi-double-action firing system of the 8mm Roth-Steyr Model 1907, and the beautifully engineered locking system of the 7.65mm Czech Model 1952 pistol. Since there is hardly any firing mechanism that hasn't been tried

Similar, but very different. Upper: 7.65mm Luger by DWM, Model 1923 commercial, value about $200. Lower: Italian 9mm Glisenti Model 1910, value in this fine condition about $100. The locking systems also differ greatly, the Glisenti being actually a retarded-blowback action.

Two interesting pistols with different locking systems. Upper: Danish 9mm Bergmann Model 1910/21, made by Pieper in Belgium, having a falling-block bolt lock. Lower: Austrian 9mm Steyr-Hahn Model 1912, with a rotating barrel lock.

Two Smith & Wessons with a vast value-span. Upper: 35 S&W Model 1913, 8,350 produced, value about $75. Lower: 32 S&W Model 1924, only 957 produced, value in this fine condition about $500. The one shown, obtained from the original buyer, is number 303, and has been fired exactly 18 times.

at some time in the past, it will be a long time before I run out of strange applications to discover!

Collecting by nationality will result in a relatively small, but definitive, collection. American pocket automatics, for example, is a good field. There are only 8 basic types (with some caliber options), three of them quite rare. They are: Colt, Smith & Wesson, Savage, Harrington & Richardson, Davis-Warner, Remington, Union, and Phoenix. The last two were made in very small numbers, while the S & W pistol saw very limited production —in 35 caliber, 8350 were made, and in 32, only 957, making it the rarest production pocket automatic in the U. S., and the most valuable. In good used condition, the price can be close to $200, and in excellent, near-new condition, around $500 would be a not unreasonable estimate.

A nationality collection of German or Belgian automatics would, or course, offer a much wider field than some other countries, as these two have produced the majority of self-loaders in existence.

The Beginning Collector

Now, for the reader who has just become interested in automatics, and is contemplating making a collection, some thoughts toward a good beginning: First, obtain as many good reference sources as possible, especially if you are somewhat unfamiliar with the relative

scarcity of certain self-loaders. This will lessen the probability of your being stung, and will help prevent your passing up what might be a fine bargain.

Any firearms magazine article on automatics should become a part of your library, particularly those which refer to the origin and history of the pistol. Past editions of the GUN DIGEST also contain much valuable information. Two that immediately come to mind are: "Military Handguns for Sporting Use" by Frank C. Barnes, 1964 edition, and "Shoulder

Two pistols with odd and interesting mechanical features. Upper: 7.65mm Steyr Model 1906-08, with hinged tip-up barrel and 2-position magazine to permit single loading and firing. Lower: 7.65mm Frommer-Stop, having a fully locked long-recoil system with rotating bolt head.

Stocks for Self-Loading Pistols" by B. William Brian, 1966 edition.

Catalogs and brochures are another good source of information. As an example, I have one put out by Golden State Arms around 1958 titled *World's Guns*. It is no longer available, but might be found at a gun show or used-book dealer; it contains two fine sections on automatics. For bibliographical data on the books listed below, see the Arms Library pages elsewhere in this issue.

In hard cover books, there are two large volumes which will be almost indispensable: *Small Arms of the World* by W. H. B. Smith and Joseph E. Smith, and *International Armament* Volume I, by George B. Johnson and Hans Bert Lockhoven. A fine book for the advanced collector is R. K. Wilson's *Textbook of Auto-*

matic Pistols, but it has been out of print since about 1948. It is hard to find and expensive. If you have decided to specialize, you will need books which thoroughly cover the material in which you are interested. Here are a few of these:

Walther Pistols and Rifles by W. H. B. Smith.

Mauser Rifles and Pistols by W. H. B. Smith.

Ten Shots Quick by Daniel K. Stern. (Savage pistols)

Mauser Self-Loading Pistols by James N. Belford and H. J. Dunlap.

System Mauser by John W. Breathed and Joseph J. Schroeder Jr.

To this list should be added the three Luger books mentioned earlier.

When you are ready to begin building a collection there are several important points to keep in mind. As with any branch of firearms collecting, condition is, of course, important. If the parts are numbered, all must match the main serial number. All parts should be original to the pistol, including, if possible, the magazine. Finish *must* be original. I belong to the purist school of thought on this. In my opinion, rebluing or plating of any automatic instantly removes all collector value. Several years ago, at a gun show, I saw a Krieghoff Luger which had been entirely chromed. From its clear markings and sharp edges, it was apparent that it had been in fine condition before this

Two Bayard pistols, one often seen, one seldom. Upper: 7.65mm (32 ACP) Model 1910, unsuccessful competitor with the Browning of the same period, and relatively scarce. Lower: 7.65mm "Baby" Model, one of the smallest pistols made in this caliber, and more common than the one above.

atrocity was committed. It even had simulated pearl grips! I try to avoid remembering this one just before dinner.

Speaking of grips, most of those on pre-WW II pistols should be either of wood or hard rubber. If an older pistol is found with plastic grips, they're probably replacements. Of course, there are exceptions to this, such as the Walther PPK, which had plastic grips originally.

When buying for a collection, even if the pistol will not be fired again, it should be in good operating condition. Here are 6 functional checkpoints:

Functional Check List

1. Firing pin, or striker. Be sure that the point has not been broken off or, in the case of striker-type pistols, that the sear projection is not broken. Keep in mind the fact that for many pistols, especially those made before WW II, *original* parts are no longer readily available. For some of the better-known pistols, replacement parts are currently being made, but these often require extensive fitting by a competent gunsmith. The only alternative is to have them made, a frequently expensive proposition. This applies to most of the parts mentioned in this checklist.

2. Extractor and ejector. In both cases, replacement would be expensive. Condition of these parts is easily seen with slide open. It should be noted that in many striker-fired pistols, the striker point acts as the ejector.

Not rare, but hard to find because of their popularity as personal protection pistols. Upper: 7.65mm Sauer Model 38H double action. Lower: 9mm Short Beretta Model 1934.

Webley self-loaders are not as well known as their revolvers, nor as easily found. Upper: 9mm Military & Police, chambered for the 9mm Browning Long cartridge. Lower: 7.65mm (32 ACP) Metropolitan Police. Other pistols by Webley include the huge 455 Navy Model, a rare experimental type in 38 ACP.

Three of the four double-action pistols in 25 ACP. Not shown is the ultra-rare Walther PP or PPK. Walther recently added a fifth to this collection, the new TPH, not available in the U.S. since the G.C.A. of 1968. From the top: Le Francais, Wiener, CZ.

3. Disconnector. This, of course, is the part which prevents more than one shot being fired with each pull of the trigger. To check its operation, hold the trigger back and cycle the slide. The pistol should remain cocked when the slide closes, but when the trigger is released and pulled again, the hammer or striker should fall with an audible snap. If not, disconnector problems can usually be cured, without costly parts replacement, by any competent gunsmith.

4. Springs. Determining the proper tension is a matter of "feel," which can only be learned. However, it might be helpful to note that everything on a self-loader should operate with a healthy snap. A weak recoil spring can be determined by holding the pistol pointing up, and easing the bolt or slide closed. If the spring does not carry it all the way to a tight closure, it is insufficient.

5. Grips. If these are cracked or broken, replacements which are near the original in appearance are sometimes difficult to find. However, very good imitations for several of the better-known pistols are available from Fitz, Scott or Sile.

6. Magazine. The heart of the feed system and, when damaged, the source of more automatic troubles than any other part. To check a magazine, inspect it for obvious dents, cracks or deformations, especially around the feed lips at the top. Inevitably, you'll find one showing signs that some imbecile has attempted to "adjust" the feed lips with pliers. Sometimes magazine damage can be repaired, and if the one in question is original, this would be best. If the magazine is missing, original replacements

can often be had from Numrich, West Hurley, N.Y., who also have other original parts from dismantled pistols. If an original magazine cannot be found, good replacements for many pistols are currently manufactured by Triple K, San Diego, Calif., who also supply many newly-made internal parts.

This completes the list of checkpoints, but keep in mind that as the rarity of the pistol increases, the possibility of finding original replacement parts decreases, so check such pistols more carefully.

Older pistols, such as those made before or during WW II, are always a good buy if in excellent condition and the price is right. This applies even if it is a relatively common type. Also, keep a sharp eye for any otherwise ordinary pistol which has small differences from usual production pieces, such as odd markings, slight changes in grips, or in caliber. As an example of the last, the Walther PP pistol in 7.65mm (32 ACP), pre-war production, is not rare. Excellent examples can be found for $60 to $75. Fewer were made in 9mm Kurz

(380 ACP), and the value goes up to about $100. However, in 6.35mm (25 ACP), it was made only experimentally, and the value jumps to around $500.

In most pistols made in 32 and 380 ACP, the 380 will be the scarcer. Among some, such as the Sauer 38H and the original Mauser HSc, the 380 is in the ultra-rare category. One exception to this rule is the Remington Model 51 pistol. More were made in 380, and the 32 is the scarce model. From these illustrations it can easily be seen how a simple difference in caliber can drastically affect value.

Sleepers and Prices

There are certain pistols, mostly in the military group which, until recently, have been ignored by both collectors and dealers. They can often still be found at very reasonable prices, and when in very good condition are an excellent buy, the sort of thing collectors will be proudly displaying in years to come. They are:
9mm Astra Models 400 and 600
9mm Radom Model 35

9mm Steyr-Hahn Model 1912
8mm Roth-Steyr Model 1907
8mm Nambu Types 14 and 94
7.65mm French Model 1935-A and 1935-S

Many of the above can be found in quite good condition for as little as $40, seldom more than $50. To a list of good buys we might add any Luger with all matching numbers in very good condition for less than $100.

For the benefit of the beginning collector, here is a list of often-encountered pieces in the non-rare category, and their approximate current value. Please note that the amount listed is a *collector's value* for pieces in *very good* to *excellent condition*, and not meant to apply to ordinary examples for protection or sporting use.

Those pistols listed 32 ACP which are not in the 380 list were either not made in that caliber, or are excessively rare. Because of the extremely wide range of rarity and values, I'll show only a brief list of pistols in 9mm Luger (Parabellum) caliber.

Sleepers and Prices

In 6.35mm (25 ACP) caliber:

Colt (original model)	$60 - $ 75
Harrington & Richardson	$40 - $ 55
Mauser Model 1910-34	$50 - $ 60
Ortgies	$30 - $ 40
CZ Model 45	$60 - $ 85
Le Francais	$35 - $ 50
Beretta (hammerless)	$35 - $ 50
Walther Model 9	$45 - $ 65
Walther Model 8	$50 - $ 70
Browning (original model)	$35 - $ 50

In 7.65mm (32 ACP) caliber:

Colt	$50 - $ 90
Savage 1908-17	$45 - $ 65
Harrington & Richardson	$40 - $ 75
Remington Model 51	$70 - $100
Warner Infallible	$40 - $ 65
Mauser 1910-34	$50 - $ 75
Mauser HSc (pre-war)	$60 - $ 80
Sauer 38H	$60 - $ 80
Sauer (old model)	$40 - $ 60
Walther Model 4	$35 - $ 50
Walther PP & PPK (pre-war)	$75 - $110
Ortgies	$40 - $ 60
Dreyse	$30 - $ 40
Frommer	$35 - $ 50
Femaru	$50 - $ 65
Bayard ("Baby")	$50 - $ 65
Browning 1900	$40 - $ 60
Browning 1910	$40 - $ 60
Browning 1922	$30 - $ 50
CZ 1927	$40 - $ 65
Astra Model 300	$40 - $ 60
Beretta 1915	$40 - $ 60
Beretta 1934	$40 - $ 60

Six of the eight 32 ACP American pocket automatics. Clockwise from top: Remington Model 51, Davis-Warner "Infallible," Smith & Wesson, Colt, Harrington & Richardson and Savage. Not shown: the Union and the Phoenix.

In 9mm Short (380 ACP) caliber:

Colt	$ 65 - $100
Savage 1917	$ 50 - $ 65
Remington Model 51	$ 60 - $ 85
Walther PP (pre-war)	$100 - $150
Ortgies	$ 50 - $ 65
Bayard ("Baby")	$ 50 - $ 65
Browning 1910	$ 45 - $ 65
Browning 1922	$ 40 - $ 60
CZ 1924-26	$ 60 - $ 75
CZ 1938	$ 60 - $ 75
Astra Model 300	$ 60 - $ 75
Beretta 1934	$ 60 - $ 75

The three lists above contain, of course, only a few of the many pistols which have been made, the ones most likely to be seen by a new collector. Regarding the prices, it should also be noted that the higher figure could be adjusted upward in certain special cases. For instance, let's say you have a 7.65mm Walther PPK, excellent condition, maximum value around $75. Now, add the fact that it has the Third Relch Emblem, the eagle holding a swastika, embossed on the grip. The value goes up to about $90. Then, suppose it is also accompanied by the original box with spare magazine, cleaning rod, and instruction sheet. The value now jumps to $100 or more. Certain markings on the slide can add still more value, and if it bears an engraved inscription which translates: "Presented to Hermann Goering in gratitude for his services to the Reich," *and* is authenticated, well, you can name your own price!

As you can see, the beginning collector has several choices. He can start a general collection or specialize. He can assemble a fine assortment for less than $50 per piece or, if money is plentiful, he can strive for the older, more esoteric names like Borchardt, Schwarzlose, Schonberger, Campo-Giro, Bergmann or Charola y Anitua.

In closing, I'd like to mention again that rarest, perhaps, of all automatics, the 45 Luger, produced experimentally for the U. S. Ordnance tests of 1907. Reportedly, Serial No. 1 was damaged beyond repair by the "torture" elements of the testing. Serial No. 2 is in the famed Sidney Aberman collection in Pittsburgh. Serial No. 3 was, at last report, owned by a prominent collector in Louisiana. It is believed that only the three were made. Possibly, however, somewhere out there, serial No. 4 exists—and maybe you'll find it! Good Luck.

●

In 9mm Parabellum (incl. Glisentis):

Polish Radom P-35, original issue	$100 - $140
Early Nazi Occupation type	$ 60 - $ 75
Late Nazi Occupation type	$ 70 - $ 85
Browning P-35 (Hi-Power)	
Pre-WW II Commercial	$100 - $125
With stock slot and tangent sight	$200 - $250
Nazi Occupation type	$ 80 - $100
Canadian Inglis type	$150 - $200
Walther P-38, pre-war Commercial	$250 - $300
WW II issue, various factory codes	$100 - $125
Walther Model 6 (rare)	$350 - $500
Astra Model 600	$ 65 - $ 85
Beretta Model 1915*	$ 65 - $ 85
Beretta Model 1923*	$ 75 - $100
Glisenti Model 1910*	$100 - $125
Mauser Model 1916 (broom-handle)	$175 - $250
Finnish Lahti Model 1935	$150 - $175
Swedish Lahti Model 1940	$100 - $125

*These three Italian pistols were designed for the 9mm Glisenti, a lower-powered version of the Parabellum cartridge. The Walther Model 6 is an unlocked, straight blowback pistol; unlike the Astra 600 it does not have sufficient compensation for standard 9mm P cartridges. It should never be fired unless greatly reduced hand-loads are used.

Luger Pistols—9mm Parabellum

WW I Military (DWM, Erfurt)	$125 - $175
WW II Military (DWM, Mauser Code)	$100 - $150
Post-WW I Commercial (DWM, Master Banner)	$200 - $250
Artillery Model (tangent sight on long barrel)	$200 - $300
Krieghoff	$350 - $750
Simson	$350 - $400
Vickers (Dutch contract)	$350 - $400
Swiss	$350 - $400
Navy Model	$450 - $500
Bulgarian contract	$500 - $600
Portuguese contract	$300 - $350

This is a very general and over-simplified list of Lugers. Many small factors can have a great effect on the value, such as special markings, the presence or absence of stock lug, sear safety, hold-open device, and so on. Where the values on this list are concerned, it is assumed that the pistol is in Very Good to Excellent condition, with all numbers matching, including the magazine. However, not all magazines were orginally numbered, such as the wooden-endpiece commercial types.

In 9mm Bergmann-Bayard (in Spain, 9mm Largo):

Astra Model 400 (no special markings)	$ 50 - $ 65
With Guardia Civil marks	$100 - $125
With Navy marks	$125 - $150
Campo-Giro Model 1913	$150 - $200
Campo-Giro Model 1913-16	$100 - $150
Bergmann Model 1910-21 (Danish)	$150 - $200

In 7.63mm Mauser (.30 Mauser) and 7.62mm Russian:

Mauser Model 1912 (broom-handle)	$125 - $175
Mauser Model 1920 (Bolo)	$175 - $200
Tokarev Model 1930	$ 75 - $100
Tokarev Model 1933	$ 40 - $ 65

Shooter's Showcase

Mag-Na-Port

EDM (elector-discharge machining) is the "secret" of this new muzzle brake and its precision-controlled installation, if that's the right word for this operation. What's EDM? Very briefly, it's a metal-erosion technique using carbon electrodes that control the area to be processed—in this instance small trapezoidal openings, into and through the barrel, that direct powder gases upward and outward to reduce recoil.

There's little question nowadays that muzzle brakes can and do reduce muzzle jump and recoil, and the Mag-Na-Port system has clearly additional value—the required slot or opening is smoothly and cleanly made, with no burring in or out resulting. For this reason lapping of the bore isn't required. No effect is had on blueing or nickeling outside the Mag-Na-Port area, so no refinishing is needed.

Any firearm (except shotguns or those having shrouded barrels) can have the Mag-Na-Port treatment, the cost a uniform $29.50, plus transport costs both ways. Delivery can usually be had in 2 weeks. Write for full information.

Hunting Accidents Drop

Pennsylvania deer hunters compiled that state's best safety record in over 15 years in 1971, with 51 total and 5 fatal accidents reported. There were more than 1.5 million hunting licenses sold in the Keystone State in 1971.

New York state recorded only three hunting fatalities in 1971, the lowest number since that state began keeping accident records. Well over one million hunting licenses were sold in the Empire State in 1971.

Aristocratie du Pistolet

Aristocratie du Pistolet (the Handgun Aristocracy) is a big, profusely illustrated book (8½"x11") published in Paris (1971) by Andre Balland. Its 358 pages carry 408 black and white illustrations. All text material is in French, note, and the price is about $25 from Ray Riling.

The authors are two Frenchmen, Raymond Caranta (our Continental European Editor) and Pierre Cantegrit, a former pistol champion.

Fifteen chapters tell the story of the most glamorous handguns made during the industrial period, from 1847 to date, with references to the men who designed or used them.

The famous "Broomhandle" Mauser automatic pistols are described, together with Lugers made in Germany and Switzerland, Colt automatic pistols, Belgian Brownings, old and new Walther's and the Swiss Hammerli products.

Among the revolvers listed are the Colt Walker, 1851 Navy and 1860 Army, the 1873 Single Action Army, Remington's "New Models," the S&W Russian, Safety Hammerless, Military and Police and 357 magnum models, plus numerous other arms, of course.

Among the rare illustrations in this book are the blow-forward 1894 Mannlicher auto pistol, 1894 and 1910 Bergmann models, the complete set of fifteen 9mm Parabellum experimental automatic pistols (not Lugers) made at the Bern Waffenfabrik from 1943 to 1947, and many more.   *Jean Delalune.*

An engraved Browning, circa 1900, as illustrated in *Aristocratie du Pistolet.*

Browning Name Change

The name of the Browning Arms Company has been shortened to "Browning." John Val Browning, company president, said the name was changed to better reflect the company's expanding lines. Since 1962 Browning has been diversifying until their products now cover a wide range—besides quality sporting arms, a new ammo line and accessories, Browning now markets fishing rods and reels, archery tackle, hunting apparel, boots and knives, power boats, Aero-Craft aluminum skiffs and canoes and the Bag-Boy line of golf carts. The new title will be: Browning, Route 1, Morgan, Utah 84050.

Williams Rustproof Trigger Shoes

A full line of lightweight, aluminum alloy trigger shoes is being made by Williams Gun Sight Company. Extra wide, they offer a much larger area for the trigger finger, resulting in a more positive pull and greater control. The inside

curve is machine grooved for a non-slip, more comfortable grip.

They're fast and easy to install—just place over trigger and tighten hex nuts with the wrench (included). They are available for most popular rifles, shotguns and handguns—cost, $2.95.

Pan Primers/Forg-Fire Flints

Green River Forge (4326—120th Ave., S.E., Bellevue, WA 98006) has a useful device for flintlock shooters. The Pan Primer, solid brass throughout, is a spring-loaded plunger tube intended for installation—in a few minutes—into the neck of a powder horn. Then a jab—fast or slow—of the spout into the pan deposits a priming charge, small or large as required. $5.50 postpaid, and well worth it in convenience alone, not to mention its rapid-use and charge-uniformity aspects.

Few things are truly "new," but Frank W. Straight Forged Flints do qualify. What are they made of? I've no idea, but their sparking life seems almost unlimited. Of gem-like hardness, and uniform in size, over 1000 shots were fired with one at Friendship in the fall of 1971, *using one edge only!* Multiply that long run by two (for the other edge), and the $3 each cost shrinks to insignificance. A smaller Forged Flint, one striking edge only, for pistols is $1.75. Both are sold on a 10-day trial guarantee, money refunded without argument or questions.

Ted Fellowes, muzzle-loading gunmaker of Seattle, Washington—who can also supply the Green River Pan Primer—says that Straight's Forged Flints are everything they're said to be.   *J.T.A.*

CIL (Box 10, Montreal 101, Quebec, and Box 831, Plattsburgh, NY 12901) has a new, color catalog for 1972-73. In it is a line of shotguns and rifles (rimfire and centerfire), plus their entire cartridge range. The new catalog is worth writing for, but please note that none of the firearms nor the handgun ammunition is available to U.S. residents. The long gun cartridges, metallics and shotshells, *are* offered in the U.S. *J.T.A.*

Woods Sport-Toters

The problem of packing hunting and fishing gear is an ever-present one It just doesn't fit well in normal type luggage.

The Woods special Sport-Toter pictured is a useful departure from the ordinary. Lightweight and roomy, it's made of 10-oz. Permasol pearl grey canvas. Reinforced at all strain points with leather and nylon webbing, the comfortable handles are made from soft black

leather and padded to prevent carrying strain. A full length heavy-duty zipper gives easy access to the bag's main compartment. A zippered side pocket can hold cartridges, fly containers or any personal items. The web straps carry "D" rings for holding fishing rods,

a rifle, shotgun or whatever. The big Sport-Toter is 30"x14", the smaller one is 21"x9".

Write to Woods Bag & Canvas Co. Ltd., 16 Lake St., Ogdensburg, NY 14669, for prices and information on the many other Woods outdoor products.

Sonic Ear-Valvs

These deservedly popular sound moderators are going to be even more so, looks like, because a new and improved model has just been announced by Sigma Engineering, the makers (11320 Burbank Blvd., No. Hollywood, CA 91601).

The latest Sonic Ear-Valv has its sound-controlling system completely covered in a soft silicone material —it's easier to insert and remove, ordinary sound levels are readily heard, and it's ventilated to allow normal air circulation into the ear canal. Dizziness and temperature hazards are thereby avoided.

The sound-filtering mechanism, a small and complex unit, acts as a sort of secondary, protective ear drum, and handles the high-fre-

quency noises and loud decibels well—the current No. 1 pollution.

Sonic Ear-Valvs, cost $4.95 a pair in a protective container, can be found in good sporting goods stores, gunshops and safety/medical equipment dealers.   J.T.A.

Federal Cartridge

Five major claybird titles were won in 1971 with Federal shotshells—the 12 Gauge Championship and the All-Around Championship in Skeet, plus the Clay Target, Doubles and High-Over-All Championship at straight trap. More Skeet shooters at the San Antonio tournament used Federals—42.7%

of them, more than used any other brand. At the 1971 Grand American, Federal loads took 43% of the 351 trophies awarded, again more than any other brand achieved.

Federal has two new books you'll probably want, both in full color. *Upland Game Birds* describes 23 species found in the U.S. and Canada. *Big Game Animals* does the same for North America. Each shows color photos of the birds or animals, and habitat maps, feeding and breeding habits, etc., are included. Postpaid for 50¢ each from Federal Book Offer, Box 7200, Maple Plain, MN 55359.
    J.T.A.

Ducks Unlimited

Ducks Unlimited, the non-profit waterfowl conservation organization, will finance construction of a record 104 prime wildlife breeding habitat areas in 1972. The program is expected to cost almost $3 million.

All DU projects, though paid for by U.S. conservationists, are in Canada, where 80% of the continent's waterfowl originate. The 1972 program will see work done on over 100,000 acres of wetlands habitat set aside for waterfowl and other wildlife purposes. 10 projects will be located in British Columbia, 36 in Alberta, 23 in Saskatchewan, 23 in Manitoba and 12 in the Maritimes.

Nipple Charger

Every caplock shooter, soon or late, rams a ball home without getting the black powder down first—at which time all the brimstone ain't in the propellant The handsome little gadget shown can

be, sometime, the lifesaver. Load it with fine grain BP, set it down into the cone, and push—in a moment or so there should be enough powder forced through the nipple to let Ol' Bacongitter sound off. All brass, the Navy Arms' well-made little widget sells for $5.

Mini Power Horn

This tiny (4¾x2 ⅜x1 ¼-inches) Freon-powered horn can be used to frighten prowlers, molesters, vicious dogs... and has dozens of other uses. Just press with your thumb and it sets loose a blast of 118 decibels.

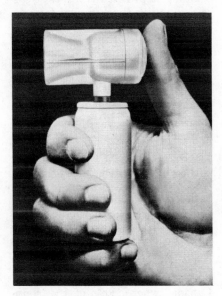

Available by mail, it is useful for boating, beach and seashore (it floats). It can be used for a ship-to-shore signal, to summon help and—most importantly—to call children.

This compact 3-oz. safety horn sells for $3.25, holds up to 100 blasts! Two refill cartridges (No. P-41,424) are $2.75, all postpaid. To order, send your name, address and check or money order to: Edmund Scientific Co., 555 Edscorp Bldg., Barrington, NJ 08007.

1972 NRA Hunting Annual Expanded

A coast-to-coast big game survey is a major feature of the 3rd edition of the National Rifle Association of America's *Hunting Annual—Denali, 1972*.

The exclusive, 12-page article contains information on licenses, hunting costs and numbers of deer, grizzly and black bear, Dall and bighorn sheep, caribou, pronghorn antelope, mountain goat and moose.

Within its 112 pages are pieces on shooting know-how for the hunter, use of scope sights, and care of game from field to freezer, plus information on hunting seasons, fees, regulations and bag limits. Special attention is given to loads for big and small game, waterfowl and upland game birds. The traveling hunter will find helpful information on the transportation of sporting arms.

Heart of the book is its Directory of North American guides, outfitters, hunting camps, shooting preserves and other services. Guides, outfitters and principal operators of the hunting camps and shooting preserves listed are NRA members who subscribe to a code of ethics published in the register. The NRA reserves the right to remove, or refuse, listing in *Denali* to any who fail to comply with the code. The NRA, however, does not offer any guarantee.

Denali, for the first time, will be available on newsstands and magazine stands across the country, price $1.50—to NRA members, only $1.00.

For more information or application for listing, write to the Director of Hunting & Conservation Division, NRA Headquarters, 1600 Rhode Island Ave., N.W., Washington, D.C., 20036.

Williams 1972-73 Blue Book of Gun Dealing

This new edition, enlarged to 96 pages, includes over 2000 new and old firearms, describing and listing

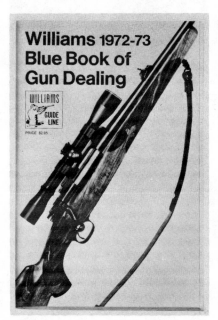

the current retail price (if any) of each, plus their value in excellent, good or poor condition. All popular scopes are listed with their trade-in value.

There's more, too—articles on How to Fit the Gun, Making Used Guns Saleable and others. A catalog section, a list of firearm manufacturers and importers, with their addresses. $2.95

Duck Stamps $5

Cost of the 1972-1973 Duck Stamp—required to be bought by everybody hunting wild fowl except those under 16—has been raised to $5, the first increase since 1959, when the price went from $2 to $3.

The first stamps were a mere $1, but that was in 1934.

A fine cause, though, and a self-serving one, too, for all sale proceeds go into a fund for wetlands and refuge acquisitions.

I want to suggest this—whether you shoot any migratory birds or not, why not contribute to the fund? Buy a Duck Stamp—it's $5 well spent.

A Fishing (?) Book?

What's a book on fishing (purportedly) doing in this sedate family organ? Good question, but there's no simple answer. Do some of you remember or know *Captain Billy's Whiz Bang*, or *Mad Magazine*? If you do, and who doesn't, you're well prepared for Poltroon's piscatorial pflood, *How to Fish Good*. I've heard that Poltroon is a pseudonym for Erwin A. (Joe) B- -r or Cl-d-Orm-nd, but I can't swallow that.

In whatever case, you'll either hate this sacrilegious insult to decent, law-abiding fisherfolk or you'll fall out of the fighting chair of your offshore cruiser from laughter or disgust, I don't know which.

Published by the Winchester Press (honest) this picture and patter book sells for $2.95, paper covers.

Powder Horn

The large genuine horn powder flask shown here is offered by Service Armament. Fitted with hand-carved wooden cap and stopper, this replica flask is priced at $10.

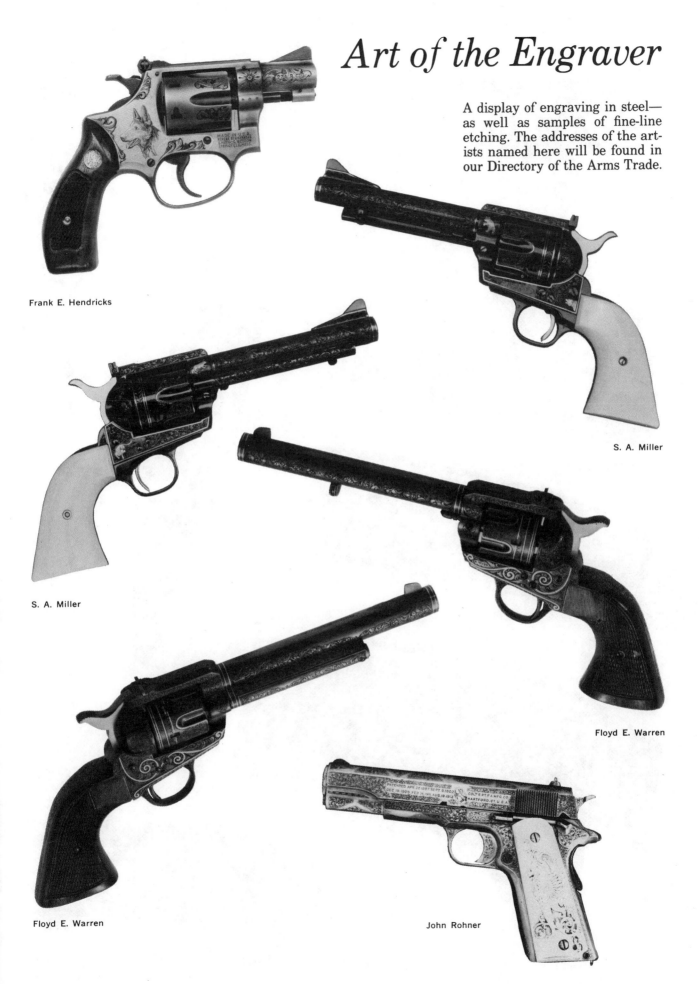

Art of the Engraver

A display of engraving in steel—as well as samples of fine-line etching. The addresses of the artists named here will be found in our Directory of the Arms Trade.

Frank E. Hendricks

S. A. Miller

S. A. Miller

Floyd E. Warren

Floyd E. Warren

John Rohner

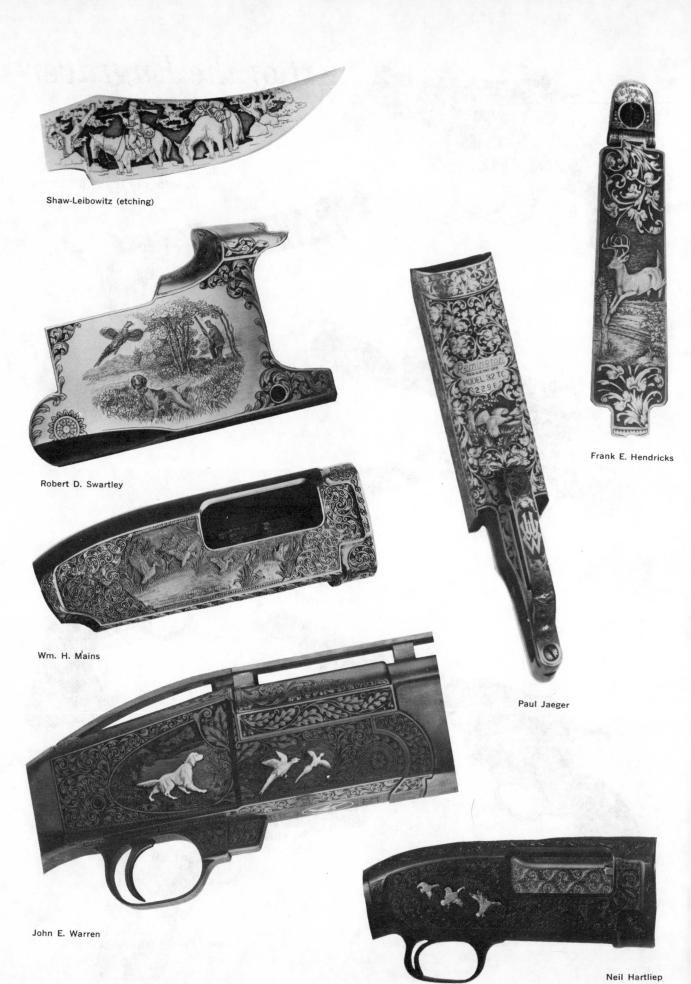

Shaw-Leibowitz (etching)

Robert D. Swartley

Wm. H. Mains

John E. Warren

Frank E. Hendricks

Paul Jaeger

Neil Hartliep

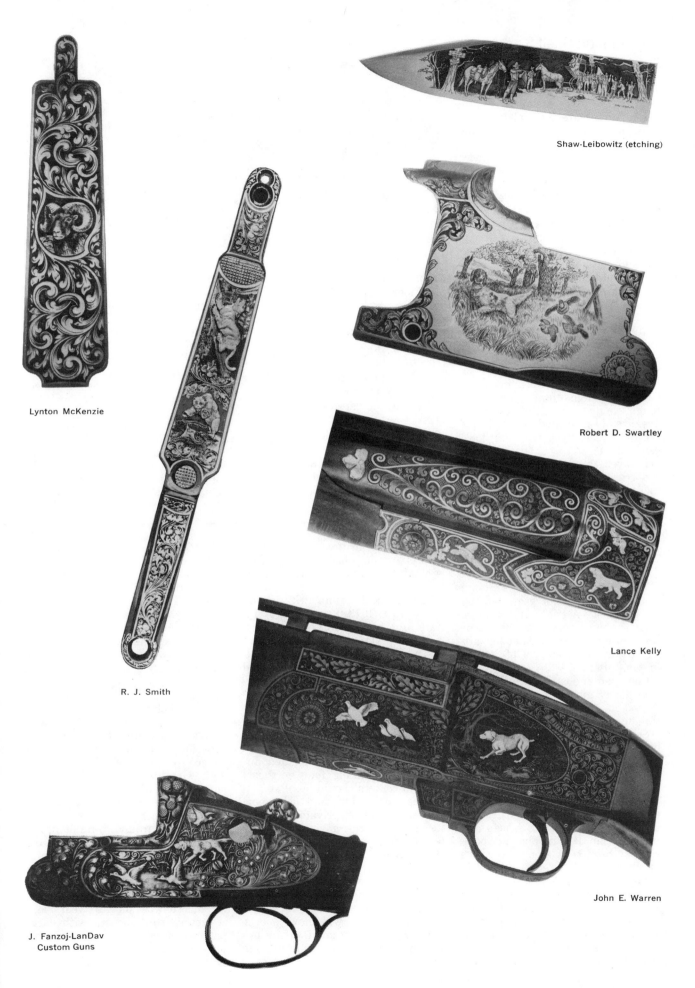

Lynton McKenzie

R. J. Smith

Shaw-Leibowitz (etching)

Robert D. Swartley

Lance Kelly

John E. Warren

J. Fanzoj-LanDav
Custom Guns

Home Made Shell Sizer

EVERY FALL finds Jake Dillman, my hunting buddy of 20 years, his son Jim, and me in blinds along the Missouri River in Western Iowa. Our favorite targets are the mallards and geese, blues and snows, that migrate down the Missouri River Valley. Pass shooting is our thing, our artillery consisting of three 10-gauge 3½" magnums and one 3" twelve.

We burn a lot of powder and, with factory fodder crowding $6 and $8 a box, reloading's a must.

Heavy shot loads and maximum powder charges result in short case life and, with new primed 10-gauge paper hulls costing $13 per 100, every old case is treated like gold.

Jim's and my 10s chambers are about the same diameter, but those of Jake's old dog are both oversize and out of round. Worse you should see the shape of some hulls we pick up! All this means a major resizing problem at reloading time. Ordinary high-brass bases are tough enough to resize, but badly oversize brass-coated steel heads are more than most reloading tools can handle.

I solved the problem by building the resizing tool shown here. The tool is simple, cheap (total less than $4) and it really does the job.

Following is a list of materials:
1 Floor flange for 1½" pipe.
1 Steel nipple for 1½" pipe, 6" long.
2 Pipe caps for 1½" pipe.
1 Steel nipple for 1½" pipe, 5" long.
1 "U" channel beam, 4" by 24".
8 ⁵⁄₁₆" by 1" capscrews
4 ⁵⁄₁₆" by ¾" capscrews
12 ⁵⁄₁₆" nuts
60" of ³⁄₁₆" by 1" flat steel (handle)

I had a local machine shop drill a hole 0.002" larger than the diameter of an unfired 12-gauge shell in the center of one pipe cap, and a similar hole drilled in the other for a 10-gauge shell.

Construction details are apparent from the illustration. The tool can be built to apply almost any amount of pressure by the choice of handle length and distance between the fixed and movable pivots. It easily resizes distorted, oversize cases that'd ordinarily be thrown away. I use a ½" steel rod, 12" long, to tap the resized cases out of the pipe cap.

It's not a fast tool, but with today's low bag limits enough hulls for a season's shooting can be salvaged in a couple of hours.

FLOYD WENSEL

1972-73 Duck Stamp Shows Emperor Geese

The 1972-73 Federal Duck Stamp pictures two emperor geese landing in overcast Arctic surroundings. The winning entry, a full color wash drawing, was created by artist Arthur M. Cook, 40 of Bloomington, Minn.

Cook, an industrial art director, had never finished higher than second in several previous tries in the duck stamp contest.

Second place this year was a tie between Lee LeBlanc of Iron River, Mich., who drew spectacled eider, and Stanley Stearns of Stevensville, Md., who also drew emperor geese. The latter species will be appearing on the duck stamp for the first time. The bird inhabits Alaska and the Aleutian Islands and has occasionally been seen along the coasts of Washington, Oregon and California.

"I was particularly pleased when I learned of the judges' choice," said Interior Secretary Rogers C. B. Morton, "because 90 percent of the world's emperor geese come from the Yukon Delta, and one of our major priorities right now is to protect the Alaska habitat that is vital to millions of wild waterfowl."

The 1972-73 stamp will go on sale July 1, 1972. Every migratory-waterfowl hunter 16 or older must buy this stamp with a State hunting license. All revenue from duck stamps, except for printing and distribution costs, is used for acquisition of wetlands for waterfowl.

New Airline Service for Northeast Ontario

NorOntair, a new scheduled airline service linking four northeast Ontario centers should be of special interest to hunters and fishermen.

Operated by a private company for the Ontario government, the 6-day-a-week service will run between Sault Ste. Marie, Sudbury, Timmins and Earlton.

Speedy and economical—the longest flight is 100 minutes and the maximum one-way adult fare is $34—the service will move sportsmen from one base of operations to another or from hunting to fishing in a matter of minutes.

NorOntair can set the sportsman down in some of the best outdoor districts. Moose and bear, lake and brook trout, walleye and northern pike are abundant ('tis said) near the NorOntair bases.

NorOntair's aircraft is the 10-passenger de Havilland Twin Otter, the crew two pilots and a stewardess.

Rare Ontario Trophy

Some lucky big-game hunter in the Geraldton district of Ontario may snag a double trophy in 1972.

Besides having an excellent chance of bagging a bull moose near Geraldton, some 250 miles northwest of Sault Ste. Marie, his moose may also be as white as the snow in which it winters.

The area around Geraldton has a big moose population for the province, with high annual hunter success. A bush pilot late last year saw a pure-white mature bull moose—not far from where a similar moose was shot 10 years ago. A young cow moose, with large patches of white around its hindquarters and flanks, was also reported in the same vicinity.

AMERICAN BULLETED CARTRIDGES

by KENNETH L. WATERS

A check list of current metallic cartridges, domestic and imported, plus a guide to performance and selection.

LATEST DEVELOPMENTS IN METALLIC CARTRIDGES

Each year along about March, America's three major ammunition makers publish colorful booklets illustrating and describing their listings of guns and ammunition currently available. Shooters who look at only the latest catalogs and fail to compare them closely with last year's editions are missing out on much that is happening in the metallic cartridge field.

Although significant new offerings are generally announced in separate news releases, little if anything is usually said concerning re-shuffling of individual loadings, changes in ballistics of existing cartridges, or calibers either discontinued or slated for discontinuance. Only by making a line-by-line comparison with last year's catalogs do these unpublicized changes come to light. In the paragraphs that follow, we'll focus attention on these alterations in line with our policy of keeping readers informed.

Last year's ABC Section reported the entrance of Smith & Wesson Fiocchi-Alcan into the metallic cartridge arena, and previous editions have commented on the growing importance of the Speer-DWM, Norma, Super Vel, CIL-Dominion, Weatherby, Sako, CCI, Hornady-Frontier and Herter lines—in addition to our "Big Three"—Winchester-Western, Remington-Peters, and Federal Cartridge.

This time we have another new entry, sponsored by an old and highly respected gunmaker—Browning—out with an extensive, if not quite complete, line-up of centerfire rifle and handgun ammunition. These too will be reviewed.

There are no "new" cartridges this year in the sense of comprising totally new calibers such as last season's 17 Remington, but this should not be taken to mean any lack of interest on the part of either manufacturers or shooters. The reinstatement of a popular old cartridge, or the introduction of new loadings in different bullet weights and/or types, can be quite as important if not more so.

Winchester-Western

That grand old cartridge, the 220 Swift, is back! Ever since its introduction in 1935, the Swift has been our highest velocity factory round, and I pointed this out last year in connection with claims to that title by the 17 Remington, but somehow my remarks were edited to say that the 17 Remington had usurped that position. It hadn't! Norma continued to load the 220 Swift with 50-gr. bullet at M.V. 4111 fps, and now in response to popular demand

Winchester-Western again lists the Swift as a factory-standard loading with 48-gr. PSP bullet at 4110 fps. Independent chronographings show the Swift to be a full 100 fs faster than the 17 Remington's bullet, weighing only half as much. Resembling the return of an old prize fighter to the ring, the "Champ" has made a come-back. Now all that's necessary is to persuade the boys at W-W,

or some other enterprising rifle maker, to once more make rifles available in this chambering.

W-W has added the 25-06 to their cartridge line-up, announcing two loadings—one with a 90-gr. bullet at M.V. 3500 fps, and the other a 120-gr. at 3120 fps—both featuring their new PEP (Positive Expanding Point) bullets. Both bullet weights have given splendid accuracy, but peculiarly—and I'm sure there will be some who say it can't be—the 90-gr. with Super-X headstamp and the 120-gr. labeled Super Speed have consistently turned in tighter groups than the 120-gr. Super-X in repeated trials. I attribute this to different lots. However, all were good, none of the 100-yard groups exceeding 1½", and several going into ¾". Just as the 243 and 6mm cut into the 257 Roberts' popularity, so will the 25-06 recapture a large following for the ¼"-bore. This is one to watch!

The 60-gr. loading for the 25-20 is now gone, leaving only the two 86-gr. loads—one in soft point, the other a plain lead bullet. This is to be regretted as the 60-gr. load was probably the most useful of them all, making a respectable short-range varmint rifle out of the 25-20. In many rifles, including my own Savage Model 23, the 60-gr. hollow point was also considerably more accurate, serving as a fine round for turkeys. I would have preferred to see them drop the 86-gr. lead bullet load.

Too, the fine old 32-40 cartridge has been discontinued, despite the use even today of Model 94s in this caliber for woods hunting, not to mention a considerable number of single shot rifles chambered for it. Like the 38-55 which went before it, no warnings that I can recall were posted of its proposed deletion, something that should have been done to give owners of these muskets a chance to stock up on ammo for them. At the very least, components—empty cases and bullets—should be made available for reloading both calibers.

There's no better place than this to repeat my urgings that Winchester and Remington (in co-operation with SAAMI) arrange for the continued production of alternate calibers. Assuming there's not a large enough market to warrant manufacture of such old cartridges by *both* companies, couldn't arrangements be made whereby Winchester would continue to produce *one* of them and Remington the other? I feel certain this sort of thing would be welcomed by shooters all across the country.

New handgun cartridges from Winchester include a 158-gr. semiwadcutter lead bullet loading in 38 Special rated at 1060 fps from 6″ barrels, and three new rounds in 357 Magnum caliber, including a light bullet, high velocity number featuring a 110-gr. jacketed hollow point, plus a pair with 158-gr. jacketed fast-moving slugs, one a hollow point and the other a flatnose soft point, each rated at 1450 fps M.V. from an 8-⅜″ barrel. In my 6″ barreled Colt Trooper, these heavier loads will repeatedly shoot 5 successive shots into 4¼″-4½″ at a measured 50 yards, with four of them contained in 3″-3½″. This should be great ammo for handgun hunters.

Apparently Winchester has dropped their 210-gr. lead bullet match load for the 45 Auto since last year's listing, for now there are only two W-W factory loads for the 45 ACP instead of three. All-in-all, this is a fair number of revisions to make in a single year, and it would appear that the Red-W crew are attempting to live up to their 1972 slogan of a Winchester line "the way you want it."

Remington-Peters

Remington's program for the past year has also been one emphasizing pruning and consolidation of their metallic cartridge line-up, this apparently an up-dating process responding to current popular trends, especially in the handgun field.

An example of this is to be seen in the introduction of a new 38 Special loading with 95-gr. semi-jacketed hollow-point bullet, intended primarily to provide improved performance (985 fps) in snubnose revolvers, and a similar 125-gr. H.P. 357 Magnum load logging an impressive 1675 fps at the muzzle of an 8-⅜″ barrel, in answer to the growing demand for higher handgun velocities and increased bullet expansion. Both loads follow this modern trend, made possible by the use of lightweight expanding jacketed bullets. Incidentally, this new 357 Magnum round has a kinetic energy (780 fp) exceeded only by the 41 and 44 Magnums, with an even flatter trajectory, considerably less recoil, and a quicker-opening bullet than its bigger brothers. Should make a top choice for six-gunning varmints.

Match shooters who may have noticed the absence from this year's Remington catalog of the accurate and popular 148-gr. Targetmaster wadcutter load will be relieved to learn that it is still being made. Concerned because this is the *only* R-P 38 Special cartridge which will function in either the Colt Gold Cup or S&W Model 52 target automatic pistols, I queried the Bridgeport headquarters and am glad to report that the error was typographical rather than a mistake in judgment.

The same explanation, I was told, applies to the fine 158-gr. semi-jacketed hollow-point 357 Magnum hunting load which likewise has been inadvertently left out of the 1972 listings. That's the only place it was omitted from, both cartridges being very much in existence.

Curious also as to why muzzle velocity of the 38 Special 158-gr. semi-jacketed hollow point is now shown as 960 fps whereas it had formerly been given as 1150 fps, it develops that the current figure was obtained by chronographing this load from a 6″-barrel revolver, while the previous practice had been to use a solid-breeched test barrel. This is certainly a more realistic policy, for which Remington is to be commended, barrel lengths now being listed for each caliber.

If you shoot a 38 Special revolver, I suggest trying Remington's new 158-gr. Semi-Wadcutter. While I haven't yet tested it at 50 yards, it will group in from 1¼″ to 2″ on the indoor 50-foot range.

Biggest news in Remington rifle cartridges is the addition of 100-gr. PSP factory loading for the 25-06. This has been expected ever since the 25-06 was first announced as a commercial standard, and should prove especially appealing to those shooters who prefer to standardize on a single loading. Like its predecessors, it is accurate, grouping in 1MOA from our Remington Model 700 test rifle. It has a higher retained velocity beyond 300 yards than the 87-gr. factory load, and a 500-yard trajectory that is slightly flatter than either the 87-gr. or 120-gr. loadings. I wouldn't be surprised if the new 100-gr. round turns out to be the best choice for deer hunting, being less highly frangible than the lighter and faster 87-gr., and probably not giving such deep penetration as the 120-gr. big game load. Almost certainly, it will enhance the fast growing popularity of the 25-06 cartridge.

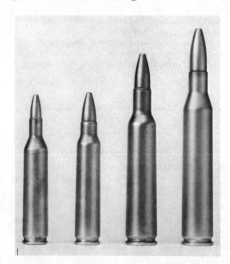

The announcement of a new 90-gr. PSP bullet loading in 6mm Remington caliber is coupled with the abandonment of the 244 Remington cartridge and its same weight bullet. But 244 owners shouldn't despair, for in reality these rounds are identical in every way except the headstamp and ballistics. M.V. has been upped from 3200 fps to 3320 fps with resultant flattening of trajectories, and an increase of 13½% in delivered energy at 300 yards. Despite this notable improvement, the 90-gr. 6mm cartridge *can* be used in 244 Remington rifles without concern.

This writer confesses to some disappointment in finding that Remington failed to implement any of the changes in their cartridge line-up which he had suggested in the spring of 1971, other than the 100-gr. loading for the 25-06. I had proposed first that the 257 Roberts be updated with the addition (actually, the reinstatement) of 87-gr. and 100-gr. spitzer bullet loadings, plus an 87-gr. for the 250 Savage in view of the re-birth of interest in that cartridge. No new bullet production would have been entailed; the 87-gr. 25-06 hollow-point bullet could readily be used to load both the 250 and 257, and the 100-gr. PSP, as already loaded in Remington's 250, could have been adapted to the 257.

Secondly, I saw then (and still see) no valid reason why the 125-gr. 7mm bullet currently being loaded in the 7mm Magnum couldn't be factory loaded for the fine 280 Remington cartridge. Similarly, the 150-gr. 7mm could be loaded in 7mm Mauser (7x57) cases for a better deer round than the old 175-gr. round nose.

Thirdly, since there is a standard Remington load with 125-gr. bullet for the 30-06, it would seem to be no trick to seat the same .308" bullet in the popular 308 Winchester-caliber cases. As with the 25 calibers, all of these additional loadings we've suggested could be accomplished with components already being manufactured, markedly increasing both the utility and versatility of popular cartridges without a parallel rise in production costs. To this writer at least, it made sense and still does.

Browning

From the extensive list of Browning centerfire ammunition, we have so far had the opportunity of testing their 22-250, 243 Win. (2 bullet weights), 6mm Rem. (also, 2 bullet weights), 7mm Rem. Magnum, 308 Win. (3 bullet weights), and 30-06 in four bullet weights. These trials were from bench-rest at 100 yards, fired in rifles of known high accuracy, strictly for analyzing consistency in grouping.

In a M77 Ruger 22-250, 5-shot groups averaged between ¾" and 1"—good but not spectacular. Both the 80- and 100-gr. 243 loads in our standard weight M70 Winchester sporter were on a par with most factory ammo (1¼"), except for a single outstanding ⅝" group with the 80-gr. Browning loads.

The 6mm, in a custom Mauser with Sharon barrel, averaged 1" with 80-gr. loads, and just under 1½" with their 100-gr. Once again there was that odd single ⅝" group with the 80-gr. loads as had occurred with the 243.

First big surprise was with the 7mm Remington Magnum, where the 150-gr. Browning factory loads grouped in just under an inch from a Remington 700 BDL rifle—impressive accuracy for high intensity factory loads.

Working up the caliber ladder, the 308 came next, fired in a heavy-barreled Winchester M70 Target rifle fitted with 15x Lyman Super Targetspot. With this rig we expected more and got it, but in one bullet weight only. The 150-gr. Browning clustered in ⅝"! The 125-gr. spitzer followed with 15/16", and the 180-gr. averaged an even 1". In a sporter-weight customized Springfield with hunting scope sight, groups opened to 1½", still at the 100-yard range.

Our final test series, involving the 30-06 cartridge, was perhaps the most interesting of all. Two highly accurate target rifles, each with bull-barrels and using the same 15x Lyman scope, gave quite different results in spite of the fact that they generally run neck-and-neck with one another. The M70 liked both 125-gr. and 220-gr. Browning loads, holding them in ¾" for 5-shots, but wouldn't do better than 1-1/16"-1-⅛" with 150- and 180-gr. loadings. By comparison, a Springfield with Eric Johnson Five-Star barrel, once used in the Wimbledon Match at Camp Perry, kept all four bullet weights in an inch or less, showing a distinct preference for the 125-gr. bullet in making ⅝" groups.

As a reference frame, these loads were also tried in a Mannlicher-Schoenauer sporter with 2½x scope, considering this rig to be more typical of the average outfit. None of the loads could be induced to stay inside less than 2", and we experienced a pair of misfires, both with the 180-gr. loads that had been least accurate in all three rifles. This can most likely be attributed to variations in ignition of that particular lot and almost certainly not typical of Browning ammo, which in all the other calibers and loads tested proved totally reliable and possessed of a high average accuracy level.

S&W-Fiocchi-Alcan

Although the appearance of this new line of handgun ammunition was reported in last year's GUN DIGEST, test samples arrived too late for testing. Since then we have put the S&W-F 38 Special, 357 Magnum and 9mm Luger rounds through accuracy trials, firing over sand bag rests from 50 yards range.

Performance of the 158-gr. 357 Magnum jacketed soft points was excellent (4"-4¼" groups) from a 6"-barreled Colt Trooper, while the S&W 125-gr. hollow points were truly outstanding, grouping in 3" and sometimes a shade less! That's match-grade accuracy from high speed hunting loads.

Compared to this sterling performance in 357 Magnum caliber, the S&W-F 38 Special ammunition proved disappointing. Fired in the same Colt Trooper used for the Magnum trials, S&W-F 148-gr. Match Wadcutters wouldn't do better than 6" groups at 50 yards. Similarly, in a like-new Colt Shooting Master 38 Special target revolver, group size was still 4½". I do *not* consider this acceptable accuracy for match-grade ammunition. As a re-check however, further trials of these wadcutters were conducted on an indoor 50-foot range with a Colt National Match Mark III Mid-Range automatic pistol and a 4"-barrel Colt Diamondback revolver. Strangely, the target automatic grouped in 1½", while the short barreled service gun took to the new ammo and produced groups of only 1" between centers of holes farthest apart!

Back at the 50-yard range, the S&W-F 158-gr. round-nose lead bullet police loads averaged no better than 5½"-5¾" in our finest target-sighted sixguns, and while match accuracy wasn't expected from these cartridges, I'd say there's room for some improvement here too.

The S&W-F 9mm loaded with 115-gr. jacketed hollow-points made 5″ groups from a finely accurate 1916 DWM Luger at 50 yards, and 3″ groups at 25 yards with completely reliable functioning, hence I won't fault this ammunition. A friend's S&W Model 39 also performed well with this 9mm load, so that I have no qualms in recommending it.

C.I.L.-Canadian

Of particular importance to U.S. shooters is the availability of this excellent Canadian manufactured ammunition in four discontinued American rifle calibers. To be had from a number of U.S. distributors are:
(1) The 22 Savage High Power with 70-gr. PSP bullet at M.V. 2800 fps.
(2) The 6.5x53 Mannlicher-Schoenauer with 160-gr. SP bullet at M.V. 2160 fps.
(3) The 32-40 Winchester with 170-gr. SP bullet at M.V. 1540 fps.
(4) The 38-55 Winchester with 255-gr. SP bullet at M.V. 1600 fps.

All this Canadian commercial ammunition is primed with Boxer (American-type) primers, cases having a single centrally-located flash-hole. They can thus be readily reloaded exactly the same as U.S.-made cases, rendering them all the more practical. I just hope they'll pick up some more of our former calibers, my mail from readers showing there's still a call for such old but popular numbers as the 25 Remington, 33 Winchester, 405 Winchester and 45-90 Winchester.

Other Tests

In 357 Magnum caliber, we have also obtained 5-shot 50-yard groups as small as 3″ using Norma 258-gr. JHP and Super Vel 110-gr. JHP factory-loaded cartridges, and while this is not an average group size, it nonetheless speaks very well for the quality and uniformity of this ammunition. Together with the S&W-F 125-gr. JHP ammo, these have given us our finest 357 accuracy on the outdoor range, beating—and I blush to admit it—our best handloads to date.

Among the various 38 Special factory cartridges, the awards for First and Second Place in the 50-yard accuracy contest go to the Remington 125-gr. JHP and 158-gr. JHP in that order, followed by Super Vel's 110-gr. JHP. Groups with these three, fired over sand bag rests, ran from 1-¾″ to 3-¾″, not infrequently grouping in 2″ to 2½″. That's not hard to take!

In 9mm Luger, I haven't personally found any factory loads that will give serious competition to our 5.5- and 5.7 grains of Unique handloads, but S&W-Fiocchi's 115-gr. hollow-points have come closest. Super Vel's 88-gr. JHP did best among factory loads in the little Star 380 automatic.

As a final point, Federal's 223 Remington-caliber factory cartridges have given us superb accuracy, grouping repeatedly in from ½″ to 1″. A recent series of 40-shots at 100 yards (eight 5-shot groups) *averaged* slightly less than ¾″. This was from a Remington 700-V varmint rifle with 15x Lyman Super Targetspot scope. If you want to give your 223 handloads some competition, try this Federal factory ammo.

Part 1. RIFLE CARTRIDGES
The Centerfires

17 REMINGTON For the shooter who already has everything he needs, but wishes to add a combination varmint cartridge and conversation piece to his battery, the 17 Remington offers a limited area of usefulness. Although it will kill varmints like lightning, it is neither as fast as the 220 Swift nor as hard hitting as a 22-250, and its extremely light bullets are more susceptible to the influence of wind over long ranges than are the high velocity 22s. In fact, I can't think of anything this caliber can do that can't be done as well or better by one or more of the 22s. The most that can be said for the 17 is that it is flat-shooting, has a low noise level and almost nonexistent recoil. Individual chronographers report that it doesn't quite reach 4000 fps at the muzzle of a 24″ barrel. Above all, the 17 should never be used on any game animal!

22 HORNET One of the most useful smallbore cartridges, and the first standard 22 specifically for varmint hunting. Since its appearance in 1930 it has earned a reputation for fine accuracy, flat trajectory, and quick bullet expansion. Effective to 175 yards on foxes, woodchucks, and jack rabbits, excellent for wild turkeys, it should definitely not be used on deer.

218 BEE Introduced in 1938 for the lever action Model 65 Winchester, its use was extended to bolt actions where its greater powder capacity, higher velocity and flatter trajectory from a stronger case made it a better choice than the Hornet. Effective on the same game species as the Hornet. Not available in any rifle today.

22 REMINGTON JET See Part II — Handgun Cartridges.

220 SWIFT Highest velocity standard sporting rifle cartridge ever produced commercially in the U.S., its 48-gr. bullet leaving the muzzle at 4110 fps is virtually a bomb, unfit for use on large game animals. As a long range varmint cartridge it is one of the finest, needing only a longer, heavier bullet less sensitive to wind.

In deference to popular demand, Winchester has resumed production of 220 Swift cartridges and components, but it remains to be seen whether rifles will ever again be offered in this caliber.

222 REMINGTON First of the post-WW II cartridges, the 222 has climbed rapidly to fame as a benchrest target and varmint round. Its better-designed bullets and finer accuracy have extended practical small varmint range to about 225 yards. This, together with its availability in numerous strong bolt action rifles, has made the older Bee and Zipper obsolete.

222 REMINGTON MAGNUM Big Brother to the standard 222, this later and longer cartridge combines increased power and velocity with the fine accuracy of its forerunner to give varmint shooters one of the best balanced, most practical 'chuck cartridges ever developed. 55- and 60-gr. spitzer bullets buck the wind better than the 50-gr. standard 222 bullet, and arrive at a 200-yard target with some 25% more energy to boot. Rifles for the 222 Magnum have been dropped because of its close similarity to the 223 Remington (or 5.56mm) in use by our military. Factory ammunition is still made by Remington in HP and PSP style, but not by Winchester.

222 SUPER RIMMED Developed in Australia, this rimmed version of our 222 Remington emigrated first to Canada and thence to the U.S. An ideal choice for chambering in single shot rifles, case dimensions (except for the rim), ballistics and loading data all duplicate those of the standard 222. Velocities may be somewhat higher however, in the longer barrels common to single shot rifles.

223 REMINGTON Adopted by the U.S. military forces as the 5.56mm with full metal jacketed 55-gr. bullets, its civilian name is 223 Remington, under which headstamp a soft point bullet is loaded. Identical ballistically to the 222 Magnum, the 223's case dimensions differ enough so that they should never be fired in a 222 Magnum chamber; they'll go in, but hazardous excess headspace will be present with a probability of case separations. Rifles for the 223 have a twist rate of 1-in-12" rather than the 1-in-14" of most 22 centerfires, this to insure bullet stability all the way out to 600-yards. Case capacity is about a grain less than the 222 Magnum and its neck is about ¹⁄₁₆" shorter, making the 222 Magnum a better choice for handloaders. Future government surplus ammunition will probably be available for the 223, however.

225 WINCHESTER Intended as a successor to the 220 Swift (in Winchester rifles), this new high performance cartridge has done more than that; it has also superseded the discontinued 219 Zipper in its role as the most powerful rimmed 22 centerfire. Although officially classified as "semi-rimless," the 225 does have a rim, easily sufficient to permit its use in single shot rifles while still fitting the bolt heads and extractors (of 270, 30-06 dimensions) of modern standard rimless cartridge repeaters. Closely similar in design to the 219 Improved Zipper (but differing in certain vital dimensions), the 225 Winchester is loaded to higher pressures than the old standard 219 Zipper, developing 540 fps greater muzzle velocity for a trajectory that is almost twice as flat. Factory cartridges in this new caliber are loaded with outstanding uniformity and provide excellent accuracy.

22/250 REMINGTON A long time favorite wildcat with both varminters and benchrest shooters, the 22/250 was standardized by Remington in 1965 and shows signs of rapidly growing popularity. Generally considered to be better designed than the Swift, it will give nearly as high velocities with bullets of the same weight. Because it is slower, case and barrel life are longer. Case capacity to bore ratio in the 22/250 is most favorable, and its short over-all loaded cartridge length of 2.35" makes it readily adaptable to short-action box magazine repeaters. Either new 22/250 Remington or Norma cases, or reformed 250 Savage brass may be used for reloading.

243 WINCHESTER One of the new 6mm or 24 caliber compromises between 22 and 25 calibers, having in large measure the best features of both. A 100-gr. bullet with high sectional density at 3,070 fs for deer and antelope, and an 80-gr. at 3,500 for long range varmints, provide accuracy equal to the Swift and far better wind-bucking and killing power. Excellent for the one-gun hunter of game not larger than deer.

244 REMINGTON Remington's first 6mm or 24-cal. rifle, never very popular because of its 1-in-12" rifling twist which kept bullet weight to 90 grains in spitzer form. Heavier bullets **can** be stabilized if made with a blunt round nose. Shooters wanted a dual-purpose rifle, however, one in which they could use 100-gr. spitzers for big game, so many picked the lesser-capacity 243. Despite the fact that neither shooters nor game could tell the difference between 90- and 100-gr. bullets, the 244 slipped and Remington ceased production of rifles in this caliber. Although officially removed from Remington's cartridge list for 1972 as a separate caliber, 6mm Remington cartridges with both 80-and 90-gr. bullets may be used interchangeably in 244 Remington rifles.

6mm REMINGTON Identical in case dimensions to the older 244 Remington, this newer cartridge is loaded with the 100-gr. bullet demanded by deer hunters. Remington lists MV as 3190 fps, and barrels have a rifling twist of 1-in-9" to stabilize the longer bullet. Despite the fact that 75- and 90-gr. 244 cartridges can also be used in 6mm rifles, shooters wanted a varmint round bearing the 6mm headstamp. Hence, in 1965 Remington announced an additional load using their new 80-gr. Power-Lokt bullet, which has proven exceptionally accurate and flat shooting. The 6mm is therefore an even better dual purpose cartridge than the 243.

25-20 WCF Prior to the coming of the Hornet and Bee, this 1893-born round was the top small-game/varmint cartridge. To-day we have better pest loads, but there is still a useful place for the 25-20 among those who hunt for stew or seek the lordly wild turkey. W-W and R-P have dropped the 60-gr. open-point varmint loading—at 2250 fps such a good little 'chuck load — and henceforth will offer only a pair of 86-gr. loads at 1460 fps. It would have been better if they had dropped the old round with plain lead bullet instead of the more accurate and faster hollow point.

25-35 WINCHESTER Another cartridge from the 1890's, this one **can** be used for deer. Currently obtainable only as a 117-gr. soft point at 2,300 fs, the 25-35's chief claim to fame lies in its reputation as one of the most accurate cartridges ever developed for lever action rifles, and one of the lightest recoiling.

250 SAVAGE Popularly known as the "250-3000" because of its velocity with an 87-gr. bullet, this fine cartridge appeared in 1915 as one of our earliest really high speed loads. 100-gr. bullets are loaded to 2,820 fs. Quick killing power, flat trajectory, and light recoil have kept this cartridge popular for over 40 years. Use 100-gr. bullets for deer and 87's for varmints. In wind-swept areas, the 100 grain is preferred, even for varmints.

256 WINCHESTER MAGNUM See Part II—Handgun Cartridges.

257 ROBERTS Named for its famous originator, Major Ned Roberts, this was to have been an extra long range varmint cartridge, but with factory production came additional bullet weights, making it one of our more versatile rounds. Although no rifles of standard make are now being chambered for the 257, W-W still offers an 87-gr. load at 3200 fps for varmints, a 100-gr. Silvertip at 2900 fps for deer/antelope, and a 117-gr. Power-Point at 2650 fps for the woods hunter. Remington lists only a single loading—the least useful 117-gr. RN—but it can be efficiently reloaded with the newer 120-gr. spitzer bullets to equal or better 243/6mm performance.

25-06 REMINGTON Wisely, Remington decided to adopt and standardize this old wildcat based as much upon popular demand as upon its proven excellence ballistically. It is without doubt one of our very finest "all-round" cartridges for American game in the contiguous 48 states (that is, not including the great bears of Alaska). Ideally, it is not an elk or moose cartridge, but as a long range load for all medium game as well as varmints, it is superb with its 87-gr. HP at 3500 fps and 120-gr. PSP at 3120 fps. Sighted for 200 yards, either bullet drops only some 19" at 400, and the heavier bullet has 1210 f.p. of energy left at that far-out range, or just slightly less than a 30-30 at only 100-yards. For all practical purposes, the 25-06 with 120-gr. bullet is the equal of the 6.5 Magnum, and treads close on the heels of the 270.

*As independently chronographed, actually about 3350. Ed.

6.5 REMINGTON MAGNUM One of a pair of short-short belted magnums developed by Remington for short-receiver bolt action rifles, powder capacity is very close to that of the 270, hence its ballistics are also much the same when using bullets of similar sectional density in equal length barrels. With its 100-gr. bullet at 3450 fps for varmints and 120-gr. game load at 3220 fps, it is even closer in performance to the 25-06, standing mid-way between the 6mm and the larger 7mm Remington Magnum. The only real advantage of the 6.5 over the 25-06 is in its ability to handle still heavier bullets, and for this purpose the 270 and 280 are even better.

264 WINCHESTER MAGNUM The third cartridge produced in Winchester's series of medium-short belted cases, the 264 offers magnum velocities and power from standard-length bolt actions. This is a cartridge with a specific purpose—the delivery of a controlled expansion bullet with flat trajectory and high residual energy at ultra long ranges. This it does. Accuracy with the 264 sometimes is less than it might be, chiefly because of a mismatching of bore-groove diameters and the bullets available. However, given the right combination, the 264 shoots very well; Sierra bullets are a good choice. With the 264 or the 6.5 Magnum, select those bullets which will stand the high rotational forces of their quick-twist rifling.

270 WINCHESTER Superior to the 257 and 6mms for western use and for game larger than deer, the 270 has earned a good reputation among open country hunters. Its flat trajectory and high velocity with 130-gr. bullet at 3140 fps makes hitting easier over long, difficult-to-estimate ranges. Thus, as a mule deer, sheep and goat cartridge it is all anyone could ask for. For larger and heavier game of the caribou, elk and moose species, Winchester loads a 150-gr. Power-Point bullet to an increased muzzle velocity of 2900 fps, while Remington offers a 150-gr. round nose Core-Lokt at 2800 for woods hunting. The 100-gr. load is excellent for varmints, and is a good choice on antelope, too.

7mm REMINGTON MAGNUM Rifle cartridge of 1962, this short-case belted magnum mates the striking power of a 180-gr. 30-06 with the velocity and flat trajectory of a 130-gr. 270. The 175-gr. load has 21½% greater muzzle energy than the 180-gr. 30-06, and the 150-gr. is traveling 12% faster than the 130-gr. 270 bullet out at 300 yards. Various "wildcat" 7mm Magnum cartridges have evidenced their game killing ability in all corners of the globe, and now we have a factory standard cartridge capable of doing the same.   In 1965, Remington added a 175-gr. factory loading having a pointed Core-Lokt bullet designed to retain high velocity over longer ranges. Starting out at the muzzle with the same 3070 fps as the round-nose bullet, remaining velocity of the new spitzer slug is 340 fs higher at 300 yards and 460 fs faster at 500 yards, even equaling the 150-gr. bullet by the time 300 yards is reached.   In 1967, Remington added still another loading, this time a 125-gr. PSP at 3430 MV, thus making available a lightweight, high speed bullet with correspondingly flat trajectory for use on the smaller species of big game under long range conditions. This load should **not** be used in taking really large game, especially at short to medium ranges where velocity is still high.

280 REMINGTON One of our very best—if not the best—"all-round" cartridges, the 280 has been sadly overlooked, bucking, as it does, the popularity and head start of the closely similar 270, and over-shadowed by the newer 7mm Remington Magnum. Originally, its attraction lay in the splendid selection of factory loads available. Four bullet weights—100-, 125-, 150- and 165-gr.—gave the 280 a flexibility unequaled by the 270 unless the latter were handloaded, and with lower chamber pressures to boot. However, shooters have shown a preference for the 7mm Magnum, with the result that Remington has discontinued the 100- and 125-gr. 280 loads, and only their M742 autoloader is still being chambered for it—most regrettable.

284 WINCHESTER Unusual for American cartridges, this short-cased round has a body diameter larger than its rim, giving it a powder capacity only about 1 grain less than the 280 Remington, even though ½-inch shorter, while retaining a "standard" size rim (common to such calibers as the 270, 280, 308 and 30-06), in order to permit use of the 284 cartridge with existing bolt face dimensions. Designed to give short action rifles (specifically the Winchester M88 lever action and M100 autoloader) ballistics equaling the longer 270 Winchester and 280 Remington cartridges, there is no reason why bolt action rifles shouldn't be chambered for it.

7mm MAUSER Originating as the Spanish military cartridge of 1893, the 7x57mm became popular the world over and today's factory loadings are better than ever. It will handle any game that the 270 will, but if used for antelope or other plains game at long range, either Federal's or Dominion's 139-gr. at 2900 fps, or Norma's 150-gr. load at 2756 fps should be specified. For varmints, Norma offers a 110-gr. bullet loading at 3068 fps MV. These modern high velocity versions have given the 7x57 new appeal. However, the standard U.S. cartridge with 175-gr. round-nose bullet of high sectional density is still the best choice for big game, especially when hunting in brush or woods.

30 CARBINE Commercial jacketed SP cartridges are loaded by W-W, R-P, Federal and Norma for use in the 30 M-1 Carbine and Ruger revolver. Winchester's 110-gr. is a hollow point; the other 3 are all RNSPs. All have a rated MV of 1970-1980 fps from an 18" barrel; at only 100-yards, velocity is down to 1540 fps with 575 f.p. energy. From this it should be obvious that the 30 Carbine is not an adequate deer load. If used on varmints, it may ricochet badly.

30-30 WCF & 32 WINCHESTER SPECIAL Old favorites of the deer hunter and rancher, these cartridges continue to be popular

more because of the light, handy carbines which use them than because of any attribute of the cartridges themselves. For the indifferent marksman they are wounders, having neither great bullet weight nor high velocity. These are deer cartridges and should not be "stretched." They're neither flat shooting nor accurate enough for varmints, nor do they have the power to be good moose killers.

30 & 32 REMINGTON Rimless versions of the 30-30 and 32 Special for the Remington line of autoloaders and slide action rifles (Models 8, 81, 14 and 141), bullet weights and velocities are the same (except no 150-gr. bullets), and there is no difference in killing power. Depends solely on which rifle action the shooter chooses as to which cartridge he uses.

300 SAVAGE Developed by Savage to approximate early 30-06 ballistics in their Model 99 lever action, this cartridge had a phenomenal acceptance for a time. It has an extremely short case neck, making it difficult to reload, but with 150- and 180-gr. factory loads it is a quick killer on deer. The lighter bullet should be chosen where flat trajectory and rapid expansion counts, but for wooded country, or for bear, moose and caribou, use the 180-gr. bullet.

30-40 KRAG Generally called the "Krag," this old military cartridge looks good in "civies." Rifles are no longer made for it, but the Krag bolt actions and Winchester Model 95 lever actions just don't seem to wear out. 180- and 220-gr. bullet loadings are available, with the former as best choice for deer, or mountain hunting requiring the flattest possible trajectory, while the latter is a long brush-cutter slow to open up and offering deeper penetration on heavy game than the faster 30-06, assuming like bullets.

308 WINCHESTER Commercial version of the 7.62mm NATO cartridge, the 308 is a big stick in a small bundle. A stubby cartridge, resembling the 300 Savage with a longer neck but still half-an-inch shorter than the 30-06, this hot little number comes within 100 fs of equaling 30-06 velocities. When first brought out, only 150- and 180-gr. bullets were available in factory loads, but now there is a 110-gr. varmint load and a dandy 200-gr. for the heavier stuff. As the new service cartridge, it will prove increasingly popular for target work as well as hunting.

30-06 SPRINGFIELD American military cartridge since 1906, this has been the standard by which all other big game cartridges were compared. Many have called it our most versatile all-round cartridge, for there are many bullets available, from the 110-gr. for varmints, through the flat-shooting 150-gr. to the 180-gr. "all-purpose," and finally up to a 220-gr. for big game and timber hunting. Except for Alaskan brown bear, buffalo, and rear-angling shots on elk, it is probably adequate for any North American game.

300 H&H MAGNUM Introduced in 1925 as the "Super-Thirty," this was the first factory cartridge giving a velocity in excess of 3000 fps with a 150-gr. bullet. Re-named "300 H&H Magnum" by Americans, it soon demonstrated its superiority as a big game cartridge and, starting in 1935, as a long range target load in the Wimbledon Cup Match at Camp Perry. By virtue of its larger belted case and heavier powder charge, the 300 H&H moves 180-gr. bullets 220 fps faster than the 30-06 with an additional quarter-ton of energy. This gives the shooter who is able to handle the increased recoil flatter trajectory with less wind deflection and more remaining knock-down power.

300 WINCHESTER MAGNUM Recognizing the average American hunter's predilection for 30-cal. rifles as the favorite all-round bore size, Winchester in 1963 introduced this modern 300 Magnum, thereby spelling the doom of the fine old 300 H&H after 38 years. MV of the new round runs 150 to 200 fps higher than the 300 H&H with equal bullet weights, delivering almost 24% greater remaining energy at 400 yards (180-gr. bullet), and 13% flatter trajectory at the same range. Ballistics also exceed by a considerable margin those of smaller bore magnums. The 300 Winchester Magnum with proper bullet weights is adequate for all our big game from deer and antelope to elk, caribou, moose and even the great bears, plus African game of similar weight.

303 BRITISH British service cartridge for over half a century, the 303 has long been popular in Canada, and now with thousands of surplus military rifles in the hands of U.S. shooters its use on this side of the border has increased enormously. Consequently, a wide variety of factory loads have been made available including the old standard 215-gr. round-nose from Remington, Norma and Dominion at 2180-2200 fps; a 180-gr. from Remington, Winchester, Federal, Dominion and Norma averaging 2540 fps (Dominion, 2610); 150-gr. Dominion and Norma at 2720 fps. and even a 130-gr. Norma load traveling 2790 fps. The 303 has thus become a quite effective multi-purpose cartridge for North American game.

32-20 WCF An almost obsolete little cartridge that refuses to die, it should have been named the 30-20 for it uses a 30-cal. bullet. Too light and under-powered for deer, and with the former 80-gr. high speed HP now gone, this old round with its 100-gr. bullet 1290 fps is best used for turkeys and edible small game.

303 SAVAGE Another light deer cartridge of the 30-30 class, but in this one some velocity was traded for more bullet weight, 180- and 190-gr. bullets being given 100 to 200 fs less speed. 30-30 killing power, with penetration slightly increased at the expense of a more arched trajectory.

8mm MAUSER Underloaded by American ammunition makers because of the wide variations in quality and bore diameter of foreign rifles chambering it, this cartridge has ballistics about like the 30-40 Krag and is a good deer slayer. As loaded by Norma and imported into this country it is quite different, acquiring 30-06 powers. Caution here is to make sure of your rifle. Strength and accuracy vary widely with the individual rifle. Given a good one, this can be a fine big game cartridge using the stepped-up loadings. Do NOT mix with 30-06 rounds!

338 WINCHESTER MAGNUM Long awaited by many big game hunters, the 338 has shown itself to be a leading contender for the all-round rifle crown, killing large game such as brown bear and bison with the aplomb of a 375 H&H, or whitetail deer with less meat destruction than a quick-expanding 270 bullet. This is a modern, high-efficiency cartridge with flat trajectory slightly bettering the 30-06-180 gr. and 270-150 gr. loads, while delivering about 25% more striking energy at 200 and 300 yards than the 30-06. The great sectional density of the heavier bullets insures penetration and resistance to deflection by wind or brush, especially when the 275-grain Speer bullets are handloaded. Recoil is greater than with lesser cartridges, but not excessive for the shooter used to firing heavy 30-06 loads in light sporting rifles. The 338 will become increasingly popular with hunters who mix elk and moose with their regular deer menu.

348 WINCHESTER Lever action cartridge for really big game as well as deer, this is one of our most powerful rimmed cases. It appeared in 1936 for the Winchester Model 71—the only rifle ever commercially chambered for it—and originally offered considerable versatility with factory loads in 150-, 200- and 250-gr. bullet weights. Today, only a single loading with 200-gr. bullet is available, no rifles are made for it, and the cartridge is making a last stand in Alaska where its power, combined with a handy, smooth-working rifle keep it in use. The old 150-gr. load isn't missed much, but at least one ammo maker should produce the hard-hitting 250-gr. load.

35 REMINGTON With 200-gr. bullet, the 35 has been found to have considerably more anchoring power than the smaller 30's and 32's. Then too, it's good for getting through brush without deflection, and leaves a better blood trail. To 200 yards there's little difference in trajectory from the 30-30 and it has the advantage of being effective on larger game such as moose at moderate ranges, without excessive recoil. Highly recommended for Eastern deer and black bear, this praise does **not** include the pointed

150-gr. load. Stick to the 200-gr. for best results.

351 WINCHESTER SELF-LOADER Chambered only in the now-obsolete Winchester '07 autoloading rifle, the 351 hangs on because of its widespread use by police departments. For close wood ranges it can be used for deer and will kill with a proper hit.

358 WINCHESTER Larger caliber version of the 308 Winchester, the 358 drives 200-gr. bullets at 2530 fps, and 250-gr. at 2250. Each gives better than 2800 f.p. energy at the muzzle, and some 2200 f.p. at 100 yards. Trajectory of the 200-gr. matches that of the 180-gr. 300 Savage to 300 yards, hence it is not restricted to short ranges only. A splendid woods cartridge for moose, elk and deer, it has, unfortunately, been overlooked by many hunters.

350 REMINGTON MAGNUM First commercial cartridge to deserve the term Short Magnum, and one of the most practical big game rounds to appear in recent years, the 350 Magnum is especially notable for the restraint built into its design. Either standard length or short actions will accommodate its squat hull and deep-seated bullets, and its power is an almost perfect compromise, for American big game, between too much and not enough. This stems directly from its powder capacity, about 7% more than that of a 30-06 when both cases are filled to the base of their necks. 200-gr. bullets have a MV of 2710 fps, while 250-grainers reach 2410 fps, both from only a 20" carbine barrel. The old 35 Remington is thus hopelessly outclassed and the 35 Whelen challenged by a cartridge that is still within the recoil limitations of once-a-year hunters. Deer hunters and those who are recoil-shy should use the 200-gr. load, which delivers noticeably less kick.

375 H&H MAGNUM World-wide big game cartridge and champion of the "mediums," the 375 H&H dates back to 1912 but can still boast no peer as an all-round load for big and dangerous game. It will dispatch the largest American game as well as most African species. If necessary, it will kill an elephant, and yet its big 270-gr. slug will travel over long ranges as flat as a 180-gr. 30-06 to kill mountain game without excessive meat destruction. There is also a 300-gr. bullet turning up over 2 tons of muzzle energy. Cartridges may be purchased in almost all of the big game regions of the world. Its one disadvantage is its quite heavy recoil.

38-40 WINCHESTER This "38" actually measures 40 caliber and should have been named "40-40." Many deer are still killed yearly by its 180-gr. bullet, loafing along at 1,330 fs, mostly because it punches a big enough hole to let out a lot of blood. It's obsolete and there are a lot of better cartridges, but for short ranges (under 100 yards), it will still do the trick.

44-40 WINCHESTER Big brother of the 38-40, this is the same type of short, low-velocity cartridge, varying only by being slightly larger in bullet diameter and weight (200 grains). Under 100 yards it will kill as well as a 30-30.

44 REMINGTON MAGNUM Originally developed as a super-powered revolver cartridge, the 44 Magnum gradually evolved into a carbine deer load. Remington and Norma load a 240-gr. Jacketed SP, and Winchester a hollow point of the same weight—all at some 1750 fps from 18½" barrels. Handy little rifles by Ruger, Winchester and Marlin, plus a bolt action from Remington, have helped popularize this round, but it should be restricted to woods ranges not exceeding 150 yards.

444 MARLIN In essence a "super" 44 Magnum since it uses the same 240-gr. .429" jacketed SP bullet but in a long, straight 2.22" case, the 444 Marlin provides 30% higher MV with 88% greater ME! At the muzzle its energy is greater even than that of the 30-06, at least on paper, but the blunt, relatively short bullet sheds velocity so fast that at only 100 yards it is down to the power level of the 7mm Mauser and 300 Savage. However, the 444 will be hitting as hard at 200 yards as the 35 Remington at 150, making it a fine deer and black bear cartridge to this range, while at 100 yards or less it is capable of handling just about any

North American big game. Its biggest need is for a heavier constructed bullet that will not break up on the tough muscles and bone structure of such game or any intervening brush. Such bullets are already available to handloaders.

45-70 Still potent after 100 years, some of which was on the battlefield, but even more in the hunting fields, this old timer asks only to be used within ranges where its trajectory isn't too steep. Other than that, its user can count on a kill (if he does his part) whether the game be a small deer or a big moose. Excessive drop makes hitting tough beyond 150 yards, despite its ability to kill well-beyond that distance.

458 WINCHESTER Second most powerful American cartridge, the 458 has already won its spurs in Africa; the special Model 70 rifle chambered for it is known as the "African" Model. It is well named, for the massive 500-gr. full-steel-jacketed and 510-gr. soft-points are an "over-dose" for practically all other game with the exceptions of Indian tiger, Asian gaur, and Alaskan brown bear. Heavy bullet weight and high speed for its caliber combine to make this more than just a good killing cartridge—it is a "stopping load," designed to break down the most ponderous and dangerous beasts, and this it will do. For an American going to Africa for elephant, buffalo and rhino it is top choice. The soft point should be used on even the largest soft-skinned game, for the solid bullet is a specialized number for elephants. Has greatest recoil of all American cartridges except the 460 Weatherby.

THE WEATHERBY CARTRIDGES

Weatherby Magnum cartridges have been factory produced for many years now, and are sold at sporting goods stores all over America and in many foreign countries. The brass cases are produced in Sweden, but all other components are American-made and assembled. They therefore qualify as American ammunition and merit inclusion in this analysis of cartridges on the U.S. market.

224 WEATHERBY VARMINTMASTER Smallest of the Weatherby's, the 224 also has the smallest capacity of any belted case. Despite its modest size, however, velocities over 3700 fps with 50-gr. bullets and 3600 fps with 55-gr. have been chronographed, making it a close competitor of the 22-250. It is thus an efficient case which, in combination with the added safety features of good base thickness and positive headspacing provided by the belt, rates as an impressive performer. For those varminters who feel a need for more velocity than the 222 or 222 Magnum, but are willing to settle for less than the 220 Swift, the 224 Weatherby is an outstanding choice.

240 WEATHERBY MAGNUM Highest velocity of all factory-loaded 24 calibers, with the single exception of Holland & Holland's 244 Magnum, this medium capacity Weatherby features an entirely new belted case of reduced dimensions, capable of driving 70-gr. 6mm bullets to 3850 fps, 90-gr. to 3500, and 100-gr. to 3395 fps. It is thus some 200-300 fs faster than the 6mm Remington, and 300-400 fs ahead of the 243 Winchester. With loads giving sufficiently fine accuracy, this should prove to be an outstanding cartridge for open country deer and antelope shooting in combination with summer use as a long range varmint round.

257 WEATHERBY MAGNUM For varmint shooting at extremely long range or for the lighter species of big game in open country, where a premium is placed on flat trajectory and rapid bullet expansion, this cartridge is outstanding. Offering the flattest trajectory of any known 25-caliber cartridge, it utilizes the maximum loads of present-day powders that can be efficiently burned in this caliber to provide the highest striking energy for its bore size. In these combined respects, it is exceeded only by the 264 Winchester Magnum in cartridges under 270 caliber, and even there the difference is negligible.

270 WEATHERBY MAGNUM Next step up in the Weatherby line, the 270 WM is also a better choice for those who place more

emphasis on big game hunting, but would still like to use the same rifle for off-season varminting. Bullets of 100, 130 and 150 grains are available with energies and trajectories close to Winchester's 264 Magnum with, however, a somewhat better bullet selection for greater flexibility. While 270 WM muzzle velocities are around 300 fps faster than the standard 270, at 300 yards the speed differential is little more than 100 fs with the lighter bullets but some 270 fs ahead in 150-gr. loadings.

7mm WEATHERBY MAGNUM This cartridge so closely parallels the 270 WM in almost all respects that little more need be said about it, except to note that there's a .007″ bigger bullet and heavier bullet selection (to 175 grains) in the 7mm. In any event, there is little to choose between the 7mm WM and the newer 7mm Remington Magnum.

300 WEATHERBY MAGNUM Weatherby says this is his most popular and versatile caliber, and it's not hard to see why. With equal bullet weights, the 300 Weatherby develops from 285 to 355 fps more muzzle velocity than the 300 H&H Magnum for a noticeable increase in power. This cartridge is also liked for the nice balance it strikes between the large and small bores. For example, the 180-gr. 300 WM load offers some 500 fs velocity advantage over the 270-gr. 375 H&H Magnum with a consequent flattening of trajectory by 27%, and yet when loaded with a 150-gr. spitzer bullet it is both faster and flatter shooting than either the 270 or 7mm Weatherby Magnums. Despite some rather extreme claims for it the 300 Weatherby Magnum is doubtless one of the finest all-round big game cartridges.

340 WEATHERBY MAGNUM This is Weatherby's newest big game cartridge, produced to satisfy those hunters who want still more bullet weight than the 300's 220 grains, but at the same time wish to retain the 300's velocity and trajectory characteristics. This it does, giving a 250-gr. bullet only 55 fs less muzzle velocity than the 220-gr. 300 WM. Recoil is up, however, and the man who selects the 340 in preference to a 300 should be reasonably sure he needs its extra punch. For the great Alaskan bear it would appear to be a better choice, but for an all-round rifle involving mostly smaller game, the 300 would get the nod. The 340 WM uses the same bullets as the 338 Winchester Magnum, but boosts bullet speeds by 150 to 210 fps. An excellent moose, elk and bear cartridge.

378 WEATHERBY MAGNUM With this truly "magnum-size" cartridge we enter the field of specialized big game calibers. The latest Weatherby catalog states that it was "designed for the purpose of killing thick-skinned animals where extremely deep penetration is needed." With bullet weights of 270- and 300-gr. at velocities of 2900 to 3180 fps, it should be obvious that while striking power is unquestionably great, so is its recoil; entirely too much, in fact, for the average hunter not used to handling such heavy comeback. Experienced African and Arctic hunters, however, accustomed to the slam of the 375 H&H and larger rifles, report the 378 WM to be a most effective cartridge for the big stuff. With the adoption of the 378, Weatherby has discontinued production of the 375 WM, although ammunition for the older caliber is still being made. Despite its designation, the 378 uses the same bullets as the 375 Weatherby and the 375 H&H Magnum.

460 WEATHERBY MAGNUM Comments made on the 378 WM apply with even greater force to this largest and most powerful of all American cartridges. Using the same oversize belted case as the 378 Weatherby, its energy of 8000 fp with 500-gr. bullet is so great that it would normally be selected for only the very largest and dangerous game including elephant, rhino and buffalo. Some authorities feel that the 378 Weatherby would be adequate for such animals were it not for African game laws requiring rifles of 40 caliber or over for those species. Here again the name may be misleading, since the 460 WM uses the same size bullets as the 458 Winchester, only at a phenomenal increase of 570 fps muzzle velocity and nearly 3000 foot pounds of ME.

AMERICANIZED IMPORTED CARTRIDGES

We include here summaries on some of the popular and significant cartridges produced in Europe for the U.S. market. Some were actually designed in this country, others of overseas origin were specifically intended for export to the States; since most of them are encountered with increasing frequency, it is reasonable to think of them as "American" by use if not by manufacture. Only those loaded with American-type "Boxer" primers are included.

6.5x54 MS An old but still liked cartridge for the Mannlicher-Schoenauer carbines, Norma offers five different versions with bullet weights of 77, 139 and 156 grains at muzzle speeds of 3117, 2580 and 2461 fps. A modest capacity round, the 6.5 MS built its reputation as a game cartridge **not** on velocity, but rather on the deep penetration of its long pencil-like round nose bullets. In its heaviest bullet weight, it has been well-liked in Maine as an effective black bear load.

6.5x55 SWEDISH Long the military cartridge of Sweden and Norway, the 6.5x55 has become quite common in the U.S., partly because of thousands of imported surplus military rifles and the fine Schultz & Larsen target rifles. With its light recoil, resistance to wind deflection and excellent accuracy, it has justified its Scandinavian reputation and is seen increasingly on our target ranges. Norma offers 6 different loadings with bullet weights of 77, 93, 139 and 156 grains at velocities somewhat above those of the smaller Mannlicher cartridge. The 139-gr. load is probably the most popular here.

7x61 S&H A modern high velocity big game round with Norma short belted case, the brain-child of Americans Phil Sharpe and Dick Hart, this shell is only 4mm longer than the old 7x57 Mauser case but velocity with 160-gr. boat-tails is 3100 fps at muzzle of a 26" barrel, according to the Norma table. In 1968, Norma improved the 7x61 case by changing its interior dimensions to provide thinner but stronger case walls, Known as the Super 7x61, exterior dimensions remain exactly the same as formerly, hence the new version will fit all rifles chambered for the older 7x61 S&H, but due to a slightly increased powder capacity, velocity is rated 50 fs higher; (3150 with 160-gr. bullet from 26" barrels).

30 U.S. CARBINE To satisfy the demand for 30 Carbine ammo, Norma produces one with full metal jacket, the other in soft point, both 110 grain. This last, the one hunter-owners most sought, is at best little more than a small game cartridge, since velocity and energy are down to 1595 fs and 622 fp respectively at only 100 yards. Fast repeat shots should not be counted on to make up for inadequate power; this cartridge should not be selected for deer or other big game hunting.

7.5 SWISS Known officially at the 7.5x55mm Schmidt-Rubin, this cartridge is intended for the Swiss military rifles, Model 1911, of the same name, and is now being imported by Norma-Precision, loaded with a 180-gr. soft point boat-tail bullet at M.V. 2650 fps. Cases have a single central flash-hole for American primers and, as factory loaded in Sweden, are both non-corrosive and non-mercuric. This should make a fine deer load for owners of these military rifles, and cases can be readily reloaded with U.S. components.

308 NORMA MAGNUM A short magnum tailored to American big game fields. Its 180-gr. bullet steps out at a velocity 400 fs faster than the 180-gr. 30-06, is 180 fs ahead of the great 300 H&H, equals the new 300 Winchester Magnum and even approaches the much larger 300 Weatherby. Advantage of the Norma cartridge (true also of the 300 Win. Mag.) is that it has the same over-all length as a 30-06, hence will fit in '06 magazines and only requires re-chambering the barrel and opening up the bolt face, plus an extractor alteration, to convert an '06 to 308 Magnum. Pressures run pretty high in this case, so only rifles with strong actions should be converted to the new cartridge. Only factory load is with 180-gr. "Dual-Core" bullets, but the cases may be reloaded with American primers and any 30-cal. bullets from 110- to 220-gr. weight. It is thus a versatile as well as powerful high performance cartridge.

NORMA 7.62mm RUSSIAN Imported by Norma-Precision for American owners of Winchester Model 1895 and surplus military rifles in this caliber, the 7.62mm is furnished with the Tri-Clad soft point 180-gr. bullet developing 2625 fps muzzle velocity and more than 2750 fp energy. This is a rimmed bottle-necked case, ballistically almost identical to our 308, thus only slightly inferior to the 30-06. Formerly loaded in this country with either 145-gr. or 150-gr. bullets at 2820 fps, those ballistics may be reproduced in these new cases by handloaders desiring a lighter, faster bullet loading.

303 BRITISH HV Another modernized old cartridge is Norma's high velocity loadings of the 303 British. As loaded by Remington with a 215-gr. bullet and by Winchester with a 180-gr., pressure limitations of the Lee-Enfield action have held velocities to a sedate 2180-2540 fps, and owners of surplus 303's have wondered how they could obtain higher speeds. The safest way is to decrease bullet weight, and this is just what Norma has done. Two Norma factory loads include a 150-gr. bullet at 2720 fps and a 130-gr. at 2789, either of which will shoot flatter and open quicker on impact than the heavier bullets. If you use a 303 for open country hunting of deer or antelope, give these new loads a try.

7.65 ARGENTINE Originally known as the 7.65mm Belgian Mauser, this cartridge was once loaded in the U.S. and chambered in such popular rifles as the Remington 30-S and Winchester 54 and 70, but was discontinued about the time of WW 2 for lack of demand. Importation of surplus Argentine military Mausers has reversed the picture and there is once again a need for this surprisingly efficient round. Norma offers a single 150-gr. soft point with 2920 fs muzzle velocity and 2105 fs at **300** yards for a midrange trajectory height of only 5.8". Regardless of the fact that this cartridge was designed over 70 years ago, in its modern version it is still an excellent deer cartridge. Bullet (not cartridge) size is the same as a 303 British—.311"-.312".

8x57-JR and 8x57-JRS Rimmed versions of the famous 8x57 Mauser cartridge, the 8x57-JR is loaded by Norma with a 196-gr. .318" bullet, while the 8x57-JRS has the same weight but in .323" diameter. Post-war rifles generally have the larger bore size, while pre-war rifles usually (but not necessarily) have the .318" bore. In any event, the proof markings on the barrel should be carefully examined and only those cartridges with the proper size bullets used. Both of the 8x57 rimmed rounds are good deer and black bear cartridges.

358 NORMA MAGNUM First of the new line of Norma Magnums, this 35-caliber number was offered to the market in 1959 and since then has steadily gained favor among big game hunters here and abroad. In the Scandinavian countries, the 358 Norma has become a favorite of moose hunters, a use for which it is well-fitted almost anywhere. A 250-gr. bullet at 2790 fps from a 23" barrel gives 4322 fp energy—some 1500 more than a 220-gr. 30-06—and energy close to the 4500 fp of a 375 Magnum. With a 200-gr. bullet, 3100 fps can be reached with permissible pressures, so that the 358 Norma may be thought of as a direct competitor of the 338 Winchester, both ballistically and as concerns adaptability to game species. It should fill the bill as a powerful "medium" bore for African hunting, and of course is a natural for Canadian and Alaskan large game.

RIMFIRE CARTRIDGES

5mm REMINGTON RIMFIRE MAGNUM Although originally announced in the fall of 1967, this 20-cal. bottle-necked high velocity rimfire was not offered on sale until 1970, for various problems arose in providing adequate breech support for case rims. These were finally overcome and this cartridge now ranks as our most powerful rimfire. It has a 38-gr. Power-Lokt HP bullet of .2045" diameter with muzzle velocity of 2100 fps and 372 f.p. Remaining speeds are 1605 fps at 100 yards, and 1400 at 150, which is about its limit on varmints. You'll need a special cleaning rod for this one, as 22-cal. rods are too large.

22 SHORT The economical shooting gallery cartridge. Accurate to 50 yards, this old load is still a popular number. Three loadings—Standard, High Speed and Gallery—give it a usefulness second only to the indispensable 22 Long Rifle. It is **not** a game cartridge, however, and its use on live targets should be restricted to rats, snakes, starlings and the like, since even in the high speed load its light bullet gives but half the energy of the Long Rifle.

22 LONG Only the High Speed loading of this little "betwixt and between" cartridge survives. Having neither the accuracy of the Short nor the power of the Long Rifle it is not recommended except for those few old repeating rifles chambered especially for it.

22 LONG RIFLE Finest and most versatile rimfire cartridge ever developed, it is today better than ever. Four loadings fit it for just about everything except big game hunting. This is everybody's cartridge, with the gilt-edged accuracy of the special

Match loads for serious competition, the Standard rounds for economical practice, the High Speeds for small game hunting (with hollow-point bullets), and the Shot cartridges for pest destruction. The High Speed with plain bullet is not recommended for **any** of these uses. For hunting, better use the hollow-point for humane kills, and even try for a head shot. Pass up shots beyond 75 yards and be content with squirrels, rabbits and birds.

22 WINCHESTER AUTOMATIC Useful only to owners of the old Winchester Model 1903 autoloader, it is less powerful than the Long Rifle.

22 WRF (or REMINGTON SPECIAL) More powerful than any Long Rifle load and a far better hunting cartridge, it deserves to be more popular. Its flat-nose bullet, of slightly greater diameter and 5 grains more weight than a Long Rifle, is faster, and turns up a third more energy. For squirrel hunters it is hard to beat, and rifles for it should again be made.

22 WINCHESTER MAGNUM RIMFIRE Now in second place to the 5mm Remington Rimfire Magnum as far as velocity and energy are concerned, the 22 WMR remains an excellent choice for the rimfire rifleman who wants greater shock power than the 22 LR offers—and wants it in other than a Remington or Winchester rifle. Chambering for the 22 WMR is offered by numerous other rifle makers, and by a few handgun manufacturers as well. It appears unlikely that the 5mm RRM will appear as a handgun round.

Part II. HANDGUN CARTRIDGES
(Rimfire & Centerfire)

22 SHORT RF This little cartridge is currently experiencing a revival of popularity because of its adaptability to rapid-fire international-type shooting in the autoloading pistols made especially for it.

22 LONG RF See Rifle Cartridge Section.

22 LONG RIFLE RF Just as with rifles, this cartridge has done more than any other to popularize shooting and training with the handgun. In either revolver or "automatic" it is highly accurate and makes a fine companion for hunter and trapper. Ammo is easily carried, yet will kill small game better than some larger centerfires. Use high speeds for hunting and standards for target work.

22 REMINGTON JET First of the CF handgun cartridges to appear, this little bottleneck was introduced in March of 1961 when Smith & Wesson announced their Magnum M53 revolver. Besides the 22 Jet this gun handles (via cylinder inserts) 22 Shorts, Longs and Long Rifles. The factory-announced muzzle velocity of 2460 fps (obtained in closed-breech test barrels) has not been achieved in revolvers with their open gap between cylinder and barrel. However, the 1870 fps reached with 6" barrels (2100 with 8⅜") makes this a respectable handgun varmint cartridge in any man's language.

221 REMINGTON FIREBALL The second 22-cal. CF cartridge to be introduced by Remington, it established a precedent in 1963 by being chambered in the first American commercial bolt action pistol. 2650 fps has been reached with a 50-gr. bullet from its 10½" barrel, equal to a factory 22 Hornet with 45-gr. bullet fired in a full-length rifle barrel.

256 WINCHESTER MAGNUM Winchester's entry in the high speed, flat trajectory handgun cartridge field had trouble getting off the ground after it was announced in April, 1961, but it has finally developed as **both** a handgun and rifle cartridge. Early published factory velocities were **lower** than those actually attained, first tables saying 2000 fps for the 60-gr. SP bullet, whereas independent chronographs registered 2350 fps from the 8½" barrel of a Ruger Hawkeye.

25 AUTO Smallest of production centerfires, this is strictly for use in defensive weapons—tiny automatics lacking both power and accuracy, firing 50-gr. metal case bullets with less energy than even the standard velocity 22 LR.

30 CARBINE In producing his Blackhawk revolver chambered for the 30 Carbine cartridge, Bill Ruger has made this round properly classifiable as a handgun load. For the considerable number of today's pistol shooters seeking a high speed, flat-shooting revolver cartridge without the heavy recoil of a 44 or 41 Magnum, but with more bullet weight and diameter than a 22 caliber, the 30 Carbine may provide the answer. Factory and GI loads produce velocities varying from 1400 to 1530 fps from our 7½" barrel test revolver, giving them some 40% more muzzle energy than the 22 Jet. As a revolver load it will be liked particularly by owners of carbines in the same caliber as a companion piece.

30 LUGER A bottle-necked cartridge for automatic pistols firing a 93-gr. metal case bullet at 1,220 fs. Flat shooting with high paper energy, expansion is lacking due to bullet construction, severely limiting its game-killing or man-stopping capabilities. However, it far out-classes the 32 ACP.

32 AUTO Next step up in the caliber scale for automatics, this is a very popular cartridge here and abroad for pocket pistols. Many are used by foreign police where it is known as the 7.65mm, but again a small (71-gr.) round nose metal case bullet gives energy only in the high speed 22 Long Rifle class and no bullet expansion. Not recommended for hunting or defense use.

32 S&W & 32 S&W LONG These are the most popular of the 32's for revolvers, the shorter load used in innumerable old "bureau-drawer specials," the accurate Long in target and light police revolvers. The Long should always be chosen if the gun will handle it. A good small game cartridge but lacks power for police work.

32 COLT SHORT & LONG A pair of "obsolete" cartridges used in old-model Colt pocket revolvers, they are less accurate and less powerful than the 32 S&W Long, and will not chamber in modern 32-caliber revolvers.

32-20 WINCHESTER Best of all the 32s for revolvers, using 100-gr. bullets in both lead and soft point types with flat nose, this is the smallest caliber practical for serious police and defensive use. Trajectory is also flatter due to higher velocity, making this a good hunting cartridge for varmints and small game. Do NOT use the "High Velocity" rifle loads in revolvers.

38 AUTO and 38 SUPER AUTOMATIC The 38 Automatic cartridge is intended to be used in the original Colt 38 Automatic pistols, Models of 1900 and 1902. When the Colt Super 38 appeared about 1925, a new, more powerful loading was offered under the name of Super 38 for this stronger pistol. These Super 38 Automatic cartridges should not be fired in the early model Colt pistols in view of their system of slide attachment and the higher pressures of the Super cartridge. Even the regular 38 Automatic is closely comparable to the 9mm Luger in power, and the 38 Super will give the 357 Magnum a run for its money in barrels of equal length. If loaded with soft point bullets, both of these 38 Auto cartridges would make good game killing loads. Either cartridge will function properly in the Super automatic pistol.

380 AUTO Designed to give more power in a straight blowback automatic pistol than is provided by the 32 ACP cartridge, and yet keep down chamber pressure and recoil to stay within the limitations of small pocket pistols, it is the smallest auto pistol cartridge which can be recommended for defense. Super Vel's modern loading of an 80-gr. JHP bullet at 1026 fps considerably increases the effectiveness of this cartridge.

9mm LUGER Improved bullet designs and modern high speed loadings have greatly upped the stopping power and all-round utility of the well-known 9mm Parabellum or Luger. To the old 124-gr. metal cased loading at 1120 fps have been added a 115-gr. JHP at 1160 fps (Rem.), a 100-gr. Power Point at 1325 fps (Win.), and either a 110-gr. SP at 1325 or 90-gr. JHP at 1422 fps by Super Vel. Long a European military pistol cartridge, the 9mm has now become an International cartridge with wide spread civilian and growing police use as well.

38 S&W A favorite cartridge for pocket revolvers, with 146-gr bullet, and adopted by the British military during World War II, when it was known as the 38-200 (as it was loaded with a 200-gr. bullet). Nothing smaller is recommended for defensive use.

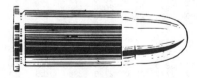

38 COLT SHORT & LONG The 38 Short was used in early Colt house defense guns and the Long was the cartridge which failed to stop fanatical Moros during the Philippine Insurrection. Either may be used in a 38 Special revolver, but both are outclassed by that cartridge for any purpose, hence seldom used.

38 SPECIAL As with the 9mm, this cartridge—once considered marginal for police, defensive and combat use—has become, with the introduction of new bullets and high speed loadings, a far more effective "stopper" than was formerly thought possible. Hollow point and expanding soft points ranging from 110-gr. and 125-gr. at 1370 fps, to 158-gr. bullets at 1150 fps (from 6" barrels) have given this old cartridge a new lease on life. In its milder loadings, it continues to be our most accurate centerfire target cartridge for handguns.

357 MAGNUM A high velocity revolver cartridge ideally suited to the needs of police officers and field shooters, its 158-gr.

bullet travels at a far higher velocity and delivers an even greater increase in striking energy than the same weight bullet from a 38 Special of equal barrel length. With metal piercing bullet it will penetrate an automobile body, and with the flat-point lead bullet it will kill game of considerable size. An even better choice of bullet for field use is the soft point Remington or Norma half-jacket which will not lead up barrels as do the ordinary lead bullets at high velocity. One of our three best long range revolver cartridges, a gun in this caliber has the added advantage of chambering all 38 Special cartridges for target work.

38-40 WINCHESTER See Part I—CF Rifle Cartridges.

41 MAGNUM Produced by Remington for Smith & Wesson revolvers in response to demands for a more potent police cartridge, this new 41 Magnum fills the gap between the 357 and 44 Magnums. Two loads are offered, one a 210-gr. SP at 1500 fps, the other a 210-gr. lead bullet at 1050 fps, both MV figures from 8¾" bbls. In the more common 6" bbl., velocities run 1342 and 986. A potent and accurate cartridge in SP version, trajectory is practically as flat as the 44 Magnum is; it penetrates even deeper, though bullet energy is less. Recoil, only 75% of a 44 Magnum's, makes it a much more pleasant load to shoot. It may well find more use in the game fields than on the policeman's beat. Recoil and gun weight are both heavy for police use, and so far the lead bullet loads have shown only medeiocre accuracy. Bullet diameter is .410" and will not interchange with the old 41 Long Colt.

44-40 WINCHESTER See Part I—CF Rifle Cartridges.

44 S&W SPECIAL Developed as a target cartridge from the earlier 44 S&W Russian, the 44 Special has never been loaded by the factories to its velocity potential. The 246-gr. lead bullets travel slowly (755 fs), which is of no matter on target ranges where their high accuracy is paramount. Only when properly handloaded is its true power capacity realized.

44 REMINGTON MAGNUM Quite in a class by itself, this extremely powerful revolver cartridge with standard factory loadings of 240-gr. lead or jacketed SP and HP bullets at 1470 fps (from 6½" barrels) ranks high in stopping power and recoil. Muzzle energy of 1150 f.p. is more than twice that of the hottest 38 Specials, but so is recoil, and gun weight too must be higher, making this a cartridge for specialized use by veteran handgunners. It most definitely cannot be recommended for beginning handgunners! Those shooters seeking a lighter load for target practice may use the mild old 44 S&W Special.

45 COLT Most famous of all American revolver cartridges and still one of the best, whether the target be criminal or beast. For close range work we would prefer its big 250-gr. bullet to the 357 Magnum. Now that new guns are again being made for the old 45, its historical background as well as its effective power should ensure a continued popularity and long life.

45 AUTO Official U.S. Army sidearm cartridge since 1911 and spanning 4 wars, this largest American round for automatic pistols has thoroughly proven itself, both in combat and on the target range. Difficult to control until mastered, but inherently accurate in accurized pistols, its already wide popularity has been given assists in the form of special target loads with 185- and 210-gr. match bullets at very low velocity, plus some stepped up prescriptions, typical of which is Super Vel's 190-gr. JHP at 1060 fps. Probably more shooters than ever before are using this cartridge for a wide range of activities from police sidearm to hunting. On competitive target ranges it often supplants the 38 Special in the centerfire matches. It is a good all-round choice for big bore pistol shooters.

45 AUTO RIM Companion of the 45 ACP, this thick-rimmed cartridge was developed for use in revolvers chambered for the 45 Auto round, without the necessity of using half-moon clips. Its 230-gr. lead bullets at 810 fps MV (from 5½" barrel) makes it suitable for either police or field use. Shallow rifling in these revolvers requires that bullets be cast hard or jacketed.

CENTER RIFLE CARTRIDGES — BALLISTICS AND PRICES

Winchester-Western, Remington-Peters, Federal, Speer-DWM, Browning and Frontier

Most of these centerfire loads are available from Winchester-Western and Remington-Peters. Loads available from only one source are marked by a letter, thus: Winchester (a); Western (b); Remington (c); Peters (d); Speer-DWM (f). Those fewer cartridges also available from Federal are marked (e). Contrary to previous practice, W-W and R-P prices are not necessarily uniform. All prices are approximate.

Cartridge	Bullet Wt. Grs.	Bullet Type	Velocity (fps) Muzzle	Velocity 100 yds.	Velocity 200 yds.	Velocity 300 yds.	Energy (ft. lbs.) Muzzle	Energy 100 yds.	Energy 200 yds.	Energy 300 yds.	Mid-Range Trajectory 100 yds.	Mid-Range Trajectory 200 yds.	Mid-Range Trajectory 300 yds.	Price for 20*
17 Remington	25	HP, PL	4020	3290	2630	2060	900	600	380	230	Not Available			$4.85
218 Bee*	46	HP	2860	2160	1610	1200	835	475	265	145	0.7	3.8	11.5	10.80
22 Hornet*	45	SP	2690	2030	1510	1150	720	410	230	130	0.8	4.3	13.0	10.35
22 Hornet* (c, d)	45	HP	2690	2030	1510	1150	720	410	230	130	0.8	4.3	13.0	10.35
22 Hornet*	46	HP	2690	2030	1510	1150	740	420	235	135	0.8	4.3	13.0	10.35
222 Remington (e)	50	PSP, MC, PL†	3200	2660	2170	1750	1140	785	520	340	0.5	2.5	7.0	4.25
222 Remington Magnum (c, d)	55	SP, PL†	3300	2800	2340	1930	1330	955	670	455	0.5	2.3	6.1	4.50
222 Remington Magnum (c, d)	55	HP, PL	3300	2830	2400	2010	1330	975	700	490	Not Available			4.85
223 Remington (c, d, e)	55	SP, PL†	3300	2800	2340	1930	1330	955	670	455	0.5	2.1	5.4	4.50
22-250 Remington	55	PSP	3810	3270	2770	2320	1770	1300	935	655	0.3	1.6	4.4	4.65
22-250 Remington (c, d)	55	HP, PL	3810	3330	2890	2490	1770	1360	1020	760	Not Available			4.90
225 Winchester (a, b)	55	PSP	3650	3140	2680	2270	1630	1200	875	630	0.4	1.8	4.8	4.65
243 Winchester (e)	80	PSP, PL†	3500	3080	2720	2410	2180	1690	1320	1030	0.4	1.8	4.7	5.85
243 Winchester (c, d)	80	HP, PL	3450	3050	2675	2330	2115	1650	1270	965	Not Available			6.25
243 Winchester (e)	100	PP, CL, PSP	3070	2790	2540	2320	2090	1730	1430	1190	0.5	2.2	5.5	5.85
6mm Remington (c, d)	80	PSP, HP, PL†	3450	3130	2750	2400	2220	1740	1340	1018	0.4	1.8	4.7	5.70
6mm Remington (c, d)	100	PCL	3190	2920	2660	2420	2260	1890	1570	1300	0.5	2.1	5.1	5.70
244 Remington (c, d)	90	PSP	3200	2850	2530	2230	2050	1630	1280	995	0.5	2.1	5.5	5.70
25-06 Remington (c, d)	87	HP	3500	3070	2680	2310	2370	1820	1390	1030	Not Available			6.20
25-06 Remington (c, d)	120	PSP, CL	3120	2850	2600	2360	2590	2160	1800	1480	Not Available			6.40
25-20 Winchester*	86	L, Lu	1460	1180	1030	940	405	265	200	170	2.6	12.5	32.0	8.25
25-20 Winchester*	86	SP	1460	1180	1030	940	405	265	200	170	2.6	12.5	32.0	9.00
25-35 Winchester	117	SP, CL	2300	1910	1600	1340	1370	945	665	465	1.0	4.6	12.5	5.75
250 Savage (a, b)	87	PSP, SP	3030	2660	2330	2060	1770	1370	1050	820	0.6	2.5	6.4	5.50
250 Savage	100	ST, CL, PSP	2820	2460	2140	1870	1760	1340	1020	775	0.6	2.9	7.4	5.50
256 Winchester Magnum* (b)	60	OPE	2800	2070	1570	1220	1040	570	330	200	0.8	4.0	12.0	10.10
257 Roberts (a, b)	87	PSP	3200	2840	2500	2190	1980	1560	1210	925	0.5	2.2	5.7	6.05
257 Roberts (a, b)	100	ST, CL	2900	2540	2210	1920	1870	1430	1080	820	0.6	2.7	7.0	6.05
257 Roberts	117	PP, CL	2650	2280	1950	1690	1820	1350	985	740	0.7	3.4	8.8	6.05
6.5 Remington Magnum (c)	100	PSPCL	3450	3070	2690	2320	2640	2090	1610	1190	Not Available			7.70
6.5mm Remington Magnum (c)	120	PSPCL	3030	2750	2480	2230	2450	2010	1640	1330	0.5	2.3	5.7	7.70
264 Winchester Magnum	100	PSP, CL	3700	3260	2880	2550	3040	2360	1840	1440	0.4	1.6	4.2	7.95
264 Winchester Magnum	140	PP, CL	3200	2490	2700	2480	3180	2690	2270	1910	0.5	2.0	4.9	7.95
270 Winchester	100	PSP	3480	3070	2690	2340	2690	2090	1600	1215	0.4	1.8	4.8	6.40
270 Winchester (e)	130	PP, PSP	3140	2880	2630	2400	2850	2390	2000	1660	0.5	2.1	5.3	6.40
270 Winchester	130	ST, CL, BP, PP	3140	2850	2580	2320	2840	2340	1920	1550	0.5	2.1	5.3	6.40
270 Winchester (c, d)	150	CL	2800	2440	2140	1870	2610	1980	1520	1160	0.6	2.9	7.6	6.40
270 Winchester (a, b, e)	150	PP	2900	2620	2380	2160	2800	2290	1890	1550	0.6	2.5	6.3	6.40
280 Remington (c, d)	150	PCL	2900	2670	2450	2220	2800	2370	2000	1640	0.6	2.5	6.1	6.20
280 Remington (c, d)	165	CL	2820	2510	2220	1970	2910	2310	1810	1420	0.6	2.8	7.2	6.20
284 Winchester (a, b)	125	PP	3200	2880	2590	2310	2840	2300	1860	1480	0.5	2.1	5.3	6.40
284 Winchester (a, b)	150	PP	2900	2630	2380	2160	2800	2300	1890	1550	0.6	2.5	6.3	6.40
7mm Mauser (e)	139	SP	2710	2440	2190	1960	2280	1850	1490	1190	0.7	3.0	7.8	6.40
7mm Mauser (e)	175	SP	2490	2170	1900	1680	2410	1830	1400	1100	0.8	3.7	9.5	6.40
7mm Remington Magnum	125	CL	3430	3080	2750	2450	3260	2630	2100	1660	0.6	1.8	4.7	7.95
7mm Remington Magnum (e)	150	PP, CL	3260	2970	2700	2450	3540	2940	2430	1990	0.4	2.0	4.9	7.95
7mm Remington Magnum (e)	175	PP	3070	2720	2400	2120	3660	2870	2240	1750	0.5	2.4	6.1	7.95
7mm Remington Magnum (c, d)	175	PCL	3070	2860	2660	2460	3660	3170	2740	2350	0.5	2.1	5.2	7.95
30 Carbine* (e)	110	HSP, SP	1980	1540	1230	1040	950	575	370	260	1.4	7.5	21.7	10.05
30-30 Winchester (c, d)	150	CL	2410	1960	1620	1360	1930	1280	875	616	0.9	4.5	12.5	5.00
30-30 Winchester (e)	150	HP	2410	2020	1700	1430	1930	1360	960	680	0.9	4.2	11.0	5.00
30-30 Winchester (a, b)	150	PP, ST, OPE	2410	2020	1700	1430	1930	1360	960	680	0.9	4.2	11.0	5.00
30-30 Winchester (e)	170	PP, HP, CL, ST, MC	2220	1890	1630	1410	1860	1350	1000	750	1.2	4.6	12.5	5.00
30 Remington	170	ST, CL	2120	1820	1560	1350	1700	1250	920	690	1.1	5.3	14.0	5.85
30-06 Springfield (a, b)	110	PSP	3370	2830	2350	1920	2770	1960	1350	900	0.5	2.2	6.0	6.40
30-06 Springfield	125	PSP	3200	2810	2480	2200	2840	2190	1710	1340	0.5	2.2	5.6	6.40
30-06 Springfield (c, d)	150	BP	2970	2710	2470	2240	2930	2440	2030	1670	0.5	2.4	6.0	6.40
30-06 Springfield (e)	150	PP	2970	2620	2300	2010	2930	2280	1760	1340	0.6	2.5	6.5	6.40
30-06 Springfield	150	ST, PCL, PSP	2970	2670	2400	2130	2930	2370	1920	1510	0.6	2.4	6.1	6.40
30-06 Springfield	180	PP, CL, PSP	2700	2330	2010	1740	2910	2170	1610	1210	0.7	3.1	8.3	6.40
30-06 Springfield (e)	180	ST, BP, PCL	2700	2470	2250	2040	2910	2440	2020	1660	0.7	2.9	7.0	6.40
30-06 Springfield	180	MCBT, MAT	2700	2520	2350	2190	2910	2540	2200	1900	0.6	2.8	6.7	9.45
30-06 Springfield	220	PP, CL	2410	2120	1870	1670	2830	2190	1710	1360	0.8	3.9	9.8	6.40
30-06 Springfield (a, b)	220	ST	2410	2180	1980	1790	2830	2320	1910	1560	0.8	3.7	9.2	6.40
30-40 Krag	180	PP, CL	2470	2120	1830	1590	2440	1790	1340	1010	0.8	3.8	9.9	6.50
30-40 Krag	180	ST, PCL	2470	2250	2040	1850	2440	2020	1660	1370	0.8	3.5	8.5	6.50
30-40 Krag (a, b)	220	ST	2200	1990	1800	1630	2360	1930	1580	1300	1.0	4.4	11.0	6.50
300 Winchester Magnum (e)	150	PP, PCL	3400	3050	2730	2430	3850	3100	2480	1970	0.4	1.9	4.8	9.35
300 Winchester Magnum (e)	180	PP, PCL	3070	2850	2640	2440	3770	3250	2790	2380	0.5	2.1	5.3	9.35
300 Winchester Mag (a, b)	220	ST	2720	2490	2270	2060	3620	3030	2520	2070	0.6	2.9	6.9	9.35
300 H&H Magnum (a, b)	150	ST	3190	2870	2580	2300	3390	2740	2220	1760	0.5	2.1	5.2	9.35
300 H&H Magnum	180	ST, PCL	2920	2670	2440	2220	3400	2850	2380	1970	0.6	2.4	5.8	9.35
300 H&H Magnum (a, b)	220	ST, CL	2620	2370	2150	1940	3350	2740	2260	1840	0.7	3.1	7.7	9.35
300 Savage (e)	150	PP	2670	2350	2060	1800	2370	1840	1410	1080	0.7	3.2	8.0	6.20
300 Savage	150	ST, PCL	2670	2390	2130	1890	2370	1900	1510	1190	0.7	3.0	7.6	6.20
300 Savage (c, d)	150	CL	2670	2270	1930	1660	2370	1710	1240	916	0.7	3.3	9.3	6.20
300 Savage (e)	180	PP, CL	2370	2040	1760	1520	2240	1660	1240	920	0.9	4.1	10.5	6.20
300 Savage	180	ST, PCL	2370	2160	1960	1770	2240	1860	1530	1250	0.9	3.7	9.2	6.20
303 Savage (c, d)	180	CL	2140	1810	1550	1340	1830	1310	960	715	1.1	5.4	14.0	6.45
303 Savage (a, b)	190	ST	1980	1680	1440	1250	1650	1190	875	660	1.3	6.2	15.5	6.45
303 British (e)	180	PP, CL	2540	2300	2090	1900	2580	2120	1750	1440	0.7	3.3	8.2	6.45
303 British (c, d)	215	SP	2180	1900	1660	1460	2270	1720	1310	1020	1.1	4.9	12.5	6.45
308 Winchester (a, b)	110	PSP	3340	2810	2340	1920	2730	1930	1340	900	0.5	2.2	6.0	6.40
308 Winchester (a, b)	125	PSP	3100	2740	2430	2160	2670	2080	1640	1300	0.5	2.3	5.9	6.40
308 Winchester (e)	150	PP	2860	2520	2210	1930	2730	2120	1630	1240	0.6	2.7	7.0	6.40
308 Winchester	150	ST, PCL	2860	2570	2300	2050	2730	2200	1760	1400	0.6	2.6	6.5	6.40
308 Winchester (e)	180	PP, CL	2610	2250	1940	1680	2720	2020	1500	1130	0.7	3.4	8.9	6.40
308 Winchester	180	ST, PCL	2610	2390	2170	1970	2720	2280	1870	1540	0.8	3.1	7.4	6.40
308 Winchester (a, b)	200	ST	2450	2210	1980	1770	2670	2170	1750	1400	0.8	3.6	9.0	6.40
32 Winchester Special (c, d, e)	170	HP, CL	2280	1920	1630	1410	1960	1390	1000	750	1.0	4.8	12.5	5.15
32 Winchester Special	170	PP, ST	2280	1870	1560	1330	1960	1320	920	665	1.0	4.8	13.0	5.15
32 Remington (c, d)	170	CL	2120	1800	1540	1340	1700	1220	895	680	1.0	4.9	13.0	6.05
32 Remington (a, b)	170	ST	2120	1760	1460	1220	1700	1170	805	560	1.1	5.3	14.5	6.05
32-20 Winchester*	100	SP	1290	1060	940	840	370	250	195	155	3.3	15.5	38.0	9.00
32-20 Winchester*	100	SP, L, Lu	1290	1060	940	840	370	250	195	155	3.3	15.5	38.0	7.20

CENTERFIRE RIFLE CARTRIDGES — BALLISTICS AND PRICES (continued)

Cartridge	Bullet Wt. Grs.	Type	Velocity (fps) Muzzle	100 yds.	200 yds.	300 yds.	Energy (ft. lbs.) Muzzle	100 yds.	200 yds.	300 yds.	Mid-Range Trajectory 100 yds.	200 yds.	300 yds.	Price for 20*
8mm Mauser (e)	170	PP, CL	2570	2140	1790	1520	2490	1730	1210	870	0.8	3.9	10.5	$6.40
338 Winchester Magnum (a, b)	200	PP	3000	2690	2410	2170	4000	3210	2580	2090	0.5	2.4	6.0	8.60
338 Winchester Magnum (a, b)	250	ST	2700	2430	2180	1940	4050	3280	2640	2090	0.7	3.0	7.4	8.60
338 Winchester Magnum (a, b)	300	PP	2450	2160	1910	1690	4000	3110	2430	1900	0.8	3.7	9.5	8.60
348 Winchester (a)	200	ST	2530	2220	1940	1680	2840	2190	1765	1509	0.4	1.7	4.7	8.95
348 Winchester (c, d)	200	CL	2530	2140	1820	1570	2840	2030	1470	1090	0.8	3.8	10.0	8.95
35 Remington (c, d)	150	CL	2400	1960	1580	1280	1920	1280	835	545	0.9	4.6	13.0	5.80
35 Remington (e)	200	PP, ST, CL	2100	1710	1390	1160	1950	1300	860	605	1.2	6.0	16.5	5.80
350 Remington Magnum (c, d)	200	PCL	2710	2410	2130	1870	3260	2570	2000	1550	Not Available			7.70
350 Remington Magnum (c, d)	250	PCL	2410	2190	1980	1790	3220	2660	2180	1780	Not Available			7.70
351 Winchester Self-Loading*	180	SP	1850	1560	1310	1140	1370	975	685	520	1.5	7.8	21.5	12.65
358 Winchester (a, b)	200	ST	2530	2210	1910	1640	2840	2160	1610	1190	0.8	3.6	9.4	7.75
358 Winchester (a, b)	250	ST	2250	2010	1780	1570	2810	2230	1760	1370	1.0	4.4	11.0	7.75
375 H&H Magnum	270	PP, SP	2740	2460	2210	1990	4500	3620	2920	2370	0.7	2.9	7.1	10.20
375 H&H Magnum	300	ST	2550	2280	2040	1830	4330	3460	2770	2230	0.7	3.3	8.3	10.20
375 H&H Magnum	300	MC	2550	2180	1860	1590	4330	3160	2300	1680	0.7	3.6	9.3	10.20
38-40 Winchester*	180	SP	1330	1070	960	850	705	455	370	290	3.2	15.0	36.5	10.70
44 Magnum* (c, d)	240	SP	1750	1360	1110	980	1630	985	655	510	1.6	8.4	—	10.95
44 Magnum (b)	240	HSP	1750	1350	1090	950	1630	970	635	480	1.8	9.4	26.0	4.50
444 Marlin (c)	240	SP	2400	1845	1410	1125	3070	1815	1060	675	Not Available			6.15
44-40 Winchester*	200	SP	1310	1050	940	830	760	490	390	305	3.3	15.0	36.5	12.85
45-70 Government	405	SP	1320	1160	1050	990	1570	1210	990	880	2.9	13.0	32.5	7.90
458 Winchester Magnum	500	MC	2130	1910	1700	1520	5040	4050	3210	2570	1.1	4.8	12.0	18.95
458 Winchester Magnum	510	SP	2130	1840	1600	1400	5140	3830	2900	2220	1.1	5.1	13.5	12.45

* Price for 50   HP—Hollow Point   SP—Soft Point   PSP—Pointed Soft Point   PP—Power Point   L—Lead   Lu—Lubaloy   ST—Silvertip
HSP—Hollow Soft Point   MC—Metal Case   BT—Boat Tail   MAT—Match   BP—Bronze Point   CL—Core Lokt   PCL—Pointed Core Lokt
OPE—Open Point Expanding   †PL—Power-Lokt (slightly higher price)   (1) Not safe in handguns or Win. M73.

WEATHERBY MAGNUM CARTRIDGES — BALLISTICS AND PRICES

Cartridge	Bullet Wt. Grs.	Type	Velocity (fps) Muzzle	100 yds.	200 yds.	300 yds.	Energy (ft. lbs.) Muzzle	100 yds.	200 yds.	300 yds.	Mid-Range Trajectory 100 yds.	200 yds.	300 yds.	Price for 20
224 Weatherby Varmintmaster	50	PE	3750	3160	2625	2140	1562	1109	1670	1250	0.7	3.6	9.0	$5.95
224 Weatherby Varmintmaster	55	PE	3650	3150	2685	2270	1627	1212	881	629	0.4	1.7	4.5	5.95
240 Weatherby	70	PE	3850	3395	2975	2585	2304	1788	1376	1038	0.3	1.5	3.9	6.95
240 Weatherby	90	PE	3500	3135	2795	2475	2444	1960	1559	1222	0.4	1.8	4.5	6.95
240 Weatherby	100	PE	3395	3115	2850	2595	2554	2150	1804	1495	0.4	1.8	4.4	6.95
257 Weatherby	87	PE	3825	3290	2835	2450	2828	2087	1553	1160	0.3	1.6	4.4	7.75
257 Weatherby	100	PE	3555	3150	2815	2500	2802	2199	1760	1338	0.4	1.7	4.4	7.75
257 Weatherby	117	SPE	3300	2900	2550	2250	2824	2184	1689	1315	0.4	2.4	6.8	7.75
270 Weatherby	100	PE	3760	3625	2825	2435	3140	2363	1773	1317	0.4	1.6	4.3	7.75
270 Weatherby	130	PE	3375	3050	2750	2480	3283	2685	2183	1776	0.4	1.8	4.5	7.75
270 Weatherby	150	PE	3245	2955	2675	2430	3501	2909	2385	1967	0.5	2.0	5.0	7.75
7mm Weatherby	139	PE	3300	2995	2715	2465	3355	2770	2275	1877	0.4	1.9	4.9	7.75
7mm Weatherby	154	PE	3160	2885	2640	2415	3406	2874	2384	1994	0.5	2.0	5.0	7.75
300 Weatherby	150	PE	3545	3195	2890	2615	4179	3393	2783	2279	0.4	1.5	3.9	8.95
300 Weatherby	180	PE	3245	2960	2705	2465	4201	3501	2925	2448	0.4	1.9	5.2	8.95
300 Weatherby	220	SPE	2905	2610	2385	2150	4123	3329	2757	2257	0.6	2.5	6.7	8.95
340 Weatherby	200	PE	3210	2905	2615	2345	4566	3748	3038	2442	0.5	2.1	5.3	8.95
340 Weatherby	210	Nosler	3165	2910	2665	2435	4660	3948	3312	2766	0.5	2.1	5.0	10.95
340 Weatherby	250	SPE	2850	2580	2325	2090	4510	3695	3000	2425	0.6	2.7	6.7	8.95
378 Weatherby	270	SPE	3180	2850	2600	2315	6051	4871	4053	3210	0.5	2.0	5.2	17.50
378 Weatherby	300	SPE, FMJ	2925	2610	2380	2125	5700	4539	3774	3009	0.6	2.5	6.2	17.50
460 Weatherby	500	RN, FMJ	2700	2330	2005	1730	8095	6025	4465	3320	0.7	3.3	10.0	17.50

Trajectory is given from scope height. Velocities chronographed using 26″ bbls. Available with Nosler bullets; add $2.00 per box.
SPE—Semi-Pointed Expanding   RN—Round Nose   PE—Pointed Expanding   FMJ—Full Metal Jacket

RIMFIRE CARTRIDGES — BALLISTICS AND PRICES

Remington-Peters, Winchester-Western, Federal & CCI

All loads available from all manufacturers except as indicated: R-P (a); W-W (b); Fed. (c); CCI (d). All prices are approximate.

CARTRIDGE	WT. GRS.	BULLET TYPE	VELOCITY FT. PER SEC. MUZZLE	100 YDS.	ENERGY FT. LBS. MUZZLE	100 YDS.	MID-RANGE TRAJECTORY 100 YDS.	HANDGUN BARREL LENGTH	BALLISTICS M.V. F.P.S.	M.E. F.P.	PRICE FOR 50
22 Short T22 (a, b)	29	C, L*	1045	810	70	42	5.6	6″	865	48	$ .92
22 Short Hi-Vel.	29	C, L	1125	920	81	54	4.3	6″	1035	69	.92
22 Short HP Hi-Vel. (a, b, c)	27	C, L	1155	920	80	51	4.2	—	—	—	1.01
22 Short (a, b)	29	D	1045	—	70	—	—	—	—	(per 500)	7.93
22 Short (a, b)	15	D	1710	—	97	—	—	—	—	(per 500)	7.93
22 Long Hi-Vel.	29	C, L	1240	965	99	60	3.8	6″	1095	77	1.01
22 Long Rifle T22 (a, b)†[1]	40	L*	1145	975	116	84	4.0	6″	950	80	1.07
22 Long Rifle (b)†[2]	40	L*	1120	950	111	80	4.2				1.71
22 Long Rifle (b)†[3]	40	L*	—	—	—	—	—	6¾″	1060	100	1.71
22 Long Rifle (d)†[4]	40	C	1165	980	121	84	4.0				.99
22 Long Rifle Hi-Vel.	40	C, L	1285	1025	147	93	3.4	6″	1125	112	1.07
22 Long Rifle HP Hi-Vel. (b, d)	37	C, L	1315	1020	142	85	3.4				1.19
22 Long Rifle HP Hi-Vel. (a, c)	36	C	1365	1040	149	86	3.4				1.19
22 Long Rifle (b, c)	No.	12 Shot	—	—	—	—	—	—	—	—	2.17
22 WRF [Rem. Spl.] (a, b)	45	C, L	1450	1110	210	123					2.95
22 WRF Mag. (b)	40	JHP	2000	1390	355	170	1.6	6½″	1550	213	2.95
22 WRF Mag. (b)	40	MC	2000	1390	355	170	1.6	6½″	1550	213	2.95
22 Win. Auto Inside lub. (a, b)	45	C, L	1055	930	111	86					2.95
5mm Rem. RFM (a)	38	PLHP	2100	1605	372	217	Not Available				4.00

†—Target loads of these ballistics available in: (1) Rem. Match; (2) W-W LV EZXS, Super Match Mark III; (3) Super Match Mark IV and EZXS Pistol Match; (4) CCI Mini-Group.   C—Copper plated   L—Lead (Wax Coated)   L*—Lead, lubricated   D—Disintegrating
MC—Metal Case   HP—Hollow Point   JHP—Jacket Hollow Point   PLHP—Power-Lokt Hollow Point

NORMA C.F. RIFLE CARTRIDGES — BALLISTICS AND PRICES

Norma ammunition loaded to standard velocity and pressure is now available with Nosler bullets in the following loads: 270 Win., 130-, 150-gr.; Super 7x61 (S&H), 160-gr.; 308 Win., 180-gr.; 30-06, 150-, 180-gr., all at slightly higher prices. All ballistic figures are computed from a line of sight one inch above center of bore at muzzle. Write for their latest prices.

Cartridge	Bullet Wt. Grs.	Type	Velocity, feet per sec.				Energy, foot pounds				Max. height of trajectory, inches			Price for 20
			V Muzzle	V 100 yds.	V 200 yds.	V 300 yds.	E Muzzle	E 100 yds.	E 200 yds.	E 300 yds.	Tr. 100 yds.	Tr. 200 yds.	Tr. 300 yds.	
220 Swift	50	PSP	4111	3611	3133	2681	1877	1448	1090	799	.2	.9	3.0	$5.35
888 Remington	50	PSP	3200	2660	2170	1750	1137	786	523	340	.0	2.0	6.2	4.10
223	55	SPP	3300	2900	2520	2160	1330	1027	776	570	.4	2.4	6.8	4.50
22-250	50	SPS	3800	3300	2810	2350	1600	1209	885	613	Not Available			4.50
	55	SPS	3650	3200	2780	2400	1637	1251	944	704	Not Available			4.50
243 Winchester	80	SP	3500	3070	2660	2290	2041	1570	1179	873	.0	1.4	4.1	5.70
	100	PSP	3070	2790	2540	2320	2093	1729	1433	1195	.1	1.8	5.0	5.70
6mm Remington	100	SPS	3190	2920	2660	2420	2260	1890	1570	1300	.4	2.1	5.3	5.70
250 Savage	87	PSP	3032	2685	2357	2054	1776	1393	1074	815	.0	1.9	5.8	5.35
	100	PSP	2822	2514	2223	1956	1769	1404	1098	850	.1	2.2	6.6	5.35
6.5 Carcano	156	SPRN	2000	1810	1640	1485	1386	1135	932	764	Not Available			7.00
6.5 Japanese	139	PSPBT	2428	2280	2130	1990	1820	1605	1401	1223	.3	2.8	7.7	7.00
	156	SPRN	2067	1871	1692	1529	1481	1213	992	810	.6	4.4	11.9	7.00
6.5 x 54 MS	139	PSPBT	2580	2420	2270	2120	2056	1808	1591	1388	.2	2.4	6.5	7.00
	156	SPRN	2461	2240	2033	1840	2098	1738	1432	1173	.3	3.0	8.2	7.00
6.5 x 55	139	PSPBT	2789	2630	2470	2320	2402	2136	1883	1662	.1	2.0	5.6	7.00
	156	SPRN	2493	2271	2062	1867	2153	1787	1473	1208	.3	2.9	7.9	7.00
270 Winchester	110	PSP	3248	2966	2694	2435	2578	2150	1773	1448	.1	1.4	4.3	6.20
	130	PSPBT	3140	2884	2639	2404	2847	2401	2011	1669	.0	1.6	4.7	6.20
	150	PSPBT	2802	2616	2436	2262	2616	2280	1977	1705	.1	2.0	5.7	6.20
7 x 57	110	PSP	3068	2792	2528	2277	2300	1904	1561	1267	.0	1.6	5.0	6.20
	150	PSPBT	2756	2539	2331	2133	2530	2148	1810	1516	.1	2.2	6.2	6.20
	175	SPRN	2490	2170	1900	1680	2410	1830	1403	1097	.4	3.3	9.0	6.20
7mm Remington Magnum	150	SPSBT	3260	2970	2700	2450	3540	2945	2435	1990	.4	2.0	4.9	7.70
	175	SPRN	3070	2720	2400	2120	3660	2870	2240	1590	.5	2.4	6.1	7.70
7 x 61 S & H (26 in.)	160	PSPBT	3100	2927	2757	2595	3415	3045	2701	2393	.0	1.5	4.3	8.20
30 U.S. Carbine	110	SPRN	1970	1595	1300	1090	948	622	413	290	.8	6.4	19.0	3.95
30-30 Winchester	150	SPFP	2410	2075	1790	1550	1934	1433	1066	799	.9	4.2	11	4.85
	170	SPFP	2220	1890	1630	1410	1861	1349	1003	750	.7	4.1	11.9	4.85
308 Winchester	130	PSPBT	2900	2590	2300	2030	2428	1937	1527	1190	.1	2.1	6.2	6.20
	150	PSPBT	2860	2570	2300	2050	2725	2200	1762	1400	.1	2.0	5.9	6.20
	180	PSPBT	2610	2400	2210	2020	2725	2303	1952	1631	.2	2.5	6.6	6.20
	180	SPDC	2610	2400	2210	2020	2725	2303	1952	1631	.7	3.4	8.9	6.70
7.62 Russian	180	PSPBT	2624	2415	2222	2030	2749	2326	1970	1644	.2	2.5	6.6	7.00
308 Norma Magnum	180	DC	3100	2881	2668	2464	3842	3318	2846	2427	.0	1.6	4.6	9.30
30-06	130	PSPBT	3281	2951	2636	2338	3108	2514	2006	1578	.1	1.5	4.6	6.20
	150	PS	2972	2680	2402	2141	2943	2393	1922	1527	.0	1.9	5.7	6.20
	180	PSPBT, SPDC	2700	2494	2296	2109	2914	2487	2107	1778	.1	2.3	6.4	6.20
	220	SPRN	2411	2197	1996	1809	2840	2358	1947	1599	.3	3.1	8.5	6.20
7.65 Argentine	150	PSP	2920	2630	2355	2105	2841	2304	1848	1476	.1	2.0	5.8	7.00
303 British	130	PSP	2789	2483	2195	1929	2246	1780	1391	1075	.1	2.3	6.7	6.25
	150	PSP	2720	2440	2170	1930	2465	1983	1569	1241	.1	2.2	6.5	6.25
	180	PSPBT	2540	2340	2147	1965	2579	2189	1843	1544	.2	2.7	7.3	6.25
7.7 Japanese	130	PSP	2950	2635	2340	2065	2513	2004	1581	1231	.1	2.0	5.9	7.00
	180	PSPBT	2493	2292	2101	1922	2484	2100	1765	1477	.3	2.8	7.7	7.00
8 x 57 JS	123	PSP	2887	2515	2170	1857	2277	1728	1286	942	.1	2.3	6.8	6.20
	159	SPRN	2723	2362	2030	1734	2618	1970	1455	1062	.2	2.6	7.9	6.20
	196	SPRN	2526	2195	1894	1627	2778	2097	1562	1152	.3	3.1	9.1	6.20
358 Norma Magnum	250	SPS	2790	2493	2231	2001	4322	3451	2764	2223	.2	2.4	6.6	8.90
44 Magnum*	240	SPFP	1750				1640				Not Available			4.45

P—Pointed   SP—Soft Point   HP—Hollow Point   FP—Flat Point   RN—Round Nose   BT—Boat Tail   MC—Metal Case
DC—Dual Core   SPS—Soft Point Semi-Pointed   NA—Not announced   *Price for 50

CENTERFIRE HANDGUN CARTRIDGES — BALLISTICS AND PRICES

Winchester-Western, Remington-Peters, Norma, Federal, Browning & S&W/Fiocchi

Most loads are available from W-W and R-P. All available Norma loads are listed. Federal cartridges are marked with an asterisk. Other loads supplied by only one source are indicated by a letter, thus: Norma (a); R-P (b); W-W (c). Prices are approximate.

Cartridge	Bullet Gr.	Bullet Style	Muzzle Velocity	Muzzle Energy	Barrel Inches	Price Per 50
22 Jet (b)	40	SP	2100	390	8⅜	$9.85
221 Fireball (b)	50	SP	2650	780	10½	4.55
25 (6.35mm) Auto*	50	MC	810	73	2	5.70
256 Winchester Magnum (c)	60	HP	2350	735	8½	10.10
30 (7.65mm) Luger Auto	93	MC	1220	307	4½	9.80
32 S&W Blank (b, c)	No bullet		—	—	—	4.35
32 S&W Blank, BP (c)	No bullet		—	—	—	4.35
32 Short Colt	80	Lead	745	100	4	5.00
32 Long Colt, IL (c)	82	Lub.	755	104	4	5.20
32 Colt New Police	100	Lead	680	100	4	6.05
32 (7.65mm) Auto*	71	MC	960	145	4	7.00
32 (7.65mm) Auto Pistol (a)	77	MC	900	162	4	6.50
32 S&W	88	Lead	680	90	3	5.00
32 S&W Long	98	Lead	705	115	4	5.20
32-20 Winchester	100	Lead	1030	271	6	7.20
32-20 Winchester	100	SP	1030	271	6	9.00
357 Magnum (b)*	158	SP	1550	845	8⅜	8.55
357 Magnum	158	MP	1410	695	8⅜	8.30
357 Magnum	158	Lead	1410	696	8⅜	7.30
357 Magnum (a)	158	JHP	1450	735	8⅜	8.55
9mm Luger (a)	116	MC	1165	349	4	8.10
9mm Luger Auto*	124	MC	1120	345	4	8.25
38 S&W Blank	No bullet		—	—	—	4.50
38 Smith & Wesson	146	Lead	685	150	4	6.55
38 S&W (a)	146	Lead	730	172	4	6.15
38 Special Blank	No bullet		—	—	—	7.00
38 Special, IL (c)	150	Lub.	1060	375	6	6.50
38 Special, IL (c)	150	MP	1060	375	6	7.75
38 Special	158	Lead	855	256	6	6.20
38 Special	200	Lead	730	236	6	6.45
38 Special	158	MP	855	256	6	7.65
38 Special (b)	125	SJHP	Not available			7.65
38 Special (b)	158	SJHP	Not available			7.65
38 Special WC (b)	148	Lead	770	195	6	6.45
38 Special Match (c)	148	Lead	770	195	6	6.45
38 Special Match, IL (b, c)	158	Lead	855	256	6	6.30
38 Special Hi-Speed*	158	Lead	1090	425	6	7.65
38 Special (a)	158	RN	900	320	6	6.20
38 Short Colt	125	Lead	730	150	6	5.60
38 Short Colt, Greased (c)	130	Lub.	730	155	6	5.60
38 Long Colt	150	Lead	730	175	6	6.20
38 Super Auto (b)	130	MC	1280	475	5	6.90
38 Auto, for Colt 38 Super (c)	130	MC	1280	475	5	6.90
38 Auto	130	MC	1040	312	4½	6.90
380 Auto*	95	MC	955	192	3¾	6.70
38-40 Winchester	180	SP	975	380	5	10.70
41 Remington Magnum (b)	210	Lead	1050	515	8¾	9.25
41 Remington Magnum (b)	210	SP	1500	1050	8¾	10.60
44 S&W Special	246	Lead	755	311	6½	8.40
44 Remington Magnum	240	SP	1470	1150	6½	11.00
44 Remington Magnum	240	Lead	1470	1150	6½	10.65
44-40 Winchester	200	SP	975	420	7½	12.85
45 Colt	250	Lead	860	410	5½	8.40
45 Colt, IL (c)	255	Lub., L	860	410	5½	8.40
45 Auto	230	MC	850	369	5	8.50
45 ACP (a)	230	JHP	850	370	5	8.75
45 Auto WC*	185	MC	775	245	5	8.95
45 Auto MC (a, b)	230	MC	850	369	5	8.75
45 Auto Match (c)	185	MC	775	247	5	9.25
45 Auto Match, IL (c)	210	Lead	710	235	5	8.75
45 Auto Match*	230	MC	850	370	5	9.25
45 Auto Rim (b)	230	Lead	810	335	5½	8.70

IL—Inside Lub. JSP—Jacketed Soft Point WC—Wad Cutter
RN—Round Nose HP—Hollow Point Lub—Lubricated
MC—Metal Case SP—Soft Point MP—Metal Point
LGC—Lead, Gas Check JHP—Jacketed Hollow Point

SUPER VEL HANDGUN CARTRIDGES — BALLISTICS AND PRICES

The cartridges listed below are perhaps the most powerful and destructive of these calibers commercially manufactured. Bullets listed can be had as components — other weights (not loaded by Super Vel) are also available.

Cartridge	Bullet Gr.	Bullet Style	Muzzle Velocity	Muzzle Energy	Barrel Inches	Price Per 50
380 ACP	80	JHP	1026	188	5	$7.45
9mm Luger	90	JHP	1422	402	5	7.90
9mm Luger	110	SP	1325	428	5	7.90
38 Special	110	JHP/SP	1370	458	6	7.45
38 Special Match	147	HBWC	775	196	6	6.25
38 Special Int.	158	Lead	1110	439	6	6.15
357 Magnum	110	JHP/SP	1690	697	6	8.35
357 Magnum	137	JHP/SP	1620	796	6	8.35
44 Magnum	180	JHP/SP	2005	1607	6	4.85†
45 Auto	190	JHP	1060	473	5	9.45

JHP—Jacketed Hollow Point SP—Jacketed Soft Point
HBWC—Hollow Base Wad Cutter †Price per 20

SHOTSHELL LOADS AND PRICES

Winchester-Western, Remington-Peters, Federal, Eley & S&W/Fiocchi

In certain loadings one manufacturer may offer fewer or more shot sizes than another, but in general all makers offer equivalent loadings. Sources are indicated by letters, thus: W-W (a); R-P (b); Fed. (c); Eley (d). Prices are approximate.

GAUGE	Length Shell Ins.	Powder Equiv. Drams	Shot Ozs.	Shot Size	PRICE FOR 25
MAGNUM LOADS					
10 (a¹, b)	3½	5	2	BB, 2, 4	$10.05
12 (a, b, c)	3	4½	1⅞	BB, 2, 4	6.30
12 (a¹, b)	3	4¼	1⅝	2, 4, 6	6.10
12 (a)	3	Max	1⅜	2, 4, 6	6.10
12 (a¹, b, c)	2¾	4	1½	2, 4, 5, 6	5.65
16 (a, b, c, d)	2¾	3½	1¼	2, 4, 6	5.00
20 (a, b, c)	3	3¼	1¼	4, 6, 7½	4.95
20 (a¹)	3	Max	1³⁄₁₆	4	5.15
20 (a¹, b, c, d)	2¾	3	1⅛	2, 4, 6, 7½	4.55
LONG RANGE LOADS					
10 (a, b)	2⅞	4¾	1⅝	4	6.10
12 (a¹, b, c, d)	2¾	3¾	1¼	BB, 2, 4, 5, 6, 7½, 9	4.55
16 (a, b, c, d)	2¾	3¼	1⅛	4, 5, 6, 7½, 9	4.20
20 (a¹, b, c, d)	2¾	2¾	1	4, 5, 6, 7½, 9	3.95
28 (a, b)	2¾	2¼	¾	6, 7½, 9.	3.95
28 (c)	2¾	2¼	⅞	4, 6, 7½, 9	3.95
FIELD LOADS					
12 (a, b, c)	2¾	3¼	1¼	7½, 8	3.60
12 (a, b, c, d)	2¾	3¼	1⅛	4, 5, 6, 7½, 8, 9	3.80
12 (a, b, c)	2¾	3	1	4, 5, 6, 8	3.75
16 (a, b, c, d)	2¾	2¾	1⅛	4, 5, 6, 7½, 8, 9	3.60
16 (a, b, c)	2¾	2½	1	6, 8	3.45
20 (a, b, c)	2¾	2½	1	4, 5, 6, 7½, 8, 9	3.50
20 (a, b, c)	2¾	2¼	⅞	6, 8	3.20
SCATTER LOADS					
12 (a, b)	2¾	3	1⅛	8	3.95
TARGET LOADS					
12 (a, b, c)	2¾	3	1⅛	7½, 8	3.85
12 (a, b, c)	2¾	2¾	1⅛	7½, 8	3.85
16 (a, b, c)	2¾	2½	1	9	3.55
20 (a, b, c)	2¾	2¼	⅞	9	3.20
28 (a, c)	2¾	2¼	¾	9	3.90
410 (a, b, c, d)	3	Max	¾	9	3.00
410 (a, b, c)	2½	Max	½	9	3.00
SKEET & TRAP					
12 (a, b, c, d)	2¾	3	1⅛	7½, 8, 9	3.80
12 (a, b, c, d)	2¾	2¾	1⅛	7½, 8, 9	3.80
16 (a, b, c)	2¾	2½	1	9	3.55
16 (c)	2¾	1⅛	1⅛	8, 9	3.55
20 (a, b, c)	2¾	2¼	⅞	9	3.20
BUCKSHOT					
12 (a, b, c)	3 Mag.	4½	—	00 Buck—15 pellets	7.85
12 (a, b, c)	3 Mag.	4½	—	4 Buck—41 pellets	7.85
12 (b)	2¾ Mag.	4	—	1 Buck—20 pellets	6.80
12 (a, b, c)	2¾ Mag.	4	—	00 Buck—12 pellets	6.80
12 (a, b, c)	2¾	3¾	—	00 Buck— 9 pellets	6.05
12 (a, b, c)	2¾	3¾	—	0 Buck—12 pellets	6.05
12 (a, b, c)	2¾	3¾	—	1 Buck—16 pellets	6.05
12 (a, b, c)	2¾	3¾	—	4 Buck—27 pellets	6.05
16 (a, b, c)	2¾	3	—	1 Buck—12 pellets	6.00
20 (a, b, c)	2¾	2¾	—	3 Buck—20 pellets	6.00
RIFLED SLUGS					
12 (a, b, c, d)	2¾	3¾	1	Slug	7.10
16 (a, b, c)	2¾	3	⅞	Slug	6.75
20 (a, b, c)	2¾	2¾	⅝	Slug	6.50
410 (a, b, c)	2½	Max	⅕	Slug	6.10

W-W 410, 28- and 10-ga. Magnum shells available in paper cases only, as are their scatter and target loads; their skeet and trap loads come in both plastic and paper.

RP shells are all of plastic with Power Piston wads except: 12 ga. scatter loads have Post Wad: all 10 ga., 410-3″ and rifled slug loads have standard wad columns.

Federal magnum, range, buckshot, slug and all 410 loads are made in plastic only. Field loads are available in both paper and plastic.

Eley shotshells are of plastic-coated paper.

¹—These loads available from W-W with Lubaloy shot at higher price.

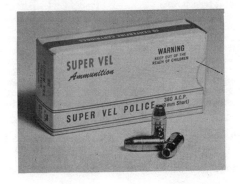

BALLISTICS

KKSP—'Kling-Kor' Soft Point   MC—Metal Cased (Hard Point)
PSP—Pointed Soft Point   PNEU—Pneumatic
SP—Soft Point   HP—Hollow Point
CPE—Copper Point Expanding   ST—'Sabretip'

DESCRIPTION	Wt. Grains	Type	Muzzle	100 Yds.	200 Yds.	300 Yds.	400 Yds.	500 Yds.	Muzzle	100 Yds.	200 Yds.	300 Yds.	400 Yds.	500 Yds.
					Velocity in Feet per Second							Energy in Foot Pounds			
22 HORNET	45	PSP	2690	2030	1510	1150	—	—	720	410	230	130	—	—
22 SAVAGE	70	PSP	2800	2440	2110	1840	—	—	1220	925	690	525	—	—
222 REMINGTON	50	PSP	3200	2600	2170	1750	—	—	1140	785	520	340	—	—
243 WINCHESTER	75	PSP	3500	3070	2660	2290	1960	1670	2040	1570	1180	875	640	465
243 WINCHESTER	100	PSP	3070	2790	2540	2320	2120	1940	2090	1730	1430	1190	995	835
244 REMINGTON	75	PSP	3500	3070	2660	2290	1960	1670	2040	1570	1180	875	640	465
6.5 x 53 MM MAN.-SCH.	160	SP	2160	1950	1750	1570	—	—	1660	1350	1090	875	—	—
6.5 x 55 MM	160	SP	2420	2190	1960	1760	1500	1420	2000	1700	1360	1110	805	715
25-20 WINCHESTER	86	SP	1460	1180	1030	940	—	—	405	265	200	170	—	—
25-35 WINCHESTER	117	SP	2300	1910	1600	1340	—	—	1370	945	665	465	—	—
250 SAVAGE	100	PSP	2820	2460	2140	1870	—	—	1760	1340	1020	775	—	—
257 ROBERTS	117	PSP	2650	2280	1950	1690	—	—	1820	1350	985	740	—	—
270 WINCHESTER	100	PSP	3480	3070	2690	2340	2010	1700	2690	2090	1600	1215	890	640
270 WINCHESTER	130	PSP	3140	2850	2580	2320	2090	1860	2840	2340	1920	1550	1260	1000
270 WINCHESTER	150	KKSP	2800	2530	2280	2050	1840	—	2790	2270	1850	1490	1200	—
7 x 57 MM MAUSER	139	PSP	2900	2590	2240	1990	1770	1580	2420	1930	1550	1220	965	770
7 x 57 MM MAUSER	160	KKSP	2650	2330	2040	1780	1550	1350	2500	1930	1480	1130	855	645
7 MM REMINGTON MAGNUM	175	SP	3070	2720	2400	2120	1870	1640	3660	2870	2240	1750	1360	1040
30-30 WINCHESTER	150	PNEU	2410	2020	1700	1430	—	—	1930	1360	960	680	—	—
30-30 WINCHESTER	170	KKSP	2220	1890	1630	1410	—	—	1860	1350	1000	750	—	—
30-30 WINCHESTER	170	ST	2220	1890	1630	1410	—	—	1860	1350	1000	750	—	—
30-30 WINCHESTER	170	MC	2220	1890	1630	1410	—	—	1860	1350	1000	750	—	—
30-30 WINCHESTER	150	ST	2410	2020	1700	1430	—	—	1930	1360	960	680	—	—
30 REMINGTON	170	KKSP	2120	1820	1560	1350	—	—	1700	1250	920	690	—	—
30-40 KRAG	180	KKSP	2470	2120	1830	1590	1400	—	2440	1790	1340	1010	785	—
30-06 SPRINGFIELD	130	HP	3150	2730	2470	2170	1920	1690	2870	2160	1770	1360	1060	820
30-06 SPRINGFIELD	150	PSP	2970	2670	2400	2130	1890	1670	2930	2370	1920	1510	1190	930
30-06 SPRINGFIELD	150	ST	2970	2670	2400	2130	1890	1670	2930	2370	1920	1510	1190	930
30-06 SPRINGFIELD	180	KKSP	2700	2330	2010	1740	1520	—	2910	2170	1610	1210	920	—
30-06 SPRINGFIELD	180	CPE	2700	2480	2280	2080	1900	1730	2910	2460	2080	1730	1440	1190
30-06 SPRINGFIELD	180	ST	2700	2470	2250	2040	1850	1670	2910	2440	2020	1660	1370	1110
30-06 SPRINGFIELD	220	KKSP	2410	2120	1870	1670	1480	—	2830	2190	1710	1360	1070	—
300 WINCHESTER-MAGNUM	180	ST	3070	2850	2640	2440	2250	2060	3770	3250	2790	2380	2020	1700
300 HOLLAND & HOLLAND MAGNUM	180	PSP	2920	2670	2440	2220	2020	1830	3400	2850	2380	1970	1630	1340
300 SAVAGE	150	PSP	2670	2390	2130	1890	1660	—	2370	1900	1510	1190	915	—
300 SAVAGE	150	ST	2670	2390	2130	1890	1660	—	2370	1900	1510	1190	915	—
300 SAVAGE	180	KKSP	2370	2040	1760	1520	1340	—	2240	1660	1240	920	715	—
300 SAVAGE	180	ST	2370	2160	1960	1770	1600	—	2240	1860	1530	1250	1020	—
303 SAVAGE	190	KKSP	1980	1680	1440	1250	—	—	1650	1190	875	660	—	—
303 BRITISH	150	PSP	2720	2420	2150	1900	1670	1470	2460	1950	1540	1200	930	720
303 BRITISH	150	ST	2720	2420	2150	1900	1670	1470	2460	1950	1540	1200	930	720
303 BRITISH	180	KKSP	2540	2180	1860	1590	1360	—	2580	1900	1380	1010	740	—
303 BRITISH	180	CPE	2540	2330	2130	1940	1760	1600	2580	2170	1810	1500	1240	1020
303 BRITISH	180	ST	2540	2300	2090	1900	1730	1580	2580	2120	1750	1440	1200	1000
303 BRITISH	215	KKSP	2180	1900	1660	1460	1250	—	2270	1720	1310	1020	750	—
308 WINCHESTER	130	HP	2930	2590	2290	2010	1770	1560	2480	1940	1520	1170	905	700
308 WINCHESTER	150	PSP	2860	2570	2300	2050	1810	1590	2730	2200	1760	1400	1090	840
308 WINCHESTER	150	ST	2860	2570	2300	2050	1810	1590	2730	2200	1760	1400	1090	840
308 WINCHESTER	180	KKSP	2610	2240	1920	1640	1400	—	2720	2010	1470	1070	785	—
308 WINCHESTER	180	ST	2610	2390	2170	1970	1780	1600	2720	2280	1870	1540	1260	1010
308 WINCHESTER	200	KKSP	2450	2210	1980	1770	1580	1410	2670	2170	1750	1400	1110	875
8 MM MAUSER	170	PSP	2570	2300	2040	1810	1600	—	2490	2000	1570	1240	965	—
32-20 WINCHESTER	115	SP	1480	1220	1050	940	—	—	560	380	280	225	—	—
32 WINCHESTER SPECIAL	170	KKSP	2280	1920	1630	1410	—	—	1960	1390	1000	750	—	—
32 WINCHESTER SPECIAL	170	ST	2280	1920	1630	1410	—	—	1960	1390	1000	750	—	—
32 REMINGTON	170	KKSP	2120	1800	1540	1340	—	—	1700	1220	895	680	—	—
32-40 WINCHESTER	170	KKSP	1540	1340	1170	1050	—	—	895	680	515	415	—	—
35 REMINGTON	200	SP	2100	1710	1390	1160	—	—	1950	1300	865	605	—	—
351 WINCHESTER SELF-LOADING	180	SP	1850	1560	1310	1140	—	—	1370	975	685	520	—	—
358 (8.8 MM) WINCHESTER	200	KKSP	2530	2210	1910	1640	1400	—	2840	2160	1610	1190	870	—
38-40 WINCHESTER	180	SP	1330	1070	960	850	—	—	705	455	370	290	—	—
38-55 WINCHESTER	255	SP	1600	1410	1240	1110	—	—	1450	1130	880	700	—	—
43 (11 MM) MAUSER	385	LEAD	1360	1150	1030	940	—	—	1580	1130	910	750	—	—
44-40 WINCHESTER	200	SP	1310	1050	940	830	—	—	760	490	390	305	—	—
44 REMINGTON MAGNUM	240	SP	1850	1450	1150	980	—	—	1820	1120	710	510	—	—

Short Range Sighting-in—It is preferable to sight-in a rifle at the "recommended sighting" range. However, it is sometimes necessary to sight-in a rifle at a distance shorter than the "recommended sighting" range because you don't have the necessary yardage available. To do this, find from the range table at what distance the bullet will first cross the line of sight. Put up a target at this distance and from a firm rest fire

and Range Table

RANGE TABLE—Values shown in this table are based on a sight height 1½" above line of bore. RECOMMENDED SIGHTING: ⊕ Indicates the most favourable sighting range in order to minimize the sighting problem at shorter and longer ranges. + Indicates inches high; — Indicates inches low.

RANGE

First Crosses Line of Sight App. Yds.	50 Yds.	75 Yds.	100 Yds.	125 Yds.	150 Yds.	200 Yds.	250 Yds.	300 Yds.	400 Yds.	500 Yds.	Bullet Wt. Grains	Bullet Type	Description
29.0	—	+1.5	—	—	⊕	−4.0	—	—	—	—	45	PSP	22 HORNET
25.0	—	—	+2.0	—	—	⊕	−4.5	—	—	—	70	PSP	22 SAVAGE
30.0	—	—	+2.0	—	—	⊕	−3.5	—	—	—	50	PSP	222 REMINGTON
30.0	—	—	—	+2.5	—	—	⊕	−3.0	−15.5	−36.5	75	PSP	243 WINCHESTER
27.5	—	—	—	+3.0	—	—	⊕	−3.5	−16.5	−35.5	100	PSP	243 WINCHESTER
30.0	—	—	—	+2.5	—	—	⊕	−3.0	−15.5	−36.5	75	PSP	244 REMINGTON
25.5	—	+1.5	—	—	⊕	−4.0	—	—	—	—	160	SP	6.5 x 53 MM MAN.-SCH.
21.0	—	—	+3.5	—	—	⊕	−5.0	−13.0	−39.0	—	160	SP	6.5 x 58 MM
16.0	+2.0	—	⊕	−4.0	—	—	—	—	—	—	86	SP	25-20 WINCHESTER
23.0	—	+1.5	—	—	⊕	−4.5	—	—	—	—	117	SP	25-35 WINCHESTER
27.5	—	—	+2.0	—	—	⊕	−3.5	—	—	—	100	PSP	250 SAVAGE
24.0	—	—	+2.5	—	—	⊕	−4.5	—	—	—	117	PSP	257 ROBERTS
31.5	—	—	—	+2.5	—	—	⊕	−3.5	−14.5	−33.5	100	PSP	270 WINCHESTER
27.5	—	—	—	+3.0	—	—	⊕	−4.0	−16.0	−35.5	130	PSP	270 WINCHESTER
28.5	—	—	+2.0	—	—	⊕	−4.0	—	−25.0	—	160	KKSP	270 WINCHESTER
27.0	—	—	—	+4.0	—	—	⊕	−4.5	−18.5	−41.0	139	PSP	7 x 57 MM MAUSER
29.0	—	—	+2.5	—	—	⊕	−4.0	—	−28.5	—	160	KKSP	7 x 57 MM MAUSER
25.0	—	—	—	+3.5	—	—	⊕	−4.0	−18.0	−43.0	175	SP	7 MM REMINGTON MAGNUM
27.0	—	+1.5	—	—	⊕	−4.0	—	—	—	—	150	PNEU	30-30 WINCHESTER
23.0	—	+1.5	—	—	⊕	−4.5	—	—	—	—	170	KKSP	30-30 WINCHESTER
23.0	—	+1.5	—	—	⊕	−4.5	—	—	—	—	170	ST	30-30 WINCHESTER
23.0	—	+1.5	—	—	⊕	−4.5	—	—	—	—	170	MC	30-30 WINCHESTER
27.0	—	+1.5	—	—	⊕	−4.0	—	—	—	—	150	ST	30-30 WINCHESTER
20.0	—	+2.0	—	—	⊕	−5.0	—	—	—	—	170	KKSP	30 REMINGTON
21.0	—	—	+3.0	—	—	⊕	−5.5	—	—	—	180	KKSP	30-30 KRAG
27.0	—	—	—	+3.0	—	—	⊕	−4.0	−19.5	−47.0	130	HP	30-06 SPRINGFIELD
25.0	—	—	—	+3.5	—	—	⊕	−4.0	−17.5	−41.0	150	PSP	30-06 SPRINGFIELD
25.0	—	—	—	+3.5	—	—	⊕	−4.0	−17.5	−41.0	150	ST	30-06 SPRINGFIELD
24.0	—	—	+2.5	—	—	⊕	−4.0	—	−32.5	—	180	KKSP	30-06 SPRINGFIELD
21.0	—	—	—	+4.0	—	—	⊕	−4.5	−20.5	−46.0	180	CPE	30-06 SPRINGFIELD
20.0	—	—	—	+4.0	—	—	⊕	−4.5	−21.0	−48.5	180	ST	30-06 SPRINGFIELD
21.0	—	—	+3.0	—	—	⊕	−5.5	−41.0	—	—	220	KKSP	30-06 SPRINGFIELD
27.5	—	—	—	+3.0	—	—	⊕	−3.5	−14.5	−32.5	180	ST	300 WINCHESTER-MAGNUM
25.0	—	—	—	+3.5	—	—	⊕	−4.0	−17.5	−39.0	180	PSP	300 HOLLAND & HOLLAND MAGNUM
26.0	—	—	+2.5	—	—	⊕	−3.5	—	−29.0	—	150	PSP	300 SAVAGE
26.0	—	—	+2.5	—	—	⊕	−3.5	—	−29.0	—	150	ST	300 SAVAGE
20.0	—	—	+3.5	—	—	⊕	−5.5	—	−43.0	—	180	KKSP	300 SAVAGE
21.5	—	—	+3.0	—	—	⊕	−5.5	—	−35.0	—	180	ST	300 SAVAGE
17.5	—	—	+3.0	—	—	⊕	−5.5	—	—	—	190	KKSP	303 SAVAGE
22.0	—	—	—	+4.5	—	—	⊕	−5.0	−23.0	−53.5	150	PSP	303 BRITISH
22.0	—	—	—	+4.5	—	—	⊕	−5.0	−23.0	−53.5	150	ST	303 BRITISH
23.0	—	—	+3.0	—	—	⊕	−5.0	−	−41.0	—	180	KKSP	303 BRITISH
19.0	—	—	—	+4.5	—	—	⊕	−5.0	−23.0	−52.5	180	CPE	303 BRITISH
17.5	—	—	—	+5.0	—	—	⊕	−5.5	−26.5	−71.0	180	ST	303 BRITISH
16.0	—	—	+4.5	—	—	⊕	−7.0	—	−54.0	—	215	KKSP	303 BRITISH
23.5	—	—	—	+3.5	—	—	⊕	−4.5	−23.5	−59.0	130	HP	308 WINCHESTER
25.0	—	—	—	+3.5	—	—	⊕	−4.5	−20.0	−47.5	150	PSP	308 WINCHESTER
25.0	—	—	—	+3.5	—	—	⊕	−4.5	−20.0	−47.5	150	ST	308 WINCHESTER
23.0	—	—	+3.0	—	—	⊕	−5.5	−38.0	—	—	180	KKSP	308 WINCHESTER
22.0	—	—	—	+4.5	—	—	⊕	−5.0	−21.5	−51.5	180	ST	308 WINCHESTER
22.0	—	—	+3.0	—	—	⊕	−5.0	−12.0	−35.0	−48.5	200	KKSP	8 MM MAUSER
22.5	—	—	+3.5	—	—	⊕	−5.5	—	−33.5	—	170	PSP	32-20 WINCHESTER
16.5	+2.0	—	—	⊕	−3.5	—	—	—	—	—	115	SP	32 WINCHESTER SPECIAL
23.0	—	+2.0	—	—	⊕	−4.5	—	—	—	—	170	KKSP	32 WINCHESTER SPECIAL
23.0	—	+2.0	—	—	⊕	−4.5	—	—	—	—	170	ST	32 REMINGTON
20.0	—	+2.0	—	—	⊕	−5.0	—	—	—	—	170	KKSP	32-40 WINCHESTER
21.0	+1.0	—	—	⊕	−2.5	—	—	—	—	—	170	KKSP	35 REMINGTON
19.5	—	+2.5	—	—	⊕	−6.0	—	—	—	—	200	SP	351 WINCHESTER SELF-LOADING
16.0	—	+3.0	—	—	⊕	−7.5	—	—	—	—	180	SP	358 (8.8 MM) WINCHESTER
20.5	—	—	+3.0	—	—	⊕	−5.0	—	−38.5	—	200	KKSP	38-40 WINCHESTER
14.5	+2.5	—	⊕	−4.0	—	—	—	—	—	—	180	SP	38-55 WINCHESTER
13.5	—	+4.0	—	—	⊕	−8.5	—	—	—	—	255	SP	43 (11 MM) MAUSER
16.0	+2.0	—	⊕	−3.5	—	—	—	—	—	—	385	LEAD	44-40 WINCHESTER
12.5	+3.0	—	⊕	−4.5	—	—	—	—	—	—	200	SP	44 REMINGTON MAGNUM
13.0	—	+4.5	—	—	⊕	−8.0	—	—	—	—	240	SP	44 REMINGTON MAGNUM

a three-shot group. The centre point of the group is the "centre of impact"—the average spot where the bullets strike. Adjust sights to bring the centre of impact to the centre of the target then fire another group. If the centre of impact is on target the rifle will be sighted in at the range recommended in the range table. It is, however, desirable to fire a target at that range as soon as possible as a double check.

FEDERAL AMMUNITION

FEDERAL CARTRIDGE CORPORATION   2700 FOSHAY TOWER   MINNEAPOLIS, MINN. 55402

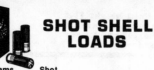

SHOT SHELL LOADS

Gauge	Shell Length Inches	Drams Equiv.	Shot Ozs.	Shot Sizes	Price Per Box
MAGNUM LOADS					
12	3	4	1⅞	BB,2,4	6.60
12	3	4	1⅝	2,4,6	6.15
12	2¾	3¾	1½	2,4,5,6	5.60
16	2¾	3¼	1¼	2,4,6	4.85
20	3	3	1¼	4,6,7½	5.05
20	2¾	2¾	1⅛	4,6,7½	4.40
HI-POWER® LOADS					
12	2¾	3¾	1¼	BB,2,4,5,6,7½,9	4.55
16	2¾	3¼	1⅛	4,5,6,7½,9	4.20
20	2¾	2¾	1	4,5,6,7½,9	3.95
28	2¾	2¼	⅞	6,7½,9	3.95
410	3	Max.	11⁄16	4,5,6,7½	3.60
410	2½	Max.	½	6,7½	3.00
FIELD LOADS					
12	2¾	3¼	1¼	7½,8,9	3.95
12	2¾	3¼	1⅛	4,5,6,7½,8,9	3.75
12	2¾	3¼	1	6,8	3.50
16	2¾	2¾	1⅛	4,5,6,7½,8,9	3.50
16	2¾	2½	1	6,8	3.35
20	2¾	2½	1	4,5,6,7½,8,9	3.40
20	2¾	2½	⅞	6,8	3.10
TARGET LOADS					
12[1]	2¾	2¾	1⅛	7½,8,8½,9	3.50
12[1]	2¾	3	1⅛	7½,8,8½,9	3.50
12	2¾	2¾	1⅛	7½,8,8½,9	3.65
12	2¾	3	1⅛	7½,8,8½,9	3.65
12[3]	2¾	3¼	1⅛	7½,8,9	3.90
16	2¾	2¾	1⅛	7½,8,9	3.50
20[2]	2¾	2½	⅞	8,9	3.20
28	2¾	2	¾	9	3.95
410	2½	Max.	½	9	3.00
BUCKSHOT & RIFLED SLUG LOADS					
12	3	Sup. Mag.	—	00 Buck, 15 Pellets	1.57
12	3	Sup. Mag.	—	No. 4 Buck, 41 Pellets	1.57
12	2¾	Mag.	—	00 Buck, 12 Pellets	1.36
12	2¾	Mag.	—	No. 1 Buck, 20 Pellets	1.36
12	2¾	Mag	—	No. 4 Buck, 34 Pellets	1.36
12	2¾	Max.	—	00 Buck, 9 Pellets	1.20
12	2¾	Max.	—	0 Buck, 12 Pellets	1.20
12	2¾	Max.	—	No. 1 Buck, 16 Pellets	1.20
12	2¾	Max.	—	No. 4 Buck, 27 Pellets	1.20
16	2¾	Max.	—	No. 1 Buck, 12 Pellets	1.20
20	2¾	Max.	—	No. 3 Buck, 20 Pellets	1.20
12	2¾	Max.	—	⅞ oz. Rifled Slug	1.42
16	2¾	Max.	—	4/5 oz. Rifled Slug	1.35
20	2¾	Max.	—	⅝ oz. Rifled Slug	1.30
410	2½	Max.	—	1/5 oz. Rifled Slug	1.22

All Plastic tubes except
[1]Paper [2]Offered in Plastic and Paper
[3]International Load.
Packaged 25 per box except Buckshot and slugs 5 per box.
Wad Columns: Triple-Plus in 12, 16, 20 Ga. Hi-Power and Fields.
Magnums, 28 Gauge, 410 use shot cup with conventional wads.
12 Gauge Target loads use plastic "Champion" air-chamber wad.
Buck and Rifled Slugs do not use shot cups.

CENTERFIRE PISTOL & RIFLE

Cartridge	Gr.	Bullet Style	Muzzle Velocity	Muzzle Energy	Barrel Length Inches	Price Per Box
PISTOL						
25 (6.35mm) Auto	50	MC	810	73	2	5.70
32 Auto	71	MC	905	128	4	6.50
357 Mag.,Ni.Pl.Cs.	158	JSP	1550	845	6	8.55
9 mm Luger Auto	123	MC	1120	345	4	8.10
380 Auto	95	MC	955	192	3¾	6.70
38 Special Match	148	WC	770	195	6	6.45
38 Special	158	Lead	855	256	6	6.20
38 Special, Hi-Vel.	158	Lead	1090	415	6	6.90
45 Auto Match	230	MC	850	370	5	8.75
45 Auto Match	185	WC	775	247	5	9.25
RIFLE						
222 Remington	50	SP	3200	1140	26	4.10
22250 Remington	55	SP	3810	1770	26	4.50
223 Remington	55	SP	3300	1330	26	4.50
*243 Winchester	80	SP	3500	2180	26	5.70
*243 Winchester	100	SP	3070	2090	26	5.70
*270 Winchester	130	HS	3140	2840	24	6.20
*270 Winchester	150	HS	2800	2610	24	6.20
*7 mm Mauser	175	HS	2490	2410	24	6.20
*7 mm Mauser	139	HS	2710	2280	24	6.20
7 mm Rem. Mag.	150	HS	3260	3540	26	7.70
7 mm Rem. Mag.	175	HS	3070	3660	26	7.70
30 Carbine	110	SP	1980	955	18	3.90
*3030 Winchester	150	HS	2410	1930	26	4.85
*3030 Winchester	170	HS	2220	1860	26	4.85
*3006 Springfield	150	HS	2970	2930	24	6.20
*3006 Springfield	180	HS	2700	2910	24	6.20
*3006 Springfield	125	SP	3200	2840	24	6.20
*300 Savage	150	HS	2670	2370	24	6.05
*300 Savage	180	HS	2370	2240	24	6.05
300 Win. Mag.	150	HS	3400	3850	26	9.10
300 Win. Mag	180	HS	3070	3770	26	9.10
*303 British	180	HS	2540	2580	26	6.25
*308 Winchester	150	HS	2860	2730	24	6.20
*308 Winchester	180	HS	2610	2720	24	6.20
*8mm Mauser	170	HS	2570	2490	23½	6.20
*32 Win. Special	170	HS	2280	1960	26	5.00
*35 Remington	200	HS	2100	1950	22	5.65
44 Magnum	240	HP-SP	1750	1630	18½	4.40

Pistol Cartridges Packaged 50 per box
Rifle Cartridges Packaged 20 per box
MC-Metal Case JSP-Jacketed Soft Point WC-Wadcutter
SP-Soft Point HS-"Hi-Shok" Soft Point HP-Hollow Point
*Caliber with "Cartridge Carrier" pack.

RIMFIRE 22'S

Cartridge	Gr.	Bullet Style	Muzzle Velocity	Barrel Length	Price Per Box
HI-POWER®					
22 Short	29	Solid	1125	24	.88
22 Short	29	Hollow Point	1155	24	.99
22 Long	29	Solid	1240	24	.93
† 22 Long Rifle	40	Solid	1285	24	1.04
† 22 Long Rifle	38	Hollow Point	1315	24	1.15
22 Long Rifle	25	No. 12 Shot	—	24	2.11
STANDARD VELOCITY					
22 Short	29	Solid	1045	24	.88
22 Long Rifle	40	Solid	1145	24	1.04

Packaged 50 per box. Items with † also available
packaged 100 per plastic box.

RWS BALLISTIC TABLES

Selected samples of the latest RWS Ballistic Data booklet, translated into English especially for GUN DIGEST. Stoeger Arms Corporation should have copies of the RWS guide by the fall of 1972.

.243 Winchester KS

		Ballistic Data				Trajectory — Inches above ⊕ or below (−) Line of Sight					
		Distance yds.	Velocity ft./sec.	Energy ft./lbs.	Time of Flight sec.	Most recommended Distance	Rifle sighted in at ⊕				Open Sight at
						200 yds.	100 yds.	150 yds.	200 yds.	300 yds.	100 yds.
Index No.	296	Muzzle	3020	1795	0						
Barrel-length in.	23.5	50	2840	1590	.051	+ 0.4	− 0.4	− 0.1	+ 0.4	+ 1.6	+ 0.2
Most recommended Distance yds.	200	100	2670	1410	.106	+ 1.6	⊕	+ 0.6	+ 1.6	+ 3.9	⊕
V 10 ft./sec.	2970	150	2530	1260	.163	+ 1.4	− 1.0	⊕	+ 1.4	+ 5.0	− 1.6
Bullet-weight grains 96 / Powder-weight grains 40		200	2390	1130	.224	⊕	− 3.1	− 1.8	⊕	+ 4.8	− 4.3
Bullet-length in. 0.90 / Max. Chamber Pressure psi 51200		300	2160	920	.356	− 7.2	− 11.9	− 9.9	− 7.2	⊕	− 14.2

7 x 57 R KS

		Ballistic Data				Trajectory — Inches above ⊕ or below (−) Line of Sight					
		Distance yds.	Velocity ft./sec.	Energy ft./lbs.	Time of Flight sec.	Most recommended Distance	Rifle sighted in at ⊕				Open Sight at
						170 yds.	100 yds.	150 yds.	200 yds.	300 yds.	100 yds.
Index No.	308 R	Muzzle	2560	2355	0						
Barrel-length in.	23.5	50	2440	2140	.060	+ 0.6	− 0.2	+ 0.3	+ 1.0	+ 2.6	+ 0.4
Most recommended Distance yds.	170	100	2330	1950	.123	+ 1.6	⊕	+ 1.0	+ 2.4	+ 5.5	⊕
V 10 ft./sec.	2530	150	2220	1770	.189	+ 0.8	− 1,5	⊕	+ 2.0	+ 6.7	− 2.1
Bullet-weight grains 162 / Powder-weight grains 46		200	2120	1615	.258	− 1.7	− 4.7	− 2,7	⊕	+ 6.2	− 5.9
Bullet-length in. 1.20 / Max. Chamber Pressure psi 42700		300	1940	1355	.406	− 11.8	− 16.5	− 13.4	− 9.4	⊕	− 18.8

7 x 64 KS

		Ballistic Data				Trajectory — Inches above ⊕ or below (−) Line of Sight					
		Distance yds.	Velocity ft./sec.	Energy ft./lbs.	Time of Flight sec.	Most recommended Distance	Rifle sighted in at ⊕				Open Sight at
						200 yds.	100 yds.	150 yds.	200 yds.	300 yds.	100 yds.
Index No.	300	Muzzle	2890	3000	0						
Barrel-length in.	25.5	50	2760	2740	.053	+ 0.4	− 0.4	− 0.1	+ 0.4	+ 1.6	+ 0.2
Most recommended Distance yds.	200	100	2630	2485	.109	+ 1.6	⊕	− 0.6	+ 1.6	+ 3.9	⊕
V 10 ft./sec.	2850	150	2510	2265	.167	+ 1.4	− 1.0	⊕	+ 1.4	+ 5.0	− 1.6
Bullet-weight grains 162 / Powder-weight grains 51		200	2390	2055	.228	⊕	− 3.1	− 1.8	⊕	+ 4.8	− 4.3
Bullet-length in. 1.20 / Max. Chamber Pressure psi 51200		300	2180	1710	.360	− 7.2	− 11.9	− 9.9	− 7,2	⊕	− 14.2

.375 H & H Magnum KS

		Ballistic Data				Trajectory — Inches above ⊕ or below (−) Line of Sight					
		Distance yds.	Velocity ft./sec.	Energy ft./lbs.	Time of Flight sec.	Most recommended Distance	Rifle sighted in at ⊕				Open Sight at
						170 yds.	100 yds.	150 yds.	200 yds.	300 yds.	100 yds.
Index No.	305	Muzzle	2590	4465	0						
Barrel-length in.	25.5	50	2470	4060	.059	+ 0.7	− 0.2	+ 0.3	+ 1.0	+ 2.6	+ 0.4
Most recommended Distance yds.	170	100	2360	3710	.121	+ 1.6	⊕	+ 1.1	+ 2.4	+ 5.6	⊕
V 10 ft./sec.	2560	150	2260	3400	.187	+ 0.8	− 1.6	⊕	+ 2.0	+ 6.7	− 2.2
Bullet-weight grains 300 / Powder-weight grains 72		200	2160	3105	.255	− 1.6	− 4.9	− 2.7	⊕	+ 6.2	− 6.1
Bullet-length in. 1.20 / Max. Chamber Pressure psi 54100		300	1980	2610	.400	− 11.7	− 16.7	− 13.5	− 9.4	⊕	− 19.1

BROWNING 22 AUTO MEDALIST PISTOL

Caliber: 22 LR, 10-shot magazine.
Barrel: 6¾", med.-heavy vent. rib.
Length: 11⁵/₁₆" over-all. **Weight:** 46 oz. less weights.
Stocks: Full wrap-around thumbrest of select checkered walnut; matching fore-end. Left hand grips available.
Features: Dry-fire mechanism permits practice without mechanical harm. Fore-end holds variable weights. Trigger adj. for weight of pull and backlash.
Sights: ⅛" undercut removable blade front; rear frame-mtd., has micrometer clicks adj. for w. and e. Sight radius, 9½".
Price: Blued . . . . $156.50   Engraved and gold inlaid $325.00
Price: Renaissance Grade, chrome plated $365.00

BROWNING INTERNATIONAL MEDALIST PISTOL

Caliber: 22LR, 10-shot magazine.
Barrel: 5.9", med.-heavy vent rib.
Length: 10¹⁵/₁₆" over-all. **Weight:** 42 oz.
Stocks: Select walnut, full wraparound with thumb rest, 1.8" max. width.
Features: The International Medalist pistol meets all International Shooting Union regulations. The regular Medalist qualifies under N.R.A. pistol regulations.
Sights: Identical to those of standard Medalist, sight radius is 8.6".
Price: Blued $149.50

COLT WOODSMAN MATCH TARGET AUTO PISTOL

Caliber: 22LR, 10-shot magazine.
Barrel: 4 inches, 6 inches.
Length: 9 inches (4" bbl.). **Weight:** 40 oz. (6" bbl.), 36 oz. (4" bbl.).
Stocks: Walnut with thumbrest.
Features: Wide trigger, automatic slide stop.
Sights: Ramp front with removable undercut blade; ⅛" standard, ¹/₁₀" on special order; Colt-Elliason adjustable rear.
Price: Colt Blue only $119.95

COLT WOODSMAN SPORT AND TARGET MODEL

Caliber: 22LR, 10-shot magazine.
Barrel: 4 inches, 6 inches.
Length: 9 inches (4" bbl.). **Weight:** 30 oz. (4" bbl.). 32 oz. (6" bbl.).
Stocks: Walnut with thumbrest; checkered.
Features: Wide trigger, automatic slide stop.
Sights: Ramp front with removable blade, adjustable rear.
Price: Colt Blue only $99.95

COLT TARGETSMAN

Same as Woodsman S&T model except: 6" bbl. only; fixed blade front sight, economy adj. rear; without auto. slide stop $84.95

COLT GOLD CUP NAT'L MATCH AUTO

Caliber: 45 ACP or Wad Cutter; 38 Spec. W.C. 7-shot magazine.
Barrel: 5", with new design bushing.
Length: 8½ inches. **Weight:** 37 oz.
Stocks: Checkered walnut, gold plated medallion.
Features: Arched or flat housing; wide, grooved trigger with adj. stop; ribbed-top slide, hand fitted, with improved ejection port.
Sights: Patridge front, Colt-Elliason rear adj. for w. and e.
Price: Colt Royal Blue $189.95

COLT GOLD CUP NAT'L MATCH Mk IV SERIES 70 AUTO

Identical to the Gold Cup except fitted with a split-finger, collet-type barrel bushing and reverse-taper barrel to match for improved accuracy.
Price: $199.95

BROWNING 22 AUTO CHALLENGER PISTOL

Caliber: 22 LR, 10-shot magazine.
Barrel: 4½ inches or 6¾ inches.
Length: 8⅞" over-all (4½" bbl.), **Weight:** 35 oz. (4½" bbl.).
Stocks: Select walnut, hand checkered, wrap-around.
Features: Steel frame, manual stop-open latch (automatic after last shot); gold plated grooved trigger; trigger pull adjustment screw on rear face of frame.
Sights: ⅛" non-glare blade front; frame-mtd. rear, screw adj. for w. & e.
Price: Blue, either bbl. $99.50   Engraved and gold inlaid . . $255.00
Price: Renaissance Grade, engraved, chrome plated, 6¾" bbl. $285.00

HI-STANDARD SUPERMATIC STANDARD CITATION

Caliber: 22 LR, 10-shot magazine.
Barrel: 5½" bull weight.
Length: 10 inches (5½" bbl.). **Weight:** 42 oz. (5½" bbl.).
Stocks: Checkered walnut with or w/o thumbrest, right or left.
Features: Adjustable trigger pull; anti-backlash trigger adjustment; double acting safety; rebounding firing pin. Back & front straps stippled.
Sights: Undercut ramp front; click adjustable square notch rear.
Price: 5½" bull barrel **$120.00**

HI-STANDARD S'MATIC CITATION MILITARY

Caliber: 22 LR, 10-shot magazine.
Barrel: 5½" bull, 7¼" fluted.
Length: 9¾ inches (5½" bbl.). **Weight:** 46 oz.
Stocks: Checkered walnut with or w/o thumbrest, right or left.
Features: Same as regular Citation plus military style grip, stippled front- and backstraps, positive magazine latch.
Sights: Undercut ramp front; frame mounted rear, click adj.
Price: Either bbl. length **$120.00**

HI-STANDARD VICTOR

Caliber: 22 LR, 10-shot magazine.
Barrel: 4½", 5½".
Length: 8¾" (4½" bbl.). **Weight:** 48 oz. (4½" bbl.), 52 oz. (5½" bbl.).
Stock: Checkered walnut.
Sights: Undercut ramp front, rib mounted click adj. rear.
Features: Vent. rib, interchangeable barrel, 2 - 2¼ lb. trigger pull, blue finish, back and front straps stippled.
Price: Either bbl. length **$160.00**

HI-STANDARD (*ISU) OLYMPIC AUTO PISTOL

Caliber: 22 Short, 10-shot magazine.
Barrel: 6¾" round tapered, with stabilizer.
Length: 11¼". **Weight:** 40 oz.
Stocks: Checkered walnut w or w/0 thumbrest, right or left.
Features: Integral stabilizer with two removable weights. Trigger adj. for pull and anti-backlash; Citation grade finish.
Sights: Undercut ramp front; click adj., square notch rear.
Price: Blued **$132.50**
*Complies with all International Shooting Union regulations.
Olympic model with frame-mounted rear sight **$145.00**

HI-STANDARD SUPERMATIC TROPHY MILITARY

Caliber: 22 LR, 10-shot magazine.
Barrel: 5½" heavy, 7¼" fluted.
Length: 9¾ inches (5½" bbl.). **Weight:** 44½ oz.
Stocks: Checkered walnut with or w/o thumbrest, right or left.
Features: Grip duplicates feel of military 45; positive action mag. latch; front- and backstraps stippled. Adj. trigger, anti-backlash screw.
Sights: Undercut ramp front; frame mounted rear, click adj.
Price: Either bbl. length **$132.50**

RUGER Mark 1 TARGET MODEL AUTO PISTOL

Caliber: 22 LR only, 9-shot magazine.
Barrel: 6⅞" or 5½" bull barrel (6-groove, 14" twist).
Length: 10⅞" (6⅞" bbl.). **Weight:** 42 oz. with 6⅞" bbl.
Stocks: Checkered hard rubber.
Features: Rear sight mounted on receiver, does not move with slide; wide, grooved trigger.
Sights: ⅛" blade front, micro click rear, adjustable for w. and e. Sight radius 9⅜" (with 6⅞" bbl.).
Price: Blued, either barrel length **$69.00**
Price: Checkered walnut panels with left thumbrest **$73.00**

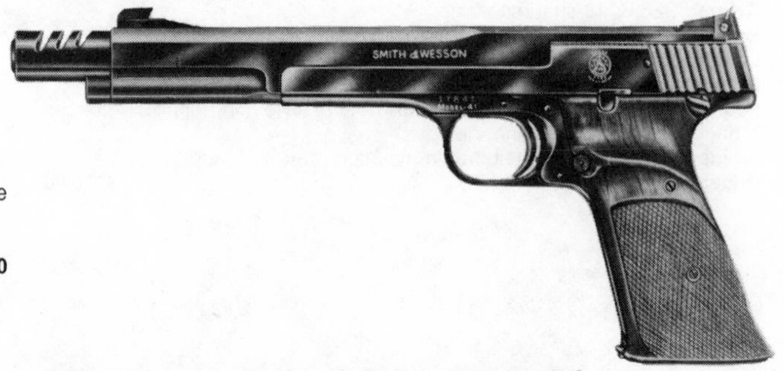

SMITH & WESSON 22 AUTO PISTOL Model 41

Caliber: 22 LR or 22 S, 10-shot clip.
Barrel: 5" or 7⅜", sight radius 9⁵⁄₁₆" (7⅜" bbl.).
Length: 12", incl. detachable muzzle brake, (7⅜" bbl. only).
Weight: 43½ oz. (7⅜" bbl.).
Stocks: Checkered walnut with thumbrest, usable with either hand.
Features: ⅜" wide, grooved trigger with adj. stop; wgts. available to make pistol up to 59 oz.
Sights: Front, ⅛" Patridge undercut; micro click rear adj. for w. and e.
Price: S&W Bright Blue, satin matted bbl., either caliber **$141.00**

SMITH & WESSON 22 MATCH HEAVY BARREL M-41

Caliber: 22 LR, 10-shot clip.
Barrel: 5½" heavy, without muzzle brake. Sight radius, 8".
Length: 9". **Weight:** 44½ oz.
Stocks: Checkered walnut with modified thumbrest, usable with either hand.
Features: ⅜" wide, grooved trigger; adj. trigger stop.
Sights: ⅛" Patridge on ramp base. S&W micro click rear, adj. for w. and e.
Price: S&W Bright Blue, satin matted top area **$141.00**

S & W 22 AUTO HEAVY BARREL EFS Model 41

Same as Model 41 Heavy Barrel but with extendible ⅛" front sight. Without muzzle brake or weights. Blued **$155.00**

SMITH & WESSON CONVERSION KIT

Converts Models 41 and 46 from 22 Short to 22 LR and vice versa. Consists of barrel, slide, magazine, slide stop and recoil spring.
Price, parts only **$65.40**
Price, factory installed and tested **$74.85**
Price, 5½" heavy bbl. only with sights for M41 or M46 .... **$37.40**

SMITH & WESSON 38 MASTER Model 52 AUTO

Caliber: 38 Special (for Mid-range W.C. with flush-seated bullet only). 5-shot magazine.
Barrel: 5".
Length: 8⅝". **Weight:** 41 oz. with empty magazine.
Features: Top sighting surfaces matte finished. Locked breech, moving barrel system; checked for 10-ring groups at 50 yards. Coin-adj. sight screws. Dry firing permissible if manual safety on.
Stocks: Checkered walnut.
Sights: ⅛" Patridge front, S&W micro click rear adj. for w. and e.
Price: S&W Bright Blue **$211.50**

STERLING TARGET "CUP" SERIES AUTO PISTOL

Caliber: 22 LR, 10-shot magazine.
Barrel: 4½", 6", and 8".
Length: 9" (4½" bbl.). **Weight:** 36 oz. (4½" bbl.).
Stocks: Checkered plastic.
Features: Adjustable trigger and balance weights; sear lock safety.
Sights: ⅛" blade front; Click adj. square notch rear.
Price: Blued (M283) **$99.00**
Price: Blued with 6" tapered barrel (M284) **$99.00**

U.S. HANDGUNS—TARGET REVOLVERS

COLT DIAMONDBACK REVOLVER
Caliber: 22 S, L or LR, or 38 Special, 6 shot.
Barrel: 2½″ or 4″, with ventilated rib.
Length: 9″ (4″ bbl.). **Weight:** 25 oz. (2½″ bbl.), 28½ oz. (4″ bbl.).
Stocks: Checkered walnut, target type, square butt.
Features: Ventilated rib; grooved, crisp trigger; swing-out cylinder; wide hammer spur.
Sights: Ramp front, adj. notch rear.
Price: Colt Blue **$139.95**
Price: Nickel finish (38 Spl. only) **$149.95**

COLT NEW POLICE PYTHON REVOLVER
Caliber: 357 Magnum (handles all 38 Spec.), 6 shot.
Barrel: 2½″, 4″ or 6″, with ventilated rib.
Length: 9¼″ (4″ bbl.). **Weight:** 41 oz. (4″ bbl.).
Stocks: Checkered walnut, target type, square butt.
Features: Ventilated rib; grooved, crisp trigger; swing-out cylinder; target hammer.
Sights: ⅛″ ramp front, adj. notch rear.
Price: Colt Royal Blue . . . . . **$199.95** Nickeled **$224.95**

SMITH & WESSON 1953 Model 35, 22/32 TARGET
Caliber: 22 S, L or LR, 6 shot.
Barrel: 6 inches.
Length: 10½ inches. **Weight:** 25 oz.
Stocks: Checkered walnut, Magna.
Sights: Front, 1/10″ Patridge, micro click rear, adjustable for w. and e.
Price: Blued **$113.50**

SMITH & WESSON 22 CENTER FIRE MAGNUM M-53
Caliber: Rem. 22 Jet and 22 S, L, LR with inserts. 6 shot.
Barrel: 4″, 6″ or 8⅜″.
Length: 11¼″ (6″ bbl.). **Weight:** 40 oz.
Stocks: Checkered walnut, target.
Features: Grooved tangs and trigger, swing-out cylinder revolver.
Sights: ⅛″ Baughman Quick Draw front, micro click rear, adjustable for w. and e.
Price: Blued **$155.00**
Price: Extra cylinder for 22 RF. (fitted) **$37.40**

SMITH & WESSON MASTERPIECE TARGET MODELS

Model: K-22 (M17).	K-22 (M48).
Caliber: 22 LR, 6 shot.	22 RF Magnum, 6 shot.
Barrel: 6″, 8⅜″.	4″, 6″ or 8⅜″
Length: 11⅛″ (6″ bbl.).	11⅛″ (6″ bbl.).
Weight: 38½ oz. (6″ bbl.).	39 oz.(6″ bbl.).
Model: K-32 (M16). (Illus.)	K-38 (M14).
Caliber: 32 S&W Long, 6 shot.	38 S&W Special, 6 shot.
Barrel: 6 inches.	6″, 8⅜″.
Length: 11⅛ inches.	11⅛ inches. (6″ bbl.)
Weight: 38½ oz. (Loaded).	38½ oz. (6″, loaded).

Features: All Masterpiece models have: checkered walnut, Magna stocks; grooved tang and trigger; ⅛″ Patridge front sight, micro. adj. rear sights. Swing out cylinder revolver.
Price: Blued, all calibers **$115.50**

SMITH & WESSON K-38 MASTERPIECE Single Action
Same as the M14 K-38 Masterpiece except single action only, and is supplied with target type hammer and trigger.
Price: Blued **$128.00**

U.S. HANDGUNS—TARGET REVOLVERS

SMITH & WESSON COMBAT MASTERPIECE
Caliber: 38 Special (M15) or 22 LR (M18), 6 shot.
Barrel: 2″ (M15) 4″ (M18)
Length: 9⅛″ (4″ bbl.). **Weight:** Loaded, 22 36½ oz, 38 30 oz.
Stocks: Checkered walnut, Magna. Grooved tangs and trigger.
Sights: Front, ⅛″ Baugham Quick Draw on ramp, micro click rear, adjustable for w. and e.
Price: Blue **$107.00**

SMITH & WESSON 1955 Model 25, 45 TARGET
Caliber: 45 ACP and 45 AR, 6 shot.
Barrel: 6½″ (heavy target type).
Length: 11⅞ inches. **Weight:** 45 oz.
Stocks: Checkered walnut target.
Features: Tangs and trigger grooved; target trigger and hammer standard, checkered target hammer. Swing-out cylinder revolver.
Sights: ⅛″ Patridge front, micro click rear, adjustable for w. and e.
Price: Blued **$148.50**

SMITH & WESSON ACCESSORIES
Target hammers with low, broad, deeply-checkered spur, and wide-swaged, grooved target trigger. For all frame sizes, $5.00 (target hammers not available for small frames). Target stocks: for large-frame guns, $10.65 to $12.30; for med/-frame guns, $8.40-$10.65; for small-frame guns, $7.10. These prices applicable only when specified on original order.
As separately-ordered parts: target hammers and triggers, $7.65; stocks, $13.75-$15.60.

U.S. HANDGUNS—SERVICE & SPORT

AMERICAN FIREARMS STAINLESS PISTOL
Caliber: 25 ACP, 8-shot.
Barrel: 2.1″.
Length: 4.4″. **Weight:** 15½ oz.
Stocks: Smooth walnut.
Sights: Fixed, open.
Price: Bright finish **$69.95**
Price: Blued steel model **$49.95**

AMERICAN FIREARMS DERRINGER
Caliber: 38 Special, 22 LR, 22 WRM, 2-shot.
Barrel: 3″.
Length: 4¾″. **Weight:** 15 oz.
Stocks: Checkered plastic.
Sights: Fixed, open.
Features: Made entirely of stainless steel, spur trigger, half-cock safety.
Price: **$67.50**

AMERICAN FIREARMS SAFEGUARD
Caliber: 380 ACP, 8-shot.
Barrel: 3½″.
Length: 5½″. **Weight:** 21 oz.
Stocks: Smooth walnut.
Sights: Fixed, open.
Features: Magazine safety, loaded chamber indicator. Made entirely from stainless steel.
Price: **$97.50**

BAUER 25 AUTOMATIC PISTOL
Caliber: 25 ACP, 6-shot.
Barrel: 2⅛″.
Length: 4″. **Weight:** 10 oz.
Stocks: Plastic pearl or checkered walnut.
Sights: Recessed, fixed.
Features: Stainless steel construction, positive manual safety, magazine safety. With padded zipper case.
Price: Satin stainless steel **$69.95**
Price: Blued stainless steel **$69.95**

BROWNING 22 AUTO NOMAD PISTOL
Caliber: 22 LR, 10-shot magazine.
Barrel: 4½″ or 6¾″.
Length: 8¹⁵⁄₁₆″ over-all (4½″ bbl.). **Weight:** 34 oz. (4½″ bbl.).
Stocks: Novadur plastic, checkered, wrap-around.
Features: Steel frame; thumb safety; bbls. interchangeable via lock screw on front of frame.
Sights: ⅛″ non-glare blade front; frame-mtd. rear, screw adj. for w. & e.
Price: Blued, either bbl. **$82.50**

BROWNING 380
Caliber: 380 ACP.
Barrel: 4⁷/₁₆″.
Weight: 23 oz. **Length:** 7¹/₁₆″.
Stock: Novadur plastic w/thumb rest.
Sights: Front, ¹/₁₀″ fixed blade. Rear, adjustable for w. & e.
Features: Fixed barrel, non-glare rear sight, magazine safety, loaded chamber indicator.
Price: Blue **$89.50**
Price: Renaissance Grade, engraved & chrome plated **$222.50**

BROWNING HI-POWER 9mm AUTOMATIC PISTOL
Caliber: 9mm Parabellum (Luger), 13-shot magazine.
Barrel: 4²¹/₃₂ inches.
Length: 7¾″ over-all. **Weight:** 32 oz.
Stocks: Walnut, hand checkered.
Features: External hammer with half-cock safety, thumb and magazine safeties. A blow on the hammer cannot discharge a cartridge; cannot be fired with magazine removed.
Sights: Fixed front; rear adj. for w.
Price: Blued **$137.50**
Price: 9mm Standard with rear sight adj. for w. and e. **$151.50**

BROWNING RENAISSANCE HI-POWER 9mm AUTO
Same as Browning Hi-Power 9mm Auto except: fully engraved, chrome plated, polyester pearl grips **$342.50**

CLERKE TARGET AUTOMATIC
Caliber: 22 LR, 380 ACP (9-shots, 22, 6-shots, 380).
Barrel: 3″.
Length: 8″ over-all. **Weight:** 30 oz.
Stocks: Checkered plastic, black, ivory or simulated rosewood.
Sights: Blade front, fixed rear.
Features: Adj. trigger, target sights available at extra cost, grip safety, blue finish.
Price: 22 LR with standard sights **$42.75**
Price: 22 LR with target sights **$50.00**
Price: 380 ACP with standard sights **$55.00**
Price: 380 ACP with target sights **$62.00**

COLT GOVT. SUPER 38 AUTO PISTOL
Caliber: 38 Super Auto, 9mm Luger 9 shot.
Barrel: 5″.
Length: 8½″. **Weight:** 39 oz.
Stocks: Checkered Coltwood. Grooved trigger.
Features: Grip and thumb safeties; grooved trigger and hammer; arched mainspring housing.
Sights: Fixed, glare-proofed ramp front, square notch rear.
Price: Blued .... **$125.00**   Nickeled **$143.75**

COLT MK IV/SERIES 70 45 GOV'T MODEL AUTO PISTOL
Identical to 38 Super and previous 45 Government Model except for addition of a split-finger, collet-type barrel bushing and reverse-taper barrel to match for improved accuracy.
Price: Blued .... **$134.95**   Nickeled **$149.95**

COLT CONVERSION UNIT
Permits the 45 and 38 Super Automatic pistols to use the economical 22 LR cartridge. No tools needed. Adjustable rear sight; 10-shot magazine. Designed to give recoil effect of the larger calibers. Not adaptable to Commander models. Blue finish **$69.95**

COLT COMMANDER AUTO PISTOL
Caliber: 45 ACP, 7 shot; 38 Super Auto, 9 shot; 9mm Luger, 9 shot.
Barrel: 4¼″.
Length: 8″. **Weight:** 26½ oz.
Stocks: Checkered Coltwood.
Features: Grooved trigger and hammer spur; arched housing; grip and thumb safeties.
Sights: Fixed, glare-proofed ramp front, square notch rear.
Price: Blued **$134.95**

COLT COMBAT COMMANDER
Same as Commander except steel frame, American walnut grips, weight 33 oz.
Price: Blue or satin nickel **$134.95**

COLT HUNTSMAN AUTO PISTOL
Caliber: 22 LR, 10-shot magazine.
Barrel: 4″, 6″.
Length: 9″ (4½″ bbl.). **Weight:** 30 oz. (4″ bbl.), 31½ oz. (6″ bbl.).
Stocks: Checkered walnut. Wide trigger.
Sights: Fixed ramp front, square notch rear, non-adjustable.
Price: Colt Blue **$74.95**

COLT POCKET AUTOMATIC
Caliber: 25 ACP, 6-shot magazine.
Barrel: 2¼″.
Length: 4⅜″ over-all. **Weight:** 12 oz.
Stocks: Fully checkered walnut.
Sights: Fixed on full-length serrated rib.
Features: Thumb and magazine safeties; round-top grooved visible hammer
Price: Colt blue **$69.95**

COLT DERINGERS
Caliber: 22 Short, single-shot.
Barrel: 2½″, side swing, blued.
Length: 4¹⁵⁄₁₆″ overall. **Weight:** 7¾ oz.
Stocks: Brown plastic, smooth.
Features: Fixed open sights, stud trigger, auto. ejection, single action, presentation case
Price: Gold frame (cased pair) **$59.95**
Price: 14K Gold frame, pearlite grips (cased pair) **$59.95**

BUDISCHOWSKY TP-70 AUTO PISTOL
Caliber: 25 ACP, 6-shot.
Barrel: 2.6″.
Length: 4⅔″. **Weight:** 12⅓ oz.
Stocks: Checkered walnut.
Sight: Fixed.
Features: Double action, exposed hammer, manual and magazine safeties. All stainless steel construction. Norarmco, manufacturer.
Price: **$100.00**

F.I.E. E27 TITAN PISTOL
Caliber: 25, 6-shot magazine
Barrel: 2⁷⁄₁₆″.
Length: 4⅝″ over-all. **Weight:** 12 oz.
Stocks: Checkered plastic.
Features: Visible hammer; fast simple takedown.
Sights: Fixed.
Price: Blued .... **$34.95**   Chromed: **$38.95**

HI-STANDARD MODEL D-100 and DM-101 DERRINGER
Caliber: 22 S, L or LR: 22 Rimfire Magnum. 2 shot.
Barrel: 3½″, over and under, rifled.
Length: 5″ over-all. **Weight:** 11 oz.
Stocks: Smooth plastic.
Features: Hammerless, integral safety hammerblock, all steel unit is encased in a black, anodized alloy housing. Recessed chamber. Dual extraction. Top break, double action.
Sights: Fixed, open.
Price: Blued .... **$49.50**   Nickel **$62.50**
Price: 22 WMR, Blue ...... **$51.50**   Nickel **$64.50**

HI-STANDARD PLINKER AUTO PISTOL
Caliber: 22 LR, 9-shot magazine.
Barrel: 4½″ or 6½″.
Length: 9″ (4½″ bbl.). **Weight:** 32 oz. (4½″ bbl.).
Stocks: Checkered plastic grips. Grooved trigger.
Features: Non slip trigger, interchangeable bbls., moulded target grips.
Sights: Fixed, ramp front, square notch rear.
Price: Blued **$64.50**

HI-STANDARD SHARPSHOOTER AUTO PISTOL
Caliber: 22 LR, 9-shot magazine.
Barrel: 5½″.
Length: 9″ over-all. **Weight:** 45 oz.
Stocks: Checkered laminated plastic.
Features: Wide, scored trigger; new hammer-sear design; new "jam-free" ejection. Slide lock, push-button take down.
Sights: Fixed, ramp front, square notch rear adj. for w. & e.
Price: Blued **$89.50**

STERLING "TRAPPER" SERIES AUTO PISTOL
Caliber: 22 LR, 10-shot magazine.
Barrel: 4½" or 6".
Length: 9" (4½" bbl.). **Weight:** 36 oz. (4½" bbl.).
Stocks: Checkered plastic.
Sights: Fixed ramp (6" bbl.) or blade (4½" bbl.) front. Square notch rear.
Features: Interchangeable safety (4½" bbl.).
Price: Blued (M286) 4½" or 6" tapered $74.50
Price: Blued (M285) 4½" heavy bbl. $69.50

STERLING MODEL 287 PPL
Caliber: 380 ACP, 32 ACP 5-shot.
Barrel: 2"
Length: 5⅜" over-all. **Weight:** 22½ oz.
Stocks: Checkered Cycolac.
Sights: Fixed, open.
Features: Trigger finger safety, extra wide trigger, external hammer.
Price: Blue $74.50

STERLING MODEL 300
Caliber: 25 ACP, 6 shot.
Barrel: 2".
Length: 4½" over-all. **Weight:** 10 oz.
Stock: Checkered Cycolac.
Sights: Fixed, open.
Price: Matte black or satin $39.95

SMITH & WESSON 9mm MODEL 39 AUTO PISTOL
Caliber: 9mm Luger, 8-shot clip.
Barrel: 4".
Length: 7⁷/₁₆". **Weight:** 26½ oz., without magazine.
Stocks: Checkered walnut.
Features: Magazine disconnector, positive firing pin lock and hammer-release safety; alloy frame with lanyard loop; locked-breech, short-recoil double action; slide locks open on last shot.
Sights: ⅛" serrated ramp front, adjustable rear.
Price: Blued .... $118.00   Nickeled $128.00

SMITH & WESSON M61 PISTOL
Caliber: 22 LR, 5-shot.
Barrel: 2⅛"
Length: 4¹³/₁₆". **Weight:** 14 oz.
Stocks: Checkered with cocking indicator pin protruding through left grip.
Features: Elementary blow-back pocket pistol with alloy frame.
Sights: Fixed square notch.
Price: Blued .... $53.50   Nickeled $63.50

RUGER STANDARD MODEL AUTO PISTOL
Caliber: 22 LR, 9-shot magazine.
Barrel: 4¾" or 6".
Length: 8¾" (4¾" bbl.). **Weight:** 36 oz. (4¾" bbl.).
Stocks: Checkered hard rubber.
Sights: Fixed, wide blade front, square notch rear.
Price: Blued $48.50
Price: With checkered walnut grips $54.50

LIBERTY RAVEN
Caliber: 25 ACP, 6-shot magazine.
Barrel: 2".
Length: 4¾". **Weight:** 15 oz.
Stocks: Plastic.
Sights: Fixed square notch.
Features: Available in either satin nickel or blue finish.
Price: $39.95

STOEGER LUGER 22 AUTO PISTOL
Caliber: 22 LR, 12-shot (11 in magazine, 1 in chamber).
Barrel: 4½" or 5½".
Weight: 30 oz.
Stocks: Checkered wood, identical to P-08.
Features: Action remains open after last shot and as magazine is removed. Grip and balance identical to P-08.
Price: 4½" Barrel $78.95
Price: 5½" Barrel $78.95

COLT DETECTIVE SPECIAL
Caliber: 38 Special, 6-shot.
Barrel: 2".
Length: 6⁹⁄₁₀" over-all. **Weight:** 23 oz.
Stocks: Full, checkered walnut, round butt.
Sights: Fixed, ramp front or blade, square notch rear.
Features: Glare-proofed sights, smooth trigger. Nickel finish, hammer shroud available as options. Two bbl. styles available—with or without shrouded ejector rod.
Price: **$99.95**

COLT COBRA REVOLVER
Caliber: 22 LR or 38 Special, 6 shot.
Barrel: 2", 3" (22 LR available in 3" only).
Length: 6¾" (2" bbl.). **Weight:** 15 oz. (2" bbl.).
Stocks: Checkered walnut, round butt. Grooved trigger.
Sights: Fixed, glare-proofed ramp front, square notch rear.
Price: Blued .... **$104.95** Nickeled **$119.95**
Price: Blued, 38 Spec. With hammer shroud installed **$109.95**

COLT AGENT REVOLVER
Caliber: 38 Special, 6 shot.
Barrel: 2" (Twist, 1-16).
Length: 6¾" over-all. **Weight:** 14 oz.
Stocks: Checkered walnut, round butt. Grooved trigger.
Sights: Fixed, glare-proofed ramp front, square notch rear.
Price: Blued .... **$104.95** With a hammer shroud installed .. **$109.95**

COLT OFFICIAL POLICE Mk III REVOLVER
Caliber: 38 Special, 6 shot.
Barrel: 4" and 6".
Length: 9¼" (4" bbl.).
Weight: 36 oz. (38 cal., 6" bbl.).
Stocks: Checkered walnut, square butt.
Sights: Fixed, glare-proofed ramp front, square notch rear.
Price: Blued **$119.95**

COLT HAMMER SHROUD
Facilitates quick draw from holster or pocket. Hammer spur projects just enough to allow for cocking for single action firing. Fits only Colt Detective Special, Cobra and Agent revolvers. Factory installed on new guns, **$5,** or as a kit for installation. Blued only **$6.00**
Factory installed on your gun (listed above). Blued only **$7.50**

COLT LAWMAN Mk III Revolver
Same as Official Police MK III but with 2" or 4" heavy barrel. Weight 36 oz. 38 Special only. Also as Metropolitan Mk III in 357 Magnum caliber.
Price: Blued .... **$119.95** Nickeled **$124.95**

COLT POLICE POSITIVE REVOLVER
Caliber: 38 Special, 6 shot.
Barrel: 4".
Length: 8¾" over-all. **Weight:** 23 oz.
Stocks: Checkered walnut, round butt. Grooved trigger.
Sights: Fixed, glare-proofed ramp front, square notch rear.
Price: Blued **$99.95**

U.S. HANDGUNS—REVOLVERS OVER $90

COLT TROOPER MK III REVOLVER
Caliber: 38 Special or 357 Magnum, 6-shot.
Barrel: 4" 6" (357 only).
Length: 9¼" (4" bbl.). **Weight:** 40 oz. (4" bbl.), 39 oz. (6" bbl.).
Stock: Checkered walnut, square butt. Grooved trigger.
Sights: Fixed ramp front with ⅛" blade, adj. notch rear.
Price: Blued **$149.95**. With wide spur hammer and target stocks . **$142.00**
Price: Nickeled **$159.95**

RUGER SECURITY SIX REVOLVER
Caliber: 357 Magnum and 38 Special, 6 shot.
Barrel: 2¾", 4" or 6".
Length: 9¼" (4" bbl.). **Weight:** 33½ oz. (4" bbl.).
Stocks: Checkered walnut, semi-target style.
Features: Solid frame with barrel, sighting rib and ejector rod housing combined in one integral unit. Can be "taken-down" using only a coin.
Sights: Fixed, or w. and e. adjustable rear.
Price: With fixed sights **$89.00**
Price: With adjustable rear sight **$97.50**

SMITH & WESSON M&P Model 10 REVOLVER
Caliber: 38 Special, 6 shot.
Barrel: 2", 4", 5" or 6"
Length: 9¼" (4" bbl.). **Weight:** 30½ oz. (4" bbl.).
Stocks: Checkered walnut, Magna. Round or square butt.
Sights: Fixed, ⅛" ramp front, square notch rear.
Price: Blued . . . . **$92.00**   Nickeled **$102.00**

SMITH & WESSON 38 M&P Heavy Barrel Model 10
  Same as regular M&P except: 4" ribbed bbl. with ⅛" ramp front sight, square rear, square butt, wgt. 34 oz.
Price: Blued . . . . **$92.00**   Nickeled **$102.00**

SMITH & WESSON 38 M&P AIRWEIGHT Model 12
Caliber: 38 Special, 6 shot.
Barrel: 2 or 4 inches.
Length: 6⅞" over-all. **Weight:** 18 oz. (2" bbl.)
Stocks: Checkered walnut, Magna. Round or square butt.
Sights: Fixed, ⅛" serrated ramp front, square notch rear.
Price: Blued . . . . **$95.00**   Nickeled **$105.00**

SMITH & WESSON TERRIOR MODEL 32
Caliber: 38 S&W, 5-shot.
Barrel: 2".
Length: 6½" over-all. **Weight:** 17 oz.
Stock: Checkered walnut.
Sights: Front, ¹/₁₀" serrated ramp, square notch rear.
Price: Blue . . . . **$92.00**   Nickeled **$102.00**

SMITH & WESSON 1953 Model 34, 22/32 KIT GUN
Caliber: 22 LR, 6 shot.
Barrel: 2", 4".
Length: 8" (4" bbl. and round butt). **Weight:** 22½ oz. (4" bbl.).
Stocks: Checkered walnut, round or square butt.
Sights: Front, ¹/₁₀" serrated ramp, micro. click rear, adjustable for w. & e.
Price: Blued . . . . **$105.50**   Nickeled **$115.50**

SMITH & WESSON Model 51 22/32 KIT GUN
  Same as Model 34 except chambered for 22 WRF Magnum; 3½" barrel; weight, 24 oz. Choice of round or square butt.
Price: Blued . . . . **$114.00**   Nickeled **$124.00**

SMITH & WESSON KIT GUN AIRWEIGHT (Model 43, not illus.)
  Same as M34 except 3½" barrel, square butt; weight 14¼ oz. 22LR.
Price: Blued . . . . **$114.00**   Nickeled **$124.00**

SMITH & WESSON 32 HAND EJECTOR Model 30
Caliber: 32 S&W Long, 6 shot.
Barrel: 2", 3", 4".
Length: 8 inches (4" bbl.). **Weight:** 18 oz. (4" bbl.).
Stocks: Checkered walnut, Magna.
Sights: Fixed, 1/10" serrated ramp front, square notch rear.
Price: Blued .... **$92.00**   Nickeled **$102.00**

SMITH & WESSON 41 M&P Model 58 REVOLVER
Caliber: 41 Magnum, 6 shot.
Barrel: 4".
Length: 9¼" over-all. **Weight:** 41 oz.
Stocks: Checkered walnut, Magna.
Sights: Fixed, 1/8" serrated ramp front, square notch rear.
Price: Blued .... **$114.50**   Nickeled **$124.50**

SMITH & WESSON 41 MAGNUM Model 57 REVOLVER
Caliber: 41 Magnum, 6 shot.
Barrel: 4", 6" or 8⅜".
Length: 11⅜" (6" bbl.). **Weight:** 48 oz. (6" bbl.).
Stocks: Oversize target type checkered Goncala Alves wood and target hammer. Tang and target trigger grooved.
Sights: 1/8" red ramp front, micro. click rear, adj. for w. and e.
Price: S&W Bright Blue or Nickel **$194.00**

SMITH & WESSON 44 MAGNUM Model 29 REVOLVER
Caliber: 44 Magnum, 44 Special or 44 Russian, 6 shot.
Barrel: 4", 6½", 8⅜".
Length: 11⅞" (6½" bbl.). **Weight:** 47 oz. (6½" bbl.), 43 oz. (4" bbl.).
Stocks: Oversize target type, checkered Goncala Alves. Tangs and target trigger grooved, checkered target hammer.
Sights: 1/8" red ramp-front, micro. click rear, adjustable for w. and e.
Price: S&W Bright Blue or Nickel **$194.00**

SMITH & WESSON HIGHWAY PATROLMAN Model 28
Caliber: 357 Magnum and 38 Special, 6 shot.
Barrel: 4", 6".
Length: 11¼" (6" bbl.). **Weight:** 44 oz. (6" bbl.).
Stocks: Checkered walnut, Magna. Grooved tangs and trigger.
Sights: Front, 1/8" Baughman Quick Draw, on plain ramp. micro click rear, adjustable for w. and e.
Price: S&W Watin Blue, sandblasted frame edging and barrel top **$118.00**
Price: With target stocks **$126.00**

U.S. HANDGUNS—REVOLVERS OVER $90

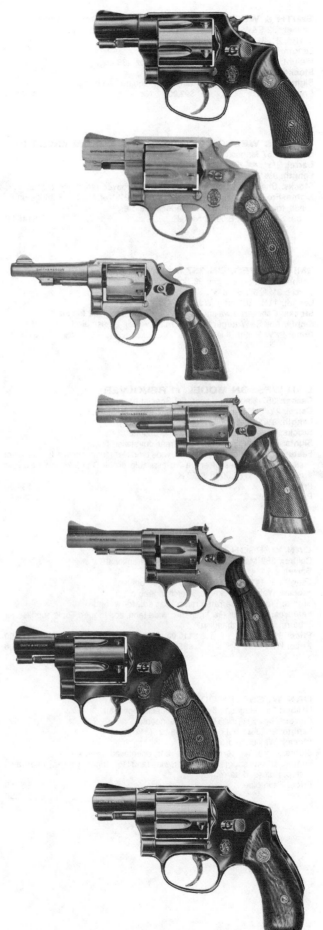

SMITH & WESSON 36 CHIEFS SPECIAL & AIRWEIGHT
Caliber: 38 Special, 5 shot.
Barrel: 2", 3".
Length: 6½" (2" bbl. and round butt). **Weight:** 19 oz. (2" bbl.; 14 oz. AIR-WEIGHT).
Stocks: Checkered walnut, Magna. Round or square butt.
Sights: Fixed, ¹⁄₁₀" serrated ramp front, square notch rear.
Price: Blued std. M-36 .... **$92.00**   Standard weight Nickel ... **$102.00**
Price: Blued AIR'W M-37 .. **$95.00**   AIRWEIGHT Nickel **$105.00**

SMITH & WESSON 60 CHIEFS SPECIAL STAINLESS
Same as Model 36 except: 2" bbl. and round butt only.
Price: Stainless steel **$120.00**

SMITH & WESSON MODEL 64 STAINLESS M&P
Caliber: 38 Special, 6-shot.
Barrel: 4".
Length: 9½" over-all. **Weight:** 30½ oz.
Stocks: Checkered walnut, service style.
Sights: Fixed, ⅛" serrated ramp front, square notch rear.
Features: Satin finished stainless steel, square butt.
Price: **$120.00**

SMITH & WESSON MODEL 66 STAINLESS COMBAT MAGNUM
Caliber: 357 Magnum and 38 Special, 6-shot.
Barrel: 4".
Length: 9½" over-all. **Weight:** 35 oz.
Stocks: Checkered Goncala Alves target.
Sights: Front, ⅛" Baughman Quick Draw on plain ramp, micro click rear adj. for w. and e. Satin finish stainless steel, grooved trigger with adj. stop.
Price: **$175.00**

SMITH & WESSON MODEL 67 K-38 STAINLESS COMBAT MASTERPIECE
Caliber: 38 special, 6-shot.
Barrel: 4".
Length: 9⅛" over-all. **Weight:** 34 oz. (loaded).
Stocks: Checkered walnut, service style.
Sights: Front, ⅛" Baushman Quick Draw on ramp, micro click rear adj. for w. and e.
Features: Stainless steel. Square butt frame with grooved tangs, grooved trigger with adj. stop.
Price: **$137.50**

SMITH & WESSON BODYGUARD Model 38 REVOLVER
Caliber: 38 Special; 5 shot, double action revolver.
Barrel: 2".
Length: 6⅜" over-all. **Weight:** 14½ oz.
Features: Alloy frame; integral hammer shroud.
Stocks: Checkered walnut, Magna.
Sights: Fixed ¹⁄₁₀" serrated ramp front, square notch rear.
Price: Blued .... **$95.00**   Nickeled **$105.00**

SMITH & WESSON BODYGUARD Model 49 REVOLVER
Same as Model 38 except steel construction. Weight 20½ oz.
Price: Blued .... **$94.50**   Nickeled **$104.50**

SMITH & WESSON CENTENNIAL Model 40 & AIRWEIGHT Model 42 REVOLVERS
Caliber: 38 Special, 5 shot.
Barrel: 2".
Length: 6½". **Weight:** 19 oz. (Standard weight), 13 oz. (AIRWEIGHT).
Stocks: Smooth walnut, Magna.
Sights: Fixed ¹⁄₁₀" serrated ramp front, square notch rear.
Price: Blued, standard wgt. **$97.00**   Nickeled, standard wgt. **$107.00**
Price: Blued AIRWEIGHT . **$103.50**   Nickeled, AIRWEIGHT **$113.50**

SMITH & WESSON 32 & 38 REGULATION POLICE
Caliber: 32 S&W Long (M31), 6 shot. 38 S&W (M33) (Illus.), 5 shot.
Barrel: 2", 3", 4". (4" only in 38 S&W).
Length: 8½" (4" bbl.).
Weight: 18¾ oz. (4" bbl., in 32 cal.), 18 oz. (38 cal.).
Stocks: Checkered walnut, Magna.
Sights: Fixed, ¹/₁₀" serrated ramp front, square notch rear.
Price: Blued .... **$92.00**   Nickeled **$102.00**

SMITH & WESSON 357 COMBAT MAGNUM Model 19
Caliber: 357 Magnum and 38 Special, 6 shot.
Barrel: 2½", 4", 6".
Length: 9½" (4" bbl.). **Weight:** 35 oz.
Stocks: Checkered Goncala Alves, target. Grooved tangs and trigger.
Sights: Front, ⅛" Baughman Quick Draw on 2½" or 4" bbl., Patridge on 6" bbl., micro click rear adjustable for w. and e.
Price: S&W Bright Blue or Nickel **$145.00**

SMITH & WESSON 357 MAGNUM M-27 REVOLVER
Caliber: 357 Magnum and 38 Special, 6 shot.
Barrel: 3½", 5", 6", 8⅜".
Length: 11¼" (6" bbl.). **Weight:** 44 oz. (6" bbl.).
Stocks: Checkered walnut. Magna. Grooved tangs and trigger.
Sights: Any S&W target front, micro click rear, adjustable for w. and e.
Price: S&W Bright Blue or Nickel **$168.00**

DAN WESSON MODEL 11 REVOLVER
Caliber: 357 Magnum, 6-shot. (38 Special optional).
Barrel: 2½", 3¾" or 6" (optional and interchangeable).
Length: 9¼" (4" bbl.). **Weight:** 38 oz. (4" bbl.).
Stocks: Walnut, interchangeable and optional.
Sights: Front, ⅛" serrated ramp, rear dovetailed fixed.
Features: Wide spur (⅜") hammer, wide tang (⅜") trigger with adj. overtravel stop. Three grades of engraving available on all Dan Wesson revolvers priced from $175.00 to $550.00.
Price: Blue **$84.00**
Price: Nickel **$94.00**

DAN WESSON MODEL 12 REVOLVER
Caliber: 357 Magnum, 6-shot. (38 Special optional).
Barrel: 2½", 4" or 6" interchangeable.
Length: 9" (4" bbl.). **Weight:** 38 oz. (4" bbl.).
Stocks: Walnut, checkered, interchangeable.
Sights: Front, ⅛" serrated ramp, rear adj. for w. and e.
Features: Wide spur (⅜") hammer; wide tang; adj. trigger. Tools supplied for barrel and grip changing.
Price: Blue .... **$110.00**   Nickel **$120.00**
Price: With fixed sights .... **$95.00**   Nickel **$94.00**

DAN WESSON MODEL 14 REVOLVER
Caliber: 357 Magnum, 6-shot. (38 Special optional).
Barrel: 2¼", 3¾" or 5¾" interchangeable.
Length: 9" (3¾" bbl.). **Weight:** 38 oz. (3¾" bbl.).
Stocks: Walnut, interchangeable.
Sights: Front, ⅛" serrated ramp, rear, dovetailed, fixed.
Features: Wide spur (⅜") hammer, wide tang (⅜") trigger with adj. overtravel stop, recessed barrel nut.
Price: Satin blue **$87.50**
Nickel **$97.50**

DAN WESSON MODEL 15 REVOLVER
Caliber: 357 Magnum, 6-shot. (38 Special optional).
Barrel: 2¼", 3¾" or 5¾" interchangeable.
Length: 9" (3¾" bbl.). **Weight:** 38 oz. (3¾" bbl.).
Stocks: Walnut, interchangeable and optional.
Sights: Front, ⅛" serrated ramp, rear, adj. for w. and e.
Features: Wide spur (⅜") hammer, wide tang (⅜") trigger with adj. overtravel stop, recessed barrel nut.
Price: Satin blue **$105.50**
Bright blue **$113.50**
Nickel **$123.50**

CHARTER ARMS "UNDERCOVER" REVOLVER
Caliber: 38 Special, 5 shot.
Barrel: 2″ or 3.
Length: 6¼″ (round butt). **Weight:** 16 oz.
Features: Wide trigger and hammer spur
Stocks: Smooth walnut, round or square butt available.
Sights: Fixed; matted ramp front, ⅛″ wide blade.
Price: Polished Blue ..... $80.00   Nickel $90.00
Price: With checkered, finger-rest bulldog grips (blue) 86.50

CHARTER ARMS UNDERCOVERETTE
Like the Undercover, but a 6-shot 32 S&W Long revolver available with 2″ barrel only, and weighing 16½ oz.
Price: Polished blue $80.00

CHARTER ARMS PATHFINDER
Same as Undercover but in 22 LR caliber, and has 3″ bbl. Fitted with adjustable rear sight, ramp front. Weight 18½ oz.
Price: Blued $87.50
Price: With checkered, finger-rest bulldog grips 94.00

CLERKE FIRST REVOLVERS
Caliber: 22 S,L,LR, 32 S&W (6-shots 22, 5-shots 32).
Barrel: 2¼″.
Length: 6¼″ over-all. **Weight:** 17 oz.
Stocks: Checkered plastic, black, ivory or simulated rosewood.
Sights: Fixed.
Features: Swing-out cylinder, double action, square butt. Available in blue finish or nickel.
Price: 22 cal. $24.00
Price: 32 S&W $29.95

F.I.E. "38" Model F38 REVOLVER
Caliber: 38 Special.
Barrel: 2″ or 4″.
Length: 6¼″ over-all. (2″ bbl.). **Weight:** 27 oz.
Features: Swing-out cylinder.
Stocks: Plastic Bulldog.
Sights: Fixed.
Price: Blued .... $49.95   4″ bbl. $53.95

F.I.E. T18 TITAN REVOLVER
Caliber: 22 LR, 6-shot.
Barrel: 1¾″.
Length: 5¾″ over-all. **Weight:** 16 oz.
Features: Swing-out cylinder with quick release.
Stocks: Checkered plastic.
Sights: Fixed.
Price: Blued $22.95

F.I.E. E14 TITANIC REVOLVER
Caliber: 32 S&W Long, 5-shot.
Barrel: 1⅞″.
Length: 6″ over-all. **Weight:** 18 oz.
Features: Solid frame, easily removable cylinder.
Stocks: Black plastic.
Sights: Fixed.
Price: Blued $34.95

FIREARMES INTERNATIONAL REGENT
Caliber: 22 LR, 8-shot or 32 S&W Long, 6-shot.
Barrel: 37″, 4″ or 6″ round (2½″ or 4″ in 32 S&W Long).
Weight: 28 oz. (4″ bbl.).
Features: Swing-out cylinder, recessed for cartridge rims.
Stocks: Checkered composition.
Sights: Fixed; ramp front.
Price: Blued, 22 LR $34.95
Price: Blued, 32 S&W Long 39.95

U.S. HANDGUNS—REVOLVERS UNDER $90

H&R Model 940 Ultra "Side-Kick" REVOLVER
Caliber: 22 S, L or LR, 9 shot.
Barrel: 6″ target weight with ventilated rib.
Weight: 33 oz.
Features: Swing-out, safety rim cylinder; safety lock and key.
Stocks: Checkered walnut with thumbrest.
Sights: Ramp front; rear adjustable for w. and e.
Price: H&R Crown-Luster Blue $62.95

H&R Model 939 Ultra "Side-Kick REVOLVER
Like the Model 940 but with a flat-sided barrel.
Price: H&R Crown-Luster Blue $64.95

HARRINGTON & RICHARDSON Model 732 Guardsman
Caliber: 32 S&W or 32 S&W Long, 6 shot.
Barrel: 2½″ or 4″ round barrel.
Weight: 23½ oz. (2½″ bbl.), 26 oz. (4″ bbl.).
Features: Swing-out cylinder with auto. extractor return. Pat. safety rim cylinder. Grooved trigger.
Stocks: Checkered, black Cycolac.
Sights: Blade front; adjustable rear on 4″ model.
Price: Blued .... **$49.95**   Chromed (Model 733) 2½″ bbl. only **$54.95**

HARRINGTON & RICHARDSON Model 622 REVOLVER
Caliber: 22 S, L or LR, 6 shot.
Barrel: 2½″, 4″, or 6″ round bbl.
Weight: 22 oz. (2½″ bbl.).
Features: Solid steel, square-built frame; snap-out safety rim cylinder; non-glare finish on frame; coil springs.
Stocks: Checkered black Cycolac.
Sights: Fixed, blade front, square notch rear.
Price: Blued, 2½″, 4″, or 6″ bbl. $37.95

HARRINGTON & RICHARDSON Model 926 REVOLVER
Caliber: 22 S, L, or LR, 9-shot, 38 S&W 5-shot.
Barrel: 4″. **Weight:** 31 oz.
Features: Top-break, double or single action
Stocks: Checkered walnut.
Sights: Fixed front, read adj. for w.
Price: Blued $64.95

HARRINGTON & RICHARDSON Model 900 REVOLVER
Caliber: 22 S, L or LR, 9 shot.
Barrel: 2½″, 4″, or 6″ round bbl.
Weight: 20 oz. (2½″ bbl.), 26 oz. (6″ bbl.).
Features: Snap-out cylinder; simultaneous push-pin extraction; coil springs; safety rim cylinder; Round-grip frame with 2½″ bbl.
Stocks: Checkered, black Cycolac.
Sights: Fixed, blade front, square notch rear.
Price: Blued $43.95

HARRINGTON & RICHARDSON SPORTSMAN Model 999 REVOLVER
Caliber: 22 S, L or LR, 9 shot.
Barrel: 6″ top-break (16″ twist), integral vent,-rib.
Length: 10½″. **Weight:** 30 oz.
Features: Wide hammer spur; rest for second finger.
Stocks: Checkered walnut, semi-thumbrest.
Sights: Front adjustable for elevation, rear for windage.
Price: Blued $69.95

U.S. HANDGUNS—REVOLVERS UNDER $90

HARRINGTON & RICHARDSON Model 925 "Defender"
Caliber: 38 S&W 5 shot.
Barrel: 2½".
Length: 7½" over-all. **Weight:** 22 oz.
Features: Top-break double action, push pin extractor.
Stocks: Smooth walnut, birds-head style, one piece wrap-round.
Sights: Rear with windage adj.
Price: H&R Crown Luster Blue $59.95

HARRINGTON & RICHARDSON Model 929 "Side-Kick"
Caliber: 22 S, L or LR, 9 shot.
Barrel: 2½", 4" or 6".
Weight: 26 oz. (4" bbl.).
Features: Swing-out cylinder with auto. extractor return. Pat. safety rim cylinder. Grooved trigger. Round-grip frame.
Stocks: Checkered, black Cycolac.
Sights: Blade front; adjustable rear on 4" and 6" models.
Price: Blued, 2½", 4" or 6" bbl. $49.95
Price: Nickel (Model 930), 4" bbl. 54.95

HI-STANDARD SENTINEL
Caliber: 22 LR, 9-shot capacity.
Barrel: 2⅜", 4" or 6".
Length: 7¼". **Weight:** 15 oz. (2⅜" bbl.).
Stocks: Checkered plastic.
Sights: Blade front, square notch rear adj. for w.
Features: One-piece frame, wide, grooved trigger. Grips in brown or white.
Price: Blued $54.95
Price: Nickel $59.95

HIGH STANDARD LONG HORN CONVERTIBLE REVOLVER
Same as the Double-Nine convertible but with a 9½" bbl., fixed sights, blued only, Weight: 40 oz.
Price: . . . . $92.50   Magnum only $87.50

HIGH STANDARD DURANGO REVOLVER
A variation of the High Standard Double-Nine with a brass finished trigger guard and backstrap. 4½" bbl., 10" over-all, weight 25 oz. 22 S, L or LR only. Walnut grips.
Price: Blued $64.95
As above but with 5½" bbl., weight 25 oz.
Price: Blued . . . . $64.95   Nickeled $69.95

HIGH STANDARD HOMBRE REVOLVER
Same as the Durango except 4½" bbl. only, no ejector rod housing or brass finish. Weight. Weight 25¼ oz.
Price: Blued . . . . $57.95   Nickeled $62.95

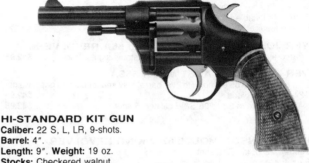

HI-STANDARD KIT GUN
Caliber: 22 S, L, LR, 9-shots.
Barrel: 4".
Length: 9". **Weight:** 19 oz.
Stocks: Checkered walnut.
Sights: Ramp target type front, rear adj. for w. & e.
Features: Swing out cylinder, blue finish.
Price: $69.95

HARRINGTON & RICHARDSON M-949 FORTY-NINER
Caliber: 22 S, L or LR, 9 shot.
Barrel: 5½" round with ejector rod.
Weight: 31 oz.
Features: Contoured loading gate; wide hammer spur; single and double action. Western type ejector-housing.
Stocks: One-piece smooth walnut frontier style.
Sights: Round blade front, adj. rear.
Price: H&R Crown-Luster Blue $47.95
Price: Nickel (Model 1950) $52.95

HIGH STANDARD DOUBLE-NINE CONVERTIBLE
Caliber: 22 S, L or LR, 9-shot (22 WRM with extra cylinder).
Barrel: 5½", dummy ejector rod fitted.
Length: 11" over-all. **Weight:** 32 oz.
Stocks: Smooth walnut, frontier style with medallion
Features: Western styling; rebounding hammer with auto safety block; spring-loaded ejection.
Sights: Fixed blade front, notched rear.
Price: Blued . . . . $79.50   Nickeled $87.50
As above but in 22 WRM only (no extra cylinder for other rimfire cartridges)
Price: Blue . . . . $74.50   Nickeled $79.50
Deluxe Double-Nine with adjustable Patridge type sights available in blue only.
Price: Convertible . . . . $92.50   Magnum only $87.50

U.S. HANDGUNS—REVOLVERS UNDER $90

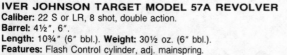

IVER JOHNSON MODEL 50A SIDEWINDER REVOLVER
Caliber: 22 S, L, LR, 8 shot.
Barrel: 6".
Length: 11¼". **Weight:** 31 oz.
Features: Wide spur hammer, half-cock safety, scored trigger, Flash Control cylinder, recessed shell head, push rod ejector.
Stocks: Plastic Stag Horn.
Sights: Fixed, blade front.
Price: Blued $46.50

IVER JOHNSON TARGET MODEL 57A REVOLVER
Caliber: 22 S or LR, 8 shot, double action.
Barrel: 4½", 6".
Length: 10¾" (6" bbl.). **Weight:** 30½ oz. (6" bbl.).
Features: Flash Control cylinder, adj. mainspring.
Stocks: Checkered thumbrest, Tenite.
Sights: Adjustable Patridge type.
Price: Blued $45.75

IVER JOHNSON TARGET MODEL 55A REVOLVER
Same as Model 57A except without adjustable sights. Price ..,.. $42.95

IVER JOHNSON CADET Model 55SA
Same as Model 55 except with 2½" barrel only, rounded tenite grips; weight 24 oz. Price, blued $42.95
Also available in 32 or 38 S&W caliber, 5 shot $42.95

IVER JOHNSON MODEL 67 VIKING REVOLVER
Caliber: 22 S, L, LR, 8-shot.
Barrel: 4½" or 6" chrome-lined heavy.
Length: 9½" (4½" bbl.). **Weight:** 34 oz. (6" bbl.).
Features: Cyl. front recessed for Flash Control, chambers also recessed for cartridge rims. Matted top, wide trigger. "Hammer-the-Hammer" action.
Stocks: Checkered, thumbrest plastic.
Sights: Adjustable Patridge type.
Price: Blued $59.50

IVER JOHNSON VIKING 67S SNUB REVOLVER
Same as M67 Viking except has 2¾" barrel, smooth rounded stocks, 7" over all, weidht 25oz. $59.50
Also available in 32 and 38 S&W calibers or Colt N.P., 5 shot 59.50

IVER JOHNSON TRAILSMAN 66 REVOLVER
Same as M67 Viking but with rebounding hammer. 6" bbl. only.
Price: $55.75

U.S. HANDGUNS—SINGLE ACTION REVOLVERS

COLT SINGLE ACTION ARMY REVOLVER
Caliber: 357 Magnum or 45 Colt, 6 shot.
Barrel: 4¾", 5½" or 7½".
Length: 11½" (5½" bbl.). **Weight:** 37 oz. (5½" bbl.).
Stocks: Checkered hard rubber. (Walnut stocks **$5.00** extra).
Sights: Fixed. Grooved top strap, blade front.
Price: Blued and case hardened in color $194.95
Price: Nickel with walnut stocks $229.95
Price: Buntline Spec., cal. 45 only. 12 bbl., wood stocks $229.95

COLT SINGLE ACTION ARMY—NEW FRONTIER
Same specifications as standard Single Action Army except: flat-top frame; high polished finish, blue and case colored; ramp front sight and target rear adj. for windage and elevation; smooth walnut stocks with silver medallion.
Price: $229.95

COLT NEW FRONTIER 22
Caliber: 22 LR, 22 Magnum.
Barrel: 4¾", 6" or 7½" (Buntline).
Length: 9⁵⁄₁₆", (10⁹⁄₁₆ in Mag., 12¾" for Buntline). **Weight:** 30 oz. (31 oz. in Mag., 28½ oz. for Buntline).
Stocks: Checkered black plastic.
Sights: Ramp front, adjustable rear.
Features: Blue finish, smooth trigger, knurled hammer spur.
Price: .... **$84.95**   (22 Magnum Dual Cyl., ...**$89.95**)
Buntline .... **$89.95**   (22 Magnum Dual Cyl., ...**$94.95**)

U.S. HANDGUNS—SINGLE ACTION REVOLVERS

COLT PEACEMAKER 22
Caliber: 22 LR, 22 Magnum.
Barrel: 4¾", 6" or 7½" (Buntline).
Length: 9⁵⁄₁₆" (10⁹⁄₁₆ in Mag., 12¾" for Buntline). **Weight:** 30 oz. (31 oz. in Mag., 28½ oz. for Buntline).
Stock: Checkered black plastic (Buntline, checkered black rubber).
Sights: Fixed. Grooved top strap, blade front.
Features: Color case hardened frame, all steel construction, smooth trigger, knurled hammer spur.
Price: Blued .... **$74.95**   with Magnum cylinder **$79.95**
Buntline .... **$79.95**   with Magnum cylinder **$84.95**

F.I.E. E15 BUFFALO SCOUT REVOLVER
Caliber: 22 LR, 6-shot.
Barrel: 4¾.
Length: 10" over-all. **Weight:** 30 oz.
Stocks: Black plastic.
Features: Slide spring ejector.
Sights: Fixed.
Price: Blued, cylinder, ejector tube and handle chromed **$32.95**
Price: Model E15M with extra interchangeable 22 WMR Mag. cylinder, blue finish **$41.95**

RUGER SUPER BEARCAT REVOLVER
Caliber: 22 S, L, or LR, 6 shot.
Barrel: 4" round, with ejector rod.
Length: 8⅞" over-all. **Weight:** 22½ oz.
Stocks: Genuine walnut with medallion.
Sights: Fixed; Patridge front, square notch rear.
Features: Alloy solid frame, patented Ruger coil-spring action; non-fluted engraved cylinder.
Price: Blued **$45.00**

RUGER SINGLE SIX REVOLVER
Caliber: 22 S, L or LR; 6 shots.
Barrel: 5½" (6 groove, 14" twist).
Length: 11⅞". **Weight:** 35 oz.
Stocks: Smooth walnut.
Sights: Fixed; blade front, square notch rear.
Features: Independent firing pin in frame; coil springs throughout; recessed chambers.
Price: Blued **$65.50**

RUGER SINGLE SIX CONVERTIBLE REVOLVER
Same as regular Single Six except furnished with two interchangeable cylinders: one-chambered for 22 S, L or LR; the other for 22 RF Magnum. Choice of 5½", 6½" or 9½" barrel.
Price: with 5½" or 6½" barrel **$69.50**
Price: 9½" barrel **$79.50**

RUGER SUPER SINGLE SIX CONVERTIBLE REVOLVER
Same as the Single Six except: frame with intergral ribs, which protect the adj. rear sight, similar to the Blackhawk; blade front sight on ramp base. 5½" or 6½" bbl.
With extra 22 Magnum cylinder in cloth pouch **$78.00**

RUGER 357 or 41 MAGNUM BLACKHAWK REVOLVER
Caliber: 41 or 357 Magnum, 6 shot.
Barrel: 4⅝" or 6½" (6-groove, 20", 41; 8-groove, 16" twist 357 twist).
Length: 12⅛" (6½" bbl.). **Weight:** 40 oz. (6½" bbl.).
Stocks: Smooth genuine walnut.
Sights: Ramp front ⅛", micro click rear adj. for w. and e.
Features: Coil springs throughout, flat-top frame, long sight radius, floating alloy firing pin in frame. Solid frame.
Price: Blued **$99.50**
Also available with brass dragoon-style grip frame, wide trigger . **$115.00**

RUGER 357 MAGNUM—9MM CONVERTIBLE BLACK-HAWK
Same as the 357 Magnum except furnished with interchangeable cylinders for 9mm Parabellum and 357 Magnum cartridges **110.00**
9mm cylinder, fitted to your 357 Blackhawk **16.00**
Also available with Dragoon-style grip frame and wide trigger . **$115.00**

U.S. HANDGUNS—SINGLE ACTION REVOLVERS

RUGER 30 CARBINE BLACKHAWK REVOLVER
Same as the 44 Magnum except fluted cylinder, round back trigger guard, weight 44 oz., 13⅛" over-all. Blued only **$99.50**

RUGER SUPER BLACKHAWK 44 MAGNUM REVOLVER
Caliber: 44 Magnum, 6 shot. Also fires 44 Spec.
Barrel: 7½" (6-groove 20" twist).
Length: 13⅜" over-all. **Weight:** 48 oz.
Stocks: Smooth genuine walnut.
Features: Large grip solid frame of steel; square-back guard; flat top-strap; non-fluted cylinder; wide, serrated trigger; wide-spur hammer.
Price: **$125.00**

RUGER 45/45 ACP CONVERTIBLE BLACKHAWK
Caliber: 45 Colt, 6-shot.
Barrel: 4⅝" or 7½" (6-groove, 10" twist).
Length: 13½" (7½" bbl.). **Weight:** 40 oz. (7½" bbl.).
Stock: Smooth walnut.
Sights: Ramp front ⅛", micro click adj. for w. and e.
Features: Same as 44 Magnum. Convertible furnished with interchangeable cylinder for 45 ACP.
Price: Blued (45 Colt) **$99.50**
Convertible **$110.00**
Also available with solid brass dragoon-style grip frame and wide trigger **$115.00**

U.S. HANDGUNS—MISCELLANEOUS

MBA GYROJET PISTOL
Caliber: 12 mm, 6-shot magazine.
Barrel: 8¼".
Length: 9¾" over-all. **Weight:** 16 oz.
Stocks: Walnut, smooth.
Sights: Fixed. Post front, square notch rear.
Features: Semi-automatic, fires rocket projectile instead of conventional cartridge.
Price: **$99.00**

MERRILL SPORTSMAN'S SINGLE SHOT
Caliber: 22 S, L, LR, 22WMR, 22WRF, 22 Rem. Jet, 22 Hornet, K-Hornet, 357, 38 Spl., 256 Win. Mag., 45 Colt/410 (3").
Barrel: 9" hinged type break-open. Semi-octagon.
Length: 10½". **Weight:** 54 oz.
Stocks: Smooth walnut with thumb & heel rest.
Sights: Front 125" blade, square notch rear adj. for w. & e.
Features: .355" rib on top, grooved for scope mounts, auto. safety, cocking indicator, hammerless.
Price: **$129.50**
Price: Extra bbls. .... **$35.00**   Wrist rest attachment **7.95**

THOMPSON-CENTER ARMS CONTENDER
Caliber: 17 Bumblebee, 17 Ackley-Bee, 17 Hornet, 17 K Hornet, 17 Mach IV, 22 S, L, LR, 22 WMR, 22 Rem. Jet, 22 Hornet, 22 K Hornet, 256 Win., 9mm Parabellum, 38 Super, 357/44 B & D, 38 Spl., 357 Mag., also 222 Rem., 30 M1, 45 ACP, 44 Mag. 5mm Rem., 45 Long Colt.
Barrel: 8¾", 10", tapered octagon. Single shot.
Length: 13¼" (10" bbl.). **Weight:** 43 oz. (10" bbl.).
Stocks: Select checkered walnut grip and fore-end, with thumb rest. Right or left hand.
Sights: Under cut blade ramp front, rear adj. for w. & e.
Features: Break open action with auto-safety. Single action only. Interchangeable bbls., both caliber (rim & center fire), and length. Grooved for scope. Engraved frame.
Price: Blued (rimfire Cals.) **$135.00**
Price: Blued (centerfire Cals.) **$144.00**
Price: Extra bbls. (Rimfire) . **$36.00**   Extra bbls. (centerfire) ... **$45.00**
Price: Bushnell Phantom scope base **$5.00**
Fitted walnut case **29.50**

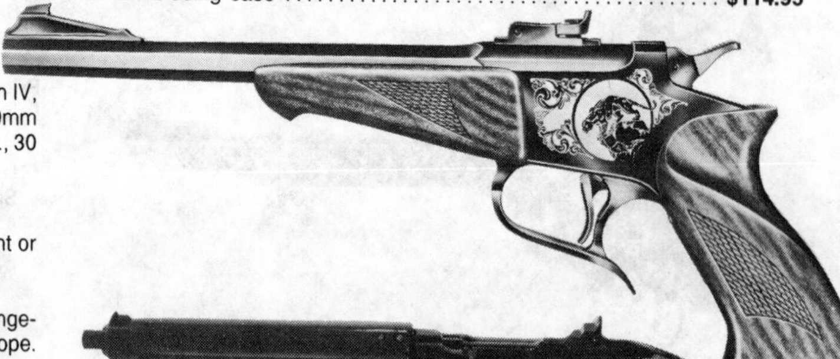

ELECTROARM FREE PISTOL
Caliber: 22 LR (bolt action, single shot).
Barrel: 9¼".
Length: 15¾". **Weight:** 50 oz.
Stock: Wood, wrap-around style, custom fitted.
Sights: Undercut blade front, fully adj. rear.
Features: Electro-mechanical sear assembly with total lock time of 3.8 milliseconds. Dual firing pins, sealed firing mechanism. Power supply is camera-type 15 volt DC battery. Trigger pull adj. from 3 to 15 grams or ½ to 3 ounces.
Price: Custom model (matte blue) **$550.00**
Price: Presentation grade (high luster blue, walnut case) **$750.00**

REMINGTON XP-100 Bolt Action Pistol
Caliber: 221 Fireball, single shot.
Barrel: 10½ inches, ventilated rib.
Length: 16¾ inches. **Weight:** 60 oz.
Stocks: Brown nylon one-piece, checkered grip with white spacers.
Features: Fits left or right hand, is shaped to fit fingers and heel of hand. Grooved trigger. Rotating thumb safety, cavity in fore-end permits insertion of up to five 38 cal., 130-gr. metal jacketed bullets to adjust weight and balance. Included is a black vinyl, zippered case.
Sights: Fixed front, rear adj. for w. and e. Tapped for scope mount.
Price: Including case **$114.95**

UNIVERSAL ENFORCER AUTO CARBINE
Caliber: 30 M1 Carbine, 30-shot magazine.
Barrel: 10¼" with 12-groove rifling.
Length: 17¾". **Weight:** 4 ½ lbs.
Stocks: American walnut with handguard.
Features: Uses surplus 5- or 15-shot magazine. 4½-6 lb. trigger pull.
Sights: Gold bead ramp front. Peep rear adj. for w. and e. 14" sight radius.
Price: Blue finish **$134.95**
Price: Nickel plated finish **$159.95**
Price: Gold plated finish **$184.95**

U.S. CENTERFIRE RIFLES—LEVER ACTION

BROWNING BLR LEVER ACTION RIFLE
Caliber: 243 or 308 Win. 4-shot detachable mag.
Barrel: 20" round tapered.
Weight: 6 lbs. 15 oz. **Length:** 39¾" over-all.
Stock: Checkered straight grip and fore-end, oil finished walnut (13¾"x1¾"x2⅜").
Sights: Square notch adj. rear, gold bead on hooded ramp front.
Features: Wide, grooved trigger; half-cock hammer safety. Receiver tapped for scope mount. Recoil pad installed.
Price: $174.50

MARLIN 336T LEVER ACTION CARBINE
Same as the 336C except: straight stock; cal. 30-30 only. Brass saddle ring, squared finger lever. .... $115.00.

MARLIN 336C LEVER ACTION CARBINE
Caliber: 30-30 or 35 Rem., 6-shot tubular magazine
Barrel: 20" Micro-Groove
Weight: 7 lbs. **Length:** 38½"
Stock: Select American walnut, capped p.g. with white line spacers.
Sights: Bead ramp front, semi-buckhorn rear adj. for w. & e.
Features: Gold plated trigger, receiver tapped for scope mount, offset hammer spur, top of receiver sand blasted to prevent glare.
Price: $115.00

MARLIN 444 LEVER ACTION RIFLE
Same as the 444 Carbine except: Straight grip stock; 24" barrel; squared finger lever. $145.00

MARLIN 444 LEVER ACTION SPORTER
Caliber: 444 Marlin, 4-shot tubular magazine
Barrel: 22" Micro-Groove
Weight: 7½ lbs. **Length:** 40½"
Stock: American walnut, capped p.g. with white line spacers, recoil pad.
Sights: Bead front, folding leaf rear adj. for w. & e.
Features: Gold plated trigger, receiver tapped for scope mount, offset hammer spur, leather sling with detachable swivels.
Price: $145.00

MARLIN GLENFIELD 30A LEVER ACTION CARBINE
Same as the Marlin 336C except: checkered walnut finished hardwood p.g. stock, 30-30 only 6-shot. $105.00

MARLIN 1894 LEVER ACTION CARBINE
Caliber: 44 Magnum, 10 shot tubular magazine
Barrel: 20" Micro-Groove
Weight: 6 lbs. **Length:** 37½"
Stock: American walnut, straight grip and fore-end.
Sights: Bead ramp front, semi-buckhorn rear adj. for w. & e.
Features: Gold plated trigger, receiver tapped for scope mount, offset hammer spur, solid top receiver sand blasted to prevent glare.
Price: $115.00

MARLIN 1895 LEVER ACTION RIFLE
Caliber: 45-70, 4-shot tubular magazine.
Barrel: 22" round.
Weight: 7 lbs. **Length:** 40½".
Stock: American walnut, straight p.g.
Sights: Bead front, semi-buckhorn rear adj. for w. and e.
Features: Solid receiver tapped for scope mounts or receiver sights, offset hammer spur.
Price: $185.00

MARLIN ZANE GREY CENTURY
Caliber: 30-30, 6-shot tubular magazine.
Barrel: 22" fully tapered octagon.
Weight: 7 lbs. **Length:** 40½".
Stock: American walnut, p.g.
Sights: Bead front, semi-buckhorn rear adj. for w. and e.
Features: Curved brass buttplate, brass fore-end cap, Zane Grey medallion, gold-plated trigger, offset hammer, receiver tapped for scope mount.
Price: $150.00

SAVAGE 99A LEVER ACTION RIFLE

Same as the 99E except: straight-grip walnut stock with schnabel fore-end, top tang safety. Folding leaf rear sight. Available in 250-300 (250 Savage) 300 Savage, 243 or 308 Win. **$159.95**

SAVAGE 99E LEVER ACTION RIFLE

Caliber: 300 Savage, 243 or 308 Win., 5-shot rotary magazine.
Barrel: 20" Chrome-moly steel.
Weight: 7 lbs. **Length:** 39¾" over-all.
Stock: Walnut finished with checkered p.g. and fore-end (13½x1½x2½).
Sights: Ramp front with step adj. sporting rear. Tapped for scope mounts.
Features: Grooved trigger, slide safety locks trigger and lever.
Price: **$135.95**

SAVAGE 99F LIGHTWEIGHT CARBINE

Same as 99E except: 22" lightweight bbl. Mag. indicator on left side. Select walnut stock with checkered p.g. and fore-end, aluminum buttplate. Wgt. 6½ lbs., 41¾" over-all. Cals. 300 Sav., 243 and 308 Win. **$154.95**

SAVAGE 99C LEVER ACTION CLIP RIFLE

Similar to M99F except: Detachable staggered clip magazine with push-button ejection (4-shot capacity: 3 in 284). Wgt. about 6¾ lbs., 41¾" over-all with 22" bbl. Cals. 243, 284, 308 .... **$164.95**

SAVAGE 99DL CARBINE

Same as 99F except: High comb Monte Carlo stock; anodized aluminum buttplate; slim fore-end; sling swivels. Wgt. 6¾ lbs., 41¾" over-all. Cals: 243 and 308 Win. **$169.95**

SEARS MODEL 100 LEVER ACTION CARBINE

Caliber: 30-30 only. 6-shot tubular mag.
Barrel: 20"
Weight: 6½ lbs. **Length:** 38" over-all.
Stock: Walnut finished hardwood straight grip stock.
Sights: Bead front sight on ramp; open notch rear adj. for w. only.
Features: Half-cock hammer safety. Solid frame receiver is tapped for scope mounts. Sears version of the Winchester 94.
Price: **$88.00**

WESTERN FIELD COMMEMORATIVE 72

Same as Standard Model except: Select walnut stock and fore-end, hand checkered p.g. and fore-end. Gold plated trigger and bbl. band. Gold filled "deer" scenes on receiver sides, brass commemorative medallion imbedded in stock.
Price: **$140.00**

WESTERN FIELD 72 LEVER ACTION CARBINE

Caliber: 30-30, 6-shot magazine.
Barrel: 20".
Weight: 7½ lbs. **Length:** 38½" over-all.
Stock: Walnut, fluted comb, p.g., rubber buttplate and p.g. cap with white spacers.
Sights: Ramp front, rear adj. for e.
Features: Trigger moves with lever on opening, hammer-block safety. Gold plated trigger. Solid top receiver with side ejection.
Price: Standard Model **$94.99**
With 2½x-7x scope and See Through mount **$124.00**

WINCHESTER 88 LEVER ACTION RIFLE

Caliber: 243 Win., 284 Win., (10" twist), 308 Win., (12" twist). 4-shot detachable mag.
Barrel: 22" round bbl.
Weight: 7¼ lbs. **Length:** 42½" over-all
Stock: One-piece basket-weave checkered p.g. stock (13¾"x1½"x2⅝").
Sights: Bead front sight on ramp, with cover; folding leaf rear.
Features: Hammerless, rotating 3-lug bolt. Side ejection, cross-bolt safety.
Price: **$164.95**

WINCHESTER 88 CARBINE

Similar to 88 rifle. Same stock dimensions. No checkering, bbl. band on fore-end. 39½" over-all, bbl. 19". 7 lbs., (not available in 284). . **$154.95**
Extra 4-shot mag. **$5.50**

U.S. CENTERFIRE RIFLES—LEVER ACTION

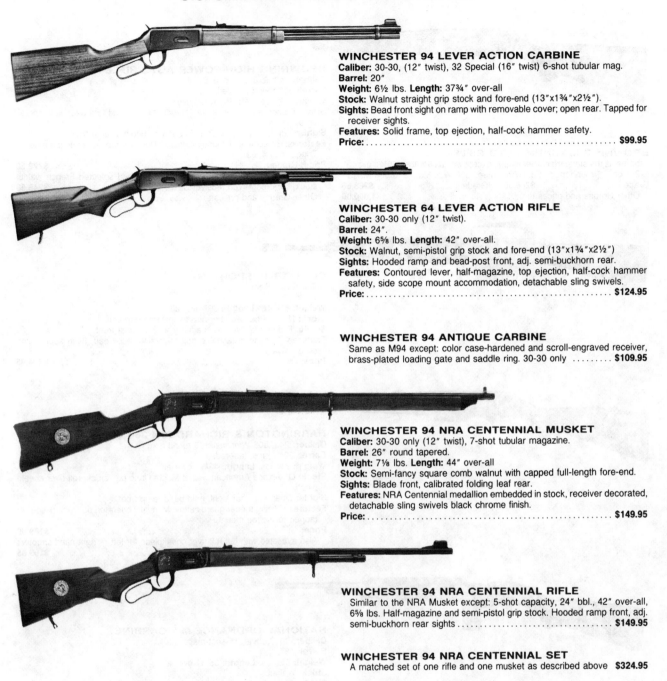

WINCHESTER 94 LEVER ACTION CARBINE
Caliber: 30-30, (12″ twist), 32 Special (16″ twist) 6-shot tubular mag.
Barrel: 20″
Weight: 6½ lbs. **Length:** 37¾″ over-all
Stock: Walnut straight grip stock and fore-end (13″x1¾″x2½″).
Sights: Bead front sight on ramp with removable cover; open rear. Tapped for receiver sights.
Features: Solid frame, top ejection, half-cock hammer safety.
Price: **$99.95**

WINCHESTER 64 LEVER ACTION RIFLE
Caliber: 30-30 only (12″ twist).
Barrel: 24″.
Weight: 6⅝ lbs. **Length:** 42″ over-all.
Stock: Walnut, semi-pistol grip stock and fore-end (13″x1¾″x2½″)
Sights: Hooded ramp and bead-post front, adj. semi-buckhorn rear.
Features: Contoured lever, half-magazine, top ejection, half-cock hammer safety, side scope mount accommodation, detachable sling swivels.
Price: **$124.95**

WINCHESTER 94 ANTIQUE CARBINE
Same as M94 except: color case-hardened and scroll-engraved receiver, brass-plated loading gate and saddle ring. 30-30 only **$109.95**

WINCHESTER 94 NRA CENTENNIAL MUSKET
Caliber: 30-30 only (12″ twist), 7-shot tubular magazine.
Barrel: 26″ round tapered.
Weight: 7⅛ lbs. **Length:** 44″ over-all
Stock: Semi-fancy square comb walnut with capped full-length fore-end.
Sights: Blade front, calibrated folding leaf rear.
Features: NRA Centennial medallion embedded in stock, receiver decorated, detachable sling swivels black chrome finish.
Price: **$149.95**

WINCHESTER 94 NRA CENTENNIAL RIFLE
Similar to the NRA Musket except: 5-shot capacity, 24″ bbl., 42″ over-all, 6⅝ lbs. Half-magazine and semi-pistol grip stock. Hooded ramp front, adj. semi-buckhorn rear sights **$149.95**

WINCHESTER 94 NRA CENTENNIAL SET
A matched set of one rifle and one musket as described above **$324.95**

U.S. CENTERFIRE RIFLES—AUTOLOADING

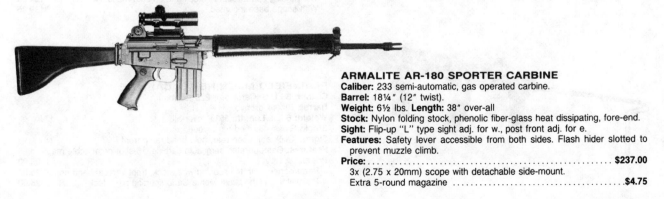

ARMALITE AR-180 SPORTER CARBINE
Caliber: 233 semi-automatic, gas operated carbine.
Barrel: 18¼″ (12″ twist).
Weight: 6½ lbs. **Length:** 38″ over-all
Stock: Nylon folding stock, phenolic fiber-glass heat dissipating, fore-end.
Sight: Flip-up "L" type sight adj. for w., post front adj. for e.
Features: Safety lever accessible from both sides. Flash hider slotted to prevent muzzle climb.
Price: **$237.00**
3x (2.75 x 20mm) scope with detachable side-mount.
Extra 5-round magazine **$4.75**

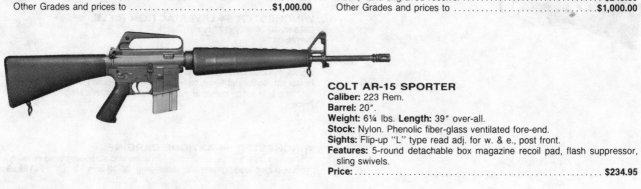

BROWNING HIGH-POWER AUTO RIFLE
Caliber: 243, 270, 30-06, 308.
Barrel: 22" round tapered.
Weight: 7⅜ lbs. **Length:** 43½" over-all.
Stock: French walnut p.g. stock (13⅝"x2"x1⅝") and fore-end, hand checkered.
Sights: Adj. folding-leaf rear, gold bead on hooded ramp front.
Features: Detachable 4-round magazine. Receiver tapped for scope mounts. Trigger pull 4 lbs.
Price: Grade I **$229.50**
Grade II. Same as Grade I except hand-rubbed selected French walnut stock, hand engraved receiver **$249.50**
Other Grades and prices to **$1,000.00**

BROWNING MAGNUM AUTO RIFLE
Same as the standard caliber model, except weighs 8½ lbs., 45¼" over-all 24" bbl., 3-round mag., Cals. 7mm Mag., 300 Win. Mag. and 338 Mag.
Grade I .... **$248.50**   Grade II **$268.50**
Other Grades and prices to **$1,000.00**

COLT AR-15 SPORTER
Caliber: 223 Rem.
Barrel: 20".
Weight: 6¼ lbs. **Length:** 39" over-all.
Stock: Nylon. Phenolic fiber-glass ventilated fore-end.
Sights: Flip-up "L" type read adj. for w. & e., post front.
Features: 5-round detachable box magazine recoil pad, flash suppressor, sling swivels.
Price: **$234.95**

HARRINGTON & RICHARDSON 360 ULTRA AUTO
Caliber: 243, 308 Winchester. 3 round mag.
Barrel: 22" round, tapered.
Weight: 7½ lbs. **Length:** 43½" over-all.
Stock: One-piece American walnut Monte Carlo p.g. stock, roll-over cheekpiece.
Sights: Open adj. rear sight, gold bead ramp front.
Features: Sliding trigger guard safety. Manually operated bolt stop. Receiver tapped for scope mount.
Price: **$189.00**
Also available with full roll-over cheekpiece for left or right hand shooters as Model 361 .... **$199.95**

NATIONAL ORDNANCE M-1 CARBINE
Caliber: 30 Carbine, 15-shot magazine.
Barrel: 18".
Weight: 5½ lbs. **Length:** 35½" over-all.
Stock: Walnut.
Sights: Blade front, rear adj. for w. and e.
Features: Gas operated, cross lock safety, hammerless, military style.
Price: **$89.95**
With scope base mounted **$99.95**
With folding "paratrooper" stock and 30-shot magazine **$124.95**
With scope base mounted **$139.95**

PLAINFIELD MACHINE CO. CARBINE
Caliber: 30 U.S. Carbine or 223 (5.7mm)
Barrel: 18" six-groove.
Weight: 6 lbs. **Length:** 35½" over-all.
Stock: Glossy finished hard wood.
Sights: Click adj. open rear, gold bead ramp front.
Features: Gas operated semi-auto carbine. 15-shot detachable magazine.
Price: **$105.00**
Paratrooper. With telescoping wire stock, front vertical hand grip **$125.00**
Plainfielder. With walnut Monte Carlo sporting p.g. stock **$125.00**

U.S. CENTERFIRE RIFLES—AUTOLOADING

PJK M-68 CARBINE
Caliber: 9mm Luger, 30-shot magazine.
Barrel: 16³⁄₁₆″.
Weight: 7 lbs. **Length:** 27″.
Stock: Black plastic.
Sights: Blade front, aperature rear adj. for e.
Features: Straight blowback operation, cross-bolt safety, removeable flash hider. Semi-automatic only.
Price: **$149.00**

REMINGTON 742 WOODMASTER AUTO RIFLE
Caliber: 243 Win., 6mm Rem., 280 Rem., 308 Win. and 30-06.
Barrel: 22″ round tapered.
Weight: 7½ lbs. **Length:** 42″ over-all
Stock: Walnut (13¼″x1⅝″x2¼″) deluxe checkered p.g. and fore-end.
Sights: Gold bead front sight on ramp; step rear sight with windage adj.
Features: Positive cross-bolt safety. Receiver tapped for scope mount. 4-shot clip mag.
Price: **$179.95**
   Extra 4-shot clip magazine **$5.25**
   Sling strap and swivels (installed) **$9.10**
   Peerless (D) and Premier (F) grades . . . . **$595.00 and $1295.00**
   Premier with gold inlays **$2000.00**
   Model 742 in foam lined case (30-06 & 308) **$199.95**

REMINGTON 742 BDL WOODSMASTER
Same as 742 except: "stepped" receiver, Monte Carlo with cheekpiece (right or left), whiteline spacers, basket-weave checkering on p.g. and fore-end, black fore-end tip, RKW finish (13⁵⁄₁₆″x1⅝″x1¹³⁄₁₆″x2½″). Cals. 30-06, 308 . . . . **$199.95**

REMINGTON 742 CARBINE
Same as M742 except: 18½″ bbl., 38½″ over-all, wgt. 6¾ lbs. Cals: 30-06, 308 Win. **$179.95**

RUGER 44 AUTOLOADING CARBINE
Caliber: 44 Magnum, 4-shot tubular magazine.
Barrel: 18½″ round tapered.
Weight: 5¾ lbs. **Length:** 36¾″ over-all
Stock: One-piece walnut p.g. stock (13⅜″x1⅝″x2¼″)
Sights: ¹⁄₁₆″ gold bead front, folding leaf rear sights.
Features: Wide, curved trigger. Sliding cross-bolt safety. Receiver tapped for scope mount.
Price: **$117.00**

UNIVERSAL 1000 AUTOLOADING CARBINE
Caliber: 30 M1, 5-shot magazine.
Barrel: 18″
Weight: 5½ lbs. **Length:** 35½″ over-all
Stock: Walnut stock inletted for "issue" sling and oiler;
Sights: Blade front aperture rear. With protective wings, adj.
Features: Gas operated, hammerless. Cross lock safety. Receiver tapped for scope mounts.
Price: **$112.50**

UNIVERSAL MODEL 1005 CARBINE
Same as Model 1000 except: Select American walnut Monte Carlo stock, no sling swivels. Blue **$124.95**

UNIVERSAL MODEL 1002 CARBINE
Same as Model 1000 except: Military type with metal handguard. Blue
Price: **$112.50**

WINCHESTER 100 AUTOLOADING CARBINE
Similar to 100 Autoloading rifle, with same stock dimensions. No checkering. Bbl. band on fore-end 39½″ over-all. Bbl. 19″. Wgt. 7 lbs. Cals. 243 (10″ twist) and 308 (12″ twist) **$164.95**
Extra magazine **$5.50**

WINCHESTER 100 AUTOLOADING RIFLE
Caliber: 243, 284 (10″ twist), and 308 (12″ twist).
Barrel: 22″ round, tapered.
Weight: 7¼ lbs. **Length:** 42½″ over-all
Stock: One piece walnut p.g. stock (13¾″x1½″x2⅝″), semi-beavertail fore-end, basketweave checkered.
Sights: Bead front and folding-leaf rear sights.
Features: Detachable box magazine. Sling swivels installed.
Price: **$174.95**

U.S. CENTERFIRE RIFLES—SLIDE ACTION

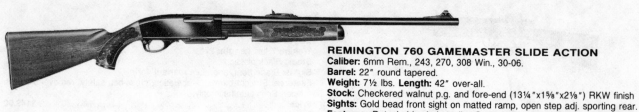

REMINGTON 760 GAMEMASTER SLIDE ACTION
Caliber: 6mm Rem., 243, 270, 308 Win., 30-06.
Barrel: 22" round tapered.
Weight: 7½ lbs. **Length:** 42" over-all.
Stock: Checkered walnut p.g. and fore-end (13¼"x1⅝"x2⅛") RKW finish
Sights: Gold bead front sight on matted ramp, open step adj. sporting rear.
Features: Detachable 4-shot clip. Cross-bolt safety. Receiver tapped for scope mount.
Price: **$154.95**
   Sling strap and swivels (installed) **$9.10**
   Extra 4-shot clip **$4.50**

REMINGTON 760 BDL GAMEMASTER
Same as 760 except: "stepped receiver," Monte Carlo stock with cheek-piece (right or left), whiteline spacer, basket-weave checkering on p.g. and fore-end, black fore-end tip, RKW finish. (13⁵/₁₆"x1⅝"x1¹³/₁₆"x2½"). Cals. 270, 30-60, 308 .... **$174.95**

REMINGTON 760 GAMEMASTER CARBINE
Same as M760 except has 18½" barrel. Wgt. 7¼ lbs., 38½" over-all. Cals: 308 Win. and 30-60 .... **$154.95**
Also in Peerless (D) and Premier (F) grades ..... **$595.00** and **$1295.00**
(F), with gold inlay **$2000.00**

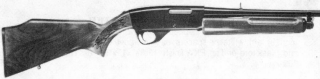

SAVAGE MODEL 170 SLIDE ACTION
Caliber: 30-30 only. 3-shot mag.
Barrel: 22" round tapered.
Weight: 6¾ lbs. **Length:** 41½" over-all.
Stock: Walnut (14"x1½"x2½"), with checkered p.g. Hard rubber buttplate.
Sights: Gold bead ramp front, folding-leaf rear.
Features: Hammerless, solid frame tapped for scope mount. Top tang safety.
Price: **$99.95**

U.S. CENTERFIRE RIFLES—BOLT ACTION

ACKLEY BOLT ACTION RIFLE
Caliber: 243, 6mm Rem., 22-250, 25-06, 257 Rob., 270, 7x57, 30-06, (4-shot mag.), 7mm Rem. Mag., 300 Win. Mag. (3-shot mag.).
Barrel: 24".
Weight: 7¼-7¾ lbs. **Length:** 43" over-all.
Stock: Walnut, rubber recoil pad with white line spacer. Hand checkered at p.g. and fore-end, swivel studs furnished.
Sights: None furnished.
Features: Ackley barrel, hinged floorplate, fully adj. trigger, Mark X Mauser action, side safety. Receiver drilled and tapped for mounts.
Price: Standard grade .... **$194.95**   Standard grade, mag. cal . **$199.95**
   Olympus grade (add $10 for mag. cals.) **$219.95**
   Olympus II grade (add $10 for mag. cals.) **$259.95**
   Varmint special: Same as Standard except: Varmint stock, 26" bbl., weight 9½ lbs., also available in 220 Swift **$279.95**

AMERICAN FIREARMS STAINLESS RIFLE
Caliber: 22-250, 243, 6mm Rem., 6mm Win. Mag., 25-06, 257 Win. Mag., 264 Win. Mag., 6.5 Rem. Mag., 6.5x55, 270 Win., 270 Win. Mag., 284 Win., 7x57, 7mm Rem. Mag. 7.62x39, 308 Win., 30-06, 300 Win. Mag., 338 Win. Mag., 458 Mag.
Barrel: 16½", 18", 20", 22", 24", 26" or 28".
Weight: 6½ to 11 lbs. **Length:** 44½" (24" bbl.)
Stock: Walnut, maple, laminated combinations. Handcheckered (13⅜"x1⅜"x2⅜" standard).
Sights: None furnished (drilled & tapped for scope mounts).
Features: Side safety, hinged floorplate, adjustable trigger. Made entirely of stainless steel. Blue or satin stainless steel.
Price: Grade I (Presentation) **$895.00**
   Grade II (Deluxe) **$595.00**
   Grade III (Standard) **$395.00**
   Grade IV (Standard 338 & 458 Mag.) **$550.00**

U.S. CENTERFIRE RIFLES—BOLT ACTION

BROWNING HIGH POWER RIFLE
Caliber: 222, 222 Mag., 22-250, 284, 243, 308, 270, 30-06, 7mm Rem. Mag., 300 Win. Mag., 308 Norma, 338 Win. Mag. 375 H&H, 458 Win. Mag.
Barrel: 22" standard, 24" Magnum.
Weight: 6⅛ to 8¼ lbs. **Length:** 43"
Stock: Checkered walnut p.g. with Monte Carlo (13⅝"x1⅝"x2⅜").
Sights: Hooded ramp front, removable adj. folding-leaf rear; except none on 458.
Features: 3-position side safety, hinged floorplate, receiver tapped for scope mount.
Price: Safari Grade .... **$276.50** to **$306.50**
 Medallion Grade .... **$460.00** to **$475.00**
 Olympian Grade .... **$720.00** to **$785.00**

CHAMPLIN RIFLE
Caliber: 270, 30-06, 7mm Rem. and 300 Win. Mag.
Barrel: 24" either round or octagon.
Weight: About 8 lbs. **Length:** 50-52"
Stock: Hand inletted oil finished select Claro walnut with Monte Carlo, ebony fore-end tip, steel p.g. cap.
Sights: 3-leaf folding rear, bead on ramp front.
Features: Available in most standard chamberings, many options to customer specifications at additional cost.
Price: **$890.00**

84 CLASSIC RIFLE
 Same as Lobo model except: Conventional stock design, weight is 7¼ lbs. Standard: **$320.00**; Grade 1: **$425.00**; Grade 2: **$675.00**; Grade 3: **$1405.00**; Grade 4: **$2950.00**.

84 PENNSY RIFLE
Caliber: All standard calibers from 17 Rem. to 460.
Barrel: 24".
Weight: 7¾ lbs. **Length:** 44½" over-all.
Stock: Walnut, contrasting p.g. cap and fore-end tip. Hand checkered.
Sights: None furnished.
Features: Sako action, Star Premium grade bbl., rubber recoil pad, sling studs, beaver tail fore-end, roll over cheek piece. "Ultra Modern" stock design.

Price: Standard grade	**$340.00**	Grade 1	**$445.00**
Grade 2	**$715.00**	Grade 3	**$1425.00**
Grade 4	**$2970.00**		

84 LOBO RIFLE
 Same as Pennsy model except: Less radical stock design, slimmer fore-end and p.g. Weight is 7¼ lbs. Standard: **$330.00**; Grade 1: **$435.00**; Grade 2: **$685.00**; Grade 3: **$1415.00**; Grade 4: **$2960.00**.

FAJEN ACRA RIFLE S-24
Caliber: 270, 30-06, 243, 308, 284, 22-250, 6mm., 25-06, 7x57, 257 Rob., 7mm Rem. Mag., 308 Norma Mag. 300 Win. Mag., 264 Win. Mag.
Barrel: 24".
Weight: 7½ lbs. **Length:** 45" over-all.
Stock: Walnut Monte Carlo, checkered p.g. and fore-end, recoil pad with white line spacer.
Sights: None furnished.
Features: Stock is glass bedded in recoil areas, hand fitted, skip-line checkering, blue finish, rosewood p.g. cap and fore-end tip. Uses Santa Barbara Mauser action.
Price: Standard cals. ..... **$169.95**   Magnum cals. **$179.95**

FAJEN ACRA M-18 RIFLE
 Same as S-24 except: Full length Mannlicker stock, 18" barrel, over-all length is 39". Not available in magnum calibers.
Price: **$189.95**

FAJEN ACRA RIFLE MODEL RA
 Same as S-24 except: Standard checkering, fitted with Tenite buttplate and p.g. cap, no fore-end tip. Standard cals. **$119.95**; Magnum cals. **$129.95**.

FAJEN ACRA VARMINT RIFLE
 Same as S-24 except: Varmint version, 26" heavy barrel, weight is 9¾" lbs. over-all length 47".
Price: Standard calibers .. **$199.50**   Magnum calibers **$209.50**

HARRINGTON & RICHARDSON 300 BOLT ACTION
Caliber: 22-250, 243, 270, 308, 30-06 (5-shot), 7mm Rem. Mag., 300 Win. Mag. (3-shot)
Barrel: 22" round, tapered.
Weight: 7¾ lbs. **Length:** 42½" over-all.
Stock: American walnut, hand checkered p.g. and fore-end, Monte Carlo, roll-over cheekpiece.
Sights: Adjustable rear, gold bead ramp front.
Features: Hinged floorplate; sliding side safety; sling swivels, recoil pad. Receiver tapped for scope mount.
Price: **$225.00**

U.S. CENTERFIRE RIFLES—BOLT ACTION

HARRINGTON & RICHARDSON 301 ULTRA CARBINE
Similar to M300, except: Mannlicher style stock (no roll-over cheek-piece) metal fore-end tip. 18″ bbl., 39″ over all, wgt. 7¼ lbs., not available in 22-250. . . . . **$239.00**

HARRINGTON & RICHARDSON 330 HUNTER'S RIFLE
Caliber: 243, 270, 30-06, 308, 7mm Rem. or 300 Win.
Barrel: 22″ round tapered.
Weight: 7⅛ lbs. **Length:** 42½″ over-all
Stock: Walnut with Monte Carlo and hand checkered p.g.
Sights: Gold bead on ramp front, rear adj. for w. & e.
Features: Hinged floorplate, adj. trigger, sliding side safety. Receiver tapped for scope mounts.
Price: **$140.00**

HARRINGTON & RICHARDSON 317 ULTRA WILDCAT
Caliber: 17 Rem., 222, 223 or 17/223 (handload) 6-shot magazine.
Barrel: 20″ round, tapered.
Weight: 5¼ lbs. **Length:** 38½″ over-all.
Stock: Walnut, hand polished, hand checkered capped p.g. and fore-end, with Monte Carlo.
Sights: None. Receiver dovetailed for integral scope mounts.
Features: Sliding side safety, adj. trigger.
Price: **$249.00**
Model 317P has better wood, basketweave checkering **$450.00**

HARRINGTON & RICHARDSON 370 ULTRA MEDALIST
Caliber: 22-250, 6mm Rem. and 243. 5-shot magazine.
Barrel: 24″ heavy varmint-target weight.
Weight: 9½ lbs. **Length:** 44¾″ over-all.
Stock: Oil finished walnut, full p.g. and roll-over comb; recoil pad installed.
Sights: None. Bbl. and receiver tapped for open sights and/or scope mounts.
Features: Sliding side safety, adj. trigger, sling swivels installed.
Price: **$245.00**

ITHACA LSA-55 BOLT ACTION RIFLE
Caliber: 243, 308, 22-250, 6mm Rem. 270 and 30-06.
Barrel: 23″ round tapered, full-floating.
Weight: About 6½ lbs. **Length:** 41½″ over-all
Stock: Hand checkered walnut, Monte Carlo with built-in swell on p.g.
Sights: Removable rear adj. for w. & e. ramp front.
Features: Detachable 3-shot magazine (5-shot available), adj. trigger, top tang safety. Receiver tapped for scope mounts.
Price: 243, 308, 22-250 & 6mm **$159.95**
Price: 270 & 30-06 . . . . **$174.95**

ITHACA LSA-55 DELUXE BOLT ACTION
Same as the std. except rollover cheekpiece, fore-end tip and pistol grip cap of rosewood with white spacers. Scope mount rings supplied. Sling swivels installed.
Price: 243, 308, 22-250 & 6mm **$199.95**
Price: 270 & 30-06 . . . . **$214.95**

ITHACA LSA-65 BOLT ACTION RIFLE
Same as the LSA-55 except in 25-06, 270 or 30-06 caliber (5-shot clip unavailable)
Price: **$174.95**
LSA-65 Deluxe **$214.95**

MOSSBERG 800 BOLT ACTION RIFLE
Caliber: 22-250, 243 and 308. 4-shot magazine.
Barrel: 22″ AC-KRO-GRUV round tapered.
Weight: 6½ lbs. **Length:** 42″ over-all.
Stock: Walnut, Monte Carlo, checkered p.g. and fore-end.
Sights: Gold bead ramp front, adj. folding-leaf rear.
Features: Top tang safety, hinged floorplate, 1″ sling swivels installed. Receiver tapped for scope mounts.
Price: **$115.40**

MOSSBERG 800 V/T VARMINT TARGET RIFLE
Model 800 with heavy 24″ bbl., target scope bases, no iron sights. Cals. 243 and 22-250 only. 44″ overall, wgt. about 9½ lbs. **$124.65**

MOSSBERG 800 SM SCOPED RIFLE
Same as M800 except has Mossberg M84 4x scope, but no iron sights. Wgt. 7½ lbs. **$131.70**

MOSSBERG 800 M MANNLICHER RIFLE
Same as M800 except has one piece Mannlicher style stock, flat bolt handle, 20″ bbl., 40″ over-all, weight 6½ lbs. **$129.95**

MOSSBERG 800D DELUXE RIFLE
Super grade M800 with special finish and Monte Carlo rollover-comb stock with wgt. 6¾ lbs. **$150.30**

U.S. CENTERFIRE RIFLES—BOLT ACTION

MOSSBERG 810A BOLT ACTION RIFLE
Caliber: 30-06 only, 4-shot magazine.
Barrel: 22″ AC-KRO-GRUV, straight taper.
Weight: 7½ to 8 lbs. **Length:** 42″ over-all.
Stock: Walnut Monte Carlo with checkered fore-end and capped p.g. recoil pad and sling swivels installed.
Sights: Gold bead on ramp front, folding-leaf rear.
Features: Receiver tapped for metallic sight or scope mounts. Top tang safety. Detachable box magazine.
Price: **$127.95**

MOSSBERG 810B BOLT ACTION RIFLE
Same as 810A except in 7mm Rem. Mag. only, length is 33 ″ over-all.
$154.95
810 BSM with M 84 4x scope **$173.40**

OMEGA III BOLT ACTION RIFLE
Caliber: 25-06, 270, 30-06, 7mm. Rem. Mag., 300 Win. Mag., 338 Min. Mag., 358 Norma Mag.
Barrel: 22″ or 24″.
Weight: 8¼ lbs. **Length:** 42″ over-all (24″ bbl.).
Stock: Choice of three styles: Monte Carlo, Cassic or Thumbhole Varminter in either Claro walnut, English walnut or laminated.
Sights: None furnished.
Features: Right or left hand action, octagonal bolt, square locking system with enclosed bolt face gives 50 degree lift. Rotary magazine holds five standard or four belted cartridges, dual safety, fully adj. trigger, interchangeable stock and fore-end. Firearms Development Co.
Price: Left or right-hand version **$397.50**
Extra set of stocks **$97.50**

RANGER ARMS TEXAS MAVERICK RIFLE
Caliber: 22-250, 243, 6mm Rem., 308 Win., 6.5 and 350 Rem. Mag.
Barrel: 22″ or 24″ round tapered.
Weight: 7¾ lbs. **Length:** 44″ over-all.
Stock: English or Claro walnut, Monte Carlo w/cheekpiece. Skip-line checkering rosewood p.g. and fore-end cap, recoil pad installed.
Sights: None. Receiver tapped for scope mounts.
Features: Push-button safety, adj. trigger, available in left or right hand models at same price.
Price: Governor Grade **$425.00**
Other grades and models (including thumb hole and Mannlicher types).
Prices to **$475.00**

REMINGTON 700 BDL BOLT ACTION RIFLE
Same as 700-ADL except: fleur-de-lis checkering; black fore-end tip and p.g. cap, white line spacers. Matted receiver top, quick release floorplate. Hooded ramp front sight. Q.D. swivels and 1″ sling **$174.95**
Available also in 6.5 Rem. Mag., 350 Rem. Mag., 7mm Rem. Mag., 264 and 300 Win. Mag., or 17 Rem. caliber. 44½″ over-all, weight 7½ lbs.**$189.95**
Peerless Grade . . . . **$595.00**   Premier Grade **$1295.00**

REMINGTON 700 BDL VARMINT
Same as 700 BDL, except: 24″ heavy bbl., 43½″ over-all, wgt. 9 lbs. Cals. 222, 223, 22-250, 6mm Rem., 243 and 25-06. No sights. **$189.95**

REMINGTON 700 ADL BOLT ACTION RIFLE
Caliber: 222, 22-250, 6mm Rem., 243, 25-06, 270, 7mm Rem. Mag., 308 and 30-06.
Barrel: 22″ or 24″ round tapered.
Weight: 7 lbs. **Length:** 41½″ to 43½″
Stock: Walnut, RKW finished p.g. stock with impressed checkering, Monte Carlo (13⅜″x1⅝″x2⅜″).
Sights: Gold bead ramp front; removable, step-adj. rear with windage screw.
Features: Side safety, receiver tapped for scope mounts.
Price: (except 7mm Rem. Mag.) **$154.95**
7mm Rem. Mag. **$169.95**

REMINGTON 700 SAFARI
Same as the 700 BDL except 375 H&H or 458 Win. Magnum calibers only. Hand checkered, oil finished stock with recoil pad installed. Delivery time is about five months. **$344.95**

REMINGTON 700 C CUSTOM RIFLE
Same as the 700 BDL except choice of 20″, 22″ or 24″ bbl. with or without sights. Jewelled bolt, with or without hinged floor plate. Select American walnut stock is hand checkered, rosewood fore-end & grip cap. Hand lapped barrel. 16 weeks for delivery after placing order **$345.00**
M700 C Custom Magnum **$357.00**
Optional extras: recoil pad **$12.00**, oil finish **$13.75**, left hand cheekpiece **$25.00**.

U.S. CENTERFIRE RIFLES—BOLT ACTION

REMINGTON 788 BOLT ACTION RIFLE
Caliber: 222 (5-shot), 22-250, 6mm Rem., 243, 30-30 and 308 (4-shot).
Barrel: 22″ round tapered (24″ in 222 and 22-250).
Weight: 7-7½ lbs. **Length:** 41⅝″ over-all.
Stock: Walnut finished hardwood with Monte Carlo and p.g. (13⅝″x1⅞″x2⅝″).
Sights: Blade ramp front, open rear adj. for w. & e.
Features: Detachable box magazine, thumb safety, receiver tapped for scope mounts.
Price: **$99.95**
Sling strap and swivels, installed **$5.40**
Model 788 with Universal Model UE 4x scope, mounts and rings in cals. 6mm Rem., 243 Win., 308 and 22-250 .... **$114.95**

REMINGTON 788 LEFT HAND BOLT ACTION
Same as 788 except cals. 6mm & 308 only and left hand stock and action.
Price: **$104.95**

RUGER 77 BOLT ACTION RIFLE
Caliber: 22-250, 6mm. Rem., 243 and 308 (5-shot), 284, 6.5 and 350 Rem. Mag. (3-shot)
Barrel: 22″ round tapered; (25-06 & 7mm Rem. Mag. 24″).
Weight: About 7 lbs. **Length:** 42″ over-all.
Stock: Checkered American walnut (13¾″x1⅝″x2⅛″) p.g. cap; sling swivel studs and recoil pad.
Sights: Optional gold bead ramp front and folding-leaf adj. rear or scope rings.
Features: Integral scope mount bases, hinged floorplate; fully adj. trigger, top tang safety.
Price: **$165.00**
With scope rings and metallic sights **$179.00**
Also available in 22-250 with heavy 24″ bbl., drilled and tapped for target scope blocks **$165.00**

RUGER MODEL 77 MAGNUM RIFLE
Same as the M77 except: caliber 270 or 30-06 (5-shot) with 22″ bbl. and 25-06 or 7mm Rem. Mag. (3-shot) with 24″ bbl. With either metallic sights or scope rings. **$165.00**
With both, metallic sights and scope rings. **$179.00**
Also available in 25-06 with heavy 24″ bbl., drilled and tapped for target scope blocks. **$165.00**

RUGER MODEL 77 ROUND TOP MAGNUM
Same as M77 Magnum except: Equipped with open sights, receiver is shaped and tapped to accommodate standard commercial scope mount bases.
Price: **$165.00**

SAVAGE 110E BOLT ACTION RIFLE
Caliber: 30-06 and 243, 4-shot. Also 7mm Rem. Mag., 3-shot at $15 extra.
Barrel: 20″ round tapered (7mm 24″ stainless).
Weight: 6¾ lbs. (7mm-7¾ lbs.) **Length:** 40½″ (20″ bbl.)
Stock: Walnut finished hardwood with Monte Carlo, checkered p.g. and fore-end, hard rubber buttplate.
Sights: Gold bead removable ramp front, step adj. rear.
Features: Top tang safety, receiver, tapped for peep or scope sights. Right or left hand models available.
Price: Right hand .... **$124.95**   Left hand (110EL) **$129.95**

SAVAGE 110D BOLT ACTION RIFLE
Same as 110E except: 22″ bbl. (24″ on Mag.); walnut stock; aluminum buttplate (recoil pad on mag.); folding-leaf rear sight; weight 6¾-8 lbs. Cals. 22-250, 243, 270 and 30-06. Also available in 7mm Rem. or 300 Win. Mag. at $15 extra.
Price: Right hand........ **$149.95**   Left hand. **$155.95**

SAVAGE 110C BOLT ACTION RIFLE
Same as the 110D except: Detachable box magazine. Cals. 243, 25-06, 270 and 30-06 (4-shot). Also in 7mm Rem. or 300 Win. Mag. (3-shot) at $15 extra.
Price: Right hand........ **$149.95**   Left hand. **$155.95**

SAVAGE 110 BARRELED ACTIONS
Same as used on the 110D rifles. No stock or sights. Cals. 243, 270 and 30-06. Also in 7mm Rem. and 300 Win. Mag. at $10 extra.
Price: Right hand .... **$94.00**   Left hand **$98.00**
Actions only. Write to Savage for prices.

SAVAGE 110 E/S SCOPEGUN
Standard Model 110E, caliber 30-06 factory fitted with 4x scope, rings and bases **$152.50**

U.S. CENTERFIRE RIFLES—BOLT ACTION

SAVAGE 340 CLIP REPEATER
Caliber: 222 Rem. (4-shot) and 30-30 (3-shot).
Barrel: 24″ and 22″ respectively.
Weight: About 6½ lbs. **Length:** 40″-42″
Stock: Walnut, Monte Carlo, checkered p.g. and fore-end white line spacers.
Sights: Gold bead ramp front, folding-leaf rear.
Features: Detachable clip magazine, sliding thumb safety, receiver tapped for scope mounts.
Price: **$89.95**

SAVAGE SCOPEGUN MODEL 340
Standard Model 340 equipped by factory with mounts and 4x scope **$115.50**

SEARS TED WILLIAMS MODEL 53
Caliber: 243 or 30-06. 5-shot mag.
Barrel: 22″ round tapered (10″ twist).
Weight: 6¾ lbs. **Length:** 42⅜″ over-all.
Stock: Walnut finished hardwood, Monte Carlo comb, checkered p.g. and fore-end.
Sights: Bead ramp front, semi-buckhorn folding rear.
Features: Wide serrated trigger, 3-position bolt head safety, receiver tapped for sights and scope mounts.
Price: **$139.95**

SMITH & WESSON MODEL A BOLT ACTION RIFLE
Caliber: 22-250, 243, 270, 308, 30-06, 7mm Rem. Mag., 300 Win. Mag.
Barrel: 23¾″ round tapered.
Weight: About 7 lbs. **Length:** 44¼″ over-all
Stock: European walnut, skip-line checkered p.g. & fore-end (rosewood tipped), Monte Carlo with cheekpiece
Sights: Silver bead hooded ramp front, folding-leaf rear.
Features: Sliding side safety, adj. trigger, hinged floorplate, receiver tapped for scope mounts.
Price: **$215.50**

SMITH & WESSON MODEL D & E BOLT ACTION RIFLES
Exactly like the Models C & B respectively, except: full-length fore-end Mannlicher stock.
Model D (no Monte Carlo) **$221.00**
Model E (Monte Carlo) **$225.00**

SMITH & WESSON MODEL B & C BOLT ACTION RIFLES
Same as Model A except: 20¾″ bbl. Cals. 243, 270, 308 and 30-06. Monte Carlo p.g. stock with schnabel fore-end. Weight 6.6 lbs. 41¼″ over-all. **$202.50**
Model C has straight p.g. stock (no Monte Carlo) **$192.50**

WEATHERBY MARK V BOLT ACTION RIFLE
Caliber: All Weatherby Cals., 22-250 and 30-06.
Barrel: 24″ or 26″ round tapered.
Weight: 6½-10½ lbs. (**Length:** 43¼″-46½″)
Stock: Walnut, Monte Carlo with cheekpiece, high luster finish, checkered p.g. and fore-end, recoil pad.
Sights: Optional (extra).
Features: Cocking indicator, adj. trigger, hinged floorplate, thumb safety, quick detachable sling swivels.
Price: Cals. 224 and 22-250, std. bbl. **$299.50**
With 26″ semi-target bbl. 309.50
Cals. 240, 257, 270, 7mm, 30-06 and 300 (24″ bbl.) 339.50
With 26″ No. 2 contour bbl. 349.50
Cal. 340 (26″ bbl.) 349.50
Cal. 378 (26″ bbl.) 455.00
Cal. 460 (26″ bbl.) 525.00

WEATHERBY MARK V RIFLE Left Hand
Available in all Weatherby calibers except 224 and 22-250 (and 26″ No. 2 contour 300WM). Complete left handed action; stock with cheekpiece on right side. Prices are $10 higher than right hand models except the 378 and 460WM are unchanged.

WEATHERBY VANGUARD BOLT ACTION RIFLE
Caliber: 25-06, 243, 270, 30-06 and 308 (5-shot), 264, 7mm Rem. and 300 Win. Mag. (3-shot).
Barrel: 24″ hammer forged.
Weight: 7⅞ lbs. **Length:** 44½″ over-all.
Stock: American walnut, p.g. cap and fore-end tip, hand inletted and checkered, 13½″ pull.
Sights: Optional, available at extra cost.
Features: Side safety, adj. trigger, hinged floorplate, receiver tapped for scope mounts.
Price: **$229.50**

U.S. CENTERFIRE RIFLES—BOLT ACTION

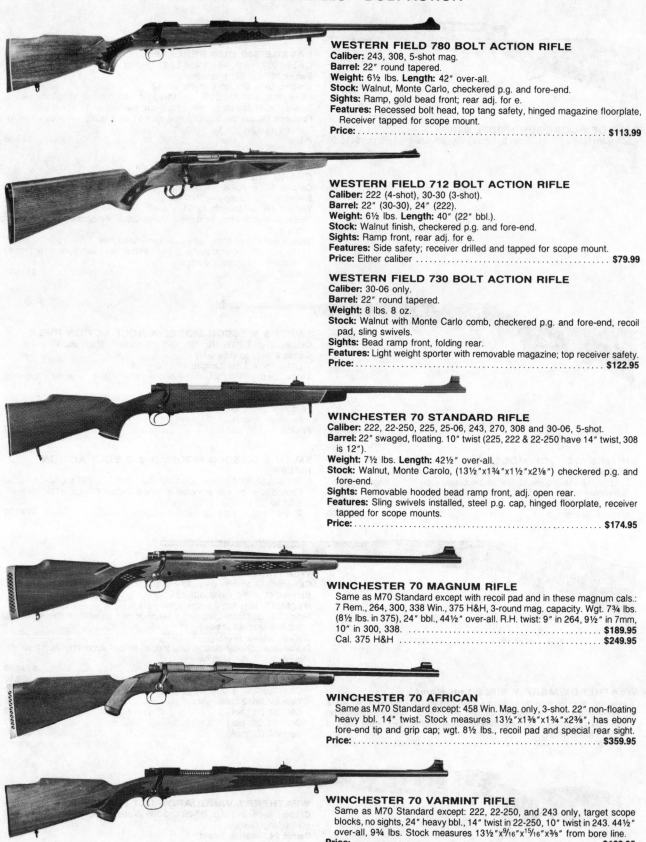

WESTERN FIELD 780 BOLT ACTION RIFLE
Caliber: 243, 308, 5-shot mag.
Barrel: 22″ round tapered.
Weight: 6½ lbs. **Length:** 42″ over-all.
Stock: Walnut, Monte Carlo, checkered p.g. and fore-end.
Sights: Ramp, gold bead front; rear adj. for e.
Features: Recessed bolt head, top tang safety, hinged magazine floorplate, Receiver tapped for scope mount.
Price: **$113.99**

WESTERN FIELD 712 BOLT ACTION RIFLE
Caliber: 222 (4-shot), 30-30 (3-shot).
Barrel: 22″ (30-30), 24″ (222).
Weight: 6½ lbs. **Length:** 40″ (22″ bbl.).
Stock: Walnut finish, checkered p.g. and fore-end.
Sights: Ramp front, rear adj. for e.
Features: Side safety; receiver drilled and tapped for scope mount.
Price: Either caliber **$79.99**

WESTERN FIELD 730 BOLT ACTION RIFLE
Caliber: 30-06 only.
Barrel: 22″ round tapered.
Weight: 8 lbs. 8 oz.
Stock: Walnut with Monte Carlo comb, checkered p.g. and fore-end, recoil pad, sling swivels.
Sights: Bead ramp front, folding rear.
Features: Light weight sporter with removable magazine; top receiver safety.
Price: **$122.95**

WINCHESTER 70 STANDARD RIFLE
Caliber: 222, 22-250, 225, 25-06, 243, 270, 308 and 30-06, 5-shot.
Barrel: 22″ swaged, floating. 10″ twist (225, 222 & 22-250 have 14″ twist, 308 is 12″).
Weight: 7½ lbs. **Length:** 42½″ over-all.
Stock: Walnut, Monte Carolo, (13½″x1¾″x1½″x2⅛″) checkered p.g. and fore-end.
Sights: Removable hooded bead ramp front, adj. open rear.
Features: Sling swivels installed, steel p.g. cap, hinged floorplate, receiver tapped for scope mounts.
Price: **$174.95**

WINCHESTER 70 MAGNUM RIFLE
Same as M70 Standard except with recoil pad and in these magnum cals.: 7 Rem., 264, 300, 338 Win., 375 H&H, 3-round mag. capacity. Wgt. 7¾ lbs. (8½ lbs. in 375), 24″ bbl., 44½″ over-all. R.H. twist: 9″ in 264, 9½″ in 7mm, 10″ in 300, 338. . . . . **$189.95**
Cal. 375 H&H **$249.95**

WINCHESTER 70 AFRICAN
Same as M70 Standard except: 458 Win. Mag. only, 3-shot. 22″ non-floating heavy bbl. 14″ twist. Stock measures 13½″x1⅜″x1¾″x2⅜″, has ebony fore-end tip and grip cap; wgt. 8½ lbs., recoil pad and special rear sight.
Price: **$359.95**

WINCHESTER 70 VARMINT RIFLE
Same as M70 Standard except: 222, 22-250, and 243 only, target scope blocks, no sights, 24″ heavy bbl., 14″ twist in 22-250, 10″ twist in 243. 44½″ over-all, 9¾ lbs. Stock measures 13½″x⁹⁄₁₆″x¹⁵⁄₁₆″x⅜″ from bore line.
Price: **$189.95**

WINCHESTER 70 TARGET RIFLE
Same as M70 except: heavy 24″ barrel, contoured aluminum handstop that fits left and right hand shooter, high comb target stock. Tapped for micrometer sights, clip slot in receiver, cals. 308 and 30-06. . . . . **$239.95**

WINCHESTER 70 MANNLICHER
Same as M70 Standard except: 19″ barrel bedded full length in Mannlicher-style stock of American walnut with Monte Carlo profile and raised cheekpiece. Length 39½″ over-all, weight about 7 lbs. Available in 243, 270, 308 Win. or 30-06. . . . . **$259.95**

WINCHESTER 70 SUPER GRADE
Same as M70 Standard except: presentation-checkered semi-fancy walnut stock, ebony p.g. cap and fore-end tip with white spacers, knurled bolt knob, non-slip rubber buttplate. Cals. 243, 270, 30-06, 300 Win. Mag. (recoil pad).
Price: **$349.95**

WINCHESTER 70 BARRELED ACTIONS
No stock, sights or scope blocks. Receivers are tapped for sights and scope mounts. Standard cals. 222, 22-250, 243, 270, 308 and 30-06. . **$128.95**
Magnum cals. 264, 300 and 338 Win., 7mm Rem. **143.95**
Varmint cals. 222, 22-250 and 243 . . . . **143.95**
Target cals. 308 and 30-06. . . . . **180.95**

WINCHESTER 70A BOLT ACTION RIFLE
Caliber: 222, 22-250, 243, 25-06, 264, 270, 7mm Rem. Mag., 30-06, 308, 300 Win Mag.
Barrel: 22″ (25-06, 264, 7mm Rem. Mag., 300 Win. Mag. have 24″).
Weight: 7⅛ to 7½ lbs. **Length:** 42½″ (22″ bbl.).
Stock: Monte Carlo, checkering at p.g. and fore-end.
Sights: Removeable hooded ramp front, adj. open rear.
Features: Sling swivels installed, three position safety, deep cut checkering.
Price: **$149.95**

WINCHESTER 70A MAGNUM RIFLE
Same as 70A except with black recoil pad and in these cals.: 264, 7mm Rem., 300 Win., 3-round mag. capacity. Wgt. 7¼ lbs., 24″ bbl., 44″″ overall. R. H. twist: 9″ in 7mm Rem., 10″ in 300 Win. **$164.95**

WINCHESTER 670 BOLT ACTION RIFLE
Caliber: 243 and 30-06, 4-shot
Barrel: 22″ full floating.
Weight: 7 lbs. **Length:** 42½″ over-all.
Stock: Monte Carlo stock (13½″x¾″x1½″x2⅛″), checkered p.g. and fore-end.
Sights: Ramp front sight and adj. open rear (both easily detachable for scope-only use).
Features: Wide serrated trigger, two position safety, red cocking indicator.
Price: **$133.95**

WINSLOW BOLT ACTION RIFLE
Caliber: All standard cartridges (magnum add $10).
Barrel: 24″ Douglas premium. (Magnums 26″)
Weight: 7-7½ lbs. **Length:** 43″ over-all.
Stock: Hand rubbed black walnut, choice of 3 styles
Sights: None. Metallics available at extra cost.
Features: Reciver tapped for scope mounts, QD swivels and recoil pad installed. 4-shot blind mag.
Price: Regal Grade **$390.00**
Regent (illus.), Regimental, Crown, Emperor and Imperial grades in ascend-order of carving, engraving and inlaying, to **$3525.00**
Regal grade Varmint in 17/222 (std or Mag.) or 17/223. Priced from**430.00**
Left hand models at $60 extra.

CLERKE SINGLE-SHOT HI-WALL RIFLE
Caliber: 222, 223, 22-250, 243, 6mm Rem., 250 Sav., 257 Rob., 25-06, 264 Win., 270, 7mm Rem. Mag., 30-30, 30-06, 300 Win., 375 H&H, 458 Win. 45-70.
Barrel: 26″ medium weight.
Stock: Walnut p.g. stock and for-end, white line spacer with black buttplate.
Sights: None furnished. Drilled and tapped.
Features: Std. model: Exposed hammer, curved finger lever, Schnabel fore-end.
Price: **$190.00**

CLERKE DELUXE-SHOT HI-WALL
Same as standard model except: Adj. trigger, features half-octagon barrel, presentation grade walnut checkered p.g. stock with cheekpiece and nickel-plated Swiss butt plate. Plain trigger. Without slot cut in bbl. for rear sight
Price: **$240.00**

H & R OFFICERS MODEL 1873
Caliber: 45-70, single shot
Barrel: 26″ round.
Weight: About 8 lbs. **Length:** 44″ over-all
Stock: Oil finished walnut, checkered at wrist and fore-end white metal tipped.
Sights: Blade front, vernier tang rear adj. for w. & e.
Features: Replica of the 1873 Springfield has engraved breech black, side lock and hammer. Each comes with commemorative plaque.
Price: **$260.00**

FETTERHOFF MODEL 72 ROLLING BLOCK
Caliber: 22 LR, 22 WMR, 22 Rem. Jet, 218 Bee, 22 Hornet, 221 Rem., 222 Rem., 223 Rem., 32-20, 30 Carbine, 30-30, 38 S & W, 357 Mag., 44-40, 44 Mag.
Barrel: Full octagon, 20″, 22″ or 24″.
Weight: 6½ lbs. **Length:** 35″ over-all (20″ bbl.).
Stock: Walnut stock and fore-end, steel buttplate.
Sights: Post front, leaf rear.
Features: Rolling block action, blue finish. Options include tang peep sight, sling swivels, sling
Price: 22 LR and 22 Mag. . **$56.50**   All other calibers **$58.50**

H & R CAVALRY MODEL CARBINE
Caliber: 45-70, single shot.
Barrel: 22″.
Weight: 7 lbs. **Length:** 41″.
Stock: American walnut with saddle ring and bridle.
Sights: Blade front, barrel mounted leaf rear adj. for e.
Features: Replica of the 1871 Springfield Carbine. Blue-black finish.
Price: **$150.00**
Deluxe version (shown) has engraved breech block, side lock and hammer
. . . . **$200.00**
Springfield Armory Museum silver plated carbine **$1,000.00**

HARRINGTON & RICHARDSON L.B.H. COMMEMORATIVE CARBINE
Caliber: 45-70, single shot.
Barrel: 22″.
Weight: 7¼ lbs. **Length:** 41″.
Stock: American walnut with metal grip adapter.
Sights: Blade front, tang mounted aperature rear adj. for w. and e.
Features: Replica of the 1871 Springfield carbine. Engraved breech block, side lock and hammer. Action color case hardened. Each comes with book entitled "In the Valley of the Little Big Horn".
Price: **$200.00**

HARRINGTON AND RICHARDSON 158 TOPPER RIFLE
Caliber: 30-30
Barrel: 22″ round tapered.
Weight: 5¼ lbs. **Length:** 37½″
Stock: Walnut finished stock and fore-end; recoil pad.
Sights: Lyman folding adj. rear and ramp front sights.
Features: Side lever break-open action with visible hammer. Easy takedown. Converts to 20 ga. Shotgun with accessory bbl. ($15 extra).
Price: **$44.95**

HYPER SINGLE RIFLE
Caliber: Choice of any rimmed cartridge. Rimless $35.00 extra.
Barrel: Choice of manufacture and length.
Weight: To customer's specifications. **Length:** To customer's specs.
Stock: To customer's specifications.
Sights: None furnished.
Features: Falling block action. Striker rotates on needle bearings and is powered by dual coil springs. Drilled and tapped for scope mounts, choice of barrel manufacture and weight. Stocked in A-A fancy wood with choice of specifications and type of wood. Set trigger **$35.00** extra, stainless bbl. **$35.00** extra, fluted bbl. **$60.00** extra.
Price: Standard rifle **$575.00**
Price: Barreled action **$300.00**
Price: Action only **$215.00**

U.S. CENTERFIRE RIFLES—SINGLE SHOT

RUGER NO. 3 CARBINE SINGLE SHOT
Caliber: 45-70.
Barrel: 22″ round.
Weight: 6 lbs. **Length:** 38½″.
Stock: American walnut.
Sights: Gold bead front, adj. folding leaf rear.
Features: Same action as No. 1 Rifle except different lever. Has auto ejector, top tang safety, adj. trigger.
Price: $165.00

RUGER NUMBER ONE SINGLE SHOT
Caliber: 22-250, 243, 6mm Rem., 25-06, 270, 30-06, 7mm Rem. Mag., 300 Win.
Barrel: 26″ round tapered with quarter-rib.
Weight: 8 lbs. **Length:** 42″ over-all.
Stock: Walnut, two-piece, checkered p.g. and fore-end (either semi-beavertail or Henry style).
Sights: None, 1″ scope rings supplied for integral mounts.
Features: Under lever, hammerless falling block design has auto ejector, top tang safety.
Price: $265.00
Available also as Light Sporter, Medium Sporter, Special Varminter or Tropical Rifle $265.00

U.S. RIMFIRE—AUTOLOADING

ARMALITE AR-7 EXPLORER CARBINE
Caliber: 22 LR, 8-shot autoloading.
Barrel: 16″ alloy (steel-lined).
Weight: 2¾ lbs. **Length:** 34½″/16½″ stowed.
Stock: Moulded grey Cycloac, snap-on rubber butt pad.
Features: Take-down design stores bbl. and action in hollow stock. Light enough to float.
Price: $59.95

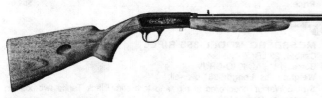

COLT COLTEER AUTOLOADING CARBINE
Caliber: 22LR, 15-shot tubular mag.
Barrel: 13⅜″ round.
Weight: 4¾ lbs. **Length:** 37″ over-all
Stock: Straight grip black walnut stock (13¾″x1⅝″x2¼″) beavertail fore-end.
Sights: Hooded gold bead front sight with notched rear adj. for w. and e.
Features: Full length magazine tube; Cross-bolt Safety. Receiver grooved for tip-off scope mount.
Price: $64.95

BROWNING AUTOLOADING RIFLE
Caliber: 22 LR, 11-shot.
Barrel: 19¼ lbs. **Weight:** 4¾ lbs. **Length:** 37″ over-all.
Stock: Checkered select walnut (13¾″x1¹³⁄₁₆″x2⅝″) with p.g. and semi-beavertail fore-end.
Sights: Gold bead front, folding leaf rear.
Features: Engraved receiver is grooved for tip-off scope mount; cross-bolt safety; tubular magazine in buttstock; easy take down for carrying or storage.
Price: Grade I . . . . **$114.50** Grade II . . . . **$172.50** Grade III **$312.50**
Also available in Grade I, 22 S (16-shot) $114.50

COLT COURIER AUTOLOADING RIFLE
Same as the Colteer except; p.g. stock with tapered fore-end (no fore-end bbl. band).
Price: $65.00

COLT STAGECOACH AUTOLOADING CARBINE
Similar to Colteer except: 16½″ bbl., 33¾″ over-all. Scroll engraved receiver, with saddle ring. 22 LR only.
Price: $74.95

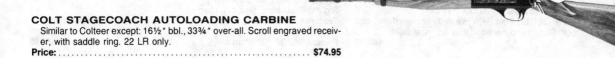

MARLIN 49DL AUTOLOADING RIFLE
Caliber: 22 LR, 18-shot tubular magazine
Barrel: 22″ Micro-Groove
Weight: 5½ lbs. **Length:** 40½″
Stock: American walnut, Monte Carlo capped p.g., checkered fore-end and p.g.,
Sights: Blade ramp front, semi-buckhorn rear adj. for w. & e.
Features: Gold plated trigger, bolt hold-open for safety and cleaning, scroll-engraved receiver grooved for tip-off scope mounts.
Price: $61.95

MARLIN 99 M1 AUTOLOADING CARBINE
Caliber: 22 LR, 9-shot tubular magazine
Barrel: 18″ Micro-Groove
Weight: 4½ lbs. **Length:** 37″
Stock: Monte Carlo American walnut with p.g. and handguard. White buttplate spacer.
Sights: Blade on band type ramp front, removable flat-top mid-sight adj. for w. & e.
Features: Gold plated trigger, bolt hold-open, serrated receiver top is grooved for tip-off scope mount, sling swivels attached.
Price: $54.95

MARLIN 99C AUTOLOADING RIFLE
Same as the Marlin 49DL except: one piece American walnut stock with checkered p.g. and fore-end.
Price: $55.95

MARLIN 989 M2 AUTOLOADING CARBINE
Same as the Marlin 99 M1 carbine except 7-shot detachable clip magazine.
Price: **$54.95**

MARLIN GLENFIELD 60 AUTOLOADER
Caliber: 22 LR, 18-shot tubular mag.
Barrel: 22″ round tapered.
Weight: About 5½ lbs. **Length:** 41″ Over-all.
Stock: Walnut finished Monte Carlo, checkered p.g. and fore-end.
Sights: Blade ramp front, step adj. rear.
Features: Chrome plated trigger, matted receiver is grooved for tip-off mounts.
Price: **$46.95**

MARLIN GLENFIELD 70 AUTOLOADER
Caliber: 22 LR, 7-shot clip.
Barrel: 18″ round tapered.
Weight: 5½ lbs. **Length:** 40½″.
Stock: Walnut finished Monte Carlo, checkered p.g.
Sights: Blade on band type ramp front, step adj. rear.
Features: Shorter clip-fed version of Model 60, rustproof receiver, grooved for tip-off scope mounts. Scope and mounts **$8.00** extra.
Price: **$46.95**

MOSSBERG MODEL 333 RIFLE
Caliber: 22 LR, 15-shot tubular mag.
Barrel: 20″.
Weight: 6¼ lbs. **Length:** 39½″ over-all.
Stock: Two-piece walnut, checkered p.g. and fore-end. Buttplate and p.g. cap w/white line spacers.
Sights: Open step adj. U-notch rear, bead ramp front.
Features: Top tang safety, automatic bolt open stop (bolt locks open after last shot), gold plated grooved trigger. Receiver grooved for scope mounting.
Price: **$64.00**

MOSSBERG MODEL 353 RIFLE
Caliber: 22 LR, 7-shot clip.
Barrel: 18″ "AC-KRO-GRUV".
Weight: 5 lbs. **Length:** 38″ over-all.
Stock: Walnut, checkered at p.g. and fore-end. Black Tenite two-position extension fore-end.
Sights: Open step adj. U-notch rear, bead front on ramp.
Features: Sling swivels and web strap on left of stock, extension fore-end folds down for steady firing from prone position. Receiver grooved for scope mounting.
Price: **$55.90**

REMINGTON 552C AUTOLOADING CARBINE
Same as the Model 552A rifle except: 21″ bbl., weight 5½ lbs., 40″ over-all.
Price: **$72.95**

REMINGTON MODEL 552BDL AUTO RIFLE
Same as Model 552A except: Du Pont RKW finished checkered fore-end and capped p.g. stock. Blade ramp front and fully adj. rear sights.
Price: **$82.95**

REMINGTON 552A AUTOLOADING RIFLE
Caliber: 22 S (20), L (17) or LR (15) tubular mag.
Barrel: 23″ round tapered.
Weight: about 5¾ lbs. **Length:** 42″ over-all.
Stock: Full-size, walnut with p.g.
Sights: Bead front, step adj. open rear.
Features: Positive cross-bolt safety, receiver grooved for tip-off mount.
Price: **$72.95**
Price: M552GS (22 Short only) **$84.95**

REMINGTON NYLON 66MB AUTO RIFLE
Caliber: 22 LR, 14-shot tubular mag.
Barrel: 19⅝″ round tapered.
Weight: 4 lbs. **Length:** 38½″ over-all.
Stock: Moulded Mohawk Brown Nylon, checkered p.g. and fore-end.
Sights: Blade ramp front, adj. open rear.
Features: Top tang safety, double extractors, receiver grooved for tip-off mounts.
Price: **$59.95**
Price: Model 66GS (22 Short only) **$69.95**

REMINGTON NYLON 66AB AUTO RIFLE
Same as the Model 66MB except: Apache Black Nylon stock, chrome plated receiver.
Price: **$64.95**

REMINGTON MOWHAWK 10C AUTO RIFLE
Same as Nylon 66 rifle except: removable 10-shot 22 LR clip magazine.
Price: **$54.95**
Extra 5-shot clip . . . . **$2.75**   Extra 10-shot clip **$3.50**

RUGER 10/22 AUTOLOADING CARBINE

Caliber: 22 LR, 10-shot rotary mag.
Barrel: 18½" round tapered.
Weight: 5 lbs. **Length:** 37" over-all.
Stock: American walnut with p.g. and bbl. band.
Sights: Gold bead front, fully adj. folding leaf rear.
Features: Detachable rotary magazine fits flush into stock, cross-bolt safety, receiver tapped and grooved for scope blocks or tip-off mount.
Price: **$56.50**

RUGER 10/22 AUTO SPORTER

Same as 10/22 Carbine except: Hand checkered p.g. and fore-end with straight buttplate, no bbl., bands, sling swivels.
Price: **$64.50**

SAVAGE 60 AUTOLOADING RIFLE

Caliber: 22 LR, 15-shot tubular mag.
Barrel: 20" round tapered.
Weight: About 6 lbs. **Length:** 40½" over-all.
Stock: Walnut, Monte Carlo, checkered p.g. and semi-beavertail fore-end.
Sights: Gold bead ramp front, Step adj. open rear.
Features: White line buttplate, top tang safety, receiver grooved for tip-off mount.
Price: **$57.95**

SAVAGE STEVENS 88 AUTOLOADING RIFLE

Same as the 60 rifle except: Checkered walnut finished stock. Blade front sight. Wgt. 5¾ lbs.
Price: **$49.95**

WEATHERBY MARK XXII AUTOLOADING RIFLE

Caliber: 22 LR only, 5- or 10-shot clip loaded
Barrel: 24" round contoured.
Weight: 6 lbs. **Length:** 42¼" over-all.
Stock: Walnut, Monte Carlo comb and cheekpiece, rosewood p.g. cap and fore-end tip. Skip-line checkering.
Sights: Gold bead ramp front, 3-leaf folding rear.
Features: Thumb operated side safety also acts as single shot selector. Receiver grooved for tip-off scope mount. Single pin release for quick take-down.
Price: **$119.50**
Extra 5-shot clip . . . .**$3.95**   Extra 10-shot clip **$4.50**

SEARS TED WILLIAMS AUTO RIFLE

Caliber: 22 S(21), L(17) or LR(15). Tubular Mag.
Barrel: 20½" round (16" twist).
Weight: 5 lbs. **Length:** 39" over-all.
Stock: Walnut finished hardwood, with p.g.
Sights: Blade front, step adj. open rear.
Features: Cross-bolt safety; burnished bolt handle, trigger and mag. cap; receiver grooved for tip-off scope mount.
Price: **$50.00**

WESTERN FIELD 868 AUTO RIFLE

Caliber: 22 LR, 15-shot tubular mag.
Barrel: 20".
Weight: 6½ lbs. **Length:** 39½" over-all.
Stock: Walnut finish p.g. and fore-end.
Sights: Ramp front, rear adj. for e.
Features: Sling swivels, plastic butt plate.
Price: **$52.95**

WESTERN FIELD 894 AUTO RIFLE

Caliber: 22 LR, 15-shot tubular mag.
Barrel: 20" round.
Weight: 6¼ lbs. **Length:** 39" over-all.
Stock: Walnut, checkered p.g. and fore-end, p.g. cap and butt plate with white line spacers.
Sights: Bead front on ramp, folding leaf rear.
Features: Top slide safety, automatic bolt hold open after last shot.
Price: **$63.95**

U.S. RIMFIRE—AUTOLOADING

WINCHESTER 290 DELUXE
Same as M290 except: select walnut stock with Monte Carlo comb (drop 2¼"), cheekpiece, white spacer, basket-weave checkering, sling swivels. Gold plated trigger and safety.
Price: **$85.95**

WINCHESTER 190 AUTO RIFLE
Same as M290 except: No checkering, pistol grip cap or buttplate spacer.
Price: **$52.95**

WINCHESTER 290 AUTOLOADING RIFLE
Caliber: 22 L (17) or LR (15), tubular mag.
Barrel: 20½" round tapered (16" twist).
Weight: 5 lbs. **Length:** 39" over-all.
Stock: 2-piece walnut finished hardwood. checkered p.g. and fore-end, (13⅝"x1¾"x2¾").
Sights: Bead post front, step adj. rear.
Features: Cross-bolt safety, composition buttplate with white line spacer, receiver grooved for tip-off scope mount.
Price: **$64.95**

WINCHESTER 190 AUTO CARBINE
Same as 190 rifle except: Carbine has barrel band and sling swivels.
Price: **$54.95**

U.S. RIMFIRE—BOLT ACTION

BROWNING T-BOLT T-1 REPEATING RIFLE
Caliber: 22 LR (S and L also, with single-shot adapter)
Barrel: 22" round, straight taper.
Weight: 5½ lbs. **Length:** 39¼" over-all.
Stock: One-piece walnut with p.g. (13½"x1⁵/₁₆x3"). Lacquer finish, no checkering.
Sights: Blade ramp front, aperture rear adj. for w. & e.
Features: 5-shot clip loading, straight-pull-back breech bolt, double extractors, side ejection. Available with left or right hand action.
Price: **$72.50**

BROWNING T-BOLT T-2 REPEATING RIFLE
Same as T-1 except: 24" bbl.; stock of figured walnut with checkered p.g. and fore-end; wgt. 6 lbs.; 41¼" over-all. Left or right hand action.
Price: **$97.50**

HARRINGTON & RICHARDSON 865 PLAINSMAN RIFLE
Caliber: 22 S, L or LR. 5-shot clip mag.
Barrel: 22" round tapered.
Weight: 5 lbs. **Length:** 39" over-all.
Stock: Walnut finished hardwood with Monte Carlo and p.g.
Sights: Blade front, step adj. open rear.
Features: Cocking indicator, sliding side safety, receiver grooved for tip-off scope mounts.
Price: **$44.95**
Price: M866 with Mannlicher stock **$49.95**

MARLIN 780 BOLT ACTION RIFLE
Caliber: 22 S, L, or LR; 7-shot clip magazine.
Barrel: 22" Micro-Groove
Weight: 5½ lbs. **Length:** 41"
Stock: Monte Carlo American walnut with checkered p.g. White line spacer at buttplate.
Sights: Blade on band ramp front sight, semibuckhorn rear adj. for w. & e.
Features: Gold plated trigger receiver anti-glare serrated and grooved for tip-off scope mount.
Price: **$50.95**

MARLIN 781 BOLT ACTION RIFLE
Same as the Marlin 780 except: tubular magazine holds 25 Shorts, 19 Longs or 17 Long Rifle cartridges. Weight 6 lbs. **$52.95**

MARLIN 782 BOLT ACTION RIFLE
Same as the Marlin 780 except: 22 Rimfire Magnum cal. only, weight about 6 lbs. Sling and swivels attached. **$56.45**

MARLIN 783 BOLT ACTION RIFLE
Same as Marlin 782 except: Tubular magazine holds 13 rounds of 22 Rimfire Magnum ammunition. **$57.95**

MARLIN GLENFIELD 20 BOLT ACTION REPEATER

Similar to Marlin 780, except: Walnut finished checkered p.g. stock, without Monte Carlo, conventional rifling. **$40.95**

MOSSBERG MODEL 340B RIFLE

Caliber: 22 S, L, LR, 7-shot clip.
Barrel: 24" "AC-KRO-GRUV".
Weight: 6 lbs. **Length:** 43½" over-all.
Stock: Walnut finish with p.g., Monte Carlo and cheek piece, sling swivels.
Sights: Mossberg S331 receiver peep with ¼-minute adjustments for w. and e. S320 Mossberg hooded ramp front.
Features: Front sight offers choice of post or aperture elements. "Magic 3-Way" clip adjusts for Short, Long or Long Rifle cartridges. Receiver grooved for scope mount.
Price: **$52.95**

MOSSBERG MODEL 341 RIFLE

Caliber: 22 S, L, LR, 7-shot clip.
Barrel: 24" "AC-KRO-GRUV".
Weight: 6½ lbs. **Length:** 43½" over-all.
Stock: Walnut, checkered p.g. and fore-end, Monte Carlo and cheek piece. Buttplate with white line spacer.
Sights: Open, U-notch rear adj. for w. and e.
Features: Sliding side safety, 8 groove rifling, "Magic 3-way" clip adjusts to Short, Long or Long Rifle cartridges.
Price: **$48.95**

MOSSBERG MODEL 640K CHUCKSTER

Caliber: 22 WMR. 5-shot clip mag.
Barrel: 24" AC-KRO-GRUV.
Weight: 6 lbs. **Length:** 44¾" over-all.
Stock: Walnut, checkered p.g. and fore-end, Monte Carlo comb and cheek-piece.
Sights: Ramp front with bead, fully adj. leaf rear.
Features: Grooved trigger, sliding side safety, double extractors, receiver grooved for tip-off scope mounts and tapped for aperture rear sight.
Price: **$55.90**

MOSSBERG MODEL 640M MAGNUM

Same as the 640K except: 20" bbl., Damascened bolt, American walnut Mannlicher stock with Monte Carlo comb and cheekpiece, checkered p.g. and fore-end. Sling swivels with leather sling. Weight about 6 lbs. 40¾" over-all.
Price: **$65.20**

REMINGTON MODEL 541-S

Caliber: 22 S,L,LR. 5-shot.
Barrel: 24"
Weight: 5½ lbs. **Length:** 42⅝".
Stock: Walnut, checkered p.g. and fore end.
Sights: None. Drilled and tapped for scope mounts or receiver sights.
Features: Clip repeater. Thumb safety. Receiver and trigger guard scroll engraved.
Price: **$134.95**
Price: Extra 10-shot clip **$3.50**

REMINGTON MODEL 581 RIFLE

Caliber: 22 S, L or LR. 5-shot clip mag.
Barrel: 24" round.
Weight: 4¾ lbs. **Length:** 42⅜" over-all.
Stock: Walnut finished Monte Carlo with p.g.
Sights: Bead post front, screw adj. open rear.
Features: Sliding side safety, wide trigger, receiver grooved for tip-off scope mounts.
Price: **$57.95**
Price: Left hand action and stock **$62.95**

REMINGTON MODEL 582 RIFLE

Same as M581 except: tubular magazine under bbl. holds 20 S, 15 L or 14 LR cartridges. Wgt. 5½ lbs.
Price: **$64.95**

U.S. RIMFIRE—BOLT ACTION

REMINGTON MODEL 592 RIFLE

Same as the M591 except: tubular magazine under bbl. holds ten 5mm Remington RFM cartridges.

Price: **$79.95**

REMINGTON MODEL 591 RIFLE
Caliber: 5mm Remington RFM. 4-shot clip mag.
Barrel: 24″ round.
Weight: 5 lbs. **Length:** 42⅜″ over-all.
Stock: Walnut finished hardwood, Monte Carlo comb, black p.g. cap and buttplate.
Sights: Bead post front, screw adj. open rear.
Features: Sliding thumb safety, detachable sights, receiver grooved for tip-off scope mounts.
Price: **$74.95**

SAVAGE/ANSCHUTZ 164 BOLT ACTION RIFLE
Caliber: 22 LR. 5-shot clip mag.
Barrel: 24″ round tapered.
Weight: 6 lbs. **Length:** 40¾″ over-all
Stock: Walnut, hand checkered p.g. and fore-end, Monte Carlo comb and cheekpiece, schnabel fore-end.
Sights: Hooded ramp gold bead front, folding-leaf rear.
Features: Fully adj. single stage trigger, sliding side safety, receiver grooved for tip-off mount.
Price: **$109.95**
Price: Model 164M in 22 WRM (4-shot) **$117.95**

SAVAGE/ANSCHUTZ MODEL 184 BOLT ACTION RIFLE
Caliber: 22 LR, 5-shot clip.
Barrel: 21½″.
Weight: 4½ lbs. **Length:** 39½″.
Stock: Walnut, Monte Carlo comb, hand checkered p.g. and fore-end, schnabel fore-end.
Sights: Hooded ramp gold bead front, folding-leaf rear.
Features: Side safety, crisp factory-set trigger, receiver grooved for scope mounting.
Price: **$77.95**

SAVAGE/ANSCHUTZ MODEL 54 SPORTER
Caliber: 22 LR. 5-shot clip mag.
Barrel: 23″ round tapered.
Weight: 6¾ lbs. **Length:** 42″ over-all.
Stock: French walnut, checkered p.g. and fore-end. Monte Carlo roll-over comb, schnabel fore-end tip.
Sights: Hooded ramp gold bead front, folding-leaf rear.
Features: Adj. single stage trigger, wing safety, receiver grooved for tip-off mount, tapped for scope blocks.
Price: **$185.00**
Price: Model 54M (22 WRM) **$195.00**

SAVAGE MODEL 65 RIFLE
Caliber: 22 S, L or LR. 5-shot clip mag.
Barrel: 20″ lightweight, free floating.
Weight: 5 lbs. **Length:** 39″ over-all.
Stock: Walnut, Monte Carlo comb. checkered p.g. and fore-end.
Sights: Gold bead ramp front, step adj. open rear.
Features: Sliding side safety, double extractors, receiver grooved for tip-off scope mount.
Price: **$48.95**
Price: Model 65M in 22 WMR (5-shot) **$52.95**

SAVAGE/STEVENS MODEL 34 RIFLE

Same as the Model 65 except: walnut finished hard wood stock, bead post front sight.
Price: **$41.95**
Price: Model 34M in 22 WMR (5-shot) **$46.95**

SAVAGE/STEVENS MODEL 46 RIFLE

Same as the Model 34 except: tubular magazine holds 22 S, 17 L or 15 LR cartridges. Available in 22 rimfire only (not magnum).
Price: **$46.95**

SAVAGE/STEVENS MODEL 46-S SCOPEGUN

Standard Model 46 equipped by factory with 4x scope **$53.95**

U.S. RIMFIRE—BOLT ACTION

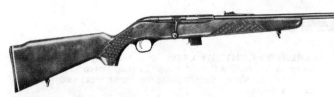

WINCHESTER 320 BOLT ACTION REPEATER
Caliber: 22 Short, Long or Long Rifle (5-shot).
Barrel: 22" round tapered.
Weight: 5⅝ lbs. **Length:** 39½" over-all.
Stock: Walnut, Monte Carlo, checkered p.g. and fore-end. 13½" pull.
Sights: Bead on ramp front, step adj. rear.
Features: Wide serrated trigger, positive safety, matted receiver is tapped for scope and micrometer sights. Sling swivels installed.
Price: $59.95
 Extra 5-shot clip $3.00
 Extra 10-shot clip $5.85

WESTERN FIELD 832 BOLT ACTION RIFLE
Caliber: 22 S, L, LR; 7-shot clip.
Barrel: 24" round tapered.
Weight: 6½ lbs. **Length:** 43" over-all.
Stock: Walnut p.g. and fore-end, checkered p.g.
Sights: Ramp front, rear adj. for e.
Features: Thumb operated safety, sling swivels.
Price: $46.95

WESTERN FIELD 822 BOLT ACTION RIFLE
 Same as MM832 except chambered for 22 WMR Magnum; 6-shot clip mag.; sling swivels; cheekpiece stock.
Price: $49.95

U.S. RIMFIRE—LEVER ACTION

BROWNING BL-22 LEVER ACTION RIFLE
Caliber: 22 S(22), L(17) or LR(15). Tubular mag.
Barrel: 20" round tapered.
Weight: 5 lbs. **Length:** 36¾" over-all.
Stock: Walnut, 2-piece straight grip western style.
Sights: Bead post front, folding-leaf rear.
Features: Short throw lever, ½-cock safety, receiver grooved for tip-off scope mounts.
Price: Grade I $82.50
Price: Grade II, engraved receiver, checkered grip and fore-end . . $102.50

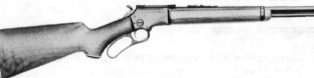

MARLIN 39D LEVER ACTION CARBINE
Caliber: 22 S (21), L (16) or LR (15), tubular magazine.
Barrel: 20½" Micro-Groove
Weight: 5¾ lbs. **Length:** 36½"
Stock: American walnut with white line spacers at p.g. cap and buttplate.
Sights: Blade front, semi-buckhorn rear adj. for w. & e.
Features: Receiver tapped for aperture sights and scope mount (adapter base incl.) offset hammer spur.
Price: $99.95

MARLIN 39 ARTICLE II LEVER ACTION RIFLE
Caliber: 22 S (26), L (21) or LR (19); tubular magazine.
Barrel: 24" Micro-Groove, full-length tapered octagon.
Weight: 6¾ lbs. **Length:** 40"
Stock: American walnut with full p.g.,
Sights: Bead front, semi-buckhorn rear adj. for w. & e.
Features: Made in limited numbers to commemorate 100th NRA anniversary. Medallion fixed to right side of action, solid brass buttplate and fore-end cap.
Price: $135.00

MARLIN GOLDEN 39M CARBINE
Caliber: 22 S(21), L(16), LR(15), tubular magazine.
Barrel: 20" micro-groove.
Weight: 6 lbs. **Length:** 36".
Stock: American walnut, straight grip.
Sights: Bead ramp front with hood, rear folding adj. for w. and e.
Features: Receiver tapped for scope mount or receiver sight, gold plated trigger, offset hammer spur, sling swivels, take-down action.
Price: $109.95

MARLIN GOLDEN 39A LEVER ACTION RIFLE
Caliber: 22 S(26), L(21), LR(19), tubular magazine.
Barrel: 24" micro-groove.
Weight: 6¾ lbs. **Length:** 40".
Stock: American walnut with white line spacers at p.g. cap and buttplate.
Sights: Bead ramp front with detachable hood, rear semi-buckhorn adj. for w. and e.
Features: Take-down action, receiver tapped for scope mount (supplied), gold plated trigger, sling swivels, offset hammer spur. Scope **$16.95** extra.
Price: $109.95

U.S. RIMFIRE—LEVER ACTION

MARLIN 39 CENTURY LTD.
Same as Golden 39M Carbine except: 20″ fully tapered octagon barrel, cartridge brass appointments, squared finger lever, brass medallion on receiver and stock.
Price: **$125.00**

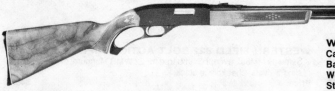

WINCHESTER MODEL 250 LEVER ACTION RIFLE
Caliber: 22 S(21), L(17) or LR(15). Tubular mag.
Barrel: 20½″ round (16″ twist).
Weight: 5 lbs. **Length:** 39″ over-all.
Stock: Two-piece walnut finished hardwood, checkered p.g. and fore-end (13⅝″ x 1¾″ x 2¾″).
Sights: Bead post ramp front, step adj. open rear.
Features: Cross-bolt safety, composition buttplate with white line spacer, receiver grooved for tip-off scope mount.
Price: **$66.95**

WINCHESTER 150 LEVER ACTION CARBINE
Same as M250 except straight stock (no p.g.), no checkering or spacers. With barrel band and swivels.
Price: **$59.95**

WINCHESTER 9422 LEVER ACTION RIFLE
Caliber: 22 S(21), L(17), LR(15). Tubular mag.
Barrel: 20½″ (16″ twist).
Weight: 5 lbs. **Length:** 37⅛″ over-all.
Stock: American walnut, 2-piece, straight grip (no p.g.).
Sights: Hooded ramp ront, adj. semi-buckhorn rear.
Features: Side ejection, received grooved for scope mounting, takedown action.
Price: **$99.95**

WINCHESTER 9422M LEVER ACTION RIFLE
Same as the 9422 except chambered for 22 WMR cartridge, has 11-round mag. capacity **$99.95**

U.S. RIMFIRE—SLIDE ACTION

REMINGTON 572 FIELDMASTER PUMP RIFLE
Caliber: 22 S(20), L(17) or LR(14). Tubular mag.
Barrel: 24″ round tapered.
Weight: 5½ lbs. **Length:** 42″ over-all.
Stock: Genuine walnut with p.g. and grooved slide handle.
Sights: Bead post front, step adj. open rear.
Features: Cross-bolt safety, removing inner mag. tube converts rifle to single shot, receiver grooved for tip-off scope mount.
Price: **$72.95**

REMINGTON MODEL 572 BDL DELUXE
Same as the 572 except: p.g. cap, RKW finish, checkered grip and fore-end, ramp front and fully adj. rear sights.
Price: **$82.95**

REMINGTON MODEL 572 SB
Similar to the 572, but has smoothbore bbl. choked for 22 LR shot cartridges.
Sling and swivels installed. **$7.50**
Price: **$82.95**

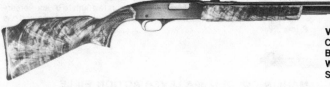

WINCHESTER MODEL 270 PUMP RIFLE
Caliber: 22 S(21), L(17) or LR(15). Tubular mag.
Barrel: 20½″ round (16″ twist).
Weight: 5 lbs. **Length:** 39″ over-all.
Stock: Walnut finished hardwood, checkered p.g. and fore-end (13⅝″ x 1¾″ x 2¾″).
Sights: Square post ramp front, adj. open rear.
Features: Cross-bolt safety, composition buttplate with white line spacer, receiver grooved for tip-off scope mount.
Price: **$68.95**

WINCHESTER 270 DELUXE PUMP RIFLE
Same as M270 except: Select walnut stock with Monte Carlo comb (drop 2¼″), cheekpiece, white spacer, basketweave checkering, swivels; gold plated trigger and safety.
Price: **$89.95**

U.S. RIMFIRE—SINGLE SHOT

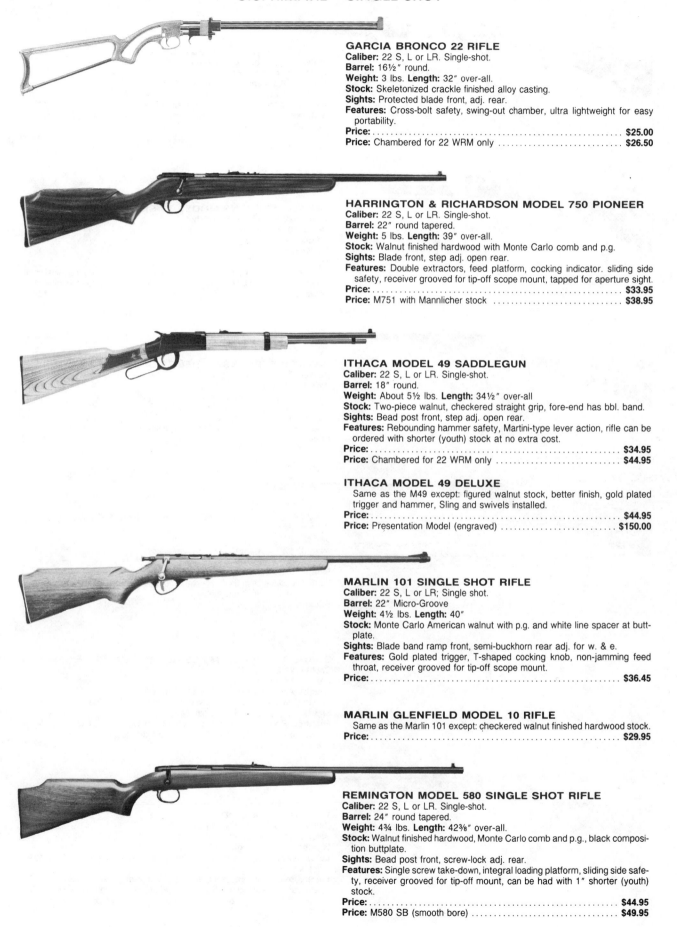

GARCIA BRONCO 22 RIFLE
Caliber: 22 S, L or LR. Single-shot.
Barrel: 16½" round.
Weight: 3 lbs. **Length:** 32" over-all.
Stock: Skeletonized crackle finished alloy casting.
Sights: Protected blade front, adj. rear.
Features: Cross-bolt safety, swing-out chamber, ultra lightweight for easy portability.
Price: **$25.00**
Price: Chambered for 22 WRM only **$26.50**

HARRINGTON & RICHARDSON MODEL 750 PIONEER
Caliber: 22 S, L or LR. Single-shot.
Barrel: 22" round tapered.
Weight: 5 lbs. **Length:** 39" over-all.
Stock: Walnut finished hardwood with Monte Carlo comb and p.g.
Sights: Blade front, step adj. open rear.
Features: Double extractors, feed platform, cocking indicator. sliding side safety, receiver grooved for tip-off scope mount, tapped for aperture sight.
Price: **$33.95**
Price: M751 with Mannlicher stock **$38.95**

ITHACA MODEL 49 SADDLEGUN
Caliber: 22 S, L or LR. Single-shot.
Barrel: 18" round.
Weight: About 5½ lbs. **Length:** 34½" over-all
Stock: Two-piece walnut, checkered straight grip, fore-end has bbl. band.
Sights: Bead post front, step adj. open rear.
Features: Rebounding hammer safety, Martini-type lever action, rifle can be ordered with shorter (youth) stock at no extra cost.
Price: **$34.95**
Price: Chambered for 22 WRM only **$44.95**

ITHACA MODEL 49 DELUXE
Same as the M49 except: figured walnut stock, better finish, gold plated trigger and hammer, Sling and swivels installed.
Price: **$44.95**
Price: Presentation Model (engraved) **$150.00**

MARLIN 101 SINGLE SHOT RIFLE
Caliber: 22 S, L or LR; Single shot.
Barrel: 22" Micro-Groove
Weight: 4½ lbs. **Length:** 40"
Stock: Monte Carlo American walnut with p.g. and white line spacer at butt-plate.
Sights: Blade band ramp front, semi-buckhorn rear adj. for w. & e.
Features: Gold plated trigger, T-shaped cocking knob, non-jamming feed throat, receiver grooved for tip-off scope mount.
Price: **$36.45**

MARLIN GLENFIELD MODEL 10 RIFLE
Same as the Marlin 101 except: checkered walnut finished hardwood stock.
Price: **$29.95**

REMINGTON MODEL 580 SINGLE SHOT RIFLE
Caliber: 22 S, L or LR. Single-shot.
Barrel: 24" round tapered.
Weight: 4¾ lbs. **Length:** 42⅜" over-all.
Stock: Walnut finished hardwood, Monte Carlo comb and p.g., black composition buttplate.
Sights: Bead post front, screw-lock adj. rear.
Features: Single screw take-down, integral loading platform, sliding side safety, receiver grooved for tip-off mount, can be had with 1" shorter (youth) stock.
Price: **$44.95**
Price: M580 SB (smooth bore) **$49.95**

U.S. RIMFIRE—SINGLE SHOT

SAVAGE MODEL 63K SINGLE SHOT RIFLE
Caliber: 22 S, L or LR. Single-shot.
Barrel: 18″ round tapered.
Weight: 4 lbs. **Length:** 36″ over-all.
Stock: Walnut finished hardwood.
Sights: Hooded bead ramp front, step adj. open rear.
Features: Cocks on opening, automatic safety, key locks trigger to prevent unauthorized use.
Price: **$34.95**

SAVAGE STEVENS MODEL 73 SINGLE SHOT RIFLE
Caliber: 22 S, L or LR. Single-shot.
Barrel: 20″ round tapered.
Weight: 4¾ lbs. **Length:** 38½″ over-all.
Stock: Walnut finished hardwood.
Sights: Bead post front, step adj. open rear.
Features: Cocks on opening, automatic safety, key locks trigger against unauthorized use, may be had with 12½″ pull stock (youth model) at same cost.
Price: **$28.50**

SAVAGE STEVENS MODEL 72 CRACKSHOT
Caliber: 22 S, L, LR.
Barrel: 22″ octagonal.
Weight: 4½ lbs. **Length:** 37″.
Stock: Walnut finished, straight grip.
Sights: Blade front, step adj. rear.
Features: Deluxe version of Model 74, color case hardened frame.
Price: **$57.50**

SAVAGE STEVENS LITTLE FAVORITE MODEL 74
Caliber: 22 S, L, LR.
Barrel: 22″ round.
Weight: 4½ lbs. **Length:** 37″.
Stock: Walnut finished, straight grip.
Sights: Blade front, step adj. open rear.
Features: Black satin finish. Hammer must be manually cocked before each shot, black plastic buttplate.
Price: **$42.50**

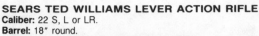

SEARS TED WILLIAMS LEVER ACTION RIFLE
Caliber: 22 S, L or LR.
Barrel: 18″ round.
Weight: About 5½ lbs. **Length:** 34½″ over-all.
Stock: Two-piece walnut, checkered straight grip, fore-end has bbl. band.
Sights: Bead post front, step adj. open rear.
Features: Rebounding hammer safety, Martini-type lever action, rifle can be ordered with shorter (youth) stock at no extra cost.
Price: **$32.00**

WINCHESTER MODEL 310 RIFLE
Caliber: 22 S, L or LR. Single-shot.
Barrel: 22″ round tapered (16″ twist).
Weight: 5⅝ lbs. **Length:** 39½″ over-all.
Stock: Walnut, fluted Monte Carlo comb, checkered p.g. and fore-end (13½″ x 1⅝″ x 2⁷/₁₆″).
Sights: Bead post ramp front, step adj. open rear.
Features: Twin extractors, sliding side safety, wide serrated trigger, receiver grooved for tip-off scope mounts tapped for aperture rear sight.
Price: **$48.95**

U.S. TARGET RIFLES—CENTERFIRE AND RIMFIRE

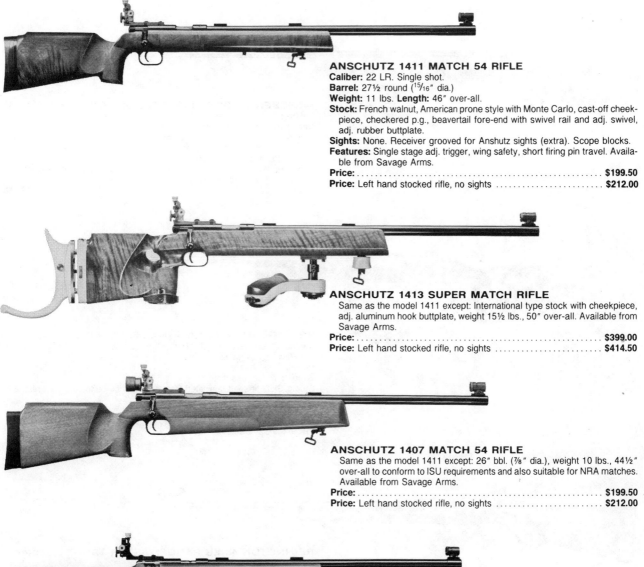

ANSCHUTZ 1411 MATCH 54 RIFLE

Caliber: 22 LR. Single shot.
Barrel: 27½ round (15/16″ dia.)
Weight: 11 lbs. **Length:** 46″ over-all.
Stock: French walnut, American prone style with Monte Carlo, cast-off cheek-piece, checkered p.g., beavertail fore-end with swivel rail and adj. swivel, adj. rubber buttplate.
Sights: None. Receiver grooved for Anshutz sights (extra). Scope blocks.
Features: Single stage adj. trigger, wing safety, short firing pin travel. Available from Savage Arms.
Price: $199.50
Price: Left hand stocked rifle, no sights $212.00

ANSCHUTZ 1413 SUPER MATCH RIFLE

Same as the model 1411 except: International type stock with cheekpiece, adj. aluminum hook buttplate, weight 15½ lbs., 50″ over-all. Available from Savage Arms.
Price: $399.00
Price: Left hand stocked rifle, no sights $414.50

ANSCHUTZ 1407 MATCH 54 RIFLE

Same as the model 1411 except: 26″ bbl. (7/8″ dia.), weight 10 lbs., 44½″ over-all to conform to ISU requirements and also suitable for NRA matches. Available from Savage Arms.
Price: $199.50
Price: Left hand stocked rifle, no sights $212.00

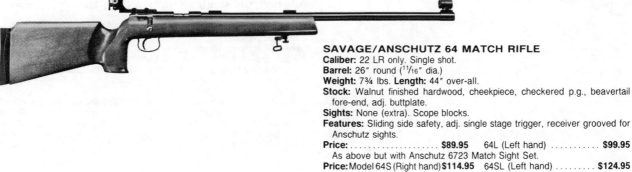

SAVAGE/ANSCHUTZ 64 MATCH RIFLE

Caliber: 22 LR only. Single shot.
Barrel: 26″ round (11/16″ dia.)
Weight: 7¾ lbs. **Length:** 44″ over-all.
Stock: Walnut finished hardwood, cheekpiece, checkered p.g., beavertail fore-end, adj. buttplate.
Sights: None (extra). Scope blocks.
Features: Sliding side safety, adj. single stage trigger, receiver grooved for Anschutz sights.
Price: . . . . **$89.95**   64L (Left hand) **$99.95**
As above but with Anschutz 6723 Match Sight Set.
Price: Model 64S (Right hand) **$114.95**   64SL (Left hand) **$124.95**

SAVAGE/ANSCHUTZ MARK 10-D TARGET RIFLE

Caliber: 22 LR, single shot.
Barrel: 26″ (25/32″ dia.).
Weight: 7¾ lbs. **Length:** 43″.
Stock: Walnut finished hardwood, cheek-piece, adj. handstop and swivels.
Sights: Front, Anschutz special globe with inserts; rear, micro click adj. for w. and e.
Features: Receiver grooved for scope mounting, factory set crisp trigger pull.
Price: $84.95

MOSSBERG MODEL 144LS TARGET RIFLE
Caliber: 22 LR only. 7-shot clip.
Barrel: 26″ round ($^{15}/_{16}$″ dia.)
Weight: About 8 lbs. **Length:** 43″ over-all.
Stock: Walnut with high thick comb, cheekpiece, p.g., beavertail fore-end, adj. handstop and sling swivels.
Features: Wide grooved trigger adj. for wgt. of pull, thumb safety, receiver grooved for scope mounting.
Price: **$70.50**

REMINGTON INTERNATIONAL FREE RIFLE
Caliber: 22 LR, 222 Rem., 222 Rem. Mag., 223 Rem., 7.62 NATO (308 Win.), 30-06 only. Single shot.
Barrel: 27¼″ heavy.
Weight: 15 lbs. **Length:** 47″
Stock: Semi-finished laminated walnut. Adj. hook buttplate, palm rest, and front sling swivel.
Sights: None. Scope blocks installed.
Features: Action is 40-XB type. 2 oz. trigger.
Price: Special order **$395.00**

REMINGTON 40-XB RANGEMASTER TARGET Center-fire
Caliber: 222 Rem., 222 Rem. Mag., 223 Rem., 7.62 NATO (308 Win.), 30-06 only. Single shot.
Barrel: 27¼″ round (Stand. dia.-¾″, Hvy. dia.-⅞″)
Weight: Std.—9¼ lbs., Hvy.—11¼ **Length:** 47″
Stock: American walnut with high comb and beavertail fore-end stop. Rubber non-slip buttplate.
Sights: None. Scope blocks installed.
Features: Adjustable trigger pull. Receiver drilled and tapped for sights.
Price: Standard single-shot, ordnance steel **$249.95**
Standard ss., stainless steel **269.95**
Repeating model **269.95**
Extra for 2 oz. trigger **40.00**

REMINGTON 40-XB RANGEMASTER TARGET Rimfire
Caliber: 22 LR only. Single shot.
Barrel: 28″ standard or heavy.
Weight: 10¾ lbs. (std.), 12 lbs., (hvy.). **Length:** 47″ over-all.
Stock: American walnut, p.g. guide rail with adj. swivel block and handstop, beavertail fore-end.
Sights: None. Receiver tapped for sights and scope blocks. (Redfield Olympic sight set optional at $35 extra.)
Features: Positive thumb safety, adj. trigger, loading platform, double extractors.
Price: **$199.95**

REMINGTON MODEL 40XB-BR

Caliber: 222 Rem., 222 Rem. Mag., 223, 6mm International, 6mm x 47, 7.62 NATO (308 Win.).
Barrel: 20″ (light varmint class), 26″ (heavy varmint class).
Weight: Light varmint class, 7¼ lbs., Heavy varmint class, 12 lbs. **Length:** 38″ (20″ bbl.), 44″ (26″ bbl.).
Stock: Select walnut.
Sights: None. Supplied with scope blocks.
Features: Unblued stainless steel barrel, trigger adj. from 1½ lbs. to 3½ lbs. Special 2 oz. trigger at extra cost. Scope and mounts extra.
Price: **$289.95**

REMINGTON 540X MATCH TARGET RIFLE

Caliber: 22 LR. Single shot.
Barrel: 26″ heavy.
Weight: 8 lbs. **Length:** 43½″ to 47″
Stock: Target style with Monte Carlo, cheekpiece and thumbrest groove. Adj. buttplate and full length guide rail.
Sights: Redfield #75 rear sight with ¼ min. clicks. #63 Globe front sight with 7 inserts. Optional.
Features: Adjustable trigger pull. Rear locking bolt with 6 lugs, double extractors.
Price: Without sights ..... **$104.95**   With sights **$124.95**
For sling with front swivel block assembly installed add **$6.95.**

WINCHESTER 52D BOLT ACTION TARGET RIFLE

Caliber: 22 LR only. Single shot.
Barrel: 28″, standard or heavy weight.
Weight: 9¾ lbs. Std. 11 lbs. Hvy. **Length:** 46″
Stock: Marksman stock of choice walnut with full length accessory channel and adj. bedding device and non-slip butt pad.
Sights: None. Barrel tapped for front sight bases.
Features: Adjustable trigger.
Price: **$177.95**

WINCHESTER 52D BARRELED ACTIONS
No stock or sights. Receiver and bbl. drilled and tapped for metallic sights or scope blocks **$138.95**

WINCHESTER 70 INT'L ARMY MATCH RIFLE

Caliber: 308 (7.62mm NATO) 5-shot.
Barrel: 24″ heavy-contour.
Weight: 11 lbs. **Length:** 43¼″ over-all.
Stock: Oil finished walnut, (12″ x 1¼″ x 1¼″) meets ISU requirements.
Sights: None. Receiver tapped for M70 sights (available at extra cost).
Features: Fore-end rail takes most std. accessories, vertically adj. buttplate, externally adj. trigger, glass bedded action.
Price: **$399.95**

WINCHESTER 52 INTERNATIONAL MATCH RIFLE

Caliber: 22 LR. Single shot.
Barrel: 28″ heavy bbl.
Weight: 13½ lbs. **Length:** 44½″
Stock: Laminated International-style, aluminum fore-end assembly, adj. palm rest.
Sights: Receiver tapped for sights and scope bases; scope blocks are included.
Features: Non-drag trigger. Lead-lapped barrel with Winchester muzzle counterbore.
Price: **$371.00**
    With Kenyon trigger **$407.00**
    With ISU trigger **$412.00**

WINCHESTER 52 INT'L MATCH BARRELED ACTIONS
No stock or sights. Receiver and bbl. drilled and tapped for metallic sights or scope blocks **$205.95**
With Kenyon trigger **$241.95**
With ISU trigger **$246.95**

BROWNING AUTO-5 LIGHT 12, 20 and SWEET 16
Gauge: 12, 20, 16 (5-shot; 3-shot plug furnished). 2¾″ chamber.
Action: Recoil operated autoloader; takedown.
Barrel: 26″ (Skeet boring in 12 & 20 ga., Cyl., Imp. Cyl., Mod. in 16 & 20 ga.); 28″ (Skeet in 12 ga., Full in 16 ga., Mod., Full); 30″ (Full in 12 ga.).
Weight: 12 ga. 7¼ lbs., 16 ga. 6¾ lbs., 20 ga. 6⅜ lbs.
Stock: French walnut, hand checkered half-p.g. and fore-end. 14¼″ x 1⅝″ x 2½″.
Features: Receiver hand engraved with scroll designs and border. Double extractors, extra bbls. interchangeable without factory fitting; mag. cut-off; cross-bolt safety.
Price: **$244.50**
Price: Vent. rib **$262.50**

Browning Auto-5 Magnum 12
Same as Std. Auto-5 except: chambered for 3″ magnum shells (also handles 2¾″ magnum and 2¾″ HV loads). 28″ Mod., Full; 30″ and 32″ (Full) bbls. 14″x1⅝″x2½″ stock. Recoil pad. Wgt. 8¾ lbs.
Price: . . . . **$248.50**   With vent. rib. Wgt. 9 lbs. **$266.50**

Browning Auto-5 Magnum 20
Same as Magnum 12 except barrels 28″ Full or Mod., or 26″ Full, Mod. or Imp. Cyl. 7 lbs. **$248.50**
With ventilated rib, 7½ lbs. **$266.50**

Browning Auto-5 Buck Special
Same as A-5 Light model except: 24″ bbl. choked for slugs, gold bead front sight on contoured ramp, rear sight adj. for w.&e. Wgt. (12 ga.) 7⅝ lbs.
Price: **$258.50**

BROWNING AUTO-5 Light 12, 16, 20, or 12 Buck Special
Same as Std. Buck Special except: with gold trigger and of less weight. Wgt. 12 ga., 7 lbs.; 16 ga., 6⅜ lbs.; 20 ga., 6 lbs. 2 oz.; 3″ Mag. 12, 8¼ lbs.
Price: **$266.50**
All Buck Specials are available with carrying sling, detachable swivels and swivel attachments for $9.00 extra.

Browning Auto-5 Light Skeet
Same as Light Standard except: 12 and 20 ga. only, 26″ or 28″ bbl. (Skeet). Wgt. 6¼-7¼ bls. **$244.50**
With vent. rib. Wgt. 6⅜-7½ lbs. **$262.50**

HI-STANDARD SUPERMATIC DELUXE AUTOS
Gauge: 12 or 20 (5-shot; 3-shot plug furnished).
Action: Gas operated autoloader (12 ga. 2¾″, 20 ga. 3″ chambers).
Barrel: 12 gauge, 30″ (Full), 26″ (Imp. Cyl.), 12 and 20 gauge, 28″ (Mod. or Full). Plain Barrel.
Stock: 14″x1½″x2½″. Walnut, checkered p.g. and semi-beavertail fore-end. Recoil pad. 20 ga. guns have longer fore-end with sloped front.
Weight: 7½ lbs. (12 ga.) 47¾″ over-all (12, 28″).
Features: 12 ga. uses all 2¾″ shells, 20 ga. all 2¾″ or 3″ shells, including rifled slugs, without adjustment.
Price: Field, plain bbl., No rib **$159.95**
Price: Deluxe rib, checkered stock, vent. rib, w/o adj. choke **184.95**
Price: Checkered stock, vent.-rib, adj. choke **189.95**
Price: Duck, 3″ Magnum, 12 ga., 30″ full, recoil pad, with vent. rib bbl.**189.95**

Hi-Standard Supermatic Deer Gun
Same as Supermatic Auto except: 12-ga. only, 22″ plain bbl., Cyl. bore, with rifle sights. Checkered walnut stock and fore-end, recoil pad. Receiver tapped for aperture sight. 41¾″ over-all, 7¾ lbs. **$169.95**

U.S. SHOTGUNS—AUTOLOADING

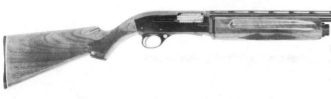

Hi-Standard Supermatic Skeet
Same as Supermatic DeLuxe except: 26″ Skeet choke bbl.; all external parts high polished; internal parts super finished; better grade American walnut stock (no recoil pad) and fore-end with cabinet finish. Weight about 7½ lbs. **$189.95**

Hi-Standard Supermatic Trap
Same features as Supermatic Skeet except: 30″ full choke barrel; stock (14⅜″x1½″x1⅞″); recoil pad. Wgt. 8 lbs. 12 ga. only **$194.95**

ITHACA MODEL 300 AUTOMATIC
Gauge: 12 ga. 2¾″ chambers, 20 ga. 3″ chambers.
Action: Recoil-operated, takedown, interchangeable barrels.
Barrel: Roto-Forged 30″ 12 ga. only (Full), 28″ (Full or Mod.), 26″ (Imp. Cyl.). Standard without rib, vent. rib, $15.00 extra.
Stock: 14″x1½″x2½″. Hand checkered walnut, p.g., fluted fore-end.
Weight: 12 ga. about 7 lbs., 20 ga. about 6½ lbs.
Features: Positive cross-bolt safety, automatic magazine cutoff permits changing loads without unloading magazine. 20 ga. guns are designed to permit quick changeover from 2¾″ to 3″ shells.
Price: **$154.95**
Price: With vent. rib **$169.95**

ITHACA MODEL 900 DELUXE AUTOMATIC
Gauge: 12 ga. 2¾″ chambers, 20 ga. 3″ chambers.
Action: Recoil-operated, takedown; interchangeable bbls., cross-bolt safety.
Barrel: Roto-Forged; 30″ 12 ga. only (Full), 28″ (Full or Mod.), 26″ (Imp. Cyl.) all with vent. rib.
Stock: 14″x1½″x2½″, hand checkered walnut, p.g. and fore-end.
Weight: 12 ga. about 7 lbs., 20 ga. about 6½ lbs.
Features: White spacers in grip cap and butt plate; attractive engraving on receiver is gold-filled, gold-plated trigger and nameplate inlaid in stock.
Price: **$184.95**

ITHACA MODEL 900 DELUXE AUTOMATIC SLUG GUN
Identical to the Model 900 Deluxe, except with 24″ barrel that carries rifle sights for slug shooting. 12 ga. 2¾″ chamber, 20 ga. 3″ chamber.
Price: **$179.95**

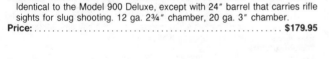

ITHACA MODEL 51 FEATHERLIGHT AUTOMATIC
Gauge: 12 ga. 2¾″ chamber.
Action: Gas-operated, rotary bolt has three locking lugs. Takedown. Self-compensating for high or low base loads.
Barrel: Roto-Forged, 30″ (Full), 28″ (Full, Mod., or Skeet), 26″ (Imp. Cyl. or Skeet). Extra barrels available. Raybar front sight. Vent. rib $25.00 extra.
Stock: 14″x1⅝″x2½″. Hand checkered walnut, white spacers on p.g. and under recoil pad.
Weight: About 7½ lbs.
Features: Hand fitted, engraved receiver, 3 shot capacity, safety is reversible for left hand shooter.
Price: Standard **$184.95**

Ithaca Model 51 Featherlight Automatic Trap
Same gun as Model 51 with vent. rib, trap recoil pad, stock dimensions are 14¼″x1½″x1⅞″. **Price:** **$219.95**

Ithaca Model 51 Featherlight Automatic Skeet
Same gun as Model 51 with vent. rib, skeet recoil pad, stock dimensions are 14″x1⅝″x2½″. **Price:** **$214.95**

ITHACA MODEL 51 MAGNUM
Same as Standard Model 51 except has 3″ chambers.
Price: Magnum Standard **$204.95**
Price: Magnum vent. rib **$229.95**

Ithaca Model 51 Featherlight Deluxe Skeet
Same gun as Model 51 Skeet with fancy American walnut stock, 28" or 29" (Skeet) barrel. **Price:** **$239.95**

Ithaca Model 51 Featherlight Deluxe Trap
Same gun as Model 51 Trap with fancy American walnut stock, 30" (full or imp. cyl.) or 28" (full or imp. mod.) barrel. **Price:** **$249.95**
Price: With Monte Carlo stock **$259.95**

ITHACA MODEL XL 300
Gauge: 12 (2¾"), 20 (2¾" or 3" chamber).
Action: Gas-operated auto loader.
Barrel: 12 ga. Field Grade - 30" (Full), 28" (Full or Mod.), 26" (Imp. Cyl.). 20 ga. Field Grade - 28" (Full or Mod.) 26" (Imp. Cyl.). Trap Grade - 30" (Full or Mod.); Skeet-26" (Skeet).
Weight: 7½ lbs. **Length:** 48" over-all.
Stock: 1½"x2½"x14" (Field Grade). Walnut.
Sights: Raybar front sight on ventilated rib.
Features: Self-compensating gas system, reversible safety.
Price: Standard .... **$169.95**   Ventilated rib **$184.95**
Price: XL 300 recoil operated, standard grade **$154.95**
Price: XL 300 recoil operated with vent. rib **$169.95**

ITHACA MODEL XL 900
Gauge: 12 (2¾"), 20 (2¾", 3" chamber); 5 shot capacity.
Action: Gas-operated autoloader.
Barrel: 12 ga., Field Grade - 30" (Full), 28" (Full or Mod.), 26" (Imp. Cyl.); 20 ga., 28" (Full or Mod.,) 26" (Imp. Cyl.), Trap - 30" (Full or Imp. Mod.), Skeet - 26" (Skeet).
Weight: 6¾ lbs. **Length:** 48" overall.
Stock: 1½"x2½"x14" (Field Grade). Walnut finish.
Sights: Ventilated rib with Raybar front sight on field grades; Bradley-type on target grades.
Features: Self-compensating gas system, reversible safety, action release button.
Price: Ventilated rib ...... **$194.95**   Trap grade (12 ga. only) .. **$209.95**
Price: Skeet grade .... **$209.95**   Slug gun **$209.95**
Price: Recoil operated ... **$184.95**   Slug, recoil operated **$179.95**

Remington 1100 Magnum
Same as 1100 except: chambered for 3" magnum loads. Available in 12 ga. (30") or 20 ga. (28") Mod. or Full, 14"x1½"x2½" stock with recoil pad, Wgt. 7¾ lbs. **$204.95**
Price: With vent. rib **$229.95**
Price: Left hand model with vent. rib **$234.95**

REMINGTON MODEL 1100 AUTO
Gauge: 12, 16, 20 (5-shot); 3-shot plug furnished.
Action: Gas-operated autoloader.
Barrel: 26" (Imp. Cyl., Mod.), 28" (Mod., Full), 30" Full in 12 ga. only.
Stock: 14"x1½"x2½" American Walnut, checkered p.g. and fore-end.
Weight: 12 ga. 7½ lbs., 16 ga. 7⅜ lbs., 20 ga. 7¼ lbs.; 48" over-all (28" bbl.).
Features: Quickly interchangeable barrels within gauge. Matted receiver top with scroll work on both sides of receiver. Crossbolt safety.
Price: .... **$184.95**   With vent. rib **$209.95**
Price: Left hand model with vent. rib **$214.95**

Remington 1100F Premier Auto
Same as 1100D except: select wood, better engraving **$1295.00**
With gold inlay **2000.00**

Remington 1100 SA Skeet
Same as the 1100 except: 26" bbl., special skeet boring, vent. rib, ivory bead front and metal bead middle sights. 14"x1½"x2½" stock. 20 and 12 ga. only. Wgt. 7½ lbs.
Price: .... **$219.95**   1100 SB (better grade walnut) ... **$244.95**
For Cutts Comp add **25.00**
Left hand model with vent. rib **$224.95**

Remington 1100 Small Gauge
Same as 1100 except: 28 ga. 2¾" (5-shot) or 410, 3" (except Skeet, 2½" 4-shot). 45½" over-all. Available in 25" bbl. (Full, Mod., or Imp. Cyl.) only.
Price: Plain bbl. .... **$194.95**   With vent. rib **$219.95**

Remington 1100 20 ga. Lightweight Magnum
Basically the same design as Model 1100, but with special weight-saving features that retain strength and dependability of the standard Model 1100.
Barrel: 28" (Full, Mod.), 26" (Imp. Cyl.).
Weight: 6½ lbs.
Price: .... **$214.95**   With vent. rib **$239.95**

Remington 1100D Tournament Auto
Same as 1100 Standard except: vent. rib, better wood, more extensive engraving **$595.00**

SEARS TED WILLIAMS 300 AUTO
Gauge: 12 and 20 (3-shot) 2¾" chamber.
Action: Gas operated autoloader with self-compensating system for light or heavy loads.
Barrel: 27", 12 and 20 ga. (with adjustable choke), 28", 12 ga. only (Mod or Full), ventilated rib.
Stock: American walnut checkered p.g. and fore-end, recoil pad.
Weight: 7 lbs. (7¼ in 12 ga. w/adj. choke); 48⅝" over-all length (47⅝" w/adj. choke).
Features: Push button action release.
Price: 12 ga. (Mod or Full) **$190.00**

Remington 1100 Deer Gun
Same as 1100 except: 12 ga. only, 22" bbl. (Imp. Cyl.), rifle sights adjustable for w. and e.; recoil pad with white spacer. Weight 7¼ lbs. **$204.95**

Remington 1100 TB Trap
Same as the 1100 except: better grade wood, recoil pad. 14⅜"x1⅜"x1¾" stock. Wgt. 8¼ lbs. 12 ga. only. 30" (Mod., Full) vent. rib bbl. Ivory bead front and white metal middle sight.
Price: .... **$254.95**   With Monte Carlo stock **$264.95**
Price: 1100TB Trap, left hand **$259.95**
Price: With Monte Carlo stock **$269.95**
Remington 1100 Extra bbls.: Plain $49.94 (20, 28 & 410, $47.95). Vent. rib $74.95 (20, 28 & 410, $70.95). Vent. rib Skeet $79.95. Vent. rib Trap $79.95 Deer bbl. $60.95, Skeet, with cutts comp. $104.95. Available in the same gauges and chokes as shown on guns.

UNIVERSAL AUTO WING SHOTGUN
Gauge: 12 only (5-shot; 3-shot plug furnished). 2¾″ chamber.
Action: Recoil operated autoloader; takedown; extra bbls. interchange without factory fitting; cross-bolt safety.
Barrels: 26″, 28″ or 30″ (Imp. Cyl., Mod., & Full). Vent. rib, Ivory bead front & middle sights.
Stock: 14¼″x1⅝″x2½″. Walnut checkered, full p.g. and grooved fore-end.
Weight: About 7 lbs.
Price: **$175.00**

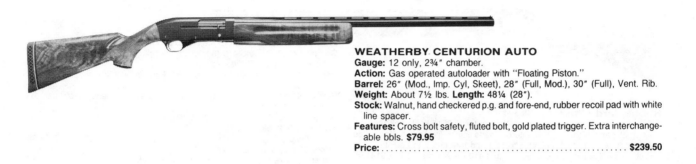

WEATHERBY CENTURION AUTO
Gauge: 12 only, 2¾″ chamber.
Action: Gas operated autoloader with "Floating Piston."
Barrel: 26″ (Mod., Imp. Cyl, Skeet), 28″ (Full, Mod.), 30″ (Full), Vent. Rib.
Weight: About 7½ lbs. **Length:** 48¼ (28″).
Stock: Walnut, hand checkered p.g. and fore-end, rubber recoil pad with white line spacer.
Features: Cross bolt safety, fluted bolt, gold plated trigger. Extra interchangeable bbls. **$79.95**
Price: **$239.50**

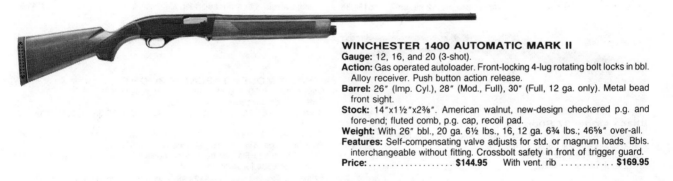

WINCHESTER 1400 AUTOMATIC MARK II
Gauge: 12, 16, and 20 (3-shot).
Action: Gas operated autoloader. Front-locking 4-lug rotating bolt locks in bbl. Alloy receiver. Push button action release.
Barrel: 26″ (Imp. Cyl.), 28″ (Mod., Full), 30″ (Full, 12 ga. only). Metal bead front sight.
Stock: 14″x1½″x2⅜″. American walnut, new-design checkered p.g. and fore-end; fluted comb, p.g. cap, recoil pad.
Weight: With 26″ bbl., 20 ga. 6½ lbs., 16, 12 ga. 6¾ lbs.; 46⅝″ over-all.
Features: Self-compensating valve adjusts for std. or magnum loads. Bbls. interchangeable without fitting. Crossbolt safety in front of trigger guard.
Price: . . . . **$144.95**   With vent. rib **$169.95**

Winchester 1400 Auto Deer Gun
Same as M1400 except: 12 ga. only, 42⅝″ over-all with 22″ bbl. specially bored for rifled slugs. Ramp front sight, adj. open rear. Stock: 14″x1½″x2⅜″. Wgt. 6½ lbs. **$159.95**

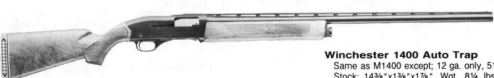

Winchester 1400 Auto Trap
Same as M1400 except; 12 ga. only, 51″ over-all with 30″ full choke bbl. Stock: 14⅜″x1⅜″x1⅞″. Wgt., 8¼ lbs. Metal, middle, red front sights. **$219.95**. With Monte Carlo Stock (14⅜″ x 1½″ x 2⅛″ x 1½″). With extended rib **$229.95**
With field grade M.C. walnut stock, specially tuned trigger and rib extension
. . . . **$229.95**

Winchester 1400 Auto Skeet
Same as M1400 except: 12 and 20 ga. only, 26″ bbl., Skeet choke, wgt. 7½ lbs. Stock: 14″ x 1½″ x 2½″. Metal, middle, red front sights. Measures 46⅝″ over-all **$219.95**
Field grade walnut stock and forearm **$189.95**
Winchester 1400 Extra Barrels: Field, 12, 16, 20 ga. **$37.95**; with vent. rib **$68.95**; Deer Gun **$48.95**; Trap, Skeet **$82.95**

Winchester 1400 Left-Hand
Winchester 1400 field model available in a left-hand version in 12 ga. 28″ Mod. only **$154.95**. With vent. rib **$179.95**. Skeet **$229.95** (12 ga. only) and Trap **$239.95** (12 ga. only).
Winchester 1400 with interchangeable choke tubes which are screwed into the barrel and tightened with supplied wrench. Available in 12, 16, and 20 ga. (28″) Full, Mod., and Imp. Cyl. tube.
Price: Field **$158.45**, Vent. **$183.45**. Also, L. H. in 12 ga. only plain **$179.95**. L. H. Vent. **$179.95**. Extra tubes in Full, Mod. or Imp. Cyl. **$4.95**. Wrench **$1.25**.

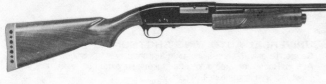

HARRINGTON & RICHARDSON 440 PUMP

Gauge: 12, 20 (2¾" and 3" chamber), 16 (2¾"). 4-shot mag.
Action: Hammerless, side ejecting, slide action.
Barrel: 24", 12 and 20 ga. (Imp. Cyl.); 26", 12 and 20 ga. (Imp. Cyl. and Mod.); 28", 12 ga. (Full and Mod.), 16 ga. (Mod. only), 20 ga. (Full and Mod.); 30", 12 ga. (Full only).
Stock: Walnut p.g. stock and fore-end; recoil pad.
Weight: 6¼ lbs. 47" over-all.
Price: **$104.95**

HARRINGTON & RICHARDSON 442 PUMP

Same as the 440 except: Full length vent. rib, checkered p.g. and fore-end.
Price: **$139.95**

HI-STANDARD FLITE-KING DELUXE PUMP GUNS

Gauge: 12, 20, 28, and 410 (6 shots; 3-shot plug furnished).
Action: "Free-falling" slide action.
Barrel: 12 ga., 30" (Full); 12, 20 ga., 28" (Mod. or Full), 26" (Imp. Cyl.); 410, 26" (Full).
Stock: 14"x1½"x2½". Walnut, checkered p.g. and fore-end. Recoil pad except: 410 & Skeet guns.
Weight: 12 ga. 7¾ lbs., 20, 410 ga. 6½ lbs.
Features: Side ejection.
Price: Field **$106.95**
Price: 12 ga., with adj. choke, 27 l. bbl **109.95**
Price: De Luxe Rib, with vent. rib, w/o adj. choke **126.95**
Price: 12 and 20 ga., as above with adj. choke **129.95**
Price: Brush, 12 ga. only with 20" cyl. bbl., grooved fore-end, adj. rifle sights. Stock (14¼"x1½"x1⅞") 39¾" over-all **$121.95**
Price: Brush Deluxe, 12 ga. only with 20" cyl. bbl., checkered p.g. and f.e., sling swivels with sling, adj. peep sight **$141.95**

Hi-Standard Flite-King Skeet

Same as Flite-King DeLuxe except: No recoil pad; 26" Skeet choke bbl.; all external parts high polished; internal parts super finished; better grade American walnut stock (14"x1½"x2½") and fore-end with cabinet finish. Wgt. 12 ga 7½ lbs., 20, 6¼ lbs., 28 and 410 ga. 6¼ lbs. **$141.95**

Hi-Standard Flite-King Trap

Same features as Flite-King Skeet except: 30" full choke; (14⅜"x1½"x1⅞") has recoil pad. About 8¼ lbs. 12 ga. only . . **$151.95**

ITHACA MODEL 37 FEATHERLIGHT

Gauge: 12, 16, 20 (5-shot; 3-shot plug furnished).
Action: Slide; takedown; bottom ejection.
Barrel: 26", 28", 30" in 12 ga. 26" or 28" in 16 or 20 ga. (Full, Mod. or Imp. Cyl.).
Stock: 14"x1⅝"x2⅝". Checkered walnut capped p.g. stock and fore-end.
Weight: 12 ga. 6½ lbs., 16 ga. 6 lbs., 20 ga. 5¾ lbs.
Features: Ithaca Raybar front sight; decorated receiver; crossbolt safety; action release for removing shells.
Price: . . . . **$129.95**   With vent. rib stock (14" x 1½" x 2½") **$154.95**

Ithaca Model 37 Supreme

Same as Model 37 except: hand checkered beavertail fore-end and p.g. stock, Ithaca recoil pad and vent. rib **$229.95**
37 Supreme also with Skeet (14"x1½"x2½") or Trap (14½"x1½"x1⅞") stocks at no extra charge. Other options available at extra charge.

Ithaca Model 37 De Luxe Featherlight

Same as Model 37 except: checkered stock with p.g. cap; beavertail fore-end; recoil pad. Wgt. 12 ga. 6¾ lbs.
Price: . . . . **$134.95**   With vent. rib **$159.95**

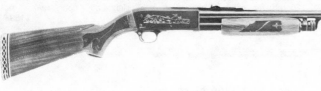

Ithaca Model 37 Deerslayer

Same as Model 37 except: 26" or 20" bbl. designed for rifled slugs; sporting rear sight, Raybar front sight; rear sight ramp grooved for Redfield long eye relief scope mount. 12, 16, or 20 gauge. With checkered stock, beavertail fore-end and recoil pad.
Price: **$144.95**
6Price: As above with special select walnut stock **$164.95**

MARLIN 120 MAGNUM PUMP GUN

Gauge: 12 ga. (2¾" or 3" chamber) 5-shot; 3-shot plug furnished.
Action: Hammerless, side ejecting, slide action.
Barrel: 26" (Imp. Cyl.), 28" (Mod.) or 30" (Full), with vent. rib.
Stock: Checkered walnut, capped p.g., semi-beavertail fore-end (14"x1½"x2⅜").
Weight: About 7¾ lbs. 45" to 49" over-all.
Features: Interchangeable bbls., slide lock release; large button cross-bolt safety.
Price: **$150.00**

U.S. SHOTGUNS—SLIDE ACTION

MOSSBERG MODEL 500 PUMP GUN
Gauge: 12, 16 (2¾"), 20; 3" (6-shot, 3-shot plug furnished).
Action: Slide, takedown; safety on top of receiver.
Barrel: 26" (Imp. Cyl.) 28" (Full or Mod.), 30" (Full), 12 ga. only. Also 12 ga. 18½" cylinder, for police only).
Stock: 14"x1½"x2½". Walnut p.g., extension fore-end. Recoil pad. 13 oz. steel plug furnished for use with Magnum barrel.
Weight: 12 ga. 6¾ lbs., 45¼" over-all (26" bbl.).
Features: Easy interchangeability of barrels; side ejection; disconnecting trigger makes doubles impossible; straight-line feed.
Price: Standard barrel **$98.75**
Price: With C-Lect Choke, 3" Mag., or 24" Slugster bbls. **$105.50**
Price: Extra barrel, 2¾" chamber **$23.75**
Price: Extra Magnum, C-Lect Choke or Slug, bbl. **$31.25**

Mossberg Model 500 Super Grade
Similar to the Model 500 except: vent. rib bbls. in 12 ga. (2¾") or 20 ga. (3"); 26" (Skeet), 28" (Mod., Full), and 30" Full (12 ga. only) 2¾" or 3" mag. Checkered p.g. and fore-end stock with fluted comb and recoil pad (14"x1½"x2½").
Price: 12 or 20 ga. **$121.00**
Price: 12 ga. 3" Magnum or C-Lect Choke 12 and 20 ga. **$130.35**

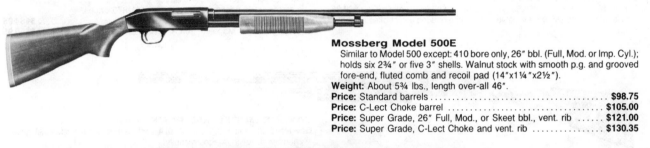

Mossberg Model 500E
Similar to Model 500 except: 410 bore only, 26" bbl. (Full, Mod. or Imp. Cyl.); holds six 2¾" or five 3" shells. Walnut stock with smooth p.g. and grooved fore-end, fluted comb and recoil pad (14"x1¼"x2½").
Weight: About 5¾ lbs., length over-all 46".
Price: Standard barrels **$98.75**
Price: C-Lect Choke barrel **$105.00**
Price: Super Grade, 26" Full, Mod., or Skeet bbl., vent. rib **$121.00**
Price: Super Grade, C-Lect Choke and vent. rib **$130.35**

Mossberg Model 500 APR Pigeon Grade
Similar to Model 500, but with vent. rib, rubber recoil pad, hand checkering, scroll engraving on action.
Price: **$143.65**
Price: 500 APTR trap gun 30" full choke barrel, M.C. stock, 14½"x1½"x2", additional barrels available. **$150.00**

Remington 870 Magnum
Same as the M870 except 3" chamber, 12 ga. 30" bbl. (Mod. or Full), 20 ga. 28" bbl. (Mod. or Full). Recoil pad installed. Wgt., 12 ga. 8 lbs., 20 ga. 7½ lbs.
Price: Plain bbl. .... **$149.95**   Vent. rib bbl. **$174.95**
Price: Left hand model **$179.95**

REMINGTON 870 ALL AMERICAN
Gauge: 12 only.
Barrel: 30" full choke.
Weight: 7 lbs.
Stock: Select walnut, fluted extension fore end, cut checkered.
Features: Receiver, trigger guard and breech fully engraved. Special "All American" shield fitted to left side of receiver. RK-W finished wood. Pistol grip cap has gold plate for initials. Supplied with luggage type, foam lined case.
Price: Standard or Monte Carlo stock **$550.00**

Remington Model 870 Brushmaster Deluxe
Carbine version of the M870 with 20" bbl. (Imp. Cyl.) for rifled slugs. 40½" over-all, wgt. 6½ lbs. Recoil pad. Adj. rear, ramp front sights. 12 or 20 ga.
Deluxe **$149.95**

REMINGTON 870 WINGMASTER PUMP GUN
Gauge: 12, 16, 20, (5-shot; 3-shot wood plug).
Action: Takedown, slide action.
Barrel: 12, 16, 20, ga., 26" (Imp. Cyl.); 28" (Mod. or Full); 12 ga., 30" (Full).
Stock: 14"x1⅝"x2½". Checkered walnut, p.g.; fluted extension fore-end; fitted rubber recoil pad.
Weight: 7 lbs., 12 ga. (7¾ lbs. with Vari-Weight plug); 6¾ lbs., 16 ga.; 6½ lbs., 20 ga. 48½" over-all (28" bbl.).
Features: Double action bars, crossbolt safety. Receiver machined from solid steel. Hand fitted action.
Price: Plain bbl. .... **$129.95**   Vent. rib **$154.95**
Price: Riot gun, 18" or 20" Riot bore, (12 ga. only) **$114.95**
Price: Riot gun, 20" Imp. Cyl., rifle sights **$119.95**

U.S. SHOTGUNS—SLIDE ACTION

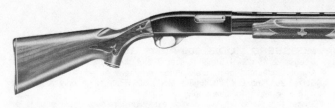

Remington 870 SA Skeet
Same as the M870 except: 26″ bbl. Skeet bored. Vent. rib with ivory front and white metal middle beads. 14″x1⅝″x2½″ stock with rubber recoil pad, 12 or 20 ga. only **$159.95**
Add **$25.00** for Cutts comp.

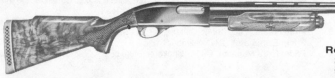

Remington 870D Tournament
Same as 870 except: better walnut, hand checkering, Engraved receiver & bbl. Vent.-rib. Stock dimensions to order **$595.00**

Remington 870F Premier
Same as M8700, except select walnut, better engraving **$1295.00**

Remington 870 Extra Barrels
Plain **$39.95**. Vent. rib **$64.95**. Vent. rib Skeet **$69.95**. Vent. rib Trap **$69.95**. With rifle sights **$50.95**. Available in the same gauges and chokes as shown on guns.

Remington 870 TB Trap
Same as the M870 except: 12 ga. only, 30″ (Mod., Full) vent. rib. bbl., ivory front and white metal middle beads. Special sear, hammer and trigger assy. 14⅜″x1½″x1⅞″ stock with recoil pad. Hand fitted action and parts. Wgt. 8 lbs. **$194.95**
Price: With Monte Carlo stock **$204.95**
Price: Left hand model **$199.95**

Remington 870 Small Gauges
Exact copies of the large ga. Model 870, except that guns are offered in 20, 28 and 410 ga. 25″ barrel (Full, Mod., Imp. Cyl.).
Plain barrel **$139.95**
D and F grade prices same as large ga. M870 prices.
Price: With vent. rib barrel **$164.95**
Price: Lightweight Magnum, 20 ga. (5¾ lbs.) **$159.95**

Savage Model 30-T
Same specifications as 12 ga., M30 except: 30″ Full Choke bbl. with 3″ chamber; Monte Carlo stock with trap dimensions (14⅝″x1½″x1½″x2¼″). Recoil pad. Over-all 50″. 8 lbs. **$129.95**

Savage Model 30 Field Grade
Same as the Model 30 except plain bbl. and receiver, hard rubber buttplate **$99.95**. As M30 AC with adj. choke **$104.95**

SAVAGE MODEL 30-D PUMP GUN
Gauge: 12, 20, and 410, 5-shot (410, 4-shot) 3-shot plug furnished. All gauges chambered for 3″ Magnum shells.
Action: Slide, hammerless, take-down; side ejection; top tang safety.
Barrel: Vent. rib. 12, 20 ga. 26″ (Imp. Cyl.); 28″ (Mod. or Full); 12 ga., 30″ (Full); 410, 26″ (Full).
Stock: 14″x1½″x2½″. Walnut, checkered p.g., grooved extension fore-end, recoil pad.
Weight: 7 lbs. (410, 6¼ lbs.). Over-all 49½″ (30″ bbl.).
Features: Decorated lightweight receiver; plated trigger.
Price: **$119.95**

Savage Model 30 Slug Gun
Same as the Model 30 Field Grade but with 22″ bbl., 12 or 20 ga. only, with rifle sights **$104.95**

SEARS TED WILLIAMS MODEL 200 PUMP GUN
Gauge: 12, (2¾″) and 20 (3″ chamber) (5 shot; 3-shot plug installed).
Action: Slide, front-locking rotating bolt.
Barrel: 28″ Full or Mod. Vent.-rib.
Stock: Walnut finished buttstock and fore-end; recoil pad, checkered p.g. with cap and fore-end. White line spacers.
Weight: About 7 lbs.; 48⅝″ over-all (28″ bbl.).
Features: Alloy receiver, non-glare serrated top; engine turned bolt; cross-bolt safety. Interchangeable bbls., no special tools required, $24 extra.
Price: **$144.00**

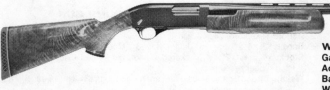

WEATHERBY PATRICIAN PUMP
Gauge: 12 only, 2¾″ chamber.
Action: Short stroke slide action.
Barrel: 26″ (Mod. Imp. Cyl, Skeet), 28″ (Full, Mod.), 30″ (Full) Vent. Rib.
Weight: About 7½ lbs. **Length:** 48⅛ (28″ bbl.)
Stock: Walnut hand checkered p.g. and fore-end, white line spacers at p.g. cap and recoil pad.
Features: Short stoke action, hidden magazine cap, crossbolt safety. Extra interchangeable bbls. **$69.95**
Price: **$169.50**

U.S. SHOTGUNS—SLIDE ACTION

WINCHESTER 12 SUPER PIGEON PUMP GUN
Gauge: 12 only, 6-shot (2-shot plug installed).
Action: Slide, one-piece receiver, takedown, side ejection.
Barrel: 26″, 28″, 30″, floating vent. rib, any standard choke.
Stock: Full fancy American walnut, dim. to order within mfg. limits, hand-finished, "A" checkering or carving (see Win. catalog), Monte Carlo, cheekpiece or offset avail. at extra charge.
Features: Receiver engraved, "1A," "1B," or "1C" type (see Win. catalog). Working parts hand fitted.
Weight: 7¾ lbs.
Price: $900.00

WESTERN FIELD 550 PUMP SHOTGUN
Gauge: 12, 20 and 410.
Action: Slide action, takedown; top tang safety.
Barrel: 12 ga., 30″ (Full), 28″ (Mod.). 20 ga., 28″ (Full or Mod.). 410, 26″ (Full).
Stock: Walnut finished p.g. stock, molded buttplate, serrated fore-end.
Weight: 8½ lbs.
Features: Straight-line feed, interchangeable bbls., trigger disconnector prevents doubling.
Price: . . . . **$92.95**   410 (with rubber buttplate) **$97.99**
As above, but with variable choke in 12, 16 or 20 ga. **$102.99**
Slug gun with 24 bbl. without choke **$102.99**
Magnum 12 ga., 30″ bbl. (Full Choke) **$102.99**
Vent. rib models available, fixed or variable choke as above **$119.45**
to **$127.95**

WINCHESTER 12 FIELD PUMP SHOTGUN
Gauge: 12 only, 6-shot (2-shot plug installed).
Barrel: 26″ (Imp. Cyl.), 28″ (Mod.), 30″ (Full), 2¾″ only.
Weight: 7¾ lbs. **Length:** 45¾″ (26″ bbl.).
Stock: 14″x1½″x2½″. Semi-fancy walnut, checkered p.g. and fore-end.
Features: Ventilated rib, hand checkered, engine turned bolt.
Price: **$350.00**

WINCHESTER 12 SKEET
Same as Model 12 except available only with 26″ Skeet bored bbl. 14″x1½″x2½″ stock with recoil pad **$375.00**

WINCHESTER 12 TRAP
Same as Model 12 except: 30″ full choke vent. rib bbl. only. 49¾″ overall. 14⅜″x1⅜″x1⅞″ stock w/recoil pad **$375.00**
With Monte Carlo stock, 14⅜″x1½″x2⅛″ **$385.00**

Winchester 1200 Skeet
Same as M1200 except: 12 and 20 ga., 26″ vent. rib bbl., b. t. fore-end. metal, middle red front sights **$205.95**

Winchester 1200 Field 3″ Magnum
Same as 1200 except: 12 and 20 ga. only, 2¾″ or 3″ shells, 28″ and 30″ full choke bbls., 3 lbs. with 38″ bbl., 48⅝″ over-all.
Price: . . . . **$144.95**   With vent. rib **$169.95**

WINCHESTER 1200 FIELD PUMP GUN
Gauge: 12, 16 and 20 (5-shot; 3-shot plug installed).
Action: Slide; front locking 4-lug rotating bolt locks into bbl. Alloy receiver, cross-bolt safety in front of trigger guard. Take-down.
Barrel: 26″ (Imp. Cyl.), 28″ (Mod., Full) and 30″ Full (12 ga. only). Metal bead front sight.
Stock: 14″x1⅜″x2⅜″. American walnut with new-design checkered p.g. and fore-end; fluted comb, recoil pad. Steel p.g. cap.
Weight: 12 ga. 6½ lbs. with 26″ bbl. 46⅝″ over-all.
Price: . . . . **$123.95**   With vent. rib **$148.95**

Winchester 1200 Trap
Same as M1200 except: 12-ga. only, 30″ Full choke vent. rib bbl., 51″ over-all. 14⅜″x1⅜″x1⅞″ stock with recoil pad, b. t. fore-end. Metal, middle, red front sights **$205.95**
With Monte Carlo stock, 14⅜″x1⁷⁄₁₆″x2⅛″x1½″ **$215.95**
With Monte Carlo stock and Winchoke **$226.95**
Field grade walnut stock, Monte Carlo **$164.95**

Winchester 1200 Deer Gun
Same as M1200 except: 12 ga. only, 22″ bbl. bored for rifled slugs; rifle-type sights, rear adj. for e. only **$138.95**
Winchester 1200 Extra Barrels: Field and Riot w/o sights, 12, 16, 20 ga. **$39.45.** Field with vent. rib, 12, 16, 20 ga. **$71.45.** Riot with sights and Deer Gun, 12 ga. **$50.45.** Trap, 12 ga., Full choke 30″ only, Skeet, 12, 20 ga. 26″ only **$81.95**
Winchester 1200 with interchangeable choke tubes which are screwed into the barrel and tightened with supplied wrench. Available in 12, 16 and 20 ga. (28″) Mod. tube. Price: Field **$137.95** Vent. rib **$162.95.** Extra tubes in Full, Mod. or Imp. Cyl. **$4.95.** Wrench **$1.25.**

U.S. SHOTGUNS—DOUBLE BARREL

BROWNING B-SS
Gauge: 12 only (2¾" and 2¾" Magnum).
Action: Top lever break-open action, top tang safety, single trigger.
Barrel: 26" (Mod. and Full or Imp. Cyl. and Mod.), 28" (Mod. and Full).
Weight: 7¼ lbs.
Stock: 14¾"x1⅝"x2½". Walnut, hand checkered. Full p.g., full beavertail fore-end.
Features: Automatic safety, automatic ejectors. Hand engraved receiver, mechanical trigger.
Price: **$234.50**

ITHACA SKB MODEL 150
Same as SKB 100 except: Beavertail fore-end and extensively etched scrollwork frame.
Price: **$239.95**

ITHACA SKB 100 FIELD GRADE DOUBLE
Gauge: 12 (2¾" chambers) and 20 (3").
Action: Top lever, hammerless, boxlock, automatic safety, single selective trigger, non-automatic extractor.
Barrel: 12 ga. 26" (Imp. Cyl., Mod.). 28⅛ or 30" (Mod., Full). 20 ga. 28" (Mod., Full). 25" (Imp. Cyl., Mod.).
Stock: 14"x1½"x2⅝". Walnut, hand checkered p.g. and fore-end, p.g. cap, fluted comb.
Weight: 7 lbs. (12 ga.); 6 lbs. (20 ga.).
Features: Automatic safety. Chrome lined action and barrels, hand engraved receiver.
Price: **$209.95**

Ithaca SKB 200E Skeet Grade
Same as 200E Deluxe Field Grade except: recoil pad, non-auto. safety. Bbls. 26" 12 ga. or 25" 20 ga. (Skeet, Skeet). Wgt. 7¼ and 6¼ lbs.
Price: **$284.95**

ITHACA SKB 200E DELUX FIELD GRADE DOUBLE
Same as 100 Grade Field except: automatic selective ejectors, bead middle sight and scroll engraving on receiver, beavertail fore-end. White line spacers. Gold plated trigger and nameplate **$279.95**

Ithaca SKB 280 English Double
Like the 200 Field Grade except: hand-checkered straight grip stock with wrap-around checkering; semi-beavertail fore-end. Receiver hand engraved with quail and English scroll. Durable, simulated oil-finished walnut stock.
Price: **$289.95**

MARLIN L. C. SMITH FIELD DOUBLE
Gauge: 12 only (2¾" chambers).
Action: Sidelock, double trigger. Case hardened frame.
Barrel: 28" (Mod. & Full).
Stock: Select walnut with capped p.g. checkered, (14"x1½"x2½").
Weight: 6¾ lbs.
Features: Vent. rib, standard extractors, top auto. tang safety.
Price: **$325.00**
Price: Deluxe Model with full beavertail fore-end, better wood and Simmons floating vent rib **$400.00**

Savage Model 500 Double
Like the Fox B-SE except 12 or 20 ga. only, game scene and case hardened finish on receiver. White spacers at buttplate and capped p.g. . . **$174.95**

SAVAGE FOX MODEL B-SE Double
Gauge: 12, 16, 20, 410 (20, 2¾" and 3"; 410, 2½" and 3" shells).
Action: Hammerless, takedown; non-selective single trigger; auto. safety. Automatic ejectors.
Barrel: 12, 20 ga. 26" (Imp. Cyl., Mod.); 12 ga. (Mod., Full); 16 ga. 30" (Mod., Full); 410, 26" (Full, Full). Vent. rib on all.
Stock: 14"x1½"x2½". Walnut, checkered p.g. and beavertail fore-end.
Weight: 12 ga. 7 lbs., 16 ga. 6¾ lbs., 20 ga. 6½ lbs., 410 ga. 6¼ lbs.
Features: Decorated, satin black finish frame; white bead front and middle sights.
Price: **$164.95**
Also available with double triggers, case hardened frame, without white line spacers and auto. ejectors as Model B **$139.95**

U.S. SHOTGUNS—DOUBLE BARREL

SAVAGE-STEVENS MODEL 311 DOUBLE
Gauge: 12, 16, 20, 410 (20 and 410, 3" chambers).
Action: Top lever, hammerless; double triggers, auto top tang safety.
Barrel: 12, 16, 20 ga. 36" (Imp. Cyl., Mod.); 12 ga. 28" (Mod., Full); 12 ga. 30" (Mod., Full); 410 ga. 26" (Full, Full).
Stock: 14"x1½"x2½". Walnut finish, p.g. fluted comb.
Weight: 7-8 lbs. **Length:** 45¾" (30" bbl.).
Features: Box type frame, case-hardened finish.
Price: **$109.95**

UNIVERSAL DOUBLE WING DOUBLE
Gauge: 12, 20 and 410, 3" chambers
Action: Top break, boxlock.
Barrel: 26" (Imp. Cyl., Mod.); 28" or 30" (Mod., Full; Imp., Mod.; Full & Full).
Stock: Walnut p.g. and fore-end, checkered.
Weight: About 7 lbs.
Features: Double triggers; Recoil pad. Beavertail style fore-end.
Price: **$134.95**
Price: 10 ga. 3½" chamber 32" Full and Full (M2030) **$164.95**

WINCHESTER 21 CUSTOM DOUBLE GUN
12, 16 or 20 ga. Almost any choke or bbl. length combination. Matted rib, 2¾" chambers, rounded frame, stock of AA-grade full fancy American walnut to customer's dimensions; straight or p.g., cheekpiece, Monte Carlo and/or offset; field. Skeet or trap fore-end.
Full fancy checkering, engine-turned receiver parts, gold plated trigger and gold oval name plate (optional) with three initials **$1,650.00**

Winchester 21 Pigeon grade
Same as Custom grade except: 3" chambers, available in 12 and 20 ga.; matted or vent. rib, leather covered pad (optional); style "A" stock carving and style "6" engraving (see Win. catalog); gold inlaid p.g. cap, gold name-plate or 3 gold initials in guard **$3,250.00**

Winchester 21 Grand American
Same as Custom and Pigeon grades except: style "B" stock carving, with style "6" engraving, all figures gold inlaid; extra pair of bbls. with beavertail fore-end, engraved and carved to match rest of gun; full leather trunk case for all, with canvas cover **$4,250.00**

U.S. SHOTGUNS—OVER-UNDER

BROWNING SUPERPOSED Standard
Gauge: 12 & 28, 2¾" chamber; 20 & 410, 3" chamber. Any combination of Full, Imp. Mod., Mod., Imp. Cyl., Skeet, and Cyl. chokes.
Action: Takedown; single selective gold plated trigger; automatic ejectors, manual safety combined in thumb piece with bbl. selector mechanism. Actions in proportion to gauge.
Barrels: 12, 20, 28 and 410 ga., 26½" or 28", vent. rib. Solid raised rib available on special order. Steel bead front sight.
Stock: 12 ga. 14¼"x1⅝"x2½"; 20, 28 and 410 14¼"x1½"x2⅜". Select walnut, hand rubbed finish, 20-line hand checkering on semi-p.g. and fore-end. Deluxe models have fancier, finer checkering.
Weight: With 28" bbls. 12 ga. 7¾ lbs.; 20 ga. 6¾ lbs.; 28 ga. 6⅝ lbs.; 410 ga. 6⅞ lbs.
Features: Grade 1, blued steel with hand engraved scroll and rosette designs. Pigeon and Diana grades, steel in silver gray tone with hand engraved game scenes showing greater artistic design with each successive grade. Midas grade has specially blued steel with deeply hand carved background and hand engraved 18K gold-inlaid game birds.
Price: Grade 1, 12 or 20 ga . . . .**$440.00** 28 or 410 ga **$550.00**
Price: (28 & 410 ga. only) Pigeon Grade **$790.00**, Diana **$1,050.00**, Midas Grade **$1,475.00**

BROWNING SUPERPOSED LIGHTNING
Same as Standard except: 7-7¼ lbs. in 12 ga. 6-6¼ lbs. in 20 ga. Grade 1 **$530.00**, Pigeon **$790.00**, Diana **$1,050.00**, Midas **$1,475.00**.

Browning Superposed Lightning Trap 12
Same as Browning Lightning Superposed except: semi-beavertail fore-end and ivory sights; stock, 14⅜" x 1⁷/₁₆" x 1⅝". 7¾ lbs. 30" (Full & Full, Full & Imp. Mod. or Full and Mod.) Grade 1 **$540.00** Pigeon **$790.00**, Diana **$1,050.00**, Midas **$1,475.00**.

Browning Superposed Magnum 12
Same as Browning Standard 12 ga. Superposed except 3" chambers; 30" (Full and Full or Full and Mod.) barrels, Stock, 14¼"x1⅝"x2½" with factory fitted recoil pad. Weight 8 lbs. Grade 1, **$530.00**, Pigeon **$790.00**, Diana **$1,050.00**, Midas **$1,475.00**.

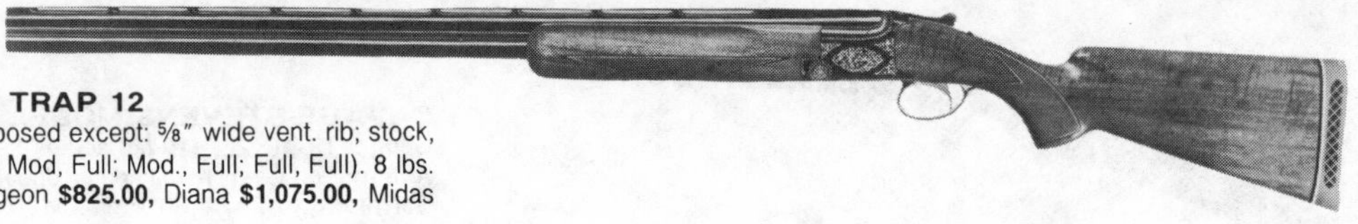

U.S. SHOTGUNS—OVER-UNDER

SUPERPOSED BROADWAY TRAP 12

Same as Browning Lightning Superposed except: ⅝" wide vent. rib; stock, 14⅜"x1⁷⁄₁₆"x1⅝". 30" or 32" (Imp. Mod, Full; Mod., Full; Full, Full). 8 lbs. with 32" bbls. Grade 1 **$560.00**, Pigeon **$825.00**, Diana **$1,075.00**, Midas **$1,515.00**.

Browning Superposed Standard Skeet

Same as Superposed Standard except: 26½" or 28" bbls. (Skeet, Skeet). Wgt. 6½-7¾ lbs. 12 and 20 ga. Grade 1 **$525.00**; (28 and 410 ga). **$560.00**, Pigeon **$825.00**, Diana **$1,075.00**, Midas **$1,515.00**

Browning Superposed Lightning Skeet

Same as Standard Skeet except: 12 and 20 ga. only. Wgt. 6½-7¾ lbs. Grade 1 **$540.00**, Pigeon **$740.00**, Diana **$1,075.00**, Midas **$1,515.00**

Browning Superposed Combinations

Standard and Lightning models are available with these factory fitted extra barrels: 12 and 20 ga., same gauge bbls.; 12 ga., 20 ga. bbls.; 20 ga., extra sets 28 and/or 410 gauge; 28 ga., extra 410 bbls. Extra barrels may be had in Lightning weights with Standard models and vice versa. Prices range from $875.00 (12, 20 ga., one set extra bbls. same gauge) for the Grade 1 Standard to about $2,500.00 for the Midas grade in various combinations, all as cased sets.

BROWNING SUPERPOSED SUPER-LIGHT

Gauge: 12, & 20 2¾" chamber.
Action: Boxlock, top lever, single selective trigger. Bbl. selector combined with manual tang safety.
Barrels: 26½" (Mod. & Full, or Imp. Cyl. & Mod.)
Stock: Straight grip (14¼" x 1⅝" x 2½") hand checkered (fore-end and grip) select walnut.
Weight: 6⅜ lbs., average.
Features: Slender, tapered solid rib. Hand rubbed finish, engraved receiver.
Price: Grade 1 .... **$560.00**
Pigeon **$825.00**
Diana **$1,075.00**
Midas **$1,515.00**

ITHACA MIRAGE O/U

Gauge: 12 only (2¾" chambers).
Action: Boxlock type, interchangeable hammer-trigger group. Single selective trigger, specify choice of firing order.
Barrel: 28", 30", or 32" (Skeet and Skeet or Extra-Full and Mod.). Vent. rib.
Weight: 8¼ lbs. **Length:** 44" over-all.
Stock: Walnut, hand checkered with schnabel fore-end, 1½"x2⅜"x14". Rubber recoil pad.
Price: Trap model $1295.00
Price: Skeet model $1295.00

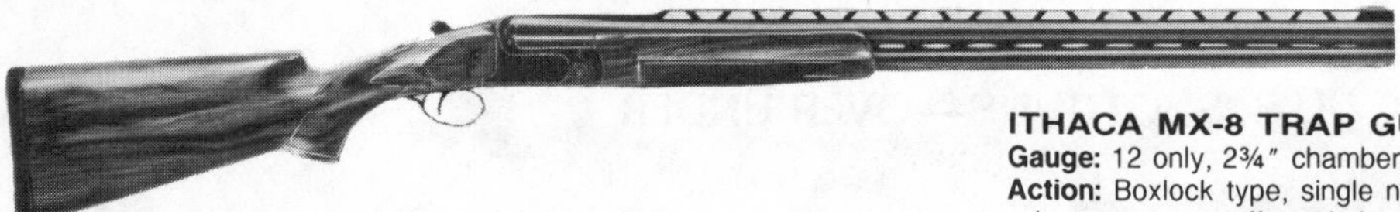

ITHACA COMPETITION I TRAP O/U

Gauge: 12 only, 2¾" chambers.
Action: Boxlock type, interchangeable hammer-trigger group. Single non-selective trigger, specify choice of firing order.
Barrel: 30" or 32", upper Full; lower, Imp.-Mod., vent rib has concave surface with deep cuts.
Stock: Interchangeable, 6 standard (1³⁄₁₆" to 1½" at comb x1⅜" to 1⅞" at heel) and 3 Monte Carlo (1⅜" to 1⁹⁄₁₆"x1⅜" to 1⁹⁄₁₆") of walnut; all have 14½" pull. Fore-end has slight taper and finger groove for firm grip.
Weight: About 7¾ lbs.
Features: Extra trigger-hammer groups are available to change firing sequence and/or trigger pull. Custom stocks also available.
Price: $795.00
Extra trigger-hammer group 75.00
Extra stock 85.00

ITHACA MX-8 TRAP GUN

Gauge: 12 only, 2¾" chambers.
Action: Boxlock type, single non-selective trigger; interchangeable trigger-hammer group offers choice of firing order.
Barrel: 30" or 32", especially bored for international clay target shooting. High concave vent rib has 5" ramp.
Stock: Custom, finely checkered (oiled or lacquer finish) European walnut, interchangeable with other models, 9 available including Monte Carlo.
Weight: About 8 lbs.
Features: Ventilated middle rib has additional vent ports for maximum heat dissipation, better balance and smoother swing.
Price: $1,295.00
Extra trigger-hammer group 75.00
Extra stock 85.00

ITHACA MX-8 COMBINATION

Same as MX-8 Trap Gun except comes with interchangeable single barrel (32" or 34").
Price: $1795.00

ITHACA COMPETITION I SKEET O/U

Gauge: 12 only, 2¾" chambers.
Action: Boxlock type, interchangeable hammer-trigger group. Single non-selective trigger.
Barrel: 26¾" (Skeet & Skeet). Vent rib has concave surface with deep cuts.
Stock: 14½"x1½"x2⅜", interchangeable walnut, custom stocks available.
Weight: About 7¾ lbs.
Features: Extra trigger-hammer groups to change firing order and/or weight of pull. Leather faced recoil pad has bevelled heel that will not catch. Extra stocks interchange for different style and dimension.
Price: $875.00
Extra trigger-hammer group 75.00

ITHACA LIGHT GAME MODEL

Gauge: 12 only (2¾" chambers).
Action: Boxlock type interchangeable hammer-trigger group. Offers choice of firing order. Single non-selective trigger.
Barrel: 27½" (Mod. and Full, Imp. Cyl. and Full, Imp. Cyl. and Mod.) Vent. rib.
Weight: 6¾ lbs. **Length:** 44½ overall.
Stock: French walnut. Hand checkered p.g., fore-end and butt, schnabel fore-end, 1½"x2⅜"x14".
Features: Hand engraved, case hardened frame.
Price: **$795.00**

ITHACA SKB 500 FIELD GRADE O-U

Gauge: 12 (2¾" chambers), 20 (3").
Action: Top lever, hammerless, boxlock; gold-plated single selective trigger; automatic ejectors, non-auto safety.
Barrel: 26" vent. rib (Imp. Cyl., Mod.); 28" (Imp. cyl., Mod. or Mod., Full); 30" (Mod., Full); 12 ga., 2¾" chambers. 26" (Imp. Cyl., Mod.); 28" (Mod., Full); 20 ga., 3" chambers.
Stock: 14"x1½"x2⅝". Walnut, checkered p.g. and fore-end, p.g. cap, fluted comb.
Weight: 7½ lbs. (12); 6½ lbs. (20).
Features: Border scroll engraved receiver. Chrome lined bbls. and action. Raybar front sight.
Price: **$299.95**

ITHACA SKB 600 TRAP GRADE O/U

Same as 500 Field Grade except 30" bbl. (Imp. Mod., Full, or Full, Full), fine scroll engraved receiver; bead middle sight; Monte Carlo stock (14½"x1½"x1½"x2"), p.g. white line spacer and recoil pad.
Price: **$374.95**
Field Grade 600, no recoil pad or Monte Carlo **$359.95**
Field Grade 12 ga., 3" Magnum **$369.95**
Trap Grade 700, select walnut oil finished stock and band engraved receiver
Price: **$425.00**

Ithaca SKB 600 Skeet Grade O/U

Same as 600 Trap except: 26" or 28" bbls. (Skeet, skeet), stock (14"x1½"x2⅝"), standard buttplate and whiteline spacer. Wgt. 7½ lbs.
Price: **$369.95**
Skeet Grade 700, select walnut oil finished stock and band engraved receiver **$425.00**

Ithaca SKB 700 Skeet Set O/U

Same as SKB 700 Skeet with above three barrels and deluxe carrying case.
Price: **$895.00**

SAVAGE MODEL 24-D O/U

Caliber: Top bbl. 22 S, L, LR or 22 Mag.; bottom bbl. 20 or 410 gauge.
Action: Two-way top lever opening, low rebounding visible hammer, single trigger, barrel selector spur on hammer, separate extractors.
Barrel: 24", separated barrels.
Weight: 6¾ lbs. **Length:** 40".
Stock: Walnut, checkered p.g. and fore-end (14"x1½"x2½").
Sights: Ramp front, rear open adj. for e.
Features: Receiver grooved for scope mounting.
Price: **$79.95**

SAVAGE MODEL 24-F.G. O/U

Same as Model 24-D except: color case hardened frame, stock is walnut finished hardwood, no checkering or cheek piece.
Price: : **$66.95**

SAVAGE MODEL 24-C O/U

Caliber: Top bbl. 22 S, L, LR; bottom bbl. 20 gauge cyl. bore.
Action: Take-down, low rebounding visible hammer. Single trigger, barrel selector spur on hammer.
Barrel: 20" separate barrels.
Weight: 5¾ lbs. **Length:** 35" (taken down 20").
Stock: Walnut finished hardwood, straight grip.
Sights: Ramp front, rear open adj. for e.
Features: Trap door butt holds two shotshells and ten 22 cartridges, comes with special carrying case. Measures 5"x22" when in case.
Price: **$74.95**

U.S. SHOTGUNS—OVER-UNDER

Savage Model 330 O/U Set
Identical to the Model 330 but with two sets of barrels, one in 12 ga. the other in 20 (Mod. & Full). Same fore-end fits both sets of bbls. Comes with padded case with pocket for extra bbl.
Price: Factory fitted **$287.95**
Price: Extra 20 ga. bbl. only (must be fitted at the factory) **$110.00**

SAVAGE 333-T
Same specifications as Model 330 except has trap specifications and features: 30" bbl. choked Imp. Mod. and Full, manually operated top tang safety (disconnects trigger from sears), stock measures 14½"x1½"x1½" at Monte Carlo, 2½" heel. Over-all length 47", taken down 30", weight 7¾ lbs. Has extra-wide ventilated rib, extractors, recoil pad.
Price: **$284.95**

SEARS TED WILLIAMS O/U SHOTGUN
Gauge: 12 ga. (2¾") or 20 ga. (2¾" and 3").
Action: Boxlock, single selective trigger, selective auto-ejectors.
Barrel: 28" (Full & Mod.), 26" (Mod. & Imp. Cyl.).
Stock: Walnut, hand checkered p.g. and fore-end.
Weight: About 6¾ lbs. 45" over-all.
Features: Hand engraved steel receiver. Top Tang safety barrel selector. Full vent rib on chrome-lined barrels. Recoil pad installed.
Price: **$335.00**

Winchester 101 Trap Gun
Same as the 101 Field gun except: Metal front and middle bead sights. 30" (Full & Full) bbl. only. 14⅜"x1⅜"x1⅞" stock with 1¼" pitch down and recoil pad. 12 ga. only. **$335.00**
With Monte Carlo stock (14⅜"x1⅜"x1⅜"x1⅞"), 30" or 32", Full and Full or Imp. Mod. and Full **$345.00**

Winchester 101 Combination Trap Set
Same as M101 Trap except: Single bbl. 32" or 34" (Full) and extra over-under bbls. 30" or 32" (Imp.-Mod & Full). Includes fitted trunk case **$535.00**
3-bbl. set: 32" single bbl. (Full), 32" single bbl. (Imp.-Mod.), and 32" over-under bbls. (Imp.-Mod. & Full) **$725.00**

Winchester 101 Single Barrel Trap Gun
Same as M101 Trap except: Single bbl. 34" (Full), 32" (Full) or 32" (Imp.-Mod.) Vent.-rib. 12 ga. only. Monte Carlo stock **$325.00**

Savage Model 24-V
Same as Model 24-DL except: 222 Rem. or 30-30 and 20 ga. only; satin-black frame and trigger; barrel band; folding leaf rear sight; rec. tapped for scope **$99.95**

SAVAGE MODEL 330 O/U
Gauge: 12, 2¾" chambers, 20 ga. 3" chambers.
Action: Top lever, break open. Selective single trigger, auto top tang safety locks trigger, coil springs.
Barrel: 26" (Mod. & Imp. Cyl.), 28" or 30" (Mod. & Full).
Stock: 14"x1½"x2½"). Walnut, checkered p.g. and fore-end, hard rubber plate.
Weight: About 7 lbs., 46½" (30" bbl.) over-all.
Features: Monoblock locking rails are engaged by locking shield that snaps forward as gun is closed. This shield overlaps the breech for added strength.
Price: **$199.95**

SAVAGE MODEL 440B O-U
Gauge: 12, 2¾" chambers, 20 ga. 3" chambers.
Action: Top lever, break open. Selective single trigger, auto. safety, all coil springs.
Barrel: 26" (Skeet & Skeet or Mod. & Imp. Cyl.), 28" (Mod. & Full), 30" 12 ga. only (Mod. & Full), all with vent rib and hard-chrome lined.
Stock: 14"x1½"x2½". French walnut, hand checkered p.g. and fore-end, hand rubbed finish, hard rubber buttplate.
Weight: 6½ lbs., length 42½"-46½" over-all.
Features: Hand engraved steel receiver. Simple extractors. Fast hammer fall.
Price: **$239.95**
Deluxe Grade 444B, with ejectors, single selective trigger and semi-beaver-tail fore-end **$289.95**

UNIVERSAL OVER WING O/U SHOTGUN
Gauge: 12, 20. 3" chamber.
Action: Top lever, hammerless, box lock, double triggers.
Barrel: 26" vent. rib (Imp. Cyl., & Mod.); 28" or 30" (Mod. & Full). Front & Middle sights.
Stock: 14"x1½"x2⅝". Walnut, checkered p.g. and fore-end. Recoil Pad.
Weight: 7½ lbs. (12); 6½ lbs. (20).
Price: **$219.95**
With single-trigger, engraved receiver and fancier stock **$249.95**

WEATHERBY REGENCY O/U SHOTGUN
Gauge: 12 ga. (2¾" chamber), 20 ga. (3" chamber).
Action: Boxlock (simulated side-lock) top lever break-open. Selective auto ejectors, single selective trigger (selector inside trigger guard).
Barrel: 28" with vent rib and bead front sight, Full & Mod., Mod. & Imp. Cyl. or Skeet & Skeet.
Stock: Amerocan walnut, checkered p.g. and fore-end (14¼"x1½"x2½").
Weight: 12 ga. 7⅜ lbs., 20 ga. 6⅞ lbs.
Features: Mechanically operated trigger. Top tang safety, Greener cross-bolt, fully engraved receiver, recoil pad installed.
Price: 12 or 20 ga. **$595.00**

WINCHESTER 101 OVER/UNDER Field Gun
Gauge: 12 and 28, 2¾"; 20 and 410, 3".
Action: Top lever, break open. Manual safety combined with bbl. selector at top of receiver tang.
Barrel: Vent. rib 26" 12, 26½", 20 and 410 (Imp. Cyl., Mod.), 28" (Mod & Full), 30" 12 only (Mod. & Full). Metal bead front sight. Chrome plated chambers and bores.
Stock: 14"x1½"x2½". Checkered walnut p.g. and fore-end; fluted comb.
Weight: 12 ga. 7¾ lbs. Others 6¼ lbs.; 44¾" over-all (28" bbls.).
Features: Single selective trigger, auto ejectors. Hand engraved receiver.
Price: 12 or 20 ga. **$314.95**
Price: 28 or 410 ga. **$331.95**

Winchester 101 Magnum Field Gun
Same as 101 Field Gun except: chambers 3" Magnum shells; 12 & 20 ga. 30" (Full & Full or Mod. & Full); hand-engraved receiver, select French walnut stock with fluted comb, hand-checkered pistol grip and beavertail fore-end with recoil pad **$314.95**

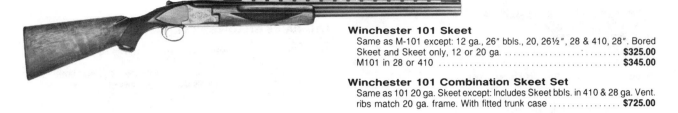

U.S. SHOTGUNS—OVER-UNDER

Winchester 101 Skeet
Same as M-101 except: 12 ga., 26″ bbls., 20, 26½″, 28 & 410, 28″. Bored Skeet and Skeet only, 12 or 20 ga. **$325.00**
M101 in 28 or 410 . . . . **$345.00**

Winchester 101 Combination Skeet Set
Same as 101 20 ga. Skeet except: Includes Skeet bbls. in 410 & 28 ga. Vent. ribs match 20 ga. frame. With fitted trunk case **$725.00**

U.S. SHOTGUNS—SINGLE BARREL

BROWNING BT-99 SINGLE BARREL TRAP
Gauge: 2¾″ 12 gauge only.
Action: Top lever break-open hammerless, engraved.
Barrel: 32″ or 34″ (Mod., Imp. Mod. or Full) with $^{11}/_{32}$″ wide, high post floating vent rib.
Stock: French walnut, hand checkered full p.g. and beavertail fore-end, factory fitted recoil pad (14⅜″x1$^{7}/_{16}$″x1⅝″).
Weight: 8 lbs. (32″ bbl.), 8⅛ lbs. (34″ bbl.).
Features: Automatic ejector, gold plated trigger has about 3½ lb. pull, no safety.
Price: **$339.50**

CLERKE FALLING BLOCK SHOTGUN
Gauge: 12, 20, 410 (2¾″ or 3″ magnums).
Weight: 6¼ lbs. (12 ga.). **Length:** 42″ to 52″ (12 ga.).
Stock: Walnut finish stock and fore-end. Full pistol grip.
Features: Exposed rebounding hammer, falling block side lever action, color case hardened frame. Vent. rib, trap grade stock and rubber recoil pad available as options.
Price: **$49.95**

GARCIA BRONCO 410 SHOTGUN
Lightweight single shot (3″ chamber), featuring swing-out chamber, skeletonized 1-pc. receiver and p.g. stock, push-button safety, 3½ lbs.
Price: **$26.95**

H & R HARRICH NO. 1
Gauge: 12 gauge only. 2¾″.
Barrel: 32″ or 34″.
Weight: 8½ lbs.
Stock: Select walnut, checkered p.g. and beavertail fore-end 14¾″x1¼″x1¼″x2″.
Features: Anson & Deeley type locking system with Kersten top locks and double under-locking lugs. Full length high line vent. rib. Hand engraved side locks.
Price: **$1500.00**

H & R TOPPER MODELS 158 and 198
Gauge: 12, 20 and 410. (2¾″ or 3″ chamber), 16 (2¾″ only).
Action: Takedown. Side lever opening. External hammer, auto ejection. Case hardened frame.
Barrel: 12 ga., 28″, 30″, 32″, 36″; 20 and 410 ga., 28″. (Full choke). 12, 16, 20 ga. available 28″ (Mod.).
Stock: Walnut finished hardwood; p.g., recoil pad. (14″x1¾″x2½″).
Weight: 5 to 6½ lbs., according to gauge and bbl. length.
Features: Self-adj. bbl. lock; coil springs throughout; auto. rebound hammer.
Price: M158 . . . . **$39.95**
  Model 198, Topper Deluxe Chrome frame, ebony finished stock. 20 ga. and 410, 28″ bbl. **$44.95**

H & R TOPPER BUCK MODEL 162
Same as M158 except 12 ga. 24″ cyl. bored bbl., adj. Lyman peep rear sight, blade front, 5½ lbs.; over-all 40″. Cross bolt safety: push-button action release, ... **$42.95**

H & R TOPPER JR. MODEL 490
Like M158 except ideally proportioned stock for the smaller shooter. Can be cheaply changed to full size. 20 ga. (Mod.) or 410 (Full) 26″ bbl. Weight 5 lbs., 40½″ over-all **$41.00**

Ithaca Model 66 Supersingle Youth
Same as the 66 Standard except: 20 (26″ Bbl., Mod.) and 410 ga. (26″ Bbl., Full) shorter stock with recoil pad **$43.95**
With vent. rib, 20 ga. only **$54.95**

ITHACA MODEL 66 SUPERSINGLE
Gauge: 12, 20, 410 (3″ chamber).
Action: Non-takedown; under lever opening.
Barrel: 12, 20 ga. 28″ (Mod., Full); 12 ga., 30″ (Full), 410, 26″ (Full).
Stock: Straight grip walnut-finish stock and fore-end.
Weight: About 7 lbs.
Features: Rebounding hammer independent of the lever.
Price: **$39.95**
  With vent. rib, 20 ga. only **$52.95**

Ithaca Model 66 RS Supersingle Buckbuster
Same as the Model 66 Standard except: 12 and 20 ga. only, 22″ bbl. with rifle sights, designed to shoot slugs **$52.95**
Heavy bbl. (12 ga. only) **$54.95**

U.S. SHOTGUNS—SINGLE BARREL

Ithaca 5E Grade Single Barrel Trap
Same as 4E except: Vent. rib bbl., better wood, more extensive engraving, and gold inlaid figures. Custom made: **$2,500.00**

Ithaca $4500 Grade Ejector
Same as 5E except: Special wood, better engraving, figures inlaid in green and yellow gold and platinum, gold plated trigger. **$4,500.00**

ITHACA 4 E GRADE SINGLE BARREL TRAP GUN
Gauge: 12 only.
Action: Top lever break open hammerless, dual locking lugs.
Barrel: 30″ or 32″, rampless rib.
Stock: (14½″x1½″x1⅞″). Select walnut, checkered p.g. and beavertail fore-end, p.g. cap, recoil pad, Monte Carlo comb, cheekpiece, Cast-on, cast-off or extreme deviation from standard stock dimensions $100 extra. Reasonable deviation allowed without extra charge.
Features: Frame, top lever and trigger guard engraved. Gold name plate in stock.
Price: Custom made:. **$1,750.00**

IVER JOHNSON CHAMPION
Gauge: 12, 20 or 410 (3″ chamber).
Barrel: 12 gauge, 28″ or 30″; 20 gauge, 28″; 410, 26″; full choke.
Stock: Walnut finish, trap style fore-end.
Features: Takedown action, automatic ejection.
Price: Either gauge **$49.95**

ITHACA PERAZZI SINGLE BARREL
Gauge: 12 (2¾″ chamber)
Action: Top lever, break open, top tang safety.
Barrel: 32″ or 34″; custom choking; ventilated rib.
Stock: Custom fitted European walnut in lacquered or oil finish.
Weight: About 8½ lbs.
Features: Hand-engraved receiver; interchangeable stocks available with some fitting.
Price: **$795.00**

SAVAGE MODEL 220L SINGLE
Gauge: 12, 16, 20, 410 (12, 20 and 410, 3″ chambers).
Action: Side lever break open; automatic top tang safety; hammerless; auto ejector.
Barrel: 12 ga. 30″; 16, 20 ga. 28″; 410 ga. 26″. Full choke only.
Stock: 14″x1½″x2½″. Walnut, p.g. full fore-end.
Weight: About 6 lbs. Over-all 52″ (30″ bbl.).
Features: Unbreakable coil springs; satin black finish.
Price: **$49.95**

Stevens M94-Y Youth's Gun
Same as Model 940 except: 26″ bbl., 20 ga. Mod. or 410 Full, 12½″ stock with recoil pad. Wgt. about 5½ lbs. 40½″ over-all. **$43.50**

SAVAGE-STEVENS MODEL 94-C Single Barrel Gun
Gauge: 12, 16, 20, 410 (12, 20 and 410, 3″ chambers).
Action: Top lever break open; hammer; auto. ejector.
Barrel: 12 ga. 28″, 30″, 36″; 16, 20 ga. 28″; 410 ga. 26″. Full choke only.
Stock: 14″x1½″x2½″. Walnut finish, checkered p.g. and fore-end.
Weight: About 6 lbs. Over-all 42″ (26″ bbl.).
Features: Color case-hardened frame, low rebounding hammer.
Price: 26″ to 32″ bbls. . . . . **$41.95** 36″ bbl. **$43.50**

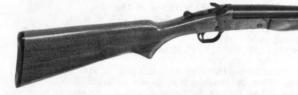

TED WILLIAMS SINGLE BARREL SHOTGUN
Gauge: 12 only, 3″ chamber.
Action: Top break, take down, external hammer.
Barrel: 26″.
Stock: Walnut p.g. stock and fore-end.
Weight: 6 lbs.
Features: Automatic ejector, variable choke. Color case hardened frame.
Price: **$49.95**

WESTERN FIELD 100 Single Barrel Gun
Gauge: 12, 16, 20, 410 (410, 3″ chamber).
Action: Hammerless; thumb slide break open.
Barrel: 12 ga., 30″; 16, 20 ga., 28″; 410 ga., 26″. All Full choke.
Stock: Walnut finished, p.g., recoil pad.
Weight: 6¼ to 7 lbs.
Features: Automatic safety, auto ejector.
Price: **$48.99**
Also available as Youth's Model. 26″ barrel, 20 or 410 gauge. Wgt. 6 lbs., 41″ over-all **$49.99**

WINCHESTER MODEL 370 Single Barrel
Gauge: 12, 20, 410 (3″ chamber); 16 and 28 (2¾″).
Action: Top break, takedown, external hammer.
Barrel: 12 ga., 30″, 32″, 36″; 16 ga., 30″, 32″; 20 and 28 ga., 28″; 410 ga., 26″. Full choke only.
Stock: Hardwood p.g. (14″x1⅜″x2⅜″), full fore-end.
Weight: 5½ to 6¼ lbs. Over-all 48¼″ (32″ bbl.).
Features: Auto. ejection, rebounding hammer. Top snap opens left or right.
Price: . . . . **$43.95** **Price:** 12 ga. 36″ bbl. **$44.95**
Also available as Youth's Model. 12½″ stock, 20 or 410 ga. Wgt. 5½ (410) or 6 lbs., 26″ bbl., 40¾″ overall **$44.95**

Marlin-Glenfield Model 50 Bolt Action
Same as the Marlin Goose Gun Except: 12 and 20 ga., 3″. No sling or swivels. Bbls. 12 ga. 28″, 20 ga. 26″ (Full). Wgt. 7 lbs., 49″ over-all (28″ bbl.)
Price: **$52.95**

MARLIN GOOSE GUN BOLT ACTION
Gauge: 12 only, 3-shot (3″ chamber).
Action: Takedown bolt action, thumb safety, detachable clip.
Barrel: 36″, Full choke.
Stock: Walnut, p.g., recoil pad, leather strap & swivels.
Weight: 7¼ lbs., 57″ over-all.
Features: Double extractors, tapped for receiver sights. Swivels and leather carrying strap. Gold-plated trigger.
Price: **$65.95**

MOSSBERG MODEL 183K BOLT ACTION
Gauge: 410, 3-shot (3″ chamber).
Action: Bolt; top-loading mag.; thumb safety.
Barrel: 25″ with C-Lect-Choke.
Stock: Walnut finish, p.g., Monte Carlo comb., rubber recoil pad w/spacer.
Weight: 6¾ lbs. 43½″ over-all.
Features: Moulded trigger guard with finger grooves, gold bead front sight.
Price: **$49.20**
  Also available in 410 ga. with 24″ bbl., detachable Full and Mod. choke tubes, as M183D **$46.25**
  Full choke, single-shot as M173 .... **$35.45**

Mossberg Model 395S Bolt Action
Same as Model 395K except 24″ barrel with adjustable folding leaf rear sight and ramp front, for use with slugs. Sling supplied **$61.20**

MOSSBERG MODEL 395K BOLT ACTION
Gauge: 12, 3-shot (3″ chamber).
Action: Bolt; takedown; detachable clip.
Barrel: 28″ with C-Lect-Choke.
Stock: Walnut finish, p.g. Monte Carlo comb; recoil pad.
Weight: 6¾ lbs. 47½″ over-all.
Features: Streamlined action; top safety; grooved rear sight.
Price: **$59.85**
  Also available in 20 ga. 3″ chamber 28″ bbl. 6¼ lbs., as M385K, **$55.35,** and in 16 ga. 28″ bbl., 6¾ lbs., as M390K **$58.40**

Savage-Stevens 59 Bolt Action
Same as Model 58 410 ga. except: tubular mag. holding five 3″ or six 2½″ shells; 3-shot plug furnished; no recoil pad. Wgt. 6 lbs. 24″ bbl., 44½″ over-all **$59.95**

SAVAGE-STEVENS 58 BOLT ACTION SHOTGUN
Gauge: 12, 16, 20 2¾″ chambers. 20 ga. also in 3″. (2-shot detachable clip).
Action: Self-cocking bolt; double extractors; thumb safety.
Barrel: 25″, Full choke.
Stock: Walnut finish, checkered fore-end and p.g., recoil pad.
Weight: 7-7½ lbs. Over-all 46″ (43½″ in 410)
Features: Crisp trigger pull.
Price: **$57.95**
  Also available in 410 ga., 3″ chamber, 3-shot detachable clip, 5½ lbs. 43½″ over-all **$48.50**

WESTERN FIELD 150 BOLT ACTION SHOTGUN
Gauge: 410 (3″ chamber).
Action: Self cocking, bolt action. Thumb safety. 3-shot magazine.
Barrel: 24″, full choke.
Weight: 5½ lbs. **Length:** 44½″ over-all.
Stock: Hardwood, Monte Carlo design.
Features: Top loading.
Price: **$46.95**

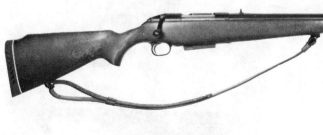

WESTERN FIELD 170 SLUG GUN
Gauge: 12 only, 2-shot clip.
Action: Self-cocking bolt action. Thumb safety, double locking lugs, detachable clip. Take-down action.
Barrel: 24″.
Weight: 6¾ lbs. **Length:** 43¼″ over-all.
Stock: Walnut finish p.g. stock.
Features: Rifle sights, rubber recoil pad; leather sling, sling swivels.
Price: **$60.89**

WESTERN FIELD 172 BOLT ACTION SHOTGUN
Gauge: 12 (3″ chamber).
Action: Self-cocking bolt. Thumb safety, double locking lugs, detachable clip.
Barrel: 28″ adj. choke, shoots rifled slugs.
Stock: Walnut, Monte Carlo design, p.g., recoil pad.
Features: Quick removable bolt with double extractors, grooved rear sight.
Price: **$58.95**
  M175 Similar to above except 20 ga., **$54.95.** Without recoil pad and adj. choke **$52.95**

ASTRA CONSTABLE AUTO PISTOL
Caliber: 22 LR, 10-shot; 32 ACP, 8-shot; and 380 ACP, 7-shot.
Barrel: 3½".
Weight: 26 oz.
Stocks: Moulded plastic.
Sights: Fixed.
Features: Double action, quick no-tool takedown, non-glare rib on slide. Imported from Spain by Garcia.
Price: **$95.00**

BERETTA MODEL 70T AUTO PISTOL
Caliber: 32 ACP, 9-shot magazine.
Barrel: 6".
Weight: 19 oz. **Length:** 9½".
Stocks: Checkered plastic wrap-around.
Sights: Fixed front, adj. rear.
Features: External hammer, target-length bbl., slide stays open after last shot. Imported from Italy by Garcia.
Price: **$85.00**

BERETTA MODEL 101 AUTO PISTOL
Same as Model 70T except 22 LR, 10-round magazine. Imported from Italy by Garcia.
Price: **$85.00**

BERETTA MODEL 76 AUTO PISTOL
Caliber: 22 LR, 10-shot magazine.
Barrel: 6".
Weight: 26 oz. **Length:** 9½".
Stocks: Checkered plastic wrap-around.
Sights: Interchangeable blade front, adj. rear.
Features: Competition-type non-glare ribbed heavy bbl., external hammer. Imported from Italy by Garcia.
Price: **$100.00**

BERETTA MODEL 70S AUTO PISTOL
Caliber: 380 ACP, 7-shot magazine.
Barrel: 3⅝".
Weight: 23¼ oz. **Length:** 6¼".
Stocks: Checkered plastic wrap-around.
Sights: Fixed front and rear.
Features: External hammer. Imported from Italy by Garcia.
Price: **$115.00**

BERETTA MODEL 90 AUTO PISTOL
Caliber: 32 ACP, 8-shot magazine.
Barrel: 3⅝".
Weight: 19½ oz. **Length:** 6¾".
Stocks: Moulded plastic wrap-around.
Sights: Fixed.
Features: Double action, chamber loaded indicator, sighting rib on slide, external hammer, stainless steel bbl. Imported from Italy by Garcia.
Price: **$160.00**

IMPORTED HANDGUNS—AUTOLOADERS

BERETTA MODEL 951 AUTO PISTOL
Caliber: 9mm Para., 8-shot magazine.
Barrel: 4½".
Weight: 31 oz. **Length:** 8".
Stocks: Moulded plastic.
Sights: Fixed.
Features: Crossbolt safety, external hammer, slide stays open after last shot. Imported from Italy by Garcia.
Price: **$180.00**

BERNARDELLI MATCH 22 AUTO PISTOL
Caliber: 22 LR, 10-shot magazine.
Barrel: 5¾".
Weight: 36 oz. **Length:** 9".
Stocks: Hand checkered walnut with thumbrest.
Sights: Post front, adj. rear.
Features: Manual and magazine safeties, external hammer, fitted case. Imported from Italy by Gold Rush.
Price: **$119.00**

BERNARDELLI MODEL 60 AUTO PISTOL
Caliber: 22 LR, 10-shot; 32 ACP, 8-shot; and 380, 7-shot.
Barrel: 3½".
Weight: 26 oz. **Length:** 6⅓".
Stocks: Checkered plastic.
Sights: Post front, click adj. rear.
Features: Manual and magazine safeties. Optional thumb rest grips, $10.00. Imported from Italy by Gold Rush, Kleingunther's, Liberty, Sloan's.
Price: **$84.50**

ERMA KGP 68 AUTO PISTOL
Caliber: 32 ACP, 6-shot; 380 ACP, 5-shot.
Barrel: 3½".
Weight: 22½ oz. **Length:** 6¾".
Stocks: Checkered walnut.
Sights: Fixed rear, adj. blade front.
Features: Sidelock manual safety. Imported from Germany by R. G. Industries.
Price: **$83.95**

ERMA KGP 69 AUTO PISTOL
Caliber: 22 LR, 8-shot magazine.
Barrel: 4".
Weight: 29 oz. **Length:** 7⁵/₁₆".
Stocks: Checkered walnut.
Sights: Fixed rear, adj. front.
Features: Stays open after last shot. Imported from Germany by R. G. Industries.
Price: **$81.95**

HECKLER & KOCH HK-4 AUTO PISTOL
Caliber: 380 ACP, 8 shots.
Barrel: 3½".
Weight: 24 oz. **Length:** 6".
Stock: Checkered black plastic.
Sights: Front, fixed, rear adj. for w.
Features: Double action, 22 LR conversion kit available. Imported from Germany by Harrington & Richardson.
Price: . . . . **$110.00**   Conversion Kit for 22 LR . . . **$37.50**

HECKLER & KOCH P9S AUTO PISTOL
Caliber: 9mm Para., 9-shot magazine.
Barrel: 4".
Weight: 33½ oz. **Length:** 5.4".
Stocks: Checkered plastic.
Sights: Fixed
Features: Double action, quick takedown, hammer cocking lever, loaded and cocked indicators. Special target model and 7.65mm Para. bbls. available. Imported from Germany by Gold Rush.
Price: **$179.00**

LLAMA MODELS VIII, IXA AUTO PISTOLS
Caliber: Super 38 (M. VIII), 45 ACP (M. IXA).
Barrel: 5".
Weight: 30 oz. **Length:** 8½".
Stocks: Checkered walnut.
Sights: Fixed.
Features: Grip and manual safeties, ventilated rib. Engraved, chrome engraved or gold damascened finish available. Imported from Spain by Stoeger Arms.
Price: **$144.95**

LLAMA XI AUTO PISTOL
Caliber: 9mm Para.
Barrel: 5".
Weight: 38 oz. **Length:** 8½".
Stocks: Moulded plastic.
Sights: Fixed front, adj. rear.
Features: Also available with engraved, chrome engraved or gold damascened finish. Imported from Spain by Stoeger Arms.
Price: **$135.95**

LLAMA MODELS XV, XA, IIIA AUTO PISTOLS
Caliber: 22 LR, 32 ACP and 380.
Barrel: 3¹¹⁄₁₆".
Weight: 23 oz. **Length:** 6½".
Stocks: Checkered plastic, thumb rest.
Sights: Fixed front, adj. notch rear.
Features: Ventilated rib, manual and grip safeties. Model XV is 22 LR, Model XA is 32 ACP, and Model IIIA is 380. Models XA and IIIA have loaded indicator; IIIA is locked breech. Imported from Spain by Stoeger Arms.
Price: **$94.95**

MAB PA15 AUTO PISTOL
Caliber: 9mm Para., 15-shot magazine.
Barrel: 4½".
Weight: 38 oz. **Length:** 8".
Stocks: Checkered plastic.
Sights: Fixed front and rear.
Features: External hammer, manual safety. 15-round magazine. Target model available on special order. Imported from France by Gold Rush.
Price: **$109.00**

MAUSER HSc AUTO PISTOL
Caliber: 32 ACP, 380 ACP, 7-shot.
Barrel: 3⅜".
Weight: 23 oz. **Length:** 6.05".
Stocks: Checkered walnut.
Sights: Fixed.
Features: Double action, manual and magazine safeties. Imported from Germany by Interarms.
Price: **$120.00**

IMPORTED HANDGUNS—AUTOLOADERS

MAUSER PARABELLUM AUTO PISTOL
Caliber: 7.65mm, 9mm Para., 8-shot.
Barrel: 6", 4" (9mm only).
Weight: 32 oz. **Length:** $8\frac{2}{3}$" (4" bbl.).
Stocks: Checkered walnut.
Sights: Fixed.
Features: Manual and grip safeties, American eagle over chamber. Imported from Germany by Interarms.
Price: **$290.00**

MKE DEFENDER AUTO PISTOL
Caliber: 32 ACP, 8-shot; 380, 7-shot.
Barrel: 4".
Weight: 23 oz. **Length:** $6\frac{1}{2}$".
Stocks: Checkered black plastic.
Sights: Fixed front, adj. notch rear.
Features: Double action with exposed hammer; safety blocks firing pin and drops hammer. Chamber loaded indicator pin. Imported from Turkey by Firearms Center.
Price: **$87.50**

SIG 210 AUTO PISTOL
Caliber: 22 LR, 7.65mm or 9mm Para., 8-shot.
Barrel: $4\frac{3}{4}$".
Weight: 34 oz. **Length:** $8\frac{1}{2}$".
Stocks: Grooved walnut or checkered plastic.
Sights: Blade front, fixed notch rear.
Features: Thumb safety, external hammer. Available with various finishes including custom engraving. Conversion unit to convert CF pistol to 22 LR $100.00. Imported from Switzerland by Gold Rush.
Prices: . . . . from **$250.00.**

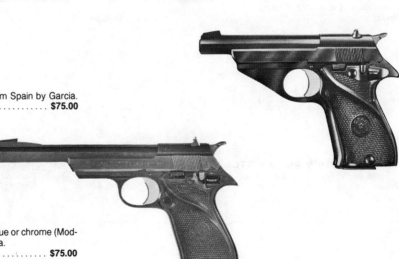

STAR MODEL FM AUTO PISTOL
Caliber: 22 LR, 10-shot magazine
Barrel: $4\frac{1}{4}$".
Weight: 32 oz.
Stocks: Checkered plastic.
Sights: Fixed front, adj. rear.
Features: External hammer, manual safety. Imported from Spain by Garcia.
Price: **$75.00**

STAR FRS AUTO PISTOL
Caliber: 22 LR, 10-shot magazine.
Barrel: 6".
Weight: 28 oz.
Stocks: Checkered plastic.
Sights: Fixed front, adj. rear.
Features: External hammer, manual safety. Available in blue or chrome (Model FRS-C). Alloy frame. Imported from Spain by Garcia.
Price: Blue **$75.00**
Price: Chrome **$80.00**

STAR STARLIGHT AUTO PISTOL
Caliber: 9mm Para., 8-shot magazine.
Barrel: $4\frac{1}{4}$".
Weight: 25 oz.
Stocks: Checkered plastic.
Sights: Fixed.
Features: Magazine and manual safeties, external hammer. Imported from Spain by Garcia.
Price: **$110.00**

IMPORTED HANDGUNS—AUTOLOADERS

STAR MODELS A, B AND P AUTO PISTOLS
Caliber: 38 Super (Model A), 9-shot; 9mm Para. (Model B), 9-shot; and 45 ACP (Model P), 7-shot.
Barrel: 5".
Weight: 37½ oz. **Length:** 8½".
Stocks: Checkered walnut.
Sights: Fixed.
Features: Magazine and manual safeties, wide-spur hammer. Imported from Spain by Garcia.
Price: **$95.00**

WALTHER PP AUTO PISTOL
Caliber: 22 LR, 32 ACP, 8-shot; 380 ACP, 7-shot.
Barrel: 3.86".
Weight: 23½ oz. **Length:** 6⁵/₁₆".
Stocks: Checkered plastic.
Sights: Fixed, white markings.
Features: Double action, manual safety blocks firing pin and drops hammer, chamber loaded indicator on 32 and 380, finger rest extra magazine provided. Imported from Germany by Interarms.
Price: (22 LR) **$145.00**
Price: (32 and 380) **$139.00**

WALTHER PP SPORT AUTO PISTOL
Same as PP except 22 LR only, choice of 6" or 8¼" bbls., target sights click adj. for w. & e., extended rounded grip.
Price: **$130.00**

WALTHER PPKS AUTO PISTOL
Same as PP except bbl. 3.27", length 5⁷/₁₆" o.a.
Price: . . . . Same as PP

WALTHER P-38 AUTO PISTOL
Caliber: 22 LR, 7.65mm or 9mm Para., 8-shot.
Barrel: 4¹⁵/₁₆".
Weight: 28 oz. **Length:** 8½".
Stock: Checkered plastic.
Sights: Fixed.
Features: Double action, safety blocks firing pin and drops hammer, chamber loaded indicator. Matte finish standard, polished blue, engraving and/or plating available. Imported from Germany by Interarms.
Price: (9mm) **$129.00**
Price: (22 LR, 7.65mm) **$160.00**

IMPORTED HANDGUNS—AUTOLOADERS

WALTHER GSP MATCH PISTOL
Caliber: 22 LR, 32 S&W wadcutter, 5-shot.
Barrel: 5¾".
Weight: 41 oz. **Length:** 11⅞".
Stock: Walnut, special hand-fitting design.
Sights: Fixed front, rear adj. for w. & e.
Features: Available with either 2.2 lb. (1000 gm) or 3 lb. (1360 gm) trigger. Spare mag., bbl. weight, tools supplied. Imported from Germany by Interarms.
Price: **$275.00**

WALTHER OSP RAPID-FIRE PISTOL
Similar to Model GSP except 22 short only, stock has adj. free-style thumb rest.
Price: **$250.00**

IMPORTED HANDGUNS—REVOLVERS

ARMINIUS REVOLVERS
Caliber: 38 Special, 32 S&W Long (6-shot); 22 Magnum, 22 LR (8-shot).
Barrel: 4" (38 Spec., 32 S&W, 22 LR); 6" (38 Spec., 22 LR); 9½" (22 Mag. only).
Weight: 35 oz. (6" bbl.). **Length:** 11" (6" bbl. 38).
Stocks: Checkered plastic.
Sights: Ramp front, fixed rear on standard models, w. & e. adj. on target models.
Features: Ventilated rib, solid frame, swing-out cylinder. Interchangeable 22 Mag. cylinder available with 22 cal versions. Imported from West Germany by Firearms Import & Export.
Price: . . . . **$31.95** to **$68.95**

APACHE REVOLVERS
Caliber: 22 LR, 8 shot; 32 S&W 7 shot; 38 Special, 6 shot.
Barrel: 4", 3" (available in 38 Special only).
Stocks: Checkered plastic.
Sights: Fixed front, rear adj. for w. & e.
Features: Ventilated rib on bbl. Imported from Germany by Jana.
Price: **$50.00**

ASTRA 357 MAGNUM REVOLVER
Caliber: 357 Magnum, 6-shot.
Barrel: 3".
Weight: 37 oz. **Length:** 8".
Stocks: Checkered walnut.
Sights: Fixed front, rear adj. for w. and e.
Features: Swing-out cylinder with countersunk chambers, floating firing pin. Imported from Spain by Garcia
Price: **$90.00**

IMPORTED HANDGUNS—REVOLVERS

BISON SINGLE ACTION REVOLVER
Caliber: 22 LR.
Barrel: 4¾".
Weight: 20 oz.
Stocks: Imitation stag.
Sights: Fixed front, adj. rear.
Features: 22 WRM cylinder also available ($5.95 additional). Imported from Germany by Jana.
Price: **$26.00**

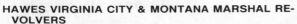

HAWES VIRGINIA CITY & MONTANA MARSHAL REVOLVERS
Same as Western Marshall except with nickel plated cylinder, back strap and trigger guard (Virginia City Marshall) or solid brass back strap and trigger guard (Montana Marshall).
Price: . . . . **$64.95** to **$99.95**

HAWES TEXAS MARSHALL REVOLVER
Similar to Western Marshall except full nickel finish and black or white Pearlite grips.
Price: . . . . **$69.95** to **$104.95**

HAWES WESTERN MARSHALL REVOLVERS
Caliber: 357 Magnum, 44 Magnum, 45 Long Colt, 22 Magnum, 22 LR, 6-shot.
Barrel: 6" (357 Mag., 44 Mag., 45) and 5½" (22 Mag., 22 LR).
Weight: 44 oz. (big bore), 40 oz. (small bore). **Length:** 11¾" and 11¼".
Stocks: Rosewood (big bore), moulded stag (small bore).
Sights: Blade front.
Features: Single action. Interchangeable cylinders available for all caliber guns: 357 Mag. with 9mm, 44 Mag. with 44/40, 45 LC with 45 ACP, 22 LR with 22 Mag. Imported from West Germany by Hawes.
Price: 357 Mag., 44 Mag., 45 LC **$89.95**
Price: Above calibers with interchangeable cylinder **$99.95**
Price: 22 Mag., 22 LR **$57.95**
Price: 22 LR with 22 Mag. cylinder **$64.95**

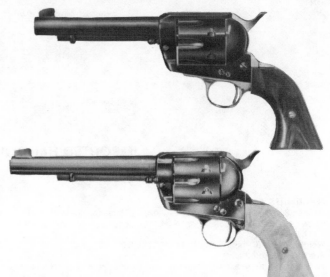

HAWES CHIEF MARSHALL REVOLVER
Caliber: 357 Magnum, 44 Magnum, 45 Long Colt; 6-shot.
Barrel: 6".
Weight: 48 oz. **Length:** 11¾".
Stocks: Smooth rosewood.
Sights: Ramp target front, rear adj. for w. & e.
Features: Single action. Extra heavy frame. Imported from West Germany by Hawes.
Price: **$109.95**

I.N.A. TIGER REVOLVER
Caliber: 38 Special, 5-shot.
Barrel: 3".
Weight: 13½ oz.
Stocks: Checkered walnut.
Sights: Fixed front, adj. rear.
Features: Swing-out cylinder. Imported from Spain by Jana.
Price: **$50.00**

LLAMA "MARTIAL" REVOLVERS
Caliber: 22 LR, 22 RFM, 38 Special.
Barrel: 6″, 4″ (except 22 LR).
Weight: 22 LR 24 oz., 38 Special 31 oz. **Length:** 9¼″ (4″ bbl.).
Stocks: Checkered walnut.
Sights: Fixed blade front, rear adj. for w. & e.
Features: Ventilated rib, wide spur hammer. Chrome plating, engraved
   finishes available. Imported from Spain by Stoeger Arms.
Price:. **$82.95**

RG30 REVOLVER
Caliber: 22 LR, 32 and 38 S&W, 6-shot.
Barrel: 4″.
Weight: 30 oz. **Length:** 9″.
Stocks: Checkered plastic.
Sights: Fixed front, rear adj. for w.
Features: Swing-out cylinder, choice of blue or nickel ($8.00 additional) finish.
   Imported from Germany by R. G. Industries.
Price:. . . . . (22) **$37.95**; (32, 38) **$39.95**

RG 38S REVOLVER
Caliber: 38 Special, 6-shot.
Barrel: 3″ and 4″.
Weight: 3″, 31 oz.; 4″, 34 oz. **Length:** 3″, 8½″; 4″, 9¼″.
Stocks: Checkered plastic.
Sights: Fixed front, rear adj. for w.
Features: Swing out cylinder with spring ejector, choice of blue or nickel finish.
   Imported from Germany by R. G. Industries.
Price: Blue **$47.95**
Price: Nickel **$54.95**

RG 57 REVOLVER
Caliber: 357 Magnum.
Barrel: 4″.
Weight: 44 oz. **Length:** 9½″.
Stocks: Checkered plastic.
Sights: Fixed rear.
Features: Swing out cylinder, spring ejector, steel frame. Imported from Ger-
   many by R. G. Industries.
Price:. **$74.95**

RG63 WESTERN STYLE REVOLVER
Caliber: 22 LR & 22 Mag., 8-shot; 32 S&W & 38 Spec., 6-shot.
Barrel: 5″.
Weight: 34-36 ozs. **Length:** 10¼″.
Stocks: Checkered plastic.
Sights: Fixed.
Features: Slide ejector rod, choice of blue or nickel. Model 63M is combo set
   with both 22 LR and 22 Mag. cylinders. Imported from Germany by R. G.
   Industries.
Price: Blue . . . .(22) **$31.95**; (22M, 38) **$39.95**; (Model 63M) **$48.95**
Price: Nickel . . . .(22) **$46.95**; (22M, 38) **$48.95**; (Model 63M) **$58.95**

RG 66 SUPER SINGLE ACTION REVOLVER
Caliber: 22 LR, 22 Mag., 6-shot.
Barrel: 4¾″.
Weight: 32 oz. **Length:** 10″.
Stocks: Checkered plastic.
Sights: Fixed front, rear adj.
Features: Slide ejector rod, choice of blue or nickel finish. Model 66M is
   combo set with both 22 LR and 22 mag. cylinders. Imported from Germany
   by R. G. Industries.
Price: Blue . . . .**$29.95**; (Model 66M) **$34.95**
Price: Nickel . . . .**$34.95**; (Model 66M) **$42.95**

RG 121 SINGLE ACTION REVOLVER
Caliber: 357 Mag., 6-shot.
Barrel: 5½"
Weight: 44½ oz. **Length:** 11¼".
Stocks: Simulated stag.
Sights: Fixed.
Features: Slide ejector rod, steel frame. Imported from Germany by R. G.
  Industires.
Price: **$82.95**

J. P. SAUER MEDALLION REVOLVER
Caliber: 38 Special, 22 LR, 6-shot.
Barrel: 3", 4" & 6" (38 Spec.) or 4" & 6" (22 LR).
Weight: 39 oz. **Length:** 11⅛" (6" bbl.).
Stocks: Checkered walnut.
Sights: Ramp front, w. & e. adj. rear.
Features: Double action. Knurled target hammer. Imported from West Germany by Hawes.
Price: **$119.95**

J. P. SAUER TROPHY REVOLVER
Caliber: 38 Special, 22 LR, 6-shot.
Barrel: 6".
Weight: 39 oz. **Length:** 11⅛"
Stocks: Checkered walnut thumbrest type.
Sights: Ventilated rib ramp front, w. & e. adj. rear.
Features: Double action. Ventilated rib, serrated target trigger, knurled target
  hammer. Imported from West Germany by Hawes.
Price: **$129.95**

IMPORTED HANDGUNS—SINGLE SHOT

HAWES FAVORITE SINGLE SHOT PISTOL
Caliber: 22 S, L, LR.
Barrel: 8".
Weight: 20 oz. **Length:** 12".
Stocks: Laminated wood or plastic.
Sights: Fixed front, adj. rear.
Features: Tilt up action, blued bbl., chromed frame. Imported by Hawes Firearms.
Price: **$35.95**

ROLLING BLOCK SINGLE SHOT PISTOL
Caliber: 22 LR, 22 WRM, 5mm Rem. Mag., 357 mag.
Barrel: 8".
Weight: 2 lbs. **Length:** 12".
Stock: Walnut.
Sights: Front adj. for w., buckhorn adj. for e.
Features: Polished brass trigger guard. Supplied with wooden display box.
  Imported by Navy Arms.
Price: **$125.00**

IMPORTED CENTERFIRE RIFLES—AUTOLOADING & LEVER ACTION

BERETTA BM-69 AUTO RIFLE

Caliber: 7.62mm NATO (308).
Barrel: 17".
Weight: 8½ lbs. **Length:** 38½".
Stock: Walnut.
Sights: Post front, adj. peep rear.
Features: Folding bipod available, $21.00. Mag. cap 20 rounds. Imported from Italy by Gold Rush.
Price: **$249.00**

CETME SPORT AUTO RIFLE

Caliber: 308, 5-shot.
Barrel: 17¾".
Weight: 10½ lbs. **Length:** 40".
Stock: Walnut with walnut fore-end.
Sights: Blade front, flip up apeture rear, scope blocks.
Features: Scope rings, bipod, 20-shot mag. avail. Imported from Spain by Mars Equipment.
Price: **$229.95**

SIG-AMT AUTO RIFLE

Caliber: 7.62mm NATO (308).
Barrel: 18.86".
Weight: 9 lbs. 9½ oz. **Length:** 38.94".
Stock: Walnut.
Sights: Adj. post front, adj. peep rear.
Features: Supplied with cleaning kit, cloth sling, bipod. 4X scope, 5, 10 and 20 round mags available. Imported from Switzerland by Benet Arms.
Price: **$348.00**

CLASSIC 1873 LEVER ACTION RIFLE

Caliber: 357 Magnum, 44-40.
Barrel: 20".
Weight: 7 lbs. **Length:** 39".
Stock: Walnut, straight grip, carbine buttplate.
Sights: Fixed front, adj. rear.
Features: Exact copy of 1873 Winchester, with full length tubular mag., center hammer, top ejection. Imported from Italy by Gold Rush, Jana.
Price: **$179.00**

ROSSI LEVER ACTION RIFLE

Caliber: 357 or 44 Magnum.
Barrel: 20".
Weight: 5¾ lbs.
Stock: Walnut, straight grip, carbine buttplate.
Sights: Fixed front, adj. rear.
Features: Capacity 10 rounds. Saddle ring, full length tubular mag. Imported from Italy by Garcia.
Price: **$115.00**

SAKO FINNWOLF LEVER ACTION RIFLE

Caliber: 243, 308.
Barrel: 23".
Weight: 6¾ lbs. **Length:** 42½".
Stock: Hand-checkered European walnut, Monte Carlo, one-piece.
Sights: Hooded front, dovetail blocks rear for tip-off scope mount or iron sights.
Features: Available with right- or left-hand stock. Hammerless, short-throw lever, solid top, side ejection, 4-shot detach. mag. Imported from Finland by Garcia.
Price: **$260.00**

IMPORTED CENTERFIRE RIFLES—BOLT ACTION

BSA MONARCH BOLT ACTION RIFLE
Caliber: 22-250, 222 Rem., 243 Win., 270 Win., 308 Win., 30-06, 7mm Rem. Mag., 300 Win. Mag.
Barrel: 22".
Weight: 7 lbs.
Stock: Hand checkered European walnut, Monte Carlo, white line spacers on p.g. cap, fore-end tip and recoil pad.
Sights: Hooded ramp front, flip up rear.
Features: Adj. trigger, hinged mag. floor plate, silent sliding safety locks bolt and trigger. Imported from England by Galef.
Price: **$167.95**

DUMOULIN BOLT ACTION RIFLE
Caliber: All commercial calibers.
Barrel: 25".
Weight: 7 lbs. **Length:** 43".
Stock: French walnut with rosewood p.g. cap and fore-end tip, standard or skip line checkering, recoil pad.
Sights: Optional, available at extra cost.
Features: Made to customer requirements using Sako or FN action, with or without engraving (3 grades available). Imported from Belgium by Firearms Center, JBL Arms.
Price: . . . . from **$285.00**

DSCHULLNIGG BOLT ACTION RIFLE
Caliber: All standard calibers.
Barrel: 24 or 26".
Weight: 7 lbs.
Stock: Select Austrian walnut with choice of finish, checkering, carving and inlay.
Sights: Fixed iron sights or choice of European scopes and mounts.
Features: Available in Grade IV (engraved) or Custom Grade (to buyer's specifications). Imported from Austria by Firearms Center.
Price: . . . . from **$650.00**

DSCHULLNIGG DOUBLE RIFLES
Caliber: All standard calibers.
Barrel: 24 or 26".
Stock: Circassian walnut, hand checkered.
Sights: Open.
Features: Double rifles, over and under rifles and drillings available on custom order basis. Imported from Austria by Firearms Center.
Price: . . . . Individually quoted to customer specifications.

FN MAUSER BOLT ACTION RIFLES
Caliber: 243, 7x57mm, 270, 308, 30-06, 264 Mag., 7mm Mag., 300 Win. Mag.
Barrel: 24".
Weight: 8½ lbs.
Stock: Hand-checkered European walnut, Monte Carlo.
Sights: Hooded front, adj. peep rear.
Features: Adj. grooved trigger, hinged floorplate, sliding safety. Also available as actions or barrelled actions. Imported from Belgium by Garcia.
Price: Standard calibers **$430.00**
Price: Magnums **$445.00**

FERLACH SPORTER RIFLE
Caliber: 243, 7x57, 270, 308 Win., 30-06, 25-06.
Barrel: 24".
Weight: 7¼ lbs.
Stock: Hand checkered Circassian walnut, Monte Carlo cheekpiece, rubber recoil pad, rosewood fore-end tip and p.g. cap, sling swivels.
Sights: Hooded ramp front, 100 and 200 yard rear. Tapped and drilled for scope mounting.
Features: 98 Mauser action, Sako trigger, side safety. Bolt knurled and forged for low scope mounting. Imported from Austria by Flaig's.
Price: 25-06 . . . . **$149.00**
Price: Other cals. **$139.00**

HERTER'S MARK U9 RIFLE
Caliber: 222, 222 mag., 223, 22-250, 25-06, 243, 6mm, 284, 308, 270, 30-06, 264, 7mm mag., 300 Win.
Barrel: 23½".
Weight: 6¼ lbs. **Length:** 42½".
Stock: American walnut, Monte Carlo, p.g.
Sights: Ramp front, rear adj. for w. and e.
Features: Also available less sights, with Mannlicher style stock, Douglas barrels (338 and 458 mag. plus above cals.). Three grades (Hunter's, Supreme, Presentation) differ in stock finish, style. Also available as actions or bbld. actions, bench rest, target or varmint versions. Imported from England by Herter's.
Price: Hunter's Grade **$109.90**
Price: Supreme Grade **$118.70**
Price: Presentation Grade **$133.70**

HERTER'S MARK J9 RIFLE

Caliber: 22-250, 25-06, 243, 6mm, 270, 308, 30-06, 264, 7mm mag., 300 Win. Mag.
Barrel: 23½".
Weight: 8 lbs. **Length:** 42½".
Stock: Black walnut, rollover cheek piece, ebonite p.g. cap and butt plate.
Sights: Ramp front, rear adj. for w. and e.
Features: Also available w/o sights, with Mannlicher or beavertail style stocks. Three grades (Hunter's, Supreme, Presentation) differ stock finish, style. Also available as actions or barreled actions. Imported from Yugoslavia by Herter's.
Price: Hunter's Grade **$90.50**
Price: Supreme Grade **$101.40**
Price: Presentation Grade **$115.40**

HUSQVARNA 8000 IMPERIAL RIFLES

Same as 9000 Crown Grade rifles except: Select European walnut Monte Carlo stock, jeweled bolt, engraved mag. floor plate, cals. 30-06 and 300 Win. Mag. only. No sights.
Price: **$265.00**

HUSQVARNA 9000 CROWN GRADE RIFLE

Caliber: 7mm Rem. Mag., 270, 30-06, 300 Win. Mag.
Barrel: 23¾".
Weight: 7¼ lbs. **Length:** 44".
Stock: Oiled French walnut Monte Carlo stock, checkered p.g. and fore-end with white line spacers.
Sights: Adj. open rear, hooded ramp front sights; receiver tapped for peep sight or scope mts.
Features: "Guided" bolt action, short stroke firing pin, adj. trigger. Hinged floorplate, sling swivels. Imported from Sweden by Tradewinds.
Price: **$210.00**

KLEINGUNTHER K14 BOLT ACTION RIFLE

Caliber: 243, 7mm Rem. Mag., 270, 30-06, 300 Win. Mag., 308.
Barrel: 24".
Weight: 7⅛ lbs. **Length:** 43½".
Stock: Walnut Monte Carlo, hand checkered p.g. and fore-end.
Sights: Less sights, tapped for scope mts.
Features: Fully adj. trigger, hinged mag. floorplate, safety in center of bolt sleeve. Imported from Austria by Kleingunther.
Price: Std. Cals. .... **$199.00**   Mag. **$212.50**

MARK X RIFLE

Caliber: 22-250; 243, 270 & 308 Win.; 30-06; 25-06; 7 mm Rem. Mag; 300 Win. Mag.
Barrel: 24".
Weight: 7½ lbs. **Length:** 44".
Stock: Hand checkered walnut, Monte Carlo, white line spacers on p.g. cap, buttplate and fore-end tip.
Sights: Ramp front with removeable hood, folding-leaf rear adj. for w. and e.
Features: Sliding safety, quick detachable sling swivels, hinged floorplate. Adj. trigger available ($10.00 additional). Also available as actions or bbld. actions. Imported from Europe by Interarms.
Price: **$173.00**

MAUSER MODEL 660 RIFLE

Caliber: 22-250, 243 Win., 25-06, 270 Win., 308, 30-06.
Barrel: 24".
Weight: 7¾ lbs. **Length:** 41".
Stock: Hand checkered walnut, Monte Carlo, with white line p.g. cap, fore-end and recoil pad spacers.
Sights: Drilled and tapped for scope mounts.
Features: Quickly interchanged bbls., new short action, adj. single stage trigger, push-button safety. Double set trigger, iron sights, engraving and hand carving all available at extra cost. Imported from Germany by Mauser Amerika.
Price: **$329.95**

IMPORTED CENTERFIRE RIFLES—BOLT ACTION

MAUSER MODEL 660 SAFARI RIFLE
Same as Model 660 except cals. 458 Win. Mag., 375 H&H Mag., 7mm Rem. Mag., 28″ bbl., 9 lbs. Fixed front and express rear sights.

Price: **$399.00**

MAUSER MODEL 3000 RIFLE
Caliber: 243 Win., 270 Win., 308, 30-06, 375 H&H Mag., 7mm Rem. Mag.
Barrel: 22″ (standard), 26″ (Magnum).
Weight: 7¼ lbs. **Length:** 43″.
Stock: Hand checkered walnut, Monte Carlo, white line spacer for p.g. and fore-end caps, vent. recoil pad.
Sights: Drilled and tapped for scope mounts.
Features: 5-round capacity standard cals., 3-round Magnums. Sliding safety, fully adj. trigger. Open sights, left hand action available at extra cost. Imported from Germany by Mauser Amerika.

Price: Standard calibers .. **$197.45**   Magnums **$229.00**

MAUSER MODEL 4000 RIFLE
Same as 3000 except 222 Rem. and 223 cals. only, hooded front and folding leaf rear sights included, 7 lbs.

Price: **$187.45**

PARKER-HALE SUPER 1200 BOLT ACTION RIFLE
Caliber: 22-250, 243 Win., 6mm Rem., 25-06, 270 Win., 30-06, 308 Win., 7mm Rem. Mag., 300 Win. Mag.
Barrel: 24″.
Weight: 7¼ lbs. **Length:** 45″.
Stock: 13.5″ x 1.8″ x 2.3″. Hand checkered walnut, rosewood p.g. and fore-end caps, fitted rubber recoil pad with white line spacers.
Sights: Bead front, folding adj. rear. Receiver tapped for scope mounts.
Features: 3-way side safety, single-stage adj. trigger, hinged mag. floorplate. Model 1200P has scroll engraved action, trigger guard and mag. floorplate, detachable swivels, no sights; not avail. in 22-250. Varmint Model (1200V) has glass-bedded action, free-floating bbl., avail. in 22-250, 6mm Rem., 25-06, 243 Win., without sights. Imported from England by Jana.

Price: .... **$164.95**   ($169.95, mag. cals.)
Price: 1200P .... **$209.95**   ($219.95, mag. cals.)
Price: 1200V **$169.95**

MIDLAND BOLT ACTION RIFLE
Caliber: 243 Win., 270 Win., 30-06, 308 Win.
Barrel: 24″.
Weight: 7 lbs. **Length:** 44½″.
Stock: Checkered walnut, p.g.
Sights: Drilled and tapped for scope mounts.
Features: Sliding side safety, hinged floorplate. Imported from England by Jana.

Price: **$120.00**

SAKO FINNBEAR BOLT ACTION RIFLE
Caliber: 25-06, 264 Mag., 270, 30-06, 300 Win. Mag., 338 Mag., 7mm Mag., 375 H&H.
Barrel: 20″ or 24″.
Weight: 7 lbs. **Length:** 39″, 43″.
Stock: Hand-checkered European walnut, Monte Carlo.
Sights: Hooded front, dovetail block for rear.
Features: Fully adj. trigger, hinged floorplate. 3-lug short lift bolt, recessed bolt-face. Carbine (20″ bbl.) has full length stock. Deluxe (24″ bbl. only) has special finish, wood inlays, recoil pad. Also available as actions or barrelled actions. Imported from Finland by Garcia.

Price: Standard **$240.00**
Price: Carbine **$270.00**
Price: Deluxe **$345.00**

SAKO FORESTER BOLT ACTION RIFLE
Caliber: 22-250, 243, 308.
Barrel: 20″ (carbine), 23″ (sporter) or 24″ (heavy bbl.).
Weight: 6½ lbs. (heavy bbl., 7½ lbs.). **Length:** 39″, 42″, 43″.
Stock: Hand-checkered European walnut, p.g., Monte Carlo.
Sights: Hooded front integral, tapered dovetail mounts rear.
Features: Fully adj. trigger, hinged floorplate. L-579 medium-length action. Carbine (20″ bbl.) has full length stock. Deluxe (23″ bbl. only) has special finish, wood inlays, recoil pad. Also available as actions or barrelled actions. Imported from Finland by Garcia.

Price: Standard **$220.00**
Price: Heavy bbl. **$245.00**
Price: Carbine **$250.00**
Price: Deluxe **$315.00**

IMPORTED CENTERFIRE RIFLES—BOLT ACTION

SAKO VIXEN BOLT ACTION RIFLE
Caliber: 222 or 223.
Barrel: 20″ (carbine), 23½″ (sporter) and 23½″ (heavy).
Weight: 6½ lbs. (heavy bbl. 7½ lbs.).
Stock: Hand-checkered European walnut.
Sights: Hooded front, dovetail block for rear.
Features: Adj. trigger, hinged floorplate, carbine has full length stock. Deluxe (23½″ bbl. only) has engraved guard, floorplate, special finish, wood inlays, recoil pad. Also available as actions or barrelled actions. Imported from Finland by Garcia.
Price: Standard **$205.00**
Price: Heavy bbl. **$230.00**
Price: Carbine **$250.00**
Price: Deluxe **$295.00**

SAKO MODEL 72 BOLT ACTION RIFLE
Caliber: 222, 223, 22-250, 243, 308, 25-06, 270, 30-06, 7mm Mag., 300 Mag., 375 H & H Mag.
Barrel: 23″ (222, 223, 22-250, 243 and 308), 24″ (other cals.).
Weight: 6½ lbs. (23″ bbl.), 7 lbs. (others).
Stock: Hand-checkered European walnut.
Sights: Hooded front, adj. rear.
Features: Adj. trigger, hinged floorplate. 222 and 223 have short action, 22-250, 243 and 308 medium action, others are long action. Imported from Finland by Garcia.
Price: Standard calibers **$185.00**
Price: Magnums **$195.00**

STEYR-MANNLICHER MODELS SL, L BOLT RIFLES
Caliber: 222 Rem., 222 Rem. Mag., 223 Rem. (Model SL): 22-250, 6mm Rem., 243 Win., 308 Win. (Model L).
Barrel: 20″ (carbine), 23⅝″ (rifle).
Weight: 6 lbs. 6 oz. **Length:** 39″ (carbine,) 42½″ (rifle).
Stock: Checkered walnut.
Sights: Hooded post front, adj. rear.
Features: Choice of single or double-set trigger. 5-round detachable rotary magazine. Also available in heavy-barreled Varmint Models, without sights, cals. 222, 223 and 22-250 only. Imported from Austria by Stoeger Arms.
Price: (Model SL) . . **$264.00** (rifle)   **$282.00** (carbine)
Price: (Model L) . . . **$284.00** (rifle);   **$302.00** (carbine)

STEYR-MANNLICHER MODEL M, S BOLT RIFLES
Caliber: 7 x 57mm, 270, 30-06 (Model M); 7mm Rem., 257 Weatherby, 264, 300 H&H, 338, 375 H&H and 458 Magnum (Model S).
Barrel: 20″ (carbine), 24″ (rifle); Model S (rifle only) 25½″.
Weight: 7 lbs. **Length:** 39″ (carbine), 43″ (rifle); Model S (rifle only) 45″.
Stock: European walnut, hand checkered.
Sights: Hooded post front, open rear.
Features: Choice of single or double-set trigger. 5-round detachable rotary magazine (4-round in magnum Model S). Model S available in single trigger rifle only. Imported from Austria by Stoeger Arms.
Price: (Model M) . . . . **$328.00** (rifle); **$346.00** (carbine)
Price: (Model S) . . . . **$364.00** (rifle only)

TRADEWINDS HUSKY MODEL 5000 BOLT RIFLE
Caliber: 270, 30-06, 308, 243, 22-250.
Barrel: 23¾″.
Weight: 6 lbs. 11 oz.
Stock: Hand checkered European walnut, Monte Carlo, white line spacers on p.g. cap, fore-end tip and butt plate.
Sights: Fixed hooded front, adj. rear.
Features: Removeable mag., fully recessed bolt head, adj. trigger. Imported by Tradewinds.
Price: **$184.50**

IMPORTED CENTERFIRE RIFLES—BOLT ACTION

TRADEWINDS MODEL 600 BOLT ACTION RIFLE
Caliber: 222 Rem., 222 Rem. Mag., 22-250, 243 Win.
Barrel: 23¾".
Weight: 6¾ lbs. **Length:** 43¾".
Stock: Hand checkered European walnut, Monte Carlo, white line spacers on p.g. cap and butt plate.
Sights: Hooded ramp front, folding rear, receiver drilled and tapped for scope mts.
Features: Sliding safety, short Mauser-type action. Model 600K has adj. double set trigger, no sights, not avail. in 243. Model 600S has adj. single trigger, avail. in 243 and 22-250 only. Imported by Tradewinds.
Price: **$162.50**

WALTHER KKJ BOLT ACTION RIFLE
Caliber: 22 Hornet, 5 shot.
Barrel: 22½".
Weight: 5½ lbs. **Length:** 41½".
Stock: Hand checkered walnut, p.g., cheek piece.
Sights: Hooded ramp front, adj. rear; dove tailed for slide-on scope mounts.
Features: Double set triggers available. Imported from Germany by Interarms.
Price: **$208.00**

WALTHER SSV BOLT ACTION RIFLE
Same as KKJ except bbl. 25½", heavier Monte Carlo stock, weight 6¾ lbs., no sights (scope rails provided). Also available in 222 Rem.
Price: 22 Hornet **$220.00**
Price: 222 Rem. **$225.00**

IMPORTED CENTERFIRE RIFLES—REPLICAS

NAVY ARMS MODEL 1875 REVOLVING RIFLE
Caliber: 38 Special, 44-40.
Barrel: 20".
Weight: 5 lbs. **Length:** 38".
Stock: Walnut, brass butt plate.
Sights: Front blade adj. for w., buckhorn rear adj. for e.
Features: Action resembles Remington Model 1875 revolver. Polished brass trigger guard. Imported by Navy Arms.
Price: **$125.00**

NAVY ARMS ROLLING BLOCK RIFLE
Caliber: 45-70, 444 Marlin.
Barrels: 26½".
Stock: Walnut finished.
Sights: Fixed front, adj. rear.
Features: Reproduction of classic rolling block action. Available in Buffalo Rifle (octagonal bbl.) and Creedmore (half round, half octagonal bbl.) models. Imported by Navy Arms.
Price: **$150.00**

IMPORTED RIMFIRE RIFLES—LEVER ACTION

ERMA EG71 LEVER ACTION RIFLE
Caliber: 22 LR, 15-shot.
Barrel: 18½".
Weight: 5 lbs., 5 ozs. **Length:** 35⅞".
Stock: Walnut.
Sights: Fixed front, adj. rear, receiver grooved for scope mts.
Features: Looks and operates like traditional 30-30. Imported from Germany by R. G. Industries.
Price: **$82.95**

NAVY ARMS MODEL 66 LEVER ACTION RIFLE
Caliber: 22 LR, 38 Special, 44-40.
Barrel: 19".
Weight: 7 lbs. **Length:** 39½".
Stock: Walnut.
Sights: Fixed front, folding rear.
Features: Replica of Winchester Model 1866 "Yellowboy." Available with three grades of engraving, selected stock and fore-end at additional cost. 22 LR also available with 16" bbl. (Trapper's Model). Imported by Navy Arms.
Price: **$120.00**

IMPORTED RIMFIRE RIFLES—AUTOLOADING

ERMA EM1.22 AUTOLOADING CARBINE
Caliber: 22 LR, 10-shot.
Barrel: 17¾".
Weight: 5¾ lbs. **Length:** 35⅜".
Stock: Walnut, semi p.g.
Sights: Fixed front, rear adj. for w. & e., grooved for scope mts. Looks and operates like U.S. M1 carbine. 15-shot mag. also available. Imported from Germany by R.G. Industries.
Price: **$83.95**

FRANCHI CENTENNIAL AUTO RIFLE
Caliber: 22 LR. (11-shot).
Barrel: 21".
Weight: 5 lbs. 2 oz. **Length:** 39⅛".
Stock: Epoxy-finished walnut.
Sights: Gold bead front, adj. rear.
Features: Quick takedown, cross-bolt safety, receiver grooved for tip-off scope mounts. Available in standard and deluxe (engraved action) grades. Imported from Italy by Stoeger Arms.
Price: **$112.75**

SQUIBMAN AUTO RIFLE
Caliber: 22 LR, 15-shot.
Barrel: 19½".
Weight: 5¾ lbs. **Length:** 40½".
Stock: Mahogany.
Sights: Bead front, partridge rear adj. for e.
Features: Detachable flash and shell deflector, cocking indicator, muzzle brake. Imported from Philippines by Century Arms.
Price: **$49.50**

TRADEWINDS MODEL 260 AUTO RIFLE
Caliber: 22 LR, 5-shot (10-shot mag. avail.).
Barrel: 22½".
Weight: 5¾ lbs. **Length:** 41½".
Stock: Walnut, with hand checkered p.g. and fore-end.
Sights: Ramp front with hood, 3-leaf folding rear, receiver grooved for scope mt.
Features: Double extractors, sliding safety. Imported by Tradewinds.
Price: **$99.95**

IMPORTED RIMFIRE RIFLES—BOLT ACTION

KLEINGUNTHER K-10 BOLT ACTION RIFLE
Caliber: 22 LR, single shot.
Barrel: 21¼".
Weight: 4.2 lbs. **Length:** 38¼".
Stock: Beechwood, walnut stained.
Sights: Hooded front, Mauser type tangent rear.
Features: Mauser type thumb safety locks firing pin. Imported from Europe by Kleingunther
Price: **$33.44**

KLEINGUNTHER K-12 BOLT ACTION RIFLE
Caliber: 22 LR, 5-shot or 10-shot.
Barrel: 21¼".
Weight: 5.7 lbs. **Length:** 40".
Stock: Hand checkered walnut, p.g., rosewood fore-end tip.
Sights: Hooded front, 2 leaf folding rear. Receiver grooved for scope mts.
Features: Adj. trigger, thumb lever safety. Imported from Europe by Kleingunther
Price: **$67.85**

IMPORTED RIMFIRE RIFLES—BOLT ACTION

KLEINGUNTHER K-13 BOLT ACTION RIFLE
Same as K-12 except chambered for 22 WMR, weight 5.9 lbs.
Price: **$106.04**

ROSSI GALLERY PUMP RIFLE
Caliber: 22 S, L or LR (Standard), 22 RFM (Magnum).
Barrel: 22½".
Weight: 5¼ lbs.
Stock: Walnut, straight grip, grooved fore-end.
Sights: Fixed front, adj. rear.
Features: Capacity 20 Short, 16 Long or 14 Long Rifle. Quick takedown. Imported from Italy by Garcia.
Price: Standard **$80.00**
Price: Magnum **$90.00**

WALTHER KKJ RIMFIRE RIFLE
Caliber: 22 LR, 5 or 8 shot; 22 WRM, 5 shot.
Barrel: 22½".
Weight: 5½ lbs. **Length:** 41½".
Stock: Hand checkered walnut, p.g., cheek piece.
Sights: Hooded ramp front, adj. rear; dove tailed for slide-on scope mounts.
Features: Double set triggers available. Imported from Germany by Interarms.
Price: 22 LR **$185.00**
Price: 22 WRM **$208.00**

TRADEWINDS MODEL 311 BOLT ACTION RIFLE
Caliber: 22 LR, 5-shot (10-shot mag. avail.).
Barrel: 22½".
Weight: 6 lbs. **Length:** 41¼".
Stock: Walnut, Monte Carlo with hand checkered p.g. and fore-end.
Sights: Ramp front with hood, folding leaf rear, receiver grooved for scope mt.
Features: Sliding safety locks trigger and bolt handle. Imported by Tradewinds.
Price: **$99.95**

WALTHER SSV RIMFIRE RIFLE
Same as KKJ except bbl. 25½", heavier Monte Carlo stock, weight 6¾ lbs. no sights (scope rails provided), 22LR (single shot) only.
Price: **$208.00**

IMPORTED TARGET RIFLES

PARKER-HALE 1200 TX TARGET RIFLE
Caliber: 7.62mm NATO (308), 30-06.
Barrel: 26".
Weight: 10½ lbs. **Length:** 46¾".
Stock: 13³/₁₆" x 1¹¹/₁₆" x 1¹⁵/₁₆". Oil finish, full beavertail, p.g., solid rubber butt pad.
Sights: Micro adj. ¼' click rear, interchangable element tubular front.
Features: Full floating bbl., epoxy bedded action, fully adj. trigger, selected bbl. Imported from England by Jana.
Price: **$219.95**

STEYR MODEL SSG-69 TARGET RIFLE
Caliber: 7.62mm NATO (308).
Weight: 11 lbs. **Length:** 45".
Stock: Oil-finished walnut with stippled Wundhammer-swell p.g. and fore-end.
Sights: Globe front, Olympic-type rear.
Features: Two-stage adjustable trigger, heavy receiver and bolt with light weight short-stroke firing pin. Imported from Austria by Stoeger Arms.
Price: **$476.00**

WALTHER U.I.T. MATCH RIFLE
Caliber: 22 LR.
Barrel: 25½".
Weight: 10 lbs., 3 oz. **Length:** 44¾".
Stock: Walnut, adj. for length and drop; fore-end guide rail for sling or palm rest.
Sights: Interchangeable post or aperture front, micro adj. rear.
Features: Conforms to both NRA and U.I.T. requirements. Fully adj. trigger. Left hand stock available on special order. Imported from Germany by Interarms.
Price: **$235.00**

WALTHER 400 MATCH RIFLE
Same as U.I.T. except adj. split stock and supplied with scope blocks instead of iron sights.
Price: **$260.00**

IMPORTED TARGET RIFLES

WALTHER KKM MATCH RIFLE
Caliber: 22 LR.
Barrel: 28″.
Weight: 15½ lbs. **Length:** 46″.
Stock: Walnut, with fully adj. hook butt plate, hand shelf and palm rest.
Sights: Olympic front with post and aperture inserts, micrometer rear click adj. for w. & e.
Features: Fully adj. match trigger. Imported from Germany by Interarms.
Price: $370.00

IMPORTED DRILLINGS, DOUBLE & COMBO RIFLES

DUMOULIN DOUBLE RIFLE
Caliber: 7x65R, 30-06, 8x57JRS, 8x60RS, 9.3x74R, 458 Win., 375 H&H, 500/465.
Barrel: 25½″.
Weight: 7.7 lbs. except 458, 375 and 500/465, 10 lbs.
Stock: French oiled walnut and German or Monte Carlo cheekpiece. Choice of standard or beavertail fore-end.
Sights: V rear, silver bead front.
Features: Anson-type action with triple Purdey locking system, Holland-type ejectors. Choice of single or double triggers, satin chrome or case hardened action finish, stock dimensions and finish. Made to customer's requirements, delivery 9-12 months. Imported from Belgium by JBL Arms.
Price: 458 Cal. . . . . $1922.00 (typical)

FERLACH O/U TURKEY RIFLE/SHOTGUN
Gauge: 12, 16, 20, and 22 Hornet, 222 Rem., 243, 257, 6.5x55, 270, 7x57, 30-06.
Action: Anson & Deeley boxlock.
Barrel: 22″ or 24″.
Weight: 6½ lbs.
Stock: Circassian walnut, hand checkered at p.g. and split fore-end, horn p.g. cap and buttplate.
Features: Double triggers, auto safety, engraved action. With or without cheekpiece, recoil pad. Imported from Austria by Flaig's.
Price: $650.00

MAUSER O/U DOUBLE RIFLE
Caliber: 243 Win., 270 Win., 30-06, 375 H&H, 7mm Rem., 458 Win. Mag.
Stock: Hand checkered p.g. stock and fore-end.
Sights: Fixed.
Features: Kersten-type double underlocking locks, auto ejectors, manual safety, bone trigger guard. Triggers fully adj. Relief-engraved receiver. Imported from Germany by Mauser Amerika.
Price: Standard . . . . $1695.00   Magnum $2050.00

SAUER DRILLING 3000-E RIFLE/DOUBLE SHOTGUN
Gauge: 12 (2¾″) and 222, 243, 30-06 or 7x65R.
Action: Blitz with Greener cross-bolt, double underlocking lugs.
Barrel: 25″ (Full & Mod.).
Weight: 6½ to 7¼ lbs.
Stock: 14½″x1⅝″x2¾″ walnut, p.g., cheekpiece, modified Monte Carlo.
Sights: Bead front, folding leaf rear.
Features: Sling swivels, matted rib, separate rifle cartridge extractor; front trigger acts as set trigger, adjustable for pull, vertical pin firing pin indicators; Greener side safety mechanism locks all 3 bbls; sear slide safety on upper tang locks right shotgun barrel when firing rifle barrel. Imported from Germany by Weatherby.
Price: Standard . . . . $750.00 Deluxe $880.00

SAUER BBF O/U RIFLE-SHOTGUN
Gauge: 16 (2¾″) and 30-30, 30-06 or 7x65R.
Action: Blitz with Kersten lock.
Barrel: 25″ (Full).
Weight: 6 lbs.
Sights: Bead front sight, folding leaf rear.
Stock: 14½″x1⅝″x2¾″ hand checkered selected walnut, with p.g., cheekpiece.
Features: Matted rib, centrally guided firing pins, front trigger for rifle barrel designed as adjustable single-set trigger. Sear safety manually operated by slide on upper tang. Imported from Germany by Weatherby.
Price: Standard . . . . $700.00 Deluxe $830.00

IMPORTED SHOTGUNS—PUMP & AUTOLOADING

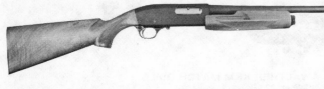

STOEGER MODEL 7 PUMP SHOTGUN
Gauge: 12 (2¾" chamber); 12 or 20 Mag. (3" chamber).
Action: Pump.
Barrel: 26" (I.C.) or 28" (Mod.), 12 std. or 20 mag.; 30" (Full), 12 or 12 Mag.
Weight: 6 lbs. **Length:** 47¼" (26" bbl.).
Stock: Walnut, checkered p.g. and fore-end.
Features: Interchangeable chrome lined bbls., cross bolt safety. Vent rib available ($35.00 additional). Imported by Stoeger Arms.
Price: . . . . **$169.95** (12 Std.)
Price: . . . . **$181.95** (12, 20 Mag.)

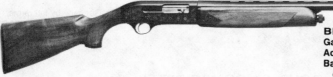

BERETTA AL AUTO SHOTGUNS
Gauge: 12 or 20 (4-shot, 3-shot plug furnished). 2¾" chambers.
Action: Gas-operated autoloader.
Barrel: 12 ga., 30 or 28" (Full), 28" (Mod.), 26" (Imp. Cyl.); 20 ga., 28" (Full or Mod.), 26" (Imp. Cyl.); 12 ga. Trap, 30" (Full); 12 or 20 ga. Skeet, 26" (Skeet).
Weight: 12 ga. 7 lbs., 20 ga. 6½ lbs., Trap 7½ lbs.
Stock: Hand checkered European walnut, p.g. Monte Carlo on trap models.
Features: AL-2 has hand-engraved receiver and ventilated rib; AL-1 has satin-finished receiver and plain bbl. AL-1 not available in 12 ga. 28" (Full), Trap or Skeet. Crossbolt safety. Imported from Italy by Garcia.
Price: AL-1 . . . . **$185.00**
Price: AL-2 . . . . **$195.00**
Price: AL-2 Trap or Skeet **$210.00**

CHARLES DALY AUTO SHOTGUN
Gauge: 12 (2¾" chamber).
Action: Gas-operated semi-auto.
Barrel: 26" (I.C.), 28" (Mod. or Full), 30" (Full), vent. rib.
Stock: Hand-checkered walnut, p.g.
Features: Button safety, 5-shot capacity (3-shot plug furnished). Imported by Charles Daly.
Price: **$220.00**

FRANCHI STANDARD AUTO SHOTGUN
Gauge: 12 or 20.
Action: Recoil-operated automatic.
Barrel: 24" (Cyl.); 26" (Imp. Cyl. or Mod.); 28" (Mod. or Full); 30", 12 ga. (Full).
Weight: 12 ga. 6¼ lbs., 20 ga. 5 lbs. 2 oz.
Stock: Epoxy-finished walnut.
Features: Chrome-lined bbl., easy takedown, 3-round plug provided. Available with plain round or ventilated rib barrel. Imported from Italy by Stoeger Arms.
Price: (Plain bbl.) . . . . **$176.95** (20 ga.); **$199.75** (12 ga.)
Price: (Vent. rib) . . . . **$207.95** (20 ga.); **$234.50** (12 ga.)

FRANCHI MAGNUM AUTO SHOTGUN
Gauge: 12 or 20, 3-inch shells.
Action: Recoil-operated automatic.
Barrel: 32", 12 ga.; 28", 20 ga., both Full.
Weight: 12 ga. 8¼ lbs., 20 ga. 6 lbs.
Stock: Epoxy-finished walnut with recoil pad.
Features: Chrome-lined bbl., easy takedown. Available with plain round or ventilated rib barrel ($35.00 additional). Imported from Italy by Stoeger Arms.
Price: . . . . **$214.75** (20 ga.); **$229.75** (12 ga.)

FRANCHI SLUG GUN
Same as Standard automatic except 22" cylinder bored bbl., adj. rear sight, sling swivels.
Price: **$234.50**

TRADEWINDS H-170 AUTO SHOTGUN
Gauge: 12 only, 2¾" chambers.
Action: Recoil-operated automatic.
Barrel: 26", 28" (Mod.) and 28" (Full), chrome lined.
Weight: 7 lbs.
Stock: Select European walnut stock, p.g. and fore-end hand checkered.
Features: Light alloy receiver, 5-shot tubular magazine, ventilated rib. Imported by Tradewinds.
Price: **$179.95**

IMPORTED SHOTGUNS—DOUBLE BARREL

ATLAS MODEL 208 DOUBLE BARREL SHOTGUN
Gauge: 12, 20, 28 and 410 (3″ chambers).
Action: Anson & Deeley-type, engraved.
Barrel: 26″ (I.C. & Mod.), 26″, 28″ (Mod. & Full).
Weight: 6-7 lbs.
Stock: Walnut with checkered semi p.g. and beavertail fore-end.
Features: Chromed bores, double trigger. Imported from Italy by Atlas Arms.
Price: **$250.00**

ATLAS 145 DOUBLE BARREL SHOTGUN
Similar to M208 except: vent. rib, choice of p.g. or straight stock, full hand engraving, entire gun of nickel-chrome steel. 12 & 20 ga., 2¾″ chambers only. Available with 2 sets of bbls., 26″ (Skeet 1 & 2), 28″ (Mod. & Full), on special order. Imported from Italy by Atlas Arms.
Price: **$350.00**

ATLAS 500 MAGNUM DOUBLE BARREL SHOTGUN
Gauge: 10 (3½″ chambers); 12, 20 (3″ chambers).
Action: Anson & Deeley box lock, Purdey type locks.
Barrel: 32″ (Full & Full), 28″ (Mod. & Full).
Weight: 8 lbs.
Stock: Hand checkered walnut, semi p.g., beavertail fore-end, recoil pad.
Features: Vent. rib, double triggers. Imported from Italy by Atlas Arms.
Price: **$270.00**

ATLAS MODEL 520 HAMMER DOUBLE SHOTGUN
Gauge: 12 (3″ chambers).
Action: Greener Crossbolt.
Barrel: 18½″ (Cyl. & Cyl.).
Weight: 6 lbs.
Stock: Hand checkered walnut, p.g., push button release fore-end.
Features: External hammers, engraved action. Imported from Italy by Atlas Arms.
Price: **$119.95**

AYA MODELS 56 & 53E DOUBLE BARREL SHOTGUNS
Gauge: 12, 20 (2¾″ chambers standard, 3″ on request).
Action: Heavy Competition sidelock frame, triple bolting.
Barrel Up to 30″ (length and choke customer specified).
Stock: Made to customer specifications.
Features: Auto safety and ejectors, loading indicators, matted rib, gas escape valves, folding front trigger, engraved frame. Made to customer requirements, 4-6 month delivery. Model 53-E same except has hand detachable locks, concave rib. Imported from Spain by JBL Arms.
Price: 56 . . . . **$641.00**
Price: 53E **$456.00**

AYA XXV/SL DOUBLE BARREL SHOTGUN
Same as 56 except 12 ga., 2¾″ chamber only, narrow top rib, 25″ bbl.
Price: **$440.00**

AYA NO. 1 DOUBLE BARREL SHOTGUN
Same as 56 except lightweight frame, concave rib, double bolting, 2¾″ chambers only.
No. 2 similar to No. 1 except without loading indicators or folding front trigger.
Price: No. 1 . . . . **$600.00**
Price: No. 2 . . . . **$331.00**

AYA 117 DOUBLE BARREL SHOTGUN
Similar to 53-E except without loading indicators; has folding front trigger.
Price: **$246.00**

BERETTA GR DOUBLE BARREL SHOTGUN
Gauge: 12 (2¾″ chambers), 20 (3″ chambers).
Action: Improved Greener action.
Barrel: 12 ga. 30″ or 28″ (Mod., Full), 26″ (Imp. Cyl., Mod.) 20 ga. 28″ (Mod., Full), 26″ (Imp. Cyl., Mod.)
Weight: 12 ga. 7 lbs., 20 ga. 6½ lbs., 12 ga. Mag. 8 lbs.
Stock: 14″ x 1½″ x 2½″ hand checkered European walnut stock and semi-beavertail fore-end.
Features: Ventilated rib. Model GR-2 has double triggers; GR-3 has single selective trigger; GR-4 has single selective trigger, auto ejectors, engraved action and select wood. Imported from Italy by Garcia.
Price: . . . .**$300.00**(GR-2) to **$465.00**(GR-4)

IMPORTED SHOTGUNS—DOUBLE BARREL

BERETTA SO DOUBLE BARREL SHOTGUNS
Gauge: 12 (2¾" chambers).
Action: Heavy underlug locking. Single selective or double triggers, gold plated on SO-7.
Barrel: 28" (Mod. and Full), 26" (I.C. and Mod.); 30" bbl. and different choke combos available.
Weight: 7 to 7¼ lbs.
Stock: Select European walnut, 14⅛" x 1½" x 2½" or custom fitted, p.g. or straight grip.
Features: Made to order to customer's specifications. SO-7 has more ornamentation. Auto safety on Field models, manual on Skeet and Trap. Imported from Italy by Garcia.
Price: SO-6 .... $2,875.00
Price: SO-7 .... $4,000.00

BERNARDELLI GAME COCK DOUBLE BARREL SHOTGUN
Gauge: 12 or 20.
Action: Hammerless boxlock, auto safety, double triggers.
Barrel: 25" (Imp. Cyl. & Mod.), 28" (Mod. & Full).
Weight: 12 ga. 6 lbs., 20 ga. 5½ lbs.
Stock: 14" x 1½" x 2½" hand-checkered walnut.
Features: Available in Standard, Deluxe (light scroll engraving, auto ejectors) or Premier (engraving, auto ejectors, non-selective single trigger). Imported from Italy by Stoeger Arms.
Price: .... $264.00 (Standard); $394.00 (Deluxe); $514.00 (Premier)

BRESCIA DOUBLE BARREL SHOTGUN
Gauge: 12, 20 (2¾" chambers).
Action: Anson & Deeley.
Barrel: 28" (Full & Mod. or I.C. & Mod.), chrome lined.
Weight: 6½ lbs.
Stock: Hand checkered walnut, p.g. or straight, recoil pad.
Features: Double triggers, engraved action. Imported from Italy by Kleingunther.
Price: $216.20

CHARLES DALY P-O-S DOUBLE BARREL SHOTGUN
Gauge: 10, 12, 20 or 410 (3" chambers except 10, 3½"; 28, 2¾").
Action: Hammerless, double triggers.
Barrel: 32" 10, 30" 12 (Full & Full); 30" 12, 28" 12 or 20, 26" 28 or 410 (Mod. & Full); 26" 12 or 20 (I.C. & Mod.).
Stock: Checkered walnut, p.g. cap and buttplate with white line spacers.
Features: Imported from Spain by Charles Daly.
Price: $150.00

CENTURY FOLDING DOUBLE BARREL SHOTGUN
Gauge: 410 (3" chambers).
Action: Hammer, side lever to open action.
Barrel: 27¾" (Full & Full).
Weight: 4¾ lbs.
Stock: Hand checkered walnut, semi p.g.
Features: Depressing button on frame allows gun to be folded for carrying or storage. Imported from Spain by Century Arms.
Price: $54.50

DARNE DOUBLE BARREL SHOTGUN
Gauge: 12, 16, 20, 24 and 28.
Action: Sliding breech.
Barrel: 25½" to 30".
Weight: 5½ lbs., min.
Stock: Hand-checkered European walnut, semi-pistol grip or straight.
Features: Available in 8 grades, stock or custom made. 5-year warranty. Imported from France by Firearms Center.
Price: .... $295.00 up

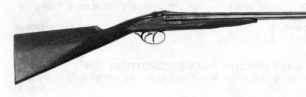

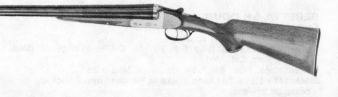

DAVIDSON MODEL 63B DOUBLE BARREL SHOTGUN
Gauge: 12, 20, 28 (2¾" chambers); 410 (3" chambers).
Action: Anson & Deeley with crossbolt (no crossbolt on 28 and 410).
Barrel: 30" 12 (Mod. & Full); 26" (I.C. & Mod.) and 28" (Mod. & Full) all except 410; 410, 25" (Full & Full) only.
Weight: 12 ga., 7 lbs.; 16, 20, 28 ga., 6½ lbs.; 410 ga., 5 lbs. 11 oz.
Stock: Hand finished checkered European walnut, white line spacers on p.g. cap and butt plate.
Features: Auto safety, manual extractors, gold-plated double triggers, engraved nickel-plated frame. Imported from Europe by Davidson.
Price: $109.95

IMPORTED SHOTGUNS—DOUBLE BARREL

DAVIDSON 69SL DOUBLE BARREL SHOTGUN
Gauge: 12, 20 (2¾″ chambers).
Action: Sidelock with detachable sideplates.
Barrel: 26″ (I.C. & Mod.), 28″ (Mod. & Full).
Weight: 12 ga., 7 lbs.; 20 ga., 6½ lbs.
Stock: Fineline checkered European walnut, white line spacer on p.g. cap and buttplate.
Features: Auto safety, manual extractors, gold-plated double triggers, engraved nickel-plated frame. Imported from Europe by Davidson.
Price: **$129.95**

DIXIE HAMMER DOUBLE BARREL SHOTGUN
Gauge: 12, 16, 20 and 410 ga. regular or Magnum.
Action: Boxlock.
Barrel: 28″ to 32″ barrels.
Stock: Straight, semi-pistol or full pistol-grip halfstocks, some with checkered grip and fore-end, some smooth.
Weight: Varies.
Features: Proofed for heaviest smokeless powder loads. Case-hardened frames with modest engraving. Imported from Belgium, Italy or Spain by Dixie Gun Works.
Price: . . . . **$125.00** to **$140.00**

DAVIDSON 63B MAGNUM DOUBLE SHOTGUN
Gauge: 10 (3½″ chambers), 12 and 20 (3″ chambers) magnum.
Barrel: 32″ 10 (Full & Full), 30″ 12 (Mod. & Full), 28″ 12, 20 (Mod. & Full), 26″ 20 (I.C. & Mod.).
Weight: 10 ga., 10 lbs. 10 oz.; 12 ga., 7½ lbs.; 20 ga. 6¾ lbs.
Stock: Hand finished checkered European walnut, beavertail fore-end, white line spacers on p.g. cap and recoil pad.
Features: Auto safety, manual extractors, gold-plated double triggers (front hinged), engraved nickel-plated action. Imported from Europe by Davidson.
Price: 12, 20 ga **$124.95**
Price: 10 ga **$159.95**

F.I.E. DOUBLE BARREL SHOTGUN
Gauge: 12, 16, 20, 410.
Action: Boxlock.
Barrel: 30″ 12 only (Full & Full); 28″ all exc. 410 (Mod.& Full); 26″ all exc. 410 (I.C.& Mod.); 26″ 410 (Mod.& Full or Full & Full).
Stock: Hand checkered walnut, beavertail fore-end, white line spacers on p.g. cap and butt plate.
Features: Raised matted rib, double triggers, engraved case hardened receiver. Imported by Firearms Import & Export.
Price: **$92.00**

FALCON DOUBLE BARREL SHOTGUN
Gauge: 12 (Model 1302), 20 (Model 1303), 28 (Model 1304), 410 (Model 1305). All 3-inch chambers except 28 ga.
Action: Anson & Deeley, gold plated double triggers.
Barrel: 30″ (Mod. and Full) 12 ga., 28″ (Mod. and Full) 12 and 20 ga., 26″ (Imp. Cyl. and Mod.) 12 and 20 ga., (Mod. and Full) 28 ga., (Full and Full) 410 ga.
Stock: Hand checkered walnut, ebonite p.g. cap and butt plate with white spacers, beavertail fore-end.
Features: Scroll engraving. Imported from Spain by American Import.
Price: **$139.00**

FALCON GOOSE DOUBLE BARREL SHOTGUN
Gauge: 10 (3½-inch chambers).
Action: Anson & Deeley with Holland type extractors, double triggers.
Barrel: 32″ (Full and Full).
Weight: 11 lbs.
Stock: Hand checkered walnut, plastic p.g. cap and rubber recoil pad with white spacers.
Features: Auto safety, rubber recoil pad, engraved action. Imported from Spain by American Import.
Price: **$175.00**

LOYOLA MAGNUM DOUBLE BARREL SHOTGUN
Gauge: 10 (3½ chambers); 12, 20 and 410 (all 3″ chambers).
Action: Hammerless, double trigger, auto. safety.
Barrel: 12, 20 ga. 26″ (Imp. Cyl., Mod.), 28″ (Full, Mod.); 10, 12 ga. 30″ (Full, Mod.); 10 ga. 32″, 12 ga. 30″ and 410 ga. 26″ (Full, Full).
Stock: Checkered walnut, p.g., fitted rubber recoil pad.
Features: Available with solid or vent. rib. ($20.00 additional). Imported from Spain by Jana.
Price: . . . . **$99.95** (12, 20, 410 ga.), **$123.50** (10 ga.)

IMPORTED SHOTGUNS—DOUBLE BARREL

MAUSER MODEL 580 DOUBLE BARREL SHOTGUN
Gauge: 12, 20 (3″ chambers).
Action: Holland & Holland type side lock.
Barrel: 28″ (Full & I.M. or I.C. & Mod.).
Weight: 7 lbs.
Stock: Hand checkered French walnut.
Features: Auto selective ejectors, choice of double or single ($50.00 additional) trigger. English scroll engraved. Imported from Germany by Mauser Amerika.
Price: **$905.00**

MERCURY MAGNUM DOUBLE BARREL SHOTGUN
Gauge: 10 (3½″), 12 or 20 (3″) magnums.
Action: Triple-lock Anson & Deeley type.
Barrel: 28″ (Full & Mod.), 12 and 20 ga.; 32″ (Full & Full), 10 ga.
Weight: 7¼ lbs. (12 ga.); 6½ lbs. (20 ga.); 10⅛ lbs. (10 ga.). **Length:** 45″ (28″ bbls.).
Stock: 14″ x 1⅝″ x 2¼″ walnut, checkered p.g. stock and beavertail fore-end, recoil pad.
Features: Double triggers, front hinged, auto safety, extractors; safety gas ports, engraved frame. Imported from Spain by Tradewinds.
Price: . . . . **$149.95** (12, 20 ga.)
Price: . . . . **$179.95** (10 ga.)

PREMIER AMBASSADOR DOUBLE BARREL SHOTGUN
Gauge: 12, 16 (2¾″); 20, 410 (3″).
Action: Triple Greener crossbolt, Purdey avail. on 410; side locks.
Barrels: 22″ exc. 410; 26″ all (Mod. & Full).
Weight: 7¼ lbs. (12) to 6¼ lbs. (410). **Length:** 44½″.
Stock: 14″ x 1⅝″ x 2½″ checkered walnut, p.g., beavertail fore-end.
Features: Cocking indicators, double triggers, auto safety. Imported from Europe by Premier.
Price: **$155.95**

PREMIER CONTINENTAL DOUBLE SHOTGUN
Same as Ambassador except outside hammers, not avail. in 410.
Price: **$141.75**

PREMIER REGENT DOUBLE BARREL SHOTGUN
Gauge: 12, 16, 28 (2¾″ chambers); 20, 410 (3″ chambers).
Action: Triple Greener crossbolt; Purdey optional on 28, 410.
Barrels: 26″ (I.C. & Mod.) exc. 28 and 410 only (Mod. & Full); 28″ (Mod. & Full); 30″ 12 only (Mod. & Full).
Weight: 7¼ lbs. (12) to 6⅛ lbs. (410). **Length:** 42½″ (26″ bbls.).
Stock: 14″ x 1⅝″ x 2½″ checkered walnut, p.g. and fore-end.
Features: Matted tapered rib, double triggers, auto safety. Extra bbl. sets avail. Imported from Europe by Premier.
Price: **$114.95**

PREMIER BRUSH KING DOUBLE BARREL SHOTGUN
Same as Regent except 12 and 20 ga. only, 22″ bbls. (I.C. & Mod.), weight 6¼ lbs. (12), 5¾ lbs. (20).
Price: **$123.40**

PREMIER MAGNUM DOUBLE BARREL SHOTGUN
Similar to Regent except 10 ga. (3½″ chambers) 32″ or 12 ga. (3″ chambers) 30″, both Full & Full. Recoil pad, beavertail fore-end.
Price: 12 ga. **$129.40**
Price: 10 ga. **$157.50**

IMPORTED SHOTGUNS—DOUBLE BARREL

ROSSI OVERLAND DOUBLE BARREL SHOTGUN
Gauge: 12, 20 and 410 (3-in. chambers).
Action: Sidelock with external hammers; Greener crossbolt.
Barrel: 12 ga., 20″ (Imp. Cyl., Mod.) 28″ (Mod., Full); 20 ga., 20″ or 26″ (Mod., Full); 410 ga., 26″ (Full, Full)
Weight: 6 lbs. (410 ga., 26″ bbls.) to 7 lbs. (12 ga., 28″ bbls).
Stock: Walnut p.g. with beavertail fore-end.
Features: Solid raised matted rib. Imported from Italy by Garcia.
Price: **$90.00**

STAR GAUGE DOUBLE BARREL SHOTGUN
Gauge: 12 (2¾″ chambers), 20 (3″ chambers).
Action: Anson & Deeley with double under-locks.
Barrel: 26″ (I.C. & Mod.), 28″ (Full & Mod.); 26″ (Full & Mod.) 20 ga. only; ventilated rib.
Weight: 7¼ lbs. (12), 6¾ lbs. (20)
Stock: Hand checkered walnut, p.g. and semi-beavertail fore-end, fitted recoil pad.
Features: Available with double (Standard) or single triggers (Deluxe). Deluxe has auto ejectors. Imported from Spain by Interarms.
Price: . . . .$149.00 (Standard); **$179.00** (Deluxe).

SARASQUETA DOUBLE BARREL SHOTGUN
Gauge: 410.
Action: Boxlock.
Barrel: 28″ (Full & Full).
Stock: Walnut, beavertail fore-end, white line spacers on p.g. cap and butt plate.
Features: Double triggers. Imported from Spain by Firearms Import & Export.
Price: **$105.95**

SARASQUETA FOLDING DOUBLE BARREL SHOTGUN
Gauge: 410.
Action: Boxlock.
Barrels: 26″ (Full & Full).
Stock: Checkered semi p.g. and fore-end.
Features: Exposed hammers, double triggers. Release button permits bbl. to fold at acute angle for carrying or storage. Imported from Spain by Firearms Import & Export.
Price: **$59.95**

SAUER ARTEMIS DOUBLE BARREL SHOTGUN
Gauge: 12 (2¾″), 20 (3″).
Action: Greener cross-bolt, removable Holland & Holland type side-locks.
Barrel: 28″ (Full & Mod.).
Stock: 14½″x1½″x2¼″ hand checkered walnut stock and beavertail fore-end.
Weight: 6½ lbs.
Features: Automatic slide safety and single selective trigger. Imported from Germany by Weatherby.
Price: Grade I . . . .$1765.00 Grade II $2170.00

SAUER ROYAL DOUBLE BARREL SHOTGUN
Gauge: 12 (2¾″), 20 (3″).
Action: Anson & Deeley, Greener cross bolt.
Barrel: 30″ 12 (Full & Mod.); 28″ (Full & Mod.); 26″ 20 (I.C.& Mod.).
Weight: 6½ lbs.(12), 6 lbs.(20).
Stock: 14¼″x1½″x2¼″ hand checkered walnut, p.g., beavertail fore-end, recoil pad.
Features: Single selective trigger, auto safety, side firing pin indicators. Imported from Germany by Weatherby.
Price: **$399.00**

A & F ZANOTTI DOUBLE BARREL SHOTGUN
Gauge: 12, 20, 28.
Action: Boxlock.
Barrel: 28″ 12 only (Mod.& Full), 26″ (I.C.& Mod.).
Stock: 12 ga. has semi-p.g. walnut stock and beavertail fore-end; 20 and 28 ga. have straight grip and slim fore-end.
Features: Single non-selective trigger, ejectors, gold stock inlay for initials. Custom made. Imported from Italy by Abercrombie & Fitch.
Price: 12 or 20 ga. . . . .$675.00 28 ga. $750.00

ZABALA DOUBLE BARREL SHOTGUN
Gauge: 10 (3½″); 12, 20, 410 (3″); 16, 20 (2¾″).
Action: Modified Anson & Deeley boxlock.
Barrels: 32″ 10, 12 only (Full & Full); 30″ 12 only (Mod.& Full); 28″ all exc. 410 (Mod.& Full); 26″ 12, 20, 28 (I.C.&Mod.); 26″ 410 only (Mod.& Full); 22″ 12 only (I.C.& I.C.).
Weight: 10½ lbs.(10), 7¾ lbs.(12) to 6 lbs.(410).
Stock: Hand checkered European walnut, p.g., beavertail fore-end, rubber recoil pad. Dimensions vary with gauge.
Features: Auto safety, plain extractors. Imported from Spain by Galef.
Price: 10 ga. . . . .$159.95 12 - 410 . . . . **$129.95**

IMPORTED SHOTGUNS—OVER-UNDER

ATLAS MODEL 800 O/U SHOTGUN
Gauge: 12, 20 (3" chambers).
Action: Merkel-type.
Barrel: 26" or 28", standard chokes, vent. rib.
Weight: 7 lbs.
Stock: 14¼"x1½"x2½" p.g., hand checkered.
Features: Highly engraved, non-ejector, non-selective single trigger. Detachable sideplates. Imported from Italy by Atlas Arms.
Price: **$295.00**

ATLAS GRAND PRIX O/U SHOTGUN
Gauge: 12, 20.
Action: Merkel-type, sidelocks.
Barrel: 26" or 28" vent. rib barrels, choice of chokes.
Weight: 7¼ lbs.
Stock: Straight or p.g. to order.
Features: Fully engraved, automatic ejectors, single selective trigger. Available on special order only. Imported from Italy by Atlas Arms.
Price: .... **$1000.00 up.**

ATLAS MODEL 95 O/U SHOTGUN
Similar to Model 800 but less engraving, p.g. 14"x1½"x2½" stock only. 3" Mag. chambers.
Price: **$280.00**

ATLAS MODEL 65 O/U SHOTGUN
Gauge: 28, 410 (3" chambers).
Action: Merkel-type.
Barrel: 26", 28"(I.C.& Mod., Mod.&Full, Skeet & Skeet).
Weight: 5½ lbs.
Stock: Hand checkered walnut.
Features: Extractors, single or double triggers. Imported from Italy by Atlas Arms.
Price: **$248.00**

AYA 37A O/U SHOTGUN
Gauge: 12, 20 (2¾" chambers).
Action: Detachable sidelocks, quadruple bolting.
Barrel: Up to 30" (length and choke customer specified).
Stock: Custom fitted, with beavertail fore-end.
Features: Ventilated rib, auto safety and ejectors, folding front trigger. Single selective or non-selective trigger, extra bbls., fitted luggage case available at additional cost. Made to customer requirements, 4-6 month delivery. Imported from Spain by JBL Arms.
Price: **$915.00**

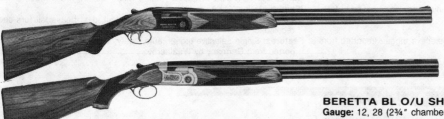

BERETTA BL O/U SHOTGUNS
Gauge: 12, 28 (2¾" chambers); 12 mag., 20 (3" chambers).
Action: Hammerless with gold-plated single-selective trigger. BL-6 has Beretta boxlock action.
Barrel: 12 ga., 30" or 28" (Mod., Full), 26" (Imp. Cyl., Mod.); 20 ga., 28" (Mod., Full), 26" (Mod., Full); 28 ga., 28" (Mod., Full), 26" (Imp. Cyl, Mod.); 12 ga. Trap, 30" (Imp. Mod., Full); 12 or 20 ga. Skeet, 26" (Skeet, Skeet).
Weight: 7¼ lbs. (12 ga.), 6 lbs (20 and 28 ga.), 7½ lbs (Trap and 12 ga. Mag.).
Stock: 14⅛"x1½"x2½" (Standard), 14⅜"x1⅜"x1¾" (Trap), hand-checkered European walnut, p.g.
Features: Hand-engraved receivers, ventilated rib. BL-4 has more engraving and checkering than BL-3, is available with two sets of barrels. BL-6 has additional hand-engraved sideplates, specially selected wood. Imported from Italy by Garcia.
Price: .... From **$230.00** (BL-1) To **$600.00** (BL-6 Trap or Skeet)

BERETTA SO SERIES O/U SHOTGUNS

Gauge: 12 (2¾" chambers).
Action: Sidelock, with modified Greener crossbolt, hand-detachable on SO-4 and 5. Single selective or double triggers, gold plated on SO-5 only.
Barrel: 28" (Mod. and Full), 26" (I.C. and Mod.). 30" and different choke combos available.
Weight: 7 to 7¼ lbs.
Stock: Select European walnut, 14⅛"x1½"x2½" or custom fitted, p.g. or straight grip.
Features: Made to order to customer's specifications. Ornamentation varies with grade, SO-2 through SO-5. Auto safety on Field models, manual on Skeet and Trap. Imported from Italy by Garcia.
Price: SO-2 .... **$1180.00** to SO-5 **$2265.00**

CONDOR O/U SHOTGUN

Gauge: 12, 20 (2¾" or 3" chambers).
Action: Purdey type double lock.
Barrel: 26" (I.C. & Mod., Skeet & Skeet); 28" (Full & Mod., I.M.& Mod.); 30" (Full & Full, Full & Mod.) 12 mag. only.
Weight: 6½ lbs. (26"20) to 7 lbs.3oz. (30"12).
Stock: 14"x1½"x2½" handcheckered walnut, p.g. and fore-end, recoil pad.
Features: Single selective trigger, auto ejectors, manual tang safety, vent. rib. Skeet Grade has extra wide rib. Imported from Italy by Kleingunther.
Price: **$345.00**

CONDOR TRAP O/U SHOTGUN

Same as Field Grade except wide rib, Monte Carlo stock, 12 ga. only, 28" (Full & Mod.); 30" or 32" (I.M.& Full, Full & Full), weight 7 lbs.7oz.
Price: **$375.00**

CHARLES DALY SUPERIOR GRADE O/U SHOTGUN

Gauge: 12, 20, 28, 410 (2¾" chambers except 20 and 410 ga. Field models, 3")
Action: Boxlock, single selective inertia trigger.
Barrel: Same as Field Grade plus 28" 12, 20, 410 (Skeet & Skeet).
Weight: 12 ga., 7¼ lbs.; others, 6 lbs. 10 oz.
Stock: 14"x1½"x2½" checkered walnut, p.g., beavertail fore-end.
Features: Ventilated rib. "Selexor" permits shooter to select auto ejection or merely extraction. Imported from Japan by Charles Daly.
Price: .... **$399.00** to **$450.00**

CHARLES DALY FIELD GRADE O/U SHOTGUNS

Gauge: 12, 28 (2¾" chambers); 12 mag., 20, 410 (3" chambers).
Action: Boxlock, single selective inertia trigger, auto safety (exc. Skeet).
Barrel: 30" 12 (Skeet&Sheet); 28" 12, 20 (Mod.&Full); 26" 12, 20, 28, 410 (Skeet&Skeet, I.C.& Mod.); 28, 410 (Mod.&Full).
Weight: 12 ga., 7 lbs.; others, about 6¼ lbs.
Stock: 14"x1½"x2½" walnut, p.g. 12 Mag. has recoil pad.
Features: Ventilated rib, selective auto ejectors. Imported from Japan by Charles Daly.
Price: 12 and 20 ga. .... **$375.00** 28 and 410 ga. **$400.00**

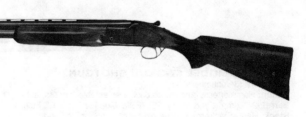

CHARLES DALY VENTURE GRADE O/U SHOTGUNS

Gauge: 12 (2¾" chambers), 20 (3" chambers).
Action: Box lock, single selective inertia trigger.
Barrel: 26" (I.C. and Mod.), 28" (Mod. and Full).
Weight: 12 ga., 7 lbs.; 20 ga., 6 lbs. 5 oz.
Stock: 14"x1½"x2½" checkered walnut, p.g.
Features: Ventilated rib, manual safety, auto ejectors. Imported from Japan by Charles Daly.
Price: **$335.00**

FOREVER YOURS O/U SHOTGUNS

Gauge: 12, 16, 20.
Action: Anson & Deeley 4-lock type, double Greener crossbolt.
Barrel: Specify length and choke desired.
Weight: 7-7½ lbs.
Stock: Checkered Circassian walnut, split fore-end, horn p.g. cap and butt-plate.
Features: Ventilated rib, auto ejectors, double triggers, engraved action. Available with or without cheekpiece, with single set trigger. Imported from Austria by Flaig's.
Price: .... **$675.00 - $750.00**

IMPORTED SHOTGUNS—OVER-UNDER

FRANCHI FALCONET O/U SHOTGUN

Gauge: 12, 16, 20, 28 and 410.
Action: Hammerless with overhead-sear trigger and auto. safety.
Barrel: 24", 12 or 20 ga. (Cyl. & Imp. Cyl.); 26", all except 410 (Imp. Cyl. & Mod.), 410 (Mod. & Full); 28", all (Mod. & Full); 30", 12 ga. (Mod. & Full); 26", all except 16 ga. (Skeet 1-Skeet 2); 30" 12 ga. Trap (Mod. & Full).
Weight: 6 lbs. (approx.) except Skeet 7½ lbs. and Trap 8¼ lbs.
Stock: Epoxy finished walnut.
Features: Chrome-lined barrels, selective single trigger, auto ejectors. Available with "Buckskin" or "Ebony" (Blue) colored Frames. Skeet and Trap models have 10mm rib, middle sight, non-auto safety. Imported from Italy by Stoeger Arms.
Price: (Ebony) . . . . **$341.75** (12, 16, 20 ga.); **$364.75** (28, 410 ga.).
Price: (Buckskin) . . . . **$354.75** (12, 16, 20 ga.); **$378.75** (28, 410 ga.).
Price: (Skeet) . . . . **$550.00** (12, 20 ga.); **$635.00** (28, 410 ga.).
Price: (Trap) . . . .**$550.00** (12,20 ga. only.).

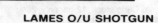

KRIEGHOFF MODEL 32 O/U SHOTGUN

Gauge: 12, 20.
Action: Boxlock.
Barrel: 28", 30".
Stock: Hand checkered walnut, p.g., beavertail fore-end.
Features: Three-way safety (manual, auto or inoperative). Selective single trigger, ejectors and ventilated rib. Other barrel lengths, chokes to order. Available with fancier walnut and relief engraving and silver and gold inlays. Extra barrels available. Imported from Germany by Europa Corp.
Price: . . . . **$595.00 to $2950.00**

LAMES O/U SHOTGUN

Gauge: 12 (2¾").
Action: Boxlock.
Barrels: 32", 30" (Full & Full or Imp.Mod.& Full), 28" (I.C.& Mod. or Mod.& Full), 26" (I.C.& Mod.).
Stock: Hand checkered walnut, semi p.g.
Features: Gold-plated single selective trigger, auto safety, vent. rib. Imported by LA Distributors.
Price: **$329.95**

LAMES O/U TRAP SHOTGUN

Gauge: 12 (2¾").
Action: Boxlock.
Barrels: 30" or 32" (Full & Full or Mod.& Full).
Stock: Hand checkered walnut, Monte Carlo, p.g., beavertail fore-end, recoil pad.
Features: Single selective trigger, manual safety, double vent. rib. Fitted 20 ga. bbl. set available. Imported by LA Distributors.
Price: **$399.95**

LAURONA MODEL 67-G O/U SHOTGUN

Gauge: 12 (3" chambers).
Action: Hammerless, gold-plated double selectable triggers, auto. safety.
Barrel: 26" (Imp. Cyl.& Mod.); 28" (Full& Mod.); 30" (Full & Full), vent. rib.
Stock: Hand-checkered walnut, p.g., vent. rubber recoil pad.
Feature: Chromed bores, vent. rib. Imported from Spain by Jana.
Price: Model 67-G **$199.95**

LAURONA MODEL 71-G O/U SHOTGUN

Same as Model 67-G except supplied with both 12 and 20 ga. bbls., 28" (Full & Mod.).
Price: **$320.00**

MAUSER 620 O/U SHOTGUN

Gauge: 12 (2¾" chambers).
Action: Greener crossbolt.
Barrel: 30" (Full & I.Mod.), 28" (Mod.& Full, I.C.& Mod. or Skeet & Skeet).
Weight: 7½ lbs. **Length:** 45" (28" bbls.).
Stock: Hand checkered walnut, p.g., beavertail fore-end, recoil pad.
Features: Single non-selective adj. trigger, vent. rib, auto ejectors. Selective or double triggers, engraving available at extra cost. Imported from Germany by Mauser Amerika.
Price: **$875.00**

IMPORTED SHOTGUNS—OVER-UNDER

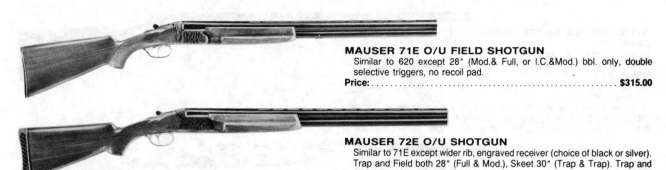

MAUSER 71E O/U FIELD SHOTGUN
Similar to 620 except 28" (Mod.& Full, or I.C.&Mod.) bbl. only, double selective triggers, no recoil pad.
Price: $315.00

MAUSER 72E O/U SHOTGUN
Similar to 71E except wider rib, engraved receiver (choice of black or silver). Trap and Field both 28" (Full & Mod.), Skeet 30" (Trap & Trap). Trap and Skeet have recoil pad.
Price: $399.00

SAUER 66 O/U SHOTGUN
Gauge: 12.
Action: Purdey type, Holland & Holland removable locks.
Barrel: 28" (Full & Mod.).
Weight: 7¼ lbs.
Stock: 14¼"x1½"x2¼" hand checkered walnut, p.g., recoil pad.
Features: Single selective trigger, selective auto. ejectors. Field model has auto. slide safety. Ventilated rib. Imported from Germany by Weatherby.
Price: Grade I . . . .$605.00 Grade II $705.00
Grade III $1135.00

A & F PERAZZI O/U SHOTGUN
Gauge: 12.
Action: Boxlock.
Barrel: 29"(Trap); 28"(Pigeon); 26"(Skeet).
Weight: 7 - 7½ lbs.
Stock: Hand checkered walnut, p.g., beavertail fore-end.
Features: Interchangeable stocks for Trap or Field, and interchangeable double or single trigger assemblies. Ventilated rib, bright-finished action. Imported from Italy by Abercrombie & Fitch.
Price: Trap, Pigeon . . . . $875.00 Skeet $950.00

SHADOW INDY O/U SHOTGUN
Gauge: 12, (2¾" chambers).
Action: Boxlock with 4 locks.
Barrel: 30" Trap (Full & Full or Field & I.M), 32" Trap (Full & I.M., Full & I.C. or I.M. & Mod.); 27½" Skeet (Skeet & Skeet); 27½" Field (Full & Mod. or Mod & I.C.).
Weight: 8 lbs. 2 oz. (30" bbl.).
Stock: French walnut, hand checkered p.g. and air ducting fore-end, rubber recoil pad. Field & Skeet: 14"x1½"x2½"; Trap: 14⅜"x1⅜"x1⅞".
Features: Aluminum airflow rib, hand engraved frame, selective safety, gold plated single trigger, chrome plated bores. Imported from Japan by Tradewinds.
Price $550.00

SHADOW GOLD GRADE O/U SHOTGUN
Specifications same as Shadow Indy; stock dimensions and chokes of customers choice. Heavily engraved with inlaid gold eagle. Delivery 6 months after acceptance of order.
Price: $1,750.00

SHADOW SEVEN O/U SHOTGUN
Gauge: 12, (2¾" chamber).
Action: Boxlock action, hand engraved.
Barrel: Field: 27" (Full & Mod. or Mod. & I.C.), 30" (Full & Mod.); Trap: 30" (Full & Full or Full & I.C.); Skeet: 27" (Skeet & Skeet).
Weight: 8 lbs. (30" bbl.).
Stock: French walnut, hand checkered p.g. and fore-end. Field and Skeet: 14"x1⅜"x1⅞"; Trap: 14⅜"x1⅜"x1⅞".
Features: Solid frame; sinble selective gold-plated trigger, automatic ejector, manual safety, ventilated rib. Imported from Japan by Tradewinds.
Price: $395.00

ZOLI GRAY EAGLE O/U SHOTGUN
Gauge: 12 (Model 300) or 20 (Model 302), 3-inch chambers.
Action: Hammerless, with auto safety and top lever release.
Barrel: 28" (Mod. and Full), 26" (Imp. Cyl. and Mod.).
Weight: 6 lbs. 13 oz. (12); 6¼ lbs. (20).
Stock: Hand checkered selected walnut, p.g., ebonite butt plate with white spacer.
Features: Ventilated rib, chrome plated bore. Imported from Italy by American Import.
Price: $239.95

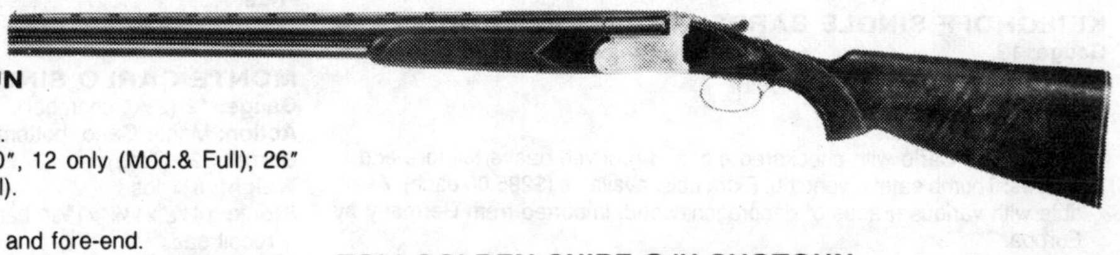

ZOLI SILVER SNIPE O/U SHOTGUN
Gauge: 12, 20 (3" chambers).
Action: Purdey type double boxlock, crossbolt.
Barrels: 26" (I.C.& Mod.), 28" (Mod.&Full), 30", 12 only (Mod.& Full); 26" Skeet (Skeet & Skeet), 30" Trap (Full & Full).
Weight: 6½ lbs. (12 ga.).
Stock: Hand checkered European walnut, p.g. and fore-end.
Features: Auto safety (exc. Trap and Skeet), vent rib, single trigger, chrome bores. Imported from Italy by Galef.
Price: Field . . . .$251.45 Skeet and Trap $302.65

ZOLI GOLDEN SNIPE O/U SHOTGUN
Same as Silver Snipe except selective auto ejectors.
Price: Field . . . .$296.95 Skeet & Trap $353.85

IMPORTED SHOTGUNS—SINGLE BARREL

ATLAS SINGLE BARREL TRAP GUN
Gauge: 12 only.
Action: Boxlock. (2¾" chamber).
Barrel: 30" or 32" (Extra Full), vent. rib, chromed bore.
Weight: 8 lbs.
Stock: 14½"x1⅜"x1⅞"x2¼" checkered walnut Monte Carlo, beavertail fore-end. Recoil pad.
Features: Engraved action, auto. ejector. Avail. with custom engraving, gold trigger and gold lettering (Deluxe). Imported from Italy by Atlas Arms.
Price: Std. .... $420.00 Deluxe $460.00

BERETTA MARK II SINGLE BARREL TRAP SHOTGUN
Gauge: 12 only; (2¾" chamber).
Action: BL type, full width hinge, top snap tip down.
Barrel: 32" or 34", (Full), matted high tapered vent. rib.
Weight: 8¼ lbs.
Stock: 14⅜" x 1⅜" x 1¾". Hand checkered European walnut, p.g.; rubber recoil pad, beavertail fore-end, Monte Carlo.
Features: Hand engraved receiver. Imported from Italy by Garcia.
Price: $400.00

BERETTA TR-2 TRAP SHOTGUN
Gauge: 12 only (2¾" chamber).
Action: Hammerless, under-bbl. release.
Barrel: 32", Full, matted vent. rib.
Weight: 8¼ lbs.
Stock: 14⅜"x1⅜"x1⅝" hand checkered European walnut Monte Carlo stock, p.g., trap-style recoil pad. Beavertail fore-end.
Features: Hand engraved receiver, matted ventilated rib, crossbolt safety. Imported from Italy by Garcia.
Price: $190.00

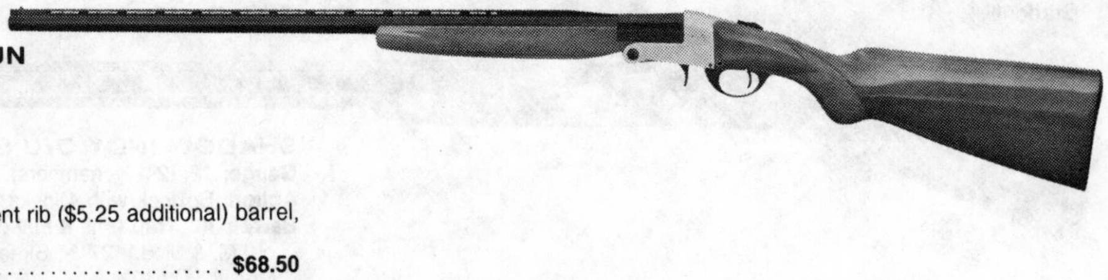

DAINO SINGLE BARREL SHOTGUN
Gauge: 12, 20, 410.
Action: Folding, underlever.
Barrel: 27½", Full or Mod.
Weight: 5½ lbs. **Length:** 44½".
Stock: Hand checkered walnut, semi p.g.
Features: Folds to 27½", choice of plain or vent rib ($5.25 additional) barrel, engraved action. Imported by Kleingunther
Price: $68.50

DICKSON BOLT ACTION SHOTGUN
Gauge: 410.
Action: Bolt, sliding thumb safety.
Barrel: 25" (Full).
Weight: 5 lbs. 5 oz.
Stock: Oiled walnut, p.g., black plastic buttplate.
Features: 3-round capacity. Imported from Europe by American Import.
Price: $37.95

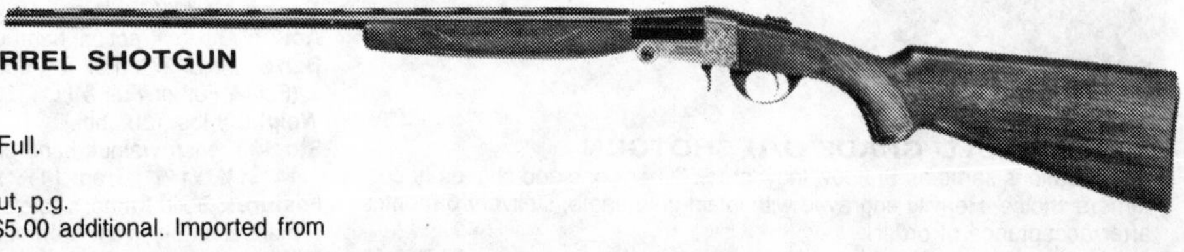

GALEF COMPANION SINGLE BARREL SHOTGUN
Gauge: 12, 20, 410 (3"); 16, 28 (2¾").
Action: Folding boxlock.
Barrel: 28" exc. 12 (30") and 410 (26"), all Full.
Weight: 5½ lbs. (12) to 4½ lbs. (410).
Stock: 14"x1½"x2⅝" hand checkered walnut, p.g.
Features: Non-auto safety, folds. Vent. rib $5.00 additional. Imported from Italy by Galef.
Price: $51.95

MAUSER MODEL 496 SINGLE BARREL SHOTGUN
Gauge: 12 (2¾" chamber).
Action: Greener-type cross bolt, 4 locking lugs.
Barrel: 32" (Mod.), 34" (Full).
Weight: 8 lbs. **Length:** 49".
Stock: Walnut Monte Carlo, p.g., beavertail fore-end.
Features: Front and middle sights, no manual safety, chrome lined bbl., auto ejector. Imported from Germany by Mauser Amerika.
Price: $465.00

KRIEGHOFF SINGLE BARREL TRAP SHOTGUN
Gauge: 12.
Action: Boxlock, short hammer fall.
Barrel: 32" or 34" (Full).
Weight: About 8½ lbs.
Stock: Monte Carlo with checkered p.g. and grooved beavertail fore-end.
Features: Thumb safety, vent. rib. Extra bbls. available ($295.00 each). Available with various grades of decoration, wood. Imported from Germany by Europa.

Price: Standard $750.00	San Remo Grade $1150.00
Monte Carlo Grade $2750.00	Crown Grade $2850.00
Super Crown Grade $3150.00	

MONTE CARLO SINGLE BARREL SHOTGUN
Gauge: 12 (2¾" chamber).
Action: Monte Carlo, bottom release.
Barrel: 32" (Trap).
Weight: 8¼ lbs.
Stock: 14½"x1⅛"x1⅝" hand checkered walnut, p.g., beavertail fore-end, recoil pad.
Features: Auto ejector, slide safety, gold plated trigger. Imported from Italy by Galef.
Price: $149.95

BLACK POWDER GUNS

The following pages catalog the black powder arms currently available to U.S. shooters. These range from quite precise replicas of historically significant arms to totally new designs created expressly to give the black powder shooter the benefits of modern technology.

Most of the replicas are imported, and many are available from more than one source. Thus examples of a given model such as the 1860 Army revolver or Zouave rifle purchased from different importers may vary in price, finish and fitting. Most of them bear proof marks, indicating that they have been test fired in the proof house of their country of origin.

A list of the importers and the retail price range are included with the description for each model. Many local dealers handle more than one importer's products, giving the prospective buyer an opportunity to make his own judgment in selecting a black powder gun. Most importers have catalogs available free or at nominal cost, and some are well worth having for the useful information on black powder shooting they provide in addition to their detailed descriptions and specifications of the guns.

A number of special accessories are also available for the black powder shooter. These include replica powder flasks, bullet moulds, cappers and tools, as well as more modern devices to facilitate black powder cleaning and maintenance. Ornate presentation cases and even detachable shoulder stocks for some black powder pistols are also available from their importers. Again, see your local dealer or the importers for their catalogs.

The black powder guns are arranged in four sections: Single Shot Pistols, Revolvers, Muskets & Rifles, and Shotguns. The guns within each section are arranged by date of the original, with the oldest first. Thus the 1836 Texas Patterson replica leads off the revolver section, and flintlocks precede precussion arms in the other sections.

BLACK POWDER SINGLE SHOT PISTOLS—FLINT & PERCUSSION

ZANOTTI FLINTLOCK PISTOL
Extremely ornate replica of an early Italian flintlock dueling pistol complete with case, bullet mould and powder flask. Carved walnut stock, deep relief engraved metal. Imported by Navy, Hawes.
Price: . . . . **$100.00 to $125.00**

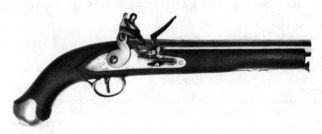

TOWER FLINTLOCK PISTOL
Caliber: 45.
Barrel: 8¼".
Weight: 40 oz. **Length:** 14" over-all.
Stock: Walnut.
Sights: Fixed.
Features: Engraved lock, brass furniture. Specifications, including caliber, weight and length may vary with importers. Available as flint or percussion. Imported by The Armoury, F.I.E., Hawes, C.V.A., Sloan's, Centennial.
Price: . . . . **$28.75 to $42.95.**

HARPER'S FERRY 1806 PERCUSSION PISTOL
Caliber: 54.
Barrel: 10".
Weight: 40 oz. **Length:** 16" over-all.
Stock: Walnut.
Sights: Fixed.
Features: Case hardened lock, brass mounted browned bbl. Replica of the first U.S. Gov't.-made flintlock pistol. Imported by Navy Arms, Sloan's.
Price: . . . . **$50.00 to $95.00**

KENTUCKY FLINTLOCK PISTOL
Caliber: 44.
Barrel: 10⅛".
Weight: 32 oz. **Length:** 15½" over-all.
Stock: Walnut.
Sights: Fixed.
Features: Case hardened lock, blued bbl.; available also as brass bbl. flint Model 1821 ($95.00, Navy). Imported by Navy, Replica, The Armoury, Century, Centennial, F.I.E., Sloan's, Jana.
Price: . . . . **$46.95 to $85.00**

BLACK POWDER SINGLE SHOT PISTOLS—FLINT & PERCUSSION

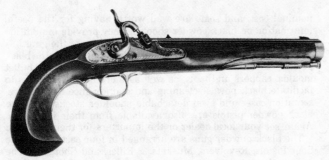

PHILADELPHIA DERRINGER PERCUSSION PISTOL
Caliber: 41.
Barrel: 3⅛".
Weight: 14 oz. **Length:** 7" over-all.
Stock: Walnut, checkered grip.
Sights: Fixed.
Features: Engraved wedge holder and bbl. Also available in flintlock version (Armoury, $29.95). Imported by C.V.A., Century, The Armoury, Hawes.
Price: . . . . $18.37 to $24.95.

SINGLE SHOT PERCUSSION TARGET PISTOL
Caliber: 44.
Barrel: 9" octagonal.
Weight: 42 oz.
Stocks: Walnut.
Sights: Bead front, rear adj. for w. and e.
Features: Engraved scenes on frame sides; brass backstrap and trigger guard; case hardened frame and hammer. Imported by Replica, Navy.
Price: . . . . $64.95 to $70.00

CHALLANGER HOPKINS & ALLEN M-L BOOT PISTOL
Caliber: 36 or 45, single shot percussion.
Barrel: 6 inch octagonal, regular or gain twist.
Weight: 34 oz.
Length: 13 inches.
Stocks: Smooth walnut, birdshead style.
Features: Underhammer lockwork, match trigger.
Sights: Fixed blade front, adj. rear.
Price: $39.95

TINGLE BLACK POWDER M1960 PISTOL
Caliber: 40, single shot, percussion.
Barrel: 8", 9", 10", or 12" octagon.
Weight: 33 oz. (8" bbl.).
Length: 11¾ inches.
Stocks: Walnut, one piece.
Features: 6-groove bbl., easily removable for cleaning; 1-in-30 twist.
Sights: Fixed blade front, w. adj. rear.
Price: $64.95
Price: With detachable shoulder stock, $19.50 extra.

KENTUCKY PERCUSSION PISTOL
Similar to above but percussion lock. Imported by Centennial, The Armory, Navy, F.I.E., Hawes, Jana, Replica.
Price: . . . . $26.95 to $85.00

KENTUCKY BELT PERCUSSION PISTOL
Caliber: 45.
Barrel: 7", rifled.
Weight: 29 oz. **Length:** 12" over-all.
Stock: Walnut.
Sights: Fixed.
Features: Engraved lock, brass furniture, steel ramrod. Available as flint or percussion. Imported by The Armoury, C.V.A., Hawes.
Price: . . . . $22.95 to $31.95.

HARPER'S FERRY MODEL 1855 PERCUSSION PISTOL
Caliber: 58.
Barrel: 11¾", rifled.
Weight: 56 oz. **Length:** 18" over-all.
Stock: Walnut.
Sights: Fixed.
Features: Case hardened lock and hammer; brass furniture; blued bbl. Shoulder stock available, priced at $35.00. Imported by Navy Arms.
Price: $90.00

THOMPSON/CENTER PATRIOT PERCUSSION PISTOL
Caliber: 45.
Barrel: 9¼".
Weight: 36 oz. **Length:** 16" over-all.
Stock: Walnut.
Sights: Patridge-type. Rear adj. for w. and e.
Features: Hook breech system; ebony ramrod; double set triggers; coil mainspring. From Thompson/Center Arms.
Price: $112.00
With accessory pack (Ohaus bullet mould, TC patches, adj. powder measure, short starter, black powder solvent, extra nipple and nipple wrench).
Price: $132.50

BLACK POWDER REVOLVERS

TEXAS PATERSON 1836 PERCUSSION REVOLVER
Caliber: 36, 5-shot.
Barrel: 6″, 7½″, 9″, 12″.
Weight: 24 oz. **Length:** 10″ (6″ bbl.).
Stocks: Walnut.
Sights: Fixed.
Features: Indian scene engraved on cylinder; folding trigger; all blue finish. Imported by Replica, Navy.
Price: . . . .$100.00 to $104.50

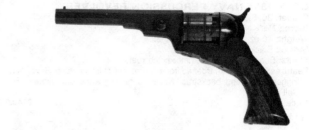

WALKER 1847 PERCUSSION REVOLVER
Caliber: 44, 6-shot.
Barrel: 9″.
Weight: 72 oz. **Length:** 15½″ over-all.
Stocks: Walnut.
Sights: Fixed.
Features: Case hardened frame, loading lever and hammer; iron back strap; brass trigger guard; engraved cylinder. Imported by Replica, Navy, Jana.
Price: . . . .$100.00 to $115.00

SECOND MODEL DRAGOON 1848 REVOLVER
Caliber: 44, 6-shot.
Barrel: 7½″.
Weight: 64 oz. **Length:** 14″ over-all.
Stocks: One piece walnut.
Sights: Fixed.
Features: Case hardened frame, loading lever and hammer; engraved cylinder scene; safety notches on hammer, safety pin in cylinder. Imported by Replica, F.I.E., Navy. First and Third Models also available from Navy priced at $110.00.
Price: . . . . $90.00 to $110.00

BABY DRAGOON 1848 PERCUSSION REVOLVER
Caliber: 31, 5-shot.
Barrel: 4″, 5″, 6″.
Weight: 24 oz. (6″ bbl.). **Length:** 10½″ (6″ bbl.).
Stocks: Walnut.
Sights: Fixed.
Features: Case hardened frame; safety notches on hammer and safety pin in cylinder; engraved cylinder scene; octagonal bbl. Imported by Replica, Navy Arms, F.I.E., Jana.
Price: . . . . $38.15 to $76.25

1849 WELLS FARGO PERCUSSION REVOLVER
Caliber: 31, 5-shot.
Barrel: 3″, 4″, 5″, 6″.
Weight: 22 oz.
Stocks: Walnut.
Sights: Fixed.
Features: No loading lever; square-back trigger guard; case hardened frame and hammer; engraved cylinder; brass trigger guard and back-strap. Imported by Replica, Navy, Jana. Bbl. lengths may vary with importer.
Price: . . . . $60.00 to $75.00

NAVY MODEL 1851 PERCUSSION REVOLVER
Caliber: 36, 6-shot.
Barrel: 7½″.
Weight: 42 oz. **Length:** 13″ over-all.
Stocks: Walnut finish.
Sights: Fixed.
Features: Brass backstrap and trigger guard; engraved cylinder with navy battle scene; case hardened frame, hammer, loading lever. Imported by Centennial, The Armoury, Navy, Hawes, Valor, Century, F.I.E., American Import, Jana.
Price: Brass frame . . . .$42.95 to $49.95
Price: Steel frame . . . .$48.95 to $90.00

POCKET MODEL 1849 PERCUSSION REVOLVER
Caliber: 31, 5-shot.
Barrel: 4″, 6″.
Weight: 26 oz.
Stocks: Walnut finish.
Sights: Fixed.
Features: Round trigger guard; Colt stagecoach hold-up scene on cylinder. Imported by Navy Arms.
Price: $75.00

BLACK POWDER REVOLVERS

COLT 1851 NAVY PERCUSSION REVOLVER
Caliber: 36, 5-shot.
Barrel: 7½".
Weight: 40 oz. **Length:** 13⅛" over-all.
Stocks: Black walnut.
Sights: Bead-type front, hammer notch rear.
Features: Color case hardened frame; barrel and cylinder blued. Silver plated trigger guard and backstrap. Naval scene engraving on cylinder. From Colt's.
Price: **$149.95**

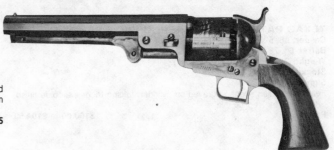

ARMY 1851 PERCUSSION REVOLVER
Caliber: 44, 6-shot.
Barrel: 7½".
Weight: 45 oz. **Length:** 13" over-all.
Stocks: Walnut finish.
Sights: Fixed.
Features: 44 caliber version of the 1851 Navy. Imported by Valor, The Armoury, Jana.
Price: . . . . **$33.50 to $65.00**

1851 SHERIFF MODEL PERCUSSION REVOLVER
Caliber: 36, 6-shot.
Barrel: 5".
Weight: 40 oz. **Length:** 10½" over-all.
Stocks: Walnut.
Sights: Fixed.
Features: Brass back strap and trigger guard; engraved navy scene; case hardened frame, hammer, loading lever. Available with brass frame from some importers at slightly lower prices. Imported by Centennial, The Armoury, Navy, Hawes.
Price: Steel frame . . . . **$54.95 to $90.00**
Price: Brass frame . . . . **$42.95 to $49.95**

NEW MODEL 1858 ARMY PERCUSSION REVOLVER
Caliber: 44, 6-shot.
Barrel: 8".
Weight: 40 oz. **Length:** 13½" over-all.
Stocks: Walnut.
Sights: Fixed.
Features: Replica of Remington Model 1858. Also available from some importers as Army Model Belt Revolver in 36 cal., shortened and lightened version of the 44. Target Model (Navy Arms) has fully adj. target rear sight, target front, 36 or 44 ($125.00). Imported by Navy, Century, F.I.E., Hawes, C.V.A., Valor, American Import, Jana, The Armoury, Gold Rush.
Price: . . . . **$50.00 to $95.00**

LYMAN 44 NEW MODEL ARMY REVOLVER
Caliber: 44, 6-shot.
Barrel: 7¾".
Weight: 42 oz. **Length:** 13½" over-all.
Stock: Walnut.
Sights: Fixed.
Features: Replica of 1858 Remington. Brass trigger guard. Solid frame with top strap. Heavy duty nipples. From Lyman Gunsight Corp.
Price: **$96.95**

LYMAN 36 NEW MODEL NAVY REVOLVER
Caliber: 36, 6-shot.
Barrel: 6½".
Weight: 42 oz. **Length:** 12⅜" over-all.
Stock: Walnut.
Sights: Fixed.
Features: Replica of 1860 Remington. Brass trigger guard. Solid frame with top strap. Heavy duty nipples. From Lyman Gunsight Corp.
Price: **$94.95**

BLACK POWDER REVOLVERS

1860 ARMY PERCUSSION REVOLVER
Caliber: 44, 6-shot.
Barrel: 8".
Weight: 40 oz. **Length:** 13⅝" over-all.
Stocks: Walnut.
Sights: Fixed.
Features: Engraved navy scene on cylinder; brass trigger guard; case hardened frame, loading lever and hammer. Some importers supply pistol cut for detachable shoulder stock, have accessory stock available. Imported by Navy, Centennial, The Armoury, Hawes, Jana, Replica.
Price:... **$44.95 to $89.95**
1861 Navy: Same as Army except 36 cal., 7½" bbl., wt. 41 oz., cut for stock; round cylinder (fluted avail.), from Replica **$89.95**

GRISWOLD & GRIER PERCUSSION REVOLVER
Caliber: 36, 44, 6-shot.
Barrel: 7½".
Weight: 44 oz. (36 cal.). **Length:** 13" over-all.
Stocks: Walnut.
Sights: Fixed.
Features: Replica of famous Confederate pistol. Brass frame, backstrap and trigger guard; case hardened loading lever; rebated cylinder (44 cal. only). Imported by Navy Arms.
Price:... **$50.00**

1862 POLICE MODEL PERCUSSION REVOLVER
Caliber: 36, 5-shot.
Barrel: 4½", 5½", 6½".
Weight: 26 oz. **Length:** 12" (6½" bbl.).
Stocks: Walnut.
Sights: Fixed.
Features: Half-fluted and rebated cylinder; case hardened frame, loading lever and hammer; brass trigger guard and back strap. Imported by Replica.
Price:... **$89.95**

RUGER 44 OLD ARMY PERCUSSION REVOLVER
Caliber: 44, 6-shot.
Barrel: 7½" (6-groove, 16" twist).
Weight: 46 oz. **Length:** 13½" over-all.
Stock: Smooth walnut.
Sights: Ramp front, rear adj. for w. and e.
Features: Stainless steel standard size nipples, chrome-moly steel cylinder and frame, same lockwork as in Super Blackhawk. From Sturm, Ruger.
Price: Blued **$115.00**
   Also available with solid brass grip frame and wide trigger **$130.00**

BLACK POWDER MUSKETS & RIFLES

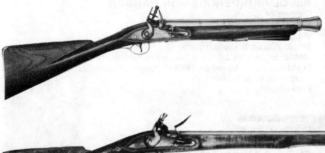

FLINTLOCK BLUNDERBUSS
Caliber: 70.
Barrel: 15½".
Weight: 6¼ lbs. **Length:** 30".
Stock: Walnut finish, hand rubbed.
Sights: None.
Features: Brass barrel and fittings, steel lock from Navy; others have steel bbl., brass fittings. Imported by Navy Arms, The Armory, Dixie.
Price:... **$37.95 to $100.00**

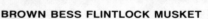

BROWN BESS FLINTLOCK MUSKET
Caliber: 70.
Barrel: 42".
Weight: 10½ lbs. **Length:** 59" over-all.
Stock: Walnut.
Sights: Fixed.
Features: Replica of Revolutionary War period model. Replica bayonet ($12.00) available. Carbine version (30½" bbl., 7¾ lbs.) also available. Can be purchased as kit ($165.00). Imported by Navy Arms.
Price:... **$275.00**

KENTUCKY FLINTLOCK RIFLE
Caliber: 44.
Barrel: 35".
Weight: 7 lbs. **Length:** 50" over-all.
Stock: Walnut stained, brass fittings.
Sights: Fixed.
Features: Available in Carbine model also, 28" bbl. Some variations in detail, finish. Kits also available from some importers. Imported by Navy Arms, Centennial, The Armory, Intercontinental, Century, Dixie and Challanger.
Price:... **$72.50 to $145.00**

BLACK POWDER MUSKETS & RIFLES

KENTUCKY PERCUSSION RIFLE
Similar to above except percussion lock. Finish and features vary with importer. Imported by Jana, Centennial, Navy Arms, Firearms Import & Export, The Armory, Century, Challanger, Dixie, Connecticut Valley, Valor, Replica.
Price: .... **$65.00** to **$229.95**

HOPKINS AND ALLEN MINUTEMAN RIFLE
Caliber: 36, 45, single-shot.
Barrel: 39".
Weight: 9½ lbs. **Length:** 55" over-all.
Stock: Maple.
Sights: Fixed.
Features: Brass furniture, patch box. Available in either flint or percussion. From Numrich Arms Corp.
Price: Either caliber, either ignition system **$179.95**

BERDAN PERCUSSION RIFLE
Caliber: 45.
Barrel: 25".
Weight: 8 lbs.
Stock: Walnut, brass fittings.
Sights: Fixed front, rear adj. for e.
Features: Double set trigger. Replica of Wesson rifle. Imported by Replica Arms.
Price: **$99.95**

REVOLVING PERCUSSION CARBINE
Caliber: 44, 6-shot.
Barrel: 18", 20".
Weight: 5 lbs. **Length:** 38" over-all.
Stock: Walnut, brass butt plate.
Sights: Blade front adj. for w., buckhorn rear adj. for e.
Features: Action based on 1858 Remington revolver. Brass trigger guard. Imported by Navy Arms.
Price: **$130.00**

ENFIELD MODEL 1861 PERCUSSION CARBINE
Caliber: 577.
Barrel: 24".
Weight: 7½ lbs. **Length:** 40¼" over-all.
Stock: Walnut.
Sights: Fixed front, adj. rear.
Features: Percussion muzzle loader, made to original 1861 English patterns. Imported from England by Jana.
Price: **$199.95**

H & R SPRINGFIELD STALKER
Caliber: 45 or 58.
Barrel: 28" round.
Weight: 8 lbs. (45 cal.), 7½ lbs. (58 cal.). **length:** 43" over-all.
Stock: American walnut.
Sights: Blade front, rear open adj. for w. and e.
Features: Action similar to Civil War Springfield. Supplied with solid brass ramrod with hardwood handle, spare nipple and nipple wrench. Blue-black finish.
Price: **$150.00**

BLACK POWDER MUSKETS & RIFLES

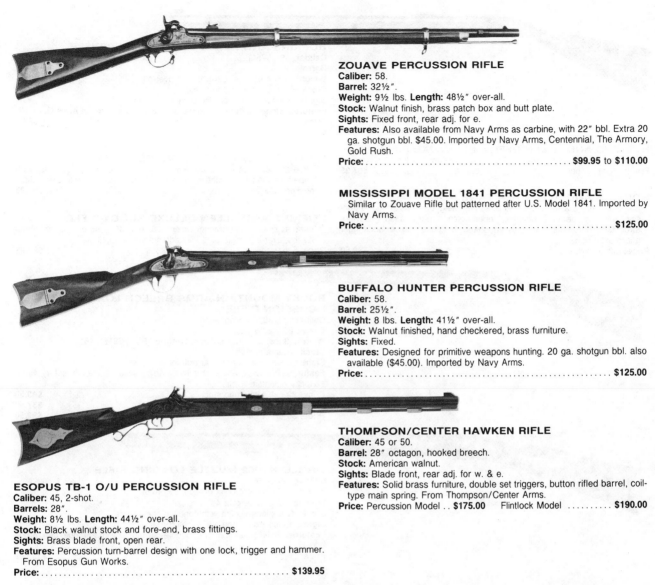

ZOUAVE PERCUSSION RIFLE
Caliber: 58.
Barrel: 32½″.
Weight: 9½ lbs. **Length:** 48½″ over-all.
Stock: Walnut finish, brass patch box and butt plate.
Sights: Fixed front, rear adj. for e.
Features: Also available from Navy Arms as carbine, with 22″ bbl. Extra 20 ga. shotgun bbl. $45.00. Imported by Navy Arms, Centennial, The Armory, Gold Rush.
Price: . . . .$99.95 to $110.00

MISSISSIPPI MODEL 1841 PERCUSSION RIFLE
Similar to Zouave Rifle but patterned after U.S. Model 1841. Imported by Navy Arms.
Price: $125.00

BUFFALO HUNTER PERCUSSION RIFLE
Caliber: 58.
Barrel: 25½″.
Weight: 8 lbs. **Length:** 41½″ over-all.
Stock: Walnut finished, hand checkered, brass furniture.
Sights: Fixed.
Features: Designed for primitive weapons hunting. 20 ga. shotgun bbl. also available ($45.00). Imported by Navy Arms.
Price: $125.00

THOMPSON/CENTER HAWKEN RIFLE
Caliber: 45 or 50.
Barrel: 28″ octagon, hooked breech.
Stock: American walnut.
Sights: Blade front, rear adj. for w. & e.
Features: Solid brass furniture, double set triggers, button rifled barrel, coil-type main spring. From Thompson/Center Arms.
Price: Percussion Model . . $175.00   Flintlock Model $190.00

ESOPUS TB-1 O/U PERCUSSION RIFLE
Caliber: 45, 2-shot.
Barrels: 28″.
Weight: 8½ lbs. **Length:** 44½″ over-all.
Stock: Black walnut stock and fore-end, brass fittings.
Sights: Brass blade front, open rear.
Features: Percussion turn-barrel design with one lock, trigger and hammer. From Esopus Gun Works.
Price: $139.95

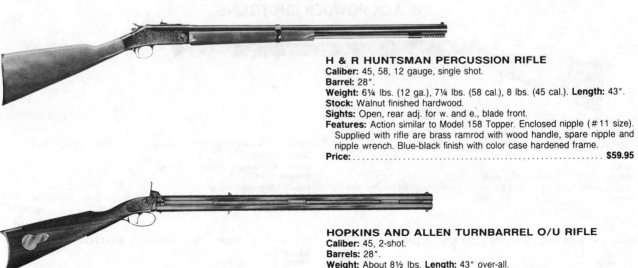

H & R HUNTSMAN PERCUSSION RIFLE
Caliber: 45, 58, 12 gauge, single shot.
Barrel: 28″.
Weight: 6¼ lbs. (12 ga.), 7¼ lbs. (58 cal.), 8 lbs. (45 cal.). **Length:** 43″.
Stock: Walnut finished hardwood.
Sights: Open, rear adj. for w. and e., blade front.
Features: Action similar to Model 158 Topper. Enclosed nipple (#11 size). Supplied with rifle are brass ramrod with wood handle, spare nipple and nipple wrench. Blue-black finish with color case hardened frame.
Price: $59.95

HOPKINS AND ALLEN TURNBARREL O/U RIFLE
Caliber: 45, 2-shot.
Barrels: 28″.
Weight: About 8½ lbs. **Length:** 43″ over-all.
Stock: Walnut.
Sights: Blade front, open notch fixed rear.
Features: Rotating barrels shoot to same point. Crescent buttplate. From Numrich Arms Corp.
Price: $139.95

BLACK POWDER MUSKETS & RIFLES

HOPKINS AND ALLEN DEER STALKER RIFLE
Caliber: 58 (.575").
Barrel: 32".
Weight: About 9½ lbs. **Length:** 49" over-all.
Stock: Walnut stock and fore-end.
Sights: Hooded front, open notch rear.
Features: Under-hammer action. Blue finish. From Numrich Arms Corp.
Price: **$87.95**

HOPKINS AND ALLEN OFFHAND DELUXE RIFLE
Same as Deer Stalker except: 36 or 45 cal., weight 8½ lbs.
Price: Either caliber **$87.95**

HOPKINS AND ALLEN 45 TARGET RIFLE
Same as Deer Stalker except: 45 cal., weight about 9½ lbs., long-range 3-aperture tang rear sight, no fore-end or ram rod ferrules. Barrel flats measure 1⅛" **$84.95**

HOPKINS AND ALLEN HERITAGE MODEL
Same as Deer Stalker except: 36 or 45 cal.; weight 8½ lbs.; hooded front sight with ring aperture, "Kentucky" open notched rear and H&A aperture target tang rear sights; brass crescent-shaped buttplate, cap box and trigger guard extension.
Price: Either caliber **$99.50**

HOPKINS AND ALLEN DELUXE BUGGY RIFLE
Same as Deer Stalker Model except: 20" bbl.; 36 or 45 cal.; weight about 6½ lbs; over-all length 37"; fully adj. notch rear sight.
Price: Either caliber **$84.95**

ROCKY MOUNTAIN ARMS BREECH LOADING PER-CUSSION RIFLE
Caliber: 22, 36, 44, single-shot.
Barrel: 20", 22½", 28".
Weight: 3 lbs., 5¼ lbs., 6½ lbs. **Length:** 35¼", 39½", 46".
Stock: Walnut or Ash.
Sights: Blade front, open rear adj. for e.
Features: Percussion. Breech-turret loading action, half-cock safety. From Rocky Mountain Arms.
Price: 22 cal. with wood stock **$49.50**
Price: With polyurethane stock **$37.50**
Price: 36 or 44 cals. **$99.50**

TINGLE M1962 MUZZLE LOADING RIFLE
Caliber: 36 or 44
Barrel: 32" octagon, hook breech, 52" twist.
Weight: 10 lbs. **Length:** 48" over-all.
Stock: One-piece walnut with concave cheekpiece.
Sights: Blade front, step adj. V-notch rear.
Features: Solid brass furniture, double-set trigger with adj. pull, percussion lock.
Price: **$139.95**

BLACK POWDER SHOTGUNS

SINGLE BARREL FLINTLOCK SHOTGUN
Gauge: 28.
Barrel: 28".
Weight: 4½ lbs. **Lenght:** 43" over-all.
Stock: Walnut finish, choice of half or full stock. Imported by The Armory.
Price: **$37.95**

TINGLE PERCUSSION SINGLE BARREL SHOTGUN
Gauge: 12 only.
Barrel: 30" straight bored, no choke.
Weight: 5 lbs.
Stock: Lacquered walnut.
Features: Mule ear side hammer lock, iron trigger guard, rubber recoil pad.
Price: Blued **$99.75**

SINGLE BARREL PERCUSSION SHOTGUN
Gauge: 12, 20, 28.
Barrel: 28".
Weight: 4½ lbs. **Length:** 43" over-all.
Stock: Walnut finish, choice of half or full stock.
Features: Finish and features vary with importer. Imported by Navy Arms, The Armory, Century, Dixie.
Price: . . . . **$32.95 to $65.00**

DOUBLE BARREL PERCUSSION SHOTGUN
Gauge: 12.
Barrel: 30" (I.C.& Mod.).
Weight: 6¼ lbs. **Length:** 45" over-all.
Stock: Hand checkered walnut, 14" pull.
Features: Double triggers, light hand engraving. Details vary with importer. Imported by Navy Arms, The Armory, Century, Dixie, and Replica.
Price: . . . . **$125.00 to $134.95**

PELLET GUNS—HANDGUNS

Guns in this section are compression powered by: A) disposable CO_2 cartridge; B) by hand pumping of air; C) by cocking a spring which compresses air. This air is released when the trigger is pulled. Calibers are 177 (BB or pellet) and 22 pellet, except for Sheridan rifles, these using a special form of 20-cal. bullet. Pellet guns are usually rifled, those for BBs only are not; 177-cal. rifles can shoot BBs also, of course.

AMPELL CO² PISTOL
Caliber: BB, 177 or 22. (BB only has 80-shot mag., others single shot.)
Barrel: 8½", rifled.
Length: 11¾". **Weight:** 36 oz.
Sights: Sq. notch rear adj. for w. and e., blade front.
Power: Standard CO_2 cylinder.
Features: Up to 365 f.p.s. M.V.; 2-lb. trigger pull. Ampell and Air Rifle HQ.
Price: **$26.50**

BENJAMIN SUPER S. S. TARGET PISTOL SERIES 130
Caliber: BB, 22 and 177; single shot.
Barrel: 8 inches; BB smoothbore; 22 and 177, rifled.
Length: 11". **Weight:** 2 lbs.
Power: Hand pumped.
Features: Bolt action; fingertip safety; adj. power.
Price: M130, BB ..... **$36.40** M132, 22 ...... **$36.40** M137, 177 .. **$36.40**

BENJAMIN 422 SEMI-AUTOMATIC PISTOL
Caliber: 22, 10-shot.
Barrel: 5⁹⁄₁₆", rifled bronze liner.
Length: 9". **Weight:** 2 lbs.
Power: Standard CO_2 cylinder. Muzzle velocity about 400 fps.
Features: Trigger and hammer safeties, checkered plastic thumbrest grips, adj. rear sight, blade front.
Price: Blued **$28.20**

CROSMAN MODEL "1300" MEDALIST II
Caliber: 22, single shot.
Barrel: 8", button rifled.
Length: 11¾". **Weight:** 37 oz.
Power: Hand pumped.
Features: Moulded plastic grip, hand size pump forearm. Cross bolt safety, self-cocking.
Price: **$31.95**

CROSMAN PEACEMAKER "44"
Caliber: 22, 6 shot.
Barrel: 4¾", button rifled.
Length: 10⅜". **Weight:** 34 oz.
Power: Crosman CO_2 Powerlet
Features: Revolving cylinder, walnut finished grips. Simulated gold hammer and trigger, positive valve design. Single-action.
Price: **$27.50**

CROSMAN FRONTIER "36"
Caliber: BB, 18-shot.
Barrel: 4¾", smoothbore.
Length: 10⅜". **Weight:** 34 oz.
Power: Crosman CO_2 Powerlet
Features: Single-action, steel barrel, revolving cylinder. Walnut finish grips.
Price: **$27.50**

PELLET GUNS—HANDGUNS

CROSMAN MARK I TARGET PISTOL
Caliber: 22, single shot.
Barrel: 7¼ inches, button rifled.
Length: 11 inches. **Weight:** 42 oz.
Power: Crosman Powerlet CO_2 cylinder.
Features: New system provides same shot-to-shot velocity, adj. from 300- to 400 fps. Checkered thumbrest grips, right or left. Patridge front sight, rear adj. for w. & e. Adj. trigger.
Price: 22 or 177 .... **$29.95**

CROSMAN MARK II TARGET PISTOL
Same as Mark I except 177 cal. **$29.95**

CROSMAN 38 TARGET REVOLVER M9
Caliber: 22, 6-shot.
Barrel: 6 inches, rifled.
Length: 11 inches. **Weight:** 43 oz.
Power: CO_2 Powerlet cylinder.
Features: Double action, revolving cylinder. Adj. rear sight.
Price: **$37.95**

CROSMAN 38 COMBAT REVOLVER
Same as 38 Target except 3½" bbl., 38 oz. **$37.95**

DAISY CO² 200 AUTOLOADING PISTOL
Caliber: BB, 175-shot semi-auto.
Barrel: 7½ inches, steel-lined, smoothbore.
Length: 11⅞", sight radius 9". **Weight:** 24 oz.
Power: Daisy CO_2 cylinders, 8½ grams (100 shots) or 12 grams (160 shots).
Features: 175-shot magazine; constant full power; valve system eliminates gas leakage; checkered thumbrest stocks; undercut ramp front sight and adjustable rear.
Price: **$24.91**

DIANA 5 TARGET PISTOL
Same as the Hy-Score 815 except: Air Rifle HQ degreases, inspects, test fires, adjusts, sights-in and repackages **$44.50**

DAISY 179 SIX GUN
Caliber: BB, 12-shot.
Barrel: Steel lined, smoothbore.
Length: 11½ inches. **Weight:** NA.
Power: Spring.
Features: Forced feed from under-barrel magazine. Single action, molded wood grained grips.
Price: **$9.31**

DAISY NRA COMMEMORATIVE PISTOL
Same as Model 179 except: Special burnishing on bbl. and receiver. Comes in picture framed, shadow-boxed carton.
Price: **$13.47**

DAISY 177 BB PISTOL
Caliber: BB, 150-shot.
Barrel: Formed steel, smoothbore.
Length: 11¼ inches. **Weight:** NA.
Power: Spring.
Features: Gravity feed, adjustable rear sight, molded plastic thumbrest grips.
Price: **$9.31**

DAISY/FWB 65 TARGET PISTOL
Caliber: 177, single shot.
Barrel: 7½", rifled, fixed to receiver.
Length: 15½". **Weight:** 42 oz.
Power: Spring, cocked by left-side lever.
Features: Recoiless operation, may be set to give recoil; Micro. rear sight, 14" radius. Adj. trigger; normal 17.6 oz. pull can be raised to 48 oz. for training. Checkered, thumbrest target grips. Air Rifle Hdqtrs. or Daisy, importer.
Price: .... **$159.23 to $198.50**

DIANA 6 TARGET PISTOL
Same as the Hy-Score 816 but with accurizing done as described above.
Price: **$64.50**

PELLET GUNS—HANDGUNS

HAMMERLI MASTER CO_2 TARGET PISTOL Model 454
Caliber: 177, single shot.
Barrel: 6.7", rifled, 12 grooves, R.H.
Length: 16". **Weight:** 38 oz.
Power: 8g. or 12g. CO_2 cyl., 40-60 plus shots.
Features: Easy manual loading; residual gas vented automatically; 4-way adj. trigger; ramp front sight, ⅞" blade (other widths avail.), micro-click rear; sight radius adj. 11½" to 13⅜". Bbl.- and grip weights available, $4 and $3.50.
Price: **$54.00**

HAMMERLI SINGLE TARGET PISTOL Model 452
Caliber: 177, single shot.
Barrel: 5.2 inches, rifled.
Length: 12 inches. **Weight:** 34 oz., including CO_2 cylinder.
Power: Standard CO_2 cylinder.
Features: Auto spring loader; adj. trigger; valve permits emptying CO_2 cylinder. Micrometer adj. rear sight. ⅛" blade front sight on ramp. H. Grieder, importer. Price incl. 10 CO_2 cylinders, 100 pellets.
Price: **$41.00**

HEALTHWAYS ML 175 CO_2 AUTOMATIC PISTOL
Caliber: BB, 100-shot repeater.
Barrel: 5¾", smooth.
Length: 9½". **Weight:** 28 oz.
Power: Standard CO_2 cylinder.
Features: 3 position power switch. Auto. ammunition feed. Positive safety.
Price: **$21.00**

HEALTHWAYS MA22 CO_2 AUTOMATIC PISTOL
Same as Healthways ML175 except rifled 22 cal. bbl., rear sight adj. for w. and e., cap. 50 lead balls. **$24.00**

HEALTHWAYS SHARPSHOOTER
Caliber: 175 (BB), 50-shot.
Barrel: 6¼".
Weight: 28 oz.
Power: Spring (barrel cocking).
Features: Easy cocking action. Loading pocket speeds and simplifies loading. Spring mechanism housed in grip.
Price: **$14.00**

HY-SCORE 816 M TARGET PISTOL
Caliber: 177, single shot.
Barrel: 7" precision rifled.
Length: 16 inches. **Weight:** 50 oz.
Power: Spring, bbl. cocking.
Features: Recoil-less firing, adj. trigger. Hooded front sight with 3 apertures, click adj. rear with 4 apertures. Plastic thumbrest target grips.
Price: In plastic case **$49.95**

HY-SCORE 814 JUNIOR PISTOL
Caliber: 177 darts BBs, single shot.
Barrel: Smoothbore.
Length: About 10 inches. **Weight:** NA.
Power: Spring, compressed by screwing in breech plug.
Features: Checkered wooden grips.
Price: Blued $5.95

HY-SCORE 815 TARGET PISTOL
Same as Hy-Score M816 except: without recoil-less system; is slightly shorter and lighter; has fixed aperture front sight. In plastic case. Also in 22 cal. **$29.95**

HY-SCORE 802 AUTOLOADING PISTOL

Caliber: 22, 6-shot repeater.
Barrel: 10¼ inches, rifled.
Length: 10¼ inches. **Weight:** 30½ oz.
Power: Spring.
Features: Thumbrest target grips. Recoil comparable to standard target pistols. 3-pound trigger pull. Shutter type loading.
Price: Blued **$29.95.** M800, same except single shot **$24.95**

MARKSMAN REPEATER PISTOL

Caliber: 177, 20-shot repeater.
Barrel: 2½ inches, smoothbore.
Length: 8¼ inches. **Weight:** 24 oz.
Power: Spring.
Features: Thumb safety. Uses BBs, darts or pellets. Repeats with BBs only.
Price: Black finish **$11.95**
Also available in either antique gold or silver finish with moulded plastic display box **$15.95**

ROGER CO² BB PISTOL

Caliber: BB, 100-shot.
Barrel: 6″, smooth.
Length: 10½″ over-all.
Power: Standard CO² cartridge.
Features: Semi-automatic. Checkered plastic thumbrest target grips. Precise Imports, importer.
Price: **$20.00**

TEX 086 AIR PISTOL

Caliber: 177, single-shot.
Barrel: 7¼″.
Length: 13½″ over-all. **Weight:** 2¾ lbs.
Power: Spring, barrel cocking.
Features: Plastic checkered thumbrest target grips. Presice Imports, importer.
Price: **$30.00**

SMITH & WESSON MODEL 77A

Caliber: 22, single shot.
Barrel: 22″, rifled.
Length: 40″. **Weight:** 6-½ lbs.
Power: Hand pumped (swinging fore-end).
Features: Adjustable notch rear sight. Monte Carlo style, walnut finish stock. Automatic safety.
Price: **$42.50**

WALTHER MODEL LPIII

Caliber: 177, single shot.
Barrel: 9⅜″, rifled.
Length: 13³/₁₆″. **Weight:** 45½ oz.
Power: Spring-air.
Features: Recoil-less operation, cocking in grip frame. Micro-click rear sight, adj. for w. & e. 4-way adj. trigger. Plastic thumbrest grips; wood grip at extra cost. Interarms, Air Rifle HQ, importers.
Price: **$98.00**

PELLET GUNS—HANDGUNS

WALTHER MODEL 53 PISTOL
Caliber: 177, single shot.
Barrel: 9⅜", rifled.
Length: 12⅜". **Weight:** 40 oz.
Power: Spring.
Features: Micrometer rear sight. Interchangeable rear sight blades. Adj. trigger. Target grips. Bbl. weight available at extra cost. Interarms, Alexandria, Va., Air Rifle HQ, importers.
Price: $56.00

WEBLEY AIR PISTOLS

Model:	Junior	Premier
Caliber:	177	177 or 22
Barrel:	6⅛"	6½"
Weight:	24 oz.	37 oz.
Power:	Spring, barrel cocking	Same
Sights:	Adj. for elev.	Adj. for w.&e.
Trigger:	Fixed	Adj.
Price:	$40.00	$44.00

Features: Harrington & Richardson, importer.

WEIHRAUCH HW-70 AIR PISTOL
Caliber: 177, single shot.
Barrel: 6¼", rifled.
Length: 12¾" over-all. **Weight:** 38 oz.
Sights: Hooded post front, square notch rear adj. for w. and e.
Power: Spring, barrel cocking.
Features: Adj. trigger. 24-lb. cocking effort, 365 f.p.s. M.V.; automatic safety. Air Rifle HQ, importer.
Price: $44.50

WINCHESTER 353 TARGET PISTOL
Caliber: 177 or 22, single shot.
Barrel: 7" rifled.
Length: 16". **Weight:** 2 lbs. 11 oz.
Power: Spring, barrel cocking.
Features: Plastic thumbrest target grips. Adj. double pull trigger, Micro rear sight, detachable bead front with hood. M.V. 378 fps.
Price: $39.95

WINCHESTER 363 TARGET PISTOL
Caliber: 177, single shot.
Barrel: 7" rifled.
Length: 16". **Weight:** 3 lbs.
Power: Spring, barrel cocking.
Features: Recoil-less firing, adj. double pull type trigger, hooded front sight with 3 apertures, click adj. rear sight. Plastic thumbrest target grips. M.V. 378 fps.
Price: $59.95

WISCHO CUSTOM MATCH PISTOL
Caliber: 177, single shot.
Barrel: 7" rifled.
Length: 15¾" over-all. **Weight:** 44 oz.
Sights: Bead front, rear adj. for w. and e.
Power: Spring, barrel cocking.
Features: Cocking effort of 17 lbs.; M.V. 472 f.p.s.; adj. trigger. Air Rifle HQ, importer.
Price: $62.50

PELLET GUNS—LONG GUNS

AMPELL BB MAGNUM RIFLE
Caliber: BB, 48-shot magazine.
Length: 38″ over-all. **Weight:** 4¼ lbs.
Sights: Blade front, rear square notch adj. for w. and e.
Power: Pump cocking spring.
Features: Hardwood stock, cross-bolt safety, 4-5 lb. trigger pull.
Price: **$26.50**

ANSCHUTZ 250 TARGET RIFLE
Caliber: 177, single shot.
Barrel: 18½″, rifled, one piece with receiver.
Length: 45″. **Weight:** 11 lbs. with sights.
Power: Spring, side-lever cocking, 11 lb. pull.
Features: Recoil-less operation. Two-stage adj. trigger. Checkered walnut
  p.g. stock with Monte Carlo comb & cheekpiece; adj. buttplate; accessory
  rail. Air Rifle Hdqtrs., Savage Arms, importers.
Price: Without sights **$179.50**
  With #6723 match sight set **$204.50**

BAVARIA/WISCHO 55N SPORTING RIFLE
Caliber: 177 or 22, single shot.
Barrel: 16¼″, rifled.
Length: 41″. **Weight:** 6¼ lbs.
Power: Spring (barrel cocking).
Features: High velocity (728 fps in 177, 590 fps in 22) and accuracy combined
  with rapid loading, can be reloaded in 5 seconds. Stock is of walnut with
  checkered p.g. and buttplate. Open rear, bead front sights; receiver grooved
  for scope mounting. Trigger is adjustable. Air Rifle Headquarters, importer.
Price: **$98.50**

BSA METEOR SUPER
Caliber: 177 or 22, single-shot.
Barrel: 18½″, rifled.
Length: 42″. **Weight:** 6 lbs.
Power: Spring, bbl. cocking.
Features: Beechwood Monte Carlo stock, recoil pad. Adjustable single-stage
  trigger. Bead front, adjustable rear sight. Positive relocation of barrel for
  same zero shot to shot. Galef, importer.
Price: **$41.95**

BENJAMIN 3030 CO^2 REPEATER
Caliber: BB only.
Barrel: 25½″, smoothbore, takedown.
Length: 36″. **Weight:** 4 lbs.
Power: Standard CO^2 cylinder.
Features: Bolt action. 30-shot repeater with permanent-magnet, shot-holder
  ammo feed.
Price: **$26.15**

BENJAMIN SERIES 3100 SUPER 100 SHOT RIFLES
Caliber: BB, 100-shot; 22, 85-shot repeater.
Barrel: 23″, rifled or smoothbore.
Length: 35″. **Weight:** 6¼ lbs.
Power: Hand pumped.
Features: Bolt action. 100-shot, piggy back full view magazine. Bar V adj. rear
  sight. Walnut p.g. stock with monte carlo.
Price: M3100, BB .... **$43.50** M3120, 22 rifled **$43.50**

BENJAMIN SERIES 340 RIFLE
Caliber: 22 and 177 pellets or BB; single shot.
Barrel: 23″, rifled.
Length: 35″. **Weight:** 6 lbs.
Power: Hand pumped.
Features: Bolt action, walnut stock and pump handle. Ramp-type front sight,
  adj. leaf type rear. Push-pull safety.
Price: M340, BB ..... **$41.95** M342, 22 ...... **$41.95** M347, 177 .. **$41.95**

PELLET GUNS—LONG GUNS

CROSMAN M-1 CARBINE
Caliber: BB, 270-shot.
Barrel: Smoothbore, steel.
Length: 35⅝″. **Weight:** 4½ lbs.
Power: Spring.
Features: Patterned after U.S. M1 carbine, uses slide action cocking, military type adj. sights. Hardwood stock.
Price: **$21.95**

CROSMAN 1400 RIFLE
Caliber: 22, single shot.
Barrel: 19½ inches, rifled steel.
Length: 35½ inches. **Weight:** About 6 lbs.
Power: Hand pumped.
Features: Bolt action. Air-Trol valve prevents air lock from over-pumping. Adj. trigger, left or right hand safety. Scope and mount optional.
Price: **$39.95**

CROSMAN 622 PELL-CLIP REPEATER
Caliber: 22, 6-shot rotating, clip
Barrel: 23″
Weight: 6½ lbs. **Length:** 40″
Power: Crosman CO_2 Powerlet, pump action
Features: Removable 6-shot pell clip. Adjustable rear sight. Scope and mount extra.
Price: **$39.50**

CROSMAN POWERMATIC "500"
Caliber: BB, 50-shot semiautomatic.
Barrel: 18″, smoothbore steel.
Length: 37¾″. **Weight:** 4½ lbs.
Power: Crosman CO_2 Powerlet.
Features: Positive safety, over 100 shots from one Powerlet. Walnut finished stock, grooved receiver for optional scope or peep sight. Rear sight is adjustable for windage and elevation.
Price: **$25.95**

CROSMAN MODEL 3500 SLIDEMASTER
Caliber: BB, 22-shot slide action.
Barrel: 18″, smoothbore steel.
Length: 35½″. **Weight:** 4 lbs.
Power: High compression spring.
Features: Fast and easy cocking, hooded post front sight and fully adjustable rear sight. Scope and mount optional. High comb Monte Carlo stock.
Price: **$18.95**

CROSMAN MODEL 760 POWERMASTER
Caliber: BB, 180 shot.
Barrel: 19½″, smoothbore steel.
Length: 35″. **Weight:** 4⅛ lbs.
Power: High compression spring.
Features: Short stroke, power determined by number of strokes. Walnut finished checkered stock and forearm. Post front sight and adjustable rear sight. Cross-bolt safety. Scope and mount optional.
Price: **$27.50**

CROSMAN TRAPMASTER SHOTGUN
Gauge: .380 inch, chambers Crosman CO_2 shotshells.
Action: One-stroke, side cocking single shot.
Barrel: 28″ true cylinder bore, full length rib.
Stock: 14¼″x1″x2″, contoured hardwood, walnut finished.
Weight: 6¼ lbs. 46½″ over-all.
Power: Crosman Giant CO_2 Powerlet.
Features: Pattern is about 14″ dia. at 40 feet (effective range). Plastic shotshells contain about 55 No. 8 pellets. Looks and feels like other shotguns.
Price: **$49.95**

CROSMAN CO_2 SKEET SET
Includes Trapmaster shotgun, box of 25 reusable plastic break-away targets, 100 shotshells, 10 giant Powerlets and Skeet Trap with remote foot release **$89.95**

PELLET GUNS—LONG GUNS

DAISY 21 DOUBLE BARREL RIFLE
Caliber: BB, two 48-shot magazines.
Barrel: 23½ inches, smoothbore.
Length: 37 inches. **Weight:** 4½ lbs.
Power: Spring, barrel cocking.
Features: Two barrels and triggers; automatic safety; beaded front ramp and open rear sights.
Price: **$24.91**

DAISY 25 PUMP GUN
Caliber: BB, 50-shot.
Barrel: 18 inches, smoothbore.
Length: 37¼ inches. **Weight:** NA.
Power: Pump cocking spring.
Features: Ramp front and adj. rear sights. BBs are spring-force fed.
Price: **$17.63**

DAISY 1894 SPITTIN' IMAGE CARBINE
Caliber: BB, 40-shot.
Barrel: 17½ inches, smoothbore.
Length: 38⅜ inches.
Power: Spring.
Features: Cocks halfway on forward stroke of lever, halfway on return.
Price: **$20.27**
Price: With 4X Scope, as M3894 .... **$28.03**
Price: With simulated silver receiver, cocking lever, saddle ring, loading port, fore-arm cap and contoured butt plate, as 3030 .... **$22.85**
Price: NRA Commemorative **$25.95**

DAISY 99 TARGET SPECIAL RIFLE
Caliber: BB, 50-shot.
Barrel: 18 inches, smoothbore.
Length: 36¼ inches.
Power: Spring.
Features: Wood stock, beavertail fore-end; sling; hooded front sight with four insert apertures, adj. aperture rear, stock medallion.
Price: **$20.75**

DAISY RIFLES

Model:	96	95	102	111	1776
Caliber:	BB	BB	BB	BB	BB
Barrel:	18″	18″	13½″	18″	13½″
Length:	36″	35″	30¼″	35″	30½″
Power:	Spring	Spring	Spring	Spring	Spring
Capacity:	700	700	350	700	350
Price:	$17.63	$13.47	$9.31	$12.43	$13.35

Price: Model 96 with 4X scope, as M496 .... **$25.95**
Features: 96 has wood M.C. stock and oversize fore-end; 95 stock is wood, fore-end plastic; 111 and 1776 have plastic stocks; 102 has wood stock; 1776 has sighting tube w/aperture and is gold finished.

DAISY HIGH POWER RIFLES

Model:	160	230	250
Caliber:	177 & BB	22	22
Barrel:	12″	15¾″	15¾″
Rifled:	No	Yes	Yes
Length:	33½″	37½″	39″
Weight:	3 lbs.	5 lbs.	5½ lbs.
Power:	Spring	Spring	Spring
Price:	$17.11	$29.07	$34.27

Features: All are barrel cocking with beechwood stocks. 160 and 220 have bead front and adj. rear sights. 230 and 250 have blade front and adj. target sights.

PELLET GUNS—LONG GUNS

DAISY MODEL 86/70 SAFARI MK. I
Caliber: BB, 240-shot.
Barrel: 11″ smooth.
Length: 34¼″. **Weight:** 2 lbs.
Sights: Ramp front, V-notch rear.
Features: Plastic stock and fore-end, force-feed magazine. Trigger-guard cocking action with cross-bolt safety.
Price: $13.47

DAISY 2299 QUICK SKILL RIFLE KIT
Caliber: BB, 50-shot
Barrel: 24 inches, smoothbore.
Length: 37⅝ inches (adult stock). **Weight:** 3¼ lbs.
Power: Spring.
Features: Kit includes rifle, shooting glasses, ammo, official targets and instruction manual. No sights, meant for instinct shooting instruction.
Price: $26.95

DAISY MODEL 450
Caliber: 177, 5-shot.
Barrel: 11″, rifled.
Length: 37″. **Weight:** 3⅛ lbs.
Stock: Monte Carlo design wood stock, beavertail fore-end.
Sights: Post-ramp front, rear adj. for w. and e.
Power: Spring, lever cocking.
Features: Automatic safety, removable "Rota-Clip" magazine.
Price: $23.00
Price: Model 400 (feather-weight version, weighs 2½ lbs.) $14.80

DAISY CO² 300 REPEATER
Caliber: BB, 5-shot semi-auto.
Barrel: 22 inches, smoothbore.
Length: 37¼ inches. **Weight:** 2 lbs. 14 oz.
Power: Daisy 8.5 or 12 gram CO² cylinder.
Features: Free-style stock, cross-bolt safety, 200 shot magazine capacity, blade front adj: open rear sights, receiver grooved for scope.
Price: $33.23
Price: With 4X scope, as CO² 3300 . . . . $41.07

DIANA 65 TARGET RIFLE
Caliber: 177, single shot.
Barrel: 18″, rifled.
Length: 43½″. **Weight:** 11 lbs. with sights & detachable bbl. sleeve.
Stock: Checkered walnut, p.g. with Monte Carlo comb & cheekpiece.
Sights: Micro. aperture rear, globe front with 4 inserts.
Power: Spring, barrel cocking.
Features: Adj. stock length. M.V. 600 fps, two-stage adj. trigger. Recoilless type action. Rubber buttplate. Imported by Air Rifle Hdqtrs.
Price: $194.95

DAISY/FWB 4300
Caliber: 177, single shot.
Barrel: 29¼″, rifled.
Length: 45″. **Weight:** 11 lbs.
Stock: Walnut, Monte Carlo cheekpiece, checkered palmswell p.g.
Sights: Globe front with inserts, micro. adj. peep rear.
Power: Spring, barrel cocking.
Features: Adj. trigger, adj. buttplate.
Price: $186.95

EL GAMO SINGLE SHOT RIFLE
Same as repeater version except: available in either 177 or 22 cal.; over-all length 41″, weight 5¼ lbs.
Price: $45.00

EL GAMO REPEATER AIR RIFLE
Caliber: 177, 25-shot.
Barrel: 17½″, 12 groove rifling.
Length: 37½″. **Weight:** 6½ lbs.
Power: Spring, barrel cocking.
Features: Micro, adj. target sights, adj. trigger; target type recoil pad, M.C. comb and cheekpiece. Precise Imports, importer.
Price: $50.00

FEINWERKBAU 300 MATCH RIFLE
Caliber: 177, single shot.
Barrel: 22¼″ rifled steel, one piece with receiver.
Length: 45″. **Weight:** 11 lbs.
Power: Hand cocked by side lever. Less than 10 lbs. pull required.
Features: Barrel and receiver recoil together, independent of stock, to eliminate felt recoil, are locked up when gun is cocked. Micro. rear peep sight, globe front with inserts. Trigger fully adj. Muzzle velocity 600 fps. Checkered walnut stock with Monte Carlo cheekpiece, palmswell p.g. Air Rifle Hdqtrs., importers.
Price: 300S (9 lb. Std.) **$254.50**; 300SL (L.H.) **$274.25**; 300ST (Tyrol. stock), 300STL (L.H. Tyrol. stock) **$309.50**

FEINWERKBAU 200 RIFLE
Same as F'bau 300 except: has slight recoil effect; 20″ bbl., 640 fps. M.V. Available from A.R.H. or Daisy.
Price: $144.50

HY-SCORE 809M TARGET RIFLE
Caliber: 22, single shot.
Barrel: 19 inch rifled.
Length: 44 inches. **Weight:** 7 pounds.
Power: Spring, bbl. cocking.
Features: Adj. target receiver sight, aperture front with 4 inserts, in addition to open adj. middle sight also with 4 apertures.
Price: $64.95

HEALTHWAYS PLAINSMAN MC22 AUTO RIFLE
Caliber: 22, 75-shot.
Barrel: 20½ inches, rifled for round lead balls.
Length: 41 inches. **Weight:** 4½ lbs.
Power: CO_2 (8- or 12-gram cylinder).
Features: Up to 50 shots automatically with 12-g. cylinder; no cocking, pumping, etc. Full size p.g. wood stock.
Price: $35.00
    Plainsman MX175. Same as MC22 except 175″ smoothbore for BBs; weighs 8 oz. less. $30.00

HY-SCORE RIFLES

Model:	808	806	813	801	807
Caliber:	177	177	22	22	22
Barrel:	12″	14½″	14¼″	15¾″	17⅜″
Rifled:	No	Yes	Yes	Yes	Yes
Length:	33″	36½″	36½″	38½″	41¾″
Weight:	3 lbs.	3¾ lbs.	4 lbs.	5 lbs.	5 lbs. 14 oz.
Power:	Spring	Spring	Spring	Spring	Spring
Price:	$14.95	$19.95	$25.95	$29.95	$39.95

Features: All are barrel cocking. All have adj. sights and regular triggers except 807, which has an adj. trigger. Staeble 2.2X scope and mt. available for all but 808. $14.95.
    M813 and scope available at a combination price of $33.40
    M801 available as 801M with click adj. receiver sight $49.95

HY-SCORE 810M OLYMPIC INTERNATIONAL RIFLE
Caliber: 177, single shot.
Barrel: 19¼″ 12-groove rifled.
Length: 44″. **Weight:** 9½ lbs.
Power: Spring (barrel cocking).
Features: Full cheekpiece, Monte Carlo stock, hand checkered; grooved fore-end, curved rubber buttplate. Adj. target receiver sight (includes 4 apertures), hooded front sight (includes 4 inserts).
Price: $99.95

MARKSMAN 4000 AIR RIFLE
Caliber: 177, 400-shot.
Barrel: 15-½″, smoothbore.
Length: 36-½″. **Weight:** 4 lbs., 2 oz.
Power: Spring, barrel cocking.
Features: Automatic safety; fixed front, adj. rear sights; shoots 177 cal. BB's pellets and darts.
Price: $24.95
    Also available as Model 4200 "shorty" with 10″ bbl. and o.a. length of 31½″.
Price: $25.95

SAVAGE/ANSCHUTZ MODEL 335 TARGET RIFLE
Caliber: 177, single shot.
Barrel: 18½″ rifled steel.
Length: 43″ over-all. **Weight:** 7 lbs. without sights.
Stock: Walnut finished hardwood. Checkered p.g., Monte Carlo with cheekpiece, rubber buttplate.
Sights: Front, globe type with insert. Rear, sporting with elevator.
Features: Receiver drilled and grooved for Anschutz 6706 target sights, adj. two-stage trigger, break action.
Price: $59.95
Price: Model 335-S with 6706 sight $84.95

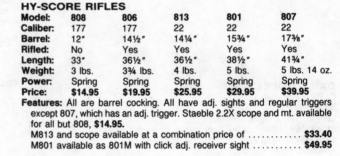

PIC CO_2 BOBCAT BOLT ACTION RIFLE
Caliber: 177, 22, single-shot.
Barrel: 19¼″.
Length: 35″ over-all. **Weight:** 4¾ lbs.
Power: Standard CO_2 cartridges.
Features: Walnut finish stock; receiver grooved for scope mounting. Precise Imports, importer.
Price: $25.00

PELLET GUNS—LONG GUNS

PRECISE/EL GAMO TOURNAMENT AIR RIFLE
Caliber: 177, 22, single shot.
Barrel: 18".
Length: 43" over-all. **Weight:** 6¾ lbs.
Power: Spring, barrel cocking.
Features: Micro. adj. rear sight, hooded front. Walnut finish stock; Monte Carlo comb with cheek piece, recoil pad. Receiver grooved for scope mounting. Precise Imports, importer.
Price: **$40.00**

PRECISE/EL GAMO CARBINE AIR RIFLE
Same as Tournament model except has plain stock without Monte Carlo comb, cheekpiece **$28.00**

SAVAGE-ANSCHUTZ 250 TARGET RIFLE
Caliber: 177, single shot.
Barrel: 18½", rifled steel fixed to receiver, movable compression cylinder.
Length: 45". **Weight:** 11 lbs. with sights.
Power: Hand cocked by side lever, about 11 lbs. cocking effort.
Features: Recoil-less shooting via oil damper and compensating piston. Two-stage trigger adj. for finger length. French walnut, Monte Carlo stock and beavertail fore-end; checkered p.g. with Wundhammer swell. Accepts Anschutz target sights.
Price: Without sights **$179.50**
Price: With #6723 Sight Set **$204.50**

SHERIDAN BLUE AND SILVER STREAK RIFLES
Caliber: 5mm (20 cal.), single shot.
Barrel: 18½", rifled.
Length: 37". **Weight:** 5 lbs.
Power: Hand pumped (swinging fore-end).
Features: Rustproof barrel and piston tube. Takedown. Thumb safety. Mannlicher type walnut stock. Left-hand models same price.
Price: Blue Streak . . . . **$44.75** Silver Streak **$45.75**
Sheridan accessories: Intermount, a base for ⅜" Tip-Off scope mounts, **$6.75**; Sheridan-Williams 5DSH receiver sight, **$7.00** Model 22 Targetrap, **$12.75**; Model 38 Targetrap **$30.00**; Sheridan 5mm pellets, **$2.75** for 500. Weaver or Bushnell 4 x scope and intermount installed **$20.20** extra.

SMITH & WESSON MODEL 77A
Caliber: 22, single shot.
Barrel: 22", rifled.
Length: 40". **Weight:** 6-½ lbs.
Power: Hand pumped (swinging fore-end).
Features: Adjustable notch rear sight. Monte Carlo style, walnut finish stock. Automatic safety.
Price: **$42.50**

WALTHER LG 55-M RIFLE
Caliber: 177, single shot.
Barrel: 16", rifled.
Length: 41⅜". **Weight:** 9 lbs. (9.7 lbs. with bbl. sleeve).
Power: Spring (barrel cocking).
Features: Micro. click adj. receiver sight, globe target front, 3 inserts. Walnut cheekpiece Monte Carlo, checkered p.g. stock. Tyrolean stock $10 extra.
Price: **$128.50**
Double set triggers available with any LG 55-M for $12 extra.

WALTHER LGV SPECIAL
Caliber: 177, single shot.
Barrel: 16", rifled.
Length: 41⅜". **Weight:** 6 lbs.
Power: Spring (barrel cocking).
Features: Micro. click adj. receiver sight; Adj. trigger. Interarms, importers.
Price: **$130.00**

WEIHRAUCH HW-25 RIFLE
Caliber: 177, single shot.
Barrel: 15½", rifled.
Length: 37½" over-all. **Weight:** 4¼ lbs.
Sights: Tapered post front, square notch rear adj. for w. and e.
Power: Spring, barrel cocking.
Features: 12 lbs. cocking effort; 500 f.p.s. M.V. Short stock dimensions intended for youths. Air Rifle Hq., importer.
Price: **$39.95**

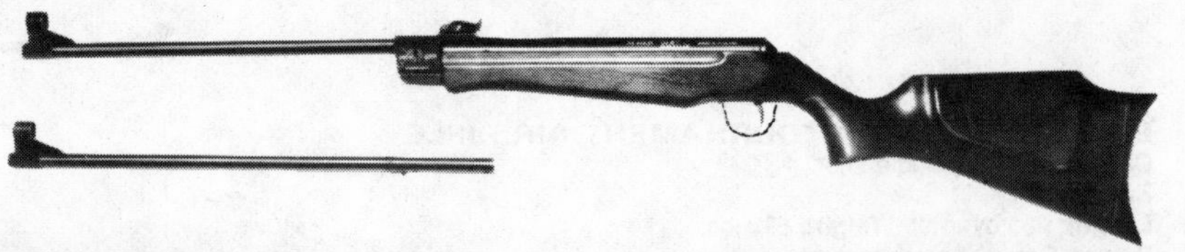

WEBLEY & SCOTT HAWK AIR RIFLE

Caliber: 177 and 22, single shot.
Barrel: 17½".
Length: 41½" over-all. **Weight:** 4½ lbs.
Power: Spring, barrel cocking.
Features: Comes with two interchangeable barrels; click adj. rear sight, hood-
ed blade front. Receiver grooved for scope mounting; automatic safety.
Harrington & Richardson, importers.
Price: **$69.95**

WEIHRAUCH 30 & 50 SERIES RIFLES

Model:	30 M-II	30S	50 M-II	50S	50E
Caliber:	177	177	177	177	177
Barrel:	16⅞"	16⅞"	18½"	18½"	18½"
Trigger:	fixed	fixed	fixed	adj.	adj.
Length:	40"	40"	43½"	43½"	43½"
Wgt., lbs.:	5½	5½	7	7	7¼
Price:	$56.50	$62.50	$67.50	$79.95	$89.95

Features: All are rifled and spring-operated by single stroke cocking. Post and
ramp front sights (except 50S and 50E have globe fronts with 4 inserts).
Open click rear sights, adj. for w. & e., except 30 Mk-11 has lock-screw
windage. Walnut finished stocks. 50E has cheek-piece, checkering, ¾" sling
swivels. MV of all 660-67 fps. Air Rifle Hdqtrs., importer.

WEIHRAUCH 35 TARGET RIFLES

Model:	35/S	35L	35E
Caliber:	177	177	177
Barrel:	19½"	19½"	22"
Wgt. lbs.:	7½	7½	8
Rear sight:	open	open	open
Front sight:	All with globe and 4 interchangeable inserts.		
Power:	All with spring (barrel cocking).		
Price:	$98.50	$109.50	$124.50

Features: Trigger fully adj. and removable. Open rear sight slick adj. for w.
and e. P.g. high comb stock with beavertail fore-end, walnut finish, except
35E have checkered walnut with standard cheekpiece. 35L has Tyrolean
cheekpiece stock. Air Rifle Hdqtrs., importer.

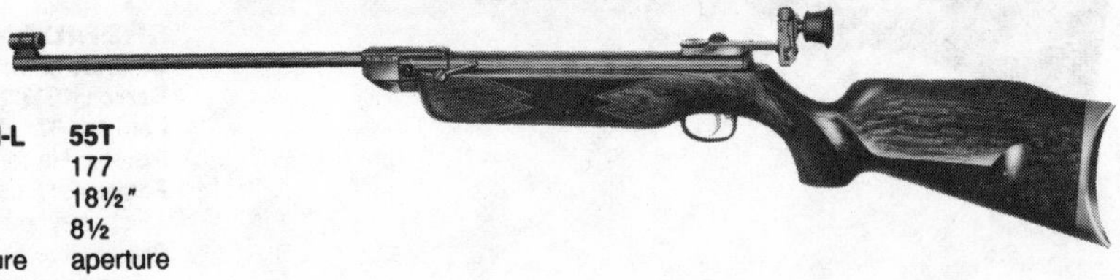

WEIHRAUCH 55 TARGET RIFLES

Model:	55SF	55SM	55MM	55MM-L	55T
Caliber:	177	177	177	177	177
Barrel:	18½"	18½"	18½"	18½"	18½"
Wgt. lbs.:	7¼	8½	8½	8½	8½
Rear sight:	open	aperture	aperture	aperture	aperture
Front sight:	All with globe and 4 interchangeable inserts.				
Power:	All with spring (bbl. cocking) .600 fps				
Price:	$132.50	$132.50	$156.50	$168.50	$174.50

Features: Trigger fully adj. and removable. Micrometer rear sight adj. for w.
and e., on all but 55SF and 55MM. P.g. high comb stock with beavertail
fore-end, walnut finish stock on 55SF, SM. Walnut stock on 55MM, Tyrolean
stock on 55T. Air Rifle Hdqtrs., importer.

WINCHESTER AIR RIFLES

Model:	416	422	423	425
Calibers:	177	177	177	22
Length:	33"	36"	36"	38"
Wgt. lbs.:	2¾	3¾	4	5
Velocity, fps:	363	480	480	543
Price:	$19.95	$27.95	$34.95	$39.95

WINCHESTER HIGH POWER AIR RIFLES

Model:	427	435	450	333
Caliber:	22	177	177	177
Length:	42"	44"	44½"	43¼"
Wgt. lbs.:	6	6½	7¾	9½
Velocity, fps:	660	693	693	576
Price:	$44.95	$64.95	$94.95	$184.95

Features: All are rifled, except 416 (smoothbore), and spring operated by
single stroke cocking. **Triggers:** 416, 422 & 423—double pull type triggers.
425, 427 & 435—adjustable double pull type triggers. 333—two stage trigger adj. for wgt., pre-travel & sear-off. **Front sights:** 416 & 422—bead post
front sights; 423—blade front sight with ramp. 425 & 427—hooded front
sights; 450 & 333—interchangeable front sight assemblies. **Rear Sights:**
416, 422 & 423—adj. screw, 425, 427, 435 & 450—Adj. micro., 333—Adj.
diopter. Also, 425, 427, 435 & 450 have dovetail bases for scope mounting.
435, 450 & 333 have rubber butt pads, cheekpieces & checkered p.g. areas.
333 has an auto. safety, when bbl. is open and red indicator when bbl. is
closed.

Chokes & Brakes

Contra-Jet Muzzle Brake

The steel tube on body of the C-J device has 48 intersecting slots that dissipate energy via the mutual interference of the emerging gases. Recoil energy is reduced nearly 38% (in cal. 308), accuracy is enhanced through lessened muzzle jump and flinching, yet no increase in muzzle blast occurs. Readily fitted by a competent gunsmith, the 3″ long, 3½ oz. Contra-Jet is available in 25, 28, 30, 35, 37 and 45 calibers. Cost is from $29.50 to $37.50, installation not included.

Cutts Compensator

The Cutts Compensator is one of the oldest variable choke devices available. Manufactured by Lyman Gunsight Corporation, it is available with either a steel or aluminum body. A series of vents allows gas to escape upward and downward, reducing recoil without directing muzzle blast toward nearby shooters. For the 12-ga. Comp body, six fixed-choke tubes are available: the Spreader—popular with Skeet shooters; Improved Cylinder; Modified; Full; Superfull, and Magnum Full. Full, Modified and Spreader tubes are available for 12, 16, 20, 28, and .410, and an Adjustable Tube, giving Full through Improved Cylinder chokes, is offered in 12, 16, 20 and 28 gauges. Barrel adaptors in various internal diameters are available at $1.00 to permit exact fitting of Cutts Expansion Chambers. Cutts Compensator installed complete with wrench and any single tube $24.50; with the adjustable tube $31.50, installed. All single choke tubes $4.00 each; adjustable tubes $11.00.

Dahl Muzzle Blast Controller

Only 1⅞″ long by ¾″ in diameter, this device is claimed to reduce recoil up to 30%. An outer sleeve, threaded onto the gun muzzle, is threaded on the inside to accept a machined plug which is bored through for bullet passage. Gas behind the bullet is bled off through slots in the plug, swirled through a number of tiny passages while contained by the sleeve, and then vented upward, this final action somewhat offsetting muzzle jump. Price is $25.00, installed.

Emsco Choke

E. M. Schacht of Waseca, Minn., offers the Emsco, a small diameter choke which features a precision curve rather than a taper behind the 1½″ choking area. 9 settings are available in this 5 oz. attachment. Its removable recoil sleeve can be furnished in dural if desired. Choice of three sight heights. For 12, 16 or 20 gauge. Price installed, $21.95. Not installed, $16.50.

Herter's Rifle Recoil Eliminator

The Recoil Eliminator is a metal tube—1¹⁵/₁₆″ long and ⅞″ diam. in the standard model, same length and 1⅛″ diam. in target type—which is screwed to the muzzle. Angled ports direct escaping gas upward and rearward, reducing recoil and muzzle jump. The target model has a shield to prevent muzzle blast from annoying nearby shooters. Weights are 2 oz. and 3 oz. respectively. Made for calibers 25 to 32. Price of standard, $3.00, $6.50 installed. Target, $4.50 and $8.00.

Vari-Choke

Herter's, Inc., supplies the Vari-Choke, which features

a ball-bearing micro-click adjustment of the pattern sleeve, rather than the spring system used by others. This model has 8 choke settings, from Full to Improved Cylinder. With Recoil Eliminator, price is $18.97 installed; without Eliminator, $15.97.

Jet-Away Choke

Arms Ingenuity Corp., makers of the Jet-Away, say that this device controls patterns through partial venting of the powder gases which normally enlarge patterns. The Jet-Away has a series of three slots in the top of the tube and a sliding control sleeve. When the sleeve is in its rearward position, all slots are uncovered, the maximum of gas is vented and patterns are densest. To obtain more open patterns, the sleeve is moved to cover one or more slots. In 12 or 20 gauge only, the Jet-Away is made of aluminum, weighs 3 ozs. $24.95 installed.

Lyman CHOKE

The LymanCHOKE is similar to the Cutts Comp in that it comes with fixed-choke tubes or an adjustable tube, with or without recoil chamber. The adjustable tube version sells for $23.50 with recoil chamber, $21.00 without, in 12, 16 or 20 gauge. Lyman also offers a Single-Choke Adaptor at $13.00 installed. This device may be used with or without a recoil-reduction chamber; cost of the latter is $2.50 extra.

Pendleton Dekicker

This Dekicker is unusual in that it is not a separate tube added onto a rifle muzzle but is machined into the barrel itself. Obviously, it cannot be installed by the customer. It must be sent to J. F. Mutter's Pendleton Gunshop, where a section of the bore a short distance behind the muzzle is relieved into an expansion chamber. Exit holes drilled at precise locations vent gas to lower apparent kick. Because metal is removed instead of being added, there is a small decrease in gun weight. Installation, including barrel polishing, is $40.00 for all calibers.

Poly-Choke

Poly-Choke Co., Inc., now is offering the Delux Signature Poly-Choke. It provides 9 choke settings (marked in 24 karat gold) to cover the complete pattern range as well as handle rifled slugs. It comes in two versions, the standard at $24.95, and the ventilated model at $27.95 installed. Fits 12, 16, 20 or 28 gauge. The Poly-Choke has been on the market for more than 30 years and is still gaining popularity.

Rex Sha-Cul Rifle Muzzle Brake

C. R. Pedersen & Son engineered the Rex Sha-Cul muzzle control tube to cut down recoil and blast. The manufacturers state that the device helps eliminate bullet wobble, thus aiding accuracy. 3″ long and 1³/₁₆″ in diam., the Sha-Cul can accommodate all calibers from 22 to 458. It requires ½″ of barrel thread to install. Sold on an "unconditional money-back guarantee," the price is $17.50, plus $3.50 installation.

Micrometer Receiver Sight   Receiver Sights

LYMAN No. 48
¼-min. clicks for w. & e. Any disc. Target or Stayset (hunting) knobs. Quick release slide, adjustable zero scales. Made for almost all modern big-game rifles. Price: **$19.50** With long slide **$21.50**

LYMAN No. 57
¼-min. clicks. Target or Stayset knobs. Quick release slide, adjustable zero scales. Made for almost all modern rifles. Price **$12.00**

LYMAN No. 60
¼-min. clicks for w. and e. Extension arm permits choice of 3 positions of eye relief. Designed for use on medium-weight, small bore target rifles. Price **$15.50**

LYMAN No. 66
Fits close to the rear of flat-sided receivers, furnished with target or Stayset knobs. Quick release slide, ¼-min. adj. For most lever or slide action or flat-sided automatic rifles. Price **$12.00**

LYMAN No. 524 HI-LO EXTENSION RECEIVER-SIGHT
Apertures above and below for metallic and scope lines of sight. ¼-min. adj. For Win. 52 Sporter, 52 Standard (old and new), 52 Heavy Barrel (target and marksman stocks); Rem. 40X. Price **$19.50**

REDFIELD No. 75
For Junior Target rifles. ¼-min. clicks for w. and e. Quick detachable extension, adj. to two positions. Available in two heights, scope or standard. For 75HW—Win. 75; 75HG and SG—Sav. 19; 75HV and SV—Stev. 416, Sears Ranger; 75HM and SM—Mossberg, master actions; 75HB and SB—Ballard; 75HR and SR—Win. SS, High Wall action only; Walnut Hill and 417; 75RT—Rem. 513T; 75RS—Rem. 513S; 75RX—Rem. 521. Price . **$16.95**

REDFIELD INTERNATIONAL MATCH
Spring loaded windage and elevation adjustments eliminate lost motion or backlash. Large adjusting screws. ¼-min. click values. Base and ⅞" disc. Fits same base as Olympic. Price **$34.95**
With base and "Sure-X" disc (see Sight Attachments). Price .. **$46.85**

REDFIELD INTERNATIONAL MARK 8
⅛-min. click adj. for windage and elevation distinguishes the Mark 8 which has all of the refinements of Redfield's International Match. Equipped with standard base and ⅞" disc. Price............................. **$39.95**
With base and Sure-X disc (see Sight Attachments). Price **$51.85**

REDFIELD OLYMPIC
Elevation, windage, and extension adjustments. New elevation compensation. ¼-min. click. Base and ⅞" disc. Made for practically all target rifles. Price **$26.95**
Extra bases. Price **3.95**
With base and Sure-X disc (see Sight Attachments). Price **$38.85**

WILLIAMS "FOOLPROOF"
Internal click adjustments. Positive locks. For virtually all rifles, plus Win., Rem. and Ithaca shotguns. Price **$12.25**
Add .50 for Twilight aperture. Extra shotgun aperture **2.00**

B-SQUARE SMLE (LEE-ENFIELD)
For No. 4 and Jungle carbine. No drilling or tapping required. ³/₃₂" disc furnished. Price **$3.95**

BUEHLER
"Little Blue Peep" auxiliary sight used with Buehler and Redfield scope mounts. Price **$3.35**
Mark IV front sight for above .... **.95**

FREELAND TUBE SIGHT
Uses Unertl 1" micrometer mounts. Complete with bases for 22-cal. target rifles, inc. 52 Win., 37, 40X Rem. and BSA Martini. Price **$50.00**

KUHARSKY AUXILIARY
Fits onto B&L or Kuharsky mounts to give emergency sighting. Includes peep rear and post front sights; extension rail slides forward for increased sight radius. Price **$9.95**

LYMAN No. 40
Mounts on left side of receiver. By releasing locking lever, slide can be adjusted for elevation. Slot in aperture permits horizontal alignment. Target disc. for Sav. 40, 45, 340, 342, Stevens 58, 322, 325, Marlin 55, Moss. 185K and H&R 349. Price................................... **$6.50**

LYMAN No. 53
Shotgun receiver sight, mounts compactly near rear of receiver. For most Win., Rem., Sav., Marlin, Mossberg, J. C. Higgins and Ithaca shotguns. Price **$6.00**

LYMAN No. 55
Located at rear of receiver; compact, easily adjusted. For almost all low-priced bolt action rifles. Price **$4.40**

WILLIAMS 5-D SIGHT
Low cost sight for shotguns, 22's and the more popular big game rifles. Adjustment for w. and e. Fits most guns without drilling or tapping. Also for Br. SMLE. Price **$7.00**

WILLIAMS GUIDE
Receiver sight for .30 M1 Car., M1903A3 Springfield, Savage 24's, Savage-Anschutz rifles and Wby. XXII. Utilizes military dovetail; no drilling. Double-dovetail W. adj., sliding dovetail adj. for E. Price **$7.25**

Sporting Leaf and Tang Sights

HOPKINS & ALLEN NUMRICH MUSKET SIGHT
Three-way rear leaf sight designed for 58 cal. muzzle loading military rifles. Fixed V-notch for 50-yard range, flip-up aperture for 100 yards and V-notch for 200 yards. Particularly suited to Springfield and Zouave rifles. Price **$4.95**

LYMAN No. 16
Middle sight for barrel dovetail slot mounting. Folds flat when scope or peep sight is used. Sight notch plate adjustable for e. White triangle for quick aiming. 3 heights; A—.400″ to .500″, B—.345″ to .445″, C—.500″ to .600″. Price **$3.00**

MARBLE FALSE BASE
New screw-on base for most rifles replaces factory base. ⅜″ dovetail slot permits installation of any Marble rear sight. Can be had in sweat-on models also. Price **$2.00**

MARBLE FOLDING LEAF
Flat-top or semi-buckhorn style. Folds down when scope or peep sights are used. Reversible plate gives choice of "U" or "V" notch. Adjustable for elevation. Price .... **$4.50—$5.96**
Also available with both w. and e. adjustment **$4.90**

MARBLE SPORTING REAR
With white enamel diamond, gives choice of two "U" and two "V" notches of different sizes. Adjustment in height by means of double step elevator and sliding notch piece. For all rifles; screw or dovetail installation. Price .... **$4.30— $5.50**

MARBLE SPORTING REAR
Single step elevator. "U" notch with white triangle aiming aid. Lower priced version of double step model. Price **$2.30**

NUMRICH KENTUCKY STYLE SIGHT
Standard dovetail, traditional notched rear sight. ¼″ high. For Kentucky and Hawken type rifles. Price **$2.75**

NUMRICH LONG RANGE REAR TARGET SIGHT
Adjustable for w. and e. with 3-size aperture target sight disc. Particularly suited for H&A Underhammer rifles. Price **$5.95**

WILLIAMS DOVETAIL OPEN SIGHT
Open rear sight with s. and e. adjustment. Furnished with "U" notch or choice of blades. Slips into dovetail and locks with gib lock. Heights from .281″ to .531″. Price with blade **$4.25**

WILLIAMS GUIDE
Open rear sight with w. and e. adjustment. Bases to fit most military and commercial barrels. Choice of square "U" or "V" notch blade, 3/16″, ¼″, 5/16″, or ⅜″ high **$5.00**
Extra blades, each 1.25

FREELAND MILITARY
Short model for use with high-powered rifles where sight must not extend beyond muzzle. Screw-on base; six plastic apertures. Price **$16.00**
Price with 6 metal apertures **19.00**

LYMAN No. 17A
7 interchangeable inserts which include 4 apertures, one transparent amber and two posts .50″ and .100″ in width. Price **$5.00**

LYMAN No. 17A XNB
For Springfield 03 and 03A3. Replaces issue front sight and barrel band. With seven inserts. Price **$8.00**

LYMAN 77 ms
Similar to M17A, except mounts to a separate base, is quickly detachable. Base **$1.75** Sight **$6.25**

REDFIELD Nos. 63 and 64
For rifles specially stocked for scopes where metallic sights must be same height as scopes. Instantly detachable to permit use of scope. Two styles and heights of bases. Interchangeable inserts. No. 64 is ¼″ higher. With base, Price **$7.95**

REDFIELD No. 65
1″ long, ⅝″ diameter. Standard dovetail base with 7 aperture or post inserts which are not reversible. For any rifle having standard barrel slot. 13/32″ height from bottom of base to center of aperture. No. 65NB same as 65 except with narrow base for Win. 64 N.R.A., 70, and Savage 40, 45, and 99 with ramp front sight base. Price **$5.95**

REDFIELD No. 66
Replaces entire removable front sight stud, locked in place by screw in front of barrel band. ¾″ from bottom of base to center of aperture. For Spgfld. 1903. Price **$5.95**

REDFIELD No. 68
For Win. 52, heavy barrel, Sav. 19 and 33, and other rifles requiring high front sight. 17/32″ from bottom of base to center of aperture. Standard dovetail size only. Price **$5.95**

REDFIELD OLYMPIC
Detachable. 10 inserts—5 steel, sizes .090″, .110″, .120″, .140″, .150″; one post insert, size .100″; four celluloid, sizes .090″, .110″, .120″, .140″. Celluloid inserts in clear, green, or amber, with or without cross hairs. For practically all rifles and with any type rear sight. Fits all standard Redfield, Lyman, or Fecker scope blocks. With base, Price **$12.95**

Globe Target Front Sights

FREELAND SUPERIOR
Furnished with six 1″ plastic apertures. Available in 4½″-62½″ lengths. Made for any target rifle. Price with base **$16.00**
Price with 6 metal insert apertures **19.00**

FREELAND JR
Same as above except standard dovetail mounting, various heights.
Price with base and 6 plastic apertures **$14.00**
Price with 6 metal insert apertures **17.00**

FREELAND TWIN SET
Two Freeland Superior or Junior Globe Front Sights, long or short, allow switching from 50 yd. to 100 yd. ranges and back again without changing rear sight adjustment. Sight adjustment compensation is built into the set; just interchange and you're "on" at either range. Set includes base and 6 plastic apertures. Twin set (long or short) **$30.00**
Price with 6 metal apertures **34.00**
Price, Junior Twin Set (long or short) plastic apertures **27.00**
Price, Junior Twin Set (long or short) metal apertures **32.00**

REDFIELD INTERNATIONAL SMALLBORE FRONT (Illustrated)
Similar to Olympic. Drop-in insertion of eared inserts. Outer sleeve prevents light leakage. Comes complete with 6 clear inserts and 6 skeleton inserts **$19.95**

REDFIELD INTERNATIONAL MILITARY BIG BORE
Same as International Match except tube only 2¼″ long. For 30 cal. use. Price **$17.90**

WOMACK DUAL RANGE
Instant change from 50 to 100 yards by rotating front knurled sleeve ½ turn. Choice of 6″ or 10″ length. Price, including 6 apertures, base and screws. Price **$21.00**

Ramp Sights

Front Sights

Williams Streamlined Ramp

Lyman ramp and front sight

JAEGER
Band type with detachable hood, gold or ivory bead. When ordering, give height and muzzle diameter. Price **$7.95**

LYMAN SLIP-ON RAMP AND FRONT SIGHT
No soldering or brazing necessary, has tapered hole. Inside dia. .550″ to .640″. Removable hood. Price for ramp, sight and hood **$9.75**

LYMAN SCREW-ON RAMP AND SIGHT
Used with 8-40 screws but may also be brazed on. Heights from .100″to .350″. Price with sight **$7.00**

MARBLE CONTOUR RAMP
For late model Rem. 725, 740, 760, 742. ⁹/₁₆″ between mounting screws. Price **$4.50**

MARBLE RAMPS
Available in either screw-on or sweat-on style. 5 heights; ³/₁₆″, ⁵/₁₆″, ³/₈″, ⁷/₁₆″, ⁹/₁₆″. Standard ³/₈″ dovetail slot. Price **$4.25**
Hoods for above ramps **$1.00**

PEDERSON "REX"
Offered as the "Rex" ramp, this is a hoodless type without barrel band. Heights available are ¼″ to ⁹/₁₆″. Blued or in the white, and without sights. Price **$2.95**

LYMAN BLADE & DOVETAIL SIGHTS
Made with gold, silver or red beads ¹/₁₆″ to ³/₃₂″ wide and in varying heights for most military and commercial rifles . . . . from **$2.50** to **$3.00**

LYMAN No. 22
Ivory bead front sight for Savage 24 series. O-U. Price **$2.75**

MARBLE STANDARD
Ivory, red, or gold bead. For all American made rifles. ¹/₁₆″ wide bead with semi-flat face which does not reflect light. Specify type of rifle when ordering **$1.90**

MARBLE-SHEARD "GOLD"
Show up well even in darkest timber. Shows same color on different colored objects; sturdily built. Medium bead. Various models for different makes of rifles so specify type of rifle when ordering. Also made for 30 or 9 mm Lugers, Colt's Single Action Army, Bisley Model, with plain sight or any other Colt's or S & W revolver with stationary front sight. Price **$3.20**

MARBLE CONTOURED
Same contour and shape as Marble-Sheard but uses standard ¹/₁₆″ or ³/₃₂″ bead, ivory, red or gold. Specify rifle type **$2.20**

NUMRICH MUSKET FRONT SIGHT
Traditional 58 cal. front sight. Can be used for 58 caliber Springfield or Zouave replacement barrels., or '41 Mississippi barrel. Price **$1.95**

NUMRICH SILVER BLADE FRONT SIGHT
Same sight as used on H&A "Minuteman" rifle and Rolling Block "Buffalo Rifle." Suited for most ML and black powder cartridge guns. Price . . **$3.45**

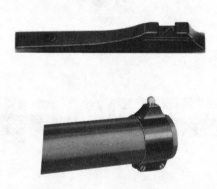

WILLIAMS SHORTY RAMP
Companion to "Streamlined" ramp, about ½″ shorter. Screw-on or sweat-on type. It is furnished in ⅛″, ³/₁₆″, ⁹/₃₂″, and ³/₈″ heights without hood only. Price **$3.75**

WILLIAMS STREAMLINED RAMP
Hooded style in screw-on or sweat-on models. Furnished in ⁹/₁₆″, ⁷/₁₆″, ³/₈″, ⁵/₁₆″, ³/₁₆″ heights. Price with hood **$5.75**
Price without hood 4.75
Lightweight alloy ramp only 4.25

WILLIAMS SHOTGUN RAMP
Designed to elevate the front bead for slug shooting or for guns that shoot high. Diameters to fit most 12, 16, 20 ga. guns. Fastens by screw-clamp, no drilling required. Price, with Williams gold bead . **$3.50**
Price, without bead 2.75

O.S.E. ADJUSTABLE HEIGHT FRONT
Screw adjustment gives .025″ change in height for each turn. 5 models give adjustments from .260″ to .880″. Fits ³/₈″ dovetail barrel or ramp slots. White or gold bead. Original Sight Exchange. Price **$2.95**

WILLIAMS GUIDE BEAD SIGHT
Fits all shotguns. ⅛″ ivory, red or gold bead. Screws into existing sight hole. Various thread sizes and shank lengths **$1.75**
Cultured Pearl Guide Bead **$3.95**

Handgun Sights

Left—FDL revolver sight.
Above—Micro handgun sight.

BO-MAR DE LUXE
Gives ⅜″ w. and e. adjustment at 50 yards on Colt Gov't 45, sight radius under 7″. For Colt, Hi-Standard, Ruger and S&W autos. Uses existing dovetail slot. Has shield-type rear blade **$16.00**

BO-MAR HIGH STANDARD RIB
Full length, 8¾″ sight radius, for all bull barrels and military. Slide alteration required **$30.00**

BO-MAR LOW PROFILE RIB
Streamlined rib with front and rear sights; 7⅛″ sight radius. Brings sight line closer to the bore than standard or extended sight and ramp. Weighs 4 oz. Made for Colt Gov't 45, Super 38, and Gold Cup 45 and 38 . **$28.00**
Extended sight and ramp, 8⅛″ radius, 5¾ oz. **34.00**
Rib & tuner—inserted in Low Profile Rib—accuracy tuner. Adjustable for barrel positioning **39.95**

BO-MAR FRONT SIGHTS
⅛″ tapered post, made for Colt, Hi-Standard, Ruger and S&W autos.
$3.00—$4.00

F.D.L. WONDERSIGHT
Micrometer rear sight for Colt and S&W revolvers. 1-min. clicks for windage. Sideplate screw controls elevation **$4.95**

MICRO
Click adjustable w. and e. rear with plain or undercut front sight in ⅒″, ⅛″, or 5⁄32″ widths. Standard model available for 45, Super 38 or Commander autos. Low model for above pistols plus Colt Service Ace. Also for Ruger with 4¾″ or 6″ barrel. Price for sets **$15.50**
Price with ramp front sight **18.50**

Shotgun Sights

FOR DOUBLE BARREL SHOTGUNS (PRESS FIT)
Marble 214—Ivory front bead, 11⁄64″ . . . **$1.00; 215**—same with .080″ rear bead and reamers . . . **$2.95. Marble 220**—Bi-color (gold and ivory) front bead, 11⁄64″ and .080 rear bead, with reamers . . . **$3.95; Marble 221**—front bead only . . . **$1.90. Marble 223**—Ivory rear .080 . . . **$1.00. Marble 224**—Front sight reamer for 214-221 beads . . . **$0.75; Marble 226** —Rear sight reamer for 223 . . . . **$0.75**

FOR SINGLE OR DB SHOTGUNS (SCREW-ON FIT)
Marble 217—Ivory front bead 11⁄64″ . . . **$1.20;** with tap and wrench**$2.50**
Marble 218—Bi-color front, 11⁄64″ . . . **1.60;** with tap and wrench . . . **3.05**
Marble 223T—Ivory rear .080 . . . **1.60;** with tap and wrench . . . **3.05**
Marble Bradley type sights 223BT—⅛″, 5⁄64″ and 11⁄64″ long. Gold, Ivory or Red bead **$1.60**

Sight Attachments

FREELAND LENS ADAPTER
Fits 1⅛″ O.D. prescription ground lens to all standard tube and receiver sights for shooting without glasses. Price without lens **$19.50**
Price, clear lens ground to prescription **12.50**
Price, yellow or green prescription lens **15.50**

MERIT ADAPTER FOR GLOBE FRONT SIGHTS
An Iris Shutter Disc with a special adapter for mounting in Lyman or Redfield globe front sights. Price **$9.00**

MERIT IRIS SHUTTER DISC
Eleven clicks gives 12 different apertures. No. 3 and Master, primarily target types, .022″ to .125″; No. 4, ½″ dia. hunting type, .025″ to .155″. Available for all popular sights. The Master Disc, with flexible rubber light shield, is particularly adapted to extension, scope height, and tang sights. All Merit Deluxe models have internal click springs; are hand fitted to minimum tolerance. Price . . . . **$8.00—$11.00**
Master . . . . **$10.00**   Master Deluxe **13.00**

Merit Master   Merit Hunting   Merit Deluxe
Target Disc   Disc #4   Lens Disc

MERIT LENS DISC
Similar to Merit Iris Shutter (Model 3 or Master) but incorporates provision for mounting prescription lens integrally. Lens may be obtained locally, or prescription sent to Merit. Sight disc is 7⁄16″ wide (Mod. 3), or ¾″ wide (Master). Lens, ground to prescription,**$7.60.** Standard tints, **$9.10.** Model 3 Deluxe **$13.00**
Master Deluxe **$16.00**

REDFIELD VARD (Variable Diopter)
For shooters with visual problems. By adjusting the focus ring to focus the lens system at a point between the front sight aperture and the bull and controlling the size of the iris diaphragm, a crisp sharp high-contrast sight picture can be achieved. Provision is made for a prescription lens holder for shooters whose requirements exceed the focus capability of the VARD. Comes with smoke-gray filter. Front thread is 9⁄32″–32NS and will fit International and Olympic sights now being produced. Older 0/1 sights with 7⁄32 thread will be converted at the plant for $3.45 on request. Maximum magnification is 1.3X. Use of the VARD adds approximately 1.5″ to the sight. Extension attaching bases listed allow the sight to move forward 1.5″ to accommodate for this extra length. Prices: VARD-IRIS Combination with filter **$39.95**
Iris Diaphragm only with filter **19.95**
Prescription lens holder **1.95**
Set of 3 filters—Yellow, Sage Green and Gray **3.95**

REDFIELD SURE-X SIGHTING DISC
Eight hole selective aperture. Fits any Redfield target sight. Each click changes aperture .004″. Price **$7.95**

REDFIELD SIGHTING DISCS
Fit all Redfield receiver sights. .046″ to .093″ aperture. ⅜″, ½″ and ⅞″ O.D. Price, each . . . . **$ .95**

WILLIAMS APERTURES
Standard thread, fits most sights. Regular series ⅜″ to ⅝″ O.D., .050″ to .125″ hole. "Twilight" series has white reflector ring. .093″ to .125″ inner hole. Price, regular series . . . **$.75.** Twilight series **$1.25**
New wide open 5⁄16″ aperture for shotguns fits 5-D and Foolproof sights. Price **$2.00**

MERIT OPTICAL ATTACHMENT
For revolver and pistol shooters. Instantly attached by rubber suction cup to regular or shooting glasses. Any aperture .020″ to .156″. Price, **$8.00.**
Deluxe (swings aside) **$10.00**

HUNTING, TARGET✦ AND VARMINT✦ SCOPES

Maker and Model	Magn.	Field at 100 Yds. (feet)	Relative Brightness	Eye Relief (in.)	Length (in.)	Tube Diam. (in.)	W&E Adjustments	Weight (ozs.)	Other Data	Price
American Import Co.										
Dickson 250	2½	43	64	3½	—	1	Int.	—	CH standard, Post available in 2½x and 4x. Aluminum tubes, centered reticles, nitrogen filled. 1" adj.	$28.95
Dickson 400	4	30	67	3½	—	1	Int.	—		30.95
Dickson 600	6	19	30	3	—	1	Int.	—		37.95
Dickson V20/154	1½-4	53-28	177-25	4-3	—	1	Int.	—		42.95
Dickson V33/257	2½-7	43-16	174-22	3	—	1	Int.	—		49.95
Dickson V40/39	3-9	30-12	196-21	3	—	1	Int.	—		55.00
Bausch & Lomb										
Custom Baltur A	2½	43	64	3¼	12¼	1	Ext.	9½	Custom models must be used with B&L or other adj. mount. Trophy models have internal ½ MOA adj. Custom variables have tapered CH. Straight powers have CH, Post $5, dot $10. Balfor B has CH; post, tapered CH, dualine, taper-dot $5, dot $10. Balvar 8B has CH; post, tapered CH, RF, dualine, taper-dot $5, dot $10.	49.95
Custom Balfor A	4	30	56	3¼	12¼	1	Ext.	9		59.95
Custom Balvar 5	2½-5	40-20	164-41	3½	12¾	1	Ext.	9½		79.95
Custom Balvar 8A	2½-8	40-12½	256-25	3½	12¾	1	Ext.	10½		99.95
Trophy Baltur B	2½	42	164	3	12⅛	1	Int.	11		49.95
Trophy Balfor B	4	30	64	3	11⅞	1	Int.	11		59.95
Trophy Balsix B	6	20	36	3	11⅞	1	Int.	10¾		69.95
Trophy Balvar 8B	2½-8	40-12½	207-20	3½	11⅞	1	Int.	12½		99.95
Browning										
22 Scope	4	24	56	2½-4	9⅜	.75	Int.	6¼	22 Scope w/mount $41.45-$42.45. CH, Post or 4-Plex optional in big game models; dot $10 extra.	31.95
Wide Angle	5	30	58	3	11½	1	Int.	9¾		76.95
	2½-8	44-16	121-14	2½	12½	1	Int.	12		109.95
Browning	2-7	44-16	241-20	3-4½	11¼	1	Int.	11½		99.95
Bushnell										
Scopechief IV	2¾	43	58	4	10	1	Int.	8½	Scopechief models have Command Post reticle with Magnetic Control Ring. Constantly centered reticles in Scopechiefs, Customs and Banners. Integral mounts $5 extra on Scopechiefs. Phantoms intended for handgun use.	58.50
Scopechief IV	4	32	64	3¾	11¾	1	Int.	10½		67.50
Scopechief IV	6	20	40	4	12½	1	Int.	11½		79.50
Scopechief IV	1½-4½	78-26	216-23	4¼-3¼	9¼	1	Int.	7¾		84.50
Scopechief IV	2½-8	44-15	160-16	4-3¼	11	1	Int.	11		88.50
Scopechief IV	3-9	39-13	160-18	3¾-3¼	11½	1	Int.	12¼		98.50
Scopechief 22	3-8	30-12	55-6	2½	11	⅞	Int.	7½	Mount rail. Similar 4x at $14.95. Battery powered Lite-Site reticles in Scopechief V models.	24.95
Scopechief V	4	30	96	3½	12¼	1	Int.	10¾		67.50
Scopechief V	1½-4	76-27½	213-27	4¼-3¼	10¾	1	Int.	12		84.50
Scopechief V	3-9	34-12½	169-27	3¾-3	12⅞	1	Int.	14		98.50
Custom DM	2½	49	64	4¼	10½	1	Int.	7¾		42.95
Custom DM	4	27	64	3¾	11½	1	Int.	9¾	Mount rail. Similar 4x at $10.95.	44.95
Custom DM	6	19	40	3¼	13	1	Int.	10¾		47.95
Custom DM	3-9	35-12½	159-18	3¾-3	12¼	1	Int.	12½		60.95
Custom 22	3-7	29-13	28-5	2	10	⅞	Int.	6½		15.95
Banner	2½	45	64	4¼	10½	1	Int.	8		34.95
Banner	4	30	64	4	11¾	1	Int.	10		38.95
Banner	6	19½	29	3¾	13¼	1	Int.	10½		41.95
Banner	10	12	26	3½	14¼	1	Int.	14½	Obj. focuses for range.	58.95
Banner	1½-4	63-28	169-25	4¼-3¼	10	1	Int.	10¼		51.95
Banner	3-9	39-13	115-13	3¾-3	11¼	1	Int.	12	With 40mm obj. $59.95.	54.95
Banner	4-12	29-10	181-18	3¼	13¼	1	Int.	15½	Obj. focuses for range.	69.95
Phantom	1 1/3	24	441	6-17	7⅝	⅞	Int.	5	Magnum Phantoms, $4 extra.	29.50
Phantom	2½	10	100	7-16	9¼	⅞	Int.	5½		39.50
Shotgun	1	92	337	6	9⅞	1	Int.	11½		69.50
Colt										
Coltmaster Jr.	4	30			12½	.75	Int.	7	Coltmaster Jr. scopes have tip-off mounts.	10.75
Coltmaster Jr.	6	20			14½	.75	Int.	8		13.75
Davis Optical										
Spot Shot 1½"	10, 12, 15, 20, 25, 30	10-4		2	25	.75	Ext.		Focus by moving non-rotating obj. lens unit. Ext. mounts included. Recoil spring $3.50 extra.	87.50
Spot Shot 1¼"	10, 12, 15, 20	10-6		2	25	.75	Ext.			67.50
Habicht										
4 S-D	4	30	64	3¼	11	1.18	Int.	13	From Del-Sports. With e. only, $62.75. With light alloy tube, (27mm), mounting rail, $69.75; same, e. only, $65.75.	63.90
Herter's										
Perfect	1	100	256	3-5	9¾	1	Int.	10¼		42.95
Mark II	2¾	44	58	3½	10¼	1	Int.	8½	A variety of reticles including dots and rangefinders available in different scopes at small price increase. Hudson Bay rimfire. 4x, $20.95.	23.95
Mark IV	4	30	64	3½	11½	1	Int.	9½		23.95
Mark VIII	8	15½	22	3½	12½	1	Int.	14½		29.95
Mark IA	3-9	14-41	157-18	3½	12½	1	Int.	14½		39.95
Mark XXI	4-12	11½-34	100-14	3½	13¼	1	Int.	12½		41.95
Hutson										
Handgunner	1	9	—	25	5¼	—	Ext.	3	CH. ⅞" obj. lens. Adj. in mount, $14.95.	45.00
Hy-Score										
No. 467	4	26	14	1¾	12	.75	Int.	7¼	Alloy tubes. Weather and fog-proof. 400 series scopes are made in Japan.	8.95
No. 469	6	19	6	1¾	12	.75	Int.	7½		11.95
Model 461-466	2½	35	64	3	9⅞	1	Int.	8		19.95
Model 462-468	4	28	64	3	11⅝	1	Int.	10		19.95
Model 463	6	22	28.1	3	11¾	1	Int.	10		20.95
Vari-Power 464	3-9	36-16	126-12	3¼	12½	1	Int.	14		29.95
Vari-Power 471	3-9	35-14	193-18	3¼	12½	1	Int.	14		36.95

Hunting, Target and Varmint Scopes—Continued

Maker and Model	Magn.	Field at 100 Yds. (feet)	Relative Brightness	Eye Relief (in.)	Length (in.)	Tube Diam. (in.)	W&E Adjustments	Weight (oz.)	Other Data	Price
Jana										
Jana 4x	4	29	—	3½	12	1	Int.	9		17.95
Economy 4x	4	29	—	3½	12	1	Int.	9	Deluxe model offers choice of dot or Dual-X reticle. Zoom offers choice of crosshair or Dual-X. Others have constantly centered reticles.	15.95
Deluxe	4	32	—	3½	12	1	Int.	9		22.50
Super	4	32	—	3½	12	1	Int.	—		29.50
JA-2	2½	32	—	—	12	1	Int.	9⅛		17.95
JA-6	6	17½	—	3⅛	12	1	Int.	9		19.95
Zoom	3-9	35-12	—	—	12½	1	Int.	13½		37.50
JA-420	4	15½	—	—	11	¾	Int.	5¼		8.75
JA-37	3-7	23-10	—	2½-3	11⅓	⅞	Int.	9½		13.95
Jason										
860	4	27¼	64	3½	12	1	Int.	9		19.95
864	6	17½	28	3¼	12	1	Int.	9	Constantly centered reticles, ball-bearing click stops, nitrogen filled tubes, coated lenses.	23.50
861	3-9	31½-12	112-12	3	13¼	1	Int.	13¾		36.95
865	3-9	31½-12	177-19	3	13½	1	Int.	15¼		39.95
Leupold										
M8	2	25	100	8-18	8.45	1	Int.	7.25		49.50
M8	3	43	45	3.85	10.13	1	Int.	8.25	Constantly centered reticles; in addition to the crosshair reticle the post, tapered (CPC), post and duplex, and duplex reticles are optional at no extra cost. Dot reticle $10.00 extra. 2x suitable for handguns and Win. 94.	59.50
M8	4	30	50	3.85	11.50	1	Int.	9.00		67.50
M8	6	18		3.85	11.7	1	Int.	10.3		79.50
M8	7½	14	32	3.60	12.60	1	Int.	12.75		84.50
M8	10	10	16	3½	13	1	Int.	13¾		97.50
M8	12	9	11	3½	14½	1	Int.	14		99.50
Vari-X II	2-7	42-18	144-17	3.7-4.12	11.00	1	Int.	10.75		89.50
Vari-X II	3-9	30.5-13	208-23	3.5-4.12	12.60	1	Int.	13.75		99.50
Lyman										
All-American	2½	43		3¼	10½	1	Int.	8¾	2, 3, or 4 minute dot reticle $10 extra. Choice of standard CH, tapered post, or tapered post and CH reticles. All-weather reticle caps. All Lyman scopes have new Perma-Center reticle which remains in optical center regardless of changes in W. & E. ⅛ or ¼ MOA clicks.	49.95
All-American	3	35		3¼	11	1	Int.	9		52.95
All-American	4	30		3¼	12	1	Int.	10		62.95
All-American	6	20		3¼	13⅞	1	Int.	12¼		69.95
◆ All-American	8	14		3¼	14⅜	1	Int.	13		89.95
◆ All-American	10	12		3¼	15½	1	Int.	13½		89.95
All-American	20	5.5		2¼	17⅛	1	Int.	15¼		109.95
◆ Super Targetspot	10, 12, 15, 20, 25, 30	12, 9.3, 8.9, 5.6, 4.3, 4	86%	2-1⅞	24-24⅜	.75	Ext.	24¼-25	Non-rotating objective lens focusing. ¼ MOA click adjustments. Sunshade, $2 extra. Steel case, $9.50 extra. 5 different dot reticles, $10.00 extra.	145.00
Marble										
A-2.5	2¾	43	164	3½	11¾	1	Int.	10¾	Duralumin tubes, nitrogen filled. Post, CH, dot or 3-post reticle. Variables have ½ MOA adj.	39.50
A-4.0	4	30	64	3½	11¾	1	Int.	10¾		39.50
VL-3.9	3-9	38½-12½	177-19	3¼	13½	1	Int.	15½		68.50
VS-3.9	3-9	37-10½	114-12	3¼	13½	1	Int.	13½		69.50
Marlin										
300	4	23	25	1½	11¾	⅞	Int.	9	Coated lenses, non-magnifying reticles. Tri-Post reticle. A 4x Glenfield M200, suitable for 22 rifles, and with ½-minute adj., is $8.00.	13.95
500	3-7	24-10	49-16	1¾	12	⅞	Int.	9½		16.95
425	4	28	64	3½	—	1	Int.	—		29.95
800	1½-5	55-19	256-49	3½	11⅜	1	Int.	13½		42.95
Glenfield 400	4	28	64	3½	12	1	Int.	9		20.00
Nickel										
Supra	2½	20	64	3½	11½	1.024	Int.	7½		90.00
Supralyt	4	20	25	3½	11½	1.024	Int.	8	¼ MOA click adjustments. Steel or alloy tubes. Weatherproof reticle caps. Crosshair, post and c.h. or post and crossbar reticles are standard. New "Diflex" coated lenses. Continental Arms Co.	90.00
Supra	4	36	81	3½	11¼	1.024	Int.	9		115.00
Supra	6	36	36	3½	12½	1.024	Int.	9		115.00
◆ Supra Varminter	6	42	49	3¼-5	12¼	1.024	Int.	11½		125.00
Supra Vari-Power	1-4	66.5-27.3	153-28	3½	10½	1.024	Int.	13.1		140.00
Supra Vari-Power	1½-6	60-21.6	176-36	3½	12	1.181	Int.	14.8		190.00
Supra Vari-Power	2½-7	38-21	125-36	3½	11¾	1.024	Int.	11		170.00
Supra Vari-Power	2½-9	42-15.6		3½	14½	1.181	Int.	17.3		190.00
Supra Vari-Power	3-10	30-12	100-18.5	3½	12½	.866	Int.	12½		180.00
Normark										
Singlepoint	1	—	—		6¾	1	Int.	7½	Usable on rifles, shotguns, handguns.	24.95
Precise Imports										
NR-15	4	23	14	2	11	.75	Int.	6¾		7.95
20257	3-7	23-13	43-8	3	11½	.75	Int.	7½	Price with mount.	13.95
20265	2½	32	164	3¾	12	1	Int.	9.6	All scopes have constanly centered reticle.	24.95
20244	4	29	64	3½	12	1	Int.	9		24.95
20249	3-9	36-13	177-19	3	13⅓	1	Int.	15		39.95
20260	10	12.2	16	3	12½	1	Int.	10½		29.95
Realist										
Apache	4	30	6	2	12½	.75	Int.	7	Scope price includes mount. Constantly centered reticles in Riflescopes. CH or P&CH standard. Dot $10 extra. Sunshades available $6.95 — $8.95. Nitrogen processed. Aluminum construction.	9.95
Apache	6	20	4	2	13¾	.75	Int.	8		12.50
Riflescope	2½	44	66	3-5	10½	1	Int.	8		55.50
Riflescope	4	31	73	3-5	12⅜	1	Int.	9		65.50
Riflescope	6	20	38	3-5	14	1	Int.	10		75.50
Brushscope	1½-4½	65-26	225-49	3-5	11	1	Int.	11½		83.50
Riflescope	3-9	34-12	144-16	3-5	13¼	1	Int.	11		103.50
Computer	6	20	38	3-5	14⅝	1	Int.	18	Supplied with special mounts and range cams for most popular rifles and calibers.	119.50
Auto/Range	4	31	73	3-5	11	1	Int.	17		119.50
	1½-4½	65-26	225-49	3-5	12¼	1	Int.	17		129.50
	3-9	34-12	144-16	3-5	12¾	1	Int.	17		129.50

Hunting, Target and Varmint Scopes—Continued

Maker and Model	Magn.	Field at 100 Yds. (feet)	Relative Brightness	Eye Relief (in.)	Length (in.)	Tube Diam. (in.)	W&E Adjustments	Weight (oz.)	Other Data	Price
Redfield										
Sportster 4X	3.9	24.5	27	3-3¾	9½	.75	Int.	6¼		31.95
Widefield 2¾	2¾	55½	49	3	10½	1	Int.	8	Constantly centered reticles; scratchproof Tuf-Coat finish; W. & E. dials adjustable to zero; weatherproof sealed. Reticle same size at all powers. Add $10 for Accu-Range, $10 for dot (not avail. in Sportster). 12X has separate parallax adj. knob, ¼" clicks.

Mounts solidly. Fine CH, Med. CH, ¼" dot. | 64.95 |
Widefield 4	4	37½	46	3	11½	1	Int.	10		74.95
Widefield 6	6	25	44	3	13½	1	Int.	11½		84.95
Magnum 12X	12	10	13.7	3-3¾	14⅞	1	Int.	13.5		119.95
Magnum Variable	1-4	85-30	289-31	3½	9¾	1	Int.	10¼		89.95
Widefield	1¾-5	70-27	100-16	3-3¾	10¾	1	Int.	11½		95.95
Widefield	2-7	49-19	121-25	3½	11¾	1	Int.	13		105.95
Widefield	3-9	39-15	144-20	3½	12½	1	Int.	14		115.95
Magnum Variable	4-12	27½-9	100-22	3-3¾	13⅞	1	Int.	14		129.95
Magnum Variable	6-18	16-5½	44.5	3½	14	1	Int.	18		139.95
3200 Target	12, 16, 20, 24,	6½, 5¼, 4, 3¾,	9, 6, 3¼, 2¼	2½	23¼	1	Int.	21		169.95
Sanders										
Bisley 2½x32	2½	42	64	3	10¾	1	Int.	8¼	Alum. alloy tubes, ¼" adj., coated lenses.

Two other scopes are also offered: a 3-9x at $56.50, and a 6x45 at $42. Rubber lens covers (clear plastic) are $2.50.

Choice of reticles in CH, PCH, 3-post. | 32.50 |
Bisley 4x33	4	28	64	3	12	1	Int.	9		36.50
Bisley 6x40	6	19	45	3	12½	1	Int.	9½		38.50
Bisley 8x40	8	18	25	3¼	12½	1	Int.	9½		40.50
Bisley 10 x40	10	12½	16	2½	12½	1	Int.	10¼		42.50
Bisley 5-13x40	5-13	29-10	64-9	3	14	1	Int.	14		60.50
Savage-Springfield										
1540	4	25	—	1¾	11¾	.75	Int.	7½		8.25
1937	3-7	25-14	—	1¾	11¾	.75	Int.	8½		14.95
3240	4	29	—	3	12	1	Int.	10¼		29.95
Scope Instruments										
2650	2½	32	164	3½	11½	1	Int.	10	Contantly centered reticles—CH or post. Nitrogen filled. Yellow haze filter.	28.95
2652	4	29	64	3¼	11½	1	Int.	9½		28.95
2654	6	21	28	3	11½	1	Int.	9½		37.95
2658	3-9	29-13	113-12	3	13¼	1	Int.	14¼		41.95
2656	3-9	29-12	177-19	3½	13¼	1	Int.	16		47.95
Sears										
No. 53801	4	30		2	11½	.75	Int.	6	First three scopes for 22's only, complete with rings for grooved receivers. Crosshair or post and crosshair reticle.
Big game scopes come with mount rings. Bases available to fit almost all H.P. rifles. Fixed crosshair reticle remains in center regardless of adjustment. No. 53824 for Sears M54.	12.75
No. 53802	4	28		2	11½	.75	Int.	8		8.75
No. 53803	3-6	30-16					Int.	6½		13.50
No. 53824	3	37		3-6	10⅜	1	Int.	8½		34.50
No. 53821	4	30		3¼	11¼	1	Int.	12		39.50
No. 53901	1				8	1	Int.	8½		39.50
Southern Precision										
562	2½	40	144	3½	12	1	Int.	9¼	Centered reticles, CH or post. All elements sealed.	21.95
564	4	30	64	3½	12	1	Int.	9¼		23.95
566	6	21	28	3¼	12	1	Int.	9¼		23.95
Stoeger										
4x	4	30	64	3	12	1	Int.	9	CH only. ½" clicks. Obj. tube diam. 1½" in fixed powers, 1⅞" in variable.	24.95
6x	6	20	28	3	12¾	1	Int.	9		29.95
8x	8	16	25	3	12	1	Int.	13		35.95
3x-9x	3-9	38-11	170-20	3	11½	1	Int.	12¾		46.95
Swift										
Stag	4	28½	64	3	11.7	1	Int.	8.5	Dot, tapered post & CH or Rangefinder reticles available on all but Zoom & Game, $2.50 extra. Rangefinder optional on Zoom & Game. All have self-centering reticles.	28.00
Aerolite	4	28½	64	3	11¾	1	Int.	9½		19.50
Aerolite	2½-8	32-13	164-16	3	13¼	1	Int.	11¼		33.00
Yukon	2½-8	32½-13	164-16	3	13¼	1	Int.	11.3		45.00
Tasco										
Zoom Utility	3-7	28-12	130-24	2¼	12	⅞	Int.	9½	Lens covers furnished. Constantly centered reticles. Write the importer, Tasco, for data on complete line.	19.95
Pistol Scope	1½	23	216	19	8⅝	⅞	Int.	7½		29.95
Sniper	2-5	36-18	150-24	3¼	11¼	1	Int.	10		39.95
Super Marksman	3-9	35-14	266-29	3.2	12⅜	1	Int.	12½		69.95
Omni-View	3-9	43-16	114-13	3	12½	1	Int.	12¼		99.95
Thompson/Center										
Puma	1½	16	—	11-20	7¾	.87	Int.	5	Handgun scope, with mount for Contender, S&W or Ruger.	39.50
Tops										
4X	4	28½	64	3	11½	1	Int.	9½	Hard-coated lenses, nitrogen filled, shock-proof tested. Write Ed Paul, importer, for data on complete line.	23.95
8X	8	14½	16	3	13	1	Int.	10		29.95
3X-9X	3-9	33-15	175-19	3	12¾	1	Int.	14		39.95

Tasco's OMNI-VIEW Zoom 3-9x with range finding 30/30 reticle and ¼ minute clicks.

Hunting, Target and Varmint Scopes—Continued

Maker and Model	Magn.	Field at 100 Yds. (feet)	Relative Brightness	Eye Relief (in.)	Length (in.)	Tube Diam. (in.)	W&E Adjustments	Weight (oz.)	Other Data	Price
United										
Golden Hawk	4	30	64		11⅞	—	Int.	9½	Anodized tubes, nitrogen filled. Write United for data on complete line.	44.50
Golden Grizzly	6	18½	44		11⅞	1	Int.	11		55.00
Golden Falcon	4-9	29½-14	100-20		13½	1	Int.	12¼		89.50
Golden Plainsman	3-12	33-12½	169-11		13½	1	Int.	12¾		110.00
Unertl										
Falcon	2¾	40	75.5	4	11	1	Int.(1′)	10	Black dural tube in hunting models. (2 oz. more with steel tube.)	57.50
Hawk	4	34	64	4	11¾	1	Int.(1′)	10.5		62.50
Condor	6	17	40	3-4	13½	1	Int.(1′)	12		78.50
◆1" Target	6,8,10	16-10	17.6-6.25	2	21½	.75	Ext.	21	Dural ¼ MOA click mounts. Hard coated lenses. Non-rotating objective lens focusing.	78.00
◆1¼" Target	8,10,12,14	12-6	15.2-5	2	25	.75	Ext.	25		104.00
◆1½" Target	8,10,12,14 16,18,20,24	11.5-3.2		2¼	25½	.75	Ext.	31		121.00
◆2" Target	8,10,12,14 16,18,24 30,36		22.6-2.5	2¼	26¼	1	Ext.	44		168.00
◆Varmint, 1¼"	6,8,10,12	14.1-7	28-7.1	2½	19½	.875	Ext.	26	¼ MOA dehorned mounts. With target mounts.	106.00 110.00
◆Ultra Varmint, 2"	8,10, 12,15	12.6-7	39.7-11	2½	24	1	Ext.	34	With dehorned mount. With calibrated head.	133.00 152.00
◆Small Game	4,6	25-17	19.4-8.4	2¼	18	.75	Ext.	16	Same as 1" Target but without objective lens focusing.	57.00
◆Vulture	8 10	11.2 10.9	29 18½	3-4	15⅝ 16⅛	1	E or I	15½	Price with internal adj. Price with ¼ MOA click mounts.	94.50 112.50
◆Programer 200	8,10,12,14 16,18,20,24 30,36	11.3-4	39-1.9		26½	1	Ext.	45	With new Posa mounts.	222.00
◆BV-20	20	8	4.4	—	17⅞	1	Ext.	21¼	Range focus unit near rear of tube. Price is with Posa mounts, Magnum clamp. With standard mounts and clamp ring, $148.00.	158.00
Universal										
Deluxe UC	2½	32	172	3½	12	1	Int.	9¼	Aluminum alloy tubes, centered reticles, coated lenses. Similar Standard series available at lower cost.	26.95
Deluxe UE	4	29	64	3½	12	1	Int.	9		26.95
Deluxe UG	6	17½	28	3¼	12	1	Int.	9		29.95
Deluxe UL	3-9	34-12	177-18	3	12¾	1	Int.	15¼		49.95
Weatherby										
Mark XXII	4	25	50	2½-3½	11¾	⅞	Int.	9¼	Focuses in top turret. ¼ MOA adj. for e., 1 MOA for w. in all models. Reticles: CH, post and CH, Lee Dot or Open Dot ($12.50 extra).	29.50
Imperial	2¾	47½	90	3¼-5	10½	1	Int.	9¼		89.50
Imperial 4x	4	33	81	3¼-4½	11⅛	1	Int.	10¼		99.50
Imperial 6x	6	21½	62	3¼-4½	12½	1	Int.	12⅜		109.50
Imperial Variable	2-7	48-17¾	324-27	4.3-3.1	11 3/16	1	Int.	12		119.50
Imperial Variable	2¾-10	37-14.6	296-22	4½-3½	12½	1	Int.	14⅛		129.50
Weaver										
Classic 300	3	37	—	4	10⅜	1	Int.	7	Classics have glossy anodized alloy, tubes, non-removable eyepieces, choice of all five reticles, dot $7.50 extra.	60.00
Classic 400	4	31	—	4	11¾	1	Int.	8		70.00
Classic 600	6	20	—	3¾	13⅝	1	Int.	9		80.00
Classic V700	2½-7	40-15		3¾	11¾	1	Int.	8¼		90.00
Classic V900	3-9	33-12		3¾	13	1	Int.	11		100.00
K1.5	1½	56		3-5	9¾	1	Int.	7		29.95
K2.5	2½	43		3-6	10⅜	1	Int.	8½		39.95
K3	3	37		3-6	10⅜	1	Int.	8½	Crosswires, post, rangefinder or Dual X reticle optional on all K and V scopes (except no RF in K1½, post in K8, 10, 12, or RF in V22). Dot $7.50 extra in K and V models only. Objective lens on K8, K10, K12, V9 and V12 focuses for range.	39.95
K4	4	31		3-5½	11¼	1	Int.	9½		49.95
K6	6	20		3-5	13⅝	1	Int.	11		54.95
K8	8	15		3-5	15⅜	1	Int.	12¼		59.95
K10	10	12		3-5	15½	1	Int.	12½		64.95
K12	12	10		3-5	15¾	1	Int.	12½		72.95
V4.5	1½-4½	54-21		3-5	10	1	Int.	8½		57.95
V7	2½-7	40-15		3-5	11⅝	1	Int.	10½		64.95
V9	3-9	33-12		3-5	13	1	Int.	13		72.95
V12	4-12	24-9		4	13		Int.	13		84.95
V22	3-6	30-16		2	12½	.875	Int.	4½	D model prices include N or Tip-Off mount.	15.95
D4	4	28	—	2	11⅝	.875	Int.	4		10.95
D6	6	18	—	2	12	.875	Int.	4		12.95
Qwik-Point	1	—	—	6	—	—	Int.	8	For rifles and shotguns. Projects red dot aiming point.	39.95
Williams										
Guide Line	4	29½	64	3¾	11¾	1	Int.	9½	Coated lenses, nitrogen filled tubes, ½ MOA adj. CH, dot, TNT or Guide reticle. Dot covers 3 MOA at 4x in all models.	75.00
Guide Line	1½-4½	78-26	196-22	4⅓-3¼	9½	1	Int.	7¾		105.00
Guide Line	2-6	60-20	169-18	3¼	10¼	1	Int.	10		105.00
Guide Line	3-9	39-13	161-18	3¾-3¼	12	1	Int.	14½		115.00
Twilight	2½	32	64	3¾	11¼	1	Int.	8½	$5 more for TNT reticle.	32.50
Twilight	4	29	64	3½	11¾	1	Int.	9½		36.50
Twilight	2-6	45-17	256-28	3	11½	1	Int.	11½		54.00
Twilight	3-9	36-13	161-18	3	12¾	1	Int.	13½		62.00
Wide Guide	4	35	64	3¼	12¼	1	Int.	14	CH, TNT or Guide reticle.	75.00
Zeiss										
Diatal D	4	31.5	64	3⅛	10½	1.24	Int.	11	Alloy tubes. Leather caps furnished. Turret dials not calibrated. Carl Zeiss, Inc., importer.	199.00
Diatal D	6	21	49	3⅛	12½	1.24	Int.	13½		219.00
Diavari D	1½-6	60-21	161-36	3⅛	12¼	1.18	Int.	16¼		299.00

◆Signifies target and/or varmint scope.

Hunting scopes in general are furnished with a choice of reticle—crosshairs, post with crosshairs, tapered or blunt post, or dot crosshairs, etc.
The great majority of target and varmint scopes have medium or fine crosshairs but post or dot reticles may be ordered.

W—Windage E—Elevation MOA—Minute of angle or 1" (approx.) at 100 yards, etc.

SCOPES & MOUNTS
TELESCOPE MOUNTS

Maker, Model, Type	W and E Adjust.	Scopes	Suitable for	Price
Bausch & Lomb				
Custom One Piece (T)	Yes	B&L, other 1" scopes.	Most popular rifles.	38.90-52.90
Custom Two Piece (T)	Yes			26.90
Trophy (T)	No	1". With int. adj.		21.90-37.90
Browning				
One Piece (T)	W only	1" split rings	Browning FN rifles.	25.00
One Piece (T)	No	¾" split rings	Browning 22 semi-auto.	5.00
One Piece Barrel Mount Base	No	Groove mount	22 rifles with grooved receiver.	6.00
Two Piece	No	¾" ring mount.	For Browning T-bolt 22.	9.50
B-Square Co.				
Mono-Mount	No	Leupold M8-2x (mounts ahead of action)	M94 Win. / M1 Carbine.	11.50 / 9.50
Buehler				
One Piece (T)	W only	¾" or 1" solid rings; ⅞", 1" or 26mm split rings. 4" or 5" spacing.	All popular models.	Solid rings—21.75 / Split rings—26.75
One Piece "Micro-Dial" Universal	Yes	Same. 4" ring spacing only.	Most popular models.	Solid—28.25 Split—33.25
Two Piece (T)	W only	Same. Rings for 26.5—27 mm adjust to size by shims.	Rem. 700, 721, 722, 725; Win. 70, 52; FN; Rem. 37; Mathieu; Schultz & Larsen; Husq.	Solid—21.75 Split—26.75
One Piece Pistol Base	W only	Uses any Buehler rings.	S&W K, Colt, Ruger, Thompson	Base only—11.25
One Piece (T)	W only	Same.	Rem. 600 rifle and XP100 pistol.	Base only—11.25
Bushnell				
Universal (T)	W only	1" split rings	All rifles with top of action tapped for 6/48 screws. Two steel 6/48 studs are screwed into receiver holes, eliminating conventional base. Rings drop over studs, are held by opposing screws which give rough windage adj. Economy mount set.	10.95 / 7.95
Dual Purpose	No	Phantom	V-block bottoms lock to chrom-moly studs seated into two 6-48 holes.	6.50
Rigid	No	Phantom	Heavy loads in Colt, S&W, Ruger revolvers, Rem. XP100, Ruger Hawkeye.	5.00
94 Win.	No	Phantom	M94 Win., end of bbl. clamp or center dovetail.	6.50
Collins				
Bulittco (T)	E only	1" split rings	Rimfire rifles with grooved receivers.	4.98
Conetrol				
One Piece (T)	W only	1" solid or split rings.	Sako dovetail bases (14.95);	Huntur $20.95
Two Piece (T)	W only	Same.	for S&K bases on M1 Carb., SMLE 4 & 5, $9.90.	Gunnur $25.85 / Custum $32.85
Griffin & Howe				
Standard Double Lever (S)	No	All standard models.	All popular models. (Garand $37.50; Win. 94 $30.00).	30.00
E. C. Herkner Echo (S)	No	All standard models.	All popular models. Solid or split rings.	14.50—19.75
Holden				
Ironsighter (T)	No	1" split rings	Many popular rifles. Rings have oval holes to permit use of iron sights. For 22 rimfire groover receivers, ¾, ⅞ or 1 inch tubes, $6.95. For long eye relief scopes on M94, $19.95.	14.95

International Guns Inc. handles the complete line of Parker-Hale (British) Roll-Over and other scope mounts.

Maker, Model, Type	W and E Adjust.	Scopes	Suitable for	Price
Jaguar				
QD, with windage (S)	W only	1", 26mm; 3 heights.	All popular models.	38.00
QD Railscope Mount	W only		For scopes with dovetail rib.	38.00
Jaeger				
QD Dovetail (T)	No	1", 26mm and 26½mm rings.	For BSA Monarch rifle (Galef, importer).	16.95
Kesselring				
Standard QD (T)	W only	¾", ⅞", 1", 26mm—30mm split or solid rings.	All popular rifles, one or two piece bases.	12.50-20.00
See-Em-Under (T)	W only	Same.	Rem. 760, 740, 788, Win. 100, 88, Marlin 336	16.50
QD Dovetail (T)	W only	1", 26mm.	Steyr 22, Sako, BSA, Brno, Krico	16.50
Kwik-Site (T)	No	1" split rings	Fits Weaver type bases. Mounts scope high to permit iron sight use. Offset base for 94 Win.	14.75 / 19.95

New See-Thru KWIK-SITE mount allows use of iron sights with scope.

SCOPES & MOUNTS

TELESCOPE MOUNTS—Continued

Maker, Model, Type	W and E Adjust.	Scopes	Suitable for	Price
Leupold				
Detacho (T)	No	1″ only.	All popular rifles. Instantly detachable, leaving W. & E. adjustable peep sight available.	15.25
			Bases for Rem. 600 series.	9.95
			Bases for Win. M94 and Rem. XP100.	5.50—10.00
M3 (T)	Yes	1″ only.	Rem. 700, 740, Win. 70, 88, 100, Wby. Mark V, FN, others. Bases reversible to give wide latitude in mounting.	24.50
Lyman All-American				
Tru-lock (T)	No	¾″, ⅞″, 1″, 26mm, split rings.	All popular post-war rifles, plus Savage 99, 98 Mauser. One or two piece bases.	11.00
Marble				
Game Getter (T)	No	1″ only.	Many popular rifles. Has see-through base to permit use of iron sights.	14.95
Marlin				
One Piece QD (T)	No	1″ split rings	Most popular models. Glenfield model. 5.00.	6.95
Numrich				
Side mount	No	1″ split rings	M1 carbine.	6.95
Pachmayr				
Lo-Swing (S)	Yes	¾″, ⅞″, 1″, 26mm solid or split loops.	All popular rifles. Scope swings aside for instant use of iron sights.	20.00
Lo-Swing (T)	Yes	¾″, ⅞″, 1″, 26mm split rings.	Adjustable base. Win. 70, 88; Rem. 721, 722, 725, 740, 760; Mar. 336; Sav. 99.	25.00
Precise Imports				
M-21 (rings only)	No	1″ tube; not over 32mm obj.	Fit Weaver bases.	3.95
M-22 (rings only)	No	1″ tube; 40mm obj. scopes		3.95
Realist				
V lock QD (T)	No	1″ split rings.	Most popular rifles.	13.00
Redfield				
JR-SR (T)	W only	¾″, 1″, 26mm.	Low, med. & high, split rings. Reversible extension front rings for 1″. 2-piece bases for Mannlicher-Schoenauer and Sako. JR-SR comes with integral folding peep sight.	20.90—43.90
Swing-Over (T) base only	No	1″. (Not for variables.)	Standard height split rings. Also for shotguns.	14.95
Ring (T)	No	¾″ and 1″.	Split rings for grooved 22's.	7.95—9.95
Frontier (T) bases	No	Takes ¾″ or 1″ rings.	See-thru bases $4.95; shotgun model $4.95; attaching base $1.	1.95
S&K				
Insta-Mount (T) base only	No	Takes Conetrol, Weaver, Herter or United rings.	M1903, A3, M1 Carbine, Lee Enfield #3, #4 #5, P14, M1917, M98 Mauser, FN Auto, AR-15.	7.50-30.00
			For M1 Garand, steel rings.	41.50
Conventional rings and bases	No	1″ split rings	Most popular rifles. For "see through underneath" risers, add $4.	19.00
Sako				
QD Dovetail (T)	W only	1″ or 26mm split rings.	Sako, or any rifle using Sako action. 3 heights and extension rings available. Garcia, importer.	18.95—20.65
Savage				
Detachable (T)	No	1″ split rings.	Most modern rifles. One or two piece bases.	9.75-10.25
No. 40 (S)	No	1″	For Savage 340.	3.00
Tasco				
700(T) and 800(S) series	No	1″ split rings, regular or high.	Many popular rifles. Swing mount, 9.95.	4.50—10.45
M722	No	Split rings.	For 22s with grooved receivers.	3.00
Unertl				
Posa (T)	Yes	¾″, ⅞″, 1″ scopes	Unertl target or varmint scope.	26.00-30.00
¼ Click (T)	Yes	¾″, 1″ target scopes	Any with regular dovetail scope bases.	27.00-28.00
Dehorned Varmint (T)	Yes	¾″, ⅞″, 1″ scopes	Add $3 for Posa.	23.00-25.00
Weaver				
Detachable Mount (T & S)	No	¾″, ⅞″, 1″, 26mm.	Nearly all modern rifles. Extension rings, 1″ $11.00	9.95
Type N (S)	No	¾″ scopes only.	Same. High or low style mounts.	2.00
Pivot Mount (T)	No	¾″, 1″, 26mm.	Most modern big bore rifles.	12.50
Tip-Off (T)	No	⅞″.	22s with grooved receivers.	3.00
Tip-Off (T)	No	1″, two-piece	Same. Adapter for Lee Enfield—$1.75	8.00
Williams				
Offset (S)	No	¾″, ⅞″, 1″, 26mm solid, split or extension rings.	Most rifles (with over-bore rings, $17.50). Br. S.M.L.E. (round rec.) $2.50 extra.	15.00
QC (T w/peep)	No	Same.	Same. Add $4.50 for micro. windage ring.	20.00
QC (T w/o peep)	No	Same.	Most 22 rifles, plus Mar. 36, 39, 93, 336, Sav. 23D, Win. 05, 07, 10.	17.50
Sight-Thru	No	1″, ⅞″ sleeves $1	Many modern rifles.	15.00
QC-TM-B22	No	Same.	For Browning 22 autoloader and Rem. 241.	17.50

(S)—Side Mount **(T)—Top Mount.** 22mm = .866″ 25.4mm = 1″ 26mm = 1.024″ 26.5mm = 1.045″ 30mm = 1.181″

Weaver's Extension Top Mounts. The extension ring permits the scope to be positioned ¾″ further forward for improved eye relief.

SPOTTING SCOPES

BAUSCH & LOMB BALSCOPE Sr.—60mm objective, 20X. Field at 100 yds. 11.1 ft. Relative brightness, 9. Wgt., 48 oz. Length closed, 16⁷⁄₁₆". Rapid prismatic focusing **$129.95**
Also 15X, 30X, and 60X eyepieces, each **29.95**
Triple eyepiece turret (without eyepiece) **19.95**
Combination auto window/camera tripod adaptor **24.95**
Carrying case **24.95**
Tele-Master camera adapter **34.95**

BAUSCH & LOMB BALSCOPE ZOOM—15X to 60X variable power. 60mm objective. Field at 1000 yds. 150 ft. (15X) to 37½ feet (60X). Relative brightness 16 (15X) to 1 (60X). Wgt., 48 oz., 16¹¹⁄₁₆" overall. Integral tripod lug. Straight eyepiece **$159.95**
With 45° eyepiece **169.95**

BAUSCH & LOMB BALSCOPE 20—40mm objective. 20X. Field at 100 yds., 7.5 ft. 15⅝" over-all, Wgt., 22 oz. **$29.95**

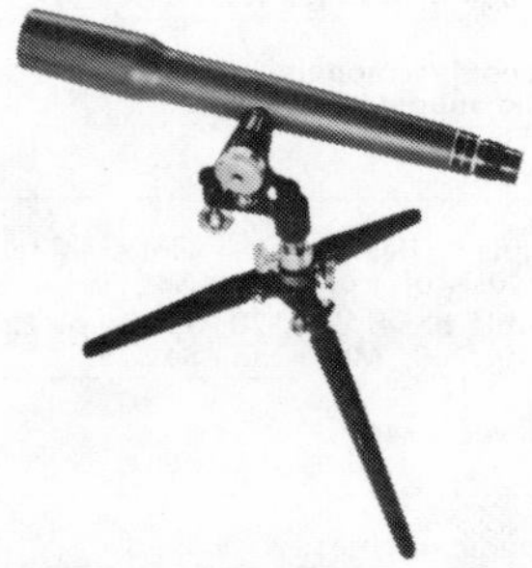

BAUSCH & LOMB BALSCOPE 10—30mm objective. 10X. Field at 100 yds. 7.5 ft. 10¼" over-all, weight, 9 oz. **$9.95**

BUSHNELL SPACEMASTER—60mm objective, 25X. Field at 100 yds., 10.5 ft. Relative brightness, 5.76. Wgt., 39 oz. Length closed, 15¼". Prism focusing, sliding sunshade **$95.00**
15X, 20X, 25X, 40X and 60X eyepieces, each **22.50**
20X wide angle eyepiece **27.50**

BUSHNELL SPACEMASTER 45°—Same as above except: Wgt., 43 oz., length closed 16¼". Eyepiece at 45° **$99.50**

BUSHNELL SPACEMASTER II—20X-45X zoom. 60mm objective. Field at 100 yards 12-7.2 ft. Relative brightness 9-1.7. Weight, 36 oz., over-all length 11⅝" **$109.00**

BUSHNELL SENTRY II—20X. 50mm objective. Field at 100 yards 12 ft. Relative brightness 6.25 .... **$54.50**
Also 32X and 48X eyepieces, each **19.50**

BUSHNELL ZOOM SPOTTER—40mm objective. 9X-30X variable power **$29.50**

HUTSON CHROMATAR 60—63.4mm objective. 22.5X eyepiece at 45D. Wgt. 24 oz. 8" over-all. 10½" foot field at 100 yards. **$119.00**
15X or 45X eyepieces, each **22.00**

HY-SCORE MODEL 460—60mm objective. 15X, 20X, 25X, 40X and 60X eyepieces included. Field at 100 yds. 15.8 to 3.2 ft. Length closed 11". Wgt., 35 oz. With tripod and case **$182.00**

PACIFIC ZOOM—60mm objective, 15X to 50X variable. Field at 100 yds., 7½-3½ ft. Aluminum body. With adj. tripod **$94.50**

PACIFIC 15x60—60mm objective, 5 eyepieces (15X, 20X, 30X, 40X, 50X), adj. tripod. 100-yd. field, 12-3¼ ft. **$89.50**

PRECISE IMPORTS, T-15—60mm objective, 15X to 30X zoom scope. About 15" long, weighs approximately 6 lbs. with adj. tripod. **$49.95**

PRECISE IMPORTS, T-19—60mm objective, interchangeable eyepieces of 15X, 20X, 30X, 40X, 60X. Sliding sunshade. Weighs about 6 lbs. with adj. tripod. **$69.95**

REDFIELD FIFTEEN-SIXTY—15X-60X zoom. 60mm objective. Field at 100 yards 15.6-3.7 ft. Relative brightness 16-1. Wgt. 48 oz., length 16¾" **$149.50**
Tripod stand **27.50**
Carrying case **29.95**

SATURN RANGER—60mm objective. 20X. Field at 100 yds., 10.4 ft. Relative brightness, 9. Eye relief, ⁹⁄₁₆". Wgt., 33 oz. Length closed, 15⁵⁄₁₆". Spiral adjustment of eyepiece. Chilford Arms **$54.50**

SATURN SCOUT—44mm objective. 20X. Field at 100 yds., 6.7 ft. Relative brightness, 4.84. Eye relief, ½". Wgt., 23 oz. Length closed, 13". Draw tube plus spiral focusing. Chilford Arms **$29.50**

SOUTHERN PRECISION MODEL 549—60mm objective and 5 eyepieces from 15X to 60X; extensible sunshade and folding tripod. Closed, 14¾", Wgt., 4¼ lbs. **$79.50**

SOUTHERN PRECISION MODEL 550—60mm objective and 4 turret-mounted eyepieces from 20X to 60X; ext. sunshade and folding tripod. Closed, 16¼", wgt., 5½ lbs. with tripod (included) **$75.00**

SOUTHERN PRECISION ZOOM MODEL 547—60mm objective, 25X to 50X; ext. sunshade folding tripod. Closed, 18", wgt. 4½ lbs. with tripod (included) **$69.50**

SOUTHERN PRECISION MODEL 546—50mm objective, 25X. Folding tripod, leather case included. Closed, 13", wgt. 3 lbs. **$27.00**

SWIFT TELEMASTER M841—60mm objective. 15X to 60X variable power. Field at 1000 yards 160 feet (15X) to 40 feet (60X). Wgt. 3.4 lbs. 17.6" over-all **$179.95**
Tripod for above **35.00**
Photo adapter **11.50**
Case for above **27.95**

SWIFT MODEL 821—60mm objective. 15X, 20X, 30X, 40X and 60X eyepieces included. Field at 100 yds., 158 to 32 ft. 18" tripod with friction clutch adj. handle. Length 13½" (without sunshade). 6 lbs. **$133.95**

TASCO 8TOZ—60mm objective. 20X to 60X variable power. Field at 1000 yards 158 feet (16X) to 40 feet (50X). Wgt. 4½ lbs. 18" overall .. **$79.95**

UNERTL RIGHT ANGLE—63.5mm objective. 24X. Field at 100 yds., 7 ft. Relative brightness, 6.96. Eye relief, ½". Wgt., 41 oz. Length closed, 19". Push-pull and screw-focus eyepiece. 16X and 32X eyepieces Priced at $18 each. **$110.00**

UNERTL STRAIGHT PRISMATIC—Same as Unertl Right Angle except: straight eyepiece and wgt. of 40 oz. **$92.00**

UNERTL 20X STRAIGHT PRISMATIC—54mm objective. 20X. Field at 100 yds., 8.5 ft. Relative brightness, 6.1. Eye relief, ½". Wgt., 36 oz. Length closed, 13½". Complete with lens covers **$74.00**

UNERTL TEAM SCOPE—100mm objective. 15X, 24X. 32X eyepieces. Field at 100 yds. 13 to 7.5 ft. Relative brightness, 39.06 to 9.79. Eye relief, 2" to 1½". Weight, 13 lbs. 29⅞" overall. Metal tripod, yoke and wood carrying case furnished (total weight, 80 lbs.) **$450.00**

WEATHERBY—60mm objective, 20X-45X zoom **$112.00**
Tripod for above **17.50**

SCOPE ATTACHMENTS

DAVIS TARGETEER—Objective lens/tube units that attach to front of low power scopes, increase magnification to 8X. 1¼" lens, **$25,** 1½" lens **$29.50**

HERMANN DUST CAPS—Connected leather straps, hand made, natural color. For all popular scopes. **$4.00**

LEE TACKHOLE DOTS—Various size dots for all scopes. Priced from .... **$7.50— $15.00**

LYMAN HAZE FILTER—For morning and late afternoon hunting. Filters out blue and violet rays allowing only the best part of the spectrum to transmit through your telescope lenses. For all reflescopes **$2.75**

PGS SCOPE SHIELDS—Flexible rubber, usable at front and rear, protect scopes from snow or rain. Made for all scopes. **$3.98**

PREMIER RETICLES—Various size dots for all scopes, also special reticles to order. Price—**$7.00** to **$18.50. PREMIER WEATHER CAPS**— transparent, high light transmission. For all popular scopes. Price **$3.50** Special sizes **$5.00**

RING MOUNTS—Custom made for German-type claw bases. Don's Gun Shop.

W. P. SIEBERT—Converts Lyman All-American and Weaver K model varmint scopes to 15X-20X. .... **$25.00-$30.00**

STORM KING LENS CAPS—A hinged glass-and-rubber protector set (2), made in various sizes for all scopes. May be unhinged or sighted through. Anderson Gun Shop. Per pair **$3.45**

VISS'S SUPREME LENS COVERS—Hinged protectors for most scope models, front and rear lenses shielded. E. D. Vissing Co. Price per pair, postpaid **$6.95**

SPOTTING SCOPE STANDS

DAVIDSON MARK 245—Bipod adjustable for elevation, 9½"-14½". Side mount with two straps. Black crinkle finish. total length folded 16½". Price **$23.95**

FREELAND ALL ANGLE—Tripod adjustable for elevation. Left or right side mount with worm drive clamp. Folding legs. Clamps available for any scope tube size. Black, gray, or green crinkle finish. Price **$22.75**
Also 12" 18", 24" extensions available **$3.00-5.00**

FREELAND OLYMPIC—Bipod adjustable for elevation. All angle mount with padded worm drive clamp. Folding legs. Clamps available for any scope tube size. Black, grey, or green crinkle finish. Price **$24.75**
Also 12", 18", 24" extensions available **$3.00-5.00**
Zoom head for tripod or bipod **$11.00**

FREELAND REGAL BIPOD—Choice of saddle or zoom head. All adjustment knobs are oversize for easy adjusting. Large "ball" carrying knob. Gray or green finish. **$26.75**
Above with stability weight **34.25**
Extensions 12"-24" **$3.00-5.00**

Shooting Publications

Write directly to the sources noted for titles listed and ask for their latest catalog. Do not order from the GUN DIGEST.

A Joint Resolution—A 4-page statement by the National Police Officers Assn. and the National Shooting Sports Foundation, outlining the role of firearms in U.S. history and voicing their stand against ill-planned restrictive gun laws. Free.[1]

Basic Pistol Marksmanship—Textbook for basic pistol courses. 25¢[2]

Basic Rifle Marksmanship—Textbook for basic rifle courses. 25¢ ea.[2]

The Elk—125-page report on the hunting and management of this game animal, more properly called *wapiti*. Extensive biblio. $1.00.[4]

Free Films—Brochure listing outdoor movies available to sportsmen's clubs. Free.[1]

The Gun Law Problem—Information about firearms legislation. Free.[2]

How to be a Crack Shot—A 14-page booklet detailing everything necessary to becoming an outstanding shot. Free.[3]

Fundamentals of Claybird Shooting—A 39-page booklet explaining the basics of Skeet and trap in non-technical terms. Many diagrams. 25¢ ea.[4]

Hunter Safety Instructor's Guide—How to conduct an NRA Hunter Safety Course. 25¢ ea.[2]

Hunting and Shooting Sportsmanship—A 4-page brochure defining the "true sportsman" and giving information on the outdoor field. Free.[1]

Junior Rifle Handbook—Information about the NRA junior program with short instruction course. (25 copies issued to each new affiliated junior club without charge.) 25¢ ea.[2]

NRA Hunter Safety Handbook—Textbook for students. 10¢ ea.[2]

National Shooting Preserve Directory—Up-to-date listing of small game preserves in the U.S. and Canada. Free.[1]

Game, Gunners and Biology—A thumbnail history of American wildlife conservation. 50¢ ea.[4]

Shooting's Fun for Everyone—The why, when, where, and how of riflery for boys and girls. 20 pp. 5¢ ea.[1]

Trap or Skeet Fundamentals—Handbooks explaining fundamentals of these two sports, complete with explicit diagrams to start beginners off right. Free.[3]

25 Foot Shooting Program—Complete information on a short range shooting program with CO^2 and pneumatic rifles and pistols. 35¢[2]

What Every Parent Should Know When a Boy or Girl Wants a Gun—Straightforward answers to the 15 questions most frequently asked by parents. 8 pp. 5¢ ea.[1]

The Cottontail Rabbit—56-page rundown on America's most popular hunting target. Where to find him, how to hunt him, how to help him. Bibliography included. $1.00 ea.[4]

For the Young Hunter—A 32-page booklet giving fundamental information on the sport. Single copies free, 15¢ each in bulk.[4]

Gray and Fox Squirrels—112-page paperbound illustrated book giving full rundown on the squirrel families named. Extensive bibliography. $1.00 ea.[4]

How to Have More Pheasant Hunting—A 16-page booklet on low cost hunting, including data on in-season stocking and how to start a small preserve. 25¢.[1]

The Mallard—80-page semi-technical report on this popular duck. Life cycle, laws and management, hunting—even politics as they affect this bird—are covered. Bibliography. $1.00 ea.[4]

NRA Booklets—Ranging from 12 to 36 pages, these are articles on specific arms or arms types. Titles available are: Sighting In; The 45 Automatic; The M1 Rifle; Telescopic Sights; Metallic Sights; Duck Hunting; U.S. Cal. 30 Carbine; Remodeling the 03A3; Remodeling the 303 Lee-Enfield; Remodeling the U.S. 1917 Rifle; M1903 Springfield Rifle; Military Rifles and Civil War Small Arms, 50¢ ea. Gun Cabinets, Racks, Cases & Pistol Boxes, 75¢. Deer Hunting, $1.00.[2]

Under the heading of "Range Plans" are 15 booklets priced from 10¢ to $1.00. All are described in an order form pamphlet available from the NRA.

NRA Digest of the Federal Gun Control Act of 1968—A 12-page booklet clearly explaining the new law and its provisions. Free to NRA members.[2]

NRA Federal Firearms Laws—A 28-page booklet digesting the several U.S. gun laws affecting the citizen today. Free to NRA members.[2]

NRA Firearms & Ammunition Fact Book—352-page book of questions and answers, ballistic charts and tables, descriptions of firearms and ammunition. NRA, Washington, D.C., 1964. $2.00 ea. ($1.75 to NRA members).

NRA Firearms Assembly Handbook, Volumes I and II—Articles describing the assembly and disassembly of various arms. Vol. I, 160 pp., covers 77 guns, Vol. II, 176 pp., 87 guns. Illustrated with exploded-view and supplementary drawings. NRA, Washington, D.C., 1960 and 1964. $3.50 ea. (2.50 to NRA members).

NRA Firearms Handling Handbook—21 major articles on the proper useage of most types of small arms available to civilians. Illus. NRA, Washington, D.C., 1962, 80 pp. $2.75 ($1.75 to NRA members).

NRA Gun Collectors Handbook—20 feature articles on all phases of gun collecting, plus a listing of all important museums. NRA, Washington, D.C., 1959. 48 pp., illus. $2.50 ($1.50 to NRA members).

NRA Handloader's Guide—Enlarged & Revised. A successor to the *NRA Illustrated Reloading Handbook*, this excellent new work covers all aspects of metallic-case and shotshell reloading. Washington, D. C., 1969, fully illus. $5.00 (NRA members, $4.00).

NRA Hunters Handbook—51 major pieces, 18 shorter ones. NRA, Washington, D.C., 1960. 72 pp., illus. $3.00 ($2.00 to NRA members).

NRA Illustrated International Shooting Handbook—18 major articles detailing shooting under ISU rules, training methods, etc. NRA, Washington, D.C., 1964. $2.50 ea. ($1.50 to NRA members).

NRA Illustrated Shotgun Handbook—50 articles covering every phase of smoothbore shooting, including exploded views of many shotguns. NRA, Washington, D.C. 1964. 128 pp. $3.00 ea. ($2.00 to NRA members).

NRA Questions and Answers Handbook—150 queries and replies on guns and shooting. NRA, Washington, D.C., 1959. 46 pp. with index, illus. $2.50 ($1.50 to NRA members).

NRA Shooters Guide—40 articles of high interest to shooters of all kinds. Over 340 illus. NRA, Washington, D.C., 1959. 72 pp., $3.00 ($2.00 to NRA members).

NRA Shooting Handbook—83 major articles plus 35 shorts on every phase of shooting. NRA, Washington, D.C., 1961. 224 pp., illus. $4.50 ($3.50 to NRA members).

Principles of Game Management—A 25-page booklet surveying in popular manner such subjects as hunting regulations, predator control, game refuges and habitat restoration. Single copies free, 15¢ each in bulk.[4]

The Ring-Necked Pheasant—Popular distillation of much of the technical literature on the "ringneck." 104-page paperbound book, appropriately illustrated. Bibliography included. $1.00 ea.[4]

Ruffed Grouse, by John Madson—108-page booklet on the life history, management and hunting of *Bonasa umbellus* in its numerous variations. Extensive biblio. $1.00.[4]

Start A Gun Club—All of the basic information needed to establish a club with clay bird shooting facilities. 24 pp. 50¢[1]

Where To Shoot Muzzle Loaders In The U.S.A.—Publ. for black powder burners, and lists more than 100 muzzle loading clubs. 10¢.[1]

The White-Tailed Deer—History, management, hunting—a complete survey in this 108-page paperbound book. Full bibliography. $1.00 ea.[4]

You and Your Lawmaker—A 22-page citizenship manual for sportsmen, showing how they can support or combat legislation affecting shooting and outdoor sports. 10¢ ea.[1]

[2]National Rifle Association of America, 1600 Rhode Island Ave., Washington, D. C. 20036

[3]Remington Arms Company, Dept. C—Bridgeport, Conn. 06602

[4]Olin Mathieson Conservation Dept., East Alton, Ill. 62024

[1]National Shooting Sports Foundation, Inc. 1075 Post Road, Riverside, Conn. 06878

Publishers: Please send review copies to John T. Amber, 20604 Collins Rd., Marengo, Ill. 60152

PERIODICAL PUBLICATIONS

Alaska Sportsman
Alaska Northwest Pub. Co., Box 4-EEE, Anchorage, Alaska 99503. $8.00 yr. Hunting and fishing articles.
American Field†
222 W. Adams St., Chicago, Ill. 60606. $9.00 yr. Field dogs and trials, occasional gun and hunting articles.
The American Rifleman (M)
National Rifle Assn., 1600 Rhode Island Ave., N.W., Wash., D.C. 20036. $7.50 yr. Firearms articles of all kinds.
The American West*
American West Publ. Co., 599 College Ave., Palo Alto, Ca. 94306. $9.00 yr.
Argosy
Popular Publ., Inc., 205 E. 42nd St., New York, N.Y. 10017. $7.00 yr.
Army (M)
Assn of the U.S. Army, 1529 18th Ave. N.W., Wash., D.C. 20036. $7.50 yr. Occasional articles on small arms
Australian Shooters' Journal
P.O. Box 90, Stafford, Brisbane, Qld., 4053 Australia. $5.50 yr. locally; $7.00 yr. overseas. Hunting and shooting articles.
Canadian Journal of Arms Collecting (Q)
Museums Restoration Service P.O. Box 2037, Sta. D, Ottawa, Ont., Canada. $4.00 yr.
Deutsches Waffen Journal
Journal-Verlag Schwend GmbH, Postfach 340, D7170 Schwabisch Hall, Germany. $11.50 yr. Antique and modern arms, their history, technical aspects, etc. German text.
Ducks Unlimited, Inc. (M)
P.O. Box 66300, Chicago, Ill. 60666.
Enforcement Journal (Q)
Natl. Police Officers Assn., Natl. Police Academy Bldg., 1890 S. Tamiami Trail, Venice, Fla. 33595. $6.00 yr.
The Field†
The Harmsworth Press Ltd., 8 Stratton St., London W.I., England. $29.50 yr. Hunting and shooting articles.
Field & Stream
Holt, Rinehart and Winston, Inc., 383 Madison Ave., New York, N.Y. 10017. $5.00 yr. Articles on firearms plus hunting and fishing.
Fishing and Hunting Guide
Fishing and Hunting Guide Ltd., P.O. Box 48, Dolton, Ill. 60419. $3.00 yr.
Fur-Fish-Game
A. R. Harding Pub. Co., 2878 E. Main St., Columbus, Ohio 43209. $3.50 yr. "Gun Rack" column by M. H. Decker.
The Gun Report
World Wide Gun Report, Inc., Box 111, Aledo, Ill. 61231. $6.00 yr. For the gun collector.
Gunsport & Gun Collector
The Clark Bldg., Suite 2100, Pittsburgh, PA 15222. Md. 20637. $5.00 yr.
Gun Week†
Sidney Printing & Publishing Co., P.O. Box 150, Sidney, Ohio 45365. $5.00 yr. U.S. and possessions; $6.00 yr. Canada; $7.00 yr. foreign. Tabloid paper on guns, hunting, shooting.
Gun World
Gallant Publishing Co., 130 Olinda Pl., Brea, Calif. 92621. $7.50 yr. For the hunting, reloading and shooting enthusiast.
Guns & Ammo
Petersen Pub. Co., 8490 Sunset Blvd., Los Angeles, Calif. 90069. $7.50 yr. Guns, shooting, and technical articles.
Guns
Guns Magazine, 8150 N. Central Park Ave., Skokie, Ill. 60076. $7.50 yr. Articles for gun collectors, hunters and shooters.
Guns Review
Ravenhill Pub. Co. Ltd., Standard House, Bonhill St., London E.C. 2, England. $10.20 yr. For collectors and shooters.
The Handgunner (M)
U.S. Revolver Assn., 59 Alvin St., Springfield, Mass. 01104. $5.00 yr. General handgun and competition articles.
The Handloader Magazine*
Dave Wolfe Pub. Co., Box 3030, Prescott, Ariz. 86301 $7.00 yr.
Hobbies
Lightner Pub. Co., 1006 S. Michigan Ave., Chicago, Ill. 60605. $6.00 yr.; Canada $7.00; foreign $7.50. Collectors departments.
International Shooting Sport*
Union Internationale de Tir, 62 Wiesbaden-Klarenthal, Klarenthalerstr., Germany. $6.00 yr., p.p. For the International target shooter.
The Journal of the Arms & Armour Society (M)
F. Wilkinson (Secy.), 40 Great James St., Holborn, London WC1, England. $4.00 yr. Articles for the collector.
Law and Order
Law and Order Magazine, 37 W. 38th St., New York, N.Y. 10018. $7.00 yr. Articles on weapons for law enforcement.
The Luger Journal
Robt. B. Marvin, Publ., P.O. Box 326, Jasper, FL 32052. $6.00 yr.

Muzzle Blasts (M)
National Muzzle Loading Rifle Assn. P.O. Box 67, Friendship, Ind. 47021. $6.00 yr. For the black powder shooter.
National Rifle Assn. Journal (British)
Natl. Rifle Assn. (BR.), Bisley Camp, Brookwood, Woking, Surrey, England.
National Sportsman's Digest
National Sportsman's Club, Box 2003, Dallas, Tex. 75221. $8.00 yr. Subs. includes membership in the Club, etc.
National Wildlife*
Natl. Wildlife Fed. Inc., 1412 16th St. N.W., Washington, D.C. $6.00 yr. World/Assoc. membership *includes Intl. Wildlife;* 12 issues $11.00.
New Zealand Wildlife (Q)
New Zealand Deerstalkers Assoc. Inc., P.O. Box 263, Wellington, N.Z. $2.00 U.S. and Canada, elsewhere on application. Hunting and shooting articles.
Ordnance* (M)
American Ordnance Assn., 819 Union Trust Bldg., Wash., D.C. 20005. $8.00 yr. Occasional articles on small arms and related subjects.
Outdoor Life
Popular Science Pub. Co., 355 Lexington Ave., New York, N.Y. 10017. $6.00 yr. Arms column by Jim Carmichel.
Outdoor World*
Country Beautiful Corp., 24198 W. Bluemound Rd., Waukesha, Wis. 53186. $7.95 yr. Conservation and wildlife articles.
Police Times (M)
1100 N.E. 125th St., No. Miami, Fla. 33161.
Popular Mechanics
Hearst Corp., 224 W. 57th St., New York, N.Y. 10019. $5.00 yr., $5.75 Canada, $7.00 foreign. Hunting and shooting articles.
Precision Shooting
Precision Shooting, Inc., 8 Cline St., Dolgeville, N.Y. 13329. $5.00 yr. Journal of the International Benchrest Shooters.
The Rifle Magazine*
Dave Wolfe Publishing Co., Box 3030, Presott, Ariz. 86301. $9.00 yr. Journal of the NBRSA.
The Rifleman (Q)
National Smallbore Rifle Assoc., 113 Southwark St., London, S. E. 1, Englnd. $7.00 (5 yrs.). Data on British Matches and International Matches, and technical shooting articles.
Rod and Gun in Canada
Rod and Gun Pub. Corp., 1219 Hotel deVille, Montreal 129, P.Q. Canada. $3.00 yr., $5.00 2 yrs., out of Canada, postage $1.00 p. yr. extra. Regular gun and shooting articles.
Saga
Gambi Public., 333 Johnson Ave., Brooklyn, N.Y. 11026. $6.00 yr. U.S., $6.50 Canada.
The Shooting Industry
Publisher's Dev. Corp., 8150 N. Central Pk., Skokie, Ill. 60076. $7.00 yr.
The Shooting Times & Country Magazine (England) †
Cordwallis Estate, Clivemont Rd., Maidenhead, Berksh., England. $20 yr. Game shooting, wild fowling and firearms articles.
Shooting Times
PJS Publications, News Plaza, Peoria, Ill., 61601 $5.85 yr. Gun ads plus articles on every gun activity.
The Shotgun News‡
Snell Publishing Co., Columbus, Nebr. 68601. $4.00 yr. Sample copy 50¢. Gun ads of all kinds.
The Skeet Shooting Review
National Skeet Shooting Assn., 212 Linwood Bldg., 2608 Inwood Rd., Dallas. Tex. 75235. $9.00 yr. (Assn. membership of $10.00 includes mag.) Scores, averages, skeet articles.
Sporting Goods Business
Gralla Publications, 1501 Broadway, New York, NY 10063. Trade journal.
The Sporting Goods Dealer
1212 No. Lindbergh Blvd., St. Louis, Mo. 63166. $4.00 yr. The sporting goods trade journal.
Sports Afield
The Hearst Corp., 250 W. 55th St., New York, N.Y. 10019. $5.00 yr. Pete Brown on firearms plus hunting and fishing articles.
Sports Age Magazine
3000 France Ave. So., Minneapolis, Minn. 55416. Trade journal.
Sports Illustrated†
Time, Inc., 541 N. Fairbanks Court, Chicago, Ill. 60611. $12.00 yr. U.S. Poss. and Canada; $16.00 yr. all other countries. Articles on the current sporting scene.
Trap & Field
1100 Waterway Blvd., Indianapolis, Ind. 46202. $7.00 yr. Official publ. Amateur Trapshooting Assn. Scores, averages, trapshooting articles.
True
Fawcett Publ., Inc., Fawcett Bldg., Greenwich, Conn. 06830. $7.00 yr. U.S. Poss., and Canada; $10.00 yr. all other countries.
Wildlife Review (Q)
Fish & Wildlife Branch. Dep't of Rec. and Conservation Parliament Bldgs., Victoria, B.C., Canada $1.00 yr.

---

* Published bi-monthly
† Published weekly
‡ Published twice per month.

M Membership requirements; write for details.
Q Published Quarterly.
All others are published monthly.

ARMS ASSOCIATIONS IN AMERICA AND ABROAD

UNITED STATES

ALABAMA

Alabama Gun Collectors Assn.
Thomas M. Stewart, 601 Eastwood Pl., Birmingham, Ala. 35216
North Alabama Gun Coll. Assn.
P.O. Box 564, Huntsville, Ala. 35804

ARIZONA

Arizona Gun Collectors
Miles S. Vaughn, 1129 S. 6th Ave., Tucson, Ariz. 85701
Arms Collectors of the Southwest
Robert Kuban, Box 543, Yuma, Ariz. 85364
International Cartridge Coll. Assn., Inc.
A. D. Amesbury, 4065 Montecito Ave., Tucson, Ariz. 85711
National Reloading Mfrs. Assn., Inc.
Box 1697, Prescott, Ariz. 86301

ARKANSAS

Arkansas Gun & Cartridge Coll. Club
M. Cutrell, 2006 E. 7th, Pine Bluff, Ark. 71601
Ft. Smith Dealers & Coll. Assn.
Tony Smith, 1407 57 Terrace, Ft. Smith, Ark. 72901

CALIFORNIA

Calif. Hunters & Gun Owners Assoc.
V. H. Wacker, 2309 Cipriani Blvd., Belmont, Cal. 94002
Greater Calif. Arms & Collectors Assn.
Donald L. Bullock, 8291 Carburton St., Long Beach, Cal. 90808
Los Angeles Gun & Ctg. Collectors Assn.
F. H. Ruffra, 20810 Amie Ave., Torrance, CA 90503
Northern California Historical Arms Coll. Assn.
Julia Lundwall, 25 Mizpah St., San Francisco Ca. 94131
San Bernardino Valley Arms Collectors, Inc.
F. Schaperkotter, 2697 Acacia Ave., San Bernardino, Cal. 92405
Santa Barbara Antique Arms Coll. Assn., Inc.
Tom McKissack, P.O. Box 6291, Santa Barbara, CA. 93111
Southern California Arms Collectors Assn.
Frank E. Barnyak, 4204 Elmer Ave., No. Hollywood, Cal. 91602
U. S. International Trap and Skeet Assn.
Box 1437, Huntington Beach, CA. 92647

COLORADO

Arapahoe Gun Collectors
Bill Rutherford, 2968 S. Broadway, Englewood, Colo. 80110
Colorado Gun Collectors Assn.
Arnie Dowd, 5970 Estes Ct., Arvada, Colo. 80002
Pikes Peak Gun Collectors Guild
Charles Cell, 406 E. Uintah St., Colorado Springs, Colo. 80903

CONNECTICUT

Antique Arms Coll. Assn. of Conn.
A. Darling, 35 Stanley St., New Haven, Conn. 06511
National Shooting Sports Fdtn., Inc.
Warren Page, President, 1075 Post Rd., Riverside, Conn. 06878
Stratford Gun Collectors Assn., Inc.
P.O. Box 52, Stratford, Conn. 06497
Ye Conn. Gun Guild, Inc.
Rob. L. Harris, P.O. Box 67, Cornwall Bridge, Conn. 06754

DELAWARE

Delaware Antique Arms Collectors
C. Landis, 2408 Duncan Rd., Wilmington, Del. 19808

DISTRICT OF COLUMBIA

American Military Inst.
Box 568, Washington, D.C. 20044
American Ordnance Assn.
819 Union Trust Bldg., Washington, D.C. 20005
National Rifle Assn.
1600 Rhode Island Ave., Washington, D.C. 20036

FLORIDA

American Police Pistol & Rifle Assn.
1100 N.E. 125th St., No. Miami, Fl. 33161 (law enforcement members only).
Florida Gun Collectors Assn.
Bob Marvin, P.O. Box 470, Jasper, Fla. 32052
National Police Officers Assn. of America
Natl. Police Hall of Fame Bldg., Venice, Fla. 33595
Tampa Bay Gun Collectors Assn.
Col. Emmet M. Jeffreys, 401 49th St., N., St. Petersburg, Fla. 33710

GEORGIA

Georgia Arms Collectors
James F. Watterson, 2915 Paces Lake Ct., N.W., Atlanta, Ga. 30339

ILLINOIS

Central Illinois Gun Collectors Assn., Inc.
Donald E. Bryan, R.R. #2, Jacksonville, Ill. 62650
Fort Dearborn Frontiersmen
Al Normath, 8845 Pleasant Ave., Hickory Hills, IL 60457
Fox Valley Arms Fellowship, Inc.
Graham Burnside, 203 Oregon Ave., Dundee, Ill. 60118
Illinois State Rifle Assn.
2800 N. Milwaukee Ave., Chicago, Ill. 60618
Illinois Gun Collectors Assn.
P. E. Pitts, P.O. Box 1524, Chicago, Ill. 60690
Little Fort Gun Collectors Assn.
Ernie Robinson, P.O. Box 194, Gurney, Ill. 60031
Mississippi Valley Gun & Cartridge Coll. Assn.
Mel Sims, Box 426, New Windsor, Ill. 61465
Sauk Trail Gun Collectors
L. D. Carlock, Rte. 1, Box 169, Prophetstown, Ill. 61277
Wabash Valley Gun Collectors Assn., Inc.
Mrs. Betty Baer, 1002 Lincoln Pk. Ave., Danville, Ill. 61832

INDIANA

American Single Shot Rifle Assn.
G. H. Crontz, 11439 Wicker Ave., Cedar Lake, Ind. 46303
Central Indiana Gun Coll. Assn.
Paul E. Daugherty, 421 E. Washington St., Hartford City, Ind. 47348
Crawfordsville Gun Club, Inc.
Rob. J. K. Edmonds, R.R. 2, Crawfordsville, Ind. 47933
Midwest Gun Traders Inc.
Glen Wittenberger, 4609 Oliver St., Ft. Wayne, IN 46806
National Muzzle Loading Rifle Assn.
Box 67, Friendship, Ind. 47021
Northern Indiana Gun Collectors Assn.
Joe Katona, 16150 Ireland Rd., Mishawaka, Ind. 46544
Southern Indiana Gun Collectors Assn., Inc.
Harold M. McClary, 509 N. 3rd St., Boonville, Ind. 47601
Tippecanoe Gun and Cartridge Collectors Club
Leonard Ledman, RR 12, Box 212, Lafayette, Ind.

IOWA

Cedar Valley Gun Coll.
R. L. Harris, 1602 Wenig Rd., N.E., Cedar Rapids, Iowa 52402
Central States Gun Collectors Assn.
Chas. J. Versluis, 701 Broadway, Watterloo, IA 50703
Eastern Iowa Gun and Cartridge Collectors Assn.
F. Fitzpatrick, 305 N. Eliza St., Maquoketa, IA. 52060
Quad City Arms Coll. Assn.
A. Squire, 1845 W. 3rd St., Davenport, IA. 52802

KANSAS

Chisholm Trail Antique Gun Coll. Assn.
P.O. Box 13093, Wichita, Kans. 67213
Four State Collectors Assn.
M. G. Wilkinson, 915 E. 10th, Pittsburgh, Kan. 66762
Kansas Cartridge Coll. Assn.
Bob Linder, Box 84, Plainville, Kans. 67663
Missouri Valley Arms Collectors Assn.
Chas. P. Samuel, Jr., Box 8204, Shawnee Mission, Kans. 66208
Solomon Valley Gun Collectors
Frank Wheeler, Box 230, Osborne, Kan. 67473

KENTUCKY

John Hunt Morgan Gun Coll. Inc.
P.O. Box 525, Paris, Ky. 40361
Kentuckiana Arms Coll. Assn.
Charles R. Phelps, Box 1776, Louisville, Ky. 40201
Kentucky Gun Collectors Assn., Inc.
J. A. Smith, Box 64, Owensboro, Ky. 42301

LOUISIANA

Ark-La-Tex Gun Collectors Assn.
Ray Franks, 1521 Earl St., Shreveport, La. 71108
Bayou Gun Club
John West, 825 Ida, New Orleans, La.
Pelican Arms Collectors
B. Thompson, 9142 Cefalu Dr., Baton Rouge, La. 70811

MARYLAND

Cumberland Valley Arms Collectors Assn.
Mrs. S. Naylor, Rte. #2, Hagerstown, Md. 21740
Maryland Arms Coll. Assn., Inc.
H. R. Moale, 2602 Hillcrest Ave., Baltimore, Md. 21234
Penn-Mar-Va Antique Arms Soc.
T. Wibberley, 54 E. Lincoln Ave., Hagerstown, Md. 21740
Potomac Arms Collectors Assn.
Bill Summerfelt, P.O. Box 93, Riverdale, Md. 20840

MASSACHUSETTS

Bay Colony Weapons Collectors Inc.
Ronald B. Santurjian, 47 Homer Rd., Belmont, Mass. 02178
Massachusetts Arms Collectors
John J. Callan, Jr., 15 Montague St., Worcester, Mass. 01603
U. S. Revolver Assn.
Stanley A. Sprague, 59 Alvin St., Springfield, Mass. 01104

MICHIGAN

Michigan Antique Arms Coll., Inc.
W. H. Heid, 8914 Borgman Ave., Huntington Woods, Mich. 48070
Michigan Rifle & Pistol Assn.
John W. Novitch, 124 Moss Ave., Highland Park, Mich. 48203
Royal Oak Gun Collectors
Margaret Parker, 13143 Borgmann, Huntington Woods, Mich. 48070

MINNESOTA

Minnesota Weapons Coll. Assn., Inc.
W. Nemitz, 1069 S. Crestview Dr., St. Paul, MN. 55119
Twin Ports Weapons Collectors
Jack Puglisi, 6504 Lexington St., Duluth, MN. 55807

MISSISSIPPI

Dixie Arms Collectors
Ruth Creecy, 1509 W. 7th, Hattiesburg, Miss. 39401
Mississippi Gun Collectors Assn.
Mrs. J. E. Swinney, Box 1332, Hattiesburg, Miss. 39401

MISSOURI

Edwardsville, Ill. Gun Collectors
A. W. Stephensmeier, 317 N. Grand Bl., St. Louis, Mo. 63103
Meramec Valley Gun Collectors
L. W. Olson, Star Route, St. Clair, Mo.
Mineral Belt Gun Coll. Assn.
G. W. Gunter, 1110 E. Cleveland Ave., Monett, Mo. 65708

MONTANA

Montana Arms Collectors Assn.
Chris Sorensen, 175 6th Ave., W.N. Kalispell, Mont. 59901
North American Sportsmen's Assn.
Box 1943—2501 4th Ave. N., Billings, Mont. 59103

NEBRASKA

Nebraska Gun & Cartridge Collectors
E. M. Zalud, 710 West 6th St., North Platte, Neb. 69101
Pine Ridge Gun Coll.
Loren Pickering, 509 Elm St., Crawford, Neb. 69339

NEW MEXICO

New Mexico Gun Collectors Assn.
P.O. Box 14145, Albuquerque, NM. 87111
Santa Fe Gun Collec. Assn.
Ernie Lang, 1085 Nugget, Los Alamos, N.M. 87544

NEW HAMPSHIRE

Maple Tree Gun Coll. Assn.
E. P. Hector, Meriden Rd., Lebanon, N.H. 03766
New Hampshire Arms Collectors Inc.
James Tillinghast, Box 5, Marlow, N.H. 03456

NEW JERSEY

Experimental Ballistics Associates
Ed Yard, 110 Kensington, Trenton, N.J. 08618
Jersey Shore Antique Arms Collectors
Bob Holloway, 1755 McGallard Ave., Trenton, N.J. 08610
New Jersey Arms Collectors Club, Inc.
Joseph Rixon, 122 Bender Ave., Roselle Park, N.J. 07204

NEW YORK

Armor & Arms Club
J. K. Watson, 51 W. 51st St., New York, N.Y. 10019
Fort Lee Arms Collectors
W. E. Sammis, R.D. 776 Brookridge Dr., Valley Cottage, N.Y. 10989
Hudson-Mohawk Arms Collectors Assn., Inc.
Bennie S. Pisarz, 108 W. Main St., Frankfort, N.Y. 13340
International Benchrest Shooters
Emory L. Tooly, 8 Cline St., Dolgeville, N.Y. 13329
Iroquois Arms Collectors Assn.
Dennis Freeman, 12144 McNeeley Rd., Akron, N.Y. 14001
Long Island Antique Gun Coll. Assn.
Frank Davison, 8 Johnson Pl., Baldwin, N.Y. 11510
Mid-State Arms Coll. & Shooters Club
Bennie S. Pisarz, 108 W. Main St., Frankfort, N.Y. 13340
New York State Arms Collectors Assn., Inc.
Marvin Salls, R. D. 1,Ilion, N.Y. 13357
Sporting Arms and Ammunition Manufacturers' Inst.
420 Lexington Ave., N.Y., N.Y. 10017
Westchester Arms Collectors Club, Inc.
F. E. Falkenbury, Jr., Secy., 75 Hillcrest Rd., Hartsdale, N.Y. 10530

NORTH CAROLINA

Carolina Gun Collectors Assn.
N. C. Bill Harvey, P.O. Box 464, Wilson, N.C. 27893

OHIO

Amateur Trap Shooting Assn.
P.O. Box 246, Vandalia, O. 45377
American Society of Arms Collectors, Inc.
Rob. F. Rubendunst, 6550 Baywood Ln., Cincinnati, O. 45224
Barberton Gun Collectors Assn.
R. N. Watters, 1108 Bevan St., Barberton, O. 44203
Central Ohio Gun and Indian Relic Coll. Assn.
Coyt Stookey, 134 E. Ohio Ave., Washington C.H., O. 43160
Lakeshore Gun Collectors
R. N. Watters, 1108 Bevan St., Barberton, Ohio 44203
Maumee Valley Gun Collectors Assn.
J. Jennings, 3450 Gallatin Rd., Toledo, O. 43606
National Bench Rest Shooters Assn., Inc.
Bernice McMullen, 607 W. Line St., Minerva, O. 44657
Ohio Gun Collectors, Assn., Inc.
Mrs. C. D. Rickey, 130 S. Main St., Prospect, O. 43342
The Stark Gun Collectors, Inc.
Russ E. McNary, 147 Miles Ave., N.W., Canton, O. 44708
Tri-State Gun Collectors
Doyt S. Gamble, 1115 N. Main St., Lima, OH 45801

OKLAHOMA

Indian Territory Gun Collectors Assn.
P.O. Box 4491, Tulsa, Okla. 74104

OREGON

Jefferson State Arms Collectors
Art Chipman, 2251 Ross Lane, Medford, Ore. 97501
Oregon Arms Coll. Assn. Inc.
Dick Hamilton, P.O. Box 152, Junction City, OR 97448
Willamette Valley Arms Coll. Assn.
M. Brooks, 2110 W. 20th, Eugene, Ore. 97405

PENNSYLVANIA

Boone & Crockett Club
C/O Carnegie Museum, 4400 Forbes Ave., Pittsburgh, Pa. 15213
Central Penn Antique Arms Assn.
Geo. Smithgall, 549 W. Lemon St., Lancaster, Pa. 17603
Forks of the Delaware Weapons Assn., Inc.
John F. Scheid, 348 Bushkill St., Easton, Pa. 18042
Lancaster Muzzle Loading Rifle Assn.
James H. Frederick, Jr., R.D. 1, Box 447, Columbia, Pa. 17512
Northern Tier Antique Gun Collectors
Cliff Breidinger, Trout Run, Pa. 17771
Pennsylvania Antique Gun Collectors Assn.
Zenas H. Hoover, 222 Phila. St., Indiana, PA 15701
Pennsylvania Gun Collectors Assn.
Arch Waugh, RD 2, Washington, Pa. 15301
Presque Isle Gun Collectors Assn.
James Welch, 156 E. 37th St., Erie, Pa. 16506
Somerset Rifle & Pistol Club
J. Richard Ross, 2 Stein Bldg., Somerset, Pa. 15501
Two Lick Valley Gun Collectors
Zenas Hoover, 222 Phila. St., Indiana, Pa. 15701

SOUTH CAROLINA

Belton Gun Club Inc.
J. K. Phillips, P.O. Box 605, Belton S.C. 29627
Natl. Arms Coll. Assn., Inc.
Jim McNelley, Box 1462, Columbia, S.C. 29201
South Carolina Arms Coll. Assn.
J. W. McNelley, 3215 Lincoln St., Columbia, S.C. 29201

SOUTH DAKOTA

Dakota Territory Gun Coll. Assn., Inc.
H. A. Jons, 1711 W. 12th St., Sioux Falls, So. Dak. 57104

TENNESSEE

Memphis Antique Weapons Assn.
F. Dauser, 3429 Jenkins, Memphis, Tenn. 38118
Memphis Gun Collectors Assn.
R. L. Haley, 3888 S. Lakewood Dr., Memphis, TN 38128
Smoky Mountain Gun Collectors Assn.
P.O. Box 22, Oak Ridge, Tenn. 37830
Tennessee Gun Collectors Assn., Inc.
M. H. Parks, 3556 Pleasant Valley Rd., Nashville, Tenn. 37204

TEXAS

Alamo Arms Collectors
Bill Brookshire, 410 Rector, San Antonio, Tex. 78216
Houston Gun Collectors Assn.
C. McKim, 5454 Stillbrooke, Houston, Tex. 77035
National Skeet Shooting Assn.
James M. Leer, Jr., 212 Linwood Bldg., 2608 Inwood Rd., Dallas, Tex. 75235
National Sportsman's Club
P.O. Box 2003, Dallas, Tex. 75221
Paso Del Norte Gun Collectors Inc.
Ken Hockett, 1216 Mescalero, El Paso, Tex. 79925
Permian Basin Rifle & Pistol Club, Inc.
E. L. Good, Box 459, Midland, Tex. 79701
Pioneer Gun Collectors Assn.
J. O. Wingate, 4611 Cherokee, Amarillo, Tex. 79109
Sabine Gun Collectors Club
Mrs. Irene Vivier, 1042 Iowa, Beaumont, Tex. 77705
Texas Gun Collectors Assn.
Mrs. Taska Clark, 3119 Produce Row, Houston, TX 77023
Waco Gun Collectors
C. V. Pruitt, 4021 N. 26th, Waco, Tex. 76708

UTAH

Utah Gun Collectors Assn.
S. Gerald Keogh, 875 20th St., Ogden, Utah 84401

VIRGINIA

North-South Skirmish Assn.
John L. Rawls, P.O. Box 114, McLean, Va. 22101
Shenandoah Valley Gun Coll. Assn.
Daniel E. Blye, P.O. Box 926, Winchester, Va. 22601
Virginia Arms Collectors & Assn.
W. H. Bacon, 4601 Sylvan Rd., Richmond, Va. 23225

WASHINGTON

Washington Arms Collectors, Inc.
Don Zwicker, 446 Pelly Ave., Renton, WA 98055

WISCONSIN

Chippewa Valley Weapons Collectors
J. M. Sullivan, 504 Ferry St., Eau Claire, Wis. 54701
Great Lakes Weapons Coll. Assn., Inc.
E. Warnke, 2249A N. 61 St., Wauwatosa, Wis. 53213
Wisconsin Gun Collectors Assn., Inc.
Rob. Zellmer, W180N8996 Leona Lane, Menomonee Falls, WI. 53051

WYOMING

Wyoming Gun Collectors
Bob Funk, 224 N. 2W., Riverton, Wyo. 82501

AUSTRALIA

Nat'l. Sporting Shooters' Assn. of Australia
G. O. Nelis, P.O. Box 90, Stafford, Brisbane, Qld., Australia 4053

CANADA

ALBERTA

Canadian Historical Arms Society
P.O. Box 901, Edmonton, Alb., Canada T5J 2L8

ONTARIO

Niagara Arms Collectors
Box 948, Beamsville, Ont. Canada
Ontario Arms Collectors Assn.
P. Peddle, 174 Ellerslie Ave., Willowdale, Ont., Canada
Oshawa Antique Gun Coll. Inc.
Gordon J. Dignem, 613 Rosmere St., Oshawa, Ont., Canada

QUEBEC

Lower Canada Arms Collectors Assn.
Secretary, P.O. Box 1162, St. B. Montreal 101, Quebec, Can.

EUROPE

ENGLAND

Arms and Armour Society of London
F. Wilkinson, 40 Great James St., Holborn, London, W.C.I.
Muzzle Loaders' Assn. of Great Britain
M. A. Malet, 43 Sandpit Lane, St. Albans, Hertfs, England
National Rifle Assn. (British)
Bisley Camp, Brookwood, Woking, Surrey, England

FRANCE

Les Arquebusiers de France,
Mme, Marckmann, 70 Rue des Chantiers, 78-Versailles, France

NEW ZEALAND

New Zealand Deerstalkers Assn.
J. M. Murphy, P.O. Box 263, Wellington, New Zealand

SOUTH AFRICA

Historical Firearms Soc. of South Africa
"Minden" 11 Buchan Rd., Newlands, Cape Town, South Africa

The Arms Library for
COLLECTOR · HUNTER · SHOOTER · OUTDOORSMAN

A selection of books—old, new and forthcoming—for everyone in the arms field, with a brief description by . . . RAY RILING

ballistics and handloading

Ballistics in the Seventeenth Century, by A. R. Hall. 1st J. & J. Harper ed. 1969 [from the Cambridge University Press ed. of 1952]. 186 pp., illus., with tables and diagrams. $13.50.
    A profound work for advanced scholars, this is a study in the relations of science and war, with reference principally to England.
The Bullet's Flight, from Powder to Target, by F. W. Mann. Ray Riling Arms Books Co., Phila., PA, 1965. A reprint of the very scarce original work of 1909. Introduction by Homer S. Powley, 384 pp. illus. $12.50.
    One of the best known and scholarly-developed works on basic ballistics.
Cartridges, by Cyril Waterworth. Farleigh Press Lindfield, N.S.W. 2070, Australia, N.D. 80 pp., illus. $1.50.
    Rifle, handgun and collectors cartridges are shown and briefly described, but no prices are given.
Cartridges of the World, by Frank C. Barnes, John T. Amber ed., Digest Books, Inc., Northfield, IL, 1972. 8½"x11", 378 pp. Profusely illus. Paperbound. $6.95.
    The third edition of a comprehensive reference for hunters, collectors, handloaders and ballisticians. Covering over 1000 cartridges, loads, components, etc., from all over the world.
Centerfire American Rifle Cartridges, 1892-1963, by Ray Bearse, A. S. Barnes & Co., S. Brunswick, NJ, 1966. 198 pp., illus. $6.98.
    Identification manual covering caliber, introduction date, origin, case type, etc. Self-indexed and cross-referenced. Headstamps and line drawings are included.
Centerfire Pistol and Revolver Cartridges, by H. P. White, B. D. Munhall and Ray Bearse. A. S. Barnes, NY, 1967, 85 pp. plus 170 pp., illus. $10.00.
    A new and revised edition covering the original Volume I, Centerfire Metric Pistol and Revolver Cartridges and Volume II, Centerfire American and British Pistol and Revolver Cartridges, by White and Munnall, formerly known as Cartridge Identification.
Complete Guide to Handloading, by Phil Sharpe. Funk & Wagnalls, NYC, 1953 (3rd ed., 2nd rev.) 734 pp., profusely illustrated, numerous line and halftone charts, tables, lists, etc., $10.00.
    The bible of handloaders ever since its first appearance in 1937, but badly dated now.
Handbook for Shooters and Reloaders, by P. O. Ackley, Salt Lake City, UT, 1970. *Vol. 1,* 567 pp., illus. $9.00. *Vol. II,* a new printing with specific new material. 495 pp., illus. $9.00. Both volumes $17.50.
Handloader's Digest, ed. by John T. Amber. Digest Books, Inc., Northfield, IL, 1972. 320 pp., very well illus., stiff paper covers. $5.95.
    This 6th edition contains the latest data on ballistics, maximum loads, new tools, equipment, reduced loads, etc., plus a fully illus. catalog section, current prices and specifications.
Home Guide to Cartridge Conversions, by Geo. C. Nonte, Jr., Stackpole Books, Harrisburg, PA, 1967. 404 pp., illus. $8.95.
    A new, revised and enlarged ed. of instructions, charts and tables for making ammunition no longer available, or which has become too expensive on the commercial market.
Hornady Handbook of Cartridge Reloading. Hornady Mfg. Co., Grand Island, Nebr., 1967. 360 pp., illus. $3.50.
    Handloader's reference, with much detail on projectiles, ballistics, etc., on many popular U.S. and imported firearms. An excellent work with particularly needed ballistic detail.
The Identification of Firearms and Forensic Ballistics, by G. Burrard. A. S. Barnes, New York, 1962. 217 pp., illus. $3.95.
    A standard, reliable, authoritative English work in the criminal-legal field of ballistics.
Interior Ballistics, How a Gun Converts Chemical Energy to Projectile Motion, by E. D. Lowry. Doubleday and Co., NY, 1968. 168 pp., including index and bibliography., illus. with 4 halftones and 17 line drawings. $4.50.
    An introduction to the history of small arms and weapons relative to the science of internal ballistics, especially for the layman and student.
Lee Reloading Handbook, by R. Lee, Lee Custom Engineering, Hartford, WI. 98 pp., illus. Paper, 98¢.
    Manual on reloading ammunition of various types.
Lyman Handbook No. 45. Lyman Gunsight Corp., Middlefield, CT, 1967. $3.50.
    Latest edition of a favorite reference for ammunition handloaders, whether novice or veteran.
Lyman Shotshell Handbook, ed. by Jim Sheridan. Lyman Gunsight Corp., Middlefield, CT, 1969. 160 pp., illus. $3.00.
    Covers reloading of all gauges, shell lengths, brands, types, etc., including reference section.
Make Muzzle Loader Accessories, by R. H. McCrory, R. H. McCory, Publ., 1971, 46 pp. Paper $2.25.
    A revised 2nd ed. covering over 20 items from powderhorns to useful tools. Well illus.

The NRA Handloader's Guide. Ashley Halsey, Jr., ed. Nat'l Rifle Assn., Washington, DC, 1969, 312 pp., illus., paperbound. $5.00.
    Revised edition of a reloading handbook, based on material published in *The American Rifleman.*
Pocket Manual for Shooters and Reloaders, by P. O. Ackley. publ. by author, Salt Lake City, UT, 1964. 176 pp., illus., spiral bound. $3.50.
    Good coverage on standard and wildcat cartridges and related firearms in popular calibers.
Principles and Practice of Loading Ammunition, by Lt. Col. Earl Naramore. Stackpole Books, Harrisburg, PA, 1954. 915 text pages, 240 illustrations. $14.95.
    Actually two volumes in one. The first part (565 pp.) deals with ballistics and the principles of cartridge making—and the chemistry, metallurgy, and physics involved. The second part (350 pp.) is a thorough discussion of the mechanics of loading cartridges. 1967 printing.
Professional Loading of Rifle, Pistol and Shotgun Cartridges ..., by G. L. Herter, Waseca, MN, 1970. 830 pp., illus. $7.50.
    Detailed technical loading information on small arms ammunition, with related articles on firearms and their use. A "condensed" paper-cover version of the above, 430 pp., illus. $4.50.
Reloading Simplified, 5th ed., by Cyril Waterworth. Farleigh Pres, Lindfield, N.S.W. 2070 Australia, 1970. 120 pp., illus. Paper, $1.50.
    Australia's only handloading manual—and an excellent one—it covers rifles, handguns and shotgun loading, plus how-to-do-it chapters.
Shooter's Bible Black Powder Guide, by George Nonte, Shooter's Bible, Inc., S. Hackensack, NJ, 1969. 214 pp., well illus. $3.95.
    Information on black powder weapons, ammunition, shooting, etc.
Shooter's Bible Reloader's Guide, 2nd ed., by R. A. Steindler. Shooter's Bible, Inc., S. Hackensack, NJ, 1968, 220 pp., fully illus. $3.95.
    Comprehensive coverage of technology and methods of handloading all types of small arms ammunition. This is a useful work.
Shotshell Handbook, by Lyman Handbook Staff. Lyman Gunsight Corp., Middlefield, CT, 1969. 160 pp., illus., stiff paper spiral-binding. $3.00.
    The first book devoted exclusively to shotshell reloading. Considers: gauge, shell length, brand, case, loads, buckshot, etc., plus excellent reference section. Some color illus.
Small Arms Ammunition Identification Guide. Normount Tech. Pub., Forest Grove, OR, 1971. 151 pp., illus. Paper, $3.00.
    A reprint of the guide originally published as FSTC-CW-07-02-66, revised.
Small Arms Ammunition Identification Guide, An Army Intelligence Document, Paladin Press, Boulder, CO, 1972. 254 pp., illus. Paper, $5.00.
    An exact reprint of FSTC-CW-7068, 1969 updated. An identification guide for most countries.
Speer Manual for Reloading Ammunition No. 8. Speer, Inc., Lewiston, ID, 1970. 382 pp., illus. $3.95.
    A popular manual on handloading, with authoritative articles on loading, ballistics, and related subjects. Decorated paper wrappers.
Why Not Load Your Own? by Col. T. Whelen. A. S. Barnes, New York, 1957, 4th ed., rev. 237 pp., illus, $5.95.
    A basic reference on handloading, describing each step, materials and equipment. Loads for popular cartridges are given.
The Winchester-Western Ammunition Handbook. Thomas Nelson & Sons, NYC, 1964. 185 pp., illus. $2.95.
    Called the world's handiest handbook on ammunition for all types of shotguns, rifles and handguns. Full of facts, photographs, ballistics and statistics.

COLLECTORS

About Cannon in 1862, by Robert F. Hudson, American Archives Publ. Co., Topsfield, MA, 1971. 44 pp., illus. Paper, $4.00.
    Reprint of an 18th century monograph on artillery pieces, with historical notes.
Accoutrement Plates, North and South, 1861-1865, by Wm. G. Gavin. Geo. Shumway, York, PA, 1963. 236 pp., 220 illus. $12.00
    The 1st detailed study of Civil War belt buckles and cartridge box insignia. Dimensions, materials, details of manufacture, relative and dollar values given.
The Age of Firearms, by Robert Held. Digest Books, Inc., Northfield, IL, 1970. New, fully rev. and corrected ed., paper covers. 192 pp., fully illus. $4.95.
    A popular review of firearms since 1475 with accent on their effects on social conditions, and the craft of making functional/artistic arms.

Air Guns, by Eldon G. Wolff. Milwaukee Public Museum, Milwaukee, WI, 1958. 198 pp., illus. Paper, $6.00.
A scholarly and comprehensive treatise, excellent for student and collectors' use, of air gun history. Every form of arm is described, and a list of 350 makers is included.

The American Bayonet, 1776-1964, by A. N. Hardin, Jr. Geo. Shumway, York, PA, 1964. 252 pp., profusely illus. $20.00.
First comprehensive book on U.S. bayonets of all services, a standard reference for collectors. All bayonets made for long arms and described in full detail, with outstanding photographs, and historical development of principal types. Full references and bibliography.

American, British & Continental Pepperbox Firearms, by Jack Dunlap. H. J. Dunlap, Los Altos, CA, 1964. 279 pp., 665 illus. $15.00.
Comprehensive history of production pepperpots from early 18th cent. through the cartridge pepperbox. Variations are covered, with much data of value to the collector.

American Engraved Powder Horns, by Stephen V. Grancsay. Originally published by The Metropolitan Museum of Art, at NYC, 1945. The 1st reprint publ. by Ray Riling Arms Books Co., Phila., PA, 1965. 96 pp. plus 47 full-page plates. $15.00.
A study based on the J. H. Grenville Gilbert collection of historic, rare and beautiful powder horns. A scholarly work by an eminent authority. Long out of print and offered now in a limited edition of 1000 copies.

American and European Swords in the Historical Collections of the U.S. National Museum, by T. T. Belote. Benchmark Pub. Co., Glendale, NY, 1970. 163 pp., illus. $7.50
A reprint of Smithsonian Institution Bulletin 163, first published in 1932.

American Knives, the First History and Collectors' Guide, by Harold L. Peterson. Scribner's, N.Y.C., 1958. 178 pp., well illus. $6.95.
A timely book to whet the appetite of the ever-growing group of knife collectors.

The American Percussion Revolver, by F. M. Sellers and Sam E. Smith. Museum Restoration Service, Ottawa, Canada, 1970. 200 pp., illus. $15.00.
All inclusive from 1826 to 1870. Over 200 illus., with profuse coverage on lesser-known arms.

American Polearms, 1526-1865, by R. H. Brown. N. Flayderman Co., New Milford, Conn., 1967. 198 pp., 150 plates. $14.50.
Concise history of pikes, spears, and similar weapons used in American military forces through the Civil War.

American Socket Bayonets, 1717-1873, by D. B. Webster, Jr. Museum Rest. Service, Ottawa, Can. 1964. 48 pp., 60 illus. paperbound. $1.50.
Concise account of major types, with nomenclature, characteristics, and dimensions. Line drawings.

The American Sword 1775-1945, by H. L. Peterson. Ray Riling Arms Books Co., 1970. 286 pp. plus 60 pp. of illus. $13.50.
1970 reprint of a survey of swords worn by U.S. uniformed forces, plus the rare "American Silver Mounted Swords," (1700-1815).

Ancient Armour and Weapons in Europe, by John Hewitt. Akademische Druck- u. Verlagsanstalt, Graz, Austria, 1967. 3 vols., 1151 total pp., illus. $50.00.
Reprint of a renowned British work first published 1855-1860; covers armor, weapons, military history and tactics through the 17th century.

The Ancient Art of Warfare, by Robert Laffont. New York Grafic Society, Greenwich, Conn., 1968. (2 vols.). 1086 pp., illus. Boxed. $29.95.
A summary on warfare since 1300 B.C., covering the principal campaigns known to history, with much on weapons, equipment, and military customs of all types. Many illustrations in full color.

Antique Arms Annual, ed. by R. L. Wilson, S. P. Stevens, Texas Gun Coll. Assn., Waco, Texas. 1971. 262 pp., profusely illus. $15.00.
A magnificent work showing hundreds of fine color photographs of rare firearms. Decorated paper covers.

Antique Firearms, by Frederick Wilkinson. Guinness Signatures, London. 1st ed., 1969. 256 pp., Well illus. $15.00.
Sixteen monographs on important aspects of firearms development from the 14th century to the era of the modern repeating rifle. Shows museum-quality arms, many in full color.

Antique Pistols, by S. G. Alexander, illus. by Ronald Paton. Arco Publ. Co., New York, 1963. 56 pp., 12 color plates. $15.00.
The large 8-color plates show 14 examples of the pistol-maker's art in England and U.S.A., 1690-1900. Commentary on each by a knowledgeable English collector.

Antique Weapons, A-Z, by Douglas J. Fryer. G. Bell & Sons, London, 1969. 114 pp. illus. $7.50.
A concise survey of collectors' arms, including firearms, edged weapons, polearms, etc., of European and Oriental design, classified by types.

Antique Weapons for Pleasure and Investment, by R. Akehurst. Arco Pub. Co., N.Y., 1969. 174 pp., illus. $5.95.
Reprint of an English book covering an extensive variety of arms, including Japanese and Hindu edged weapons and firearms.

Les Armes Americaines 1870-1871 de las Defense Nationale, by P. Lorain and J. Boudriot. Librarie Pierre Petitot, Paris, France, 1970. French text, 96 pp., illus. $12.50.
Covers all U.S. weapons bought by the French government a century ago.

Armes a Feu Francaises Modeles Reglementaires, by J. Boudriot. Paris, 1961-1968. 4 series of booklets; 1st and 2nd series, 5 booklets; 3rd and 4th, 6 booklets. Each series, $6.75, $9.75, $10.75, $11.75, resp.
Detailed survey of all models of French military small arms, 1717-1861, with text in French and fine scale drawings. Each series covers a different period of development; the last covers percussion arms.

Armes Blanches Militaires Francaises, by Christian Aries. P. Petitot, Paris, 1968. Unpaginated, paperbound, 11 volumes. $9.50 per vol., $95.00 complete.
Pictorial survey of French military swords, in French text and line drawings in exact detail. The classifications in the various volumes are the author's own and do not follow any specific sequence. The work must be used as a complete set for maximum benefit.

Le Armi da Fuoco Portatili Italiane, dalle Origini al Risorgimento, by Gen. Agostino Gaibi. Bramante Editrice, Milan, Italy, 1962. 527 pp., 320 illus. (69 in color), in slip case. $65.00.
A magnificently produced volume covering Italian hand firearms from their beginning into the 18th cent. Italian text. Superb illus. of historic weapons, engraving, marks, related equipment. A companion book to *Armi e Armature Italiane.*

Armi e Armature Europee, by B. Thomas-O. Gamber-H, Schedelmann, Bramante Editrice, Milano, Italy, 1965, 246 pp., magnificently illus., mainly in full color. $40.00. Ed. ltd. to 1600 copies.
Italian text version of *Arms and Armor of Europe* by the same authors in German text. Text and commentary cover 50 pp., and there are 196 pp. of illus.

Armi e Armature Italiane, Fino al XVIII Secolo, by Aldo Mario Aroldi. Bramante Editrice, Milan, Italy, 1961. 544 pp., profusely illus. (Much in color). In slip case, $65.00.
A luxurious work on the golden age of Italian arms and makers through the 18th cent., emphasizing body and horse armor, edged weapons, crossbows, early firearms. Italian text. Beautiful and scholarly work for the advanced collector.

Armi e Armature Orientali, by Gianni Vianello, Bramante Editrice, Milano, Italy, 1966. 423 pp. Magnificently illustrated, mainly in full-color tip-ins. $56.00 with slip case. Ed. ltd. to 1600 copies.
A new addition to a notable series of fine books in the arms and armor field. The introduction is 68 pp., 105 pp. of commentary on the 250 pp. of illus.

Arming the Troops, by Paul C. Boehret, Publ. by the author at Chalfont, Pa., 1967. 39 pp., illus. $7.50. The same in paper wrappers $5.00.
A catalog of arms makers of the early years of U.S. history, from 1775 to 1815.

The Armourer and his Craft, by Charles ffoulkes. Frederick Ungar Publ. Co., N.Y., 1967. 199 pp., illus. $18.50.
Standard British reference on body armor, 11th-16th cent.; covering notable makers, construction, decoration, and use. 1st ed. 1912, now reprinted.

Armourers Marks, by D. S. H. Gyngell. Thorsons, Ltd., England, 1959. 131 pp., illus. $7.95.
Some of the marks of armourers, swordsmiths and gunsmiths of almost every foreign country.

Arms Archives, by H. B. Lockhoven, International Small Arms Publ., Cologne, W. Germany, 1969. Unpaginated, English and German text, looseleaf format. Available in 4 series—Handguns, Longarms, Automatic Weapons, and Antique Firearms. Each installment is $9.50. Special binders holding a complete series of 3 installments are $5.50 each.
A major breakthrough in weapons literature. Scaled photographs of arms and their cartridges, fully described.

Arms and Armor, by Vesey Norman. Putnam's N.Y.C., 1964. 128 pp., 129 illus. $5.95.
Authoritative, compact coverage of European armor and weapons prior to the age of firearms. Excellent illus., many in color.

Arms & Armor from the Atelier of Ernst Schmidt, Munich, by E. Andrew Mowbray, compiler. Mowbray Co., Providence, R.I., 1967. 168 pp., well illus. $11.95.
Principally a compilation of plates from the extremely rare Schmidt catalog displaying the famous replicas of medieval armor and weapons made in his shop from about 1870 to 1930. Limited edition.

Arms and Armor in Colonial America, 1526-1783, by H. L. Peterson. Crown, New York, reprint ed., 1964. 350 pp., illus. $3.95.
Well-organized account of arms and equipment used in America's colonization and exploration, through the Revolutionary period.

Arms and Armour, by Frederick Wilkinson, A. & C. Black Ltd., London. Reprint of 1969, 63 pp., well illus. $2.95.
A concise work for young readers describing edged weapons, polearms, armor, etc., mainly of European origin.

Arms and Armour, 9th to 17th Century, by Paul Martin, C. E. Tuttle Co., Rutland, Vt., 1968. 298 pp., well illus. $15.00.
Beautiful illustrations and authoritative text on armor and accessories from the time of Charlemagne to the firearms era.

Arms and Armour of the Western World, by B. Thomas, O. Gamber & H. Schedelmann, McGraw Hill, N.Y.C., 1964. 252 pp., illus. (much in color), $27.50.
Museum quality weapons and armor shown and described in a magnificent book, which gives the association of specimen arms with the men and events of history. Superb photographs in color. Pub. 1963 in German as "Die Schonsten Waffen . . ." price $25.00.

Arms Collection of Colonel Colt, by R. L. Wilson. Herb Glass, Bullville, N.Y., 1964. 132 pp., 73 illus. Lim. deluxe ed., $16.50; trade ed., $6.50.
Samuel Colt's personal collection is well-described and photographed, plus new technical data on Colt's arms and life. 51 Colt guns and other revolving U.S. and European arms are included.

Arms and Equipment of the Civil War, by Jack Coggins, Doubleday & Co., Inc, NY, 1962. 160 pp., $5.95.
Tools of war of the blue and the grey. Infantry, cavalry, artillery, and navy: guide to equipment, clothing, organization, and weapons. Over 500 illus.

Arms Making In the Connecticut Valley, by F. J. Deyrup. George Shumway Publ., York, Pa., 1970. Reprint of the noted work originally publ. in 1948 by Smith College. 290 pp., line maps, $10.00.
A scholarly regional study of the economic development of the small arms industry 1798-1870. With statistical appendices, notes, bibliography.

Arms of the World—1911, ed. by Joseph J. Schroeder, Jr., Digest Books, Inc., Northfield, IL, 1972, 420 pp., profusely illus. $5.95.
Reprint of the Adolph Frank ALFA 21 catalog of 1911 in 4 languages—English, German, French, Spanish.

The Art of the Gunmaker, by J. F. Hayward; Vol. I, 1500-1660; Vol. II, 1660-1830. St. Martin's Press, New York, 1962-64. Vol. I: 303 pp. plus 64 pp. of illus., $15.00; Vol. II: 352 pp., 220 illus., $18.50.
Comprehensive survey of firearms development and ornamentation by leading makers in Europe and the U.S. Prepared by a museum expert with excellent illus., this book offers valuable new information.

Artillery and Ammunition of the Civil War, by Warren Ripley. Van Nostrand Reinhold Co., New York, N.Y., 1st ed., 1970. 384 pp., well illus. with 662 black and white photos and line drawings. $22.50.
A fine survey covering both Union and Confederate cannon and projectiles, as well as those imported.

Artillery of the United States Land Service. Vol. I, Field Artillery 1848-1865, comp. by D. E. Lutz, Antique Ordnance Artificers, Jackson, MI, 1970. 64 pp. Paper, $5.00.
First of series containing drawings of artillery used during the Civil War. Limited ed., each copy numbered.

Artillery Through the Ages, by A. Manucy, Normount Armament Co., Forest Grove, OR, 1971. 92 pp., illus. Paper, $2.50
A short history of cannon, emphasizing types used in America.

Arts of the Japanese Swords, by B. W. Robinson. Chas. E. Tuttle Co., Rutland, Vt., 1961. 110 pp. of descriptive text with illus., plus 100 full page plates, some in full color. $15.00.
An authoritative work, divided into 2 parts—the first on blades, tracing their history to the present day; the second on mounts and fittings. It includes forging processes; accounts of the important schools of swordsmiths; techniques employed, plus a useful appendix on care and cleaning.

Badges & Emblems of the British Forces 1940, Arms and Armour Press, London, 1968. 64 pp. Paper, $3.00.
Reprint of a comprehensive guide to badges and emblems worn by all British forces in 1940, including Welfare, Aux. Services, Nursing Units, etc. Over 350 illus.

Ballard Rifles in the H. J. Nunnemacher Coll., by Eldon G. Wolff. Milwaukee Public Museum, Milwaukee, Wisc., 2nd ed. 1961. Paper, 77 p. plus 4 pp. of charts and 27 plates. $2.50.
A thoroughly authoritative work on all phases of the famous rifles, their parts, patent and manufacturing history.

The Bannerman Catalogue 1903, Francis Bannerman Sons, New York, N.Y. Reprint released in 1960. 116 pp., well illus., $3.50.
A reprint in facsimile of this dealer's catalog of military goods of all descriptions, including weapons and equipment.

The Bannerman Catalog 1965, Francis Bannerman Sons, Blue Point, N.Y. The 100th anniversary ed., 1966. 264 pp., well illus. $5.00.
Latest dealer catalog of nostalgic interest on military and collector's items of all sorts.

Basic Documents on U.S. Marital Arms, commentary by Col. B. R. Lewis, reissue by Ray Riling, Phila., Pa., 1956 and 1960.
Rifle Musket Model 1855. The first issue rifle of musket caliber, a muzzle loader equipped with the Maynard Primer, 32 pp. $2.00.
Rifle Musket Model 1863. The Typical Union muzzle-loader of the Civil War, 26 pp. $1.50.
Breech-Loading Rifle Musket Model 1866. The first of our 50 caliber breechloading rifles, 12 pp. $1.50.
Remington Navy Rifle Model 1870. A commercial type breech-loader made at Springfield, 16 pp. $1.50.
Lee Straight Pull Navy Rifle Model 1895. A magazine cartridge arm of 6mm caliber. 23 pp. $2.75.
Breech-Loading Rifle Musket Model 1868. The first 50-70 designed as such. 20 pp. $1.50.
Peabody Breech-Loading Arms (five models)—27 pp. $2.25.
Ward-Burton Rifle Musket 1871—16 pp. $2.00.
Springfield Rifle, Carbine & Army Revolvers (cal. 45) model 1873 including Colt and Smith & Wesson hand arms. 52 pp. $2.25.
U.S. Magazine Rifle and Carbine (cal. 30) Model 1892 (the Krag Rifle) 36 pp. $2.50.

Bayonets Illustrated, by Bert Walsh, Bashall Eaves, Ireland, 1970. 49 pp., illus. $5.00.
162 detailed line drawings of bayonets from many countries and periods.

Bayonets, an Illustrated History and Reference Guide, by F. J. Stephens. Arms and Armour Press, London, 1968. 76 pp., stiff paper wrappers, 134 photographs. $5.00.
A general historical survey of all categories of the weapon, from the U.S. and many other countries.

Bellifortis [The War Hero], by Conrad Kyeser. Verlag des Vereins Deutscher Ingenieure, Dusseldorf, W. Germany. 1967. Two large facsimile volumes, 391 pp., combining Latin and German text. Superbly illus.
For the advanced collector, this is a reproduction of the oldest [A.D. 1405] German manuscript on weapons and warfare. Limited to 1,000 copies, bound in white half-vellum and boxed. $120.00.

Bilderatlas zum Grundriss der Waffenlehre, by K. T. VonSauer. Pawlas, Nurnberg, Germany, 1968. Paper folder containing 28 pp. text and 26 plates. $7.50.
Facsimile of an 1869 set of plates depicting military rifles of Germany, with explanatory pamphlet in German text.

Blunderbusses, by D. R. Baxter. Stackpole Books, Harrisburg, Pa., 1970. 80 pp., 60 illus. $4.95.
Traces blunderbuss development from the 16th century, covering basic designs, firing systems, the double blunderbuss and revolving pepperbox design.

The Book of Colt Firearms, by R. Q. Sutherland and R. L. Wilson, Privately printed, Kansas City, Mo., 1971. 604 pp. 9x12", profusely illus. $50.00.
This exhaustive large work, highly informative and scholarly, contains 40 color plates showing 420 Colt firearms, plus 1258 black and white photographs.

The Book of the Continental Soldier, by Harold L. Peterson. Stackpole Books, Harrisburg, Pa, 1968. 287 pp., of large format profusely illus. with halftone, line, and including art work by H. Charles McBarron, Jr., Clyde A. Risley and Peter Copeland, $12.95.
A thorough and commendable work in every pertinent aspect. Covers in satisfying detail every facet of the soldier's existence.

Book of the 22, by Richard Arnold, Barnes & Co., N.Y.C., 1962. 188 pp., illus., $2.95.
Authoritative data for the 22 rifleman and pistoleer, detailing arms of this caliber in the use throughout the world, history of the weapons and cartridges.

Bowie Knives, by R. Abels. Pub. by the author, NYC, 1960. 48 pp. profusely illus. Paper covers. $2.00.
A booklet showing knives, tomahawks, related trade cards and advertisements.

Brass Spikes & Horsehair Plumes: A Study of U.S. Army Dress Helmets, 1872-1903, by Gordon Chappell, Arizona Pioneers Hist. Soc., Tucson, Ariz. 1966. 50 pp., illus. Paper covers. $2.00.
Historical monograph on military headgear of the period.

The Breech-Loader in the Service, 1816-1917, by Claud E. Fuller, N. Flayderman, New Milford, Conn., 1965. 381 pp., illus. $14.50.
Revised ed. of a 1933 historical reference on U.S. standard and experimental military shoulder arms. Much patent data, drawings, and photographs of the arms.
A voluminous work that covers handloading—and other things—in great detail. Replete with data for all cartridge forms.

British and American Infantry Weapons of World War II, by A. J. Barker. 1st ed., 1969, Arco Publishing Co., New York, N.Y. 76 pp., illus., $3.50.
A British officer's survey that includes numerous specialized weapons, all are illustrated and described.

British Military Bayonets from 1700 to 1945, by R. J. W. Latham. Arco Publ. Co., N.Y.C., 1969. 94 pp., ilus. $8.50.
History and identification catalog of British bayonets, with fine illustrations, marks, dimensions, and equipment of various British army units.

British Military Firearms 1650-1850, by H. L. Blackmore. Arco Publ. Co. Inc., New York, 1962. 296 pp. and 83 plates of photographs, line drawings, appendices and index. $10.00.
This excellent work admirably and authoritatively covers the subject in every detail. Highly recommended.

British Military Longarms 1715-1815, by D. W. Bailey, Stackpole Books, Harrisburg, PA, 1971. 80 pp., $4.95.
The Regulation service longarms of the British Army and Navy during a century of conflict in Europe, America and India, are fully described and illus.

British Military Swords, From 1800 to the Present Day, by J. W. Latham, Crown Publishers, NY, 1967, 91 pp., illus. $3.95.
Survey of British swords used by various branches of the Army, with data on their manufacture, specifications, and procurement.

British Pistols and Guns, 1640-1940, by Ian Glendenning. Arco Publ. Co., NY, 1967. 194 pp., photos and drawings. $7.50.
Historical review of British firearms, with much data and illustration of furniture and decoration of fine weapons.

British Smooth-Bore Artillery, by Maj.-Gen. B. P. Hughes. Stackpole Books, Harrisburg, PA, 1969. 144 pp., illus. $14.95.
On the muzzle-loading artillery of the 18th and 19th centuries, covering dimensions, ammunition, and application.

The British Soldier's Firearm, 1850-1864, by C. H. Roads. Herbert Jenkins, London, 1964. 332 pp., illus. $12.50.
Detailed account of development of British military arms at the acme of the muzzle-loading period. All models in use are covered, as well as ammunition.

Buttons of the British Army 1855-1970, by Howard Ripley, Arms & Armour Press, London, 1971. 64 pp. $5.00.
Guide for collectors with over 650 buttons illus.

The Canadian Bayonet, by R. B. Manarey, Century Press, Alberta, Can. 1970. 51 pp. $5.00.
Illustrated history of the Canadian bayonet.

The Canadian Gunsmiths 1608-1900, by S. James Gooding. Museum Restoration Service, Canada, 1962. 322 pp., illus. $17.50.
Comprehensive survey of the gunmakers of Canada and the products of their skill, from early settlement to the age of the breech-loader.

Cartridge Headstamp Guide, by H. P. White and B. D. Munhall. H. P. White Laboratory, Bel Air, MD, 1963. 263 pp., illus. $10.00.
An important reference on headstamping of small arms ammo, by manufacturers in many countries. Clear illus. of 1936 headstamps of every type.

Cartridges for Collectors, by Fred A. Datig. Borden Publishing Co., Alhambra, Calif, Vol. I (Centerfire), 1958; Vol. II (Rimfire and Misc.) Types, 1963; Vol. III (Additional Rimfire, Centerfire, and Plastic,) 1967. Each of the three volumes 176 pp., well illus. and each priced at $7.50.
Vol. III supplements the first two books and presents 300 additional specimens. All illus. are shown in full-scale line drawings.

Cavalry Equipment 1874, 4 reprint of *U.S. Ordnance Memoranda No. 18* by Francis Bannerman Sons, Blue Point, NY, 1969. 119 pp., 12 plates. $6.50.
An officers' report on details of equipment issued to U.S. cavalry units.

Civil War Carbines, by A. F. Lustyik. World Wide Gun Report, Inc., Aledo, ILL, 1962. 63 pp., illus. paper covers, $2.00.
Accurate, interesting summary of most carbines of the Civil War period, in booklet form, with numerous good illus.

Civil War Collector's Encyclopedia, by Francis A. Lord, Stackpole books, Harrisburg, PA, 1963, 384 pp., 350 illus. $17.95.
A reference work on Civil War relics, for museums, students, writers, and collectors of Union and Confederate items. Identifies arms, uniforms, accoutrements, ordnance material, currency, postage, etc. Many patent drawings. Lists of manufacturers and vendors, North and South, are given.

Civil War Guns, by Wm. B. Edwards, Stackpole Books, Harrisburg, PA, 1962. 464 pp., over 400 illus. $5.95.
Comprehensive survey of Civil War arms, identification data, procurement procedures, and historical data. Important information on replicas, imitations, and fakes.

Classic Bowie Knives, by Robert Abels. R. Abels, Inc., NY, 1967. 97 pp., illus. with numerous fine examples of the subject. $7.50.
A nostalgic story of the famous blades, with trade advertisements on them, and photos of users.

The Collecting of Guns, ed. by Jas. E. Serven. Stackpole Books, Harrisburg, PA, 1964. 272 pp., illus. $24.50.
A new and massive compendium of gun lore for serious collectors by recognized experts. Separate chapters cover major categories and aspects of collecting. Over 600 firearms illus. Handsomely designed, deluxe binding in slip case. Reprint of 1966, $5.95.

Collector's Guide to American Cartridge Handguns, by Dewitt E. Sell. Stackpole Books, Harrisburg, PA, 1963, 234 pp., illus. $3.98.
Catalogs the important U.S. makers in its field, with histories of the firms and their production models. Photos, descriptions and features of many older and current handguns are included.

Collector's Guns, by Don Myrus, Arco Publ. Co., Inc., NY, 1962. 128 pp., illus. $3.50.
The fascinating story of firearms—from the early hand cannon to the Peacemaker—with over 200 rare photographs and illus.

A Collector's Pictorial Book of Bayonets, by F. J. Stephens, Stackpole Books, Harrisburg, PA, 1971. 127 pp., illus. $5.95.
Instant identification of bayonet types, plus their history and use.

Colt Firearms from 1836, by James E. Serven. Foundation Press, La Habra, Cal, 1969. 6th printing, 398 pp., very well illus. $19.95.
A dependable survey of the Colt company and its products. In addition to historical data, each Colt model is illus. and described, with production figures.

Colt's Variations of the Old Model Pocket Pistol, 1848 to 1872, by P. L. Shumaker. Borden Publishing Co., Alhambra, CA, 1966. A reprint of the 1957 edition. 150 pp., illus. $6.00.
A useful tool for the Colt specialist and a welcome return of a popular source of information that had been long out-of-print.

The Complete Book of Gun Collecting, by Charles E. Chapel. Coward-McCann, Inc., N.Y.C., 1960. 222 pp., illus. $4.95.
Answers hundreds of questions for the beginner, and is a reference for the advanced collector and student of firearms. It covers hand cannon of the 14th century to arms of the present day.

Confederate Arms, by Wm. A. Albaugh III, and E. N. Simmons. Stackpole Books, Harrisburg, PA, 1957. 278 pp., illus. $3.95.
Contains much heretofore unpublished information on the arms and associated material of the Confederacy.

Confederate Handguns, by Wm. A. Albaugh III. Hugh Benet Jr., and Edw. N. Simmons. Geo. Shumway, York, PA, 1963. 272 pp., 125 illus. $5.95.
Every known true Confederate pistol and revolver is described and illus., with the story of its maker and procurement by the C.S.A. Much new information includes listing of C. W. makers and dealers, information on replicas and fakes. Indispensable to the collector and student of these arms and their period.

Cut and Thrust Weapons, by E. Wagner, Spring Books, Longdon, 1967. 491 pp., line drawings. $17.50.
English translation of a survey of European edged weapons, their traditions, manufacture, and use.

Deanes' Manual of the History and Science of Fire-arms, by J. Deane. Standard Publications, Huntington, WV, 1946 facsimile reprint of the rare English original of 1858. 291 pp., three folding plates. $6.00.
A history of firearms, plus design and manufacture of military and sporting arms.

Decoy Collector's Guide 1963-1964-1965, ed. by H. D. Sorenson, Burlington, IA, 1971. Irregular pagination, illus., $15.00.
This volume includes all of the 12 booklets originally published as quarterlies.

Decoy Collector's Guide 1966-67 Annual, ed. by H. D. Sorenson, Burlington, IA, 1966. 125 pp., illus. $5.00.
Well-illustrated articles on American decoys.
Decoy Collector's Guide, 1968, ed. by H. D. Sorenson, 1967, Burlington, IA 128 pp, 75 photos. Spiral bound. $5.00.
History, decoy patents, carving, collecting, etc.
Digest of Patents Relating to Breech-Loading and Magazine Small Arms (1836-1873), by V. D. Stockbridge, WA, 1874. Reprinted 1963 by E. N. Flayderman, Greenwich, Conn. 180 pp., 880 illus. $12.50.
An exhaustive compendium of patent documents on firearms, indexed and classified by breech mechanism types, valuable reference for students and collectors.
Early Firearms of Great Britain and Ireland from the Collection of Clay P. Bedford. The Metropolitan Museum of Art, NY, 1971. 187 pp., illus. $17.50.
Authoritative account of an exceptional body of historic firearms, and a detailed survey of three centuries of gunmaking.
Early Indian Trade Guns—1625 to 1775, by T. M. Hamilton. Museum of the Great Plains, Lawton, Okla. 1969. 34 pp., well illus., paper covers. $2.50.
Detailed descriptions of subject arms, compiled from early records and from the study of remnants found in Indian county.
Early Loading Tools and Bullet Molds, by R. H. Chamberlain. The Farm Tribune, Porterville, GA, 1971. 75 pp., illus. Paper covers, $3.00.
An excellent aid to collectors.
Early Percussion Firearms, by Lewis Winant, Wm. Morrow & Co., Inc., N.Y.C., 1959. 292 pp., illus. $2.98.
A history of early percussion firearms ignition—from Forsyth to Winchester 44-40, from flintlocks of the 18th century to centerfires. Over 230 illus. of firearms, parts, patents, and cartridges—from some of the finest collections here and abroad.
Edged Weapons, by Fred. Wilkinson. Guinness Signatures, London, 1970, 256 pp., plus 14-page index. Excellently illus., many in full color. $12.95.
Scholarly treatment of all kinds of blades—from flint to steel, rapiers, smallswords, knives, daggers, hunting weapons, polearms, etc., plus construction and decoration.
The Encyclopedia of Military History, by R. Ernest and Trevor N. Dupuy. Harper & Row, New York, NY, 1970. 1st ed., 1406 pp., well illus., in line and halftone. $20.00.
This massive single volume covers the subject from 3500 B.C. to the present time. A complete reference guide to the world's military history; narration of war and combat, tactics, strategy and weaponry. Over 250 maps, illus. of weapons, fortifications, etc.
English, Irish and Scottish Firearms, by A. Merwyn Carey. Arco Publishing Co., Inc., NY, 1967. A reprint. 121 pp., illus. in line and halftone. $6.50.
Out-of-print since 1954, this work covers the subject from the middle of the 16th century to the end of the 19th.
English Pistols & Revolvers, by J. N. George. Arco Publ. Co., Inc., N.Y.C., 1962, 256 pp., 28 plates, $6.50.
The 2nd reprinting of a notable work first publ. in 1938. Treats of the historical development and design of English hand firearms from the 17th cent. to the present. A much better book than the former reprint, particularly as to clarity of the tipped-in plates.
English Sporting Guns and Accessories, by Macdonald Hastings. Ward Lock & Co., London. 1st ed., 1969. 96 pp., well illus. $4.00.
A delightful monograph on shotguns and accessory equipment for hunting from 1800 to the advent of the breech loader, including historic arms and ammunition.
European & American Arms, by Claude Blair, Batsford, London, and Crown Publ., N.Y.C., 1962, 192 pp., 9"x12". Profusely and magnificently illus. $6.95.
A complete visual encyclopedia on all sorts of arms of Europe and America with over 600 photographs of pieces from nearly all the major collections of Western Europe, America, and Russia, from about 1100 to 1850. A splendid text describes historical and technical developments.
European Armour in the Tower of London, by A. R. Dufty. H. M. Stationery Office, London, England, 1968. 17 pp. text, 164 plates, $12.60.
Pictorial record of almost 400 pieces of armor, helmets, and accouterments in the famous Tower of London collection.
European Arms & Armour, by Chas. H. Ashdown, Brussel & Brussel, NY, 1967. A reprint, 384 pp., illus. with 42 plates and 450 drawings. $5.95.
Historical survey of body armor up to the era of gunpowder, with some coverage on weapons and early firearms.
European Hand Firearms of the 16th, 17th, and 18th Centuries, by H. J. Jackson and C. E. Whitlaw. Bramhall house, New York, NY. A reprint of the noted original. 108 pp., fine photographic plates. $5.95.
A work for scholars and collectors, including a list of arms makers. Not without error.
The Evolution of the Colt, by R. L. Wilson, R. Q. Sutherland, Kansas City, MO, 1967. 54 pp., illus. $3.00.
Pictures the fine Colt arms of the publisher from percussion to cartridge. Includes a Colt bibliography.
Famous Guns from the Smithsonian Collection, by H. W. Bowman. Arco. Publ. Co., Inc., NY, 1967. 112 pp., illus. $3.50.
The finest of the "Famous Guns" series.
Famous Guns from the Winchester Collection, by H. W. Bowman. Arco Publ. Co., NYC, 1958 and later. 144 pp., illus. $3.50.
The gems of the hand and shoulder arms in the great collection at New Haven, CT.
Feuerwaffen von 1300 bis 1967, by Hans-Bert Lockhoven. International Small Arms Publ., Cologne, W. Germany, 1969. 96 pp., illus. $6.95.
Review of the principal developments in military smallarms from early times, German text.
'51 Colt Navies, by N. L. Swayze. Gun Hill Publ. Co., Yazoo City, MS, 1967. 243 pp., well illus. $15.00.
The first major effort devoting its entire space to the 1851 Colt Navy revolver. There are 198 photos of models, sub-models, variations, parts, markings, documentary material, etc. Fully indexed.
Firearms Curiosa, by Lewis Winant, Ray Riling, Philadelphia, PA, 2nd and deluxe reissue 1961, 281 pp., well illus. $5.00.
Reissue publ. by Bonanza Books, N.Y.C., 1965. $2.98.
An important work for those with an interest in odd, distinctive and unusual forms and firing.
The Firearms Dictionary, by R. A. Steindler. Stackpole Books, Harrisburg, PA, 1970. 256 pp., nearly 200 illus. $7.95.
A super single-source reference to more than 1800 English and Foreign gun-related words, phrases and nomenclature, etc. Highly useful to all armsmen—collectors, shooters, hunters, etc.
Firearms in England in the Fourteenth Century, by T. F. Tout. Geo. Shumway, York, PA, 1958. 58 pp., illus., Paper covers. $4.00.
Reprint of a 1911 monograph on the history and manufacture of early British firearms, by a distinguished historian.
Flintlock Guns and Rifles, by F. Wilkinson, Stackpole Books, Harrisburg, PA, 1971. 80 pp., $4.95.
Illus. reference guide for 1650-1850 period showing makers, mechanisms and users.
The Flintlock, Its Origin and Development, by Torsten Lenk; J. T. Hayward, Editor, Holland Press, London, 1964. 192 pp., 134 illus. $6.95.
First English-text version of the 1939 Swedish work termed "the most important book on the subject." Original illus. are reproduced, and a new index and bibliography complete this valuable book.
Flintlock Pistols, by F. Wilkinson. Stackpole Books, Harrisburg, PA, 1968. 75 pp., illus. $4.95.
Illustrated reference guide by a British authority, covering 17th-19th century flintlock pistols.
Forsyth & Co.—Patent Gunmakers, by W. Keith Neal and D. H. L. Back. G. Bell & Sons, London, 1st ed., 1969, 280 pp., well illus. $12.95.
An excellent study of the invention and development of the percussion system by the Rev. Alexander Forsyth in the early 19th century. All Forsyth types are covered, plus a diary of events from 1768 to 1852.
.45-70 Rifles, by J. Behn, Rutgers Book Center, Highland Park, NJ, 1972. New ed., 150 pp., illus. $5.95.
Covers the official U.S. Army small arms cartridge and the weapons for its use.
The French Army in America, by E. P. Hamilton. Museum Restoration Service, Ottawa, 1967. 108 pp., illus. $3.00.
Concise historical coverage, illus. with contemporary documents and manual-of-arms plates. Text in English and French. Paper wrappers.
French Military Weapons, 1717-1938, by James E. Hicks. N. Flayderman & Co., New Milford, CT, 1964. 281 pp., profusely illus. $9.50.
A valuable reference work, first publ. 1938 as *Notes on French Ordnance*, this rev. ed. covers hand, shoulder, and edged weapons, ammunition and artillery, with history of various systems.
The Fuller Collection of American Firearms, by H. L. Peterson. Eastern National Park & Monument Assn., 1967. 63 pp., illus. $2.50.
Illustrated catalog of principal military shoulder arms in the collection. Decorated paper wrappers.
Gamle Danske Militaervaben, by Th. Moller. Host & Sons, Denmark, 1st reprinting, 1968. 64 pp., well illus. in line. Heavy paper covers. $4.00.
Old Danish military weapons, with Danish and English text, covering Weapons from 1971 to 1832, plus accoutrements.
The Gatling Gun, by Paul Wahl & D. R. Toppel. Arco Publ., N.Y.C., 1971. 168 pp., illus. $5.95.
History of the famed rapid-fire weapon used by many of the world's armies and navies from 1861.
German Mauser Rifle—Model of 1898, by J. E. Coombes and J. L. Aney. A reprint in paper covers by Francis Bannerman Sons, New York, NY, of their 1921 publication. 20 pp., well illus. $1.50.
Data on the subject weapon and its W. W. I development. Bayonets and ammunition are also described and illus.
German Pistols and Holsters 1934 to 1945, by R. D. Whittington III. Brownlee Books, College Station, Tex., 1969. 1st ed., limited to 2000 numbered copies, 223 pp., well illus., in halftone. $15.00.
A manual for collectors on subject items issued to the military, police and NSDAP. Covers all models of various designs, including those of foreign manufacture.
German Submachine Guns and Assault Rifles. WE, Inc., Old Greenwich, CT, 1967. 161 pp. $5.95.
Aberdeen Proving Ground reports on over 50 models of World War II German rapid-fire weapons are reprinted.
Die Geschichtliche Entwicklung Der Handfeuerwaffen, by M. Thierbach, Akademische Druck, Graz, Austria, 1965. Vol. 1, 590 pp., German text: Vol. II, 36 Plates. $37.00.
The famous German work on history and development of firearms, accessories and ammunition, first published in 1886 in Dresden.
A Glossary of the Construction, Decoration and Use of Arms and Armor in all Countries and in all Times, by Geo. C. Stone, Jack Brussel, NY, 2nd reprint, 1966, 694 pp., illus. $9.95.
The outstanding work on its subject, authoritative and accurate in detail. The major portion is on oriental arms.
The Great Guns, by H. L. Peterson and Robt. Elman. Grosset & Dunlap, NY, 1972. $14.95.
Basic and general history with 70 full color illustrations and 140 photos of some of the finest guns from American collections. A well written text.
Great Weapons of World War I, by Com. G. Dooly, Walker & Co., NY, 1969, 340 pp., illus. $14.50.
Describes all the important weapons and system developments used during WWI.
The Gun and its Development, by W. W. Greener. Bonanza Books, NY, 1967. A reprint. 804 pp., profusely illus. $5.95.
A facsimile of the famous 9th edition of 1910. Covers history and development of arms in general with emphasis on shotguns.
The Gun Collector's Handbook of Values, by C.E. Chapel. Coward-McCann, N.Y.C., 1970. 398 pp., illus. $12.50.
The 9th rev. ed. of the best-known values reference for collectors with prices for 1971-1972.
Gunmakers of Indiana, by A. W. Lindert. Publ. by the author, Homewood, IL, 1968, 3rd ed. 284 pp., illus. Large format. $15.00.
An extensive and historical treatment, illus. with old photographs and drawings.
Guns of the Old West, by C. E. Chapel. Coward-McCann Inc., N.Y.C., 1961. 306 pp., illus. $6.95.
A definitive book on American arms that opened the frontier and won the West. Shows arms, rare pictures, advertisements, and pertinent associated material.
Guns Through the Ages, by Geoffrey Boothroyd. Sterling Publ. Co., N.Y.C., 1962, 192 pp., illus. $1.69.
A detailed illustrated history of small arms from the invention of gunpowder to today. Covers ignition methods, proof marks, fakes, ammo, etc. Bibliography.
Haandskydevaabens Bedommelse, by Johan F. Stockel. Udgivet Af Tojuhusmuseet, Copenhagen, Denmark, 2nd limited reprint, 1966. Vol. I, 397 pp., plus 6 plates, Vol. II, 1080 pp. illus. Both $35.00.
Printed in Danish but considered by scholars to be the finest and most complete source for the "marks" and "touches" of gunmakers. Both are well illus.
Hall's Breechloaders, by R. T. Huntington, Geo. Shumway, Publ. 1972. 369 pp., illus. $15.00. Paper, $12.00.
Definitive treatise on John H. Hall and his inspectors. Shows all known models of the Hall rifle, appurtenances and pistol.
Handbuch Der Waffenkunde, by Wendelin Boeheim. Akademische D. U. V., Graz, Austria, 1966, 694 pp., illus. $14.00.
One of the famous works of 1890—long out-of-print. Now in a new printing, German text. Historical weapons and armor from the Middle Ages through the 18th century.
Handfeuerwaffen, by J. Lugs, Deutscher Militarverlag, Berlin, 1956. 2 Vol., 315 pp., illus. German text, $40.00.
Noted reference on small arms and their development in many nations. All types of weapons are listed described, and illustrated, with data on manufacturers.

Die Handfeuerwaffen, by Rudolf Schmidt, Vienna, Austria, 1968, Vol. I, text 225 pp., Vol. II, 76 plates. $20.00.
Reprint of an important 1875 German reference work on military small arms, much prized by knowledgeable collectors. The fine color plates in Vol. II show detailed and exploded views of many longarms and handguns.

Henry Deringer's Pocket Pistol, by John E. Parsons, Morrow, NYC, 1952. Over 70 illustrations. $7.50.
An excellent and complete account of this famous maker, coupled with an extensive story on Deringer's imitators, the later cartridge derringers, etc.

Hints to Riflemen, by H. W. S. Cleveland. Distributor, Robert Halter, New Hope, PA, 286 pp., illustrated. $6.50.
A reprint of the original 1864 edition, to which *Practical Directions for the use of the Rifle* has been added.

History and Collecting Case Pocket Knives, by D. P. Ferguson. D. P. Ferguson, Fairborn, OH, 1970. 24 pp., illus., paper, $1.00.
Handbook on knives made by W. R. Case & Sons Cutlery Co.

A History of Body Armor, by H. L. Peterson, Charles Scribner's Sons, NY, 1968. 64 pp., illus. $4.95.
From the fur and leather armor of primitive man to the nylon body armor and steel helmet of today.

A History of the Colt Revolver, by C. T. Haven and F. A. Belden. Bonanza Books, NY, 1967. A reprint. 711 pages large format, profusely illus. in line and halftone. $8.95.
A great and massive work, including details on other Colt arms from 1836 to 1940. A must for every Colt collector.

A History of Firearms, by W. Y. Carman. Routledge & Kegan Paul Ltd., London, England, 1955. 207 pp., illus. $4.50.
A concise coverage, from earliest times to 1914, with emphasis on artillery.

A History of Firearms, by H. L. Peterson. Chas. Scribner's Sons, N.Y.C., 1961. 57 pp., profusely illus. $4.95.
From the origin of firearms through each ignition form and improvement to the M-14. Drawings by Daniel D. Feaser.

History of Modern U.S. Military Small Arms Ammunition, by F. W. Hackley, W. H. Woodin and E. L. Scranton, Macmillan, NYC, 1967. 315 pp., 8½"x11", over 500 exact-scale drawings and 100 photos, $25.00.
A superb work based on years of research by the capable authors. Covers cartridges for handguns, rifles and machine guns; miscellaneous, experimental and unidentified rounds, etc.

A History of Shooting, by Jaroslav Lugs, Spring Books, Feltham, England. 1st printing, 1968. 227 pp., well illus., with contemporary drawings and photographs. $4.98.
Historical survey dealing mainly with marksmanship, duelling and exhibition shooting in Europe and America.

A History of Spanish Firearms, by James D. Lavin. Arco Co., NY, 1965. 304 pp., illus. $9.95.
This history, beginning with the recorded appearance of gunpowder in Spain, traces the development of hand firearms through their golden age—the eighteenth century—to the death in 1825 of Isidro Soler. Copious reproductions of short and long arms, list of gun makers and their "marks" a glossary, bibliography and index are included.

A History of Weaponry, by Courtlandt Canby, Hawthorne Books, Inc., NY, 1963, 112 pp., illus. $2.98.
From the caveman's club to the M-14 rifle, from Greek fire to the ICBM.

The History of Winchester Firearms 1866-1966, ed. by T. E. Hall and P. Kuhlhoff, Winchester-Western Press, New Haven, CT, 1966. 159 pp., illus. $10.00.
Called the collector's item of the century, this 3rd ed. of Geo. R. Watrous' work rises to new glory in its scope and illustrations, beautifully produced, with a slip case showing old hunting scenes by A. B. Frost and Frederic Remington. Limited ed.

Home Service Helmet 1878-1914 With Regimental Plates, The Collectors Series, London, n.d., 32 pp., illus. Paper, $4.00.
Taken from the Wilkinson-Latham collection.

Identifying Old U.S. Muskets, Rifles & Carbines, by Col. A. Gluckman. Stackpole Books, Harrisburg, PA, 1965, 487 pp., illus. $10.00.
Collector's guide to U.S. long arms, first publ. 1959. Numerous models of each type are described and shown, with histories of their makers.

Illustrated British Firearms Patents 1714-1853, comp. and ed. by Stephen V. Grancsay and Merrill Lindsay. Winchester Press. NY, 1969. Unpaginated. $15.00.
Facsimile of patent documents with a bibliography. Limited, numbered ed. of 1000, bound in ¾ leather and marbled boards.

Insignia, Decorations and Badges of the Third Reich and Occupied Countries, by R. Kahl, Military Collectors Service, Kedichem, Holland, 1970. 135 pp., $9.95.
Handbook of regalia with descriptive text and over 800 line illus.

An introduction to British Artillery in North America, by S. J. Gooding. Museum Rest. Serv., Ottawa, 1965. 54 pp., illus., Paperbound. $2.00.
Concise account of such equipment used in America 1750-1850.

Japanese Armour, by L. J. Anderson. Stackpole Books, Harrisburg, PA, 1968. 84 pp., illus. $4.95.
British reference on museum quality armor made by the Myochin and Saotome families between the 15th and 20th centuries.

Japanese Polearms, by R. M. Knutsen. Holland Press, London, 1963. 271 pp., well-illus. Line drawings and photos. $18.00.
Each category of Japanese spear is described and illus. in this hist. treatment, including schools of spear and sword fencing. Lists leading makers and glossary.

Japanese Sword Blades, by Alfred Dobree, George Shumway, York, PA, 1967. 39 pp., illus., in paper wrapers. $4.50.
A two-part monograph, reprinted from a notable work.

The Kentucky Rifle, by J. G. W. Dillin. Geo. Shumway, York, PA, 1967. 5th ed. 202 pp., illus. $20.00
A respected work on the long rifles developed in colonial days and carried by pioneers and soldiers. Much information of value to collectors and historians. Limited ed.

Kentucky Rifle Patchboxes & Barrel Marks, by Roy F. Chandler, Valley View Offset, Duncannon, PA, 1971. 400 pp., $20.00.
Reference work illustrating hundreds of patchboxes, together with the mark or signature of the maker.

Robert Klaas Sword and Dagger Catalog, Robt. Klaas, Solingen-Ohligs, W. Germany 1938. 32 pp., illus. Paper, $5.00.
Reprint of the original 1938 catalog. A rare reference work. 16 pp. of swords and daggers with original prices.

The Leather Jacket Soldier, by O. B. Faulk. Socio-Technical Pub., Pasadena, CA, 1971, 80 pp., illus. $10.00.
History of such Spanish military equipment of the late 18th century as lances, horse accoutrements, guns, uniforms, etc.

Longrifles of North Carolina, by John Bivins, Jr. Geo. Shumway, York, PA, 1968, 200 pp., profusely illus. $24.00.
Historical survey of North Carolina gunmakers and their production during the 18th and 19th centuries. Over 400 gunsmiths are included. Fine photographs.

Longrifles of Note, by Geo. Shumway, Geo. Shumway, York, PA, 1967. 90 pp., illus. Paper covers $3.95.
A review of 35 fine American long rifles, with detailed illustrations showing their art work, plus descriptive material.

The Luger Pistol, by Fred A. Datig. Privately published, Los Angeles, CA, 1962. 328 pp. well-illus. $8.50.
Larger, revised ed. of the story behind the most famous pistol of all time.

Manhattan Firearms, by Waldo E. Nutter, Stackpole Books, Harrisburg, PA, 1958. 250 pp., illus., in halftone. $7.95.
Complete history of the Manhattan Firearms Mfg. Co., and its products. Excellent specialized reference.

The Mantons: Gunmakers, by W. Keith Neal and D. H. L. Back, Walker & Co., NY, 1966, 300 pp., illus. $10.95.
Well-documented account of the life and work of John and Joseph Manton, and others of the British gunmakers. A long list, with serial numbers, etc., of Manton guns, is included.

Manual of Rifling and Rifle Sights, by Lt.-Col. Viscount Bury, M.P., Ray Riling Arms Books Co., Phila., PA, 1971. 47 pp., Paper, $5.00.
Reprint of 1864 London edition done for the British National Rifle Ass'n. 141 illus., plus 3 folding plates.

The Manufacture of Armour and Helmets in 16th Century Japan, by Sakakibara Kozan. Holland Press, London, 1963. 156 pp., 32 pp. of illus. $20.00.
Important reference on styles and steps of making Japanese armor, first publ. Tokyo, 1800. Eng. trans., revised by H. R. Robinson of Tower of London Armouries.

Mauser-Gewehre & Mauser-Patente, by R. H. Korn. Akademische Druck Graz, Austria, 1971. 440 pp. German text, most completely illustrated with copious line drawings, charts, many of them folding plates. $27.50.
Fine reprint of the extremely-rare original. Truly a must for every Mauser buff, it has never been surpassed.

Metal Uniform Insignia of the US Army in the Southwest, 1846-1902, by S. B. Brinckerhoff, Arizona Pioneers Hist. Soc., Tucson, Ariz., 1965. 28 pp., illus. Paper covers. $1.50.
Monograph on buttons, badges, buckles, and other uniform insignia.

Metallic Cartridges, T. J. Treadwell, compiler. The Armoury, NYC, 1959. Unpaginated. 68 plates. Paper, $2.95. Cloth, $5.95.
A reduced-size reproduction of U.S. Ordnance Memoranda No. 14, originally publ. in 1873, on regulation and experimental cartridges manufactured and tested at Frankford Arsenal, Philadelphia, Pa.

Militaria, by Frederick Wilkinson. Hawthorn Books, New York, NY, 1969. 1st U.S. ed. 256 pp., well illus. in halftone. $5.95.
Introduction to military items of interest to collectors, including prints, medals, uniforms, military miniatures, weapons, badges etc.

Military Arms of Canada, by Upper Canada Hist. Arms Soc. Museum Restoration Serv., West Hill, Ont., 1963. 43 pp., illus. $1.50.
Booklet cont. 6 authoritative articles on the principal models of Canadian mil. small arms. Gives characteristics of each, makers, quantities produced.

Military Edged Weapons of the World, 1880-1965, by H. A. Mauerer, College Pt., NY, 1967. 151 pp., illus. $4.50.
Various swords, blades, etc., in a private collection are dimensioned, described, and photographed. A guide for collectors. Paper wrappers.

Military Headgear in the Southwest, 1846-1890, by S. B. Brinckerhoff, Arizona Pioneers Hist. Soc., Tucson, Ariz., 1963. 16 pp., illus. Paper covers. $1.50.
Historical monograph, reprinted from the journal *Arizoniana*. With bibliography.

Military Sharps Rifles and Carbines, by R. E. Hopkins. Hopkins, Campbell, Calif., 1967. 141 pp., illus. $11.50.
A guide to the principal types, with photographs, patent data, technical details, etc.

Miniature Arms, by Merrill Lindsay. Winchester Press, New York, NY, 1970. 111 pp., illus. $5.95.
A concise study of small-scale replicas of firearms and other weapons of collector interest. Fine color photographs.

Monographie der K. K. Osterr.-Ung: Blanken und Handfeuer-Waffen, by Anton Dolleczek. Akademische Druck, Graz, Austria, 1970. 197 pp., illus. $10.00.
Facsimile reprint of a standard 1896 German work on military weapons. In German text, illus. with line drawings and color plate of regimental colors.

Montgomery Ward & Co. 1894-1895, reproduction of a 600-page catalog, ed. by Jos. J. Schroeder, Jr., Digest Books, Inc., Northfield, IL, 1970. profusely illus. $4.95.
A nostalgic look at the past, and for the gun enthusiast a look at models and prices prevailing in the late 19th century.

The NRA Collector's Series, Digest Books, Inc., Northfield, IL, 1971, 84 pp. paper covers $2.95.
Reprint of the three predecessors of *American Rifleman* magazine and the first edition of *American Rifleman*.

The NRA Gun Collectors Guide, by staff members of NRA. National Rifle Assn., Washington, D.C., 1972. 256 pp., well illus. $4.50.
A wealth of information on collecting and collectors arms, with 64 major and 41 short articles, selected from the last 18 years of in "The American Rifleman."

Louis Napoleon on Artillery: The Development of Artillery from the 14th to the 17th Century, by W. Y. Carman, Arms and Armour Press, Middlesex, England, 1967. 24 pp., illus. Paper covers. $2.75.
A reprinting of rare original material—10 finely engraved plates, with 70 drawings, on the development of artillery, plus brief text.

The New Highland Military Discipline, by Geo. Grant. Museum Restoration Service, Ottawa, 1967. 32 pp., illus. $1.50.
Reprint of a Scottish drill manual, regimental history, with illus. contemporary and modern. Paper wrappers.

The 9-pdr. Muzzle Loading Rifle, by J. D. Chown. Museum Restoration Service, Ottawa, 1967. 32 pp., illus. $1.50.
Reprint of an early Canadian artillery manual, with historical notes. Paper wrappers.

Simeon North: First Official Pistol Maker of the United States, by S. North and R. North, Rutgers Book Center, Highland Park, NJ, 1972. 207 pp., illus. $7.95.
Exact reprint of the original. Includes chapters on New England pioneer manufacturers and on various arms.

Notes on Canadian Shotshells, by N. Krevosheia and A. M. Provick, compilers. N. Krevosheia, Edmonton, Canada, 1967. Paper wrappers, 32 pp., illus. $2.00.
An illustrated handbook for collectors with line drawings and photos of domestic, contract, export and miscellaneous shells and their boxes, etc.

Notes on U.S. Ordnance, vol. II, 1776-1941, by James E. Hicks. Modern Books & Crafts, Greens Farms, Conn., 1971. 252 pp., illus. $8.00.
Updated version of a standard work on development of military weapons used by U.S. forces, from handguns to coast artillery and aerial bombs. This is not to be confused with Hicks 1940 United States Ordnance, referring mainly to Ordnance correspondence as Vol. II.

One Hundred Great Guns, by Merrill Lindsay. Walker & Co., NY, 1967. 379 pp., fine color illus. $9.95.
Deluxe illus. history of firearms, covering all principal types of small arms and their makers. Bibliography.
A super-deluxe edition is available at $75.00.

Ordnance Memoranda No.22. The Fabrication of Small Arms for the U.S. Service, by Lt. Col. James G. Benton. Benchmark Pub. Co., Glendale, NY, 1970. 229 pp., 35 plates. $9.50.
Reprint of an 1878 War Dept. pub. on U.S. production of military firearms and edged weapons.

Oriental Armour, by W. R. Robinson. Reprint by Outlet Book Co., New York, NY, 1970. 256 pp., well illus. $4.95.
Traces the subject material from earliest times until it was finally discarded.

The Original Mauser Magazine Sporting Rifles. Shooter's Bible, S. Hackensack, NJ, 56 pp., illus., paperbound. $1.00.
Facsimile reprint of a Mauser firearms brochure, with English text.

An Outline of the History and Development of Hand Firearms, from the Earliest Period to About the End of the Fifteenth Century, by R. C. Clephan [Original ed., 1906]. A reprint in 1946 by Standard Publications, Inc., Huntington, W.Va. 60 pp., illus. $4.00.
A worthy facsimile of a very scarce, concise and scholarly work.

The Peacemaker and Its Rivals, by John E. Parsons. Morrow, NYC, 1950. 140 pp., illustrated. Appendix, bibliography, and index. $7.50.
Detailed history and development of the Single Action Army Colt, with an over-all study of the six-shooter's significance in American history.

The Pennsylvania-Kentucky Rifle, by Henry J. Kauffman. Bonanza Books, NY, 1968. A reprint. 374 pp., illus. $4.95.
A classic work first publ. in 1960 on early long rifles. Makers descriptions, and manufacturing methods are covered.

Percussion Revolvers of the United States, by R. Thalheimer. Von Hoffman Press, St. Louis, 1970. 224 pp., illus, $7.95.
Reference work on U.S. and Confederate percussion revolvers, plus a history of firearms from the hand-cannon to percussion revolvers.

Photographic Supplement of Confederate Swords, by Wm. A. Albaugh III. Wm. A. Bond, Vernon, TX, 1963. 205 pp., 300 photos. $6.95.
Over 200 specimens of C. W. Edged weapons are shown, with data on their owners and makers. Useful for collectors and students.

The Powder Flask Book, by Ray Riling. Bonanza Books, NY 1968. A reprint. 520 pp., large format, profusely illus. First re-issue of the 1953 original ed. $9.95. A limited number of the originals are available for inscription and autograph at $35.00.
Covers the literature on flasks, their makers, and users—hunters, shooters and the military—as well as showing the arms, cased or not, short and long. A relative price listing for collector advantage is included.

Price List of the U.S. Cartridge Company's Ammunition, A 1969 reprint of the 1891 original, publ. by J. C. Tillinghast, Marlow, N.H. 29 pp., illus., paper covers. $2.50.
Displays many of the now hard-to-find cartridges.

A Primer of World Bayonets. G. Hughes, London, 1969. Unpaginated, illus. Paper, $5.00.
A comprehensive (2 vol.) manual on the bayonet.

Quellen zur Geschichte de Feuerwaffen, by A. Essenwein [ed./compiler] Akademische Druck, Graz, Austria, 1969. One volume of text [German] plus another of fascinating plates. 178 pp., text and 197 plates. $50.00.
A fine facsimile of a rare and most interesting German source book on the "History of Firearms," taken from original drawings of 1390-1700. A treasury for the serious scholar and/or artillery buff.

The Rampant Colt, by R. L. Wilson. Thomas Haas, Spencer, Ind., 1969. 107 pp., well illus. $10.00.
Study of Samuel Colt's coat-of-arms and the rampant colt figure used on Colt firearms and in advertising.

Rapiers, by Eric Valentine. Stackpole Books, Harrisburg, Pa., 1968. 76 pp., 58 photos., 3 drawings. $4.95.
A desirable monograph, first on its subject, to be publ. in English. Covers methods of authentication, renovation, cleaning and preservation.

Red Coat and Brown Bess, by Anthony D. Darling. Museum Restoration Service, Ottawa, Ontario, Can., 1970. Paper covers, 63 pp., very well illus., in line and halftone. $3.00.
An unusually excellent treatise on the British Army in 1774-1775. Includes detailed text and illus. of various models of the "Brown Bess," plus "Records of the Battles, Sieges and Skirmishes of the American Revolution."

Regulation Military Swords, by J. Wilkinson-Latham, Star Products, London, 1970. 32 pp., illus. Paper, $4.00.
Survey of military swords of U.S., England, France and Germany.

Remington Arms in American History, by A. Hatch, Rinehart & Co., NY, 1956. 359 pp., illus. $6.50.
Collector's guide with appendix of all Remington arms, ballistics tables, etc.

Remington Catalog [Price List] of 1885, a reprint in facsimile, by The Wyoming Armory, Inc., Cheyenne, Wyo., 1969. 48 pp., well illus., paper covers. $2.50.
All rifles, handguns, cane gun, sights, cartridges, shotguns, accessories etc. A priced catalog.

The Remington Historical Treasury of American Guns, by Harold L. Peterson. Thomas Nelson & Sons, N.Y.C., 1966. 199 pp., illus. $2.95.
A historical saga woven into first-rate Americana through the facts and details of the Remington firm and their products.

The Revolver, Its Description, Management, and Use, by P. E. Dove. Arms and Armour Press, London, 1968. 57 pp., 6 engravings, stiff paper wrappers. $3.75.
A facsimile reprint of a rare classic, dealing principally with the Adams revolver compared to the qualities of the Colt.

Revolving Arms, by A. W. F. Taylerson, Walker and Co., New York, 1967. 123 pp., illus. $8.50.
A detailed history of mechanically-rotated cylinder firearms in Europe and the U.S. Primarily on handguns, but other types of revolving guns are included.

Rifled Infantry Arms, by J. Schon; trans. by Capt. J. Gorgas, USA. Dresden, 1855; facsimile reprint by W. E. Meuse, Schuylersville, NY, 1965. 54 pp., illus. $2.50.
Reprint of classic essay on European military small arms of the mid-19th century. Paper covers.

The Rifled Musket, by Claud E. Fuller. Stackpole Books, Harrisburg, Pa., 1958. 302 pp., illus. $4.95.
The authoritative work of the late Claud E. Fuller and basically an account of the muskets whose model dates fell within the Civil War years —1861, 1863 and 1864. Part Two treats of the contract muskets. Some reproduced material, notably Bartlett & Gallatin's "Digest of Cartridges," is almost wholly illegible, as is much of an 1860 Ordnance Dept. report.

Romance of Knife Collecting, by Dewey P. Ferguson, Dewey P. Ferguson, Fairborn, OH, 1970. 100 pp., illus. Paper covers, spiral binding. $5.00.
From stone to steel knives, care, patterns, counterfeiting, history of knife companies, etc.
Price Guide to above title, by D. P. Ferguson, same place, 1972. 60 pp., illus. Paper covers. $4.00.

G. Roth Aktiengesellschaft. Horn Co., Burlington, Vt., 1968. 28 pp., illus., paperbound. $2.50.
Reprint of a German cartridge catalog of 1913, with drawings and dimensions.

Royal Sporting Guns at Windsor, by H. L. Blackmore. H. M. Stationery Office, London, England, 1968. 60 pp. text, 52 plates. $9.54.
Catalog of the most decorative and interesting guns in the Royal Armoury collection at Windsor Castle.

Russian Military Swords, 1801-1917, by E. Mollo. Historical Research Unit, London, Eng., 1969. 56 pp., illus. $7.50.
First book in English to examine and classify the various swords used by the Russian Army from Alexander I to the Revolution. 42 photos, 27 line drawings, 10 in color.

Russian Pistols in the 17th Century, by L. Tarassuk. Geo. Shumway, York, Pa., 1968. 35 pp. plus plates. $4.00.
Monograph on museum quality Russian handguns of the 17th century. Fine, detailed photographs.

Samuel Colt's New Model Pocket Pistols, by S. G. Keogh. Priv. publ., 1964. 31 pp., 20 illus., paperbound. $3.00.
"The story of the 1855 Root model revolver," with detailed classification data and descriptions. Well-illus.

The Samurai Swords, by J. M. Yumoto. Tuttle Co., Rutland, Vt., 1958. 191 pp., illus. $4.50.
Detailed information on evaluation of specimens, including origin and development of the Japanese blade.

Savage Automatic Pistols, by James R. Carr. Publ. by the author, St. Charles, Ill., 1967. A reprint. 129 pp., illus. with numerous photos. $6.50.
Collector's guide to Savage pistols, models 1907-1922, with features, production data, and pictures of each. A reprint of the circa 1912 Savage promotional and instructive booklet titled *It Banishes Fear* is recommended to accompany the above. Paper wrappers, 32 pp. $1.50.

Schuyler, Hartley & Graham Catalog. publ. by Norm Flayderman, Greenwich, Conn., 1961. 176 pp., illus. $9.50.
A reprint of a rare 1864 catalog of firearms, military goods, uniforms, etc. An extensive source of information for Civil War collectors.

Scottish Swords and Dirks, by John Wallace. Stackpole Books, Harrisburg, Pa., 1970. 80 pp., illus, $4.95.
An illustrated reference guide to Scottish edged weapons.

Scottish Swords from the Battlefield at Culloden, by Lord Archibald Campbell, Mowbray Co., Providence, RI, 1971. 63 pp., illus. $5.00.
Modern reprint of an exceedingly rare 1894 limited private ed.

Sears, Roebuck & Co. Catalogue No. 117, J. J. Schroeder, ed. A reprint of the 1908 work. Digest Books, Inc., Northfield, Ill., 1969, profusely illus., paper covers. $3.95.
This reprint of a famous catalog brings to all arms collectors a treasured replica of the collectibles and prices of yesteryear.

The Sharps Rifle, by W. O. Smith. Morrow, NYC, 1943, reprinted 1965. 138 pp., illus. $10.00.
Study of America's first successful breech-loader patented 1848, with information on its history, development, and operation.

Shosankenshu, by H. L. Joly. Holland Press, London, 1963. Unpaginated. $12.50.
List of Japanese artists' names and kakihan found on sword furniture by the late European authority. Completed in 1919, previously unpubl., this is a facsimile of Joly's MS. and line drawings. Lists nearly 3,000 names.

Shotgun Shells: Identification, Manufacturers and Checklist for Collectors, by F. H. Steward. B. and P. Associates, St. Louis, Mo., 1969. 101 pp., illus., paper covers. $4.95.
Historical data for the collector.

Single-Shot Rifles, by James J. Grant. Wm. Morrow & Co., NYC, 4th printing 1964. 385 pp., illus. $8.50.
A detailed study of these rifles by a noted collector.

Small Arms, by Frederick Wilkinson, Hawthorne Books, Inc., New York, 1966. 256 pp., illus. $4.95.
A history of small firearms, techniques of the gunsmith, equipment used by combatants, sportsmen and hunters.

Small Arms and Ammunition in the United States Service, 1776-1865, by B. R. Lewis. Smithsonian Inst., Washington, D.C., 1968. 338 pp. plus 52 plates. $12.50.
2nd printing of a distinguished work for historians and collectors. A limited number of deluxe, signed and numbered copies (1st reprinting 1960) are available in full leather and gilt top at $25.

Smith and Wesson 1857-1945, by Robert J. Neal and Roy J. Jenks. A. S. Barnes and Co., Inc., NYC, 1966. 500 pp., illus. with over 300 photos and 90 radiographs. $25.00.
A long-needed book, especially for knowledgeable enthusiasts and collectors. Covers an investigation of the series of handguns produced by the Smith and Wesson Company.

The Soldier's Manual, by J. H. Nesmith. (First publ. in Philadelphia in 1824.) Geo. Shumway, York, Pa., 1963. 108 pp., frontis, and 11 color plates. $4.95.
Facsimile reproduction of an important early American militia drill manual, covering exercises with musket, pistol, sword, and artillery. The color plates depict accurately the picturesque uniforms and accoutrements of elite militia corps of Phila. and vicinity. Intro. by Anne S. K. Brown traces the origin of the text matter and the early engravers.

Southern Derringers of the Mississippi Valley, by Turner Kirkland. Pioneer Press, Tenn., 1971. 80 pp., illus., paper covers. $1.00.
A guide for the collector, and a much-needed study.

Sporting Guns, by Richard Akehurst. G. P. Putnam's Sons, New York, NY, 1968. 120 pp., excellently illus. and with 24 pp. in full color. $5.95.
One of the noted Pleasures and Treasures series. A nostalgic tracing of the history of shooting, and of the guns and rifles used by the sportsman.

Springfield Armory, Pointless Sacrifice, by C. L. Dvarecka. Prolitho Pub., Ludlow, Mass., 1968. 177 pp., illus. Paper covers. $1.00.
Story of the armory's closing; contains names, particulars and the quantities made of Springfield arms.

Springfield Muzzle-Loading Shoulder Arms, by C. E. Fuller, F. Bannerman Sons, NYC, reprinted 1968. 176 pp., illus. $12.50.
Long-awaited reprint of an important 1930 reference work on weapons produced at Springfield Armory, 1795-1865, including ordnance reports, tables, etc., on flintlock and percussion models.

Stahlhelm; Evolution of the German Steel Helmet, by F. R. Tubbs, F. R. Tubbs, 1971. 104 pp., illus. Paper, $5.50.
Helmets used by the German Army from 1916 to date. Shields, frontal plates, liners, detailed drawings, camouflage, etc.

Stevens Pistols and Pocket Rifles, by K. L. Cope, Museum Restoration Service, Ottawa, Can., 1971. 104 pp. $8.50.
All are shown, identified, detailed, variations, listings of dates, etc.

The Story of Allen and Wheelock Firearms, by H. H. Thomas. C. J. Krehbiel, Cincinnati, 1965, 125 pp., illus. $6.50.
Brief history of the Allen & Wheelock guns produced in mid-19th century, and their maker. Well illus. with descriptions of specimens.

The Story of Pope's Barrels, by Ray M. Smith. Stackpole Books, Harrisburg, PA, 1964., 211 pp., illus. $10.00.
Detailed account of the achievements and life of Harry M. Pope, master rifle bbl. maker.

Superimposed Load Firearms 1360-1860, by D. R. Baxter. Privately printed for the author in Hong Kong, 1966. $22.00. Foreword by Keith Neal. Ltd. ed., 500 copies only.
Excellently illustrated with photographs, diagrams, figures and patent drawings. Covers over-under arms of all countries, and a list of gunmakers and inventors is included.

Sword, Lance and Bayonet, by Charles ffoulkes and E. C. Hopkinson. Arco Publishing Co., NY, 1967. 145 pp., well illus. in line and halftone. $7.50.
A facsimile reprint of the first attempt at a consecutive account of the arms, both general and official use, since the discarding of armor.

The Sword and Same, by H. L. Joly and I. Hogitaro, Holland Press Ltd., London, 1971. 241 pp. plates and line drawings. $18.00.
New printing of Arai Hakuseki, "The Sword Book in Honcho Gunkiko" and "The Book of Same Ko Hi Sei Gi of Inaba Tsurio."

Swords for Sea Service, by Commander W. E. May, R. N. & P. G. W. Annis, H.M. S.O., London, 1970. 398 pp. in 2 volumes, $30.00.
Study based on the swords, dirks and cutlasses in the National Maritime Museum in Greenwich, plus many other outside weapons, and information on the British sword trade, industry, makers and retailers. 140 black and white plates, 3 color plates and many other illus.

The 36 Calibers of the Colt Single Action Army, by David M. Brown. Publ. by the author at Albuquerque, NM, new reprint 1971. 222 pp., well-illus. $15.00.
Edited by Bev Mann of *Guns Magazine.* This is an unusual approach to the many details of the Colt S.A. Army revolver. Halftone and line drawings of the same models make this of especial interest.

Thoughts on the Kentucky Rifle in its Golden Age, by Joe Kindig, Jr. George Shumway, York, PA, 1970. A facsimile reprint of the 1960 original. 561 pp., replete with fine arms and data on many makers. $14.50.
Covers mainly the arms and their makers in the Lancaster area of Pennsylvania. An authoritative work.

Toxophilus, by Roger Ascham. S. R. Pub. Ltd., Yorkshire, Eng., 1968. 230 pp., illus. $7.00
A facsimile reprint of the 1788 ed. still regarded as the classic text on archery.

Treasury of the Gun, by H. L. Peterson, Crown Publishing Co.'s reprint, NYC, 1965. 252 pp. profusely illus., some in color. $7.95.
A beautiful production, presenting a new high in authoritative text. Virtually every significant type of firearm of the past 650 years is shown.

A Treatise on Ancient Armour and Weapons, by F. Grose, Benchmark Publ., Glendale, NY, 1970. Irreg. pagination, illus. $12.50.
Reprint of a 1786 monograph from the collection in the Tower of London and other sites.

Underhammer Guns, by H. C. Logan. Stackpole Books, Harrisburg, PA, 1964. 250 pp. illus. $4.98.
A full account of an unusual form of firearm dating back to flintlock days. Both American and foreign specimens are included.

Uniforms and Badges of the Third Reich, by Rudolph Kahl, Military Collectors Service, Kedichem, Holland, 1970.
Volume I; NSDAP. 76 pp., 260 illus. $6.95.
Volume II: SA, NSKK, and SS. 120 pp., 523 illus. $8.95.
Volume III: HJ, NSFK, and RAD. 100 pp., 452 illus. $7.95.

Uniforms of the American, British, French, and German Armies in the War of the American Revolution, 1775-1783, by Lt. Charles M. Lefferts, We Inc., Old Greenwich, CT, 1970. 292 pp., illus. $8.00.
Reprint of the original 1926 ed. and the only book on its subject today.

U.S. Cartridge Co. Collection of Firearms, We, Inc., Old Greenwich, CT., 1970. 142 pp., illus. $6.00.
Describes each arm in detail as to manufacture, action, period of use, function, markings, patents, makers, etc.

U.S. Firearms: The First Century, 1776-1875, by D. F. Butler. Winchester Press, NY, 1971. 320 pp., illus. $15.00.
A rich mine of carefully researched information and data on American firearms of this period. Illustrated with photos, schematics and historical documents.

U.S. Martial and Semi-Martial Single-Shot Pistols, by C. E. Chapel, Coward-McCann Inc., NYC, 1962. 352 pp., over 150 illus. $7.50.
Describes in detail all single shot martial pistols used by the US armed forces and by military units of the states. A definitive guide.

U.S. Military Firearms, 1776-1956, by Maj. Jas. E. Hicks. J. E. Hicks & Son. La Canada, Calif., 216 pp., incl. 88 pages of fine plates. $12.50.
Covering 180 years of America's hand and shoulder weapons. The most authoritative book on this subject. Packed with official data.

U.S. Military Small Arms 1816-1865, by R. M. Reilly. The Eagle Press, Inc., Baton Rouge, La., 1970. 275 pp., illus. $22.50.
Describes and superbly illustrates every known type of primary and secondary martial firearm of the period 1816-1865. Limited, numbered ed.

U.S. Sword Bayonets, 1847-1865, by R. V. Davis, Jr. Priv. prt., Pittsburgh, PA, 1963. 36 pp., 17 pl., paper. $4.00
Histories, production data, and good photos of U.S. military sword bayonets of Civil War era.

U.S. Weapons Development 1920-25. An abridged reprint from official sources, this Section 1 covering rifles, pistols and some miscellaneous items. Design Publ., Inc. Hyattsville, Md. [circa 1968]. 57 pp., illus., paper covers. $5.00.
Dependable material for the collector and shooter.

A Universal Military Dictionary, by Captain George Smith. The rare original book was published at London in 1779. This facsimile reprint was released in 1969 by Museum Restoration Service, Ottawa, Ontario, Can. 336 pp., 16 fold-out plates. $27.50.
A most useful reference for mean of arms interest. Offered only in a numbered, limited issue of 700 copies.

Waffen: Beitrag zur Historischen Waffenkunde, by J. H. Hefner-Alteneck. Akademische Druck, Graz, Austria, 1969. 58 pp., German text plus 100 plates. $30.00.
A descriptive text complements the fine illustrations depicting armor and weapons used in Europe from the middle ages through the 17th century.

Weapons, by E. Tunis. World Publishing Co., NYC, 1954. 153 pp., a large book, well-illus. $4.95.
A pictorial history of arms with complementing narrative. Coverage: from the first tied stone thrown by pre-historic man to super bombs.

Weapons of the British Soldier, by Col. H. C. B. Rogers. Seeley Service & Co., London, 1960. 259 pp., illus. in line and halftone plus full color frontis. $7.50.
The story of weapons used by the British soldier throughout the ages and the many developments in personal arms during the course of history.

The Webley Story, by Wm. C. Dowell, Skyrac Press, Leeds, Eng. 337 pp., profusely illus. $21.00.
Detailed study of Webley pistols and revolvers, covering over 250 specimens. This important reference also gives detailed listing of English small arms cartridge patents through 1880.

The Whitney Firearms, by Claud Fuller. Standard Publications, Huntington, W. Va., 1946. 334 pp., many plates and drawings. $12.50.
An authoritative history of all Whitney arms and their maker. Highly recommended. An exclusive with Ray Riling Arms Book Co.

Winchester—The Gun That Won the West, by H. F. Williamson. Combat Forces Press, Washington, D.C., 1952. Later eds. by Barnes, NY 494 pp., profusely illus. $5.95.
A scholarly and essential economic history of an honored arms company, but the early and modern arms introduced will satisfy all but the exacting collector.

The Winchester Book, by Geo. Madis. Art & Reference House, Lancaster, Texas, 1971. 542 pp., illus. $20.00.
First release of 1,000 autographed deluxe copies at this special price. After these are sold only a standard ed. will be available, the price the same. $20.00.

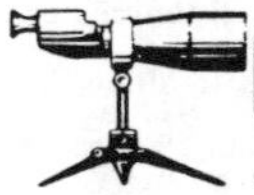

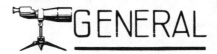

GENERAL

A.B.C. of Snap Shooting, by Horace Fletcher, Americana Archives Publ. Co., Topsfield, MA., 1971. 48 pp., illus. Paper, $3.00.
Authentic reproduction of a rare 1881 original.

The Adaptable Black Bear, by J. R. Matson. Dorrance & Co., Phila., Pa., 1967. 147 pp., illus. $4.00.
Complete picture of the black bear, its adaptation to environment, habits, disposition and behavior in the wild.

Age of Great Guns, by Frank E. Comparato. Stackpole Books, Harrisburg, Pa. 1965, 386 pp. illus. $11.95.
Of cannon kings and cannoneers who forged the fire-power of artillery. A highly acclaimed work of importance to artillery enthusiasts.

Air Gun Batteries, by E. G. Wolff. Public Museum, Milwaukee, Wisc., 1964. 28 pp., illus., paperbound. 75¢.
Study of discharge mechanisms on reservoir air guns.

Air Organizations of the Third Reich, Volume I, R. J. Bender, compiler. R. J. Bender, Mountain View, CA, 192 pp., illus., some in color. $9.95.
Concise survey of the World War II Luftwaffe organizations. Shows uniforms, weapons, identification marks and badges.

The Album of Gunfighters, by J. Marvin Hunter and Noah H. Rose, Warren Hunter, Helotes, Texas, 1965. 4th printing. 236 pp., wonderfully illus., with spectacular oldtime photos. $17.50.
For the serious gunfighter fan there is nothing to equal this factual record of the men-behind-the-star and the human targets that they faced.

To All Sportsmen; and Particularly to Farmers and Gamekeepers, by Col. Geo. Hanger, Richmond Publ. Co., Richmond, England, 1971. 226 pp. $9.50.
Reprint of an 1814 work on hunting, guns, horses, veterinary techniques, etc.

The American B.B. Gun, by A. T. Dunathan, A. S. Barnes, S. Brunswick, NJ, 1971. 154 pp., illus. $10.00.
Identification reference and a price guide for B.B. guns, plus a brief history and advertising plates.

American Bird Decoys, by W. J. Mackey Jr. Dutton, NYC, 1965. 256 pp., illus. $10.00.
The history and fine points of decoys for all gamebird species, with much data for collectors and hunters.

American Game Birds of Field and Forest, by F. C. Edminster, Book Sales, NY, 1972 490 pp. 99 plates. $6.95.
18 species; their origin, history, range, food, diseases, etc.

American Indian Tomahawks, by H. L. Peterson, Museum of the American Indian Heye Foundation, 1971. 142 pp., $10.00.
Brief description of various types and their makers. 314 illustrations, and many line drawings.

Americans and their Guns, compiled by Jas. B. Trefethen, ed. by Jas. E. Serven, Stackpole Books, Harrisburg, Pa., 1967. 320 pp., illus. $9.95.
The National Rifle Association of America story through nearly a century of service to the nation. More than a history—a chronical of help to novice and expert in the safe and proper use of firearms for defense and recreation, as well as a guide for the collector of arms.

America's Camping Book, by Paul Cardwell, Jr. C. Scribner's Sons, New York, NY 1st ed., 1969. 591 pp., well illus., in line and halftone. $10.00.
A fine illustrated guide to camping and woodcraft, with data on equipment, techniques, emergencies and nature study.

Ammunition General, TM 9-1900 to 11A-1-20, Dept. of the Army, Paladin Press, Boulder, CO, 1971. 320 pp., Paper, $6.00.
Reprint of army manual covering propellants, low and high explosives, chemical agents, rockets, etc. 215 illus., 19 color plates.

The Anatomy of Firearms, by R. L. Wallack, Simon & Schuster, NYC, 1965. 320 pp., illus. $6.95.
Guide to guns of all types, ammunition, ballistics, repairs and adjustments, and related topics.

Animals in Africa, by Peter and Philippa Scott. Clarkson N. Potter, NY, 1963. Profusely, magnificently illus. Unpaginated. Large format. $7.95.
The enchanting story, in words and pictures, of a journey by the authors through the National Parks of Kenya to Murchison Falls Park in Uganda. Over 180 pictures in black-and-white, 20 in full color.

Animals of East Africa, by C. A. Spinage. Houghton Mifflin Co., Boston, Mass., 1963. 151 pp., illus. $7.50.
The life history, unusual observations and little known facts about these animals. Over 90 photographs, some in color.

Archery: Its Theory and Practice, by H. A. Ford. Geo. Shumway, York, PA, 1971. 128 pp., illus. $6.00.
Reprint of the scarce 1856 ed.

Archery, by C. J. Longman and H. Walrond. Frederick Ungar Co., NY, 1967. 534 pp., illus. in line and halftone. $5.95.
Reproduction of a standard, important British reference work, first publ. in 1894, on the history, uses and techniques of archery.

Arco Gun Book, ed. by Larry Koller. Arco Publ. Co. Inc., NYC, 1962 397 pp., illus. $7.50.
A concise encyclopedia for arms collectors, shooters and hunters.

Armour, by Viscount Dillon. Geo. Shumway, York, PA, 1968. 78 pp., illus., paperbound. $4.00.
Facsimile of British monographs titled *An Elizabethan Armourer's Album* and *Armour Notes.*

Armoured Fighting Vehicles, by Malcolm McGregor, Walker & Co., New York, 1967. 56 pp., illus. $15.00.
Describes 12 tanks and armored cars, representative of those used in the two World Wars. The illustrations in full-color are true scale drawn from actual models.

Armoured Forces, by R. M. Ogorkiewicz. Arco Pub. Co., NY, 1970. 475 pp., illus. $7.95.
A history of the armored forces and their vehicles.

Arms of the World: The 1911 Alfa Catalogue. Edited by Joseph J. Schroeder, Jr. Digest Books, Northfield, IL., 701 pp., Paper, $5.95.
Reprint in 4 languages of thousands of guns, cartridges, swords, helmets, tools, etc. Profusely illus., and priced the 1911 way.

The Art of Archerie, by Gervase Markham. A reprint of the 1634 original, publ. in London. Geo. Shumway, York, PA, 1968. 172 pp. $12.00.
This classic treatise, written to keep alive the art of archery in warfare, treats with the making of longbows and their use. A scholarly introduction to the new issue by S. V. Grancsay adds an enlightening historical perception.

Art for Conservation; The Federal Duck Stamps, by Jene C. Gilmore, with introd. by Robt. Hines, Barre Publ., Barre, MA, 1971. 94 pp., illus. $14.95.
Contains all the duck stamp illustrations from 1934 to 1972 with pertinent biographical, historical and philatelic data.

The Art and Science of Taking to the Woods, by C. B. Colby and B. Angier, Stackpole Books, Harrisburg, Pa. 1970, 288 pp. illus. $7.95. Also in paper covers. $3.95.
Illustrated camper's manual covering all types of outdoor living and transportation, for novice and expert alike.

The Art of Shooting, by C. E. Chapel. Barnes, NYC, 1960. 424 pp., illus. $3.95.
A comprehensive, simplified guide to every aspect of pistol, revolver, and rifle shooting. A history of rifle development is included.

The Art of Survival, by C. Troebst. Doubleday & Co., Garden City, NY. 1965. 312 pp. illus. $5.95.
Narratives of devices of survival in difficult terrain or circumstances and evaluation of rescue and life-saving procedures.

The Art of the Decoy: American Bird Carvings, by Adele Earnest. Clarkson N. Potter, Inc., NYC, 1966. $4.95.
The origin of a lost art explained, plus some data on the most famous carvers. Over 106 black-and-white photos, 35 line drawings and an 8-page insert in full color.

The Artillerist's Manual, by Lieut, John Gibbon, Benchmark Pub. Co., Glendale, NY, 1970. 568 pp., illus. $16.50.
Reprint of an 1860 textbook on U.S. artillery, covering guns, ammunition, transportation, many other facets.

Artillery and Ammunition of the Civil War, by Warren Ripley. Van Nostrand Reinhold Co., NY, 1970. 384 pp., illus. $22.50.
Well-illustrated survey, covering Union and Confederate cannon and projectiles, as well as imported pieces.

Artillery of the U.S. Land Service: 1848-1865, compiled by D. E. Lutz. Antique Ordnance Artificers, Jackson, Mich., 1970. 64 pp., illus. Paper wrappers. $5.00.
Known as Vol. I, **Field Artillery, 1848-1865,** and the first of a series containing drawings of the artillery used during the Civil War. Mainly taken from manuscripts in the National Archives.

Asian Fighting Arts, by D. F. Draeger and R. W. Smith. Kodansha International Ltd., Tokyo, Japan. 2nd printing, 1969. 207 pp., well illus., in line and halftone. $12.50.
A work of monumental research, interesting to all involved in the science of fighting techniques. Covers eleven Asian skills, ranging from Chinese T'ai-chi and Burmese Bando to Japanese Jujitsu and the lethal Pentjak-silak of Indonesia.

Author and Subject Index to the American Rifleman Magazine 1961-1970, by W. R. Burrell, Galesburg, MI, 1971. 64 pp. $6.50.
Alphabetical listing by author, title and subject.

Bannerman Military Goods Catalog, 1907. Benchmark Publ. Co., NY, 260 pp., illus. Paper, $3.95.
Exact reprint of original catalog with thousands of items listed.

Bayonet Fighting, by the Dept. of the Army, Normount Armament Co., Forest Grove, OR, 1972. 76 pp., illus. Paper, $1.50.
Reprint of FM 23-25. Its principles, purpose, use, positions, training, etc.

Baron von Steuben and his Regulations, by Joseph R. Riling, Ray Riling Arms Books Co., Philadelphia, Penna., 1966. 207 pp., illus. $12.50.
A documented book on this great American Major General and the creation by him of the first official "Regulations." Includes the complete facsimile of these regulations.

Being Your Own Wilderness Doctor, by Dr. E. Russel Kodet and Bradford Angier. Stackpole Books, Harrisburg, Pa., 1968. 127 pp., illus. In line drawings. $3.95.
Called the "outdoorsman's emergency manual" It offers security of knowing what to do best—in case of the worst.

A Bibliography of Military Books up to 1642, by Maurice J. D. Cockle. A new reprint of the Holland Press, London, 1965. 320 pp., illus. $15.00.
Describes the important military books from the invention of gunpowder to subject date. A standard reference.

Birds in Our Lives, ed. by A. Stefferud and A. L. Nelson. Gov't. Prtg. Office, Washington, D.C. 20402, 1966, 576 pp., 80 drawings, 372 photos. $9.00.
61 authors have contributed to this great book, the illus. by Bob Hines. A successful effort to bring any and all readers an appreciation of—and an interest in—the part birds play in their lives.

Black Powder Guide, by Geo. Nonte, Jr. Shooter's Bible Publ., S. Hackensack, NJ, 1969. 214 pp., fully illus., $3.95.
A complete guide to muzzle-loading firearms of all types, their loading, repair and maintenance.

Black Powder Snapshots, by Herb Sherlock. Standard Publications. Huntington, W. VA, 50 pp., illus. $10.00.
Deluxe large volume containing 23 major Sherlock drawings and 95 punchy, marginal sketches.

The Book of the American West, ed. by Jay Monaghan. Julian Messner, New York, 1963. 608 pp., 200 illus. (many in color). $9.95.
A special chapter on frontier firearms is a feature of this massive work. 10 experts on Western hist. in as many fields of study contributed to the book. Illus. includ. works by the best contemporary artists.

The Book of the American Woodcock, by Wm. G. Sheldon, Ph.D. University of Mass. Press, Amherst, 1967. 227 pp., bibliography, appendices and index. $8.50.

Bow & Arrow Archer's Digest, ed. by Jack Lewis. Digest Books, Inc., Northfield, Ill., 1971. 320 pp., profusely illus. $5.95.
Comprehensive treatment of the art and science of archery.

The Boy's Book of Backyard Camping, by A. A. Macfarlan. Stackpole Books, Harrisburg, Pa. 1st ed. 1968. 160 pp., illus. in line. $4.50.
"How to use at-home space for the development of camping skills." Chapters on tents, equipment, cooking—all for out-of-doors enjoyment.

Boys in the Revolution, by Jack Coggins, Stackpole Books, Harrisburg, Pa., 1967. 96 pp., illus. $4.50.
Young Americans tell their part in the war for independence—what they did, what they wore, the gear they carried, the weapons they used, the ships they sailed on, the campaigns in which they fought.

British and American Tanks of WW II, by P. Chamberlain and C. Ellis. Arco Pub. Co., New York., 1969 222 pp., illus. $9.95.
Complete, illus. history of American, British and Commonwealth tanks, 1939-1945. Photos, and precise specifications of each.

The British Code of Duel, Richmond Publ. Co., Richmond, England, 1971. 144 pp. Reprint of the 1824 ed. Reference on the laws of honour and the character of gentlemen. Together with **The Art of Duelling,** same publ., 1971. 70 pp. Reprint of the 1836 London ed. Both books $9.00.
Information useful to young Continental tourists.

Camper's Digest, by Cecil Coffey. Digest Books, Inc., Northfield, Ill. 60093 320 pp., paper covers, over 500 illus. $4.95.
Everything needed to be known about camping. Trails, tools, clothes, cooking, hundreds of camp grounds listed, and more.

The Camping Manual, compiled by Fred Sturges, Stackpole Books, Harrisburg, PA, 1967. 160 pp., illus. $3.95.
An excellent refresher on the fundamentals, with a digest of the newest methods and latest advice for those who want to enjoy camping more.

Carbine Handbook, by Paul Wahl. Arco Publ. Co., N.Y.C., 1964. 80 pp., illus. $6.00. Paperbound, $3.95.
A manual and guide to the U.S. Carbine, cal. .30, M1, with data on its history, operation, repair, ammunition, and shooting.

The Chi-Com Series, by Granville Rideout, Yankee Publ. Co., Ashburnham, MA, 1971. 246 pp., illus. $12.95
New definitive reference work on Chinese Communist weapons in Southeast Asia. Limited and numbered ed.

The Classic Decoy Series, Ed Zern, text; M. C. Weiller, illustrator. Winchester Press, New York, NY 1969. A beautiful work picturing 24 American duck decoys in full color, printed on special paper and loose for framing. Decorated covers in slip case. Anecdotal text on each species shown. $100.00.
This deluxe collectors' work is offered in a strictly limited issue of 1000 copies, each signed by the artist and numbered.

The Code of Honor; or Rules for the Government of Principals and Seconds in Duelling, by John Lyde Wilson, Ray Riling Arms Books Co., Phila., PA, 1971. 48 pp. Paper, $5.00.
Reprint of the rare 1858 edition.

A Colt Bibliography, by G. M. Ford. Privately produced by the author, Bothell, WA, 1968. 32 pp., mimeographed stapled sheets. $3.00.
Lists articles, books, etc., of interest to the Colt collector, gunsmith and or historian.

Colt Commemorative Firearms, by R. L. Wilson. Chas. Kidwell, Wichita, KS, 1969. 108 pp., $10.00.
A chronological listing and a precise description of all Colt commemoratives from 1961 through 1969.

The Complete Book of the Air Gun, by G. C. Nonte Jr. Stackpole Books, Harrisburg, PA, 1970. 288 pp., illus. $7.95.
From Plinking to Olympic competition, from BB guns to deluxe rifles, pistols, the air shotgun.

The Complete Book of Game Conservation, by Chas. Coles, Barrie & Jenkins, London, 1971. 394 pp., $18.50.
Definitive work on the subject. 181 illustrations including color reproductions of rare prints and original paintings.

Complete Book of Rifles and Shotguns, by Jack O'Connor, Harper & Bros., N.Y.C., 1961, 477 pp., illus. $6.95.
A splendid two-part book of encyclopedic coverage on every detail of rifle and shotgun.

Complete Book of Shooting, by Jack O'Connor et al. Outdoor Life—Harper & Row, N.Y.C., 1965. 385 pp., illus. $5.95.
Fundamentals of shooting with rifle, shotgun, and handgun in the hunting field and on target ranges.

The Complete Book of Trick and Fancy Shooting, by Ernie Lind, Winchester Press, NY, 1972. 159 pp., illus. $5.95.
Step-by-step instructions for acquiring the whole range of shooting skills with rifle, pistol and shotgun; includes practical hints on developing your own shooting act.

The Complete Cannoneer, compiled by M. C. Switlik. Antique Ordnance Artificers, Jackson, MI, 1971. 106 pp., illus., paper covers. $4.50.
A must for the modern cannoneer. Compiled in two sections. Part first contains "School of the Piece" as orginally published in Artillery Drill by George S. Patton, in 1861. Part second contains current observations on the safe use of cannon.

Coping with Camp Cooking, by M. W. Stephens and G. S. Wells. Stackpole Books, Harrisburg, PA 1966. 94 pp., illus., decorated boards. $2.95.
Hints and recipes selected from the editors' writings appearing in *Camping Guide Magazine.*

The Crossbow, by Sir Ralph Payne-Gallwey, Holland Press Ltd., London, 1971. 375 pp., illus. $21.00.
New printing of the only work devoted to the crossbow and such related weapons as the siege engine, balistas, catapults, Turkish bows and the Chinese repeating crossbow.

Crusade for Wildlife, by J. B. Trefethen. Stackpole Books, Harrisburg, PA, 1961. 377 pp., illus. $7.50.
History of the Boone and Crockett Club and its efforts to preserve wildlife in America, with accounts of the plight of threatened species.

Current American War Medals and Decorations, 1963-69, by E. E. Kerrigan. Medallic Publishing Co., Noroton Heights, CT 1st ed. 1969. Paper covers, 23 pp., illus. $3.00.
This supplement updates the author's *American War Medals and Decorations,* listing recently created awards and recipients.

Daggers, Bayonets & Fighting Knives of Hitler's Germany, by John R. Angolia. James Bender Pub. Co., Mountain View, CA. 1st ed. 1971. 334 pp., profusely illus. $14.95.
An exceptionally fine, useful compilation for collector, historian and student.
The Daggers and Edged Weapons of Hitler's Germany, by Maj. J. P. Atwood, Publ. privately for the author in Berlin, Germany, 1965. 240 pp. illus. New edition, 1967. $15.00.
Lavishly illus. with many plates in full color, this is an outstanding production, easily the best information (for the collector) on the subject.
Daggers and Fighting Knives of the Western World: From the Stone Age Unitl 1900, by Harold L. Peterson, Walker and Co., New York, 1967. 256 pp., illus. $2.98.
The only full-scale historical and analytical work on this subject, from flint knives of the stone age to British and American naval dirks.
Decoys and Decoy Carvers of Illinois, by P. W. Parmalee and F. D. Loomis. Northern Illinois University Press, DeKalb, IL. 1st ed., 1969, 506 pp., illus. $17.50.
A comprehensive and handsome survey, replete with photographs—many in color. The work of the makers is analyzed, with comments on Illinois duck shooting over the past century.
Description of U.S. Military Rifle Sights, by Edw. A. Tolosky, E. A. Tolosky, Publ., 1971. 117 pp. Paper, $8.50.
Covers period from 1861 to 1940. New and excellent work for collectors and fans of the U.S. Military. Definitive text, full-size line drawings.
Design and Development of Fighting Vehicles, by R. M. Ogorkiewicz. Doubleday, N.Y.C., 1968. 208 pp. plus 174 plates. $7.95.
A review of design and engineering problems of battle tanks and other armored vehicles since World War II, with evaluations of tank design.
The Details of the Rocket System, by Col. Wm. Congreve. Museum Restoration Service, Ottawa, Canada, 1970. 85 pp., illus. $10.00.
Reprint of the 1814 1st ed. with details, photos and plates of rockets and their launchers. Edition limited and numbered.
The Diary of Colonel Peter Hawker, by Col. P. Hawker, Richmond Publ. Co., Richmond, England. 1971. 759 pp., illus. $16.95.
Reprint of the 1893 ed. covers shooting in every way and how to outwit your opponent!
Die Handwaffen, by Werner Eckardt and Otto Morawietz. H. G. Schulz, Hamburg, 1957. 265 pp., 15 plates, 175 illus. $10.00.
An important work (in German) on German Service arms from their beginnings through World War II. A symposium on the subject—ancient, obsolete, semi-modern and modern.
The Double-Armed Man, by Wm. Neade, Geo. Shumway, Publ., York, PA, 1971. 51 pp., 7 woodcuts. $8.00.
Facsimile ed. of a little book published in London in 1625. Describes use of the longbow in combination with the pike. Limited to 400 numbered copies.
Eat the Weeds, by B. C. Harris. Barre Publ., Barre, MA, 1968. 223 pp., illus., paper covers $3.95.
Practical directions for collecting and drying herbs, for using edible plants and fruits as food and for medical purposes or as substitutes for cultivated vegetables.
Elephant, by Commander D. E. Blunt. A reprint by Neville Spearman, Ltd., London, 1971. 260 pp., illus. $10.00.
A hunter's account of the ways of the elephant in Africa and elsewhere—on hunting and conservation practices.
Encyclopedia of Continental Army Units; Battalions, Regiments and Independent Corps, by Fred A. Berg, Stackpole Books, Harrisburg, PA, 1972. 160 pp. $6.95.
The official and unofficial designations, organizational history, commanding officers and ethnic composition for every unit of the Continental Army for which these facts are known.
Encyclopedia of Firearms, ed. by H. L. Peterson. E. P. Dutton, N.Y.C., 1964. 367 pp., 100 pp. of illus. incl. color. $13.50.
Fine reference work on firearms, with articles by 45 top authorities covering classes of guns, manufacturers, ammunition, nomenclature, and related topics.
Encyclopedia of Modern Firearms, Vol. 1, compiled and publ. by Bob Brownell, Montezuma, IA, 1959. 1057 pp. plus index, illus. $22.50. Dist. by Bob Brownell, Montezuma, IA 50171.
Massive accumulation of basic information of nearly all modern arms pertaining to "parts and assembly." Replete with arms photographs, exploded drawings, manufacturers' lists of parts, etc.
The Exercise of Arms, by Jacob de Gehyn, McGraw-Hill Book Co., NY, 1971. 250 pp. plus separate commentary by J. B. Kist, Dutch historian. $45.00.
Exact facsimile of original 1807 ed. now in Dutch archives, and based on concepts of troop organization and training developed by Prince Johann II. 117 copper engravings.
Special deluxe-bound ed. in full hard covers, limited to ten (10) copies. $1,000.00.
Explosives and Demolitions, U.S. Field Manual 5-25, Normount Armament Co., Forest Grove, OR. 215 pp., illus., paperbound. $4.00.
A reprint of the Army FM dated 14 May 1959.
Falconry, by Gilbert Blaine, Neville Spearman, London, 1970. 253 pp., illus. $7.50.
Reprint of a 1936 classic on training, handling, types, furniture, etc., of hawks, plus a glossary and list.
Die Faustfeuerwaffen von 1850 dis zur Gegenwart, by Eugene Heer, Akademische D.-u. V., Graz, Austria, 1972. 234 pp. of German texts, 215 pp. of illus. $25.00.
First volume in a series which will cover the history of Swiss firearms from 1800. The handguns issued between 1850 and 1950 are described and illustrated in considerable detail.
Fell's Guide to Guns and How to Use Them, by B. G. Wels. Frederick Fell, New York, NY 1969. 173 pp., illus. in line and halftone. $4.95.
Aspects of the safe use of firearms for sportsmen, hunters and collectors.
Firearms, by Walter Buehr. Crowell Co., N.Y.C., 1967. 186 pp., illus. $5.95.
From gunpowder to guided missile, an illustrated history of firearms for military and sporting uses.
Firearms Dictionary, by R. A. "Bob" Steindler. Stackpole Books, Harrisburg, PA, 288 pp., illus. $7.95.
Firearm Silencers, by D. B. McLean. Normount Armament Co., Forest Grove, OR, 1968. 123 pp., illus., paperbound. $4.00.
The history, design, and development of silencers for U.S. military firearms.
Firearms, Traps & Tools of the Mountain Men, by Carl P. Russell. A. A. Knopf, NY, 1967. 448 pp., illus. in line drawings. $15.00.
Detailed survey of fur traders' equipment in the early days of the west.
The Fireside Book of Guns, by Larry Koller. Simon & Schuster, N.Y.C., 1959. 284 pp., illus. in artistic photography and full-color plates. $12.95
On all counts the most beautiful and colorful production of any arms book of our time, this work adequately tells the story of firearms in America—from the first explorers to today's sportsmen.
Four Studies on the History of Arms, by Arne Hoff, et al. Tjhusmuseet, Copenhagen, 1964. 145 pp., illus., paperbound. $6.75.
A Danish museum publication containing in English text scholarly monographs on arms topics of historic interest.
Frederic Remington and the Spanish-American War, by Douglas Allen, Crown Publ., Inc, NY, 1971. 178 pp.. Deluxe numbered and autographed ed. limited to 150 copies, slip-cased. $50.00.
Copiously illustrated with reproductions of the artists drawings, paintings and bronzes of the Spanish-American War period.
Free for the Eating, by Bradford Angier, Stackpole Books, Harrisburg, PA, 1966. 191 pp., illus. $4.95.
Discusses and illustrates 100 wild plants and 300 ways to use them.
More Free for the Eating, Wild Foods, by Bradford Angier, Stackpole Books, Harrisburg, PA, 1969. 192 pp., illus. $4.95.
A sequel to *Free for the Eating,* being a nature-study cookbook with an additional 200 ways to prepare common wild plants.
The A. B. Frost Book, by Henry M. Reed. Charles E. Tuttle Co., Rutland, VT, 1967. 149 pp., of large format with over 70 plates, 44 in color, and many line drawings. $20.00.
A collection of the sketches, drawings and paintings by a famous outdoor artist (1851-1928). Includes his noted sporting and shooting masterpieces.
Fundamentals of Small Arms, U.S. TM9-2205. Normount Armament Co., Forest Grove, OR. 236 pp., illus., paperbound. $3.50.
Reprint of the U.S. Army technical manual dated 7 May 1952.
Game Animals, by Leonard Lee Rue III. Harper & Row, NY, 1968. 655 pp., incl. appendix and index. Illus. with maps and photos. $6.50.
A concise guide to and field book of North American species.
Game and Bird Calling, by A. C. Becker, Jr., A. S. Barnes and Co., NY, 1972. 147 pp., illus. $7.95.
Discusses various types of calls and techniques used by hunters—tyros and professionals.
Game and Fish Cookbook, by H. and J. Barnett. Grossman Publ., New York, NY 1968, 162 pp., illus. $7.95.
Special culinary attention to fish and game, with interesting and different touches.
Game in the Kitchen, by B. Flood and W. C. Roux (eds.). Barre Publ., Barre, MA 1st ed., 1968, 234 pp., illus. $7.50.
A fish and game cookbook, with menus and information on preservation, cooking and serving.
Gas, Air and Spring Guns of the World, by W. H. B. Smith. Stackpole Books, Harrisburg, PA, 1957. 279 pp., well illus. $4.98.
A detailed, well-documented history of the air and gas gun industry throughout the world. It includes ancient and modern arms, and it devotes a chapter to accurate velocity tests of modern arms.
German Infantry Weapons, ed. by D. B. McLean. Normount Armament Co., Forest Grove, OR, 1966. 191 pp., illus., paperbound. $3.00.
World War II German weapons described and illustrated, from military intelligence research.
German Infantry Weapons of World War II, by A. J. Barker. Arco Publ. Co., New York, NY 1969, 76 pp., illus. $3.50.
Historical and statistical data on all types of the subject weapons, ammunition, etc.
German Machineguns, by D. D. Musgrave & S. H. Oliver, Mor Associates, WA, DC, 1971. 472 pp., $17.50.
Covers aircraft and ground types, including rare and little-known weapons, plus information on ammunition, accessories, and mounts. Over 500 illus..
German Mauser Rifle, Model of 1898, by Coombes & Aney. F. Bannerman, N.Y.C., 1921. 20 pp., illus., paperbound. $1.50.
Reprint of a pamphlet describing a famous military rifle, its bayonets, ammunition, and accessories.
German Secret Weapons of World War II, by I. V. Hogg. Arco Pub. Co., NY, 1970. 80 pp., illus. $3.50.
Compact, comprehensive account of Germany's secret weapons, eccentric and brilliant. Includes plans and technical details.
German Tanks of World War II, by F. M. von Senger und Etterlin. Stackpole Books, Harrisburg, PA, 1969. 176 pp., nearly 300 photos and drawings. Large format. $11.95.
A fully illustrated and definitive history of German armoured fighting vehicles, 1926-1945. Written in English.
German Weapons-Uniforms-Insignia 1841-1918, by Maj. J. E. Hicks. J. E. Hicks & Son, La Canada, CA, 1958. 158 pp., illus. $6.00.
Originally published in 1937 as *Notes on German Ordnance 1841-1918,* this new edition offers the collector a wealth of information gathered from many authentic sources.
The Golden Guide to Guns, by Larry Koller. Golden Press, N.Y.C., 1966. 160 pp., illus., paperbound, pocket-size. $1.00.
Introduction to rifles, shotguns, and handguns for all uses. Profusely illus., much in color.
Gourmet Cooking for Free, by Bradford Angier. Stackpole Books. Harrisburg, PA 1970. 190 pp. illus. $4.95.
Cookery of large and small game, seafood and wild plants.
Great American Guns and Frontier Fighters, by Will Bryant, Grosset & Dunlap, NY, 1961. 160 pp., illus. $3.95.
Popular account of firearms in U.S. history and of the events in which they played a part.
Great Weapons of World War II, by J. Kirk and R. Young. Bonanza Books, NY, 1968. 348 pp., profusely illus. The latest reprint. $4.95.
Covers, in text and picture, great and powerful weapons, planes, tanks as well as small arms, miscellaneous arms and naval attack vessels.
Grundriss der Waffenlehre, ed. by J. Schott, Akademische D. U. V., Graz, Austria, 1971. 395 pp. of German text, plus a 24 pp. Atlas. $22.50
Facsimile reprint of the 1876 ed. written by Edw. Zernin and publ. in Darmstadt and Leipzig.
Guide to the Soviet Navy, by Siegfried Breyer, U.S. Naval Institute, Annapolis, MD, 1971. 353 pp. $10.00.
Compact, comprehensive, up-to-date view of organization, construction, weapons, equipment, forces, bases and ports. Over 100 photos, plans, tables and maps, specifications and profiles.
Guide to United States Machine Guns, by K. F. Schreier, Jr., Normount Armament Co., Forest Grove, OR, 1971. 178 pp., illus. Paper, $4.00.
All machine guns procured by the U.S. Armed Forces and some of an experimental nature.
Gun Digest, 26th ed., ed. by John Amber. Digest Books, Inc., Northfield, IL, 1972, 480 pp., profusely illus., 32 pp. in full color, paper cover. $6.95.
Known as the world's greatest gun book because of its factual, informative data for shooters, hunters, collectors, reloaders and other enthusiasts. Truly of encyclopedic importance.
Gun Digest Treasury, ed. by J. T. Amber, 4th ed., 1972. Digest Books, Inc. Northfield, IL. 352 pp. illus. Paper, $5.95.
The best from 25 years of the GUN DIGEST, selected from the annual editions.

The Gun, 1834, by Wm. Greener, with intro. by D. B. McLean. Normount Technical Publ., Forest Grove, OR, 1971. 240 pp., illus. Paper, $4.50.
Reprint of the 1835 British ed. on various small firearms.
Gundogs, Their Care and Training, by M. Brander. A. & C. Black, London, Eng., 1969. 97 pp., illus. $4.95.
A British manual on hunting dogs.
Gun Fun with Safety, by G. E. Damon. Standard Publications, Huntington, W. VA, 1947. 206 pp., well illus. $6.00.
A long out-of-print work that is still much sought. A fine general coverage of arms and ammunition, old and new, with chapters on shooting, targets, etc., with safety always upper-most.
The Gun that Made the Twenties Roar, by W. J. Helmer, Macmillan Co., NY 1969. 286 pp. illus. $7.95.
Historical account of John T. Thompson and his invention, the Thompson submachine gun. Includes virtually a complete manual in detail.
Gun Trader's Guide, by Paul Wahl, Shooter's Bible, Inc., NY, 1968. 5th rev. ed. 220 pp., 8"x10", profusely illus. Paperbound. $3.95.
Complete guide to the identification of modern firearms and giving their current market values.
The Gunfighter, Man or Myth? by Joseph G. Rosa, Oklahoma Press, Norman, OK, 1969. 229 pp., illus., (including weapons). $5.95.
A well-documented work on gunfights and gunfighters of the West and elsewhere. Great treat for all gunfighter buffs.
The Gunfighters, by Dale T. Schoenberger, The Caxton Printers, Ltd., Caldwell, ID, 1971. 207 pp., illus. $12.95.
Startling expose of our foremost Western folk heroes.
The Gun-Founders of England, by Charles ffoulkes, Geo. Shumway, York, PA, 1969. 133 pp., illus. $10.00.
Detailed study of cannon, casting. Describes preparation of moulds, castings, mfg. of powder and shot, etc.
The Gunner's Bible, by Bill Riviere. Doubleday, N.Y.C., 1965. 192 pp., illus. Paperbound. $1.95.
General Guide to modern sporting firearms and their accessories, for all shooters.
Gunology, by P. M. Doane. Winchester-Western, N.Y.C., 1968. 64 pp., illus., paperbound. $2.95.
A comprehensive course for professional sporting arms salesmen. Of great help to the arms man are the hundreds of questions on arms and hunting.
Guns, by Dudley Pope. Delacorte Press, N.Y.C., 1965. 256 pp., illus. $9.98.
Concise history of firearms, stressing early museum-quality weapons. Includes small arms as well as artillery, naval, and airborne types. Fine photographs, many in color.
Guns, by F. Wilkinson, Grosset & Dunlap, NY, 1971. 168 pp., $3.95.
From the discovery of gunpowder to the complex weapons of today. Over 100 photos in color.
Guns & Ammo 1972 Annual, Guns & Ammo magazine, Petersen Publ. Co., Los Angeles, CA, 1972. 378 pp. illus. Paper covers. $3.95.
Annual catalog of sporting firearms and accessories, with numerous articles for gun enthusiasts.
Guns Annual for 1973, edited by Jerome Rakusan, Publishers Development Corp., Skokie, IL, 1972. 134 pp., well illus., decorated paper wrappers. $2.00.
An annual publication describing and illustrating firearms available in current markets, plus articles by experts in the field of collecting, shooting, ammunition, etc.
Guns Illustrated 1973, 5th ed., ed. by Joe J. Schroeder, Jr., Digest Books, Inc., Northfield, IL 1972. 288 pp., profusely illus., paper covers. $3.95.
Revised and up-dated with latest models, prices, specifications and data on handguns, rifles, shotguns, scopes, sights. Original technical articles.
Guns; An Illustrated History of Artillery, ed. by Jos. Jobe, New York Graphic Society, Greenwich, CT, 1971. 216 pp., illus. $30.00.
Traces the history and technology of artillery from its beginnings in the 14th century to its 20th century demise in the face of aerial bombs and guided missiles.
Guns and Rifles of the World, by Howard L. Blackmore, The Viking Press, NY, 1965. 290 pp. 1042 halftone and line illustrations. $9.98.
One of the finest books to come out of England. Covers firearms from the handgun to air, steam, and electric guns.
Guns and Shooting, by Maj. Sir Gerald Burrard. Barnes & Co., N.Y.C., 1962. 147 pp. $1.95.
Expanded from the author's earlier *In the Gunroom*, this contains 153 often-asked questions on shotguns and rifles, with authoritative answers covering guns, ammunition, ballistics, etc.
Guns and Shooting, a Bibliography, by R. Riling. Greenberg, N.Y.C., 1951. 434 pp., illus. $20.00.
A selected listing, with pertinent comments and anecdote, of books and printed material on arms and ammunition from 1420 to 1950.
The Guns of Harpers Ferry, by S. E. Brown Jr. Virginia Book Co., Berryville, VA, 1968. 157 pp., illus. $12.50.
Catalog of all known firearms produced at the U.S. armory at Harpers Ferry, 1798-1861, with descriptions, illustrations and a history of the operations there.
The Hall Carbine Affair; An Essay in Historiography, by R. Gordon Wasson, Privately Printed, Danbury, CT, 1971. 250 pp., illus. Deluxe slip-cased ed. of 250 copies. $75.00.
Based on the original work (limited to 100 copies) of 1941 and a 1948 revised ed. of only 750 copies. This issue, enlarged and re-researched, relates to sales and purchases of Hall carbines in the Civil War, in which J. Pierpont Morgan was involved.
Handbook on German Military Forces, a reprint of *TM-E30-451*, originating with U.S. Military Intelligence. Publ. by the Military Press, Gaithersburg, Md. 1970. 550 pp., copious illus., many in color. $14.95.
A rare restricted handbook [many destroyed] covering military systems, doctrines, SS Policy, home defense, etc.
Handbook on German Military Forces, by Founder's Ltd., Des Moines, IA. Paper, 372 pp., illus. $7.50.
Reprint of a restricted Military Intelligence Division handbook TM-E-30-451.
Handbook for Hythe, by H. Busk, Richmond Pub. Co., Richmond, England, 1971. 194 pp., illus. $8.50.
Reprint of the 1860 ed. explaining laws of projectiles with an introduction to the system of musketry.
Handbook on Japanese Military Forces, a reprint of *TM-E30-480*, originating with U.S. Military Intelligence. Publ. by the Military Press, Gaithersburg, Md., 1970. 550 pp., illus., 24 pp., in color. $14.95.
A rare restricted work [many destroyed] on military systems, doctrines, police, home defense, etc.
Handbook of Self-Defense for Law Enforcement Officers, by John Martone. Arco Publ. Co., New York, NY, 1968. 1st ed., 4th printing, 111 pp., $3.50.
A clearly-illustrated manual on offensive and defensive techniques recommended for the use of policemen.
Hardtack and Coffee, or The Unwritten Story of Civil War Army Life, by John D. Billings, Benchmark Publ. Corp., Glendale, NY, 1970. 408 pp., illus. $9.50.
Reprint of original 1887 ed., with data on army life in tents, huts, enlisting, foraging, punishment, etc.
Hatcher's Notebook, by Maj. Gen. J. S. Hatcher. Stackpole Books, Harrisburg, Pa., 1952. 2nd ed. with four new chapters, 1957. 629 pp., illus. $11.95.
A dependable source of information for gunsmiths, ballisticians, historians, hunters, and collectors.
Hibbard, Spencer, Bartlett & Co. Catalog. American Reprints, St. Louis, MO, 1969. 92 pp., illus. Paper, $5.00.
Reprint of 1884 catalog on guns, rifles, revolvers, ammo, powder flasks, etc. Descriptions and contemporary prices.
History of the British Army, by P. Young and J. P. Lawford. G. P. Putnam's Sons, NY, 1970. 304 pp., profusely illus., much in color. $15.00.
Traces history of the British Army from the early 17th century to the present.
A History of the Dress of the British Soldier, by Lt. Col. John Luard, Frederick Muller Ltd., London, 1971. 171 pp., illus. 50 plates. $15.00.
Reprint of the 1852 ed., limited to 400 numbered copies.
A History of Knives, by Harold L. Peterson. Charles Scripner's Sons, N.Y.C., 1966. 64 pp., illus. $5.00.
The fine drawings of Daniel D. Feaser combine with the author's commendable text to produce an important work. From the earliest knives of prehistoric man through the evolution of the metal knife.
History of Small Arms Ammunition 1917-19. A reprint of an official U.S. Ordnance source work, *circa* 1920. Design Publ. Hyattsville, Md. Reprinted 1968, 40 pp., illus., paper covers. $5.00.
Another scarce work for the seeker of authoritative material.
A History of War and Weapons, 449 to 1660, by A. V. B. Norman and D. Pottinger. Thomas Y. Crowell Co., NY, 1966. 224 pp., well illus. with sketches. $6.95.
An excellent work for the scholar on the evolution of war and weapons in England. Many sketches of arms and weapons of all sorts add importance.
The History of Weapons of the American Revolution, by Geo. C. Neumann. Harper & Row, NY, 1967, 373 pp., fully illus. $15.00.
Collector's reference covering long arms, handguns, edged and pole weapons used in the Revolutionary War.
The Hitler Albums, Vol. I, by Roger J. Bender, R. J. Bender Publ. Co., Mountain View, CA, 1970. 144 pp., $10.95.
Complete photographic study of Mussolini's state visit to Germany in September, 1937. 175 photos and illus..
Home Book of Taxidermy and Tanning, by G. J. Grantz, Stackpole Books, Harrisburg, PA, 1969, 160 pp., illus. $7.95.
Amateur's primer on mounting fish, birds, animals, and trophies.
Home in Your Pack, by Bradford Angier, Stackpole Books, Harrisburg, PA, 1965. 192 pp., illus. $4.50.
An outdoorsman's handbook on equipment, woodcraft, and camping techniques.
Horse Equipments and Cavalry Accoutrements 1891. a reprint of U.S. Ordnance Memoranda No. 29 by Francis Bannerman Sons, Blue Point, NY, 1969, 23 pp., plus 20 plates. $3.50.
U.S. army cavalry equipment described and illustrated in line.
How to Build Your Home in the Woods, by Bradford Angier, Stackpole Books, Harrisburg, PA, 1967, 310 pp., illus. $7.00.
Detailed instructions on building cabins, shelters, etc., with natural materials. How to obtain food from nature, and how to live in the wilderness in comfort.
How to Defend Yourself, your Family, and your Home, by Geo. Hunter. David McKay, N.Y.C., 1967, 307 pp., illus. $6.95.
The only book available for the public at large that advocates their ownership of firearms—including handguns. Covers laws of self-defense, setting up home protection, and much else.
How to Live in the Woods on Pennies a Day, by Bradford Angier, Stackpole Books, Harrisburg, PA, 1971. 192 pp., illus. $6.95.
New reprint on modern-day wilderness living in America, plus cooking and recipes.
The Identification and Registration of Firearms, by Vaclav "Jack" Krcma, C. C. Thomas, Springfield, IL, 1971. 173 pp., illus. $14.50.
Analysis of problems and improved techniques of recording firearms data accurately.
Indian and Oriental Armour, by Lord Egerton of Tatton. Stackpole Books, Harrisburg, PA, 1968. 178 pp., well illus., some in color. $14.95.
New edition of a rare work which has been a key reference for students of the subject, plus a creditable source on Oriental history.
Infantry Equipment 1875. A reprint of U.S. Ordnance Memoranda No. 19 by Francis Bannerman Sons, Blue Point, NY, 1969. 62 pp., plus 9 plates. $6.50.
A report covering materials, supplies, etc., to outfit troops in field and garrison.
Instinct Shooting, by Mike Jennings. Dodd, Mead & Co., N.Y.C., 1959. 157 pp., 20 line drawings, illus. $3.95.
All about Lucky McDaniel and his surprisingly successful discovery of a new aerial shooting technique, one which will let almost anyone, novices preferred, hit flying targets with only minutes of instruction.
Instructions to Young Sportsmen: Guns and Shooting, by Col. P. Hawker, Richmond Publ. Co., Richmond, England, 1971. 507 pp., illus. $13.95.
Reprint of the 1833 British work on guns, shooting and killing game.
Introduction to Muzzle Loading, by R. O. Ackerman. Publ. by the author, Albuquerque, NM, 1966. 20 pp., illus. with author's sketches. $1.50.
This booklet, in paper wrappers, will be Book No. 1 of a projected series. Contains a glossary of muzzle loading terms, and is aimed at the novice.
An Introduction to Tool Marks, Firearms and the Striagraph, by J. E. Davis. Chas. C. Thomas, Springfield, IL, 1st ed., 1958. 282 pp. $8.50.
Textbook on micro-contour analysis in criminalistics, with emphasis upon the striagraph in analysis of evidence.
Ironmaker To The Confederacy, by C. B. Dew. Yale Univ. Press, New Haven, 1966. 345 pp., illus. $10.00.
History of Joseph R. Anderson's Tredegar Iron works in Richmond, VA, which produced weapons and military equipment essential to the Confederacy's armed forces.
Jane's Weapons Systems: 1970-71, by R. T. Pretty and D. H. R. Archer, Editors. Jane's Yearbooks, London, 1970. 606 pp. illus. $55.00.
Catalog of military hardware of the major nations.
Japanese Infantry Weapons, ed. by D. B. McLean. Normount Armament Co., Forest Grove, OR, 1966. 241 pp., well illus., paperbound. $3.50.
Survey of World War II Japanese weapons, based on military intelligence research.
The Japanese Sword and Its Fittings, by members of the Japanese Sword Society of New York. Cooper Union Museum, N.Y.C., 1966. Paper covers. 26 pp. of text plus many illus. $3.50.
The authoritative text in the form of a catalog describing the illus. of items in the possession of members of the society.

John Groth's World of Sport, by J. Groth. Winchester Press. NY, 1970. 160 pp., illus. $6.95.
Exotic and exciting sports recorded by a man whose vital drawings convey the essence of the action. 40 color paintings.

Johnson Rifles and Light Machine Guns, ed. by D. B. McLean. Normount Armament Co., Forest Grove, OR, 1968. 55 pp., illus., paperbound. $2.00.
Manual on the only recoil-operated auto-loading rifle issued to U.S. forces.

Knife Throwing as a Modern Sport, by H. K. McEvoy and C. V. Gruzanski. Charles C. Thomas, Springfield, IL, 1965. 57 pp., illus. $5.50.
For first time, a concise, easy-to-read and complete story on this modern sport.

A Knight and His Armour, 95 pp. $3.25.
A Knight and His Castle, 108 pp., $3.25.
A Knight and His Horse, 96 pp., $3.25.
A Knight and His Weapons, 95 pp., $3.25.
A series planned for young readers, by R. E. Oakeshott. Lutterworth Press, London, 1966. All illus. Of interest to adults as well.

Knights in Armor, by S. Glubok, Harper & Row, NY, 1969. 48 pp., illus. $5.50.
Story of European body armor told for young readers.

Kuhlhoff on Guns, by Pete Kuhlhoff, Winchester Press, NY, 1970. 180 pp., illus. $5.95.
A selection of firearms articles by the late Gun Editor of *Argosy* Magazine.

Lewis Automatic Machine Gun, publ. originally by Savage Arms Co., Utica, NY. A reprint by L. A. Funk, Puyallup, WA, 1969. 47 pp., illus., paper covers. $1.50.
This facsimile covers the Model 1916 gun, explaining all features of operation, action, nomenclature, stripping and assembly.

The Machine Gun, Vol, II, Part VII, by Lt. Col. G. M. Chinn. Paladin Press, Boulder, Col., n.d. 215 pp., illus. $15.00.
Reprint of a 1952 Navy publication of Soviet WW II rapid fire weapons.

Machine Guns and Gunnery for Machine Guns. Normount Armament Co., Forest Grove, OR, 1968. 218 pp., illus. Paper, $3.00.
Complete manual on 30- and 50-caliber machine guns and 45-caliber sub-machine guns.

Marlin Catalog of 1897. A reprint in facsimile by the Wyoming Armory, Inc., Cheyenne, WY, 1969. 192 pp. Well illus., paper covers, $3.50.
All models are covered, cartridges, sights, engraving, accessories, reloading tools, etc.

Marlin Catalog, 1905, Wyoming Armory, Inc., Cheyenne, WY, 1971. 128 pp. Paper, $4.00.
Reprint. Rifles, shotguns, pistols, tools, cartridge information, factory engraving and carving illustrated and described.

Mexican Military Arms, The Cartridge Period, by James B. Hughes, Jr. Deep River Armory, Inc., Houston, TX, 1967. 135 pp., photos and line drawings. $4.50.
An interesting and useful work, in imprinted wrappers, covering the period from 1866 to 1967.

Military Modelling, by Donald Featherstone, A. S. Barnes and Co., NY, 1971. 159 pp., illus. $6.95.
Describes the art of moulding and casting, soldering, glueing, painting and construction of small figures.

Military Uniforms, 1686-1918, by Rene North. Grosset & Dunlap, NY, 1970. 159 pp., illus. $3.95.
Concise survey of European and U.S. military dress and its history during the principal wars. Profusely illus., with some colored drawings.

Military Uniforms of the World in Color, by Preben Kannik, translated by W. Y. Carman. MacMillan Co., N.Y., NY, 1968. 278 pp. incl. index, 512 illus. figures in full color. $4.95.
An excellent handbook for the collector and student. The descriptive text gives good details of equipment.

The Minute Men, by J. R. Galvin. Hawthorn Books, N.Y.C., 1967. 286 pp. $6.95.
History of the colonial militia to the beginning of the Revolutionary War, including data on the battles of Lexington and Concord.

Modern ABC's of Bow and Arrow, by G. H. Gillelan. Stackpole Books, Harrisburg, PA, 1967. 160 pp., illus. $4.95.
Survey of techniques for beginners and experts in target archery as well as bowhunting.

Modern ABC's of Guns, by R. A. Steindler. Stackpole Books, Harrisburg, PA, 1965. 191 pp., illus. $4.95.
Concise lexicon of today's sporting firearms, their components, ammunition, accessory equipment and use.

Modern Police Firearms, by Duke Roberts and A. P. Bristow. Glencoe Press, Beverly Hills, CA, 1969. 170 pp., illus., in line and halftone. $5.95.
An informative work covering all pertinent details, with chapters on safety, ballistics, maintenance, marksmanship, chemical agents, the shotgun, plus legal and ethical aspects.

Navies of the World, by Hans Busk, Richmond Publ. Co., Richmond, England, 1971. 456 pp., illus. $13.50.
Reprint of the London 1859 ed.

The New Way of the Wilderness, By Calvin Rutstrum. Macmillan Co., New York, NY 1st ed., 1966 [4th printing]. 276 pp., illus. in line. $4.95.
An outdoorsman's manual on traveling and living in the open, with chapters on transportation, equipment, food, hunting and fishing for food.

L. D. Nimschke, Firearms Engraver, by R. L. Wilson. John J. Malloy, publisher, Teaneck, NJ, 1965. Quarto, 107 pp., profusely illus. $17.50.
Showing a wide variety of designs, initials and monograms and ever-so-many portions of collectors' arms. A thoroughly interesting work for the collector and an inspiration to the engraver.

No Second Place Winner, by Wm. H. Jordan, publ. by the author, Shreveport, LA (Box 4072), 1962. 114 pp., illus. $6.00.
Guns and gear of the peace officer, ably discussed by a U.S. Border Patrolman for over 30 years, and a first-class shooter with handgun, rifle, etc.

The Order of the Death's Head, by Heinz Hohne, Coward-McCann, Inc., NY, 1970. 690 pp., illus. $12.50.
The Story of Hitler's S.S., the most horrifying organization ever invented by the Germans. Based on Himmler's personal staff files, the Nuremberg trials and the Reich Security Office.

The Other Mr. Churchill, by Macdonald Hastings. Dodd Mead, N.Y.C., 1965. 336 pp., illus. $1.98.
Important biography of a great London gunmaker and forensic ballistics expert, who contributed much to the color and excellence of British firearms tradition.

Pageant of the Gun, by Harold L. Peterson. Doubleday & Co., Inc., Garden City, NY, 1967. 352 pp., profusely illus. $3.95.
A storehouse of stories on firearms, their romance and lore, their development and use through 10 centuries. A most satisfying history of firearms chronologically presented.

Paradise Below Zero, by Calvin Rutstrum. Macmillan Co., New York, NY 1st ed., 1968. 244 pp., illus. in line and halftone. $5.95.
On the rewards and methods of camping and travel in Eskimo country, including check lists of provisions, tools, equipment, clothing and ways of getting about.

The Pictorial Field-Book of the Revolution, 1775-1783; or "Illustrations by Pen and Pencil of the History, Biography, Scenery, Relics and Traditions of the War for Independence," by Benson J. Lossing, Benchmark Publ. Corp. Glendale, NY, 1970. 1555 pp. in 2 Vol. $36.50.
Reprint of the original 1855 ed. Over 1100 engravings and index.

The Pictorial Field-Book of the War of 1812; or "Illustrations by Pen and Pencil of the History, Biography, Scenery, Relics and Traditions of the Last War for American Independence," by Benson J. Lossing, Benchmark Publ. Corp., Glendale, NY, 1970. 1084 pp.,. $24.50.
Reprint of the 1869 ed. Several hundred engravings.

Picture Book of the Continental Soldier, by C. K. Wilbur. Stackpole Books, Harrisburg, PA, 1969. 96 pp., well illus. $4.95.
A wealth of detailed material in text and fine drawings, depicting Revolutionary War weapons, accouterments, field equipment, and the routine of the solder's life. Included are artillery, edged weapons, muskets, rifles, powder horns, etc.

Pocket Guide to Archery, by H. T. Sigler. Stackpole Co., Harrisburg, PA, 1960. 96 pp., illus. $2.95.
Useful introduction to the subject, covering equipment, shooting techniques, and bow hunting of small game and deer.

Presenting America's Aristocracy of Fine Cutlery, Grawolf Trading Co., Milwaukee, WI, 1971. Vol. 2 of a limited, numbered ed. Paper, $3.50.
Unpaginated with hundreds of illus. and explanations.

Reading the Woods, by Vinson Brown. Stackpole Books, Harrisburg, PA, 1969. 160 pp. illus. $5.95.
Clues to the past, present and future development of wooded areas by observation of signs of change, decay, influences of water and wildlife, and the impact of man's presence.

The Records and Badges of Every Regiment and Corps in the British Army, by H. M. Chichester and Geo. Burges-Short. Fred. Muller, Ltd., London, 1970. A reprint of the 2nd ed. of 1900. 240 illus., in the text and 24 color plates $27.50.
A magnificent facsimile with gilt top giving the history, uniforms, colors and insignia in satisfying detail of much-wanted data on subject.

The Redbook of Used Gun Values 1972, publ. by Publishers Dev. Corp., Skokie, IL, 1971, 130 pp., illus., paper covers. $2.50.
Lists many types and modifications of rifles, shotguns and handguns, arranged by makers, with prices estimated according to condition.

Remington Arms Revised Price-List, 1902. Arthur McKee, Northport, NY, n.d. 64 pp. Paper covers. $3.50.
Reprint, fully illustrated.

Remington Firearms, 1906 Catalog, Arthur McKee, Northport, NY, n.d., 48 pp., illus. Paper covers. $3.50.
Reprint. Guns, parts, ammo., prices, etc.

Riot Control—Materiel and Techniques, by Rex Applegate. Stackpole Books, Harrisburg, PA 1969. 320 pp., illus. $9.95.
Originally released as *Kill or Get Killed,* later as *Crowd and Riot Control.* Designed for law officer training, plus deployment of personnel, chemicals and special equipment for best results.

Round Shot and Rammers, by H. L. Peterson. Stackpole Books, Harrisburg, PA, 1969. 128 pp., illus. $9.95.
Artillery in America Through the Civil War years, with much detail on manufacture, history, accessory equipment, and use of all types of cannon. Fine line drawings show the guns, their equipment, and the men who used them.

Russian Infantry Weapons of World War II, by A. J. Barker and John Walter, Arco Publ. Co., NY, 1971. 80 pp., $3.50.
History and development of World War II infantry weapons used by the Red Army. Each weapon is fully described and illus..

Sam Colt: Genius, by Robt. F. Hudson, American Archieves Publ. Co., Topsfield, MA, 1971. 160 pp., illus. Plastic spiral bound. $6.50.
Historical review of Colt's inventions, including facsimiles of patent papers and other Colt information.

Scloppetaria, by Capt. H. Beaufroy, Richmond Publ. Co., Richmond, England, 1971. 251 pp. $11.00.
Reprint of the 1808 edition written under the pseudonym "A Corporal of Rifelmen". Covers rifles and rifle shooting, the first such work in English.

Second World War Combat Weapons, by Hoffschmidt & Tantum. WE, Inc., Old Greenwich, CT, 1968. 212 pp., illus. $7.95.
German weapons, vehicles, and projectiles illustrated and described. First of a 7-vol. series.

Secret Fighting Arts of the World, by J. F. Gilbey. Tuttle, Rutland, VT 1963. 150 pp., illus. $3.75.
20 chapters on advanced techniques of unarmed combat, described in anecdotal form.

Secret Weapons of the Third Reich, by L. E. Simon, We, Inc., Old Greenwich, CT, 1971. 248 pp., illus. $8.95.
Review of German World War II military research and its products.

Shooter's Bible, No. 63, John Olson, ed. Shooter's Bible, Inc., S. Hackensack, NJ, 1972. 576 pp., illus. $4.95.
An annually-published guide to firearms, ammunition, and accessories.

Shooter's Bible Game Cook Book, by Geraldine Steindler. Follett Publ. Co., Chicago IL 1965. 224 pp., illus., cloth, $6.95; paper, $4.95.
Full information on preparing game for the table, including recipes and methods of field-dressing.

Shooter's Bible Gun Trader's Guide, by Paul Wahl. Shooter's Bible, S. Hackensack, NJ, 5th edition, 1968. 220 pp., illus., paperbound. $3.95.
Revised guide to market values of modern firearms, with identification data on U.S. and imported guns.

The Shooter's Guide: or Complete Sportsman's Companion, by B. Thomas, Richmond Publ. Co., Richmond, England, 1971. 264 pp., illus. $9.00.
Reprint of an 1816 British handbook on hunting small game, game laws, dogs, guns and ammunition.

Shooting, by M. Turner and St. Tucker, Cogswell & Harrison, London, 1970. 176 pp., illus. $2.95.
Instruction manual for novices and the young in sports.

Shooting Muzzle Loading Hand Guns, by Charles T. Haven. Guns Inc., MA, 1947. 132 pp., illus. $6.50.
A good summary of shooting methods, both contemporary and modern. Duelling with M.L. handguns is also covered.

The Shorebirds of North America, by Peter Matthiesen, ed. by Gordon Stout, with species accounts by R. S. Palmer. Viking Press, N.Y.C., 1967, 288 pp., 32 6-color plates, 10"x14", $22.50. De Luxe ltd. ed., extra bound, $50.00.
A magnificent book, probably the outstanding work on the shorebirds of the northern western world. 32 chapters cover 59 species. The illustrations are superb.

Silencers. Paladin Press, Boulder, CO, 1971 205 pp., illus. $9.95.
Reprint of Frankford Arsenal Report R-1896. The functional and physical details on foreign and domestic silencers, including patent drawings, engineering data, manufacture, etc..

Silencers, Snipers & Assassins, by J. David Truby, Paladin Press, Boulder, CO, 1972. 209 pp., illus. $15.95.
Traces development of silencers from their invention by Hiram Maxim in 1908 to American snipers' use during the Korean conflict.

Six-guns and Saddle Leather, by Ramon F. Adams. University of Oklahoma Press, Norman, OK, 1969, 801 pp., $19.95.
A bibliography of books and pamphlets on western outlaws and gunmen. A brand new revised and enlarged edition.

Sketch Book 76: The American Soldier 1775-1781, by R. Klinger and R. A. Wilder, Arlington VA, 1967. 53 pp., illus. Paper covers. $2.50.
Sketches, notes, and patterns compiled from a study of clothing and equipment used by the American foot soldier in the Revolutionary War.

Skills for Taming the Wilds, by Bradford Angier, Stackpole Books, Harrisburg, PA, 1967. 320 pp., illus. $6.95.
A handbook of woodcraft wisdom, by a foremost authority, showing how to obtain maximum comfort from nature.

Small Arms Identification and Operation Guide—Eurasian Communist Countries, by Harold E. Johnson, Inco., 1972. 218 pp., illus. Paper covers. $4.00.
Reprint of 1970 U.S. Army manual FSTC-CW-07-03-70.

Small Arms Lexicon and Concise Encyclopedia, by Chester Mueller and John Olson. Stoeger Arms, So. Hackensack, NJ, 1968. 312 pp., 500 illus. $14.95.
Definitions, explanations, and references on antiques, optics, ballistics, etc., from A to Z. Over 3,000 entries plus appendix.

Small Arms of the World, by W. H. B. Smith and J. E. Smith. 9th ed., 1969. Stackpole Books, Harrisburg, PA. 786 pp., profusely illus. $17.95.
A most popular firearms classic for easy reference. Covers the small arms of 42 countries, clearly showing operational principles. A timeless volume of proven worth.

The Sportsman's Eye, by James Gregg, Winchester Press, NY, 1971. 210 pp., illus. $6.95.
How to make better use of your eyes in the outdoors.

Stoeger's Catalog & Handbook: New York World's Fair 1939 Jubilee Issue, Stoeger Arms, NY, 1970. 512 pp., illus. Paper, $4.95.
Reprint describing pre-W.W.II sporting arms.

Stoeger Mail Order and Gun Parts Catalog, compiled and published by Stoeger Arms, So. Hackensack, NJ, 1971. 416 pp., illus. $3.95.
Mail-order catalog listing over 1000 parts for pistols, rifles and shotguns, domestic and foreign. Includes gunsmith tools and accessories.

Stories of the Old Duck Hunters and Other Drivel, by Gordon MacQuarrie and compiled by Zack Taylor. Stackpole Books, Harrisburg, PA, 1967. 223 pp., illus. $5.95.
An off-beat relaxing and enjoyable group of 19 best-remembered outdoor stories, previously publ. in magazines.

Submachine Guns Caliber .45, M3 and M3A1, U.S. FM23-41 and TM 9-1217. Normount Armament Co., Forest Grove, OR, 1967. 141 pp., illus., paperbound. $3.00.
Reprint of two U.S. Army manuals on submachine guns.

Swords & Daggers, by Frederick Wilkinson. Hawthorn Books, NY, 1968. 256 pp., well illus. $5.95.
Good general survey of edged weapons and polearms of collector interest, with 150 pp. of illustrations and descriptions of arms from Europe, Africa and the Orient.

Swords of Hitler's Third Reich, by Major J. R. Angolia, F. J. Stephens, Essex, England, 1969. Over 100 pp., well illus. $8.95.
A comprehensive work on the swords of the German Army, Navy, Air Force, SS, Police, Fire Dept., and many other government departments—plus belts, hangers, and accouterments—all described and illus.

Tanks; An Illustrated History of Fighting Vehicles, by Armin Halle & Carlo Demand, New York Graphic Society, Greenwich, CT, 1971. 175 pp., illus. $24.95.
Comprehensively traces the development and technology of one of man's most complex and ingenious weapons.

Teaching Kids to Shoot, by Henry M. Stebbins. Stackpole Books, Harrisburg, PA 1966. 96 pp. illus. $2.95.
Designed for parents and leaders who want to develop safety conscious firearms-users.

Tear Gas Munitions. by T. F. Swearengen, Charles C. Thomas, Springfield, IL, 1966. 569 pp., illus. $34.50.
An analysis of commercial (riot) gas guns, tear gas projectiles, grenades, small arms ammunition, and related tear gas devices.

Technical Dictionary for Weapon Enthusiasts, Shooters and Hunters, by Gustav Sybertz. Publ. by J. Neumann-Neudamm, 3508 Melsungen, W. Germany, 1969, 164 pp., semi-soft covers. $7.50.
A German-English and English-German dictionary for the sportsman. An excellent handy work.

Tenting on the Plains, by Elizabeth Bacon Custer, Univ. of Oklahoma Press, Norman, OK, 1971. 706 pp. in 3 volumes, plus a 30-page intro. by Jane R. Stewart. Slip-cased. $8.85.
Deals with period after the Civil War when General Custer was stationed in Texas and Kansas.

The Thompson Gun, publ. by Numrich Arms, West Hurley, NY, 1967, 27 pp., illus., paper covers. $1.95.
A facsimile reprint, excellently done, of a 1923 catalog of Thompson sub-machine guns.

Thompson-Submachine Guns, compiled from original manuals by the publ. Normount Armament Co., Forest Grove, OR, 1968. Over 230 pp., well illus., many exploded views. Paper wrappers. $4.00.
Five reprints in one book: Basic Field Manual, Cal. 45, M1928AI (U.S. Army); Cal. 45, Model 1928, (for British); Cal., 45 (U.S. Ordnance); Model M1, Cal., 45 (U.S. Ordnance) and Ultra Modern Automatic Arms (Auto-Ordnance Corp.).

The Tournament, its periods and phases, by R. C. Clephan. Frederick Ungar Co., NY, 1967. A reprint. 195 pp., illus. with contemporary pictures plus half-tones of armor and weapons used by contestants, $9.95.
A rare and eagerly-sought work, long out-of-print. A scholarly, historical and descriptive account of jousting.

Training Your Own Bird Dog, by Henry P. Davis, G. P. Putnam's Sons, New York, NY. New rev. ed., 1969, 168 pp., plus 10 pp. of field trial records. Illus. with photographs. $5.95.
The reappearance of a popular and practical book for the beginner starting his first bird dog—by an internationally recognized authority.

A Treatise on Ancient Armour and Weapons, by Francis Grose. Benchmark Pub. Co., Glendale, NY, 1970. Irregular pagination. $12.50.
Reprint of a 1786 British monograph showing numerous items from the Tower of London and other sites.

A Treatise of Artillery, by John Muller. Museum Restoration Service, Ottawa, Canada, 1965. 216 pp., plus many plates. $17.50.
A creditable reprint of a famous and excellent original work of the third ed. of 1780, printed in London. This reprint limited to 350 numbered copies. The plates should be highly useful to the artillery buff.

Triggernometry, by Eugene Cunningham. Caxton Printers Lt., Caldwell, ID, 1970. 441 pp., illus. $7.95. A classic study of famous outlaws and lawmen of the West—their stature as human beings, their exploits and skills in handling firearms. A reprint.

The True Book About Firearms, by R. H. Walton, Frederick Muller, Ltd., London, 1965. 143 pp., illus. $3.50.
How modern weapons work, are used and their effect on history.

Unconventional Warfare Devices and Techniques, a reprint of Army TM 31-200-1 234 pp., illus., paper covers. $10.00.
Published primarily for U.S. Army Special Forces. Deals with destructive techniques and their applications to targets in guerrilla warfare.

Uniforms, Organization and History of the Waffen SS, by R. J. Bender and H. P. Taylor. R. J. Bender, Mountain View, Cal., 1969. 160 pp., photographs and drawings. $9.95.
The first of 4 contemplated volumes on the subject, with accompanying historical text.

United States Military Medals & Ribbons, by Philip K. Robles, Charles E. Tuttle Co., Rutland, VT, 1971. 187 pp., $12.50.
A definitive work; 139 plates in full color.

Use and Maintenance of the Browning "Hi-Power" Pistol, (No. 2 MK 1 and Commercial Models), by D. B. McLean. Normount Armament Co., Forest Grove, OR, 1966. 48 pp., illus., paperbound. $1.50.
Covers the use, maintenance, and repair of various Browning 9mm parabellum pistols.

Warriors' Weapons, by Walter Buehr. Crowell Co., NYC, 1963. 186 pp., illus. $5.95.
Illustrated history of pre-gunpowder arms, from stone ax to crossbow and catapult.

Weapons of the American Revolution, and Accoutrements, by Warren Moore. Funk & Wagnalls, NY, 1967. 225 pp., fine illus. $10.00.
Revolutionary era shoulder arms, pistols, edged weapons, and equipment are described and shown in fine drawings and photographs, some in color.

The Weapons Merchants, by Bernt Engelmann, Crown Publ., inc., Inc., NY, 1968. 224 pp., illus. $4.95.
A true account of illegal traffic in death-dealing arms by individuals and governments.

Weapons and Tactics, Hastings to Berlin, by Jac Weller, St. Martin's Press, New York, 1966. 238 pp., illus. $6.00.
Primarily on the infantry weapons of today, with basic data on those of the past.

Weapons of War, by P. E. Cleator. Crowell Co., NYC, 1968. 224 pp., illus. $6.95.
A British survey of warfare from earliest times, as influenced by the weapons available for combat.

A. A. White Engravers, Inc. A catalog, unpaginated, n.d. Paper covers. $2.00.
Current prices and illus. for the engraving of arms.

Wild Game Cookbook, by L. E. Johnson. Benjamin Co., NYC, 1968. 160 pp. $2.95.
Recipes, sauces, and cooking hints for preparation of all types of game birds and animals.

Wild Sanctuaries ..., by Robert Murphy. E. P. Dutton & Co., Inc., New York, NY, 1968, 288 pp., over 250 photographs in color and monochrome, plus 32 maps, including those of the flyways. $12.95.
Concerns America's national wildlife refuges. An all-encompassing treatise on its subject with fascinating pertinent text.

The Wild Turkey, its History and Domestication, by A. W. Schorger, Univ. of Oklahoma Press, Norman, Okla., 1966. 625 pp., illus. $15.00.
Detailed coverage of habitats, characteristics, breeding, and feeding of the American wild turkey. Bibliography.

Wilderness Cookery, by Bradford Angier. Stackpole Books, Harrisburg, PA, 1969. 256 pp., illus. $4.95.
An excellent work, one that will be of big interest to hunters, fishermen, campers, et al.

The Wilderness Route Finder, by C. Rutstrum, Macmillan Co., NY, 1970. 214 pp. $4.95.
Complete guide to finding your way in the wilderness.

Wildwood Wisdom, by Ellsworth Jaeger. The Macmillan Company, New York, NY, 1964. 491 pp. well-illus. by author. $6.95.
An authoritative work, through many editions; about all there is to know about every detail for the outdoorsman.

Williams 1970-71 Blue Book of Gun Dealing. Williams Gun Sight Co., Davison, Mich., 1970. 76 pp., illus., paperbound. $2.50.
Suggested price ranges for many models of rifles, shotguns, handguns, sights, etc., with other useful information for the gun trader.

The World of the White-Tailed Deer, by L. L. Rue III. J. B. Lippincott Co., Phila., 1967. A reprint. 137 pp., fine photos. $5.95.
An eminent naturalist-writer's account of the year-round activities of the white-tailed deer.

The World's Assault Rifles (and Automatic Carbines), by D. D. Musgrave and T. B. Nelson. T. B. N. Enterprises, Alexandria, VA, 1967. 546 pp., profusely illus. $17.50.
High velocity small-bore combat rifles are shown and described in much detail, arranged by type and nationality. A companion volume to *The World's Submachine Guns*, by Nelson and Lockhoven.

The World's Submachine Guns (and Machine Pistols), by T. B. Nelson and H. B. Lockhoven. T. B. N. Enterprises, Alexandria, VA, 1962. 739 pp., profusely illus. $15.50.
The 2nd printing (1964) of the first work with descriptive data on all significant SMGs to date, arranged by national origin. A glossary in 22 languages is included. It is a companion volume to the *The World's Assault Rifles* by Musgrave and Nelson.

You and Your Retriever, by R. W. Coykendall, Jr. Doubleday & Co., Garden City, NY, 1963. 155 pp., illus. $4.95.
A text on early, intermediate and advanced training of retrievers, with full information for handlers.

The Young Sportsman's Guide to Camping, by J. L. Holden. Thomas Nelson & Sons, Camden, NJ, 1962. 96 pp., illus. $2.75.
A concise and dependable guide to basic techniques of camping in comfort and safety.

The Young Sportsman's Guide to Dogs, by J. R. Falk. Thomas Nelson & Sons, Camden, NJ, 1964. 96 pp., illus. $2.75.
A creditable and concise work on the history and characteristics of 29 breeds of dogs, both working and nonsporting types.

The Young Sportsman's Guide to Target Shooting, by Gene Seraphine. Thomas Nelson & Sons, Camden, NJ, 1964. 94 pp., illus. $2.95.
A basic introduction to marksmanship, including selection of firearms, sights, equipment, ammunition and range behavior.

Gunsmithing

Antique Firearms: Their Care, Repair and Restoration, by Ronald Lister. Crown Publ., New York, 1964. 220 pp., 66 plates, 24 fig. $2.98.
A workshop manual for collectors and gunsmiths, giving correct procedures for every step in preserving firearms.

Artistry in Arms. The R. W. Norton Gallery, Shreveport, LA., 1970. 42 pp., illus. Paper, $2.50.
The art of gunsmithing and engraving.

Checkering and Carving of Gun Stocks, by Monte Kennedy. Stackpole Books, Harrisburg, PA, 1962. 175 pp., illus. $10.00.
Rev., enlarged clothbound ed. of a much sought-after, dependable work.

Complete Guide to Gunsmithing, by C. E. Chapel. Barnes & Co., NYC, 1962. 479 pp., illus. $6.95.
2nd rev. edition, known earlier as *Gun Care and Repair,* of a comprehensive book on all details of gunsmithing for the hobbyist and professional.

Firearms Blueing and Browning, by R. H. Angier. Stackpole Books, Harrisburg, PA, 151 pp., illus. $5.00.
A useful, concise text on chemical coloring methods for the gunsmith and mechanic.

Gun Engraving Review, by E. C. Prudhomme, G. E. R. Publ. Co., Shreveport, LA., 1965. 150 pp., profusely illus. (some in color.) $21.95.
Excellent examples of the gun engraver's art to serve as a guide to novice or expert. Selection of tools, techniques and a directory of engravers is given.

Gunsmith Kinks, by F. R. [Bob] Brownell. F. Brownell & Son., Montezuma, I. 1st ed., 1969. 496 pp., well illus. $9.95.
A widely useful accumulation of shop kinks, short cuts, techniques and pertinent comments by practicing gunsmiths from all over the world.

The Gunsmith's Manual, by J. Stelle and W. Harrison, Rutgers Book Center, Highland Park, NJ, 1972. 376 pp., illus. $9.95.
Exact reprint of the original. For the American gunsmith in all branches of the trade.

Gunsmithing, by Roy F. Dunlap. Stackpole Books, Harrisburg, PA, 714 pp., illus. $10.00.
Comprehensive work on conventional techniques, incl. recent advances in the field. Valuable to rifle owners, shooters, and practicing gunsmiths.

Gunsmithing Simplified, by H. E. Macfarland. Washington, DC, 1950, A. S. Barnes, NYC, 1959. 303 pp., illus. $6.95.
A thorough dependable concise work with many helpful short-cuts.

Gunstock Finishing and Care, by A. D. Newell. Stackpole Books, Harrisburg, PA. A new printing, 1966. 473 pp. illus. $9.50.
Amateur's and professional's handbook on the selection, use and application of protective and decorative coatings on gun stocks.

Hobby Gunsmithing, by Ralph Walker, Digest Books, Inc., Northfield, IL, 1972, 320 pp., illus. Paper, $5.95.
Kitchen table gunsmithing for the budding hobbyist.

Home Gun Care & Repair, by P. O. Ackley. Stackpole Books, Harrisburg, PA, 1969. 191 pp., illus. $5.95.
Basic reference for safe tinkering, fixing, and converting rifles, shotguns, handguns.

Home Gunsmithing Digest, by Tommy Bish. Digest Books, Inc., Northfield, IL, 1970, 320 pp., very well illus. within stiff decorated paper covers. $4.95.
An unusually beneficial assist for gun owners doing their own repairs, maintenance, etc. 45 chapters on tools, techniques and theories.

HOW . . . by L. Cowher, W. Hunley, and L. Johnston. NMLR Assn., IN, 1961. 107 pp., illus. Paper covers. $2.95.
This 1961 rev. ed., enlarged by 3 chapters and additional illustrations, covers the building of a muzzle-loading rifle, target pistol, and powder horn, and tells how to make gunflints.

How to Convert Military Rifles, by Harvey Williams, *et al.* Digest Books, Inc., Northfield, IL, 1970. 88 pp., very well illus., stiff paper covers. $1.95.
The 6th and latest ed. of a popular work formerly distributed by the author's company. Gives step-by-step instructions to convert a military rifle to a good looking and easy to handle sporter.

Introduction to Modern Gunsmithing, by H. E. MacFarland. Stackpole Books, Harrisburg, PA, 1965. 320 pp., illus. $6.95.
Up-to-date reference for all gunsmiths on care, repair, and modification of firearms, sights, and related topics.

Lock, Stock and Barrel, by R. H. McCrory. Publ. by author at Bellmore, NY, 1966. Paper covers, 122 pp., illus. $4.00.
A handy and useful work for the collector or the professional with many helpful procedures shown and described on antique gun repair.

Make Muzzle Loader Accessories, by Robert H. McCrory. R. H. McCrory, Bellmore, NY, 1967. 46 pp., paper wrappers, illus. with sketches. $2.25.
A capably executed handbook on how to make a powder horn, capper, nipple wrench, loading block and spring vise.

Master French Gunsmith's Designs of the 17th-18th Centuries, compiled by S. V. Grancsay. Winchester Press, New York, NY, 1970. A brand new work of 208 pp., beautifully illus. in facsimile. Numbered, limited issue of 1000 copies. $24.95.
Magnificient ornamentation of weapons taken from a superb collection of design books, gathered by a world authority. An inspiration and a must for the gunsmith-engraver.

The Modern Gunsmith, by James V. Howe. Funk & Wagnalls. NYC, 1970 reprint ed. (2 vols.). 910 pp., illus. $25.00.
Guide for amateur and professional gunsmiths on firearms design, construction, repair, etc.

The Modern Kentucky Rifle, How to Build Your Own, by R. H. McCrory. McCrory, Wantagh, NY, 1961. 68 pp., illus., paper bound. $3.50.
A workshop manual on how to fabricate a flintlock rifle. Also some information on pistols and percussion locks.

The NRA Gunsmithing Guide, National Rifle Association, Wash., DC, 1971. 336 pp., illus. Paper. $5.50.
Information of the past 15 years from the "American Rifleman," ranging from 03A3 Springfields to Model 92 Winchesters.

Professional Gunsmithing, by W. J. Howe, Stackpole Books, Harrisburg, PA, 1968 reprinting. 526 pp., illus. $10.00.
Textbook on repair and alteration of firearms, with detailed notes on equipment and commercial gunshop operation.

Recreating the Kentucky Rifle, by Wm. Buchele. Geo. Shumway, York, PA, 1970. 189 pp., illus. $10.00.
How to build a Kentucky rifle, illustrated with line drawings and separate full-scale drawings. In paper covers. $6.50.

Restocking a Rifle, by Alvin Linden. Stackpole Books, Harrisburg, PA, 1969. 138 combined pp., of text. Well illus. Large format. $9.95.
A re-issue in one volume of the 3 earlier Linden instruction guides on: Stock Inletting; Shaping; Finishing of the Springfield, Enfield and Winchester M70 rifles.

---

handguns

Automatic Firearm Pistols, by Elmer Swanson, Wesmore Book Co., Weehawken, NJ. 1st (and only) ed. 1955, 210 pp., well illus. $15.00.
A veritable catalog exclusively on automatic handguns for collectors, with many line drawings and descriptions, plus then-market market values of each.

Automatic Pistols, by H. B. C. Pollard, WE Inc., Old Greenwich, CT, 1966. 110 pp., illus. $5.95.
A facsimile reprint of the scarce 1920 original. Covers historical development of military and other automatics, shooting, care, etc.

Book of Pistols & Revolvers, by W. H. B. Smith. Stackpole Books, Harrisburg, PA, 1968. 758 pp., profusely illus. $6.00.
Rev. and enlarged, this encyclopedic reference, first publ. in 1946, continues to be the best on its subject.

Browning Hi-Power Pistols. Normount Armament Co., Forest Grove, OR, 1968. 48 pp., illus., paperbound. $1.50.
A handbook on all models of Browning Hi-Power Pistols, covering their use, maintenance and repair.

Colt Commemorative Firearms, by R. L. Wilson. Charles Kidwell, Wichita, Kans., 1969, Unpaginated, well illus. paper covers $5.95. In hard deluxe covers, limited issue of 1000 copies, each numbered. $10.00.
Description and fine color photographs of commemorative handguns issued by the Colt company, 1961-1969, all replicas of famous earlier models.

Combat Shooting for Police, by Paul B. Weston. Charles C. Thomas, Springfield, IL, 1967. A reprint. 194 pp., illus. $8.50.
First publ. in 1960 this popular self-teaching manual gives basic concepts of defensive fire in every position.

The Encyclopedia of the Third Reich, Book 1, by R. B. Marvin. Universal Research, Inc., Fort Lauderdale, Fla., 1969, from offset typewritten copy. 37 pp., very clear and sharp illustrations, paper covers. $4.00
This volume considers only handguns, but is a concise collector's guide to the main types of W.W. II German pistols and revolvers.

Fired In Anger, by Robt. Elman. Doubleday, Garden City, NY, 1968. 416 pp., illus. with 250 photos. $7.95.
Describes and illustrates the personal handguns used by famous and infamous Americans, including soldiers, outlaws and historical figures.

Georgian Pistols; The Art and Craft of the Flintlock Pistol, 1715-1840, by Norman Dixon, Geo. Shumway, York, PA, 1971. 184 pp., illus. $14.00.
The art of the Georgian gunmaker, describing the evolution of the holster pistol and the duelling pistol, with the parallel changes in style of the turn-off pistol.

German Pistols and Revolvers 1871-1945, by Ian V. Hogg, Stackpole Books, Harrisburg, PA, 1971. 160 pp. $12.95.
Over 160 photos and drawings showing each weapon, plus exploded views of parts, including markings, firms, patents, mfg. codes, etc.

The Handbook of Handgunning, by Paul B. Weston. Crown Publ., NYC, 1968. 138 pp., illus. with photos. $4.95.
"New concepts in pistol and revolver shooting," by a noted firearms instructor and writer.

Handbuch der Faustfeuerwaffen, by Gerhard Bock and W. Weigel. J. Neumann-Neudamm, Melsungen, Germany, 1968. 4th and latest ed., 724 pp., including index. Profusely illus. $21.00.
A truly encyclopedic work in German text on every aspect of handguns. Highly recommended for those who read German.

The Handgun, by Geoffrey Boothroyd. Crown Publishers, Inc., New York, NY, 1970. 564 pp., profusely illus., plus copious index. $19.95.
A massive and impressive work, excellently covering the subject from matchlocks to present-day automatics. Many anecdotes, much comment and pertinent data, including ammunition, etc.

Home Gunsmithing the Colt Single Action Revolvers, by Loren W. Smith, Ray Riling Arms Books Co., Phila., PA, 1971. 119 pp., illus. $7.95.
Detailed, information on the operation and servicing of this famous and historic handgun.

Japanese Hand Guns, by F. E. Leithe, Borden Publ. Co., Alhambra, CA, 1968. Unpaginated, well illus. $8.50.
Identification guide, covering models produced since the late 19th century. Brief text material gives history, descriptions, and markings.

Law Enforcement Handgun Digest, by Dean Grennell and Mason Williams. Digest Books, Inc., Northfield, IL, 1972. 320 pp., illus. Paper covers. $5.95.
Written especially for law enforcement officers and handgun-enthusiasts. From selection of weapon to grips, ammo, training, etc.

The Luger Pistol (Pistole Parabellum), by F. A. Datig. Borden Publ. Co., Alhambra, CA, 1962. 328 pp., well illus. $8.50.
An enlarged, rev. ed. of an important reference on the arm, its history and development from 1893 to 1945.

Lugers at Random, by Charles Kenyon, Jr. Handgun Press, Chicago, IL. 1st ed., 1970. 416 pp., profusely illus. $15.00.
An impressive large side-opening book carrying throughout alternate facing-pages of descriptive text and clear photographs. A new boon to the Luger collector and/or shooter.

Lugers Unlimited, by F. G. Tilton, World-Wide Gun Reports, Inc., Aledo, IL, 1965. 49 pp., illus. Paper covers $2.00.
An excellent monograph about one of the most controversial pistols since the invention of hand firearms.

Mauser Pocket Pistols 1910-1946, by Roy G. Pender, Collectors Press, Houston, TX, 1971. 307 pp., $14.50.
Comprehensive work covering over 100 variations, including factory boxes and manuals. Over 300 photos. Limited, numbered ed.

The Mauser Self-Loading Pistol, by Belford & Dunlap. Borden Publ. Co., Alhambra, CA. Over 200 pp., 300 illus., large format. $12.50.
The long-awaited book on the "Broom Handles," covering their inception in 1894 to the end of production. Complete and in detail: pocket pistols, Chinese and Spanish copies, etc.

Mauser, Walther & Mannlicher Firearms, by W.H.B. Smith, with a intro. by John T. Amber. Stackpole Books, Harrisburg, PA, 1971. 673 pp., illus. $14.95.
W.H.B. Smith's three classics, now in one convenient volume.

Military Pistols and Revolvers, by I. V. Hogg. Arco Pub. Co., NY, 1970. 80 pp., illus. $3.50.
The handguns of the two World Wars shown in halftone illus., with brief historical and descriptive text.

The Modern Handgun, by Robert Hertzberg. Arco Publ. Co., New York, NY, 1965. 112 pp., well illus. $3.50.
Pistols and revolvers of all types are traced from their beginnings. Data on modern marksmanship included.

Modern Pistol Shooting, by P. C. Freeman. Faber & Faber, London, England, 1968, 176 pp., illus. $5.00.
How to develop accuracy with the pistol. Fine points in technique are covered, with information on competitive target shooting.

The Official U.S. Army Marksmanship Guide, first authorized reproduction of the original U.S.A. work. J&A Publ., NY, 1972. 144 pp., over 90 illus. $4.95.
Every detail from sight alignment to International Pistol Programs—technical and fundamental for championship shooting in easy-to-read illus. form.

The "Parbellum" Automatic Pistol, the English version of the official DWM handbook on Luger pistols. Normount Armament Co., Forest Grove, OR, 1968. 42 pp., illus. Paper wrappers. $1.25.
A user's handbook, a reference work for collectors. A reprint of the original detailed instructions on use, disassembly and maintenance. Includes three folding plates.

Pistol and Revolver Guide, by George Nonte. Stoeger Arms Corp., So. Hackensack, NJ, 1967. 192 pp., well illus. Paper wrappers. $3.95.
A history of the handgun, its selection, use and care, with a glossary and trade directory.

The Pistol Shooter's Treasury, by Gil Hebard. Gil Hebard, Knoxville, IL, 1969. 1st ed., 112 pp. illus. in halftone and full color. Color decorated paper covers. $2.50.
A gathering of the experts, by an expert—classic articles on how to shoot a handgun and prepare for competition.

Pistolen Atlas, by Karl R. Pawlas, Nuremberg, Germany, 1970. Arranged alphabetically by maker and model in loose-leaf binding. Each vol. $10.00.
Carefully planned and researched for the "automatic arms buff," shooter and collector, depicts hundreds of auto. pistols of all nations and of all calibers with excellent illus. and descriptive text in English, French, German and Spanish. 13 volumes projected, of which vols. 1, 2, 3, 5, 6, 7 and 8 are now ready.

Pistols, A Modern Encyclopedia, by Stebbins, Shay & Hammond. Stackpole Co., Harrisburg, PA, 1961. 380 pp., illus. $4.98.
Comprehensive coverage of handguns for every purpose, with material on selection, ammunition, and marksmanship.

Pistols of the World, by Claude Blair, Viking Press, NYC, 1968. 206 pp., plus plates, $9.98.
Authoritative review of handguns since the 16th century, with chapters on major types, manufacture, and decoration. Fine photographic illustrations.

Pistols, Revolvers, and Ammunition, by M. H. Josserand and J. Stevenson, Crown Publ. Co., NY, 1972. 341 pp., illus. $7.50.
Basic information classifying the pistol, revolver, ammunition, ballistics and rules of safety.

Report of Board on Tests of Revolvers and Automatic Pistols. From The *Annual Report* of the Chief of Ordnance, 1907. Reprinted by J. C. Tillinghast, Marlow, NH, 1969. 34 pp., 7 plates, paper covers. $3.00.
A comparison of handguns, including Luger, Savage, Colt, Webley-Fosbery and other makes.

The Revolver, 1818-1865, by Taylerson, Andrews, & Frith. Crown Publ., NYC, 1968. 360 pp., illus. $7.50.
Noted British work on early revolving arms and the principal makers, giving production data and serial numbers on many models.

The Revolver, 1865-1888, by A. W. F. Taylerson. Crown Publ., NYC, 1966. 292 pp., illus. $3.49.
Detailed study of 19th-century British and U.S. revolvers, by types and makers, based on study of patent records.

The Revolver 1889-1914, by A. W. F. Taylerson. Crown Pub. NY, 1971. 324 pp., illus. $7.50.
The concluding volume of this definitive work deals with Continental arms, American rimfire and centerfire, British centerfire, and obsolescent arms in use.

Saga of the Colt Six-Shooter, and the famous men who used it, by G. E. Virgines. Frederick Fell Co., New York, NY, 1969. 220 pp., well illus. $7.95.
History of the Colt Single action army revolver since 1873, with much information of interest to collectors and shooters.

Sixguns by Keith, by Elmer Keith. Stackpole Co., Harrisburg, PA, 1968 (reprint of 1961 edition.) 335 pp., illus. $4.95.
Long a popular reference on handguns, this work covers all aspects, whether for the shooter, collector or other enthusiasts.

Smith and Wesson Catalog of 1901, a reprint facsimile by The Wyoming Armory, Inc., Cheyenne, WY, 1969. 72 pp., well illus., paper covers. $2.25.
All models, engraving, parts and break-down lists, etc.

The Story of Colt's Revolver, by Wm. B. Edwards, Castle Books, NY, 1971. 470 pp. $9.98.
Biography of Samuel Colt and his invention. Hundreds of photos, diagrams, patents and appendix of original advertisements.

System Mauser, a Pictorial History of the Model 1896 Self-Loading Pistol, by J. W. Breathed, Jr., and J. J. Schroeder, Jr. Handgun Press, Chicago, IL, 1967. 273 pp., well illus. 1st limited ed. hardbound. $12.50.

10 Shots Quick, by Daniel K. Stern. Globe Printing Co., San Jose, CA, 1967. 153 pp., photos. $8.50.
History of Savage-made automatic pistols, models of 1903-1917, with descriptive data for shooters and collectors.

U.S. Pistols and Revolvers Vol. 1, D. B. McLean, compiler. Normount Armament Co., Forest Grove, OR, 1968. 2nd printing, 198 pp., well illus., paper covers. $3.50.
A useful and reliable work from authoritative sources on M1911/M1911A1 Colt Pistols; M1917 S & W revolvers; M1917 and Detective Special Colt revolvers. Excellent for their use, maintenance and repair.

United States Single Shot Martial Pistols, by C. W. Sawyer, WE, Inc., Old Greenwich, CT, 1971. 101 pp., illus. $5.00.
History of pistols used by the U.S. Armed Services 1776-1871.

U.S. Test Trials 1900 Luger, by Michael Reese II. Coventry Publ. Co., Gretna, LA, 1970. illus. $7.00.
For the Luger Pistol collector.

The Webley-Fosbery Automatic Revolver. A reprint of the original undated booklet pupl. by the British makers. Deep River Armory, Houston, TX, 1968. 16 pp., illus., paper. $3.00.
An instruction manual, parts list and sales brochure on this scarce military handgun.

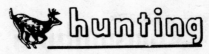

hunting

African Hunting, by Wm. C. Baldwin. Abercrombie & Fitch Library, NY, 1967. 451 pp., illus. $12.95.
Limited printing of a much-desired book giving vivid accounts of big game hunting exploits in Africa. First publ. in 1863.

After Wild Sheep in the Altai and Mongolia, by Prince Demidoff. Abercrombie & Fitch Library, NY, 1966. 324 pp., with photographs and drawings. $10.00.
Limited printing of a famous British work of 1900, on hunting big game in Asia. Long out-of-print.

American Partridge & Pheasant Shooting, by Frank Schiey. Abercrombie & Fitch Library, NYC, 1968. 238 pp., illus. $7.95.
Facsimile of an American sporting classic work, including detailed engravings of game birds.

The American Sportsman, by Elisha J. Lewis. Abercrombie & Fitch Library, NY, 1967, 510 pp., illus. $10.95.
Limited issue of a scarce classic American work on the hunting field, first publ. in 1851.

Animals of East Africa, by C. A. Spinage. Houghton Mifflin Co., Boston, MA, 1963. 151 pp. illus. $7.50.
Foreword by Sir Julian Huxley, F.R.S., who calls this "The best collection of wild life photographs I have seen." Excellent for those planning a safari.

The Art of Hunting Big Game in North America, by Jack O'Connor. Alfred A. Knopf, NY, 1967, 404 pp., line drawings and photos. $10.00.
A complete book on the subject, from tracing the origin of game on this continent to the various techniques practised in the sport on different species. Rifles and cartridges discussed at length.

Art of Successful Deer Hunting, by F. E. Sell, Stackpole Books, Harrisburg, PA, 1971. 192 pp., paper, $2.95.
Illus. re-issue of "The Deer Hunter's Guide." Western hunting lore for rifle and bow-hunter.

The Art of Wing Shooting, by W. B. Leffingwell. Abercrombie & Fitch Library, NYC, 1968. 190 pp., illus. $7.95.
An outstanding treatise on shotgun marksmanship, first publ. 1894, with explicit drawings on techniques of leading the target.

Asian Jungle, African Bush, by Charles Askins. Stackpole Books, Harrisburg, PA, 1959. 258 pp., illus. $5.95.
A where-to-go and how-to-do guide for game-rich Indo-China. The African section deals with game, the use of various arms and ammo on specific species.

The Australian Hunter, by Col. Allison with Ian Coombes. Cassell Australia Ltd., No. Melbourne, Australia, 1970. 212 pp., 58 photos., and 60 distribution maps and drawings. $11.50.
A comprehensive guide to game, equipment, hunting and photography.

Bell of Africa, by W. D. M. Bell, with foreword and introduction by Wally Taber and Col. T. Whelen. N. Spearman and Holland Press, London, 1960. 236 pp., illus. $5.75.
On elephants and the hunter extracted from Bell's own papers, it includes an appendix on rifles and rifle shooting.

Big Game Hunting in the West, by Mike Cramond. Mitchell Press, Vancouver, B.C., Can., 1965. 164 pp., illus. $5.95.
Accounts of hunting many species of big game and predators are given plus a section on rifles, equipment, and useful tips for the field.

Big Game Hunting Around the World, by B. Klineburger and V. Hurst, Exposition Press, NY, 1969. 376 pp., illus. $15.00.
From hunting tigers in India to polar bears in the Arctic.

Big Game Shooting in Africa, ed. by Major H. C. Maydon. Seeley, Service & Co., London, n.d., 445 pp. illus. $8.50.
Vol. 14 of the Lonsdale Library, with chapters by various British writers on African big game and on hunting in various sections of Africa.

Bird Hunting Know-How, by D. M. Duffey. Van Nostrand, Princeton, NJ, 1968. 192 pp., illus. $5.95.
Game-getting techniques and sound advice on all aspects of upland bird hunting, plus data on guns and loads.

The Bobwhite Quail, its Life and Management, by Walter Rosene. Rutgers University Press, New Brunswick, NJ. 1st ed., 1969. 418 pp., photographs, maps and color plates. $20.00.
An exhaustive study of an important species which has diminished under the impact of changing agricultural and forestry practices.

The Book of Saint Albans, by Dame Juliana Berners, Abercrombie & Fitch, NY, 1966. Illus. $18.00.
Reprint of the rare 1810 Haselwood ed. on hawking, hunting, fishing etc. The first English sporting book.

Bow & Arrow Archer's Digest, by J. Lewis, Digest Books, Northfield, IL, 1971. 320 pp., illus. Paper, $5.95.
The encyclopedia for all archers, from picking a bow to varmint calling.

Bowhunting for Deer, by H. R. Wambold. Stackpole Books, Harrisburg, PA, 1964. 160 pp., illus. $5.95.
Useful tips on deer, their habits, anatomy, and how-when-where of hunting, plus selection and use of tackle.

A Boy and His Gun, by Edward C. Janes. A. S. Barnes & Co., New York, NY. 207 pp., illus., $5.00.
Introduction to rifles, shooting and hunting techniques for young shooters with practical hints on game shooting with rifle or shotgun.

Buckshot and Hounds, by C. J. Milling. A. S. Barnes, NY, 1967. 132 pp., illus. $4.95.
Deer-driving methods and traditions of the South and West, with present-day adaptations described.

Calling All Game, by Bert Popowski. Stackpole Books, Harrisburg, PA, 1952, 306 pp. Illus. $7.50.
Practical methods of attracting game, from quail to moose, using artificial decoys and calls.

Charles Morgan on Retrievers, ed. by Ann Fowler and D. L. Walters. Abercrombie & Fitch, NYC, 1968, 168 pp., illus. $12.50.
Based on years of success in schooling hunting dogs, this work gives full details of an expert's proven methods to guide experienced trainers.

Complete Book of Bow and Arrow, by G. H. Gillelan, Stackpole Books, Harrisburg, PA, 1971. 320 pp., illus. $9.95.
Encyclopedic reference on archery, gear, rules, skill, etc.

Complete Book of Hunting, by Clyde Ormond. Harper & Bros., NYC, 1962. 467 pp., well-illus. $6.95.
Part I is on game animals, Part II is on birds. Guns and ammunition, game, habitats, clothing, equipment, etc. hunters' tips are discussed.

The Complete Deer Hunt, by Joe DeFalco. Madison Publ. Co., New York, NY, 1970. 133 pp., well illus., in line and halftone. Stiff paper covers. $3.95.
A concise work covering field dressing, skinning, equipment and arms, methods of hunting, etc.

Complete Guide to Hunting Across North America, by Byron Dalrymple. Outdoor Life, Harper & Row, NY, 1970. 848 pp., illus. with photos and 50 maps. $10.00.
A large reference work on hunting conditions, locating game, clothing, techniques, transportation, equipment for every region, etc.
Crow Shooting, by Bert Popowski. A. S. Barnes and Co., NYC, 1946. (4th printing 1957). 216 pp., illus. $5.00.
Practical and entertaining, telling how to locate roosts, build blinds and employ cover; the use of various decoys for shooting with rifle or shotgun.
Crow Shooting Secrets, by Dick Mermon. Winchester Press, New York, 1970. 149 pp., illus. $5.95.
An expert shares his secrets and touches all the bases.
Danger, by B. East, E. P. Dutton, NY, 1970. 323 pp., illus. $5.95.
The dangers in hunting and the weird things that can happen.
The Deer Hunter's Bible, by Geo. Laycock. Doubleday, Garden City, NY, 1963. 154 pp., illus. paperbound. $1.95.
Handy summary of deer hunting lore, by an expert. Guns, loads, bowhunting, care of vension, field techniques are covered.
The Deer of North America, edit. by W. P. Taylor. Stackpole Books. Harrisburg, PA, 1956. 668 pp., illus. incl. full-color plates. $12.50.
Leading authorities in all parts of the deer range have contributed their intimate studies of the animal.
Elephant, by D. E. Blunt, Neville Spearman, London, 1971. 260 pp., illus. $10.00.
Reprint of a rare book, a hunter's account of the ways of an elephant.
The End of the Game, by P. H. Beard. Viking Press, NYC, 1965. 256 pp., fine illus. $12.95.
Account of recent changes in African game country and decline of the game population.
Game Bird Hunting in the West, by Mike Cramond. Mitchell Press, Vancouver, B.C., Can., 1967. 246 pp., illus. $5.95.
Identification and hunting methods for each species of waterfowl and upland game birds, plus a section on shotgun types, equipment, and related subjects for the hunter.
Good Hunting, by Jas L. Clark, Univ. of Oklahoma Press, Norman, Okla., 1966. 242 pp., illus. $7.95.
Fifty years of collecting and preparing habitat groups for the American Museum.
The Great Arc of the Wild Sheep, by J. L. Clark, Univ. of Oklahoma Press, Norman, Okla., 1964. 247 pp., illus. $8.95.
Every classified variety of wild sheep is discussed, as found in North America, Asia & Europe. Numerous hunting stories by experts are included.
Great Game Animals of the World, by Russell B. Aitken. Winchester Press, NY, 1969. 192 pp. profusely ills. in monochrome and color. $22.50.
Accounts of man's pursuit of big game in all parts of the world, told in many fine pictures.
Great True Hunts, ed. by Peter Barrett. Prentice-Hall, Englewood Cliffs, NJ, 1967. 278 pp., illus. $4.95.
Big game hunting stories from *True* magazine, telling of hunting exploits of famous men around the world.
Green Hills of Africa, by Ernest Hemingway. Charles Scribner's Sons, NY, 1963. 285 pp. illus. $6.95.
A famous narrative of African big-game hunting, first published in 1935.
The Grizzly Bear, edited by B. D. and E. Haynes, Univ. of Oklahoma Press, Norman, Okla., 1966. 386 pp., illus. $6.95.
Collected stories about various encounters with the grizzly by mountain men, settlers, naturalists, scouts and others.
Grizzly Country, by Andy Russell. A. A. Knopf, NYC, 1968, 302 pp., illus. $7.95.
Many-sided view of the grizzly bear and his world, by a noted guide, hunter and naturalist.
Grouse and Grouse Hunting, by Frank Woolner. Crown Pub., Co., NY, 1970. 192 pp., illus. $7.50.
The history, habits, habitat and methods of hunting one of America's great game birds.
Guide to Safaris, by Burk H. Steizner. Charles Scribner's Sons, New York, NY, 1970. 178 pp., illus. $6.95.
Discussions of the different African regions, types of safari, minimal costs, etc. Highly informative for the would-be safari-goers seeking basic information.
Gun Dog, by Richard A. Wolters, E. P. Dutton, New York, NY, 1969. 1st ed., 11th Printing. 150 pp., well illus. $5.95.
A popular manual for upland bird shooters who want to train their dogs to perfection in minimum time.
The Gun on Saltings and Stubble, by N. M. Sedgwick. Herbert Jenkins, Ltd., Eng., 1949. 221 pp. $3.50.
Wildfowling on Britain's coastal estuaries.
How to Hunt American Game, by R. B. Vale. Stackpole Books, Harrisburg, PA. 5th printing, 1954. 199 pp., illus. $4.00.
Wildlife habits, conservation and the encouragement of hunting. Including the author's experiences in hunting game throughout America.
How to Hunt Small American Game, by L. A. Anderson. Funk and Wagnalls, New York, NY, 1969. 167 pp., well illus. $5.95.
A new basic guide for the small game hunter, similar to the author's 1959 *How to Hunt Deer and Small Game.* Written for beginner and expert, covers game, guns, equipment and game habits.
How to Hunt Whitetail Deer, L. A. Anderson. Funk & Wagnalls, NYC, 1968. 116 pp., illus. $5.95.
Useful reference for deer hunters, both novice and experienced, giving basic information and valuable pointers.
A Hunter's Wanderings in Africa, by Frederick Courteney Selous. Abercrombie & Fitch Library, NY, 1967. 455 pp., illus. $11.95.
Limited ed. of a rare and much-sought original work of 1881. A world-famous big game hunter tells of his African exploits.
The Hunter's World, by C. F. Waterman. Random House, NY, 1970. 250 pp., illus. $15.00.
A book for those who welcome an expert's guidance, one who understands the terrain, feed, cover, etc., of the game they hunt. Profusely illus. in color.
Hunting Dog Know-How, by D. M. Duffey, Van Nostrand, Princeton, NJ, 1965. 177 pp., illus. $5.95.
Covers selection, breeds, and training of hunting dogs, problems in hunting and field trials.
Hunting Our Biggest Game, by Clyde Ormond. Stackpole Books, Harrisburg, PA, 1956. 197 pp., illus. $8.95.
Practical advice for hunters on moose, elk, bear, wild sheep, trophy data, field methods, etc.
Hunting Our Medium Size Game, by Clyde Ormond. Stackpole Books, Harrisburg, PA, 1958. 219 pp., illus. $5.00.
Covers deer, whitetails and mules; black bear; antelope; coyotes; bobcats and cougar. Included are sections on equipment, use of rifles, and care of venison.
Hunting Pronghorn Antelope, by Bert Popowski. Stackpole Books, Harrisburg, PA, 1959. 227 pp., illus. $6.50.
Hunting the Ruffed Grouse, by Nick Sisley. Copyright, Nick Sisley, 1970. 136 pp., illus. $3.50.
A must for hunting this great game bird. The author, a grouse expert, is vice president of the Ruffed Grouse Society of America.
Hunting with Bow and Arrow, by George Laycock and Erwin Bauer. Arco Publ. Co., Inc., NYC, 1966. $3.50.
A practical guide to archery as a present-day sport. Mentions equipment needed and how to select it. Illus. instructions on how to shoot with ease and accuracy.
The Imperial Collection of Audubon Animals, original text by John James Audubon and Rev. John Bachman, illus. by John James and John Woodhouse Audubon. A magnificent quarto reproduction of the rare original by Hammond, Inc., Maplewood, NJ, 1967. 307 pp., 150 animals pictured in full color. $6.95.
Each illus. accompanied by engaging text, as in the 1st ed. of 1848, including accounts of Audubon's exploring trips. A most useful work for hunters who want to know their game.
Inside Safari Hunting, by D. Holman. G. P. Putnam's Sons, NY, 1970. 296 pp., illus. $6.95.
The work of the white hunter in Africa, based on the experiences of a second-generation professional.
Jack O'Connor's Big Game Hunts, by Jack O'Connor. E. P. Dutton, N.Y.C., 1963. 415 pp., illus. $5.95.
26 detailed chronicles of successful trips for big game, selected from *Outdoor Life.*
Krider's Sporting Anecdotes, edited by Milnor H. Klapp. Abercrombie & Fitch Library, NY, 1966. 292 pp., illus. $8.00.
Limited issue of the much-wanted work on Philadelphia's renowned gunsmith, John Krider, publ. first in 1853. A rich fund of knowledge on upland shooting, dogs and match shooting, etc.
Living Off the Country, by B. Angier. Stackpole Books, Harrisburg, PA, 1959. 241 pp., illus. $5.00.
In a simple and entertaining manner the author explains how to live off nature when emergency arises and how to stay alive in the woods.
Modern ABC's of Bird Hunting, by Dave Harbour, Stackpole Books, Harrisburg, PA, 1966. 192 pp., illus. $4.95.
From city's edge to wilderness this gives the occasional hunter the quickest way on how to increase his bag. Covers all game birds of the U.S. and Canada.
Modern Hunting with Indian Secrets, by Allan A. Macfarlan. Stackpole Books, Harrisburg, PA, 1971. 222 pp., $6.50.
How to acquire the new-old skills of the Redman, how to apply them to modern hunting.
The New Hunter's Encyclopedia, edited by Leonard Miracle and James B. Trefethen, plus specialized articles by over 60 outstanding contributors. Stackpole Books, Harrisburg, PA, 1972. 1054 pp., with 2047 photos, diagrams, drawings and full-color plates. $24.95.
A massive work covering every detail of every sort of hunting in the U.S., Canada and Mexico.
Nine Centuries of Hunting Weapons, by L. G. Boccia, Editrice Edam, Firenze, Italy, 1967. 181 pp., illus. with many fine photos of superb museum quality in full color. $15.00.
In Italian text, a historical survey of hunting weapons of Italian origin and their makers.
North American Big Game 1971 Edition, ed. by Robt. C. Alberts, Boone and Crockett Club, Pittsburgh, PA, 1971. 403 pp., illus. $15.00.
Tabulations of outstanding trophies compiled by the B & C Club.
On Your Own in the Wilderness, by Col. T. Whelen and B. Angier. Stackpole Books, Harrisburg, PA, 1958. 324 pp., illus. $5.00.
Two eminent authorities give complete, accurate, and useful data on all phases of camping and travel in primitive areas.
Paw Prints; How to Identify Rare and Common Mammals by Their Tracks. O. C. Lempfert, NY, 1972. 71 pp., illus. with actual size prints. $7.50.
An authoritive manual for hunters and outdoorsmen.
Pocket Guide to Animal Tracks, by L. M. Henderson, Stackpole Books, Harrisburg, PA, 1968. 57 pp., profusely illus., and bound in paper boards. $2.95.
Delightful text plus Henderson's most accurate line drawings show many signatures—paw and hoof prints, habits and characteristics, of 44 North American Small and big game.
The Practical Hunter's Dog Book, by John R. Falk, Winchester Press, NY, 1971. 314 pp., illus. $8.95.
Helps to choose, train and enjoy your gun dog.
Prehistoric Animals and Their Hunters, by I. W. Cornwall. F. A. Praeger, NY, 1968. 214 pp., illus. $7.50.
Describes animal species and hunting methods used in this period, plus uses made of the kills.
The Puma, Mysterious American Cat, by S. P. Young and E. A. Goldman, Dover Publ., NY, 1964, 358 pp., illus. Paper covers $3.00.
A two-part work: the first on the history, economic status and control: the second on classifications of the races of the puma.
Ranch Life and the Hunting Trail, by Theodore Roosevelt, 1894. A fine reprint by the Winchester Press, New York, NY, 1969, with introduction by Kermit Roosevelt. 168 pp., and includes the Frederic Remington illustrations from the original and those added from the 1908 edition. $6.98.
The far west of the 1880's of hunting and bags, of men and manners.
The Rifle and Hound in Ceylon, by Samuel White Baker. Abercrombie & Fitch Library, NY, 1967. 422 pp., well illus. $12.95.
Limited printing of a classic description of elephant-hunting, deer-coursing and elk-hunting in the East. First published in the 1850s.
Rowland Ward's Records of Big Game, 14th ed., comp. by G. A. Best, Rowland Ward Pub., Ltd., 1971. 438 pp., illus. $45.00.
New edition of the authoritive record of big game kills in Africa, by species.
Safari, by Elmer Keith. Safari Publ., La Jolla, CA, 1968. 166 pp., illus. $7.95.
Guide to big game hunting in Africa, with anecdote and expert advice on hunting many species of game. Information on guns, ammunition, equipment, and planning the safari is included. Fine photographs.
Safari by Jet, through Africa and Asia, by Sister Maria del Rey, Charles Scribner's Sons, New York, NY, 1962. 308 pp., profusely illus., with photos, and line. $5.95.
Off-beat reading about an African-Asian grand tour, with tales of the land and the people of Tanganyika, Ceylon, the Philippines, Hong Kong, Taiwan, et al.
Selected American Game Birds, by David Hagerbaumer and Sam Lehman, The Caxton Printers, Ltd., Caldwell, ID, 1972. The entire text of this book is executed in decorated calligraphy. $30.00.
Twenty-six of David Hagerbaumer's exquisite original watercolors, representing 29 bird species. A must for every book collector and art lover.
Shots at Whitetails, by Larry Koller. A. A. Knopf, NY, 1970. 359 pp., illus. $7.95.
A new reprint, with all information on guns, loads, scopes, etc., brought up to date.

A Sporting Chance . . . , by D. P. Mannix. E. P. Dutton & Co., NY, 1967. 248 pp., illus. with 50 photos. $1.98.
Unusual methods of hunting the exotic species from hounds to falcons. Inspiring reading for those desiring to get away from the commonplace.

Sporting Guns, by Richard Akehurst. G. P. Putnam's Sons, NYC, 1968. 120 pp., illus. $5.95.
History of shooting and of the guns and rifles developed to meet the hunter's needs, with anecdotes of the hunting field.

The Sportsman's Companion, by Lee Wulff. Harper & Row, N.Y.C., 1968. 413 pp., illus. $11.95.
Compendium of writings by various experts on hunting and fishing for American game. A useful reference for the outdoorsman.

Sportman's Guide to Game Animals, by Leonard Lee Rue III. Harper & Row [Outdoor Life Books], New York, NY, 1st ed., 2nd printing, 1969. 635 pp., illus. with photographs and maps. $6.50.
Exhaustive and capable coverage of the behavior and habits of all North American game animals.

The Standard Book of Hunting and Shooting, R. B. Stringfellow, ed. 1st ed., in 1950 by the Greystone Press, New York, NY, 564 pp., very well illus. $10.00.
An excellent anthology on hunting in America, giving meaningful information on all major species and on all types of guns, sights, ammunition, etc. An abridgement of the larger *Hunters Encyclopedia.*

Three Years' Hunting & Trapping America and the Great Northwest, by J. Turner-Turner Abercromble & Fitch Library, N.Y.C., 1967. 182 pp., illus. $10.95.
Reprint of an 1888 account of a determined quest for valuable furs in one of the world's least hospitable regions.

Topflight; A Speed Index to Waterfowl, by J. A. Ruthven & Wm. Zimmerman, Moebius Prtg. Co., Milwaukee, WI, 1968. 112 pp., $4.95.
Rapid reference for specie identification. Marginal color band of book directs reader to proper section. 263 full color illustrations of body and feather configurations.

Tracks of an Intruder, by Gordon Young. Winchester Press, NY, 1970. 191 pp., illus. $5.95.
Fascinating, first hand account of how an American naturalist gained recognition as a master hunter from the Montagnard Lahu tribesmen of Southeast Asia.

Travel & Adventure in Southeast Africa, by F. C. Selous. A & F Press, N.Y.C., 1967. 522 pp., illus. $11.95.
New edition of a famous African hunting book, first published in 1893.

A Treasury of African Hunting, ed. by Peter Barrett. Winchester Press, NY, 1970. 251 pp., illus. $6.95.
Outstanding accounts by noted writers and experts on African hunting, covering big game and small in many sections of the continent.

The Treasury of Hunting, by Larry Koller, Odyssey Press, N.Y.C., 1965. 251 pp., illus. $7.95.
Concise accounts of all types of hunting in the U.S. Excellent illustrations, many color photographs taken in various hunting fields.

Trophy Hunter in Asia, by E. T. Gates, Winchester Press, NY, 1971. 272 pp., illus. $12.50.
Hunting the rarest of game animals.

The Truth About Hunting in Today's Africa and how to go on a safari for $690.00, by G. L. Herter, Herter's, Inc., Waseca, Minn., 1970. 314 pp., well illus. $3.95.
Tells how to arrange safari costs, plus new data on weights, rifles and bullets derived from actual field tests.

The Unnatural Enemy, by Vance Bourjaily. The Dial Press, 1963. 182 pp., illus. $2.49.
Beautifully written episodes of bird-hunting.

The Upland Game Hunter's Bible, by Dan Holland. Doubleday, N.Y.C., 1961. 192 pp., illus. paper covers. $1.95.
Hunter's manual on the principal species of American upland game birds and how to hunt them.

The Varmint and Crow Hunter's Bible, by Bert Popowski. Doubleday & Co., N.Y.C., 1962. 185 pp., 150 illus. Paper covers. $1.95.
Hunting and trapping techniques described by a well-known authority. Chapters on woodchucks, crows, foxes, snakes, guns, etc.

Water Dog. by R. A. Wolters, E. P. Dutton & Co., NY, 1964. 179 pp., illus. $5.95.
Rapid training manual for working retrievers.

Waterfowl in the Marshes, by A. C. Becker Jr. A. S. Barnes and Co., New York, NY, 1969. 155 pp., photographs. $7.50.
A highly informative and practical guide to waterfowl hunting in America.

Whitetail, by George Mattis. World Publ. Co., New York, NY, 1969. 273 pp., including index. Illus. $6.95.
Fundamentals and fine points of compelling interest for the deer hunter.

Wild Fowl Decoys, by Joel Barber. Dover Publ., N.Y.C., 1954. 156 pp., 134 illus., paperbound. $4.00.
A fine work on making, painting, care and use of decoys in hunting, recently reprinted. Full data on design and construction.

Wildfowling, by James Andrews, et al. Seeley, Service & Co., London, n.d. 352 pp., illus. $7.50.
Articles by British sportsmen on shooting wildfowl, guns, punting, and conditions in various areas. Vol. 29 of the Lonsdale Library.

Winchester-Western 1970-71 Hunting Guide, by E. L. Kozicky and J. B. Madson. Winchester Press, NY, 1970. 126 pp., illus. Paper covers. $1.95.
A compendium of hunting information, seasons, licenses, prospects and best hunting areas.

RIFLES

The Big-Game Rifle, by Jack O'Connor, Alfred A. Knopf, N.Y.C., 1951. 371 pp., plus XI pp. Well illus. $10.00.
Discusses construction, purpose and use for all types of big game as well as ammo., sights, accessories, etc.

Bolt Action Rifles, by Frank de Haas, ed. by John T. Amber, Editor of GUN DIGEST. Digest Books, Inc., Northfield, IL, 1971. 320 pp., illus. Paper, $6.95.
The definitive work, covering every major design since the Mauser of 1871.

The Book of Rifles, by W. H. B. Smith. Stackpole Books, Harrisburg, PA, 1963 (3rd ed.). 656 pp., profusely illus. $6.00.
An encyclopedic reference work on shoulder arms, recently up-dated. Includes rifles of all types, arranged by country of origin.

The Boy's Book of Rifles, by C. E. Chapel. Coward-McCann, N.Y.C., 1948, rev. ed., 1960. 274 pp., illus. $3.95.
For all young men of Boy Scout age at every phase of small-caliber marksmanship and safe gun handling. It tells how to qualify for NRA medals and Scout Merit Badges for Marksmanship.

Boy's Single-Shot Rifles, by Jas. J. Grant, William Morrow & Co., Inc., NY, 1967. 608 pp., illus. $10.00.
A wealth of important new material on an ever-popular subject, authoritatively presented. By the author of *Single Shot Rifles* and *More Single Shot Rifles.*

The Breech-Loading Single-Shot Match Rifle, by N. H. Roberts and K. L. Waters, D. Van Nostrand Co., Princeton, NJ, 1967. 293 pp., fine photos. $12.50.
Account of the Schuetzen rifle in America, with material on famous shooters, gunsmiths, ammunition, and related topics.

Browning Automatic Rifles, Normount Armament Co., Forest Grove, OR, 81 pp., illus. Paper, $2.00.
Reprint of Ordnance Manual TM 9-1211, on all types of caliber 30's.

Carbines Cal. .30 M1, M1A1, M2 and M3, by D. B. McLean. Normount Armament Co., Forest Grove, OR, 1964. 221 pp., well illus., paperbound. $3.00.
U.S. field manual reprints on these weapons, edited and reorganized.

Description and Instructions for the Management of the Gallery-Practice Rifle Caliber .22—Model of 1903. Inco., 1972. 12 pp., 1 plate. Paper, $1.00.
Reprint of 1907 War Dept. pamphlet No. 1925.

Description of Telescopic Musket Sights, Inco, 1972. 10 pp., 4 plates. Paper, $1.00.
Reprint of 1917 War Dept. pamphlet No. 1957, first publ. in 1908.

Fifteen Years in the Hawken Lode, by John D. Baird, The Buckskin Press, Chaska, MI, 1971. 120 pp., illus. $10.00.
Complements "The Hawken Rifle" by the same author. Collection of thoughts and observations over many years on the famed Hawkens.

The First Winchester, by John E. Parsons. Winchester Press, New York, NY, 1969. 207 pp., well illus., $8.95.
This new printing of *The Story of the 1866 Repeating Rifle* [1st publ. 1955] is revised, and additional illustrations included.

Garand Rifles M1, M1C, M1D, by Donald B. McLean. Normount Armament Co., Forest Grove, OR, 1968. Over 160 pp., 175 illus., paper wrappers. $3.00.
Covers all facets of the arm: battlefield use, disassembly and maintenance, all details to complete lock-stock-and-barrel repair, plus variations, grenades, ammo., and accessories; plus a section on 7.62mm NATO conventions.

Hawken Rifles; The Mountain Man's Choice, by John D. Baird, The Buckskin Press, Chaska, MI, 1971. 95 pp., illus. $10.00.
History and collector's reference on Hawken rifles, developed and used in the West in the fur trade.

How to Select and Use Your Big Game Rifle, by Henry M. Stebbins, Combat Forces Press, Washington, 1952. 237 pp., illus. $6.50.
Concise valuable data on rifles, old and new—slide action, lever, semi automatic, and single shot models are covered.

The Hunting Rifle, by Jack O'Connor. Winchester Press, NY, 1970. 352 pp., illus. $8.95.
An analysis, with wit and wisdom, of contemporary rifles, cartridges, accessories and hunting techniques.

Johnson Semi-Automatic Rifle, Rotary Feed Model, 1941 Instruction Manual, by the Johnson Arms Co. Design Publ., Hyattsville, Md., 1969. 72 pp. illus., paper covers. $4.00.
A reprint of the original instruction manual.

The Lee-Enfield Rifle, by E. G. B. Reynolds. Arco Publ. Co., NY, 1968. 224 pp., drawings and photos. $9.50.
New U.S. edition of a standard reference on models and modifications of the famous British military rifle.

Major Ned H. Roberts and the Schuetzen Rifle, by Gerald O. Kelver, G: O. Kelver, Publ., Mentone, IN, 1972. 99 pp., illus. $4.00.
Selected writings on old single shot rifles, sights, loads, etc.

Maynard Catalog of 1880, a reprint in facsimile by the Wyoming Armory, Inc., Cheyenne, WY, 1969. 32 pp., illus., paper covers. $2.25.
All models, sights, cartridges, targets etc.

Modern Breech-Loaders, Sporting and Military, by W. W. Greener, with intro. by D. B. McLean. Normount Technical Publ., Forest Grove, OR, 1971. 256 pp., illus. Paper, $4.50.
Reprint of original 1870 ed. Covers rifles, carbines, and the "new" breech-loading pistols.

Pictorial History of the Rifle, By G. W. P. Swenson. Ian Allan Ltd., Shepperton, Surrey, England, 1971. 184 pp., illus. $9.50.
Essentially a picture book, with over 200 rifle illustrations. The text furnishes a concise history of the rifle and its development.

The Rifle: and How to Use it, by H. Busk, Richmond Publ. Co., Richmond, England, 1971. 225 pp., illus. $9.00.
Reprint of the 1859 ed. Covers mid-19th century military rifles.

The Rifle Book, by Jack O'Connor. Random House (Knopf), N.Y.C., 1948. 3rd ed., 1964. 338 pp., illus. $10.00.
A definitive work, out-of-print until recently, which covers actions, design, ammunition, sights and accessories.

Rifles, a Modern Encyclopedia, by H. M. Stebbins. Book Sales, New York, NY, 1970. A reprint of the original of 1958. 376 pp., well illus. $4.98.
A comprehensive work covering subject for target and game. A limited number of original, deluxe and numbered full-leather bound copies at $25.00.

Rifles AR15, M16, and M16A1, 5.56 mm, by D. B. McLean. Normount Armament Co., Forest Grove, OR, 1968. Unpaginated, illus., paper covers. $3.50.
Descriptions, specifications and operation of subject models are set forth in text and picture.

Schuetzen Rifles, History and Loading, by Gerald O. Kelver, Gerald O. Kelver, Publisher, Brighton, CO, 1972. Illus. $4.00.
Reference work on these rifles, their bullets, loading, telescopic sights, accuracy, etc. A limited, numbered ed.

Sharps Firearms, *v. 3, Pt. 3, Model 1874 Rifles,* by Frank M. Sellers and Dewitt Bailey II. Frank M. Sellers, Denver, Colo., 1969. 20 pp., illus., paper covers. $7.50.
A separately printed section of a continuing comprehensive collector's reference. This current work shows and describes the known M1874 variations.

Shooter's Bible Gunsight Guide, by George Nonte. Shooter's Bible, Inc., So. Hackensack, NJ, 1968. 224 pp., illus. $3.95.
Catalog data, descriptions and comment, plus articles on all types of modern gun sights.

Shooting the Percussion Rifle, by R. O. Ackerman. Publ. by the author, Albuquerque, N.M., 1966. 19 pp., illus. in line by the author. Paper wrappers, $1.50.

This well prepared work is Book No. 2 of a projected series. This one gives basic information on the use of the muzzle-loading rifle.

Single Shot Rifles and Actions, by Frank de Haas. Ed. by J. T. Amber. Published by Digest Books, Inc., Northfield, IL, 1969. 342 pp., illus. paper bound. $7.95.

A definitive book on over 60 single shot actions and rifles, their use, repair, remodelling, etc.

Sir Charles Ross and His Rifle, by Robt. Phillips and J. J. Knap, Museum Restoration Service, Ottawa, Canada., 1969. 32 pp., illus. Paper covers. $2.00.

The story of the man who invented the "Ross Model 1897 Magazine Sporting Rifle," the 1900 under the name of Bennett, and many others.

Small Bore Target Shooting, by H. G. B. Fuller. Herbert Jenkins, London, 1964. 264 pp., well illus. $8.50.

Authoritative English work, covering rifle types, buying hints, ammunition, accessories, and range technique.

Sniper Rifles of Two World Wars, by W. H. Tantum IV. Museum Restoration Service, Ottawa, Can., 1967. 32 pp., illus. $1.50.

Monograph on high-accuracy rifles used by troops in world wars I and II and in Korea. Paper wrappers.

Springfield Rifles, M1903, M1903A1, M1903A4, compiled by the publ. Normount Armament Co., Forest Grove, OR, 1968. Over 115 pp., illus., paper wrappers. $2.50.

Routine disassembly and maintenance to complete ordnance inspection and repair; bore sighting, trigger adjustment, accessories, etc.

The '03 Springfields, by Clark S. Campbell, Ray Riling Arms Books Co., Phila, PA, 1971. 320 pp., illus. $16.50.

New, completely revised, enlarged and updated ed. based on the 1957 issue.

Twenty-Two Caliber Varmint Rifles, by C. S. Landis. Stackpole Books, Harrisburg, PA, 1947. 521 pp., profusely illustrated. $7.50.

A vast amount of data on the many Wildcat 22's, including numerous scale drawings of cartridges and chambers.

United States Rifle, Cal. .30, Model of 1917, a reprint of an official government booklet by Normount Publ. Co., Forest Grove, OR, 1969. 80 pp., line illus., paper covers. $2.00.

A training manual issued by the War Department in 1918. A much-wanted and useful booklet.

United States Rifle 7.62 mm, M14 and M14E2, a reprint of an official government booklet by Normount Armament Co., Forest Grove, OR, 1968. 50 pp., illus., paper covers. $2.00.

U.S. Army Field Manual 23-8, first published in 1965.

Westley Richards Modern Sporting Rifles and Cartridges. A reprint of an original undated catalog of the British makers. Safari Outfitters, Richfield, Conn., 1968. 60 pp. illus., paper. $4.95.

Facsimile of issue, covers big game rifles and ammunition.

Winchester '73 & '76, the First Repeating Center-Fire Rifles, by D. F. Butler. Winchester Press, New York, NY, 1st ed. 1970. 95 pp., well and tastefully illus. in line, halftones and photos. Color frontispiece. $7.95.

A complete history of the subject arms and their then-new ammunition, plus details of their use on America's western frontiers.

American Partridge and Pheasant Shooting, Frank Schley. Abercrombie & Fitch Library, NY, 1967. 222 pp., illus. with detailed engravings of game birds. $7.95.

Limited printing of the rare sporting classic of 1877, considered for years the most important book available on the use of the scattergun.

The Art of Wing Shooting, by Wm. B. Leffingwell. Abercrombie & Fitch Library, NY, 1967. 192 pp., illus. $7.95.

Limited issue of a practical treatise on the use of the shotgun, first publ. in 1894. Contains a wealth of period anecdotes.

Automatic and Repeating Shotguns, by R. Arnold. Barnes & Co., N.Y.C., 1960. 173 pp., illus. $2.95.

Their history and development, with expert professional advice on choosing a gun for clay target shooting, game shooting, etc.

Book of Shotgun Sports, by Sports Illustrated eds. J. B. Lippincott Co., Phila, PA, 1967. 88 pp., illus. $3.50.

Introduction to target shooting, game shooting, and gunmanship.

Clay Pigeon Marksmanship, by Percy Stanbury and G. L. Carlisle. Herbert Jenkins, London, 1964. 216 pp., illus. $6.00.

Handbook on learning the skills, with data on guns & equipment and competition shooting at all types of clay targets; by two eminent British writers.

Field, Skeet and Trapshooting, by C. E. Chapel. Revised ed. Barnes & Co., NYC, 1962. 291 pp., illus. $6.95.

A useful work on shotgun shooting, including gun types, ammo, accessories, marksmanship, etc.

The Fowler in Ireland. by Sir Ralph Payne-Gallwey, Richmond Publ. Co., Richmond, England, 1971. 503 pp., illus. $13.95.

Reprint of the 1882 work on wildfowling and wildlife in Ireland.

The Game Shot's Vade Mecum, by Michael Brander, A. & C. Black, London, 1st ed., 1965. 242 pp., illus. $6.00.

A British guide on the use of the shotgun in the hunting field, covers selection, marksmanship, game behavior and hunt management.

The Golden Age of Shotgunning, by Bob Hinman, Winchester Press, NY, 1971. 175 pp., illus. $8.95.

The story of American shotgun and wingshooting from 1870 to 1900.

Gough Thomas's Gun Book, by G. T. Garwood. A. & C. Black, London, England, 1969. 160 pp., illus. $8.95.

Excerpts of articles on the shotgun published in *Shooting Times*, by a noted British authority. Wide-ranging survey of every aspect of the shotgun, its use, behavior, care, and lore.

Gough Thomas's Second Gun Book, by G. T. Garwood, A. & C. Black, London, 1971. 227 pp., illus. $10.00.

More—and excellent—shotgun lore for the sportsman.

High Pheasants, by Sir Ralph Payne-Gallwey, Richmond Publ. Co., Richmond, England, 1970. 79 pp. $6.60.

The first and last word on its subject.

How to Shoot Straight, by Macdonald Hastings. A. S. Barnes and Co., New York, NY, 1970. 133 pp., illus., index ed. $5.95.

A companion volume to the author's *Churchill on Game Shooting,* and designed as a standard work on the modern game gun—a "teach-yourself" book.

New England Grouse Shooting, by W. H. Foster, Chas. Scribner's, NY, 193 pp., illus. $12.50.

Many interesting and helpful points on how to hunt grouse.

The New Wildfowler in the 1970's by N. M. Sedgwick, et al. Barrie & Jenkins, London, Eng., 1970. 375 pp., illus. $11.50.

A compendium of articles on wildfowling, hunting practices and conservation. An updated reprint.

Parker, America's Finest Shotgun, by P. H. Johnson. Outlet Book Co., Inc., NY, 1968. 260 pp., illus. $3.95.

An account of a great sporting arm—from post Civil War until 1947, when it was sold to Remington. Values, models, etc.

Pigeon Shooting, by Richard Arnold. Faber & Faber, London, Eng., 1966. 162 pp., illus. $5.00.

A practical, specialized work on pigeon shooting in flight, over decoys, how to make hideouts, decoys, etc.

Rough Shooting, by G. A. Gratten & R. Willett. Faber & Faber, London, Eng., 1968. 242 pp., illus. $6.75.

The art of shooting, dogs and their training, games, rearing and their diseases, proof marks, etc.

Score Better at Trap, by Fred Missildine. Winchester Press, NY, 1971. 192 pp., illus. $5.95.

Step-by-step instructions, fully illustrated, on mastering the game by one of the world's leading coaches. In paper covers, $2.95.

Shooting For Beginners, by E. N. Barclay. Percival Marshal & Co., London, 1963. 74 pp., illus. $1.75.

Concise introduction to British techniques and customs in shotgunning for game birds.

Shooting Preserve Management (The Nilo System), by E. L. Kozicky and John Madson, Winchester Press, New York, NY, 1969. 312 pp., photos., line drawings and diagrams. $10.00.

The new look in 13 chapters, a full account of American field shooting at Nilo Farms, the show-case of the shooting-preserve concept.

The Shotgun, by T. D. S. & J. A. Purdey. A. & C. Black, London, Eng., 1969. 144 pp., illus. with Photos and diagrams. $3.95.

Reprinted 4th ed. of a well-known British work by two members of the notable gunsmith family. Covers the gun and its use in the field, at traps, and for skeet.

The Shotgun Book, by Jack O'Connor. Alfred A. Knopf, NY, 1965. 332 pp., plus index, illus. with line and photos. $10.00.

The definitive, authoritative shotgun book with up-to-date chapters on wild-fowling, upland gunning, trap and Skeet shooting. It includes practical advice on shotgun makes, models and functions, as well as data on actions.

Shotgun and Shooter, by G. Carlisle and P. Stanbury, Barrie & Jenkins, London, 1970. 217 pp., illus. $6.95.

On guns, wildfowling, dog training, decoys, safety, etc.

Shotgun Marksmanship, by P. Stanbury & G. L. Carlisle. A. S. Barnes & Co., NY, 1969. 224 pp., illus. $6.95.

A new and revised edition for beginners, veterans, skeet shooters, hunters, etc. Valuable tips on improving marksmanship, etc.

The Shotgun Stock, by Robt. Arthur. A. S. Barnes & Co., NY, 1971. 175 pp., illus. $12.00.

The first and only book about the shotgun stock. Its design, construction, and embellishment. A much-needed work.

The Shotgunner's Bible, by George Laycock. Doubleday & Co., Garden City, NY, 1969. 173 pp., illus., paper covers. $1.95.

Coverage of shotguns, ammunition, marksmanship, hunting of various types of game, care and safety, etc.

Shotguns & Cartridges, by Gough Thomas. A. & C. Black, London, Eng., 1970. 136 pp., illus. $5.00.

An excellent work on the choice and use of guns and loads, by the gun editor of *The Shooting Times* (England).

Shotguns by Keith, by E. Keith. Stackpole Books, Harrisburg, PA, 1967. 307 pp., illus. A new edition, $2.98.

Guns and their accessories from history to ornamentation, their ammunition, and the practical use of American, English and European arms.

Skeet Shooting with D. Lee Braun, Robt. Campbell, ed. Grosset & Dunlap, NY, 1967. 160 pp., illus. Paper covers $1.95.

Thorough instructions on the fine points of Skeet shooting.

Successful Shotgun Shooting, by A. A. Montague. Winchester Press, NY, 1970. 160 pp., illus. $5.95.

The work of a superb shot and a great teacher; even the experts can read with profit.

Sure-Hit Shotgun Ways, by F. E. Sell, Stackpole Books, Harrisburg, PA, 1967. 160 pp., illus. $5.95.

An expert with the scatter gun uncomplicates its effective use in every field, gives quick-skill methods for the sportsman.

Trapshooting with D. Lee Braun and the Remington Pros., ed. by R. Campbell. Remington Arms Co., Bridgeport, CT, 1969. 157 pp., well illus., $5.95. Also in paper covers. $2.95.

America's masters of the scattergun give the secrets of professional marksmanship.

Wing & Shot, by R. G. Wehle, Country Press, Scottsville, NY, 1967. 190 pp., illus. $8.50.

Step-by-step account on how to train a fine shooting dog.

IMPORTANT NOTICE TO BOOK BUYERS

GLOSSARY FOR GUNNERS

Action Breech mechanism of a gun, by which it is loaded and unloaded.

Air Space Space in a loaded cartridge case not occupied by powder or bullet base.

Anvil In a primer or cartridge case, a fixed point against which the priming mixture is compressed, and thereby detonated, by the action of the firing pin.

Ball Earlier term for "bullet," and still used in some military terminology.

Ballistics Science of projectiles in motion.

Barrel The part(s) of a gun through which passes the bullet or shot, traveling from breech to muzzle.

Base Wad Compressed paper or other material inside a shotshell, varying in size and form.

Battery Cup Type of shotshell ignition form in which the cap or primer is held.

Belted Case Cartridge case with a band or belt at base, just ahead of extractor groove, and on which case (otherwise "rimless") positions in rifle chamber. See "Headspace."

Black Powder A mixture of charcoal, sulphur and saltpeter used as a propellant. Gives off much smoke when burned. See "Smokeless Powder."

Bore The inside of the barrel of a gun.

Bore Diameter In rifled arms, the diametrical measurement between tops of lands.

Breech Bolt The part of a breech that resists the rearward force of the combustion that occurs when a cartridge is fired.

BT Boat-tail, referring to the base taper given certain bullets to give them greater efficiency at long ranges.

Bullet The projectile *only,* not to be applied to the cartridge, which see. See also "Ball."

Bullet Mould Metallic device with a cavity(s) into which molten lead (or lead alloy) can be poured and allowed to harden into the projectile.

Caliber Bore or groove diameter expressed (in English) in decimals of an inch, otherwise in the metric system. Frequently compounded to indicate powder capacity of cartridge case; to show date of adoption; to show case length or to show proprietor, etc. E.g., 30-40, 30-06, 8x57mm or 375 Holland & Holland.

Cannelure Circumferential groove(s) around a bullet or cartridge case. In the latter refers to extractor groove, in lead bullets the lubrication grooves, in jacketed bullets the expansion point and/or where case is crimped.

Caplock Used of a muzzleloading gun whose ignition system employs a percussion cap, a small thimble-like metal cup containing a detonating mixture. This cup, placed on a "nipple," transmits flame to the powder charge when struck by the gun's hammer.

Cartridge A complete round of ammunition, made up, simply, of a cartridge case, primer, bullet (or shot) and powder.

Cartridge Case Commonly, the brass or copper envelope that contains powder, primer and projectile, but applicable to shotshells, too, whether of all brass (not common), paper and metal or plastic and metal.

CF Centerfire (cartridges); those ignited by means of (generally) a separate and replaceable primer.

Chamber That part of the bore, at the breech, formed to accept the cartridge.

Choke The constriction of a shotgun bore at the muzzle to various degrees, designed to control pellet charge spread at the target.

Chronograph An instrument which measures the velocity of a projectile.

Clip See "Magazine."

Cordite A nitroglycerine smokeless powder used mainly in Great Britain.

Crimp The bending inward of the case mouth perimeter, in order to grip and hold the bullet, or to keep the shot in a paper case intact.

Cylinder In a revolver, a cartridge container that rotates (generally) around an axis parallel to and below the barrel.

Die In handloading ammunition, any of a number of tools used to size bullets or cases, seat bullets, etc.

Drams Equivalent Term used to indicate that a certain charge of smokeless powder gives ballistics equal to a stated volumetric charge of black powder.

Drift The bullet's movement to right or left, away from the line of the bore, caused by bullet rotation or spin.

Drilling A three-barrel gun, popular in Europe, which usually combines smoothbore and rifled barrels.

Ejector Correctly the device(s) at the barrel breech or within the action that forcibly expels the fired case from the gun. See "Extractor."

Energy In bullets, the amount of work done, at given ranges, expressed in foot pounds.

Erosion More or less gradual wearing away of rifling by combustion gas, heat and bullet friction.

"Everlasting" Case Brass cartridge case made from heavy stock, intended for extended reloading life.

Extractor Device that removes or partially removes the fired cartridge case from the chamber. See "Ejector."

Firing Pin A part of the action, actuated by the trigger, that hits the primer and fires the cartridge.

Flintlock Used of a muzzleloading gun fired by means of a piece of flint, held in the hammer or "cock" jaws, striking against a steel "frizzen." Incandescent particles of steel scraped from the frizzen fall into a "pan" holding powder. This ignited powder flames through the "touch-hole," thus firing the main charge.

Follower A metal platform in a clip or magazine that pushes the cartridges upward at the proper angle for feeding into the chamber.

Gas Check A cup (usually copper) used on the base of a lead bullet to protect it from hot powder gases.

Gauge Unit of bore measurement in shotguns, determined by the number of solid lead round balls, of the bore diameter, obtainable from one pound of lead. E.g., 12 gauge means a bore of such size that 12 balls of that size make a pound of lead.

Gilding Metal A copper-zinc alloy used as bullet jacket material; usually 5% to 10% zinc.

Grooves Spiral cuts in a bore which cause the bullet to spin as it travels down the barrel.

Groove Diameter In rifled arms, the diametrical measurement between bottoms of grooves.

Group Number of shots fired into a target (number and range optional), usually with one sight setting.

Hammer A part of the action (in some guns) actuated by the trigger. The hammer drives the firing pin against the primer, thus igniting the cartridge powder charge.

Hangfire Abnormal delay in cartridge ignition not exceeding 0.3 seconds (300 milliseconds) after primer receives adequate blow from firing pin.

H.P. Hollow point, a design feature of certain bullets. See "Mushroom."

Headspace For rimmed cartridges, the distance from the face of the breechblock to the barrel seat for the forward surface of the case rim. For a rimless bottleneck cartridge, the distance from the face of the breechblock to a predetermined point on the shoulder of the chamber. For rimless straight cartridges, the distance from the face of the breechblock to the shoulder or ledge in the chamber. Belted cases headspace on the forward edge of the belt.

Lands That portion of the bore remaining after the rifling or grooves have been cut.

Leading Lead deposited on bore by bullets passing through.

Magazine Device or reservoir to hold extra cartridges, of many types and names. "Clip," once reserved for the slender metal strip from which cartridges are stripped into a magazine well, now refers to separate, detachable magazines also, as with those for autoloading pistols, many rifles and shotguns.

Matchlock An early form of firearm in which the priming charge was ignited by a cord or "match" of slow-burning material.

M.C. Metal Case, a form of bullet completely covered forward with copper or copper alloy (usually) jacket. Generally a military bullet type, and also termed "solids," and F.M.J. (full metal jacketed).

Mid-Range Usually used in connection with trajectory, referring to a point midway between muzzle and target or game.

Misfire Failure of priming agent to explode when primer is struck an adequate blow by a firing pin or failure of the exploding primer to ignite the powder.

MRT Mid Range Trajectory. See above.

Mushroom The capacity of certain bullets to expand on or after impact, also the term given to some soft point or hollow point bullets. See "S.P." and "H.P."

Muzzle End of barrel opposite to breech; point from which bullet or shot leaves barrel.

Muzzle-Loader Gun loaded through the front end of the bore, using loose powder and ball (or shot) or paper cartridges.

M.E. Muzzle Energy. See "Energy."

M.V. Muzzle Velocity. See "Velocity."

Nipple On muzzle-loading guns, the small metal cone at the rear of the barrel (or cylinder) through which the flame from the percussion cap passes to ignite the powder charge.

Ogive The radius of the curve of the nose of a bullet, usually expressed in calibers.

O.P.E. Open Point Expanding, a term for bullets of hollow point form made by Western Cartridge Co.

Over-bore Capacity Condition in which the volume of a cartridge case exceeds the amount of powder which can most efficiently be burned.

Pan See "Flintlock."

Paradox Smoothbore gun in which the final few inches of barrel are rifled to increase efficiency of round ball or bullet use. Also called "Explora" and "Fauneta" guns by Westley Richards.

Patching, Cloth Used to form a gas seal around the projectile (round ball or conical bullet) of a muzzle-loading gun and engage the rifling.

Pattern Of pellets from a shotgun, usually expressed as so many pellets within a 30-inch circle at 40 yards.

Percussion Cap Small metallic cup containing fulminating material that explodes when struck by gun's hammer. See "Nipple."

Pistol Said by some to derive from Pistoia, an early gun making center in Italy. Any small, concealable, short-barreled (2"-10") hand weapon, generally *not* a revolver.

Pressure The gas pressure generated in a cartridge on its being fired, usually expressed in (greatest) pounds per square inch (p.s.i.).

Primer In a centerfire cartridge, the small cup containing a detonating mixture, which is seated in a recess in the base of the case. In a rimfire, a similar mixture inside the folded rim of the case.

Proprietary Cartridge One developed and sold exclusively by one business organization.

Ramrod Rod, of wood or metal, used to force home the projectile in a muzzle-loading gun and sometimes to hold cleaning implements.

Rebated Rim Type of cartridge case rim smaller in diameter than the case is at a point just forward of the extractor groove.

Recoil The backward thrust of a gun caused by the reaction to the powder gases pushing the bullet forward.

Revolver A multi-shot handgun, using a revolving cylinder as a cartridge container.

RF Rimfire cartridges. Those containing their primer mixture in the rim, which is where they are struck by the firing pin.

Rifling Spiral grooving cut into the bore of rifles and handguns to impart spin to their bullets, thus assuring point-on flight and accuracy.

Rim The projecting edge of the base or "head" of certain cartridges.

Rook Cartridge Low powered cartridge developed in England for shooting pest birds and animals.

Shot Lead or lead-alloy spheres used as projectiles in smoothbore guns.

Shotgun A smoothbore gun using cartridges loaded with shot.

Shoulder The sloping portion of a bottleneck cartridge case that joins the body and neck.

Sizing In handloading cartridges, sizing (or resizing) brings the fired cartridge case back to the (full or partial) dimensions of the new or unfired case. Bullets are also sized.

Smokeless Powder Gunpowder which gives off almost no smoke when burned. See "Black Powder." Usually made by nitrating and otherwise chemically treating purified cotton waste.

S.P. Soft Point, a term used for bullets with partial metal jacketing, having some lead exposed at the front.

Trajectory Curved path of bullet in flight, a parabola.

Twist Angle of the rifling relative to the axis of the bore. Usually uniform, and expressed in turns or part-turns in so many inches. Less common, "progressive" or "gain" twist, usually starting at a rate at breech that becomes gradually faster.

Velocity Projectile speed, usually measured in feet per second (f.p.s.) at the muzzle and other distances such as 100 yards, 200 yards, etc.

Vent Orifice through the nipple.

Wad A disc of paper, felt, plastic or other material used in shotshells; sometimes in metallic cases, too, but not commonly today.

a. Filler Wad—placed between the powder and card or Nitro wad to cushion the shot from the thrust of the hot powder gases, and to bring the shot to the proper height for correct crimping.

b. Over-powder Wad—placed between powder and filler wads, sometimes called Nitro wads.

c. Top Wad—thin card placed on top of the shot in roll crimp shells—star crimp shells do not require a top wad.

d. Base Wad—these are permanently built into the shell at the base to hold the paper tube to the brass and give added support to the thin brass wall.

Wheel-lock Used of a muzzleloading gun fired by means of a piece of flint or pyrites, held in the hammer jaws, which is held over a serrated steel wheel. This wheel, set in motion by a tensioned spring, protrudes through the bottom of the "pan" (wherein powder has been placed) and bears against the flint. Sparks are created, as in the flintlock, and the gun is fired by a flame passing through the touch-hole.

Wildcat Cartridge designed by a private experimenter; not available as a factory-loaded round.

WCF Winchester Center Fire.

WRF Winchester Rim Fire.

Zero That sight setting which gives bullet group desired, and from which subsequent changes in sight settings will be made.

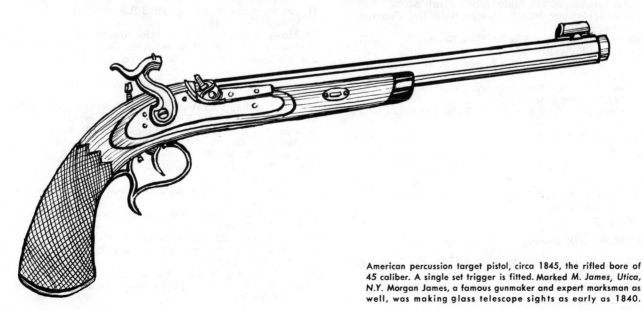

American percussion target pistol, circa 1845, the rifled bore of 45 caliber. A single set trigger is fitted. Marked M. James, Utica, N.Y. Morgan James, a famous gunmaker and expert marksman as well, was making glass telescope sights as early as 1840.

Directory of the Arms Trade

AMMUNITION (Commercial)

Alcan Shells, (See: Smith & Wesson-Fiocchi, Inc.)

Cascade Cartridge Inc., (See Omark)

Federal Cartridge Co., 2700 Foshay Tower, Minneapolis, Minn. 55402

Frontier Cartridge Co., Inc., Box 906, Grand Island, Neb. 68801

Omark-CCI, Inc., Box 856, Lewiston, Ida. 83501

Remington Arms Co., Bridgeport, Conn. 06602

Service Armament, 689 Bergen Blvd., Ridgefield, N.J. 07657

Smith & Wesson-Fiocchi, Inc., 3640 Seminary Rd., Alton, IL 62002

Speer-DWM, Box 896, Lewiston, Ida. 83501

Super-Vel Cartridge Co., Box 40, Shelbyville, Ind. 46176

Weatherby's, 2781 E. Firestone Blvd., South Gate, Calif. 90280

Winchester-Western, East Alton, Ill. 62024

AMMUNITION (Custom)

Ed Agramonte, Inc., 41 Riverdale Ave., Yonkers, NY 10701

Ammodyne, Box 1589, Los Angeles, Calif. 90053

B&K Custom Rel. Serv., Rte. 1, Lake 13, Farwell, Mich. 48622

Bill Ballard, P.O. Box 656, Billings, Mont. 59103

Caldwell's Loading Serv., 1314 Monroe Dr., N.E., Atlanta, Ga. 30306

Russell Campbell, 219 Leisure Dr., San Antonio, Tex. 78201

Colorado Shotgun Ammunition, 365 S. Moore, Lakewood, CO 80226

Cumberland Arms, 1222 Oak Dr., Manchester, Tenn. 37355

Custom Ammo & Gunsmithing, 390 S. Main, Moab, Utah 84532

J. Dewey Gun Co., Clinton Corners, N.Y. 12514

E. W. Ellis Sport Shop, RFD 1, Box 139, Corinth, N.Y. 12822

Ellwood Epps, 80 King St., Clinton, Ont., Canada

David J. Gaida, 1109 S. Millwood, Wichita, KS 67203

R. H. Keeler, 1304 S. Oak, Port Angeles, Wash. 98362

KWT Inc., 710 Cooper-Foster Pk. Rd., Lorain, O. 44053 (tungsten bullets)

Dean Lincoln, 390 S. Main, Moab, Utah 84532

Pat B. McMillan, 1828 E. Campo Bello Dr., Phoenix, Ariz. 85022

Mansfield Gunshop, Box 83, New Boston, N.H. 03070

Man-Tol Shells, Box 134, Bunnell, Fla. 32010

Numrich Arms Corp., 203 Broadway, W. Hurley, N.Y. 12491

Robert Pomeroy, Morrison Ave., East Corinth, ME 04427 (custom shells)

Sanders Cust. Gun Serv., 2358 Tyler Lane, Louisville, Ky. 40205

Shooter's Service & Dewey, Inc., Clinton Corners, N.Y. 12514

Super Vel Cartridge Corp., Shelbyville, Ind. 46176

3-D Co., Inc., Box 4411, Lincoln, Neb. 68504

James C. Tillinghast, Box 568, Marlow, N.H. 03456

Whitney Cartridge Co., P.O. Box 608, Cortez, CO 81321 (shotshells)

AMMUNITION (Foreign)

Abercrombie & Fitch, Madison at 45th St., New York, N.Y. 10017

Canadian Ind. Ltd. (C.I.L.), Box 10, Montreal, Que., Canada

C-I-L Ammunition Inc., P.O. Box 831, Plattsburgh, N.Y. 12901

Centennial Arms Co., 3318 W. Devon Ave., Chicago, (Lincolnwood) Ill. 60645 (Hirtenberg, Austrian)

Colonial Ammunition Co., Box 8511, Auckland, New Zealand

DWM, Speer Prods. Inc., Box 896, Lewiston, Ida. 83501

Gevelot of Canada, Box 1593, Saskatoon, Sask., Canada

Hy-Score Arms Co., 200 Tillary, Brooklyn, N.Y. 11201

Paul Jaeger Inc., 211 Leedom St., Jenkintown, Pa. 19046

S. E. Laszlo, 200 Tillary, Brooklyn, N.Y. 11201

NORMA-Precision, South Lansing, N.Y. 14882

Oregon Ammo Service, Box 19341, Portland, Ore. 97219

RWS (Rheinische-Westfalische Sprengstoff) see: Stoeger

Stoeger Arms Corp., 55 Ruta Ct., So. Hackensack, N.J. 07606 (RWS)

James C. Tillinghast, Box 568, Marlow, N.H. 03456

ANTIQUE ARMS DEALERS

Robert Abels, P.O. Box 428, Hopewell Junction, NY 12533 (Catalog $1.00)

Ed Agramonte, Inc., 41 Riverdale Ave., Yonkers, NY 10701

F. Banne man Sons, Inc., Box 126, L.I., Blue Point, N.Y. 1 715

Wm. Boggs, 1243 Grandview Ave., Columbus, Ohio 43212

Ellwood Epps Sporting Goods, 80 King St., Clinton, Ont., Canada

Farris Muzzle Guns, 1610 Gallia St., Portsmouth, Ohio 45662

A. A. Fidd, Diamond Pt. Rd., Diamond Pt., N.Y. 12824

N. Flayderman & Co., Squash Hollow, New Milford, Conn. 06776

Fulmer's Antique Firearms, Detroit Lakes, Minn. 56501

Herb Glass, Bullville, N.Y. 10915

Gold Rush Guns, P.O. Box 33, Afton, Va. 22920

Gold Rush Guns Shop II, 2211 Clement St., San Francisco, Cal. 94121

Goodman's for Guns, 1101 Olive St., St. Louis, Mo. 63101

Griffin's Guns & Antiques, R.R. 4, Peterboro, Ont., Canada

The Gun Shop, 6497 Pearl Rd., Cleveland, O. 44130

Heritage Firearms Co., 27 Danbury Rd., Rte. 7, Wilton, Conn 06897

Holbrook Arms Museum, 12953 Biscayne Blvd., N. Miami, Fla. 33161

Ed Howe, 2 Main, Coopers Mills, Me. 04341

Jackson Arms, 6209 Hillcrest Ave., Dallas, Tex. 75205

Jerry's Gun Shop, 9220 Ogden Ave., Brookfield, Ill. 60513

Lever Arms Serv. Ltd., 771 Dunsmuir St., Vancouver 1, B.C., Canada

Wm. M. Locke, 3607 Ault Pk. Rd., Cincinnati, O. 45208

John J. Malloy, Briar Ridge Rd., Danbury, Conn. 06810

Charles W. Moore, R.D. 2, Schenevus, N.Y. 12155

Museum of Historical Arms, 1038 Alton Rd., Miami Beach, Fla. 33139

National Gun Traders, Inc., 225 S.W. 22nd Ave., Miami, Fla. 33135

New Orleans Arms Co., Inc., 240 Chartres St., New Orleans, La. 70130

Old West Gun Room, 3509 Carlson Blvd., El Cerrito, Cal. 94530 (write for list)

Pioneer Guns, 5228 Montgomery, Norwood, O. 45212

Powell & Clements Sporting Arms, 210 E. 6th St., Cincinnati, O. 45202

Glode M. Requa, Box 35, Monsey, N.Y. 10952

Martin B. Retting Inc., 11029 Washington, Culver City, Calif. 90230

Ridge Guncraft, Inc., 234 N. Tulane Ave., Oak Ridge, Tenn. 37830

S.G. Intl., P.O. Box 702, Hermosa Beach, CA. 90254

Safari Outfitters Lt., Rte. 7, Ridgefield, CT 06877

San Francisco Gun Exch., 74 Fourth, San Francisco, Calif. 94103

Santa Ana Gunroom, P.O. Box 1777, Santa Ana, Calif. 92702

Ward & Van Valkenburg, 402-30th Ave. No., Fargo, N. Dak. 58102

M. C. Wiest, 234 N. Tulane Ave., Oak Ridge, Tenn. 37830

Yeck Antique Firearms, 579 Tecumseh, Dundee, Mich. 48131

BULLET & CASE LUBRICANTS

Alpha-Molykote, Dow Corning Corp., 45 Commerce Dr., Trumbull, Ct. 06601

Birchwood-Casey Co., Inc., 7900 Fuller Rd., Eden Prairie, Minn. 55343 (Anderol)

Bullet Pouch, Box 4285, Long Beach, Calif. 90804 (Mirror-Lube)

Chopie Mfg. Inc., 531 Copeland, La Crosse, Wis. 54601 (Black-Solve)

Cooper-Woodward, Box 972, Riverside, Cal. 92502 (Perfect Lube)

Green Bay Bullets, 233 N. Ashland, Green Bay, Wis. 54303 (EZE-Size case lube)

Herter's, Inc., Waseca, Minn. 56903 (Perfect Lubricant)

Javelina Products, Box 337, San Bernardino, Cal. 92402 (Alox beeswax)

Jet-Aer Corp., 100 Sixth Ave., Paterson, N.J. 07524

Lenz Prod. Co., Box 1226, Sta. C, Canton, O. 44708 (Clenzoil)

Lyman Gun Sight Products, Middlefield, Conn. 06455 (Size-Ezy)

Micro Shooter's Supply, Box 213, Las Cruces, N. Mex. 88001 (Micro-Lube)

Mirror Lube, American Spl. Lubricants, Box 4275, Long Beach, CA 90804

Nutec, Box 1187, Wilmington, Del. 19899 (Dry-Lube)

Pacific Tool Co., Box 4495, Lincoln, Neb. 68504

Phelps Rel. Inc., Box 4004, E. Orange, N.J. 07019

RCBS, Inc., Box 1919, Oroville, Calif. 95965

SAECO Rel. Inc., 726 Hopmeadow St., Simsbury, Conn. 06070

Scientific Lubricants Co., 3753 Lawrence Ave., Chicago, Ill. 60625

Shooters Accessory Supply (SAS), Box 250, N. Bend, Ore. 97459

Sports Distr. Co., Rte. 1, Rapid City, S.D. 57701 (Reloader No. 7)

Testing Systems, Inc., 2836 Mt. Carmel, Glenside, PA 19038

CHOKE DEVICES & RECOIL ABSORBERS

Arms Ingenuity Corp., Box 1, Weatogue, Conn. 06089 (Jet-Away)

Contra-Jet, 7920 49th Ave. So., Seattle, Wash. 98118

Dahl's Gun Shop, Rt. 2, Billings, Mont. 59101

Diverter Arms, Inc., 6520 Rampart St., Houston, TX 77036 (shotgun diverter)

Edwards Recoil Reducer, 269 Herbert St., Alton, Ill. 62002

Emsco Chokes, 101 Second Ave., S.E., Waseca, Minn. 56093

Herter's Inc., Waseca, Minn. 56093. (Vari-Choke)

Lyman Gun Sight Products, Middlefield, Conn. 60455 (Cutts Comp.)

Mag-Na-Port Arms, Inc., 34341 Groesbeck, Fraser, MI 48026 (muzzle-brake system)

C. R. Pedersen & Son, Ludington, Mich. 49431 (Sha-Cul Brake)

Pendleton Dekickers, 1210 S. W. Hailey Ave., Pendleton, Ore. 97801

Poly-Choke Co., Inc., Box 296, Hartford, Conn. 06101

St. Louis Precision Products, 902 Michigan Ave., St. Louis, Mich. 48880 (Gun-Tamer)

CHRONOGRAPHS AND PRESSURE TOOLS

Avtron, 10409 Meech Ave., Cleveland, Ohio, 44105

B-Square Co., Box 11281, Ft. Worth, Tex. 76110

Chronograph Specialists, P.O. Box 5005, Santa Ana, Calif. 92704

Diverter Arms, Inc., 6520 Rampart St., Houston, TX 77036 (press. tool)

Herter's, Waseca, Minn. 56093

Micro-Sight Co., 242 Harbor Blvd., Belmont, Calif. 94002 (Techsonic)

Oehler Research, P.O. Box 9135, Austin, Tex. 78756

Sundtek Co., P.O. Box 744, Springfield, Ore. 97477

Telepacific Electronics Co., Inc., 3335 W. Orange Ave., Anaheim, CA 92804

M. York, 19381 Keymar Way, Gaithersburg, MD 20760 (press. tool)

CLEANING & REFINISHING SUPPLIES

ADSCO, Box 191, Ft. Kent, Me. 04743 (stock finish)

Allied Products Co., 734 N. Leavitt, Chicago, Ill. 60612 (Cor-O-Dex)

Armite Labs., 1845 Randolph St., Los Angeles, CA 90001 (pen oiler)

Backus Co., 411 W. Water St., Smethport, Pa. 16749 (field gun-cleaner)

Ber Big Enterprises, P.O. Box 291, Huntington, CA 90255 (gunsoap)

Birchwood-Casey Chem. Co., 7900 Fuller Rd., Eden Prairie, Minn. 55343 (Anderol, etc.)

Bisonite Co., Inc., Box 84, Buffalo, N.Y. 14217

Jim Brobst, 299 Poplar St., Hamburg, Pa. 19526 (J-B Compound)

Geo. Brothers, Great Barrington, Mass. 01230 (G-B Linspeed Oil)

Browning Arms, Rt. 4, Box 624-B, Arnold, Mo. 63010

J. M. Bucheimer Co., Airport Rd., Frederick, MD 21701

Bullet Pouch, Box 4285, Long Beach, Cal. 90804 (Mirror Lube)

Burnishine Prod. Co., 8140 N. Ridgeway, Skokie, Ill. 60076 (Stock Glaze)

C & R Distr. Corp., 449 E. 21st So., Salt Lake City, Utah 84115

Cherry Corners Gun Shop, 8010 Lafayette Rd., Rte. 1, Lodi, Ohio 44254 (buffing compound)

Chopie Mfg. Inc., 531 Copeland, La Crosse, Wis. 54601 (Black-Solve)

Clenzoil Co., Box 1226, Sta. C, Canton, O. 44708

Craftsman Wood Serv. Co., 2729 S. Mary, Chicago, Ill. 60608

Custom Industries, 18900 Detroit Ave., Lakewood, O. 44107

Dex-Kleen, Box 509, Des Moines, Ia. 50302 (gun wipers)

J. Dewey Gun Co., Clinton Corners, N.Y. 12514

Dri-Slide, Inc., Industrial Park, Fremont, Mich. 49412

Dry Film Gun Coatings, 1521—43rd St., W. Palm Beach, Fla. 33407

Forty-Five Ranch Enterpr., 119 S. Main St., Miami, Okla. 74354

Garcia Sptg. Arms Corp., 329 Alfred Ave., Teaneck, N.J. 07666

Gun-All Products, Box 244, Dowagiac, Mich. 49047

Percy Harms Corp., 7349 N. Hamlin, Skokie, Ill. 60076

Frank C. Hoppe Div., P.O. Box 97, Parkesburg, Pa. 19365

Hunting World, 247 E. 50th St., N.Y. 10022 (P-H Safari Kit)

J & G Rifle Ranch, Turner, MT 59542

Jet-Aer Corp., 100 Sixth Ave., Paterson, N.J. 07524 (blues & oils)

K.W. Kleinendorst, Taylortown Rd., Montville, N.J. 07045 (rifle clg. rods)

Knox Laboratories, 2335 S. Michigan Ave., Chicago, Ill. 60616

LPS Res. Labs. Inc., 2050 Cotner Ave., Los Angeles, Calif. 90025

Carl Lampert Co., 2639 So. 31st St., Milwaukee, Wis. 53215 (gun bags)

LEM Gun Spec., Box 31, College Park, Ga 30337 (Lewis Lead Remover)

Liquid Wrench, Box 10628, Charlotte, N.C. 28201 (pen. oil)

Lynx-Line Gun Products, Box 3985, Detroit, Mich. 48227

Marble Arms Co., 1120 Superior, Gladstone, Mich. 49837

Micro Sight Co., 242 Harbor Blvd., Belmont, Ca. 94002 (bedding)

Mill Run Prod., 1360 W. 9th, Cleveland, O. 44113 (Brite-Bore Kits)

Mint Luster Cleaners, 1102 N. Division, Appleton, Wis. 54911

Mirror-Lube Div., Amer. Spec. Lubricants, Box 4275, Long Beach, CA 90804

Mistic Metal Mover, Inc., R.R. 2, P.O. Box 336, Princeton, Ill. 61356

Mitchell Chemical Co., Wampus Lane, Milford, CT 06460 (Gun Guard)

New Method Mfg. Co., Box 175, Bradford, Pa. 16701 (gun blue)

Numrich Arms Co., West Hurley, N.Y. 12491 (44-40 gun blue)

Nutec, Box 1187, Wilmington, Del. 19899 (Dry-Lube)

Outers Laboratories, Box 37, Onalaska, Wis. 54650 (Gunslick kits)

R.E.I., 101 Wolpers, Park Forest, Ill. 60466 (whale oil lube)

Radiator Spec. Co., Charlotte, N.C. 28201 (liquid wrench)

Realist Inc., N. 93 W. 16288 Megal Dr., Menomonee Falls, Wis. 53051

Reardon Prod., 323 N. Main St., Roanoke, Ill. 61561 (Dry-Lube)

Reese Arms Co., R.R. 1, Colona, IL 61241 (Dry-film lube)

Riel & Fuller, 423 Woodrow Ave., Dunkirk, N.Y. 14048 (anti-rust oil)

Rig Products Co., Box 279, Oregon, Ill. 61061 (Rig Grease)

Rocket Chemical Co., Inc., 5390 Napa St., San Diego, Calif. 92110 (WD-40)

Rusteprufe Labs., 605 Wolcott St., Sparta, Wis. 54656

Saunders Sptg. Gds., 338 Somerset, No. Plainfield, NJ 07060 (Sav-Bore)

Service Armament, 689 Bergen Blvd., Ridgefield, N. J. 07657 (Parker-Hale)

Sheldon's Inc., Box 508, Antigo, Wis. 54409 (shotgun brushes)

Shooter's Serv. & Dewey (SS&D), Clinton Corners, N.Y. 12514

Silicote Corp., Box 359, Oshkosh, Wis. 54901 (Silicone cloths)

A. D. Soucy, Box 191, Ft. Kent, Me. 04743 (ADSCO stock finish)

Southeastern Coatings, Ind., (SECOA), Bldg. 132, P.B.I. Airport, W. Palm Beach, Fla. 33406 (Teflon Coatings)

Sportsmen's Labs., Inc., Box 732, Anoka, Minn. 55303 (Gun Life lube)

Sun Ray Chemicals, 371-30th Ave., San Francisco, Calif. 94121

Surcon, Inc., P.O. Box 277, Zieglerville, Pa. 19492

Taylor & Robbins, Box 164, Rixford, Pa. 16745 (Throat Saver)

Testing Systems, Inc., 2836 Mt. Carmel, Glenside, PA 19038 (gun lube)

Texas Platers Supply Co., 2458 W. Five Mile Parkway, Dallas, TX 75233 (plating kit)

C. S. Van Gorden, 120 Tenth Ave., Eau Claire, Wis. 54701 (Instant Blue)

WD-40 Co., 5390 Napa St., San Diego, Ca 92110

W&W Mfg. Co., Box 365, Belton, Mo. 64012 (shotgun cleaner)

Webber Gage Division, 24500 Detroit Rd., Cleveland, O. 44111 (Luger oil)

West Coast Secoa, Inc., 3915 U.S. Hwy. 98 So., Lakeland, Fla. 33803

Williams Gun Sight, 7389 Lapeer Rd., Davison, Mich. 48423 (finish kit)

Winslow Arms Co., P.O. Box 578, Osprey, Fla. 33595 (refinishing kit)

Wisconsin Platers Supply Co., see: Texas Platers Supply Co.

Woodstream Corp., P.O. Box 327, Lititz, Pa. 17543 (Mask)

COMPONENTS—BULLETS, POWDER, PRIMERS

Accuracy Bullet Co., 2443 41st St., San Francisco, Calif. 94116 (Perfecast bullets)

Alcan, (see: Smith & Wesson-Fiocchi, Inc.)

Ammo-O-Mart, P.O. Box 66, Hawkesbury, Ont., Canada (Curry bullets)

Austin Power Co. (see Red Diamond Dist. Co.)

Bahler Die Shop, Box 386, Florence, Ore. 97439 (17 cal. bull.)

Lee Baker, P.O. Box 1486, Valdosta, GA 31601 (17 cal. bull.)

Joe J. Balickie, 6108 Deerwood Pl., Raleigh, NC 27607

Ballistic Research Industries, see: S & W-Fiocchi (12 ga. Sabot bullets)

Bitterroot Bullet Co., Box 412, Lewiston, Ida. 83501

Centrix, 2116 N. 10th Ave., Tucson, Ariz. 85705

Kenneth E. Clark, 18738 Highway 99, Madera, CA 93637 (Bullets)

Colorado Custom Bullets, Rt. 1, Box 507-B, Montrose, Colo. 81401

Curry Bullets Canada, P.O. Box 66, Hawkesbury, Ont., Canada

Division Lead, 7742 W. 61 Pl., Summit, Ill. 60502

DuPont, Explosives Dept., Wilmington, Del. 19898

Elk Mountain Shooters Supply, 2020 Road 44, Pasco, Wash. 99301 (Alaskan bullets)

Farmer Bros. Mfg. Co., 1102 Washington St., Eldora, IA 50627 (Lage shotshell wads)

Forty Five Ranch Enterprises, 119 S. Main, Miami, Okla. 74354

Godfrey Reloading Supply, R.R. 1, Box 688, Brighton, Ill. 62012 (cast bullets)

Lynn Godfrey, see: Elk Mtn. Shooters Supply

G. J. Godwin, 455 Fox Lane, Orange Park, Fla. 32073 (cast bullets)

Green Bay Bullets, 233 No. Ashland, Green Bay, Wis. 54303 (lead)

Frank A. Hemsted, Box 281, Sunland, Calif. 91040

Hercules Powder Co., 910 Market St., Wilmington, Del. 19899

Herter's Inc., Waseca, Minn. 56093

Hi-Precision Co., 109 Third Ave., N.E., Orange City, Ia. 51041

B. E. Hodgdon, Inc., 7710 W. 50th Hwy., Shawnee Mission, Kans. 66202

Hornady Mfg. Co., Box 1848, Grand Island, Neb. 68801

N. E. House Co., Middletown Rd., E. Hampton, Conn. 06424 (zinc bases only)

David Ingram, Box 4263, Long Beach, CA 90804 (17/20 cal. bullets)

Jurras Munition Corp., Box 140, Shelbyville, Ind. 46176

Kush Plastics, P.O. Box 366, Palatine, IL 60067 (shotshell wads)

L. L. F. Die Shop, 1281 Highway 99 North, Eugene, Ore. 97402

LAGE wads, see Farmer Bros.

Lee's Precision Bullets, P.O. Box 1486, Valdosta, GA 31601 (17 cal.)

Ljutic Ind., Inc., Box 2117, Yakima, WA 98902 (Monowads)

Lyman Gun Sight Products, Middlefield, Conn. 06455

Markell, Inc., 4115 Judah St., San Francisco, Calif. 94112

Meyer Bros., Wabasha, Minn. 55981 (shotgun slugs)

Michael's Antiques, Box 233, Copiague, L.I., NY 11726 (Balle Blondeau)

Miller Trading Co., 20 S. Front St., Wilmington, N.C. 28401

G. E. Murphy, 2443-41 Ave., San Francisco, CA 94116 (Acc. Perfecast bullets)

Norma-Precision, So. Lansing, N.Y. 14882

Northridge Bullet Co., P.O. Box 1208, Vista, Ca. 92083

Nosler Bullets, P.O. Box 688, Beaverton, OR 97005

Oregon Ammo Service, Box 19341, Portland, Ore. 97219

Robert Pomeroy, Morrison Ave., East Corinth, ME 04427

Red Diamond Distributing Co., 1304 Snowdon Dr., Knoxville, TN 37912 (black powder)

Remington-Peters, Bridgeport, Conn. 06602

Sanderson's, 724 W. Edgewater, Portage, Wis. 53901 (cork wad)

Sierra Bullets Inc., 421 No. Altadena Dr., Pasadena, Ca. 91107

Sisk Bullet Co., Box 398, Iowa Park, TX 76367

Smith & Wesson-Fiocchi, Inc., 3640 Seminary Rd., Alton, IL 62002

Speedy Bullets, Box 1262, Lincoln, Neb. 68501

Speer Products Inc., Box 896, Lewiston, Ida. 83501

C. H. Stocking, Rte. 3, Hutchinson, Minn. 55350 (17 cal. bullet jackets)

Super-Vel Cartr. Corp., 129 E. Franklin St., Shelbyville, Ind. 46176

Taylor Bullets, P.O. Box 21254, San Antonio, Tex. 78221

James C. Tillinghast, Box 568, Marlow, N.H. 03456

Vitt & Boos, Sugarloaf Dr., Wilton, Conn. 06897

Winchester-Western, New Haven, Conn. 06504

F. Wood, Box 386, Florence, Ore. 97439 (17 cal.)

Xelex Ltd., Hawksbury, Ont., Canada (powder, Curry bullets)

Zero Bullet Co., P.O. Box 1012, Cullman, AL 35055

CUSTOM GUNSMITHS AND CUSTOM GUN WORK

A & M Rifle Co., Box 1713, Prescott, AZ 86301

Abe-Van Horn, 5124 Huntington Dr., Los Angeles, CA 90032

P. O. Ackley, Inc., 5448 Riley Lane, Salt Lake City, UT 84107

Ed Agramonte, Inc., 41 Riverdale Ave., Yonkers, NY 10701

Ahlman Cust. Gun Shop, R.R. 1, Box 20, Morristown, Minn. 55052

R. E. Anderson, 706 S. 23rd St., Laramie, Wyo. 82070

Andrews' Ammunition & Arms, 7114 So. Albion, Littleton, Colo. 80120

R. J. Anton, 1016 Riehl St., Waterloo, Ia. 50703

Arms Divs., M. R. Co., 968 Radcliffe Rd., Baltimore, Md. 21204

Bacon Creek Gun Shop, Cumberland Falls Rd., Corbin, Ky. 40701

Bain and Davis Sptg. Gds., 599 W. Las Tunas Dr., San Gabriel, Calif. 41776

Joe J. Balickie, 6108 Deerwood Pl., Raleigh, N.C. 27607

Barber's Southpaw Conversions, 26 N.W. 2nd, Portland, Ore. 97209

Barta's, Rte. 1, Box 129-A, Cato, Wis. 54206

Bayer's Gun Shop, 213 S. 2nd, Walla Walla, Wash. 99362

Bennett Gun Works, 561 Delaware Ave., Delmar, N.Y. 12054

Irvin L. Benson, Saganaga Lake, Ontario, Canada

Gordon Bess, 708 River St., Canon City, Colo. 81212

Bruce Betts Gunsmith Co., 26 Rolla Gardens Dr., Rolla, Mo. 65401

John Bivins, Jr., 446 So. Main St., Winston-Salem, N.C. 27101

Edwin T. Blackburn, Jr., 1880A Embarcadero Rd., Palo Alto, CA 94303

Boone Mountain Trading Post, Averyville Rd., St. Marys, Pa. 15857

T. H. Boughton, 410 Stone Rd., Rochester, N.Y. 14616

Kay H. Bowles, Pinedale, Wyo. 82941

Wm. A. Boyle, Box 5-770, College, Alaska 99701

L. H. Brown, Rte. 2, Airport Rd., Kalispell, Mont. 59901

Lenard M. Brownell, Box 6147 Sheridan, WY 82801

George Bunch, 7735 Garrison Rd., Hyattsville, Md. 20784

Tom Burgess, Rte. 3, Kalispell, MT 59901 (metalsmithing only)

Leo Bustani, P.O. Box 8125, W. Palm Beach, Fla. 33407

Gus Butterowe, 2520 W. Mockingbird Lane, Dallas, Tex. 75235

Cameron's Guns, 16690 W. 11th Ave., Golden, Colo. 80401

Dick Campbell, 1445 S. Meade, Denver, Colo. 80219

Carpenter's Gun Works, Gunshop Rd., Box C, Plattekill, N.Y. 12568

Carter Gun Works, 2211 Jefferson Pk. Ave., Charlotteville, Va. 22903

Cassell's Gun Shop, 403 West Lane, Worland, Wyo. 82401

Ray Chalmers, 18 White Clay Dr., Newark, Del. 19711

N. C. Christakos, 2832 N. Austin, Chicago, IL 60634

Kenneth E. Clark, 18738 Highway 99, Madera, Calif. 93637

Cloward's Gun Shop, 2045 Eastlake Ave. E., Seattle, WA 98102

Crest Carving Co., 14849 Dillow St., Westminster, Ca. 92683

Philip R. Crouthamel, 817 E. Baltimore, E. Lansdowne, Pa. 19050

Custom Rifle Shop, 4550 E. Colfax Ave., Denver, Colo. 80220

Jim Cuthbert, 715 S. 5th St., Coos Bay, Ore. 97420

Dahl's Gunshop, Rt. 2, Billings, Mont. 59101

Dave's Gun Shop, 3994 Potters Rd. West, Ionia, Mich. 48846

Dee Davis, 5658 So. Mayfield, Chicago, Ill. 60638

Jack Dever, Box 577, Jackson, Wyo. 83001 (S. S. Work)

J. Dewey Gun Co., Clinton Corners, N.Y. 12514

Joe E. Dillen, 1206 Juanita S.W., Massillon, Ohio 44646

Dominic DiStefano, 4303 Friar Lane, Colorado Springs, CO 80907

Don's Gun Shop, 128 Ruxton Ave., Manitou Springs, Colo. 80829,

Drumbore Gun Shop, 119 Center St., Lehigton, PA 18235

Charles Duffy, Williams Lane, W. Hurley, N.Y. 12491

Gerald D. Eisenhauer, Rte. #3, Twin Falls, Ida. 83301

Bill English, 4411 S. W. 100th, Seattle, Wash. 98146

Ellwood Epps, 80 King St., Clinton, Ont., Canada

Ken Eyster, Heritage Gunsmiths Inc., 6441 Bishop Rd., Centerburg, O. 43011

N. B. Fashingbauer, Box 366, Lac Du Flambeau, Wis. 54538

Ted Fellowes, 9245-16th Ave., S.W., Seattle, Wa. 98106 (muzzle loaders)

Loxley Firth Firearms, 8563 Oswego Rd., R. D. 4, Baldwinsville, N.Y. 13027

Marshall F. Fish, Westport, N.Y. 12993

Jerry Fisher, 1244—4th Ave. West, Kalispell, Mont. 59901

Flagler Gun Clinic, Box 8125, West Palm Beach, Fla. 33407 (Win. 92 & 94 Conv.)

Freeland's Scope Stands, 3737—14th Ave., Rock Island, Ill. 61201

Fred's Gun Shop, Box 725, Juneau, Alaska 99801

Frederick Gun Shop, 10 Elson Drive, Riverside, R.I. 02915

Frontier Arms, Inc., 420 E. Riding Club Rd., Cheyenne, Wyo. 82001

Fuller Gunshop, Cooper Landing, Alas. 99572

Geo. M. Fullmer, 2499 Mavis St., Oakland, Cal. 94501 (metal work)
Georgia Gun & Smith, 222 Jones Shaw Rd., Marietta, GA 30060
Gibbs Rifle Products, Viola, Ida. 83872
Ed Gillman, Upper High Crest Dr., R.F.D. #1, Butler, N.J. 07405
A. R. Goode, R.D. 1, Box 84, Thurmont, MD 21788
E. M. Greashaw, S. Centerville, RR 2, Sturgis, Mich. 49041
Griffin & Howe, 589-8th Ave., New York, N.Y. 10017
Dale M. Guise, Rt. 2, Box 239, Gardners, Pa. 17324 (Rem. left-hand conversions)
H & R Custom Gun Serv., 68 Passaic Dr., Hewitt, N.J. 07421
Paul Haberly, 2364 N. Neva, Chicago, IL 60635
Chas. E. Hammans, Box 788, Stuttgart, AR 72160
Harkrader's Cust. Gun Shop, 111 No. Franklin St., Christiansburg, Va. 24073
Elden Harsh, Rt. 4, London, O. 43140
Rob't W. Hart & Son, 401 Montgomery St., Nescopeck, Pa. 18635 (actions, stocks)
Hal Hartley, Box 147, Blairs Fork Rd., Lenoir, N.C. 28654
Hubert J. Hecht, 55 Rose Mead Circle, Sacramento, CA 95831
Edw. O. Hefti, 300 Fairview, College Sta., Tex. 77840
Iver Henriksen, 1211 So. 2nd, Missoula, Mont. 59801
Wm. Hobaugh, Box 657, Philipsburg, Mont. 59858
Richard Hodgson, 9081 Tahoe Lane, Boulder, Colo. 80301
Hoenig-Rodman, 853 So. Curtis Rd., Boise, ID 83705
Hollis Gun Shop, 917 Rex St., Carlsbad, N.M. 88220
Wm. R. Horvath, 742 S. Scott Dr., Farwell, Mich. 48622
Huckleberry Gun Shop, 10440 Kingsbury Rd., Delton, Mich. 49046 (rust blueing)
Hurst Custom Gunstocks, RFD 1, Box 1000, Exmore, Va. 23350
Hurt's Specialty Gunsmithing, Box 1033, Muskogee, Okla. 74401
Hyper-Single Precision SS Rifles, 520 E. Beaver, Jenks, OK 74037
Independent Machine & Gun Shop, 1416 N. Hayes, Pocatello, Ida. 83201
Jackson's, Box 416, Selman City, TX 75689
Paul Jaeger, 211 Leedom, Jenkintown, Pa. 19046
J. J. Jenkins, 462 Stanford Pl., Santa Barbara, CA 93105
Jerry's Gun Shop, 9220 Ogden Ave., Brookfield, Ill. 60513
Jerry's Gun Shop, 1527 N. Graceland Ave., Appleton, Wis. 54911
Johnson Automatics Assoc., Inc., Box 306, Hope Valley, R.I. 02832
Johnson's Gun Shop, 1326 N. Blackstone, Fresno, Calif. 93703
Johnson's Kenai Rifles, Box 6208, Annex Br., Anchorage, Alaska 99502
Kennedy Gun Shop, Rt. 6, Clarksville, Tenn. 37040
Monte Kennedy, R. D. 2-B, Kalispell, Mont. 59901
Kennon's Custom Rifles, 5408 Biffle, Stone Mtn., Ga. 30083
Kerr Sport Shop, Inc., 9584 Wilshire Blvd., Beverly Hills, Calif. 90212
Kess Arms Co., 12515 W. Lisbon Rd., Brookfield, Wis. 53005
Kesselring Gun Shop, 400 Pacific Hiway 99 No., Burlington, Wash. 98233
Knights Gun Store, Inc., 103 So. Jennings, Ft. Worth, Tex. 76104
Ward Koozer, Box 18, Walterville, Ore. 97489
R. Krieger & Sons, 34923 Gratiot, Mt. Clemens, Mich. 48043
Lacy's Gun Service, 1518A West Blvd., Charlotte, N.C. 28208
Sam Lair, 520 E. Beaver, Jenks, OK 74037

LanDav Custom Guns, 7213 Lee Highway, Falls Church, VA 22046
Harry Lawson Co., 3328 N. Richey Blvd., Tucson, Ariz. 85716
John G. Lawson, 1802 E. Columbia, Tacoma, Wa. 98404
Gene Lechner, 636 Jane N.E., Albuquerque, NM 87123
Ledel, Inc., Main and Commerce Sts., Cheswold, Del. 19936
Art LeFeuvre, 1003 Hazel Ave., Deerfield, Ill. 60015
LeFever Arms Co., R.D. 1, Lee Center, N.Y. 13363
Max J. Lindauer, R.R. 1, Box 114, Washington, Mo. 63090
Robt. L. Lindsay, Box 805, Gaithersburg, Md. 20760 (services only)
Ljutic Ind., Box 2117, Yakima, WA 98902 (Mono-Wads)
Llanerch Gun Shop, 2800 Township Line, Upper Darby, Pa. 19083
McCormick's Gun Bluing Service, 4936 E. Rosecrans Ave., Compton, Calif. 90221
Harry McGowen, Momence, IL 60954
Pat B. McMillan, 1828 E. Campo Bello Dr., Phoenix, Ariz. 85022
R. J. Maberry, 511 So. K, Midland, Tex. 79701
Harold E. MacFarland, Star Route, Box 84, Cottonwood, Ariz. 86326
Maryland Gun Exchange, Rte. 5, Frederick, Md. 21701
Mathews & Son, 10224 S. Paramount Blvd., Downey, Calif. 90241
Maurer Arms, 2366 Frederick Dr., Cuyahoga Falls, Ohio 44221
Middaugh's Nodak, 318 2nd St., Bismarck, N.D. 58501
C.D. Miller Guns, St. Onge, SD 57779
Earl Milliron, 1249 N.E. 166th Ave., Portland, Ore. 97230
Mills (D.H.) Custom Stocks, 401 N. Ellsworth, San Mateo, Calif. 94401 (antique)
Mitchell's Gun Repair, Rt. 1, Perryville, Ark. 72126
Natl. Gun Traders, Inc., 225 S.W. 22nd Ave., Miami, Fla. 33135
Clayton N. Nelson, 1725 Thompson Ave., Enid, Okla. 73701
Newman Gunshop, 119 Miller Rd., Agency, Ia. 52530
Nu-Line Guns, Inc., 3727 Jennings Rd., St. Louis, Mo. 63121
Oak Lawn Gun & Sports, Inc., 9618 Southwest Hwy., Oak Lawn, Ill. 60453
O'Brien Rifle Co., 324 Tropicana No. 128, Las Vegas, Nev. 89109
Pachmayr Gun Works, 1220 S. Grand Ave., Los Angeles, Calif. 90015
Harry Pagett Gun Shop, 125 Water St., Milford, Ohio 45150
Charles J. Parkinson, 116 Wharncliffe Rd. So., London, Ont., Canada
Pendleton Gunshop, 1210 S. W. Haley Ave., Pendleton, Ore. 97801
C. R. Pedersen & Son, Ludington, Mich. 49431
Al Petersen, Box 8, Riverhurst, Sask., Canada
A. W. Peterson Gun Shop, 1693 Old 44 No., Mt. Dora, Fla. 32757 (ML rifles, also)
Gene Phipps, 10 Wood's Gap Rd., Floyd, Va. 24091
Purcell's Gunshop, 915 Main St., Boise, Idaho 83702
Ready Eddie's Gun Shop, 501 Van Spanje Ave., Michigan City, IN 46360
Marion Reed Gun Shop, 1522 Colorado, Bartlesville, Okla. 74003
Fred Renard, Rt. 1, Symsonia, Ky. 42082
Ridge Guncraft, Inc., 234 N. Tulane, Oak Ridge, Tenn. 37830
Riedl Rifles, P.O. Box FR, Azusa, CA 91702
Rifle Shop, Box 657, Philipsburg, Mont. 59858
Riflemen's Hdqs., Rte. 3, RD 550-E, Kendallville, IN 46755
Carl Roth, P.O. Box 2593, Cheyenne, WY 82001
Royal Arms, Inc., 10064 Bert Acosta, Santee, Calif. 92071
M. L. Ruffino, Rt. 2, Milford, ME 04461

Sam's Gun Shop, 25 Squam Rd., Rockport, Mass. 01966
Sanders Custom Gun Serv., 2358 Tyler Lane, Louisville, Ky. 40205
Sandy's Custom Gunshop, Rockport, Ill. 62370
Saratoga Arms Co., R.D. 3, Box 387, Pottstown, Pa. 19464
Roy V. Schaefer, 965 W. Hilliard Lane, Eugene, Ore. 97402
George Schielke, Washington Crossing, Titusville, N.J. 08560
N.H. Schiffman Cust. Gun Serv., P.O. Box 7373, Murray, UT 84107
Schuetzen Gun Works, 1226 Prairie Rd., Colorado Springs, Colo. 80909
Schumaker's Gun Shop, 208 W. 5th Ave., Colville, Wash 99114
Schwab Gun Shop, 1103 E. Bigelow, Findlay, O. 45840
Schwartz Custom Guns, 9621 Coleman Rd., Haslett, Mich. 48840
Schwarz's Gun Shop, 41-15th St., Wellsburg, W. Va. 26070
Jim Scott, Hiway 2-East, Leon, IA 50144
Joseph M. Sellner, 1010 Stelton Rd., Piscataway, N.J. 08854
Shaw's, 1655 S. Euclid Ave., Anaheim, Calif. 92802
Shilen Rifles, Inc., 930 N. Belt Line, Suite 134B, Irving, Tex. 75060
Harold H. Shockley, Box 355, Hanna City, Ill. 65126 (hot bluing & plating)
Shooters Service & Dewey Inc., Clinton Corner, N.Y. 12514
Walter Shultz, R.D. 3, Pottstown, Pa. 19464
The Sight Shop, 1802 E. Columbia Ave., Tacoma, Wa. 98404
Silver Dollar Guns, 7 Balsam St., Keene, NH 03431
Simmons Gun Spec., 700 Rogers Rd., Olathe, Kans. 66061
Simms Hardward Co., 2801 J St., Sacramento, Calif. 95816
Skinner's Gun Shop, Box 30, Juneau, Alaska 98801
Markus Skosples, 1119-35th St., Rock Island, Ill. 61201
Jerome F. Slezak, 1290 Marlowe, Cleveland, O. 44107
John Smith, 912 Lincoln, Carpentersville, Ill. 60110
K. E. Smith, 8766 Los Choches Rd., Lakeside, Calif. 92040
Smitty's Gunshop, 308 S. Washington, Lake City, Minn. 55041
Snapp's Gunshop, 6911 E. Washington Rd., Clare, Mich. 48617
R. Southgate, Rt. 2, Franklin, Tenn. 37064 (new Kentucky rifles)
Sportsman's Den, 1010 Stelton Rd., Piscataway, N.J. 08854
Sportsmens Equip. Co., 915 W. Washington, San Diego, Calif. 92103
Jess L. Stark, 12051 Stroud, Houston, TX 77072
Ikey Starks, 1058 Grand Ave., So. San Francisco, Calif. 94080
Keith Stegall, Box 696, Gunnison, Colo. 81230
Suter's House of Guns, 332 N. Tejon, Colorado Springs, Colo. 80902
Swanson Custom Firearms, 1051 Broadway, Denver, Colo. 80203
A. D. Swenson's 45 Shop, 3223 W. 154th St., Gardena, Calif. 90249
T-P Shop, 212 E. Houghton, West Branch, Mich. 48661
Talmage Ent., 1309 W. 12th St., Long Beach, Calif. 90813
Taylor & Robbins, Box 164, Rixford, Pa. 16745
Daniel Titus, 119 Morlyn Ave., Bryn Mawr, PA 19010
Tom's Gunshop, 600 Albert Pike, Hot Springs, Ark. 71901
Dave Trevallion, 3442 S. Post Rd., Indianapolis, IN 46239
Trinko's Gun Serv., 1406 E. Main, Watertown, Wis. 53094

Herb. G. Troester's Accurizing Serv., Cayuga, ND 58013
C. Hunt Turner, 618 S. Grove, Webster Groves, Mo. 63119 (shotguns only)
Upper Missouri Trading Co., Inc., Crofton, MO 68730
Roy Vail, R. 1, Box 8, Warwick, N.Y. 10990
J. W. Van Patten, Box 145, Foster Hill, Milford, Pa. 18337
Herman Waldron, Box 475, Pomeroy, WN 99437 (metalsmithing)
Walker Arms Co., R. 2, Box 38, Selma, Ala. 36701
Harold Waller, 1288 Camillo Way, El Cajon, Calif. 92021
R. A. Wardrop, Box 245, Mechanicsburg, Pa. 17055
Watertown Shooting Supplies, Box 233 Thomaston Rd., Rte. 6, Watertown, Conn. 06795
Weatherby's, 2781 Firestone Blvd., South Gate, Calif. 90280
Weber Rifle Actions, Box 515, Woodbridge, Calif. 95258
Wells Sport Store, 110 N. Summit St., Prescott, Ariz. 86301
R. A. Wells, 3452 N. 1st, Racine, Wis. 53402
Robert G. West, 6626 S. Lincoln, Littleton, Colo. 80120
Western Stocks & Guns, 2206 E. 11th, Bremerton, Wash. 98310
M. C. Wiest, 234 N. Tulane Ave., Oak Ridge, Tenn. 37830
W. C. Wilber, 400 Lucerne Dr., Spartanburg, SC 29302
Williams Gun Sight Co., 7389 Lapeer Rd., Davison, Mich. 48423
Lou Williamson, 129 Stonegate Ct., Bedford, TX 76021
Wilson Gun Store Inc., R.D. 1, Rte. 225, Dauphin, Pa. 17018
Robert M. Winter, Box 484, Menno, SD 57045
Lester Womack, Box 17210, Tucson, AZ 85710
W. H. Womack, 2124 Meriwether Rd., Shreveport, La. 71108
Russ Zeeryp, 1026 W. Skyline Dr., Morristown, Tenn. 37814

DEALERS IN COLLECTORS' CARTRIDGES

Antique Arsenal, 365 So. Moore St., Lakewood, Colo. 80226
J. A. Belton, 52 Sauve Rd., Mercier, Chateauguay Cty, Quebec, Canada
Peter Bigler, 291 Crestwood Dr., Milltown, N.J. 08850 (ctlg. $1.50)
Geo. Blakeslee, 3135 W. 28th St., Denver, CO 80211
Cameron's, 16690 W. 11th Ave., Golden, Colo. 80401
Carter Gun Works, 2211 Jefferson Pk. Ave., Charlottesville, Va. 22903
Gerry Coleman, 163 Arkell St., Hamilton, Ont., Canada
Chas. E. Duffy, Williams Lane, West Hurley, N.Y. 12419
Tom M. Dunn, 1342 So. Poplar, Casper, Wyo. 82601
Ellwood Epps, 80 King St., Clinton, Ont., Canada
Ed Howe, 2 Main St., Coopers Mills, Me. 04341
Walt Ireson, 47 Chedoke Ave., Hamilton 12, Ont., Canada
Jackson Arms, 6209 Hillcrest Ave., Dallas, Tex. 75205
Oregon Ammo Service, Box 19341, Portland, Ore. 97219 (catlg. $2.00)
Powder Horn, 3093 W. Monmouth, Englewood, CO 80110
Martin B. Retting Inc., 11029 Washington, Culver City, Calif. 90230
Perry Spangler, 519 So. Lynch, Flint, Mich. 48503 (list 50¢)
Jon Taylor House of Cartridges, 12 Cascade Bay, Brandon, Manit., Can.
Ernest Tichy, 365 S. Moore, Lakewood, Colo. 80226
James C. Tillinghast, Box 568, Marlow, N.H. 03456 (list 50c)

ENGRAVERS, ENGRAVING, TOOLS

E. Averill, Rt. 1, 60 Chestnut St., Cooperstown, N.Y. 13326

Joseph Bayer, Sunset Ave., Sunset Hill, RD 1, Princeton, N.J. 08540

Sid Bell, Box 188, Tully, N.Y. 13159

John T. Bickett, 401 Westmark Ave., Colorado Springs, CO 80906

Weldon Bledsoe, 6812 Park Place Dr., Fort Worth, Tex. 76118

Henry D. Bonham, Box 656 (Main St.), Brownville, Me. 04414

Ray Bossi, 3574 University Ave., San Diego, CA 92104

Max E. Bruehl, 781 No. 9th Ave., Canton, IL 61520

Burgess Vibrocrafters (BVI), Rt. 83, Grayslake, Ill. 60030

Chizar Engr. Serv., 690—12th Ave., San Francisco, Cal. 94118

Carl E. Courts, 2421 E. Anaheim St., Long Beach, Cal. 90804

Creative Carvings Inc., R.D. 2, Tully, N.Y. 13159

Bill Dyer, P.O. Box 75255, Oklahoma City, Okla. 73107

J. M. Evans, Box 1850, Los Gatos, CA 95030

Ken Eyster, Heritage Gunsmiths Inc., 6441 Bishop Rd., Centerburg, O. 43011

Ken Flood, 63 Homestead, Stratford, Conn. 06497

Jos. Fugger, c/o Griffin & Howe, 589-8th Ave., N.Y., N.Y. 10017

Donald Glaser, 1520 West St., Emporia, Kans. 66801

Griffin & Howe, 589-8th Ave., N.Y., N.Y. 10017

F. R. Gurney, Engraving Methods Ltd., #207-10344 Jasper Ave., Edmonton, Alberta, Can.

Neil Hartliep, Box 733, Fairmont, Minn. 56031

Frank E. Hendricks, Rt. 2, Box 189J, San Antonio, Tex. 78228

Bob Izenstark, 101 Wolpers Rd., Park Forest, IL 60466

Jaqua's Sporting Goods, 225 N. Main St., Findlay, O. 45840

Paul Jaeger, 211 Leedom, Jenkintown, Pa. 19046

Robert C. Kain, R.F.D. Rte. 30, Newfane, Vermont 05345

Lance Kelly, P.O. Box 1072, Pompana Beach, Fla. 33061

Kleinguenther's, P.O. Box 1261, Seguin, TX 78155

Lynton S.M. McKenzie, 240 Chartres St., New Orleans, La. 70130 (booklet $3.00)

Wm. H. Mains, 2895 Seneca St., Buffalo, N.Y. 14224

Rudy Marek, Rt. 1, Box 1A, Banks, Ore. 97106

Franz Marktl, c/o Davis Gun Shop, 7211 Lee Hwy., Falls Church, VA 22046

S. A. Miller, Central P.O. Box 619, Naha, Okinawa

Frank Mittermeier, 3577 E. Tremont Ave., New York, N.Y. 10465

Albin Obiltschnig, Ferlach, Austria

Pachmayr Gun Works, Inc., 1220 S. Grand Ave., Los Angeles, Calif. 90015

Hans Pfeiffer, 286 Illinois St., Elmhurst, IL 60126

E. C. Prudhomme, 302 Ward Bldg., Shreveport, La. 71101

R. E. I. Engravings, 101 Wolpers, Park Forest, Ill. 60466

John R. Rohner, Sunshine Canyon, Boulder, Colo. 80302

Robert P. Runge, 94 Grove St., Ilion, N.Y. 13357

Shaw-Leibowitz, Rt. 1, Box 421, New Cumberland, W.Va. 26047 (etchers)

Russell J. Smith, 231 Springdale Rd., Westfield, Mass. 01085

Robt. Swartley, 2800 Pine St., Napa, Calif. 94559

Ray Viramontez, 5258 Robinwood, Dayton, O. 45431

Floyd E. Warren, Rt. 3, Box 87, Cortland, O. 44410

John E. Warren, P.O. Box 72, Eastham, Mass. 02642

A. A. White Engr., Inc., P.O. Box 68, Manchester, Conn. 06040

GAME CALLS

Black Duck, 1737 Davis, Whiting, Ind. 46394

Burnham Bros., Box 100-C, Marble Falls, Tex. 78654

Electronic Game Calls, Inc., 210 W. Grand, Wisconsin Rapids, Wis. 54494

Faulk's, 616 18th St., Lake Charles, La. 70601

Lohman Mfg. Co., 320 E. Spring, Neosho, Mo. 64850

M. L. Lynch, 306 Edgewood Blvd., Birmingham, Ala. 35209

Mallardtone, 2901 16th St., Moline, Ill. 61265

Phil. S. Olt Co., Box 550, Pekin, Ill. 61554

Penn's Woods Products, Inc., 19 W. Pittsburgh St., Delmont, Pa. 15626

Sport-Lore, Inc., 1757 Cherry St., Denver, Colo. 80220

Johnny Stewart Wildlife Calls, Box 7954, Waco, Tex. 76710

Thomas Game Calls, P.O. Box 336, Winnsboro, TX 75494

Weems Wild Calls, Box 7261, Ft. Worth, Tex. 76111

Wightman Electronics, Box 989, Easton, Md. 21601

Wildlife Prod. Inc., Prof. Bldg., 513 East Perkins Ave., Sandusky, Ohio 44870 (Lectro Hunter)

Tex Wirtz Ent., Inc., 1925 W. Hubbard St., Chicago, Ill. 60622

GUN CASES, CABINETS AND RACKS

Alco Carrying Cases Inc., 601 W. 26th St., New York, N.Y. 10001

Amer. Safety Gun Case Co., Holland, Mich. 49424

Aremac Co., 101 N. Verity Parkway, Middletown, O. 45042

Artistic Wood Specialties, 923-29 W. Chicago Ave., Chicago, Ill. 60622

Morton Booth Co., Box 123, Joplin, Mo. 64801

Boyt Co., Box 1108, Iowa Falls, Ia. 50126

Brewster Corp., Old Lyme, Conn. 06371

Browning, Rt. 4, Box 624-B, Arnold, MO 63010

Castle Sptg. Gods., Inc., 498 Nepperhan Ave., Yonkers, N.Y. 10701

Challanger Mfg. Co., 118 Pearl St., Mt. Vernon, NY 10550

Cincinnati Ind. Inc., (Cindus), Cincinnati (Lockland), O. 45215

Coladonato Bros., Box 156, Hazleton, Pa. 18201

Dutton's, 7840 Phillips Highway, Jacksonville, Fla. 32216 (single rack)

Ellwood Epps Sporting Goods, Clinton, Ont., Canada

Farber Bros., Inc., 821 Linden Ave., Memphis, Tenn. 38101 (truck pouch)

Ferrell Co., Rte, 3, Gallatin, Tenn. 37066 (Redi-Rack)

Flambeau Plastics Corp., 801 Lynn, Baraboo, Wis. 53913

Gun-Ho Case Mfg. Co., 110 East 10th St., St. Paul, Minn. 55101

Gun Racks, Inc., P.O. Box 22675, Houston, Tex. 77027

B. E. Hodgdon, Inc., 7710 W. 50 Hiway, Shawnee-Mission, Kans. 66202

Ithaca Gun Co., Terrace Hill, Ithaca, N.Y. 14850

J-K Imports, Box 403, Novato, Cal. 94947 (leg 'o mutton case)

Jumbo Sports Prods., P.O. Box 280-Airport Rd., Frederick, MD 21701

Kolpin Bros. Co., Inc., Box 231, Berlin, Wis. 54923

Marble Arms Corp., 1120 Superior, Gladstone, Mich. 49837

National Sports Div., 19 E. McWilliams St., Fond du Lac, Wis. 54935

Nortex Co., 2821 Main St., Dallas, Tex. 75226 (automobile gun rack)

Paul-Reed, Inc., P.O. Box 227, Charlevoix, Mich. 49720

Penguin Industries, Inc., Box 97, Parkesburg, Pa. 19365

Precise Imp. Corp., 3 Chestnut, Suffern, N.Y. 10901

Pretto Cabinet Co., 1201 E. Walnut, Oglesby, Ill. 61348

Protecto Plastics, Inc., 201 Alpha Rd., Wind Gap, Pa. 18091 (carrying cases)

Richland Arms Co., 321 W. Adrian, Blissfield, Mich. 49228

Saf-T-Case, Box 10592, Dallas, Tex. 75207

San Angelo Die Castings, Box 984, San Angelo, Tex. 76901

Buddy Schoellkopf, 4100 Platinum Way, Dallas, Tex. 75237

Sile Distr., 7 Centre Market Pl., New York, N.Y. 10013 (leg o'mutton case)

Stearn Mfg. Co., Div. & 30th St., St. Cloud, Minn. 56301

Sure Shoot'n, Box 195, Jacksonville, Ill. 62650 (leg o'mutton case)

Western Holder Co., Box 33, Menomonee Falls, Wis. 53051

Woodstream Corp., Box 327, Lititz, Pa. 17543

Yield House, Inc., RFD, No. Conway, N.H. 03860

GUNS & GUN PARTS, REPLICA AND ANTIQUE

Antique Gun Parts, Inc., 569 So. Braddock Ave., Pittsburgh, Pa. 15221 (ML)

Armoury Inc., Rte. 25, New Preston, Conn. 06777

Artistic Arms, Inc., Box 23, Hoagland, IN 46745 (Sharps-Borchardt replica)

Bannerman, F., Box 126, Blue Point, Long Island, N.Y. 11715

Shelley Braverman, Athens, N.Y. 12015 (obsolete parts)

Carter Gun Works, 2211 Jefferson Pk. Ave., Charlottesville, Va. 22903

Cornwall Bridge Gun Shop, Cornwall Bridge, CT 06754 (parts)

R. MacDonald Champlin, Stanyan Hill, Wentworth, N.H. 03282 (replicas)

David E. Cumberland, 3509 Carlson Blvd., El Cerrito, CA 94530 (Replica Gatling guns)

Darr's Rifle Shop, 2309 Black Rd., Joliet, Ill. 60435 (S.S. items)

Dixie Gun Works, Inc., Hwy 51, South, Union City, Tenn. 38261

Ellwood Epps Sporting Goods, 80 King St., Clinton, Ont., Canada

Kindig's Log Cabin Sport Shop, R.D. 1, P.O. Box 275, Lodi, Ohio 44254

Edw. E. Lucas, 32 Garfield Ave., Old Bridge, N.J. 08857 (45-70)

R. M. Marek, Rt. 1, Box 1-A, Banks Ore. 97106 (cannons)

Numrich Arms Co., West Hurley, N.Y. 12491

Replica Models, Inc., 610 Franklin St., Alexandria, VA 22314

Riflemen's Hdqs., Rt. 3, RD 550-E, Kendallville, IN 46755

S&S Firearms, 88-21 Aubrey Ave., Glendale, N.Y. 11227

Rob. Thompson, 1031-5th Ave., N., Clinton, Ia. 52732 (Win. only)

C. H. Weisz, Box 311, Arlington, Va. 22210

Wescombe, 10549 Wilsey, Tujunga, CA 91042 (Rem. R.B. parts)

GUN PARTS, U. S. AND FOREIGN

American Firearms Mfg. Co., Inc., 1200 Warfield, San Antonio, Tex. 78216 (clips)

Badger Shooter's Supply, Owen, Wisc. 54460

Shelley Braverman, Athens, N.Y. 12015

Philip R. Crouthamel, 817 E. Baltimore, E. Lansdowne, Pa. 19050

Charles E. Duffy, Williams Lane, West Hurley, N.Y. 12491

Federal Ordnance Inc., P.O. Box 36032, Los Angeles, Calif. 90036

Greeley Arms Co., Inc., 223 Little Falls Rd., Fairfield, N.J. 07006

Gunner's Armory, 2 Sonoma, San Francisco, Calif. 94133

H&B Gun Corp., 1228 Fort St., Lincoln Park, Mich. 48166

Hunter's Haven, Zero Prince St., Alexandria, Va. 22314

Bob Lovell, Box 675, Roseville, CA 95678

Numrich Arms Co., West Hurley, N.Y. 12491

Pacific Intl. Import Co., 2416-16th St., Sacramento, CA 95818

Potomac Arms Corp. (see Hunter's Haven)

Reed & Co., Shokan, N.Y. 12481

Martin B. Retting, Inc., 11029 Washington, Culver City, Cal. 90230

Ruvel & Co., 3037 N. Clark, Chicago, IL 60614

Santa Barbara of America, Ltd., 930 N. Beltline Rd., 132, Irving, TX 75060 (barrels and barreled actions)

Sarco, Inc., 192 Central, Stirling, N.J. 07980

R. A. Saunders, 3253 Hillcrest Dr., San Antonio, Tex. 78201 (clips)

Sherwood Distr. Inc., 7435 Greenbush Ave., No. Hollywood, CA 91605

Simms, 2801 J St., Sacramento, CA 95816

Clifford L. Smires, R.D., Columbus, N.J. 08022 (Mauser rifles)

Sporting Arms, Inc., 9643 Alpaca St., So. El Monte, CA 91733 (M-1 carb. access.)

N. F. Strebe, 4926 Marlboro Pike, S.E., Washington, D.C. 20027

Triple-K Mfg. Co., 568-6th Ave., San Diego, CA 92101

GUNS (Foreign)

Abercrombie & Fitch, Madison at 45th, New York, N.Y. 10017

Alaskan Rifles, Box 30, Juneau, Alaska 99801

American Import Co., 1167 Mission St., San Francisco, Calif. 94103

Armi Fabbri, Casella 206, Brescia, Italy 25100

Armoury Inc., Rte. 25, New Preston, Ct. 06777

Atlas Arms, Inc., 7952 Waukegan Rd., Niles, Ill. 60648

Benet Arms Co., Box 33, Afton, Va. 22920

Blumenfeld Co., 80 W. Virginia Ave., Memphis, Tenn. 38100

Browning, Rt. 4, Box 624-B, Arnold, Mo. 63010

Centennial Arms Corp., 3318 W. Devon, Chicago, (Lincolnwood) Ill. 60645

Century Arms Co., 3-5 Federal St., St. Albans, Vt. 05478

Connecticut Valley Arms Co., Candlewood Hill Rd., Higganum, CT 06441 (CVA)

Continental Arms Corp., 697 Fifth Ave., New York, N.Y. 10022

W. H. Craig, Box 927, Selma, Ala. 36701

Crusader Arms Co., Box 2801, 800 S. 4th St., Louisville, Ky. 40202

Charles Daly, Inc., 90 Chambers St., New York, N.Y. 10007

Dave's House of Guns, 9130 Viscount Row, Dallas, Tex. 75247

Davidson Firearms Co., 2703 High Pt. Rd., Greensboro, N.C. 27403 (shotguns)

Davis Gun Shop, 7213 Lee Highway, Falls Church, VA 22046 (Fanzoj, Ferlach)

Dixie Gun Works, Inc., Hwy 51, South, Union City, Tenn. 38261 ("Kentucky" rifles)

Euroarms, Via Solferino 13/A, 25100 Brescia, Italy

Europa Corp., P.O. Box 48-1367, Miami, Fla. 33148

FFV Sports Inc., 63 E. 64th St., New York, NY 10021 (Husqvarna)

J. Fanzoj, P.O. Box 25, Ferlach, Austria 9170

R. C. Fessler & Co., 1634 Colorado Blvd., Los Angeles, Calif. 90041

Firearms Center Inc. (FCI), 113 Spokane, Victoria, TX 77901

Firearms Imp. & Exp. Co., 2470 N.W. 21st St., Miami, Fla. 33142

Firearms International Corp., 515 Kerby Hill Rd., Washington, DC 20022

Flaig's Lodge, Millvale, Pa. 15209

Freeland's Scope Stands, Inc., 3737 14th Ave., Rock Island, Ill. 61201

J. L. Galef & Son, Inc., 85 Chambers, New York, N.Y. 10007

Garcia Sptg. Arms Corp., 329 Alfred Ave., Teaneck, N.J. 07666

Gevarm (see Blumenfeld Co.)

Gevelot of Can. Ltd., Box 1593, Saskatoon, Sask., Canada

Gold Rush Guns, Box 33, Afton, Va. 22920 (SIG)

H. F. Grieder, Box 487, Knoxville, Ill. 61448 (Hammerli)

Harden & Knight, 5959 S.W. 49th St., Miami, Fla. 33155

Harrington & Richardson Arms Co., 320 Park Ave., Worcester, Mass. 01610 (HK pistol)

Hawes Firearms Co., 8224 Sunset Blvd., Los Angeles, Calif. 90046

Healthways, Box 45055, Los Angeles, Calif. 90061

Herter's, Waseca, Minn. 56093

Husqvarna, see FFV Sports Inc.

Interarmco, see: Interarms (Walther)

Interarms Ltd., 10 Prince St., Alexandria, Va. 22313 (Mauser)

Intercontinental Arms, 2222 Barry Ave., Los Angeles, Calif. 90064

International Firearms Co., Ltd., Montreal 1, Que., Canada

International Distr., Box 7566, Miami, Fla. 33155

Ithaca Gun Co., Terrace Hill, Ithaca, N.Y. 14850 (Perazzi)

Italguns, Via Leonardo da Vinci 36, 20090 Trezzano, Milano, Italy

JBL Arms Co., 4315 Warren St., Davenport, IA 52806

J-K Imports, Box 403, Novato, Cal. 94947 (Italian)

Paul Jaeger Inc., 211 Leedom St., Jenkintown, Pa. 19046

Jana Intl. Co., Box 1107, Denver, Colo. 80201 (Parker-Hale)

J. J. Jenkins, 462 Stanford Pl., Santa Barbara, CA 93105

Guy T. Jones Import Co., 905 Gervais St., Columbia, S. Car. 29201

Kassnar Imports, P.O. Box 3895, Harrisburg, PA 17105

Kleinguenther's, P.O. Box 1261, Seguin, TX 78155

Krieghoff Gun Co., P.O. Box 48-1367, Miami, FL 33148

L. A. Distributors, 4 Centre Market Pl., New York, N.Y. 10013

Jos. G. Landmann, 2308 Preetz/Holstein, W. Germany (JGL)

S. E. Laszlo, 200 Tillary St., Brooklyn, N.Y. 11201

Lever-Arms Serv. Ltd., 771 Dunsmuir, Vancouver 1, B.C., Canada

Liberty Arms Organization, Box 306, Montrose, Calif. 91020

McQueen Sales Co. Ltd., 1760 W. 3rd Ave., Vancouver 9, B.C., Canada

Marketing Unlimited, Inc., 1 Ranch Rite Rd., Yakima, WN 98901

Mars Equipment Corp., 3318 W. Devon, Chicago, Ill. 60645

Mauser Amerika, 34575 Commerce, Fraser, MI 48026

McKeown's Guns, R.R. 1, Pekin, Ill. 61554

Navy Arms Co., 689 Bergen Blvd., Ridgefield, N.J. 07657

Omnipol, Washingtonova 11, Praha 1, Czechoslovakia

Harry Owen, P.O. Box 774, Sunnyvale, Ca. 94088.

Pachmayr Gun Works, 1220 S. Grand Ave., Los Angeles, Calif. 90015 (Fabbri)

Pacific Intl. Import Co., 2416 - 16th St., Sacramento, CA 91605

Palmetto Imp., Inc., P.O. Box 4008, Columbia, SC 29204

Parker-Hale, Whittall St., Birmingham 4, England

Ed Paul Sptg. Goods, 172 Flatbush Ave., Brooklyn, N.Y. 11217 (Premier)

Precise Imp. Corp. (PIC), 3 Chestnut, Suffern, N.Y. 10901

Premier Shotguns, 172 Flatbush Ave., Brooklyn N.Y. 11217

J.L. Quick & Son Co., 1301 Laurence St., Birmingham, AL 35210

RG Industries, Inc., 2485 N.W. 20th St., Miami, FL 33142 (Erma)

Replica Arms Co., Box 640, Marietta, O. 45750

Richland Arms Co., 321 W. Adrian St., Blissfield, Mich. 49228

Sanderson's, 724 W. Edgewater, Portage, Wis. 53901

Savage Arms Corp., Westfield, Mass. 01085 (Anschutz)

Service Armament, 689 Bergen Blvd., Ridgefield, N.J. 07657 (Greener Harpoon Gun)

Sherwood Dist., Inc., 9470 Santa Monica Blvd., Beverly Hills, Ca. 90210

Simmons Spec., Inc., 700 Rogers Rd., Olathe, Kans. 66061

Skinner's Gun Shop (see Alaskan Rifles)

Sloan's Sprtg. Goods, Inc., 88 Chambers St., New York, N.Y. 10001

Solingen Cutlery, Box 306, Montrose, Calif. 91020

Spesco Corp., 3540 Browns Mill Rd. S.E., Atlanta, Ga. 30315

Sportex Intl. Ltd., 10389 W. Olympic Blvd, W. Los Angeles, CA 90064

Stoeger Arms Co., 55 Ruta Ct., S. Hackensack, N.J. 07606

Tradewinds, Inc., P.O. Box 1191, Tacoma, Wash. 98401

Universal Firearms Corp., 3746 E. 10th Ct., Hialeah, Fla. 33013

Valor Imp. Corp., 5555 N.W. 36th Ave., Miami, FL 33142

Voere (see Marketing Unlimited)

Waffen-Frankonia, Box 380, 87 Wurzburg, W. Germany

Weatherby's, 2781 Firestone Blvd., So. Gate, Calif. 90280 (Sauer)

Dan Wesson Arms, 293 So. Main, Monson, Mass. 01057

Zavodi Crvena Zastava, 29 Novembra St., No. 12, Belgrade, Yugosl.

GUNS (Pellet)

Air Rifle Hq., 247 Court St., Grantsville, W. Va. 26147

AmPell Playtime Prods., Inc., 24 E. Main St., Honeoye, NY 14471

Benjamin Air Rifle Co., 1525 So. 8th St., St. Louis, Mo. 63104

Continental Arms Corp., 697 5th Ave., New York, N.Y. 10022

Crosman Arms Co., Inc., Fairport, N.Y. 14450

Daisy Mfg. Co., Rogers, Ark. 72756 (also Feinwerkbau)

Fanta Air Rifles, Box 8122, La Crescenta, Calif, 91214

J. L. Galef & Son, Inc., 85 Chambers St., New York, N.Y. 10007 (B.S.A.)

H. F. Grieder, Box 487, Knoxville, IL 61448 (Hammerli)

Harrington & Richardson Arms Co., 320 Park Ave., Worcester, Mass. 01610 (Webley)

Healthways, Box 45055, Los Angeles, Calif. 90061

Gil Hebard Guns, Box 1, Knoxville, Ill. 61448

Hy-Score Arms Co., 200 Tillary St., Brooklyn, N.Y. 11201

Interarms, 10 Prince, Alexandria, Va. 22313 (Walther)

International Dist., Box 7566, Miami, Fla. 33155 (Hammerli-Master)

Kerrco, Inc., Box 368, Hastings, Nebr. 68901

Marksman Products, P.O. Box 2983, Torrance, CA 90509

Precise Imports Corp. (PIC), 3 Chestnut, Suffern, N.Y. 10901

Sears, Roebuck & Co., 825 S. St. Louis, Chicago, Ill. 60607

Service Armament, 689 Bergen Blvd., Ridgefield, N.J. 07657 (Webley, Jaguar)

Sheridan Products, Inc., 3205 Sheridan, Racine, Wis. 53403

Smith & Wesson, Inc., Springfield, Mass. 01101

Solingen Cutlery, Box 306, Montrose, Calif. 91020

Stoeger Arms Corp., 55 Ruta Ct., S. Hackensack, N.J. 07606 (Peerless)

Stuart Distr. Co., 6 Riverside Dr., Baltimore, Md. 21221

Dan Wesson Arms, 293 S. Main, Monson, Mass. 01057

GUNS, U.S.-made

Agawam Arms Co., 916 Suffield St., Agawam, Mass. 01001

American Firearms Mfg. Co., Inc., 1200 Warfield, San Antonio, Tex. 78216

ArmaLite, 118 E. 16th St., Costa Mesa, Calif. 92627

Artistic Arms, Inc., Box 23, Hoagland, IN 46745 (Sharps-Borchardt)

Auto Mag Corp., 2480 E. Colorado Blvd., Pasadena, CA 91107

Bauer Firearms, 34750 Klein Ave., Fraser, MI 48026

Caraville Arms, P.O. Box 377, Thousand Oaks, CA 91360

Challanger Mfg. Corp., 118 Pearl St., Mt. Vernon, NY 10550 (Hopkins & Allen)

Champlin Firearms, Inc., Box 3191, Enid, Okla. 73701

Charter Arms Corp., 265 Asylum, Bridgeport, Conn. 06610

Clerke Products, 2219 Main St., Santa Monica, Ca. 90405

Colt's, 150 Huyshope Ave., Hartford, Conn. 06102

Commando Arms, Inc., Box 10214, Knoxville, Tenn. 37919

Cumberland Arms, 1222 Oak Dr., Manchester, Tenn 37355

Day Arms Corp., 7515 Stagecoach Ln., San Antonio, Tex. 78227

84 Gun Co., Inc., P.O. Box 54, Eighty Four, PA 15330

Electroarm pistol, see: Independent Research

Esopus Gun Works, Port Ewen, NY 12466 (muzzle loaders)

S. L. Fetterhoff & Co., 911 Monterey Road, So. Pasadena, CA 91030 (rolling block)

Firearms Development, Inc., 218 Austin St., Denton, Tex. 76201

Firearms Imp. & Exp. Co., 2470 N.W. 21st St., Miami, FL 33142 (FIE)

Firearms Intl. Corp., (see: Garcia)

Golden Age Arms Co., 657 High St., Worthington, O. 43085

Gyrojet (see Intercontinental Arms)

Wendell Hanson, 740 Burdick St., Ortonville, MN 56278

Harrington & Richardson, Park Ave., Worcester, Mass. 01610

A. D. Heller, Inc., Box 268, Grand Ave., Baldwin, NY 11510

High Standard Mfg. Co., 1817 Dixwell Ave., Hamden, Conn. 06514

Hopkins & Allen, see: Challenger Mfg. Corp.

Independent Res. & Development, Inc. (I.R.D.), P.O. Box 28188, San Antonio, TX 78228 (Electroarm)

Intercontinental Arms, Inc., 2222 Barry Ave., Los Angeles, Ca. 90064

Ithaca Gun Co., Ithaca, N.Y. 14850

Iver Johnson Arms & Cycle Works, Fitchburg, Mass. 01420

Jackson Hole Arms Corp., Box T, Jackson, Wyo. 83001

J & R carbine, (see: PJK Inc.)

Ljutic Ind., Inc., P.O. Box 2117, Yakima, WA 98902 (Mono-Gun)

MBAssociates, (see Intercontinental Arms)

Marlin Firearms Co., 100 Kenna Dr., New Haven, Conn. 06473

O. F. Mossberg & Sons, Inc., 7 Grasso St., No. Haven, Conn. 06473

W. L. Mowrey Gun Works, Inc., Box 711, Olney, TX 73674

Natl. Ordance Inc., 9643 Alpaca, S. El Monte, CA 91733

Navy Arms Co., 689 Bergen Blvd., Ridgefield, N.J. 07657

Norarmco, 41471 Irwin, Mt. Clemens, MI 48043 (D.A. 25 auto)

Numrich Arms Corp., W. Hurley, N.Y. 12491

PJK, Inc., 1527 Royal Oak Dr., Bradbury, Ca 91010 (J&R Carbine)

Plainfield Machine Co., Inc., Box 447, Dunellen, N.J. 08812

Potomac Arms Corp., P.O. Box 35, Alexandria, Va. 22313 (ML replicas)

R G Industries, 2485 N.W. 20th SE., Miami, FL 33142

Ranger Arms Co., Box 704, Gainesville, Tex. 76240 (Texan Mag.)

Remington Arms Co., Bridgeport, Conn. 06602

Riedl Rifles, P.O. Box FR, Azusa, CA 91702 (S.S.)

Rocky Mountain Arms Corp., Box 224, Salt Lake City, UT 84110

Savage Arms Corp., Westfield, Mass. 01085

Sears, Roebuck & Co., 825 S. St. Louis, Chicago, Ill. 60607

Seventrees Ltd., 315 W. 39th St., New York, N.Y. 10018

Smith & Wesson, Inc., Springfield, Mass. 01101

Sporting Arms, Inc., 9643 Alpaca St., So. El Monte, CA 91733 (M-1 carbine)

Sterling Arms Corp., 2207 Elmwood Ave., Buffalo, N.Y. 14216

Sturm, Ruger & Co., Southport, Conn. 06490

Thompson-Center Arms, Box 2405, Rochester, N.H. 03867 (Contender pistol)

Tingle, 1125 Smithland Pike, Shelbyville, Ind. 46176 (muzzleloader)

Universal Firearms Corp., 3746 E. 10th Ct., Hialeah, Fla. 33013

Ward's, 619 W. Chicago, Chicago, Ill. 60607 (Western Field brand)

Weatherby's, 2781 E. Firestone Blvd., South Gate, Calif. 90280

Dan Wesson Arms, 293 So. Main St., Monson, Mass. 01057

Western Valley Arms Co., 524 W. Main St., Alhambra, CA 91801

Winchester Repeating Arms Co., New Haven, Conn. 06504

Winslow Arms Co., P.O. Box 578, Osprey, Fla. 33595

GUNSMITH SCHOOLS

Colorado School of Trades, 1545 Hoyt, Denver, Colo. 80215

Lassen Community College, Highway 139, Susanville, Calif. 96130

Oregon Technical Institute, Klamath Falls, Ore. 97601

Penn. Gunsmith School, 812 Ohio River Blvd., Avalon, Pittsburgh, Pa. 15202

Trinidad State Junior College, Trinidad, Colo. 81082

GUNSMITH SUPPLIES, TOOLS, SERVICES

Adams & Nelson Co., 4125 W. Fullerton, Chicago, Ill. 60639

Alamo Heat Treating Co., Box 55345, Houston, Tex. 77055

Albright Prod. Co., P.O. Box 695, Bishop, CA 93514 (trap buttplates)

Alley Supply Co., Box 458, Sonora, Calif. 95370

American Edelstaal, Inc., 1 Atwood Ave., Tenafly, NJ 07670

American Firearms Mfg. Co., Inc., 1200 Warfield, San Antonio, Tex. 78216 (45 Conversion Kit)

Anderson & Co., 1203 Broadway, Yakima, Wash. 98902 (tang safe)

Armite Labs., 1845 Randolph St., Los Angeles, Cal. 90001 (pen oiler)

Atlas Arms Inc., 2952 Waukegan Rd., Niles, Ill. 60648

B-Square Co., Box 11281, Ft. Worth, Tex. 76110

Jim Baiar, Rt. 1-B, Box 352, Columbia Falls, Mont. 59912 (hex screws)

Bonanza Sports Mfg. Co., 412 Western Ave., Faribault, Minn. 55021

Brown & Sharpe Mfg. Co., Precision Pk., No. Kingston, R.I. 02852

Bob Brownell's, Main & Third, Montezuma, Ia. 50171

W. E. Brownell, 1852 Alessandro Trail, Vista, Calif. 92083 (checkering tools)

Maynard P. Buehler, Inc., 17 Orinda Hwy., Orinda, Calif. 94563 (Rocol lube)

Burgess Vibrocrafters, Inc. (BVI), Rte. 83, Grayslake, Ill. 60030

M. H. Canjar, 500 E. 45th, Denver, Colo. 80216 (triggers, etc.)

Centerline Prod., Box 14074, Denver, Colo. 80214

Chicago Wheel & Mfg. Co., 1101 W. Monroe St., Chicago, Ill. 60607 (Handee grinders)

Christy Gun Works, 875-57th St., Sacramento, Calif. 95819

Clymer Mfg. Co., 14241 W. 11 Mile Rd., Oak Park, Mich. 48237 (reamers)

Colbert Industries, 10107 Adella, South Gate, Calif. 90280 (Panavise)

A. Constantine & Son, Inc., 2050 Eastchester Rd., Bronx, N.Y. 10461 (wood)

Cougar & Hunter, 6398 W. Pierson Rd., Flushing, Mich. 48433 (scope jigs)

Craft Industries, 719 No. East St., Anaheim, Ca. 92800 (Gunline tools)

Dayton-Traister Co., P.O. Box 93, Oak Harbor, Wa. 98277 (triggers)

Dem-Bart Hand Tool Co., 7749 15th Ave. N.W., Seattle, WA 98107 (checkering tools)

Die Supply Corp., 11700 Harvard Ave., Cleveland, Ohio 44105

Ditto Industries, 527 N. Alexandria, Los Angeles, Cal. 90004 (clamp tool)

Dixie Diamond Tool Co., Inc., 6875 S.W. 81st St., Miami, Fla. 33143 (marking pencils)

Dremel Mfg. Co., P.O. Box 518, Racine, Wis. 53401 (grinders)

Chas. E. Duffy, Williams Lane, West Hurley, N.Y. 12491

Dumore Co., 1300 - 17th St., Racine, Wis. 53403

E-Z Tool Co., P.O. Box 3186, East 14th Street Sta., Des Moines, Ia. 50313 (taper lathe attachment)

Edmund Scientific Co., 101 E. Glouster Pike, Barrington, N.J. 08007

F. K. Elliott, Box 785, Ramona, Calif. 92065 (reamers)

Foredom Elec. Co., Rt. 6, Bethel, Conn. 06801 (power drills)

Forster Appelt Mfg. Co., Inc., 82 E. Lanark Ave., Lanark, Ill. 61046

Keith Francis, Box 343, Talent, Ore. 97540 (reamers)

Frantz Tools, 913 Barbara Ave., Placentia, Cal. 92670

G. R. S. Corp., Box 1157, Boulder, Colo. 80302 (Gravermeister)

Gilmore Pattern Works, 1164 N. Utica, Tulsa, Okla. 74110

Gold Lode, Inc., P.O. Box 31, Addison, Ill. 60101 (gold inlay kit)

Grace Metal Prod., Box 67, Elk Rapids, Mich. 49629 (screw drivers, drifts)

Gopher Shooter's Supply, Box 246, Faribault, Minn. 55021 (screwdrivers, etc.)

The Gun Case, 11035 Maplefield SE., El Monte, Calif. 91733 (triggers)

Gunline Tools (see Craft Ind.)

H. & M. 24062 Orchard Lake Rd., Farmington, Mich. 48024 (reamers)

Half Moon Rifle Shop, Rt. 1B, Box 352, Columbia Falls, MT 59912 (hex screws)

Hartford Reamer Co., Box 134, Lathrup Village, Mich. 48075

O. Iber Co., 626 W. Randolph, Chicago, Ill. 60606

Paul Jaeger Inc., 211 Leedom St., Jenkintown, PA. 19046

Kasenite Co., Inc., 3 King St., Mahwah, N.J. 07430 (surface hrdng. comp.)

LanDav Custom Guns, 7213 Lee Highway, Falls Church, VA 22046

John G. Lawson, 1802 E. Columbia Ave., Tacoma, WA 98404

Lea Mfg. Co., 237 E. Aurora St., Waterbury, Conn. 06720

Lock's Phila. Gun Exch., 6700 Rowland Ave., Philadelphia, Pa. 19149

Marker Machine Co., Box 426, Charleston, Ill. 61920

Michaels of Oregon Co., P.O. Box 13010, Portland, Ore. 97213

Viggo Miller, P.O. Box 4181, Omaha, Neb. 68104 (trigger attachment)

Miller Single Trigger Mfg. Co., Box 69, Millersburg, Pa. 17061

Frank Mittermeier, 3577 E. Tremont, N.Y., N.Y. 10465

Moderntools Corp, Box 407, Dept. GD, Woodside, N.Y. 11377

N&J Sales, Lime Kiln Rd., Northford, Conn. 06472 (screwdrivers)

Karl A. Neise, Inc., 5602 Roosevelt Ave., Woodside, N.Y. 11377

P & S Sales, P.O. Box 45095, Tulsa, OK 74145

Palmgren, 8383 South Chicago Ave., Chicago, Ill. 60167 (vises, etc.)

C. R. Pedersen & Son, Ludington, Mich. 49431

Ponderay Lab., 210 W. Prasch, Yakima, Wash. 98902 (epoxy glass bedding)

Redford Reamer Co., Box 6604, Redford Hts. Sta., Detroit, MI 48240

Richland Arms Co., 321 W. Adrian St., Blissfield, Mich. 49228

Riley's Supply Co., 121 No. Main St., Avilla, Ind. 46710 (Niedner buttplates, caps)

Rob. A. Saunders, (see Amer. Firearms Mfg.)

Ruhr-American Corp., So. Hwy #5, Glenwood, Minn. 56334

A. G. Russell, 1705 Hiway 71N, Springdale, AR 72764 (Arkansas oilstones)

Schaffner Mfg. Co., Emsworth, Pittsburgh, Pa. 15202 (polishing kits)

Schuetzen Gun Works, 1226 Prarie Rd., Colo. Springs, Colo. 80909

Shaw's, 1655 S. Euclid Ave., Anaheim, Calif. 92802

A. D. Soucy, Box 191, Fort Kent, Me. 04743 (ADSCO stock finish)

L. S. Starrett Co., Athol, Mass. 01331

Technological Devices, Inc., P.O. Box 3491, Stamford, Conn. 06905 (Accu-Orb circle cutters)

Texas Platers Supply Co., 2458 W. Five Mile Parkway, Dallas, TX 75233 (plating kit)

L.B. Thompson, 568 E. School Ave., Salem, O. 44460 (rust bluing/browning services)

Timney Mfg. Co., 5624 Imperial Hwy., So. Gate, Calif. 90280 (triggers)

Stan de Treville, Box 2446, San Diego, Calif 92112 (checkering patterns)

Twin City Steel Treating Co., Inc., 1114 S. 3rd, Minneapolis, Minn. 55415 (heat treating)

R. G. Walters Co., 3235 Hancock, San Diego, Ca. 92110

Ward Mfg. Co., 500 Ford Blvd., Hamilton, O. 45011

Will-Burt Co., P.O. Box 160, Orrville, O. 44667 (vises)

Williams Gun Sight Co., 7389 Lapeer Rd., Davison, Mich. 48423

Wilson Arms Co., Box 364, Stony Creek, Branford, Conn. 06405

Wilton Tool Corp., 9525 W. Irving Pk. Rd., Schiller Park, Ill. 60176 (vises)

Wisconsin Platers Supply Co., see: Texas Platers

W. C. Wolff Co., Box 232, Ardmore, PA 19003 (springs)

Woodcraft Supply Corp., 313 Montvale, Woburn, MA 01801

HANDGUN ACCESSORIES

A & R Sales Co., 99163¾ Rush St., So. El Monte, CA 91733

Barami Corp, 6250 E. 7 Mile Rd, Detroit, Mich. 48234 (Hip-Grip)

Bar-Sto Precision Machine, 633 S. Victory Blvd., Burbank, CA 91502

B. L. Broadway, Rte. 1, Box 381, Alpine, CA 92001 (machine rest)

C'Arco, P.O. Box 2043, San Bernardino, CA 92406 (Ransom Rest)

Case Master, 4675 E. 10 Ave., Miami, Fla. 33013

Central Specialties Co., 6030 Northwest Hwy., Chicago, Ill. 60631

John Dangelzer, 3056 Frontier Pl., N.E., Albuquerque, N.M. 87106 (flasks)

Bill Dyer, 503 Midwest Bldg., Oklahoma City, Okla. 73102 (grip caps)

R. S. Frielich, 396 Broome St., New York, N.Y. 10013 (cases)

Hunt Eng., 121—17th St., Yucaipa, Calif. 92399 (Multi-Loader)

Jeffersontown Speclty. Co., Inc., 9815 Taylorsville Rd., Jeffersontown, KY 40299 (pin pads)

R. G. Jensen, 16153½ Parthenia, Sepulveda, Calif. 91343 (auxiliary chambers)

Lee Prec. Mfg., 21 E. Wisconsin, Hartford, WI 53027 (pistol rest holders)

Matich Loader, Box 958, So. Pasadena, Calif. 91030 (Quick Load)

J. McArthur, 1961 Overlook Ave., Youngstown, O. 44509 (sling)

Pachmayr, 1220 S. Grand, Los Angeles, Calif. 90015 (cases)

Platt Luggage, Inc., 2301 S. Prairie, Chicago, Ill. 60616 (cases)

Jules Reiver, 4104 Market St., Wilmington, Del. 19899 (cases)

Roger A. Smith, 19320 Heber St., Glendora, Ca. 91740 (Wrist-Loc)

Sportsmen's Equipment Co., 415 W. Washington, San Diego, Calif. 92103

M. Tyler, 1326 W. Britton, Oklahoma City, Okla. 73114 (grip adaptor)

HANDGUN GRIPS

Beckelhymer's, Hidalgo & San Bernardo, Laredo, Tex. 78040

Belmont Prods., Rte. #1, Friendsville, TN 37737

Cloyce's Gun Stocks, Box 1133, Twin Falls, Ida. 83301

Crest Carving Co., 8091 Bolsa Ave., Midway City, CA 92655

Custom Combat Grips, 148 Shepherd Ave., Brooklyn, N.Y. 11208

J. M. Evans, Box 1850, Los Gatos, CA 95030 (custom-made)

Fitz, Box 49797, Los Angeles, Calif. 90049

Herret's, Box 741, Twin Falls, Ida. 83301

Hogue Custom Grips, Box 1001, Cambria, CA 93428

Mershon Co., Inc., 1230 S. Grand Ave., Los Angeles, Calif. 90015

Mustang Pistol Grips, 13830 Hiway 395, Edgemont, Calif. 92508

Safety Grip Corp., Box 456, Riverside St., Miami, Fla. 33135

Sanderson Custom Pistol Stocks, 17695 Fenton, Detroit, Mich. 48219

Jay Scott, 81 Sherman Place, Garfield, N.J. 07026

Sile Dist., 7 Centre Market Pl., New York, N.Y. 10013

John W. Womack, 3006 Bibb St., Shreveport, La 71108

HEARING PROTECTORS

American Optical Corp., Mechanic St., Southbridge, Mass. 01550 (ear valve)

Bausch & Lomb, 635 St. Paul St., Rochester, N.Y. 14602

David Clark Co., 360 Franklin St., Worcester, Mass. 01604

Curtis Safety Prod. Co., Box 61, Webster Sq. Sta., Worcester, Mass. 01603 (ear valve)

Hodgdon, 7710 W. 50 Hiway, Shawnee Mission, Kans. 66202

Human Acoustics, Inc., 888 E. Williams St., Carson City, Nev. 89701

Sigma Eng. Co., 11320 Burbank Blvd., No. Hollywood, Ca. 91601 (Lee-Sonic ear valve)

Willson Prods Div., P.O. Box 622, Reading, Pa. 19603 (Ray-O-Vac)

HOLSTERS & LEATHER GOODS

American Sales & Mfg. Co., P.O. Box 677, Laredo, Tex. 78040

Andy Anderson, 6100 Vineland Ave., No. Hollywood, CA 91606 (Gunfighter Custom Holsters)

Berns-Martin, 1307 Spring St. N.W., Atlanta, GA 30309

Bianchi Holster Co., 212 W. Foothill Blvd., Monrovia, Calif. 91016

Edward H. Bohlin, 931 N. Highland Ave., Hollywood, Calif. 90038

Boyt Co., Box 1108, Iowa Falls, Ia. 51026

Brauer Bros. Mfg. Co., 817 N. 17th, St. Louis, Mo. 63106

Browning, Rt. 4, Box 624-B, Arnold, MO 63010

J. M. Bucheimer Co., Airport Rd., Frederick, Md. 21701

Cole's Acku-Rite, Box 25, Kennedy, N.Y. 14747

Colt's, 150 Huyshope Ave., Hartford, Conn. 06102

Daisy Mfg. Co., Rogers, Ark. 72756

Eugene DeMayo & Sons, Inc., 2795 Third Ave., Bronx, N.Y. 10455

Filmat Enterpr., Inc., 200 Market St., East Paterson, N.J. 07407

Flintrop Arms Co., 4034 W. National Ave., Milwaukee, Wis. 53215

Goerg Ent., 3009 S. Laurel, Port Angeles, Wash. 98362

Gunfighter (See Anderson)

Hoyt Holster Co., P.O. Box 1783, Costa Mesa, Cal. 92626

Don Hume, Box 351, Miami, Okla. 74354

The Hunter Co., 1215 12th St., Denver, Colo. 80204

Jet Sports Corp., 4 Centre Market Pl., New York, N.Y. 10013

Jumbo Sports Prods., P.O. Box 280, Airport Rd., Frederick, MD 21701

George Lawrence Co., 306 S. W. First Ave., Portland, Ore. 97204

MMGR Corp., 5710 12th Ave., Brooklyn, N.Y. 11219

S. D. Myres Saddle Co., Box 9776, El Paso, Tex. 79988

Alfonso Pineda, 4850 Lankershim Blvd., No. Hollywood, CA 91062 (custom holstermaker)

Pony Express Sport Shop, 17460 Ventura Blvd., Encino, Calif. 91316

Red Head Brand Co., 4100 Platinum Way, Dallas, Tex. 75237

R. E. Roseberry, 810 W. 38th, Anderson, Ind. 46014

Safariland Leather Products, 1946 S. Myrtle Ave., Monrovia, Calif. 91016

Safety Speed Holster, Inc., 910 So. Vail, Montebello, Calif. 90640

Saguaro Holsters, 1508 Del Carlo Circle, Seagoville, TX 75159 (custom)

San Francisco Gun Exchange, 75 Fourth St., San Francisco, Calif. 94103

Buddy Schoellkopf Products, Inc., 4100 Platinum Way, Dallas, Tex. 75237

Seventrees, Ltd., 315 W. 39 St., New York, N.Y. 10018

Sile Distr., 7 Centre Market Pl., New York, N.Y. 10013

Smith & Wesson Leather Co., 2100 Roosevelt, Springfield, Mass. 01101

Swiss-Craft Co., Inc., 33 Arctic St., Worcester, MA 01604

Tandy Leather Co., 1001 Foch, Fort Worth, Texas 76107

Tayra Corp., 1529-19th St. N.W., Canton, O. 44709

Whitco, Box 1712, Brownsville, Tex. 78520 (Hide-A-Way)

Woodland Sport and Gift Shop, Box 107, Mayfield, N.Y. 12117

HUNTING, CAMP GEAR, CLOTHING, ETC.

Abercrombie & Fitch, 45th & Madison Ave., N.Y., N.Y. 10017

Alpine Designs, Box 1081, Boulder, Colo. 80302

Alpine Hut, Box 1456, Wenatchee, Wash. 98801

Eddie Bauer, 1737 Airport Way So., Seattle, Wash. 98134

L. L. Bean, Freeport, Me. 04032

Bear Archery Co., R.R. 1, Grayling, Mich. 49738 (Himalayan backpack)

Bernzomatic Corp., 740 Driving Pk. Ave., Rochester, N.Y. 14613 (stoves & lanterns)

Big Beam, Teledyne Co., 290 E. Prairie St., Crystal Lake, Ill. 60014 (lamp)

Thos. Black & Sons, 930 Ford St., Ogdensburg, N.Y. 13669 (ctlg. 25¢)

Browning, Rte. 1, Morgan, Utah 84050

Camouflage Mfg. Co., P.O. Box 5437, Pine Bluff, AR 71601

Camp and Trail Outfitters, 21 Park Place, N.Y., N.Y. 10007

Camp Trails, P.O. Box 14500, Phoenix, Ariz. 85031 (packs only)

Challanger Mfg. Co., Box 550, Jamaica, N.Y. 11431 (glow safe)

Coleman Co., Inc., 250 N. St. Francis, Wichita, Kans. 67201

Colorado Outdoor Sports Co., 5450 N. Valley Hwy., Denver, Colo. 80216

Converse Rubber Co., 392 Pearl St., Malden, Mass. 02148 (boots)

Corcoran, Inc., Zero Canton Street, Stoughton, Mass. 02072

Dana Safety Heater, J. L. Galef & Son, Inc., 85 Chamber St., N.Y. N.Y. 10007

DEER-ME Prod. Co., Box 345, Anoka, Minn. 55303 (tree steps)

Dunham's Footwear, RFD 3, Brattleboro, Vt. 05301 (boots)

Edmont-Wilson, 1300 Walnut St., Coshocton, O. 43812 (gloves)

Fabrico Mfg. Corp., 1300 W. Exchange, Chicago, Ill. 60609

Farber Bros., Inc., 821 Linden Ave., Memphis, TN 38101 (Westex Truck Pouch)

Filmat Enterpr., Inc., 200 Market St., East Paterson, N.J. 07407 (field dressing kit)

Freeman Ind., Inc., 100 Marblehead Rd., Tuckahoe, N.Y. 10707 (Trak-Kit)

Game-Winner, Inc., 700 Wharton Dr. S.W., Atlanta, GA 30336 (camouflage suits)

Gander Mountain, Inc., Box 248, Wilmot, Wis. 53192

Gerry Mountain Sports, Inc. (see Colorado Sports)

Gokey, 94 E. 4th St., St. Paul, Minn. 55101

Greenford Products, Inc., 64 Old Orchard, Skokie, Ill. 60076 (heaters & ranges)

Gun Club Sportswear, Box 477, Des Moines, Ia. 50302

Gun-Ho Case Mfg. Co., 110 E. 10th St., St. Paul, Minn. 55101

Hawthorn Co., Div. of Kellwood Co., New Haven, Mo. 63068 (tents)

Herter's Inc., Waseca, Minn. 56093

Himalayan Back Packs, Box 950, Monterey, CA 93940

Bob Hinman, 1217 W. Glen, Peoria, Ill. 61614

Holubar Mountaineering, Box 7, Boulder, Colo. 80302

Humphrey Prod., P.O. Box 2008, Kalamazoo, Mich. 49003 (camping equipment)

Hunting World, 247 E. 50th St., New York, N.Y. 10022

Kelty Pack, Inc., Box 3645, Glendale, Calif. 91201

Peter Limmer & Sons, Box 66, Intervale, N.H. 03845 (boots)

Marble Arms Corp., 1120 Superior, Gladstone, Mich. 49837

Moor & Mountain, 14 Main St., Concord Center, Mass. 01742

National Sports Div., 19 E. McWilliams St., Fond du Lac, Wis. 54935

Nimrod & Wayfarer Trailers, 500 Ford Blvd., Hamilton, O. 45011

Charles F. Orvis Co., Manchester, Vt. 05254 (fishing gear)

Palco Prods., 15 Hope Ave., Worcester, MA 01603

Paulin Infra-Red Prod. Co., 30520 Lakeland Blvd., Willowick, OH 44094

Portablind, 705 Exchange Park, Dallas, TX 75235

Powerwinch Corp., 184 Garden St., Bridgeport, Conn. 06605

Primus-Sievert, 354 Sackett Pt. Rd., No. Haven, CT 06473 (stoves)

Raemco, Box 882, Somerville, N.J. 08876 (stoves)

Red Head Brand Co., 4100 Platinum Way, Dallas Tex. 75237

Red Wing Shoe Co., Rte. 2, Red Wing, Minn. 55066

Refrigiwear, Inc., 71 Inip Dr., Inwood, L.I., N.Y. 11696

Reliance Prod. Ltd., 1830 Dublin Ave., Winnipeg 21, Man., Can. (tent peg)

Buddy Schoellkopf, Inc., 4100 Platinum Way, Dallas, Tex. 75237

Servus Rubber Co., 1136 2nd St., Rock Island, Ill. 61201 (footwear)

Sportsgear, Inc., 4909 Fremont Ave. So., Minneapolis, Minn. 55409 (pack sack & port. chair)

Sportsmen Prod. Inc., Box 1082, Boulder, Colo. 80302 (snowshoes)

Stearns Mfg. Co., Division & 30th St., St. Cloud, Minn. 56301

Sterno Inc., 105 Hudson St., Jersey City, N.J. 07302 (camp stoves)

Burt Stumpf, 408 Morrison Ave., Waterloo, Ill. 62298 (Easy-Way hunting vest)

10-X Mfg. Co., 100 S.W. 3rd St., Des Moines, IA 50309

Thermos Div., KST Co., Norwich, Conn. 06361 (Pop Tent)

Therm'x Corp., Inc., 1280 Columbus, San Francisco, Calif. 94133

Norm Thompson, 1805 N.W. Thurman St., Portland, Ore. 97209

Trailwise-The Ski Hut, 1615 University Ave., Berkeley, Calif. 94703

Travel Industries, Box 108, Oswego, Kan. 67356 (Dreamer pickup fleet)

Trigg Mfg. Co., Box 850, Danville, Ky. 40422 (clothing)

U-C-Lite Mfg. Co., 290 E. Prairie St., Crystal Lake, Ill. 60014 (Big beam car- and hand-flashlights)

Eug. Usow Mfg. Co., 1934 N. Washtenaw, Chicago, Ill. 60647 (clothing)

Ute Mountain Corp., Box 3602, Englewood, Colo. 80110 (Metal Match)

Utica Duxbak Corp., 815 Noyes St., Utica, N.Y. 13502

Visa-Therm Prod., Inc., P.O. Box 486, Bridgeport, Conn. 06601 (Astro/Electr. vest)

Vogt Mfg. Co., 100 Fernwood Ave., Rochester, N.Y. 14621 (fluorescent belt)

Waffen-Frankonia, Box 380, 87 Wurzburg, W. Germany

Ward Mfg. Co., 500 Ford Blvd., Hamilton, O. 45015 (trailers)

Weinbrenner Shoe Corp., Polk St., Merrill, WI 54452

Wilson Certified Foods, Inc., Box 7345, Omaha, Neb. 68107

Wisconsin Shoe Co., 1039 So. Second, Milwaukee, Wis. 53204

Woods Bag & Canvas Co., Ltd., 16 Lake St., Ogdensburg, N.Y. 13669

Woodstream Corp., Box 327, Lititz, Pa. 17543 (Hunter Seat)

Woolrich Woolen Mills, Woolrich, Pa. 17779

Yankee Mechanics, Lacey Place, Southport, CT 06490 (hand winches)

Zeus Portable Generator Co., 500 Mildred, Primos, Ohio 19018

HUNTING KNIVES, AXES AND HATCHETS

Adanac Sptg. Gds., 505 Bellingham Ntl. Bk. Bldg., Bellingham, Wash. 98225

John Applebaugh, Box 68, Blackwell, Okla. 74631 (custom-knives)

B.H.S. Mfg. Co., Box 24, Troy, MI 48084 (pocket axe)

L. L. Bean, Freeport, Maine 04032

Bear Archery Co., R.R. 1, Grayling, MI 49738

Lee Biggs, 3816 Via La Silva, Palo Verde, CA 92266 (custom-knives)

Ralph Bone Knife Co., 806 Avenue J, Lubbock, Tex. 79401

H. Gardner Bourne, 1252 Hope Ave., Columbus, O. 43212 (custom-knives)

D. L. Brown, 1803 Birdie Dr., Toledo, O. 43615 (custom-knives)

L. E. "Red" Brown, 301 E. Neece St., Long Beach, CA 90805 (custom-knives)

Buck Knives, Inc., P.O. Box 1267, El Cajon, CA 92022

Ray Busch, 940 Orion, Mandeville, LA 70005 (custom-knives)

Pete Callan, 17 Sherline Ave., New Orleans, LA 70124 (custom-knives)

W. R. Case Knives, 20 Russell Blvd., Bradford, Pa. 16701

Challanger Mfg. Co., 118 Pearl St., Mt. Vernon, NY 10550

Cooper Knives, P.O. Box 1423, Burbank, CA 91505 (custom, ctlg. 50¢)

Custom Knifemaker's Supply, P.O. Box 11448, Dallas, TX 75223

Dan-D Custom Knives, Box 4479, Yuma, AZ 85364

Davis Custom Knives, 118 W. 14th, Airway Heights, WA 99001

Philip Day, Rte. 1, Box 465T, Bay Minetter, AL 36507 (custom-knives)

J. R. Dennard, 907 Greenwood Pl., Dalton, GA 30720 (custom-knives)

Chas. E. Dickey, 803 N.E. A St., Bentonville, AR 72712 (custom-knives)

T. M. Dowell, 139 St. Helen's Pl., Bend, OR 97701 (TMD custom-knives, ctlg. 25¢)

John Ek, 3214 NW 54th St., Miami, Fla. 33142 (custom-knives)

Fischer Custom Knives, Rt. 1, Box 170-M, Victoria, TX 77901

H. H. Frank, c/o Loveless, Box 837, Lawndale, CA 90260 (custom-knives)

James Furlow, 2499 Brookdale Dr. N.E., Atlanta, GA 30345 (custom-knives)

Garcia Sptg. Arms Corp., 329 Alfred Ave., Teaneck, NJ 07666

Gerber Legendary Blades, 14200 S.W. 72nd St., Portland, OR 99223

Gutman Cutlery Co., Inc., 3956 Broadway, New York, NY 10032

Gyrfalcon Inc., Kutz Bldg., 1104 Fernwood Ave., Camp Hill, PA 17011 (Skachet)

H & B Forge Co., Rte. 2, Greenwich, OH 44837 (tomahawks)

Lloyd A. Hale, Washington, AR 71862 (custom-knives)

C. M. (Pete) Heath, 119 Grant St., Winnecone, WI 54986 (custom-knives)

G. H. Herron, 920 Murrah Ave., Aiken, SC 29801 (custom-knives)

Gil Hibben, Box 773, Springdale, AR 72764 (custom-knives)

Chubby Hueske, 4808 Tamarisk Dr., Bellaire, TX 77401 (custom-knives)

Indian Ridge Traders, P.O. Box X-50, Ferndale, MI 48220

Jet-Aer Corp., 100 Sixth Ave., Paterson, NJ 07524 (G96 knives)

LaDow (Doc) Johnston, 2322 W. Country Club Parkway, Toledo, OH 43614 (custom-knives)

KA-BAR Cutlery, Inc., 5777 Grant Ave., Cleveland, OH 44105

Jon W. Kirk, 800 N. Olive, Fayetteville, AR 72701 (custom-knives)

W. Kneubuhler, P.O. Box 327, Pioneer, OH 43554 (custom-knives)

Kustom Made Knives, 418 Jolee, Richardson, TX 75080

J. I. Lane, Rte. 5, Carbondale, IL 62901 (custom-knives)

Lile Handmade Knives, Rte. 1, Box 56, Russellville, AR 72801

LocKnife, Inc., 11717 E. 23rd St., Independence, MO 64050

R. W. Loveless, Box 837, Lawndale, CA 90260 (custom-knives, ctlg. $1)

Bob Ludwig, 1028 Pecos Ave., Port Arthur, TX 77640 (custom-knives)

MAC Intl. Corp., 4848 W. Main, Skokie, IL 60076

Marble Arms Corp., 1120 Superior, Gladstone, MI 49837

Joe S. Martin, Box 6652, Lubbock, TX 79413 (custom-knives)

John T. Mims, 620 S. 28th Ave., Apt. 327, Hattiesburg, MS 39401 (custom-knives)

Mitchell Knives, 511 Ave. B, So. Houston, TX 77587 (custom)

W. F. Moran, Jr., Rt. 5, Frederick, MD 21701 (custom-knives, ctlg. 50¢)

Morseth Sports Equip. Co., 1705 Hiway 71N, Springdale, AR 72764 (custom-knives)

Normark Corp., 1710 E. 78th St., Minneapolis, MN 55423

Ogg Custom Knives, Rt. 1, Box 230, Paris, AR 72855

Olsen Knife Co., Inc., 7 Joy St., Howard City, MI 49329

Randall-Made Knives, Box 1988, Orlando, FL 32802 (ctlg. 25¢)

Razor Edge, Box 203, Butler, WI 53007 (knife sharpener)

F. J. Richtig, Clarkson, NB 68629 (custom-knives)

Ruana Knife Works, Box 574, Bonner, MT 59823 (ctlg. 50¢)

Sanders, 2358 Tyler Lane, Louisville, KY 40205 (Bahco)

N. H. Schiffman, P.O. Box 7373, Murray, UT 84107 (custom-knives)

Jack D. Schmier, 16787 Mulberry Ct., Fountain Valley, CA 92708 (custom-knives)

Bob Schrimsher, Wm. Rodgers Cutlery, P.O. Box 11448, Dallas, TX 75223

John J. Schwarz, 41 Fifteenth St., Wellsburg, WV 26070 (custom-knives)

Sewell Custom Knives, 1307 Spring St. N.W., Atlanta, GA 30309

C. R. Sigman, Star Rte., Box 3, Red House, WV 25168

Skachet, (see: Gyrfalcon Inc.)

Jos. T. Smith, 6048 Cedar Crest Dr., So. Haven, MS 38671 (custom-knives)

W. J. Sonneville, 1050 Chalet Dr. W., Mobile, AL 36608 (custom-knives)

Bernard Sparks, Box 32, Dingle, ID 83233 (custom-knives)

Stone Knives, 703 Floyd Rd., Richardson, TX 75080

Thompson/Center, P.O. Box 2405, Rochester, NH 03867

Thunderbird Custom Knives, 912 So. 2nd St., Blackwell, OK 74631

Tru-Balance Knife Co., 2110 Tremont Blvd., Grand Rapids, MI 49504

True-Temper, 1623 Euclid, Cleveland, OH 44100

Unique Inventions, Inc., 3727 W. Alabama St., Houston, TX 77027 (throwing knife)

W-K Knives, P.O. Box 327, Pioneer, OH 43554

Western Cutlery Co., 5311 Western Ave., Boulder, CO 80302

Ronnie Wilson, P.O. Box 2012, Weirton, WV 26062 (custom-knives)

Don Zaccagaino, P.O. Box Zack, Pahokee, FL 33476 (custom-knives)

LOAD TESTING & CHRONOGRAPHING

Carter Gun Works, 2211 Jefferson Pk. Ave., Charlottesville, Va. 22903

Custom Ballistics' Lab., 3354 Cumberland Dr., San Angelo, Tex. 76901

Horton Ballistics, North Waterford, Me. 04267

Hutton Rifle Ranch, Box 898, Topanga, CA 90290

Jurras Co., Box 163, Shelbyville, Ind. 46176

Kennon's, 5408 Biffle, Stone Mountain, Ga. 30083

Plum City Ballistics Range, RFD 1, Box 128, Plum City, Wis. 54761

Shooters Service & Dewey, Inc., Clinton Corners, N.Y. 12514 (daily fee range also)

Gene West, 137 Baylor, Pueblo, Colo. 81005

H. P. White Lab., Box 331, Bel Air, Md. 21014

METALLIC SIGHTS

B-Square Eng. Co., Box 11281, Ft. Worth, Tex. 76110

Bo-Mar Tool & Mfg. Co., Box 168, Carthage, Tex. 75633

Maynard P. Buehler, Inc., 17 Orinda Highway, Orinda, Calif. 94563

Christy Gun Works, 875 57th St., Sacramento, Calif. 95819

Cornwall Bridge Gun Shop, Cornwall Bridge, CT 06754 (vernier)

E-Z Mount, Ruelle Bros., P.O. Box 114, Ferndale, MT 48220

Firearms Dev. Lab., Box 278, Scotts Valley, Calif. 95060

Freeland's Scope Stands, Inc., 3734-14th Ave., Rock Island, Ill. 61201

P. W. Gray Co., Fairgrounds Rd., Nantucket, Mass. 02554 (shotgun)

Paul T. Haberly, 2364 N. Neva, Chicago, IL 60635

Paul Jaeger, Inc., 211 Leedom St., Jenkintown, PA 19046

Lyman Gun Sight Products, Middlefield, Conn. 06455

Marble Arms Corp., 1120 Superior, Gladstone, Mich. 49837

Merit Gunsight Co., P.O. Box 995, Sequim, Wash. 98382

Micro Sight Co., 242 Harbor Blvd., Belmont, Calif. 94002

Miniature Machine Co., 212 E. Spruce, Deming, N.M. 88030

Oxford Corp., 100 Benbro Dr., Buffalo, N.Y. 14225 (Illum. Sight)

C. R. Pedersen & Son, Ludington, Mich. 49431

Poly Choke Co., Inc., P.O. Box 296, Hartford, CT 06101

Redfield Gun Sight Co., 1315 S. Clarkson St., Denver, Colo. 80210

Ruelle Bros. Co., P.O. Box 114, Ferndale, MI 48220

Schwarz's Gun Shop, 41 - 15th St., Wellsburg, W. Va. 26070

Simmons Gun Specialties, Inc., 700 Rodgers Rd., Olathe, Kans. 66061

Slug Site Co., 3835 University, Des Moines, Ia. 50311

Tradewinds, Inc., Box 1191, Tacoma, WA 98401

Williams Gun Sight Co., 7389 Lapeer Rd., Davison, Mich. 48423

W. H. Womack, 2124 Meriwether Rd., Shreveport. La. 71108

MISCELLANEOUS

Accurizing Service, Herbert G. Troester, Cayuaga, ND 58013

Adhesive Flannel, Forest City Prod., 722 Bolivar, Cleveland, O. 44115

Ammo Pouch, Creed Ent., 13167 E. Garvey Ave., Baldwin Park, CA 91706

Archery, Bear Co., R.R. 1, Grayling, Mich. 49738

Arms Books, Normount Technical Publications, Box 211, Forest Grove, OR 97116

Arms Books, Handgun Press, 5832 S. Green, Chicago, IL 60621

Arms Booksellers, CB Press, Box 4087, Bartonville, OK 61607

Arms Bookseller, Norm Flayderman, RFD 2, Squash Hollow, New Milford, Conn. 06776

Arms Bookseller, Rutgers, Mark Aziz, 127 Raritan Ave., Highland Park, N.J. 08904

Arms Research, American Arms Co., 1641 Maplecrest Dr., Bloomington, Ind. 47401

Barrel Band Swivels, Phil Judd, 83 E. Park St., Butte, Mont. 59701

Barrel Bedding Device, W. H. Womack, 2124 Meriwether Rd., Shreveport, La. 71108

Bedding Kit, Bisonite Co., Box 84, Buffalo, N.Y. 14217

Bedding Kit, Fenwal, Inc., Resin Systems Div., 400 Main St., Ashland, Mass. 01721

Bench Rest Accessory Case, Walden Leisure Prods., 1040 Matley Lane, Bldg. 4, Reno, NV 89502

Bench Rest Pedestal, Jim Brobst, 299 Poplar, Hamburg, Pa. 19526

Bench Rest Stands, Suter's, 332 Tejon, Colorado Springs, Colo. 80902

Binocular/Camera Harness, Jack Worsfold Assoc., Box 25, Forest Hill, Md. 21050

Bootdryers, Baekgaard Ltd., 1855 Janke Dr., Northbrook, Ill. 60062

Bore Collimator, Alley Supply Co., Box 458, Sonora, Calif. 95370

Bore Collimator, Collins Co., Box 40, Shepherdsville, Ky. 40165

Bore Lamp, Spacetron, Inc., Box 84, Broadview Ill. 60155

Borescope, Eder Inst. Co., 5115 N. Ravenswood Ave., Chicago, Ill. 60640

Bore Sighter, Rifleman's Bore Sighter Co., P.O. Box 1701, Saginaw, Mich. 48605

Breech Plug Wrench, Swaine Machine, 195 O'Connell, Providence, R.I. 02905

Can Thrower, Trius Prod., Box 25, Cleves, O. 45002

Cannons, South Bend Replicas Inc., 61650 Oak Rd., So. Bend, IN 46614 (ctlg. $1)

Capper, Muzzle-Loading, Pat Burke, 3339 Farnsworth Rd., Lapeer, Mich. 48446

Cartridge Boxes, Llanerch Gun Shop, 2800 Township Line, Upper Darby, Pa. 19083

Cartridge Boxes, Shooters Supplies, 1589 Payne Ave., St. Paul, MN 55101

Cartridge Box Labels, Milton Brynin, Box 162, Fleetwood Sta., Mt. Vernon, N.Y. 10552

Cartridge Box Labels, Jasco, Box 49751, Los Angeles, Calif. 90049

Cartridge Box Labels, Peterson Label Co., P.O. Box 186Z, Redding Ridge, CT 06876

Cartridge Carrier, N.H. Schiffman, P.O. Box 7373, Murray, UT 84107

Case Gauge, Plum City Ballistics Range, Box 128, Plum City, Wis. 54761

Chrome Brl. Lining, Marker Mach. Co., Box 426, Charleston, Ill. 61920

Color Hardening, Alamo Heat Treating Co., Box 55345, Houston, Tex. 77055

Cronoscope, Wein Prod. Inc., 115 W. 25th St., Los Angeles, Ca. 90007

Crossbows, Midwest Crossbow Co., 9043 So. Western, Chicago, Ill. 60620

Crow Caller, Wightman Elec. Inc., Box 989, Easton, Md. 21601

Custom Bluing, J. A. Wingert, 124 W. 2nd St., Waynesboro, Pa. 17268

Decoys, Carry-Lite, Inc., 3000 W. Clarke, Milwaukee, Wis. 53245

Decoys, Deeks, Inc., Box 2309, Salt Lake City, Utah 84114

Decoys, G & H Decoy Mfg. Co., P.O. Box 937, Henryetta, Okla. 74437

Decoys, Sports Haven Ltd., Box 19323, Portland, Ore. 97219

Decoys, Tex Wirtz Ent., Inc., 1925 W. Hubbard St., Chicago Ill. 60622

Decoys, Woodstream Corp., Box 327, Lititz, Pa. 17543

Distress Flares, Marsh Coulter Co., 118 Park, Tecumseh, Mich. 49286

Dog House, Canine Pal Sales, 421 E. 39th Ave., Gary, Ind. 46409 (portable)

Dryer, Thermo-Electric, Golden-Rod, (Phinney-Hale, Inc., Box 5286, Oxnard, CA 93030

E-Z Loader, Del Rey Prod., P.O. Box 91561, Los Angeles, CA 90009

Ear-Valv, Sigma Eng. Co., 11320 Burbank Blvd., N. Hollywood, Cal. 91601 (Lee-Sonic)

Emergency Food, Tony Bolton Foods, Micro Dr., Woburn, Mass. 01801

Emergency Food, Chuck Wagon, Micro Dr., Woburn, Mass. 01801

Flares, Colt Industries, Huyshope Ave., Hartford, Conn. 06102

Flares, Goble Assoc., Box 1057, Escondido, Calif. 92025

Flares, Intercontinental Arms, 2222 Barry Ave., Los Angeles, Ca. 90064 (MBA)

Flat Springs, Alamo Heat Treating Co., Box 55345, Houston, Tex. 77055

Game Hoist, Flanders Mfg. Co., Box 33363, Houston, Tex. 77033

Game Hoist, PIC, 3 Chestnut, Suffern, N.Y. 10901

Game Scent, Buck Stop, Inc., 3015 Grow Rd., Stanton, Mi 4888

Game Scent, Pete Rickard, R.D. 1, Carlisle Rd., Box 1002, Cobleskill, N.Y. 12043 (Indian Buck lure)

Gas Pistol, Penguin Ind., Inc., Box 97, Parkesburg, Pa. 19365

Gun Bedding Kit, Resin Div., Fenwal, Inc., 400 Main St., Ashland, Mass. 01721

Gun Jewelry, Sid Bell, Originals, Box 188, Tully, N.Y. 13159

Gun Jewelry, Al Popper, 614 Turnpike St., Stoughton, Mass. 02072

Gun Lock, Bor-Lok Prods., 105 5th St., Arbuckle, CA 95912

Gun Lock, E & C Enterprises, P.O. Box 823, So. Pasadena, CA. 91030

Gun Lock Chain, Lundy Corp., 1123-24 Davenport Bk. Bldg., Davenport, Ia. 52801

Gun Socks Covers, E & C Enterprises, P.O. Box 823, So. Pasadena, CA. 91030

Gun Socks Covers, East-Tenn Mills, Inc., Box 1030, Johnson City, Tenn. 37601

Hollow Pointer, Goerg Ent., 3009 S. Laurel St., Port Angeles, Wash. 98362

Hugger Hooks, Roman Products, Box 891, Golden, Colo. 80401

Hull Bag, D. Titus, 119 Morlyn, Bryn Mawr, Pa. 19010

Hunting Bag, Dan Barr, Rte. 1, Thornville, OH 43076

Hunting Blind, Sports Haven Ltd., Box 19323, Portland, Ore. 97219

Insect Repellent, Armor, Div. of Buck Stop, Inc., 3015 Grow Rd., Stanton, Mich. 48888

Insert Barrels, (22 RF), H. Owen, P.O. Box 774, Sunnyvale, Calif. 94088

Leather Rest-Bags, B. Tuller, 29 Germania, Galeton, Pa. 16922

Lightnin-Loader, Hunter Mfg. Co., Box 2882, Van Nuys, Cal. 91404

Magazine Clip (Colyer), Great Northern Trading Post, 13001 Hwy. 65 N.E., Rte. 4, Anoka, Minn. 55303

Magazine Clips, Amer. Firearms Mfg. Co., Inc., 1200 Warfield, San Antonio, Tex. 78216

Master Lock Co., 2600 N. 32nd St., Milwaukee, WI 53245

Military Museum, Lt. Col. E.H. Hoffman, 768 So. Main St., Woodstock, Va. 22664

MINI Lights, Avery Corp., Box 99, Electra, Tex. 76360

Miniature Guns, C. H. Stoppler, 1426 Walton Ave., N.Y., N.Y. 10452

Monte Carlo Pad, Frank A. Hoppe Div., P.O. Box 97, Parkesburg, Pa. 19365

Multiple Shell Catcher, The I and I Co., 709 Twelfth St., Altoona, PA 16601

Muzzle-Top, Allen Assoc., 7502 Limekiln, Philadelphia, PA 19150 (plastic gun muzzle cap)

Nipple Wrenches, Chopie Mfg. Inc., 531 Copeland Ave., La Crosse, Wis. 54601

Pell Remover, A. Edw. Terpening, 838 W. Darlington Rd., Tarpon Springs, Fla. 33589

Personal Firearms Record Book, Box 201, Park Ridge, Ill. 60068

Portable Bench, Walden Leisure Prods., 1040 Matley Lane, Bldg. 4, Reno, NV 89502

Portable Gun Rest, Central Specialties Co., 630 Northwest Hwy., Chicago, Ill. 60631 (Gun-Rak)

Porto-Bench, Universal Std. Prods., 926 N. Memorial, Racine, WI 53404

Powder Horns, Thos. F. White, 5801 Westchester Ct., Worthington, O. 43085

Powder Storage Magazine, C & M Gunworks, 4201 36th Ave., Moline, IL 61265

Pressure Testg. Machine, M. York, 19381 Keymar Way, Gaithersburg, MD 20760

Ransom Handgun Rests, C'Arco, P.O. Box 2043, San Bernardino, CA 92406

Rifle Slings, Bianchi, 212 W. Foothill Blvd., Monrovia, Cal. 91016

RIG, NRA Scoring Plug, Rig Prod. Co., Box 279, Oregon, Ill. 60161

Rubber Cheekpiece, W. H. Lodewick, 2816 N. E. Halsey, Portland, Ore. 97232

Rust Bluing/Browning, L.B. Thompson, 568 E. School Ave., Salem, O. 44460

Safe-T-Shell, Inc., 4361 Woodhall Rd., Columbus. O. 43221 (shotgun)

Safeties, Williams Gun Sight Co., 7389 Lapeer Rd., Davison, Mich. 48423

Salute Cannons, Naval Co., Rt. 611, Doylestown, Pa. 18901

Save-Bore, Saunders Sptg. Gds., 338 Somerset St., N. Plainfield, NJ 07060

Scope Safeties, W. H. Lodewick, 2816 N.E. Halsey, Portland, Ore. 97232

Scrimshaw Engraving, C. Milton Barringer, 217-2nd Isle N., Port Richey, FL 33568

Scrimshaw Engraving, A. Douglas Jacobs, Box 1236, Cutchogue, NY 11935

Sharpening Stones, Russell's Arkansas Oilstones, 1705 Hiway 71N., Springdale, AR 72764

Shell Cracker, Stoneco, Inc., 5401 No. Federal Blvd., Denver, Colo. 80200

Shell Shrinker Mfg. Co., Box 6143, Lubbock, Tex. 79413

Shooting Bench/Porto, Universal Standard Prods. Inc., 926 N. Memorial Dr., Racine, WI 53404

Shooting Coats, 10-X Mfg. Co., 100 S. W. 3rd, Des Moines, Iowa 50309

Shooting/Testing Glasses, Clear View Sports Shields, P.O. Box 255, Wethersfield, Conn. 06107

Shooting Glasses, Bausch & Lomb, Inc., 635 St. Paul St., Rochester, NY 14602

Shooting Glasses, Bushnell Optical Corp., 2828 E. Foothill Blvd., Pasadena, CA 91107

Shooting Glasses, M. B. Dinsmore, Box 21, Wyomissing, Pa. 19610

Shooting Glasses, Mitchell's, Box 539, Waynesville, Mo. 65583

Shooting Glasses, Ray-O-Vac, Willson Prods. Div., P.O. Box 622, Reading, PA 19603

Shooting Ranges, Shooting Equip. Inc., 2001 N. Parkside Ave., Chicago, Ill. 60639

Shotgun Recoil Kit, CHB, 3063 Hiram, Wichita, Kan. 67217

Shotgun Sight, bi-ocular, Trius Prod., Box 25, Cleves, O. 45002

Shotshell Catcher, Old Mill Trap & Skeet, 300 Mill Ridge Rd., Secaucus, N.J. 07094 (Seymour)

Shotshell Pouches, Filmat Enterpr., Inc., 200 Market St., East Paterson, N.J. 07407

Sighting-In-Device, F & H Machining, 4645 Cambio Ct., Fremont, CA 94536

Silver Grip Caps, Bill Dyer, P.O. Box 75255, Oklahoma City, Okla. 73107

Snap Caps, Filmat, 200 Market, East Paterson, N.J. 07407

Snowshoes, Sportsmen Prod. Inc., Box 1082, Boulder, Colo. 80302

Springfield Safety Pin, B-Square Co., P.O. Box 11281, Ft. Worth, Tex. 76110

Springs, W. Wolff Co., Box 232, Ardmore, Pa. 19003

Stock-Lo-Kater, Bill Matthews Co., 5004 Encinita Ave., Temple City, Ca. 91780

Supersound, Edmund Scientific Co., 101 E. Gloucester Pike, Barrington, NJ 08007 (safety device)

Swivels, Michaels, P.O. Box 13010, Portland, Ore. 97213

Swivels, Sile Dist., 7 Centre Market Pl., New York, N.Y. 10013

Swivels, Williams Gun Sight Co., 7389 Lapeer Rd., Davison, Mich. 48423

Targ-Dots, Peterson Label Co., P.O. Box 186Z, Redding Ridge, CT 06876

Taxidermy, D. Anderson, 140 E. 13800 South, Draper, UT 84020

Taxidermy, Jack Atcheson, 2309 Hancock Ave., Butte, Mont. 59701

Taxidermy, Clearfield, 603 Hanna St., Clearfield, Pa. 16830

Taxidermy, Jonas Bros., 1037 Broadway, Denver, Colo. 80203

Taxidermy, Knopp Bros., N. 6715 Division St., Spokane, Wash. 99208

Taxidermy, Mac's, 417 N. Grand Ave., Waukesha, Wis. 53186

Teenuts, Dot Product Supply Co., 10544 Lunt Ave., Rosemont, Ill. 60018

Trap buttplates, Albright Prod. Co., P.O. Box 695, Bishop, CA 93514

Trap, claybird, Deerback Prod., 8239 Hayle Ave., Dallas, Tex. 75227

Trap, claybird, Outers Lab., Inc., Box 37, Onalaska, Wis. 54650

Trap claybird, Trius Prod., Box 25, Cleves, O. 45002

Triggers, Canjar Rifle Acc., 500 E. 45th St., Denver, Colo. 80216

Trigger Guards, Beesley Mfg. Co., P.O. Box 17075, Salt Lake City, Utah 84117 (Bee-Safe)

Trigger Guards, Michaels, P.O. Box 13010, Portland, Ore. 97213

Trigger Pull Gauge,Ohaus, 29 Hanover Rd., Florham Park, NJ 07932

Trigger Release, Schwab Gun Shop, 1103 E. Bigelow, Findlay, O. 45840

Trigger Shoe, Flaigs, Babcock Blvd., Millvale, Pa. 15209

Trigger Shoe, Pacific Tool Co., Box 4495, Lincoln, Neb. 68504

Trigger Shoe, Melvin Tyler, 1326 W. Britton, Oklahoma City, Okla. 73114

Trophies, L. G. Balfour Co., Attleboro, Mass. 02703

Trophies, Blackinton & Co., 140 Commonwealth, Attleboro Falls, Mass. 12763

Trophies, F. H. Noble & Co., 559 W. 59th St., Chicago, Ill. 60621

Universal 3-shot Shotgun Plug, LanDav Custom Guns, 7213 Lee Highway, Falls Church, VA 22046

Worldhunting Info., Jack Atcheson, 2309 Hancock Ave., Butte, Mont. 59701

World Hunting Info., Denver Jonas Bros., 1037 Broadway, Denver, CO 80203

MUZZLE LOADING BARRELS OR EQUIPMENT

Luther Adkins, Box 281, Shelbyville, Ind. 47176 (breech plugs)

Armoury, Inc., Rte. 25, New Preston, Conn. 06777

Barney's Cannons, Inc., 61650 Oak Rd., South Bend, IN 46614 (ctlg. $1)

Dan Barr, Rte. 1, Thornville, OH 43076 (hunting bag)

Henry S. Beverage, New Gloucester, Me. 04260 (brass bullet mould)

John Bivins, Jr., 446 So. Main, Winston-Salem, N.C. 27101

Jesse F. Booher, 2751 Ridge Ave., Dayton, Ohio 45414

G. S. Bunch, 7735 Garrison, Hyattsville, Md. 20784 (flask repair)

Pat Burke, 3339 Farnsworth Rd., Lapeer, Mich. 48446 (capper)

Challanger Mfg. Co., 118 Pearl St., Mt. Vernon, NY 10550 (Hopkins & Allen)

Caution Tool Co., Scout Rd., Southbury, CT 06488

Cherry Corners Gun Shop, Rte. 1, 8010 Lafayette Rd., Lodi, Ohio 44254

Cornwall Bridge Gun Shop, Cornwall Bridge, CT 06745

Earl T. Cureton, Rte. 6, 7017 Pine Grove Rd., Knoxville, Tenn. 37914 (powder horns)

John N. Dangelzer, 3056 Frontier Pl. N.E., Albuquerque, N. Mex. 87106 (powder flasks)

Ted Fellowes, 9245 16th Ave. S.W., Seattle, Wash. 98106

Firearms Imp. & Exp. Corp., 2470 N.W. 21st St., Miami, Fla. 33142

Golden Age Arms Co., 657 High St., Worthington, Ohio 43085 (ctlg. $1)

A. R. Goode, R.D. 1, Box 84, Thurmont, MD 21788

Green River Forge, 4326 120th Ave. S.E., Bellevue, WA 98006 (Forge-Fire flints)

Virgil W. Hartley, 1602 S. Hunter Rd., Indianapolis, IN 46239 (ML pouch)

International M. L. Parts Co., 19453 Forrer, Detroit, MI 48235

JJJJ Ranch, Wm. Large, Rte. 1, Ironton, Ohio 45638

Art LeFeuvre, 1003 Hazel Ave., Deerfield, Ill. 60015 (antique gun restoring)

Kindig's Log Cabin Sport Shop, R.D. 1, Box 275, Lodi, OH 44254

Les' Gun Shop (Les Bauska), Box 511, Kalispell, Mont, 59901

Lever Arms Serv. Ltd., 771 Dunsmuir, Vancouver 1, B.C., Canada

J. Lewis Arms Mfg., 3931 Montgomery Rd., Cincinnati, Ohio 45212 (pistol)

McKeown's Guns, R.R. 1, Pekin, IL 61554 (E-Z load rev. stand)

Maryland Gun Exchange Inc., Rt. 40 West, RD 5, Frederick, MD 21701

Maywood Forge, Foley, MN 56329 (cannons)

Jos. W. Mellott, 334 Rockhill Rd., Pittsburgh, Pa. 15243 (barrel blanks)

W. L. Mowrey Gun Works, Inc., Box 711, Olney, Tex. 73674

Muzzle Loaders Supply Co., Rte. 25, New Preston, CT 06777

Numrich Corp., W. Hurley, N.Y. 12491 (powder flasks)

R. Parris & Son, R.D. 5, Box 61, Gettysburg, Pa. 17325 (barrels)

Penna. Rifle Works, 319 E. Main St., Ligonier, Pa. 15658 (ML guns, parts)

Fred Renard, Rte. 1, Symsonia, Ky. 42082 (ML)

H. M. Schoeller, 569 So. Braddock Ave., Pittsburgh, Pa. 15221

Shilo Ind., Inc., 173 Washington Pl., Hasbrouck Heights, NJ 07604 (4-cavity mould)

C. E. Siler, 181 Sandhill School, Asheville, N.C., 28806 (flint locks)

Thos. F. White, 5801 Westchester Ct., Worthington, O. 43085 (powder horn)

Lou Williamson, 129 Stonegate Ct., Bedford, TX 76021

PISTOLSMITHS

Alamo Heat Treating, Box 55345, Houston, Tex. 77055

Allen Assoc., 7448 Limekiln Pike, Philadelphia, Pa. 19138 (speed-cock lever for 45 ACP)

Bain and Davis Sptg. Gds., 559 W. Las Tunas Dr., San Gabriel, Cal. 91776

Bar-Sto Precision Machine, 633 So. Victory Blvd., Burbank, CA 91502 (S.S. bbls. f. 45 Acp)

Behlert & Freed, Inc., 33 Herning Ave., Cranford. N.J. 07016 (short actions)

R. M. Champlin, Stanyan Hill, Wentworth, N.H. 03282

F. Bob Chow, Gun Shop, 3185 Mission, San Francisco, Calif. 94110

J.E. Clark, Rte. 2, Box 22A, Keithville, LA 71047

Custom Gunshop, 33 Herning Ave., Cranford, N.J. 07016

Day Arms Corp., 7515 Stagecoach Lane, San Antonio, Tex. 78227

Alton S. Dinan, Jr., P.O. Box 6674, Canaan, Conn. 06018

Dominic DiStefano, 4303 Friar Lane, Colorado Springs, CO 80907 (accurizing)

Dan Dwyer, 915 W. Washington, San Diego, Calif. 92103

Giles' 45 Shop, Rt. 1, Box 47, Odessa, Fla. 33556

H. H. Harris, 1237 So. State, Chicago, Ill. 60605

Gil Hebard Guns, Box 1, Knoxville, Ill. 61448

Rudy Marent, 9711 Tiltree, Houston, Tex. 77034 (Hammerli)

Maryland Gun Exchange, Inc., Rte. 40 W., RD 5, Frederick, Md. 21701

Match Arms Co., 831 Mary St., Springdale, Pa. 15144

Pachmayr Gun Works, 1220 S. Grand Ave., Los Angeles, Calif. 90015

Geo. E. Sheldon, 7 Balsam St., Keene, N.H. 03431

R. L. Shockey Guns, Inc., 1614 S. Choctaw, E. Reno, Okla. 73036

Silver Dollar Guns, 7 Balsam St., Keene, N.H. 03431 (45 auto only)

Sportsmens Equipmt. Co., 915 W. Washington, San Diego, Calif. 92103

A. D. Swenson's 45 Shop, 3223 W. 145th St., Gardena, Calif. 90249

Dave Woodruff, 116 Stahl Ave., Wilmington Manor, New Castle, DE 19720

REBORING AND RERIFLING

A & M Rifle Co., Box 1713, Prescott, AZ 86301

P.O. Ackley Inc., 5448 Riley Lane, Salt Lake City, UT 84107

Bain & Davis Sptg. Gds., 559 W. Las Tunas Dr., San Gabriel, Calif. 91776

Carpenter's Gun Works, Gunshop Rd., Box C, Plattekill, N.Y. 12568

Fuller Gun Shop, Cooper Landing, Alaska 99572

Ward Koozer, Box 18, Walterville, Ore. 97489

Les' Gun Shop, Box 511, Kalispell, Mont. 59901

Morgan's Cust. Reboring, 707 Union Ave., Grants Pass, OR 97526

Nu-Line Guns, 3727 Jennings Rd., St. Louis, Mo. 63121

Al Petersen, Riverhurst, Saskatchewan, Canada

Schuetzen Gun Works, 1226 Prairie Rd., Colorado Springs, Colo. 80909

Sharon Rifle Barrel Co., P.O. Box 106, Kalispell, Mont. 59901

Siegrist Gun Shop, R.R. #1, Whittemore, MI 48770

Snapp's Gunshop, 6911 E. Washington Rd., Clare, Mich. 48617

R. Southgate, Rt. 2, Franklin, Tenn. 37064 (Muzzleloaders)

J. W. Van Patten, Box 145, Foster Hill, Milford, Pa. 18337

Robt. G. West, 6626 So. Lincoln, Littleton, Colo. 80120

RELOADING TOOLS AND ACCESSORIES

Acme Ind. Inc., Box 101, Kaukauna, WI 54130 (loader & wingtraps)

Alcan, (See: Smith & Wesson-Fiocchi, Inc.)

Alpha-Molykote, Dow Corning Corp., 45 Commerce, Trumbull, Ct. 06601

Anchor Alloys, Inc., 966 Meeker Ave., Brooklyn, N.Y. 11222 (chilled shot)

Anchor Plastics, Inc., P.O. Box 300, Logansport, IN 46947

Anderson Mfg. Co., Royal, Ia. 51357 (Shotshell Trimmers)

Aurands, 229 E. 3rd St., Lewistown, Pa. 17044

Automatic Reloading Equipment, Inc., 1602 Babcock St., Costa Mesa, CA 92627

B-Square Eng. Co., Box 11281, Ft. Worth, Tex. 76110

Bahler Die Shop, Box 386, Florence, Ore. 97439

Bair Machine Co., Box 4407, Lincoln, Neb. 68504

Bill Ballard, P.O. Box 656, Billings, Mont. 59103

Belding & Mull, P.O. Box 428, Philipsburg, Pa. 16866

Belmont Prods., Rte. 1, Friendsville, TN 37737 (lead cutter)

H. S. Beverage, New Gloucester, Me. 04260 (brass bullet mould)

Blackhawk SAA East, C2274 POB, Loves Park, Ill. 61111

Blackhawk SAA West, Box 285, Hiawatha, KS 66434

Bonanza Sports, Inc., 412 Western Ave., Faribault, Minn. 55021

Gene Bowlin, 3602 Hill Ave., Snyder, Tex. 79549 (arbor press)

Brown Precision Co., 5869 Indian Ave., San Jose, Calif. 95123 (Little Wiggler)

A. V. Bryant, 72 Whiting Rd., East Hartford, Ct. 06424 (Nutmeg Universal Press)

C-H Tool & Die Corp., Box L, Owen, Wis. 54460

Camdex, Inc., 18619 W. Seven Mile Rd., Detroit, Mich. 48219

Carbide Die & Mfg. Co., Box 226, Covina, Calif. 91706

Carter Gun Works, 2211 Jefferson Pk. Ave., Charlottesville, Va. 22903

Cascade Cartridge, Inc., (See Omark)

Chellife Corp., 607 Spring Valley Rd., Richardson, TX 75080

Clymer Mfg. Co., 14241 W. 11 Mile Rd., Oak Park, MI 48237 (½-jack. swaging dies)

Lester Coats, 416 Simpson St., No. Bend, Ore. 97459 (core cutter)

Cole's Acku-Rite Prod., P.O. Box 25, Kennedy, N.Y. 14747 (die racks)

Container Development Corp., 424 Montgomery St., Watertown, Wis. 53094

Cooper Engineering, 612 E. 20th, Houston, Tex. 77008

Cooper-Woodward, Box 972, Riverside, Calif. 92502 (Perfect Lube)

Design & Development Co., 1002 N. 64th St., Omaha, Neb. 68132

J. Dewey Gun Co., Clinton Corners, N.Y. 12514 (bullet spinner)

Diverter Arms, Inc., 6520 Rampart St., Houston, TX 77036 (bullet puller)

Division Lead Co., 7742 W. 61st Pl., Summit, Ill. 60502

Eagle Products Co., 1520 Adelia Ave., So. El Monte, Cal. 91733

W. H. English, 4411 S. W. 100th, Seattle, Wash. 98146 (Paktool)

Ellwood Epps Sptg. Goods, 80 King St., Clinton, Ont., Canada

Farmer Bros. Mfg. Co., 1102 Washington St., Eldora, IA 50627 (Lage wads)

The Fergusons, 27 W. Chestnut St., Farmingdale, N.Y. 11735

Fitz, Box 49797, Los Angeles, Calif. 90049 (Fitz Flipper)

Flambeau Plastics, 801 Lynn, Baraboo, Wis. 53913

Forster-Appelt Mfg. Co., Inc., 82 E. Lanark Ave., Lanark, Ill. 61046

Gene's Gun Shop, 3602 Hill Ave., Snyder, Tex. 79549 (arbor press)

Goerg Enterprises, 3009 S. Laurel, Port Angeles, WA 98362 (hollow pointer)

Gopher Shooter's Supply, Box 246, Faribault, Minn. 55021

Griffin Shooter's Supplies, 7801-A9 Hillmont, Houston, TX 77040 (Electric operator for MEC tools)

The Gun Clinic, 81 Kale St., Mahtomedi, Minn. 55115

Hart Products, 401 Montgomery St., Nescopeck, Pa. 18635

Ed Hart, U.S. Rte. 15, Cohocton, NY 14826 (Meyer shotgun slugs)

Frank A. Hemsted, Box 281, Sunland, Cal. 91040 (swage dies)

Hensley & Gibbs, Box 10, Murphy, Ore. 97533

E. C. Herkner Co., Box 5007, Boise, Ida. 83702

Herter's Inc., RR1, Waseca, Minn. 56093

B. E. Hodgdon, Inc., 7710 W. 50 Hiway, Shawnee Mission, Kans. 66202

Hollywood Reloading, see: Whitney Sales, Inc.

Hulme Firearm Serv., Box 83, Millbrae, Calif. 94030 (Star case feeder)

Hunter Bradlee Co., 2800 Routh St., Dallas, TX 75201 (powder measure)

Independent Mach. & Gun Shop, 1416 N. Hayes, Pocatello, Ida. 83201

JASCO, Box 49751, Los Angeles, Calif. 90049

J & G Rifle Ranch, Turner, Mont. 59542 (case tumblers)

Javelina Products, Box 337, San Bernardino, Cal. 92402 (Alox beeswax)

Kexplore, Box 22084, Houston, Tex. 77027

Kuharsky Bros., 2425 W. 12th, Erie, Pa. 16500 (primer pocket cleaner)

Kush Plastics, P.O. Box 366, Palatine, IL 60067 (shotshell wads)

Lachmiller Div. of Peng. Ind., P.O. Box 97, Parkesburg, Pa. 19365

Lage universal shotshell wad, see: Farmer Bros.

LanDav, 7213 Lee Highway, Falls Church, VA 22046 (X-15 bullet puller)

Lee Engineering, 21 E. Wisconsin St., Hartford, Wis. 53027

Leon's Reloading Service, 3945 No. 11 St., Lincoln, Neb. 68521

L. L. F. Die Shop, 1281 Highway 99 N., Eugene, Ore. 97402

Ljutic Industries, 918 N. 5th Ave., Yakima, Wash. 98902

Lock's Phila. Gun Exch., 6700 Rowland, Philadelphia, Pa. 19149

J. T. Loos, P.O. Box 41, Pomfret, CT. 06258 (primer pocket cleaner)

Lyman Gun Sight Products, Middlefield, Conn. 06455

McKillen & Heyer, Box 627, Willoughby, O. 44094 (case gauge)

Paul McLean, 2670 Lakeshore Blvd., W., Toronto 14, Ont., Canada (Universal Cartridge Holder)

Pat B. McMillan, 1828 E. Campo Bello Dr., Phoenix, Ariz. 85022

MTM Molded Prod., 5680 Webster St., Dayton, OH 45414

Magma Eng. Co., P.O. Box 881, Chandler, AZ 85224

Mayville Eng. Co., Box 267, Mayville, Wis. 53050 (shotshell loader)

Merit Gun Sight Co., P.O. Box 995, Sequim, Wash. 98382

Minnesota Shooters Supply, 1915 E. 22nd St., Minneapolis, Minn. 55404

Murdock Lead Co., Box 5298, Dallas, Tex. 75222

National Lead Co., Box 831, Perth Amboy, N.J. 08861

Normington Co., Box 156, Rathdrum, Ida. 83858 (powder baffles)

John Nuler, 12869 Dixie, Detroit, Mich. 48239 (primer seating tool)

Ohaus Scale Corp., 29 Hanover Rd., Florham Park, N.J. 07932

Omark-CCI, Inc., Box 856, Lewiston, Ida. 83501

Pacific Tool Co., Box 4495, Lincoln, Neb. 68504

C. W. Paddock, 1589 Payne Ave., St. Paul, Minn. 55101 (cartridge boxes)

Perfection Die Co., 1614 S. Choctaw, El Reno, Okla. 73036

Personal Firearms Record Book, Box 201, Park Ridge, Ill. 60068

Phelps Reloader Inc., Box 4004, E. Orange N.J. 07019

Ferris Pindell, R.R. 3, Box 205, Connersville, IN 47331 (bullet spinner)

Plum City Ballistics Range, Box 128, Plum City, Wis. 54761

Ponsness-Warren, Inc., P.O. Box 861, Eugene, OR 97401

Potter Eng. Co., 1410 Santa Ana Dr., Dunedin, Fla. 33528

Marian Powley, 19 Sugarplum Rd., Levittown, Pa. 10956

Quinetics Corp., 3740 Colony Dr., San Antonio, Tx. 78230 (kinetic bullet puller)

RCBS, Inc., Box 1919, Oroville, Calif. 95965

Redco, Box 15523, Salt Lake City, Utah 84115

Redding-Hunter, Inc., 114 Starr Rd., Cortland, N.Y. 13045

Remco, 1404 Whitesboro St., Utica, N.Y. 13502 (shot caps)

B. T. Reynolds, 835-B Arcadia Ave., Arcadia, CA 91006 (bullet gauge)

Rifle Ranch, Rte. 1, Prescott, Ariz, 86301

Rochester Lead Works, Rochester, N.Y. 14608 (lead-wire)

Rorschach Precision Prods., P.O. Box 1613, Irving, Tex. 75060

Rotex Mfg. Co. (see Texan)

Ruhr-American Corp., So. East Hwy. 55, Glenwood, Minn. 56334

SAECO Rel. Inc., P.O. Box 778, Carpinteria, Calif. 93013

Savage Arms Co., Westfield, Mass. 01085

Scientific Lubricants Co., 3753 Lawrence Ave., Chicago, Ill. 60625

Shoffstalls Mfg. Co., 740 Ellis Place, E. Aurora N.Y. 14052

Shooters Accessory Supply, Box 250, N. Bend, Ore. 97459 (SAS)

Shooters Serv. & Dewey, Inc., Clinton Corners, N.Y. 12514 (SS&D) (bullet spinner)

Sil's Gun Prod., 490 Sylvan Dr., Washington, Pa. 15301 (K-spinner)

Jerry Simmons, 713 Middlebury St., Goshen, Ind. 46526 (Pope de- & recapper)

Rob. B. Simonson, Rte. 7, 2129 Vanderbilt Rd., Kalamazoo, Mich. 49002

Smith & Wesson-Fiocchi, Inc., 3640 Seminary Rd., Alton, IL 62002

Star Machine Works, 418 10th Ave., San Diego, Calif. 92101

Sullivan Arms Corp., see: Anchor Plastics

Texan Reloaders, Inc., P.O. Box 5355, Dallas, Tex. 75222

VAMCO, Box 67, Vestal, N.Y. 13850

W. S. Vickerman, 505 W. 3rd Ave., Ellensburg, Wash. 98926

Walker Mfg. Inc., 8296 So. Channel, Harsen's Island, MI 48028 (Berdan decapper)

Weatherby, Inc., 2781 Firestone Blvd., South Gate, Calif. 90280

Webster Scale Mfg. Co., Box 188, Sebring, Fla. 33870

Whit's Shooting Stuf, 2121 Stampede Ave., Cody, Wyo. 82414

Whitney Cartridge Co., P.O. Box 608, Cortez, CO 81321 (shotshells)

Whitney Sales, Inc., P.O. 875, Reseda, CA 91335 (Hollywood)

L. E. Wilson, Inc., Box 324, Cashmere, Wash. 98815

Xelex, Ltd., Hawksbury, Ont., Canada (powder)

Zenith Ent., Rt. 1, Box 52z, Del Mar, Calif. 92014

A. Zimmerman, 127 Highland Trail, Denville, N.J. 07834 (case trimmer)

RIFLE BARREL MAKERS

A & M Rifle Co., Box 1713, Prescott, AZ 86301

P.O. Ackley, Inc., 5448 Riley Lane, Salt Lake City, UT 84107

Apex Rifle Co., 7628 San Fernando, Sun Valley, Calif. 91352

Christy Gun Works, 875 57th St., Sacramento, Calif. 95819

Clerke Prods., 2219 Main St., Santa Monica, Calif. 90405

Cuthbert Gun Shop, 715 So. 5th, Coos Bay, Ore. 97420

Darr's Rifle Shop, 2309 Black Rd., Joliet, IL 60435

J. Dewey Gun Co., Clinton Corners, N.Y. 12514

Douglas Barrels, Inc., 5504 Big Tyler Rd., Charleston, W. Va. 25312

Federal Firearms Co., Inc., Box 145, Oakdale, Pa. 15071 (Star bbls., actions)

A. R. Goode, R.D. 1, Box 84, Thurmont, MD 21788

Hart Rifle Barrels, Inc., RD 2, Lafayette, N.Y. 13084

Wm. H. Hobaugh, Box 657, Philipsburg, Mont. 59858

Hoffman Rifle Barrel Co., Bucklin, Kans. 67834

Intern'l Casting Co., 19453 Forrer, Detroit, Mich. 48235

Johnson Automatics, Box 306, Hope Valley, R.I. 02832

Les' Gun Shop, Box 511, Kalispell, Mont. 59901

McGowen Rifle Barrels, Rte. 3, St. Anne, Ill. 60964

D. M. Manley, 295 Main St., Brookville, PA 15825

Nauman Gun Shop, 1048 S. 5th, Douglas, Wyo. 82633

Nu-Line Guns, Inc., 3727 Jennings Rd., St. Louis, Mo. 63121

Numrich Arms, W. Hurley, N.Y. 12491

R. Paris & Son, R.D. 5, Box 61, Gettysburg, Pa. 17325

Rheinmetall (see John Weir)

SS & D, Inc., Clinton Corners, N.Y. 12514 (cold-formed bbls.)

Sanders Cust. Gun Serv., 2358 Tyler Lane, Louisville, Ky. 40205

Sharon Rifle Barrel Co., P.O. Box 106, Kalispell, Mont. 59901

Ed Shilen Rifles, 4510 Harrington Rd., Irving, Tex. 75060

Titus Barrel & Gun Co., Box 151, Heber City, Ut. 84032

John E. Weir, 3304 Norton Ave., Independence, Mo. 64052

Wilson Arms, Box 364, Stony Creek, Branford, Conn. 06405

RIFLE RESTS

E. L. Beecher, 2155 Demington Dr., Cleveland Hgts., O. 44106

Cole's Acku-Rite Prod., Box 25, Kennedy, N.Y. 14747

Frontier Arms, Inc., 420 E. Riding Club Rd., Cheyenne, Wyo. 82001

The Gun Case, 11035 Maplefield, El Monte, Cal. 91733

Harris Engr., Inc., Box 305, Fraser, Mich. 48026 (bi-pods)

Rob. W. Hart & Son, 401 Montgomery St., Nescopeck, Pa. 18635

Rec. Prods., Res., Inc., 158 Franklin Ave., Ridgewood, N.J. 07450 (Butts Bipod)

Ten Ring Mfg. Co., Box 157, New City, N.Y. 10956 (Rifle-Mate)

Basil Tuller, 29 Germania, Galeton, PA 16922 (Protecktor sandbags)

W. H. Womack, 2124 Meriwether Rd., Shreveport, La. 71108

SCOPES, MOUNTS, ACCESSORIES, OPTICAL EQUIPMENT

Alley Supply Co., P.O. Box 458, Sonora, Calif. 95370 (Scope collimator)

American Import Co., 1167 Mission, San Francisco, Calif. 94103

Anderson & Co., 1203 Broadway, Yakima, Wash. 98902 (lens cap)

Ball-One Buck Scope Lens Cover, Box 426, Midway City, CA 92655

Bausch & Lomb Inc., 635 St. Paul St., Rochester, N.Y. 14602

Bennett, 561 Delaware, Delmar, N.Y. 12054 (mounting wrench)

Bridge Mount Co., Box 3344, Lubbock, Tex. 79410 (one-piece target mts.)

Browning Arms, Rt. 4, Box 624-B, Arnold, Mo. 63010

Maynard P. Buehler, Inc., 17 Orinda Highway, Orinda, Calif. 94563

Bullitco, Box 40, Shepherdsville, Ky. 40165 (Scope collimator)

D. P. Bushnell & Co., Inc., 2828 E. Foothill Blvd., Pasadena, Calif. 91107

Chilford Arms Mfg. Co., 9 First St., San Francisco, Calif. 94105

Kenneth Clark, 18738 Highway 99, Madera, Calif. 93637

Collins Co., Box 40, Shepherdsville, Ky. 40165 (Scope collimator)

Colt's, Hartford, Conn. 06102

Compass Instr. & Optical Co., Inc., 104 E 25th St., New York, N.Y. 10010

Conetrol, Hwy 123 South, Seguin, Tex. 78155

Continental Arms Corp., 697-5th Ave., New York, N.Y. 10022 (Nickel)

Davis Optical Co., P.O. Box 6, Winchester, Ind. 47934

Del-Sports, Main St., Margaretville, N.Y. 12455 (Kahles)

Diana Imports, Main St., Margaretville, N.Y. 12455 (Habicht)

Don's Gun Shop, 128 Ruxton, Manitou Springs, Colo. 80829 (claw mtg. rings)

Duo Mount see: Firearms Service

Firearms Service, 2 Lewelling Blvd., San Lorenzo, CA 94580

Flaig's, Babcock Blvd., Millvale, Pa. 15209

Freeland's Scope Stands, Inc. 3734 14th, Rock Island, Ill. 61201

Bert Friedberg & Co., 820 Mission St., San Francisco, Cal. 94103

Griffin & Howe, Inc., 589-8th Ave., New York, N.Y. 10017

E. C. Herkner Co., Box 5007, Boise, Idaho 83702

Herter's Inc., Waseca, Minn. 56093

J. B. Holden Co., Box H-1495, Plymouth, Mich. 48170

The Hutson Corp., P.O. 1127, Arlington, Tex. 76010

Hy-Score Arms Corp., 200 Tillary St., Brooklyn, N.Y. 11201

Paul Jaeger, 211 Leedom St., Jenkintown, Pa. 19046 (Nickel)

Jana Intl. Co., Box 1107, Denver, Colo. 80201

Jason Empire, 1211 Walnut, Kansas City, Mo. 64106

Kesselring Gun Shop, 400 Pacific Hiway 99 No, Burlington, Wash. 98283

Kuharsky Bros., 2425 W. 12th St., Erie, Pa. 16500

Kwik-Site, 27367 Michigan, Inkster, Mich. 48141 (rings)

LanDav, 7213 Lee Highway, Falls Church, VA 22046 (steel leverlock side mt.)

T. K. Lee, Box 2123, Birmingham, Ala. 35201 (reticles)

E. Leitz, Inc., Rockleigh, N.J. 07647

Leupold & Stevens Inc., P.O. Box 688, Beaverton, Ore. 97005

Jake Levin and Son, Inc., 1211 Walnut, Kansas City, Mo. 64106

Lyman Gun Sight Products, Middlefield, Conn. 06455

Marble Arms Co., 1120 Superior St., Gladstone, Mich. 49837

Marlin Firearms Co., 100 Kenna Dr., New Haven, Conn. 06473

O. F. Mossberg & Sons, Inc., 7 Grasso Ave., North Haven, Conn. 06473

Normark Corp., 1710 E. 78th St., Minneapolis, Minn. 55423 (Singlepoint)

Numrich Arms, West Hurley, N.Y. 12491

Nydar Div., Swain Nelson Co., Box 45, Glenview, Ill. 60025 (shotgun sight)
PGS, Peters' Inc., 622 Gratiot Ave., Saginaw, Mich. 48602 (scope shields)
Pachmayr Gun Works, 1220 S. Grand Ave., Los Angeles, Calif. 90015
Pacific Tool Co., Box 4495, Lincoln, Neb. 68504
Ed Paul's Sptg. Goods, Inc., 172 Flatbush Ave., Brooklyn, N.Y. 11217 (Tops)
Pickering Co., 2110 Walnut, Unionville, Mo. 63565
Precise Imports Corp., 3 Chestnut, Suffern, N.Y. 10901 (PIC)
Premier Reticles, Ocala, Fla. 32670
Ranging Inc., P.O. Box 9106, Rochester, N.Y. 14625
Realist, Inc., N. 93 W. 16288, Megal Dr., Menomonee Falls, Wis. 53051
Redfield Gun Sight Co., 5800 E. Jewell Ave., Denver, Colo. 80222
S & K Mfg. Co., Box 247, Pittsfield, Pa. 16340 (Instamount)
Sanders Cust. Gun Serv., 2358 Tyler Lane, Louisville, Ky. 40205 (MSW)
Savage Arms, Westfield, Mass. 01085
Scope Inst. Co., 25-20 Brooklyn-Queens Expressway West, Woodside, N.Y. 11377
Sears, Roebuck & Co., 825 S. St. Louis, Chicago, Ill. 60607
Selsi Co., 40 Veterans Blvd., Carlstadt, N.J. 07072
W. H. Siebert, 22443 S.E. 56th Pl., Issaquah, Wn. 98027
Singlepoint (see Normark)
Southern Precision Inst. Co., 3419B Commerce St., San Antonio, Tex. 78215
Stoeger Arms Co., 55 Ruta Ct., S. Hackensack, N.J. 07606
Swift Instruments, Inc., 952 Dorchester Ave., Boston, Mass. 02125
Tasco, 1075 N.W. 71st, Miami, Fla. 33138
Thompson-Center Arms, P.O. Box 2405, Rochester, N.H. 03867 (handgun scope)
Tradewinds, Inc., Box 1191, Tacoma, Wash. 98401
John Unertl Optical Co., 3551-5 East St., Pittsburgh, Pa. 15214
United Binocular Co., 9043 S. Western Ave., Chicago, Ill. 60620
Universal Firearms Corp., 3746 E. 10th Ct., Hialeah, Fla. 33013
Vissing Co., Box 437, Idaho Falls, Idaho 83401 (lens cap)
H. P. Wasson, Box 181, Netcong, N.J. 07857 (eyeglass apertures)
Weatherby's, 2781 Firestone, South Gate, Calif. 90280
W. R. Weaver Co., 7125 Industrial Ave., El Paso, Tex. 79915
Williams Gun Sight Co., 7389 Lapeer Rd., Davison, Mich. 48423
Carl Zeiss Inc., 444 Fifth Ave., New York, N.Y. 10018 (Hensoldt)

STOCKS (Commercial and Custom)

Abe-Van Horn, 5124 Huntington Dr., Los Angeles, CA 90032
Ahlman's Inc., R.R. 1, Box 20, Morristown, MN 55052
R. E. Anderson, 706 So. 23rd St., Laramie, Wyo. 82070
Dale P. Andrews, 7114 So. Albion, Littleton, Colo. 80120
R. J. Anton, 1016 Riehl St., Waterloo, Ia. 50703
Jim Baiar, Rt. 1-B, Box 352, Columbia Falls, Mont. 59912
Joe J. Balickie, Custom Stocks, 6108 Deerwood Pl., Raleigh, N.C. 27607
Bartas, Rte. 1, Box 129-A, Cato, Wis. 54206
John Bianchi, 212 W. Foothill Blvd., Monrovia, Calif. 91016 (U. S. carbines)
Al Biesen, West 2039 Sinto Ave., Spokane, Wash. 99201
E. C. Bishop & Son Inc., Box 7, Warsaw, Mo. 65355
Nate Bishop, Box 158, Minturn, CO 81645

Kay H. Bowles, Pinedale, Wyo. 82941
Brown Precision Co., 5869 Indian Ave., San Jose, CA 95123
Lenard M. Brownell, Box 6147, Sheridan, WY 82801
Cadmus Ind. Sporting Arms, Inc., 6311 Yucca St., Hollywood, Calif. 90028 (U. S. carbines)
Calico Hardwoods, Inc., 1648 Airport Blvd., Windsor, Calif. 95492 (blanks)
Dick Campbell, 1445 So. Meade, Denver, Colo. 80219
Cloward's Gun Shop, 2045 Eastlake Ave. E., Seattle, Wa. 98102
Mike Conner, Box 208, Tijeras, NM 87059
Crane Creek Gun Stock Co., Box 268, Waseca, Minn. 56093
Crest Carving Co., 8091 Bolsa Ave., Midway City, CA 92655
Charles De Veto, 1087 Irene Rd., Lyndhurst, O. 44124
Custom Gunstocks, 1445 So. Meade, Denver, Colo. 80219
Reinhart Fajen, Box 338, Warsaw, Mo. 65355
N. B. Fashingbauer, Box 366, Lac Du Flambeau, Wis. 54538
Ted Fellowes, 9245 16th Ave. S. W., Seattle, Wash. 98106
Clyde E. Fischer, Rt. 1, Box 170-M, Victoria, Tex. 77901
Jerry Fisher, 1244-4th Ave., Kalispell, Mont. 59901
Flaig's Lodge, Millvale, Pa. 15209
Horace M. Frantz, Box 128, Farmingdale, N.J. 07727
Freeland's Scope Stands, Inc., 3734 14th Ave., Rock Island, Ill. 61201
Aaron T. Gates, 3229 Felton St., San Diego, Calif. 92104
Dale Goens, Box 224, Cedar Crest, N.M. 87008
Gould's Myrtlewood, 1692 N. Dogwood, Coquille, Ore. 97423 (gun blanks)
Rolf R. Gruning, 315 Busby Dr., San Antonio, Tex. 78209
Gunstocks-Rarewoods, Haleiwa, Hawaii 97612 (blanks)
Gunwoods (N.Z.) Ltd., Box 18505, New Brighton, Christchurch, New Zealand (blanks)
Half Moon Rifle Shop, Rte. 1B, Box 352, Columbia Falls, MT 59912
Hank's Stock Shop, 1078 Alice Ave., Ukiah, Calif. 95482
Harper's Custom Stocks, 928 Lombrano St., San Antonio, Tex. 78207
Harris Gun Stocks, Inc., 12 Lake St., Richfield Springs, N.Y. 13439
Elden Harsh, Rt. 4, London, O. 43140
Hal Hartley, Box 147, Blairsfork Rd., Lenoir, N.C. 28654
Hayes Gunstock Service Co., 914 E. Turner St., Clearwater, Fla. 33516
Hubert J. Hecht, 55 Rose Mead Circle, Sacramento, CA 95831
Edward O. Hefti, 300 Fairview, College Sta., Tex. 77840
Herter's Inc., Waseca, Minn. 56093
Richard Hodgson, 9081 Tahoe Lane, Boulder, CO 80301
Hollis Gun Shop, 917 Rex St., Carlsbad, N.M. 88220
Hurst Custom Gunstocks, RFD 1, Box 1000, Exmore, Va. 23350
Jackson's, Box 416, Selman City, Tex. 75689 (blanks)
Paul Jaeger, 211 Leedom St., Jenkintown, Pa. 19046
I. D. Johnson, Rt. 1, Strawberry Point, Ia. 52076 (blanks)
Monte Kennedy, R.D. 2B, Kalispell Mont., 59901
Leer's Gun Barn, Rt. 3, Sycamore Hills, Elwood, Ind. 46036
LeFever Arms Co., Inc., R.D. 1, Lee Center, N.Y. 13363
Maryland Gun Exchange, Rte. 5, Frederick, Md. 21701
Maurer Arms, 2366 Frederick Dr., Cuyahoga Falls, O. 44221
Leonard Mews, R.2, Box 242, Hortonville, WI 54944
Robt. U. Milhoan & Son, Rt. 3, Elizabeth, W. Va. 26143
C. D. Miller Guns, St. Onge, S.D. 57779
Mills (D.H.) Custom Stocks, 401 N. Ellsworth Ave., San Mateo, Calif. 94401

Nelsen's Gun Shop, 501 S. Wilson, Olympia, Wash. 98501

Oakley and Merkley, Box 2446, Sacramento, Calif. 95801 (blanks)

Ernest O. Paulsen, Chinook, Mont. 59523 (blanks)

Peterson Mach. Carving, Box 1065, Sun Valley, Calif. 91352

Andrew Redmond, Inc., No. Anson, Me. 04958 (birchwood blanks)

Richards Micro-Fit Stocks, P.O. Box 1066, Sun Valley, CA. 91352 (thumbhole)

Roberts Wood Prod., 1400 Melody Rd., Marysville, Calif. 95901

Carl Roth, Jr., P.O. Box 2593, Cheyenne, Wy. 82001

Royal Arms, Inc., 10064 Bert Acosta Ct., Santee, Calif. 92071

Sanders Cust. Gun Serv., 2358 Tyler Lane, Louisville, Ky. 40205 (blanks)

Santa Barbara of Amer. Ltd., 930 N. Beltline Rd., #32, Irving, Tx. 75060

Saratoga Arms Co., R.D. 3, Box 387, Pottstown, Pa. 19464

Roy Schaefer, 965 W. Hilliard Lane, Eugene, Ore. 97402 (blanks)

Shaw's, 1655 S. Euclid Ave., Anaheim, Calif. 92802

Walter Shultz, R.D. 3, Pottstown, Pa. 19464

Sile Dist., 7 Centre Market Pl., New York, N.Y. 10013

Ed Sowers, 8331 DeCelis Pl., Sepulveda, Calif. 91343

Sportsmen's Equip. Co., 915 W. Washington, San Diego, Calif. 92103 (carbine conversions)

Keith Stegall, Box 696, Gunnison, Colo. 81230

Stinehour Rifles, Box 84, Cragsmoor, N.Y. 12420

J. R. Sundra, 683 Elizabeth St., Bridgeville, Pa. 15017

Swanson Cust. Firearms, 1051 Broadway, Denver, Colo. 80203

V. S. Swenson, Rt. 1, Ettrick, Wis. 54627

Talmage Enterpr., 1309 W. 12 St., Long Beach, CA 90813

D. W. Thomas, Box 184, Vineland, N.J. 08360

Trevallion Gunstocks, 3442 S. Post Rd., Indianapolis, IN 46239

Roy Vail, Rt. 1, Box 8, Warwick, N.Y. 10990

Harold Waller, 1288 Camillo Way, El Cajon, CA 92021

Weatherby's, 2781 Firestone, South Gate, Calif. 90280

Western Stocks & Guns, Inc., 2206 E 11th, Bremerton, Wash. 98311

Joe White, Box 8505, New Brighton, Christchurch, N.Z. (blanks)

Lou Williamson, 129 Stonegate Ct., Bedford, TX 76021

Robert M. Winter, Box 484, Menno, S.D. 57045

Fred Wranic, 6919 Santa Fe, Huntington Park, Calif. 90255 (mesquite)

Paul Wright, 4504 W. Washington Blvd., Los Angeles, Calif. 90016

SURPLUS GUNS, PARTS AND AMMUNITION

Century Arms, Inc., 3-5 Federal St., St. Albans, Vt. 05478

W. H. Craig, Box 927, Selma, Ala. 36701

Cummings Intl. Inc., 41 Riverside Ave., Yonkers, N.Y. 10701

Eastern Firearms Co., 790 S. Arroyo Pkwy., Pasadena, Calif. 91105

Hunter's Lodge, 200 S. Union, Alexandria, Va. 22313

Lever Arms Serv. Ltd., 771 Dunsmuir St., Vancouver 1, B.C., Canada

Mars Equipment Corp., 3318 W. Devon, Chicago, Ill. 60645

National Gun Traders, 225 S.W. 22nd, Miami, Fla. 33135

Pacific Intl. Imp. Co., 2416-16th St., Sacramento, CA. 95818

Plainfield Ordnance Co., Box 447, Dunellen, N.J. 08812

Potomac Arms Corp., Box 35, Alexandria, Va. 22313

Ruvel & Co., 3037 N. Clark St., Chicago, Ill. 60614

Service Armament Co., 689 Bergen Blvd., Ridgefield, N.J. 07657

Sherwood Distrib. Inc., 9470 Santa Monica Blvd., Beverly Hills, CA 90210

Z. M. Military Research Corp., 31 Legion Dr., Bergenfield, NJ 07621

TARGETS, BULLET & CLAYBIRD TRAPS

Black Products Co., 13513 Calumet Ave., Chicago, Ill. 60627

Caswell Target Carriers, Box 344, Anoka, Minn. 55303

Cole's Acku-Rite Prod., Box 25, Kennedy, N.Y. 14747 (Site Rite targets)

Detroit Bullet Trap Co., 2233 N. Palmer Dr., Schaumburg, Ill. 60172

Dupont Target Co., Dupont, Ind. 47231 (motorized target carrier)

Gopher Shooter's Supply, Box 246, Faribault, Minn. 55021 (Lok-A-Leg target holders)

Millard F. Lerch, Box 163, 10842 Front St., Mokena, Ill. 60448 (bullet target)

National Target Co., 4960 Wyaconda Rd., Rockville, Md. 20853

Outers Laboratories, Inc., Onalaska, Wis. 54650 (claybird traps)

Peterson Label Co., P.O. Box 186Z, Redding Ridge, CT 06876 (paste-ons)

Police Ordnance, 3027 Enterprise St., Costa Mesa, Calif. 92626 (Multi-Rotating target system)

Professional Tape Co., 355 E. Burlington Rd., Riverside, Ill. 60546 (Time Labels)

Ranger Arms Co., Box 704, Gainesville, Tex. 76240 (paper targets)

Recreation Prods. Res. Inc., 158 Franklin Ave., Ridgwood, N.J. 07450 (Butts bullet trap)

Remington Arms Co., Bridgeport, Conn. 06602 (claybird traps)

Scientific Prod. Corp., 5417A Vine St., Alexandria, Va. 22310 (Targeteer)

Sheridan Products, Inc., 3205 Sheridan, Racine, Wis. 53403 (traps)

Shooting Equip. Inc., 2001 N. Parkside Ave., Chicago, Ill. 60639 (electric range)

Sterling-Fleischman Inc., 176 Penna Ave., Malvern, Pa. 19355

Time Products Co. (See Prof. Tape Co.)

Trius Prod., Box 25, Cleves, O. 45002 (claybird, can thrower)

Valentine Equip. Co., 2630 W. Arthington, Chicago, Ill. 60612 ("Crazy Quail" clay target game)

Winchester-Western, New Haven, Conn. 06504 (claybird traps)

Wisler Western Target Co., 1685 Industrial Way, Sparks, Nev. 89431 (NRA targets)

X-Ring Prod. Co., Outers Lab., Onalaska, Wis. 54650 (traps)